Common Formulas

Distance

$d = rt$

d = distance traveled
t = time
r = rate

Temperature

$F = \dfrac{9}{5}C + 32$

F = degrees Fahrenheit
C = degrees Celsius

Simple Interest

$I = Prt$

I = interest
P = principal
r = annual interest rate
t = time in years

Compound Interest

$A = P\left(1 + \dfrac{r}{n}\right)^{nt}$

A = balance
P = principal
r = annual interest rate
n = compoundings per year
t = time in years

Coordinate Plane: Midpoint Formula

Midpoint of line segment joining (x_1, y_1) and (x_2, y_2)

$\left(\dfrac{x_1 + x_2}{2}, \dfrac{y_1 + y_2}{2}\right)$

Coordinate Plane: Distance Formula

d = distance between points (x_1, y_1) and (x_2, y_2)

$d = \sqrt{(x_2 - x_1)^2 + (y_2 - y_1)^2}$

Quadratic Formula

Solutions of $ax^2 + bx + c = 0$

$x = \dfrac{-b \pm \sqrt{b^2 - 4ac}}{2a}$

Rules of Exponents

$a^0 = 1$

$a^m \cdot a^n = a^{m+n}$

$(ab)^m = a^m \cdot b^m$

$(a^m)^n = a^{mn}$

$\dfrac{a^m}{a^n} = a^{m-n}, \quad a \neq 0$

$\left(\dfrac{a}{b}\right)^m = \dfrac{a^m}{b^m}, \quad b \neq 0$

$a^{-n} = \dfrac{1}{a^n}, \quad a \neq 0$

$\left(\dfrac{a}{b}\right)^{-n} = \dfrac{b^n}{a^n}, \quad a \neq 0, \ b \neq 0$

Basic Rules of Algebra

Commutative Property of Addition

$a + b = b + a$

Commutative Property of Multiplication

$ab = ba$

Associative Property of Addition

$(a + b) + c = a + (b + c)$

Associative Property of Multiplication

$(ab)c = a(bc)$

Left Distributive Property

$a(b + c) = ab + ac$

Right Distributive Property

$(a + b)c = ac + bc$

Additive Identity Property

$a + 0 = a$

Multiplicative Identity Property

$a \cdot 1 = 1 \cdot a = a$

Additive Inverse Property

$a + (-a) = 0$

Multiplicative Inverse Property

$a \cdot \dfrac{1}{a} = 1, \quad a \neq 0$

Properties of Equality

Addition Property of Equality

If $a = b$, then $a + c = b + c$.

Multiplication Property of Equality

If $a = b$, then $ac = bc$.

Cancellation Property of Addition

If $a + c = b + c$, then $a = b$.

Cancellation Property of Multiplication

If $ac = bc$, and $c \neq 0$, then $a = b$.

Zero Factor Property

If $ab = 0$, then $a = 0$ or $b = 0$.

Instructor's Annotated Edition

Elementary Algebra

Third Edition

Ron Larson
The Pennsylvania State University
The Behrend College

Robert P. Hostetler
The Pennsylvania State University
The Behrend College

With the assistance of
David E. Heyd
The Pennsylvania State University
The Behrend College

Houghton Mifflin Company
Boston   New York

Sponsoring Editor: Jack Shira
Managing Editor: Cathy Cantin
Senior Associate Editor: Maureen Ross
Associate Editor: Laura Wheel
Assistant Editor: Carolyn Johnson
Supervising Editor: Karen Carter
Project Editor: Patty Bergin
Editorial Assistant: Christine E. Lee
Art Supervisor: Gary Crespo
Marketing Manager: Ros Kane
Senior Manufacturing Coordinator: Sally Culler
Composition and Art: Meridian Creative Group

We have included examples and exercises that use real-life data as well as technology output from a variety of software. This would not have been possible without the help of many people and organizations. Our wholehearted thanks go to all for their time and effort.

Trademark acknowledgment: TI is a registered trademark of Texas Instruments, Inc.

Printed in the U.S.A.

Library of Congress Catalog Card Number: 99-71984

ISBN: 0-395-97674-X

123456789–DOW–04 03 02 01 00

Contents

A Word from the Authors

Welcome to *Elementary Algebra*, Third Edition. In this revision, we have continued to focus on developing students' proficiency and conceptual understanding of algebra. We hope you enjoy the Third Edition.

In response to suggestions from elementary and intermediate algebra instructors, we have revised and reorganized the coverage of topics for the Third Edition. We combined the content of the first two chapters of the previous edition and streamlined them into Chapter 1 "The Real Number System" for the Third Edition. To improve the flow of the material, the business applications have been incorporated into Section 3.4 "Ratios and Proportions." "Geometric and Scientific Applications" is now Section 3.5. Compound inequalities and set notation are now introduced in Section 3.6 "Linear Inequalities." And a new section, "Absolute Value Equations and Inequalities," has been added to Chapter 3. In order to be more efficient and to improve the flow of the text, Chapter 4, which previously introduced the coordinate plane and graphs of equations, now includes Section 4.3 "Relations, Functions, and Graphs," Section 4.4 "Slope and Graphs of Linear Equations," Section 4.5 "Equations of Lines," and Section 4.6 "Graphs of Linear Inequalities." And finally, Chapter 9 "Radical Expressions and Equations" now includes higher order roots.

In order to address the diverse needs and abilities of students, we offer a straightforward approach to the presentation of difficult concepts. In the Third Edition, the emphasis is on helping students learn a variety of techniques—symbolic, numeric, and visual—for solving problems. We are committed to providing students with a successful and meaningful course of study.

Our approach begins with Motivating the Chapter, a new feature that introduces each chapter. These multipart problems are designed to show students the relevance of algebra to the world around them. Each Motivating the Chapter feature is a real-life application that requires students to apply the concepts of the chapter in order to solve each part of the problem. Problem-solving and critical thinking skills are emphasized here and throughout the text in applications that appear in the examples and exercise sets.

To improve the usefulness of the text as a study tool, we added Objectives, which highlight the main concepts that students will learn throughout the section. Each objective is restated in the margin at the point where the concept is introduced, to help keep students focused as they read the section. The Chapter Summary was revised for the Third Edition to make it a more comprehensive and effective study tool. It now highlights the important mathematical vocabulary (Key Terms) and primary concepts (Key Concepts) of the chapter. For easy reference, the Key Terms are correlated to the chapter by page number and the Key Concepts by section number.

As students proceed through each chapter they have many opportunities to assess their understanding. They can check their progress after each section with the Exercise sets (which are correlated to Examples in the section), midway through the chapter with the Mid-Chapter Quiz, and at the end of the chapter with the Review Exercises (which are correlated to the sections) and the Chapter Test. The exercises and test items were carefully chosen and graded in difficulty to allow students to gain confidence as they progress. In addition, students can assess their understanding of previously learned concepts through the Integrated Review exercises that precede the section exercise sets and the Cumulative Tests that follow Chapters 3, 6, and 9.

In the Third Edition, we combined the Technology and Discovery features of the Second Edition. Technology Tips provide point-of-use instructions for using a graphing utility. Technology Discovery features encourage students to explore mathematical concepts with graphing utilities and scientific calculators. Both are highlighted and can easily be omitted without loss of continuity in coverage of material.

To show students the practical uses of algebra, we highlight the connections between the mathematical concepts and the real world in the multitude of applications found throughout the text. We believe that students can overcome their difficulties in mathematics if they are encouraged and supported throughout the learning process. Too often, students become frustrated and lose interest in the material when they cannot follow the text. With this in mind, every effort has been made to write a readable text that can be understood by every student. We hope that your students find our approach engaging and effective.

Ron Larson

Robert P. Hostetler

Features

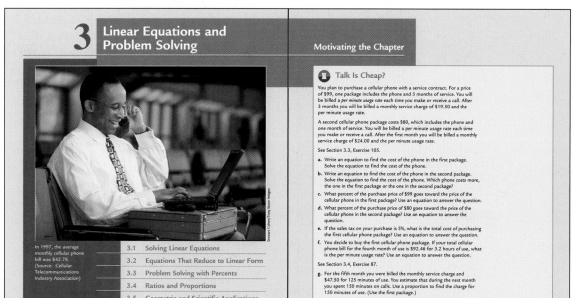

Motivating the Chapter

Talk Is Cheap?

You plan to purchase a cellular phone with a service contract. For a price of $99, one package includes the phone and 3 months of service. You will be billed a *per minute usage rate* each time you make or receive a call. After 3 months you will be billed a monthly service charge of $19.50 and the per minute usage rate.

A second cellular phone package costs $80, which includes the phone and one month of service. You will be billed a per minute usage rate each time you make or receive a call. After the first month you will be billed a monthly service charge of $24.00 and the per minute usage rate.

See Section 3.3, Exercise 105.

a. Write an equation to find the cost of the phone in the first package. Solve the equation to find the cost of the phone.

b. Write an equation to find the cost of the phone in the second package. Solve the equation to find the cost of the phone. Which phone costs more, the one in the first package or the one in the second package?

c. What percent of the purchase price of $99 goes toward the price of the cellular phone in the first package? Use an equation to answer the question.

d. What percent of the purchase price of $80 goes toward the price of the cellular phone in the second package? Use an equation to answer the question.

e. If the sales tax on your purchase is 5%, what is the total cost of purchasing the first cellular phone package? Use an equation to answer the question.

f. You decide to buy the first cellular phone package. If your total cellular phone bill for the fourth month of use is $92.46 for 3.2 hours of use, what is the per minute usage rate? Use an equation to answer the question.

See Section 3.4, Exercise 87.

g. For the fifth month you were billed the monthly service charge and $47.50 for 125 minutes of use. You estimate that during the next month you spent 150 minutes on calls. Use a proportion to find the charge for 150 minutes of use. (Use the first package.)

See Section 3.6, Exercise 87.

h. You determine that the most you can spend each month on phone calls is $75. Write a compound inequality that describes the number of minutes you can spend talking on the cellular phone each month if the per minute usage rate is $0.35. Solve the inequality. (Use the first package.)

In 1997, the average monthly cellular phone bill was $42.78. (Source: Cellular Telecommunications Industry Association)

114 / 115

Chapter Opener *New*

Every chapter opens with *Motivating the Chapter*. Each of these multipart problems incorporates the concepts presented in the chapter in the context of a single real-world application. *Motivating the Chapter* problems are correlated to sections and exercises and can be assigned as students work through the chapter or can be assigned as individual or group projects. The icon 🔵 identifies an exercise that relates back to *Motivating the Chapter*.

Section Opener *New*

Every section begins with a list of learning objectives. Each objective is restated in the margin at the point where it is covered.

Historical Note

Historical notes featuring mathematicians or mathematical artifacts are included throughout the text.

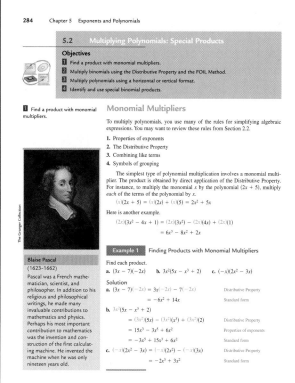

284 Chapter 5 Exponents and Polynomials

5.2 Multiplying Polynomials: Special Products

Objectives

1 Find a product with monomial multipliers.
2 Multiply binomials using the Distributive Property and the FOIL Method.
3 Multiply polynomials using a horizontal or vertical format.
4 Identify and use special binomial products.

1 Find a product with monomial multipliers.

Blaise Pascal
(1623–1662)
Pascal was a French mathematician, scientist, and philosopher. In addition to his religious and philosophical writings, he made many invaluable contributions to mathematics and physics. Perhaps his most important contribution to mathematics was the invention and construction of the first calculating machine. He invented the machine when he was only nineteen years old.

Monomial Multipliers

To multiply polynomials, you use many of the rules for simplifying algebraic expressions. You may want to review these rules from Section 2.2.

1. Properties of exponents
2. The Distributive Property
3. Combining like terms
4. Symbols of grouping

The simplest type of polynomial multiplication involves a monomial multiplier. The product is obtained by direct application of the Distributive Property. For instance, to multiply the monomial x by the polynomial $(2x + 5)$, multiply *each* of the terms of the polynomial by x.

$$(x)(2x + 5) = (x)(2x) + (x)(5) = 2x^2 + 5x$$

Here is another example.

$$(2x)(3x^2 - 4x + 1) = (2x)(3x^2) - (2x)(4x) + (2x)(1)$$
$$= 6x^3 - 8x^2 + 2x$$

Example 1 Finding Products with Monomial Multipliers

Find each product.

a. $(3x - 7)(-2x)$ b. $3x^2(5x - x^3 + 2)$ c. $(-x)(2x^2 - 3x)$

Solution

a. $(3x - 7)(-2x) = 3x(-2x) - 7(-2x)$ Distributive Property
$$= -6x^2 + 14x$$ Standard form

b. $3x^2(5x - x^3 + 2)$
$$= (3x^2)(5x) - (3x^2)(x^3) + (3x^2)(2)$$ Distributive Property
$$= 15x^3 - 3x^5 + 6x^2$$ Properties of exponents
$$= -3x^5 + 15x^3 + 6x^2$$ Standard form

c. $(-x)(2x^2 - 3x) = (-x)(2x^2) - (-x)(3x)$ Distributive Property
$$= -2x^3 + 3x^2$$ Standard form

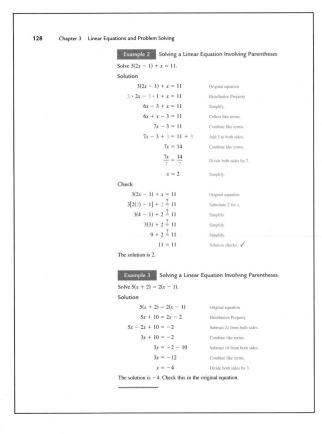

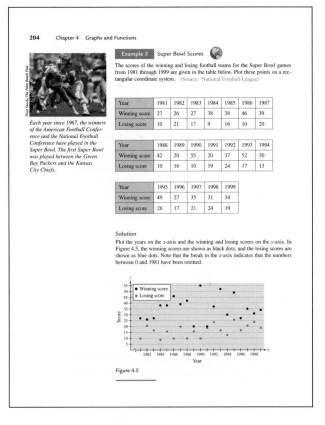

Examples

Each example was carefully chosen to illustrate a particular mathematical concept or problem-solving technique. The examples cover a wide variety of problems and are titled for easy reference. Many examples include detailed, step-by-step solutions with side comments, which explain the key steps of the solution process.

Applications

A wide variety of real-life applications are integrated throughout the text in examples and exercises. These applications demonstrate the relevance of algebra in the real world. Many of the applications use current, real data. The icon indicates an example involving a real-life application.

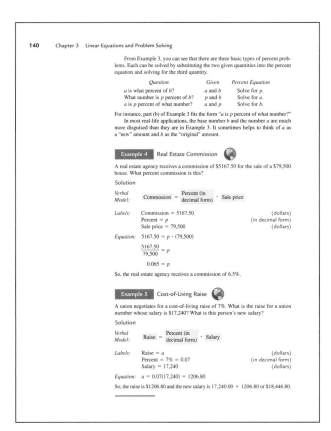

140   Chapter 3   Linear Equations and Problem Solving

From Example 3, you can see that there are three basic types of percent problems. Each can be solved by substituting the two given quantities into the percent equation and solving for the third quantity.

Question	Given	Percent Equation
a is what percent of b?	a and b	Solve for p.
What number is p percent of b?	p and b	Solve for a.
a is p percent of what number?	a and p	Solve for b.

For instance, part (b) of Example 3 fits the form "a is p percent of what number?" In most real-life applications, the base number b and the number a are much more disguised than they are in Example 3. It sometimes helps to think of a as a "new" amount and b as the "original" amount.

Example 4   Real Estate Commission

A real estate agency receives a commission of $5167.50 for the sale of a $79,500 house. What percent commission is this?

Solution

Verbal Model: $\text{Commission} = \dfrac{\text{Percent (in decimal form)}}{} \cdot \text{Sale price}$

Labels: Commission = 5167.50   (dollars)
Percent = p (in decimal form)
Sale price = 79,500   (dollars)

Equation: $5167.50 = p \cdot (79,500)$

$\dfrac{5167.50}{79,500} = p$

$0.065 = p$

So, the real estate agency receives a commission of 6.5%.

Example 5   Cost-of-Living Raise

A union negotiates for a cost-of-living raise of 7%. What is the raise for a union member whose salary is $17,240? What is this person's new salary?

Solution

Verbal Model: $\text{Raise} = \dfrac{\text{Percent (in decimal form)}}{} \cdot \text{Salary}$

Labels: Raise = a (dollars)
Percent = 7% = 0.07   (in decimal form)
Salary = 17,240   (dollars)

Equation: $a = 0.07(17,240) = 1206.80$

So, the raise is $1206.80 and the new salary is 17,240.00 + 1206.80 or $18,446.80.

Problem Solving

This text provides many opportunities for students to sharpen their problem-solving skills. In both the examples and the exercises, students are asked to apply verbal, numerical, analytical, and graphical approaches to problem-solving. In the spirit of the AMATYC and NCTM standards, students are taught a five-step strategy for solving applied problems, which begins with constructing a verbal model and ends with checking the answer.

Geometry

Coverage and integration of geometry in examples and exercises have been enhanced throughout the Third Edition.

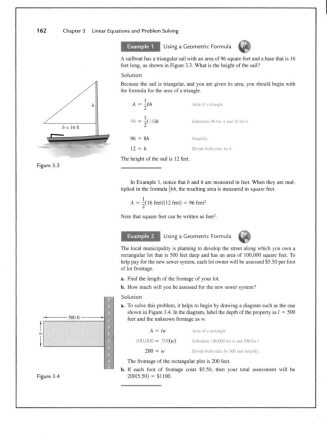

162   Chapter 3   Linear Equations and Problem Solving

Example 1   Using a Geometric Formula

A sailboat has a triangular sail with an area of 96 square feet and a base that is 16 feet long, as shown in Figure 3.3. What is the height of the sail?

Solution

Because the sail is triangular, and you are given its area, you should begin with the formula for the area of a triangle.

$A = \dfrac{1}{2}bh$ Area of a triangle

$96 = \dfrac{1}{2}(16)h$ Substitute 96 for A and 16 for b.

$96 = 8h$ Simplify.

$12 = h$ Divide both sides by 8.

The height of the sail is 12 feet.

$b = 16$ ft

Figure 3.3

In Example 1, notice that b and h are measured in feet. When they are multiplied in the formula $\frac{1}{2}bh$, the resulting area is measured in *square* feet.

$A = \dfrac{1}{2}(16 \text{ feet})(12 \text{ feet}) = 96 \text{ feet}^2$

Note that square feet can be written as feet².

Example 2   Using a Geometric Formula

The local municipality is planning to develop the street along which you own a rectangular lot that is 500 feet deep and has an area of 100,000 square feet. To help pay for the new sewer system, each lot owner will be assessed $5.50 per foot of lot frontage.

a. Find the length of the frontage of your lot.
b. How much will you be assessed for the new sewer system?

Solution

a. To solve this problem, it helps to begin by drawing a diagram such as the one shown in Figure 3.4. In the diagram, label the depth of the property as $l = 500$ feet and the unknown frontage as w.

$A = lw$ Area of a rectangle

$100,000 = 500(w)$ Substitute 100,000 for A and 500 for l.

$200 = w$ Divide both sides by 500 and simplify.

The frontage of the rectangular plot is 200 feet.

b. If each foot of frontage costs $5.50, then your total assessment will be $200(5.50) = 1100.

500 ft

Figure 3.4

FEATURES

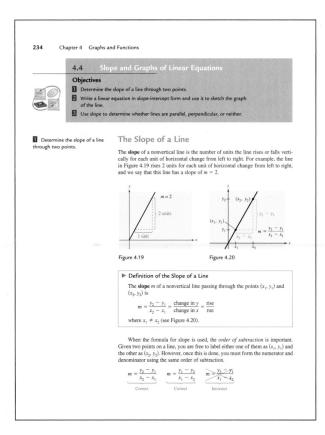

Definitions and Rules

All important definitions, rules, formulas, properties, and summaries of solution methods are highlighted for emphasis. Each of these features is also titled for easy reference.

Graphics

Visualization is a critical problem-solving skill. To encourage the development of this skill, students are shown how to use graphs to reinforce algebraic and numeric solutions and to interpret data. The numerous figures in examples and exercises throughout the text were computer generated for accuracy.

Technology Tips

Point-of-use instructions for using graphing utilities appear in the margins. They provide convenient reference for students using graphing technology. In addition, they encourage the use of graphing technology as a tool for visualization of mathematical concepts, for verification of other solution methods, and for facilitation of computations. The *Technology Tips* can easily be omitted without loss of continuity in coverage.

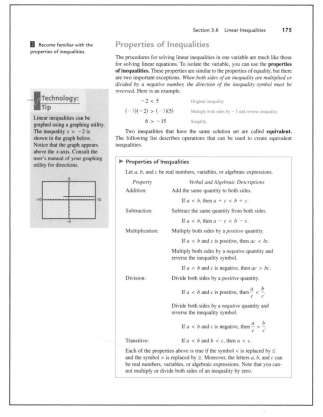

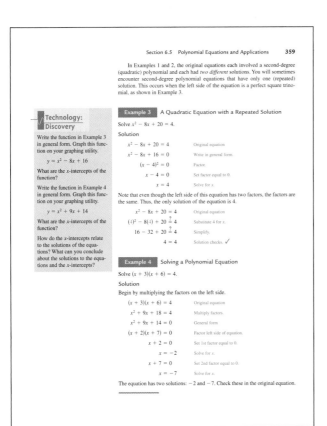

FEATURES

Technology Discovery

Utilizing the power of technology (scientific calculator and graphing utility), *Technology Discovery* invites students to engage in active exploration of mathematical concepts and discovery of mathematical relationships. These activities encourage students to use their critical thinking skills and help them develop an intuitive understanding of theoretical concepts. *Technology Discovery* features can easily be omitted without loss of continuity in coverage.

Study Tips

Study Tips offer students specific point-of-use suggestions for studying algebra, as well as pointing out common errors and discussing alternative solution methods. They appear in the margins.

Discussing the Concept

Each section concludes with a *Discussing the Concept* feature. Designed as a section wrap-up activity to give students an opportunity to think, talk, and write about mathematics, each of these activities encourages students to synthesize the mathematical concepts presented in the section. *Discussing the Concept* can be assigned as an independent or collaborative activity or can be used as a basis for a class discussion.

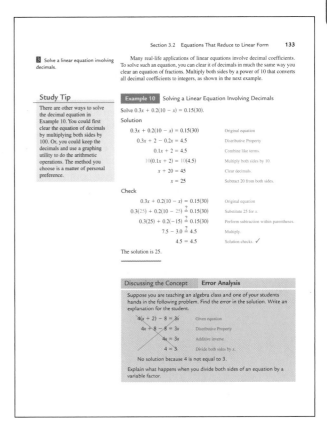

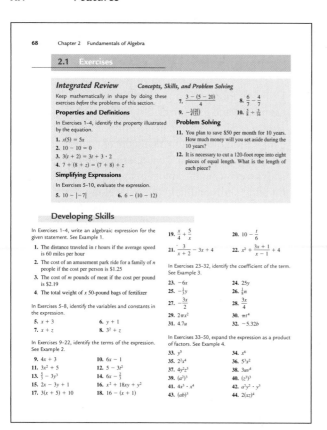

Integrated Review

Each exercise set (except in Chapter 1) is preceded by *Integrated Review* exercises. These exercises are designed to help students keep up with concepts and skills learned in previous chapters. Answers to all *Integrated Review* problems are given in the back of the book.

Exercises

The exercise sets have been reorganized in the Third Edition. Each exercise set is grouped into three categories: *Developing Skills*, *Solving Problems*, and *Explaining Concepts*. The exercise sets offer a diverse variety of computational, conceptual, and applied problems to accommodate many teaching and learning styles. Designed to build competence, skill, and understanding, each exercise set is graded in difficulty to allow students to gain confidence as they progress. Detailed solutions to all odd-numbered exercises are given in the *Student Solutions Guide*, and answers to all odd-numbered exercises are given in the back of the book.

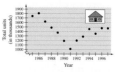

Chapter Summary

The *Chapter Summary* has been completely revised in the Third Edition. Designed to be an effective study tool for students preparing for exams, it highlights the *Key Terms* (referenced by page) and the *Key Concepts* (referenced by section) presented in the chapter.

Review Exercises

The *Review Exercises* at the end of each chapter have been reorganized in the Third Edition. They are grouped into two categories: *Reviewing Skills* and *Solving Problems*. Exercises in *Reviewing Skills* are correlated to sections in the chapter. The *Review Exercises* offer students additional practice in preparation for exams. Answers to all odd-numbered exercises are given in the back of the book.

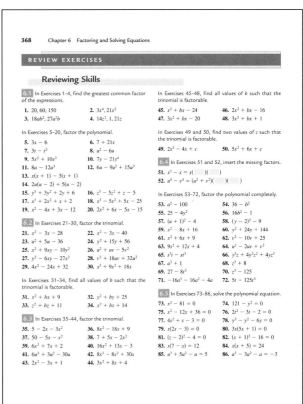

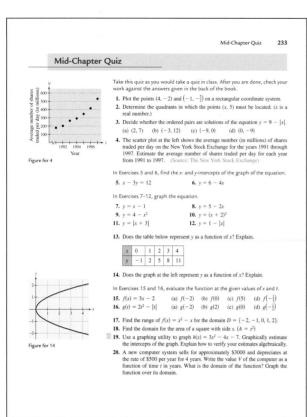

Mid-Chapter Quiz

Take this quiz as you would take a quiz in class. After you are done, check your work against the answers given in the back of the book.

1. Plot the points $(4, -2)$ and $\left(-1, -\frac{5}{2}\right)$ on a rectangular coordinate system.

2. Determine the quadrants in which the points $(x, 5)$ must be located. (x is a real number.)

3. Decide whether the ordered pairs are solutions of the equation $y = 9 - |x|$.
   (a) $(2, 7)$ (b) $(-3, 12)$ (c) $(-9, 0)$ (d) $(0, -9)$

4. The scatter plot at the left shows the average number (in millions) of shares traded per day on the New York Stock Exchange for the years 1991 through 1997. Estimate the average number of shares traded per day for each year from 1991 to 1997. (Source: The New York Stock Exchange)

In Exercises 5 and 6, find the x- and y-intercepts of the graph of the equation.

5. $x - 3y = 12$ 6. $y = 6 - 4x$

In Exercises 7–12, graph the equation.

7. $y = x - 1$ 8. $y = 5 - 2x$
9. $y = 4 - x^2$ 10. $y = (x + 2)^2$
11. $y = |x + 3|$ 12. $y = 1 - |x|$

13. Does the table below represent y as a function of x? Explain.

x	0	1	2	3	4
y	-1	2	5	8	11

14. Does the graph at the left represent y as a function of x? Explain.

In Exercises 15 and 16, evaluate the function at the given values of x and t.

15. $f(x) = 3x - 2$ (a) $f(-2)$ (b) $f(0)$ (c) $f(5)$ (d) $f\left(-\frac{1}{3}\right)$
16. $g(t) = 2t^2 - |t|$ (a) $g(-2)$ (b) $g(2)$ (c) $g(0)$ (d) $g\left(-\frac{1}{2}\right)$

17. Find the range of $f(x) = x^2 - x$ for the domain $D = \{-2, -1, 0, 1, 2\}$.

18. Find the domain for the area of a square with side s. ($A = s^2$)

19. Use a graphing utility to graph $h(x) = 3x^2 - 4x - 7$. Graphically estimate the intercepts of the graph. Explain how to verify your estimates algebraically.

20. A new computer system sells for approximately $3000 and depreciates at the rate of $500 per year for 4 years. Write the value V of the computer as a function of time t in years. What is the domain of the function? Graph the function over its domain.

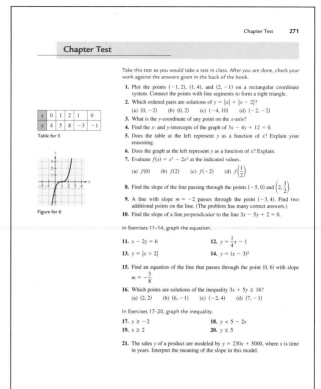

Chapter Test

Take this test as you would take a test in class. After you are done, check your work against the answers given in the back of the book.

1. Plot the points $(-1, 2)$, $(1, 4)$, and $(2, -1)$ on a rectangular coordinate system. Connect the points with line segments to form a right triangle.

2. Which ordered pairs are solutions of $y = |x| + |x - 2|$?
   (a) $(0, -2)$ (b) $(0, 2)$ (c) $(-4, 10)$ (d) $(-2, -2)$

3. What is the y-coordinate of any point on the x-axis?

4. Find the x- and y-intercepts of the graph of $3x - 4y + 12 = 0$.

5. Does the table at the left represent y as a function of x? Explain your reasoning.

x	0	1	2	1	0
y	4	5	8	-3	-1

Table for 5

6. Does the graph at the left represent y as a function of x? Explain.

7. Evaluate $f(x) = x^3 - 2x^2$ at the indicated values.
   (a) $f(0)$ (b) $f(2)$ (c) $f(-2)$ (d) $f\left(\frac{1}{2}\right)$

8. Find the slope of the line passing through the points $(-5, 0)$ and $\left(2, \frac{3}{2}\right)$.

9. A line with slope $m = -2$ passes through the point $(-3, 4)$. Find two additional points on the line. (The problem has many correct answers.)

10. Find the slope of a line perpendicular to the line $3x - 5y + 2 = 0$.

In Exercises 11–14, graph the equation.

11. $x - 2y = 6$ 12. $y = \frac{1}{4}x - 1$
13. $y = |x + 2|$ 14. $y = (x - 3)^2$

15. Find an equation of the line that passes through the point $(0, 6)$ with slope $m = -\frac{3}{8}$.

16. Which points are solutions of the inequality $3x + 5y \le 16$?
   (a) $(2, 2)$ (b) $(6, -1)$ (c) $(-2, 4)$ (d) $(7, -1)$

In Exercises 17–20, graph the inequality.

17. $y \ge -2$ 18. $y < 5 - 2x$
19. $x \ge 2$ 20. $y \le 5$

21. The sales y of a product are modeled by $y = 230x + 5000$, where x is time in years. Interpret the meaning of the slope in this model.

Mid-Chapter Quiz

Each chapter contains a *Mid-Chapter Quiz*. This feature allows students to perform a self-assessment midway through the chapter. Answers to all questions in the *Mid-Chapter Quiz* are given in the back of the book.

Chapter Test

Each chapter ends with a *Chapter Test*. This feature allows students to perform a self-assessment at the end of the chapter. Answers to all questions in the *Chapter Test* are given in the back of the book.

Cumulative Test

The *Cumulative Tests* that follow Chapters 3, 6, and 9 provide a comprehensive self-assessment tool that helps students check their mastery of previously covered material. Answers to all questions in the *Cumulative Tests* are given in the back of the book.

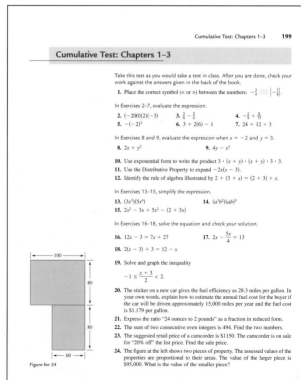

Cumulative Test: Chapters 1–3

Take this test as you would take a test in class. After you are done, check your work against the answers given in the back of the book.

1. Place the correct symbol ($<$ or $>$) between the numbers: $-\frac{3}{4}$ ☐ $\left|-\frac{7}{8}\right|$.

In Exercises 2–7, evaluate the expression.

2. $(-200)(2)(-3)$ 3. $\frac{3}{8} - \frac{5}{6}$ 4. $-\frac{7}{9} \div \frac{8}{75}$
5. $-(-2)^3$ 6. $3 + 2(6) - 1$ 7. $24 + 12 \div 3$

In Exercises 8 and 9, evaluate the expression when $x = -2$ and $y = 3$.

8. $2x + y^2$ 9. $4y - x^3$

10. Use exponential form to write the product $3 \cdot (x + y) \cdot (x + y) \cdot 3 \cdot 3$.

11. Use the Distributive Property to expand $-2x(x - 3)$.

12. Identify the rule of algebra illustrated by $2 + (3 + x) = (2 + 3) + x$.

In Exercises 13–15, simplify the expression.

13. $(3x^3)(5x^4)$ 14. $(a^3b^2)(ab)^5$
15. $2x^2 - 3x + 5x^2 - (2 + 3x)$

In Exercises 16–18, solve the equation and check your solution.

16. $12x - 3 = 7x + 27$ 17. $2x - \frac{5x}{4} = 13$
18. $2(x - 3) + 3 = 12 - x$

19. Solve and graph the inequality
   $$-1 \le \frac{x + 3}{2} < 2.$$

20. The sticker on a new car gives the fuel efficiency as 28.3 miles per gallon. In your own words, explain how to estimate the annual fuel cost for the buyer if the car will be driven approximately 15,000 miles per year and the fuel cost is $1.179 per gallon.

21. Express the ratio "24 ounces to 2 pounds" as a fraction in reduced form.

22. The sum of two consecutive even integers is 494. Find the two numbers.

23. The suggested retail price of a camcorder is $1150. The camcorder is on sale for "20% off" the list price. Find the sale price.

24. The figure at the left shows two pieces of property. The assessed values of the properties are proportional to their areas. The value of the larger piece is $95,000. What is the value of the smaller piece?

Figure for 24

Supplements

Elementary Algebra, Third Edition, by Larson and Hostetler is accompanied by a comprehensive supplements package, which includes resources for both students and instructors. All items are keyed to the text.

Printed Resources

For the Student

Study and Solutions Guide by Carolyn Neptune, Johnson County Community College
(0-395-97673-1)
- Detailed, step-by-step solutions to all Integrated Review exercises and to all odd-numbered exercises in the section exercise sets and in the review exercises
- Detailed, step-by-step solutions to all Mid-Chapter Quiz, Chapter Test, and Cumulative Test questions

Graphing Calculator Keystroke Guide by Benjamin N. Levy and Laurel Technical Services
(0-395-87777-6)
- Keystroke instructions for the following graphing calculators: (Texas Instruments) *TI-80*, *TI-81*, *TI-82*, *TI-83*, *TI-85*, and *TI-92*; (Casio) *fx-7700GE*, *fx-9700GE*, and *CFX-9800G*; (Hewlett Packard) *HP-38G*; and (Sharp) *EL-9200/9300*
- Examples with step-by-step solutions
- Extensive graphics screen output
- Technology tips

For the Instructor

Instructor's Annotated Edition
(0-395-97674-X)
- Includes entire student edition
- Instructor's answer section, which includes answers to all even-numbered exercises, Technology Discovery boxes, Technology Tip boxes, and Discussing the Concept activities
- Annotations at point of use that offer strategies and suggestions for teaching the course and point out common student errors

Test Item File and Instructor's Resource Guide by Cheryl Leech, The Pennsylvania State University, The Behrend College
(0-395-97672-3)
- Printed test bank with approximately 3300 test items, coded by level of difficulty
- Technology required test items, coded for easy reference
- Chapter test forms with answer key
- Two final exams
- Transparency masters

- Notes to the instructor, which include information on standardized tests such as the Texas Academic Skills Program (TASP), the Florida College Level Academic Skills Test (CLAST), and the California State University Entry Level Mathematics (ELM) Exam. A list of skills covered by the test and the corresponding sections in the text where the topics are covered are also provided.
- Alternative assessment strategies

Media Resources

For Students and Instructors

Web Site (*www.hmco.com*)
Contains, but is not limited to, the following student and instructor resources:
- Study guide (for students), which includes section summaries, additional examples with solutions, and starter exercises with answers
- Chapter projects and additional real-life applications
- Geometry review
- ACE Algebra Tutor
- Graphing calculator programs
- Math Matters and Career Interviews

HM³ Tutor
(Instructor's version Windows: 0-618-04208-3)
This networkable, interactive tutorial software offers the following features:
- Algorithmically generated practice and quiz problems
- A variety of multiple-choice and free-response questions, varying in degree of difficulty
- Animated examples and interactivity within lessons
- Hints and full solutions available for every problem
- Integrated classroom management system (for instructors), which includes a syllabus builder and the capability to track and report student performance
- Non-networkable student version (Windows: 0-395-97656-1)

For the Student

Videotape Series by Dana Mosely
(0-395-97682-0)
- Comprehensive section-by-section coverage
- Detailed explanations of important concepts
- Numerous examples and applications, often illustrated via computer-generated animations
- Discussion of study skills

For the Instructor

Computerized Test Bank
(Windows: 0-395-97677-4; Macintosh: 0-395-97678-2)
- Test-generating software for IBM and Macintosh computers
- Approximately 3300 test items
- Also available as a printed test bank

Acknowledgments

We would like to thank the many people who have helped us prepare the Third Edition of this text. Their encouragement, criticisms, and suggestions have been invaluable to us.

Third Edition Reviewers

Mary Kay Best, Coastal Bend College; Connie L. Buller, Metropolitan Community College; Maggie W. Flint, Northeast State Technical Community College; William Hoard, Front Range Community College; Jennifer L. Laveglia, Bellevue Community College; Aaron Montgomery, Purdue University North Central; William Naegele, South Suburban College; Jeanette O'Rourke, Middlesex County College; Judith Pranger, Binghamton University; Kent Sandefer, Mohave Community College; Robert L. Sartain, Howard Payne University; Jon W. Scott, Montgomery College; John Seims, Mesa Community College; Ralph Selensky, Eastern Arizona College; Charles I. Sherrill, Community College of Aurora; Bettie Truitt, Black Hawk College; Betsey S. Whitman, Framingham State College; George J. Witt, Glendale Community College.

We would also like to thank the staff of Larson Texts, Inc. and the staff of Meridian Creative Group, who assisted in proofreading the manuscript, preparing and proofreading the art package, and checking and typesetting the supplements.

On a personal level, we are grateful to our wives, Deanna Gilbert Larson and Eloise Hostetler, for their love, patience, and support. Also, a special thanks goes to R. Scott O'Neil.

If you have suggestions for improving this text, please feel free to write to us. Over the past two decades we have received many useful comments from both instructors and students, and we value these comments very much.

Ron Larson
Robert P. Hostetler

ACKNOWLEDGMENTS

How to Study Algebra

Your success in algebra depends on your active participation both in class and outside of class. Because the material you learn each day builds on the material you learned previously, it is important that you keep up with the course work every day and develop a clear plan of study. To help you learn how to study algebra, we have prepared a set of guidelines that highlight key study strategies.

Preparing for Class

The syllabus your instructor provides is an invaluable resource that outlines the major topics to be covered in the course. Use it to help you prepare. As a general rule, you should set aside two to four hours of study time for each hour spent in class. Being prepared is the first step toward success in algebra. Before class,

❏ Review your notes from the previous class.

❏ Read the portion of the text that will be covered in class.

❏ Use the objectives listed at the beginning of each section to keep you focused on the main ideas of the section.

❏ Pay special attention to the definitions, rules, and concepts highlighted in boxes. Also, be sure you understand the meanings of mathematical symbols and of terms written in boldface type. Keep a vocabulary journal for easy reference.

❏ Read through the solved examples. Use the side comments given in the solution steps to help you follow the solution process. Also, read the *Study Tips* given in the margins.

❏ Make notes of anything you do not understand as you read through the text. If you still do not understand after your instructor covers the topic in question, ask questions before your instructor moves on to a new topic.

❏ If you are using technology in this course, read the *Technology Tips* and try the *Technology Discovery* exercises.

Keeping Up

Another important step toward success in algebra involves your ability to keep up with the work. It is very easy to fall behind, especially if you miss a class. To keep up with the course work, be sure to

❏ Attend every class. Bring your text, a notebook, and a pen or pencil. If you miss a class, get the notes from a classmate as soon as possible and review them carefully.

❏ Take notes in class. After class, read through your notes and add explanations so that your notes make sense to *you*.

❏ Reread the portion of the text that was covered in class. This time, work each example *before* reading through the solution.

❐ Do your homework as soon as possible, while concepts are still fresh in your mind.

❐ Use your notes from class, the text discussion, the examples, and the *Study Tips* as you do your homework. Many exercises are keyed to specific examples in the text for easy reference.

Getting Extra Help

It can be very frustrating when you do not understand concepts and are unable to complete homework assignments. However, there are many resources available to help you with your study of algebra.

❐ Your instructor may have office hours. If you are feeling overwhelmed and need help, make an appointment to discuss your difficulties with your instructor.

❐ Find a study partner or a study group. Sometimes it helps to work through problems with another person.

❐ Arrange to get regular assistance from a tutor. Many colleges have a math resource center available on campus, as well.

❐ Consult one of the many ancillaries available with this text: the *Student Solutions Guide*, tutorial software, videotapes, and additional study resources available at our website at *www.hmco.com*.

Preparing for an Exam

The last step toward success in algebra lies in how you prepare for and complete exams. If you have followed the suggestions given above, then you are almost ready for exams. Do not assume that you can cram for the exam the night before—this seldom works. As a final preparation for the exam,

❐ Read the *Chapter Summary*, which is keyed to each section, and review the concepts and terms.

❐ Work through the *Review Exercises* if you need extra practice on material from a particular section.

❐ Take the *Mid-Chapter Quiz* and the *Chapter Test* as if you were in class. You should set aside at least one hour per test. Check your answers against the answers given in the back of the book.

❐ Review your notes and the portion of the text that will be covered on the exam.

❐ Avoid studying up until the last minute. This will only make you anxious.

❐ Once the exam begins, read through the directions and the entire exam before beginning. Work the problems that you know how to do first to avoid spending too much time of the exam on any one problem. Time management is extremely important when taking an exam.

❐ If you finish early, use the remaining exam time to go over your work.

❐ When you get an exam back, review it carefully and go over your errors. Rework the problems you answered incorrectly. Discovering the mistakes you made will help you improve your test-taking ability.

STUDY PLAN

1

The Real Number System

Jerry Driendl

The average daily temperature in Pittsburgh, Pennsylvania, in December of 1998 was 37.8°F. This was 6.3°F above the normal average daily temperature of 31.5°F. (Source: The National Weather Service)

Motivating the Chapter

 ## December in Pennsylvania

A city in Pennsylvania has an average daily high temperature of 0° Celsius for the month of December. The temperature records for the first 14 days of December 1997 are given in the table.

Day	1	2	3	4	5	6	7
Low temperature (°C)	$-3°$	$-5°$	$-12°$	$-20°$	$-6°$	$-\frac{4}{3}°$	$0°$
High temperature (°C)	$2.5°$	$1°$	$-4°$	$-15°$	$0°$	$5°$	$8°$

Day	8	9	10	11	12	13	14
Low temperature (°C)	$0°$	$2°$	$-1°$	$-2°$	$-9°$	$-10°$	$-8°$
High temperature (°C)	$2°$	$7.2°$	$3°$	$2°$	$-4°$	$-4\frac{1}{2}°$	$-4°$

Here are some of the types of questions you will be able to answer as you study this chapter. You will be asked to answer Questions (a) to (f) in Section 1.1, Exercise 71.

a. Write the set A of *integer* high temperatures.

b. Write the set B of *rational* low temperatures.

c. Write the set C of *nonnegative* low temperatures.

d. Write the high temperatures in *increasing* order.

e. Write the low temperatures in *decreasing* order.

f. What day(s) had high and low temperatures that were opposite numbers?

The answers to Motivating the Chapter are given in the section exercise answers in the back of the book. For instance, the answers to parts a–f are given in the answers to Section 1.1. Odd-numbered exercises are given in the student answer key and even-numbered exercises are given in the instructor's answer key.

You will be asked to answer Questions (g) to (l) in Section 1.3, Exercise 153.

g. What day had a high temperature of greatest departure from the monthly average high temperature of 0°?

h. What successive days had the greatest change in high temperature?

i. What successive days had the greatest change in low temperature?

j. Find the average high temperature for the 14 days.

k. Find the average low temperature for the 14 days.

l. In which of the preceding problems is the concept of absolute value used?

Objectives

1 Define sets and use them to classify numbers as natural, integer, rational, or irrational.

2 Plot numbers on the real number line.

3 Use the real number line and inequality symbols to order real numbers.

4 Find the absolute value of a number.

---

1 Define sets and use them to classify numbers as natural, integer, rational, or irrational.

Study Tip

Whenever we formally introduce a mathematical term in this text, the word will occur in boldface type. Be sure you understand the meaning of each new word; it is important that each word become part of your mathematical vocabulary.

Sets and Real Numbers

The ability to communicate precisely is an essential part of a modern society, and it is the primary goal of this text. Specifically, this section introduces the language used to communicate numerical concepts.

The formal term that is used in mathematics to talk about a collection of objects is the word **set.** For instance, the set $\{1, 2, 3\}$ contains the three numbers 1, 2, and 3. Note that a pair of braces $\{\ \}$ is used to list the members of the set. Parentheses $(\ )$ and brackets $[\ ]$ are used to represent other ideas.

The set of numbers that is used in arithmetic is called the set of **real numbers.** The term *real* distinguishes real numbers from *imaginary* numbers—a type of number that is used in some mathematics courses. You will not study imaginary numbers in Elementary Algebra.

If each member of a set A is also a member of a set B, then A is called a **subset** of B. The set of real numbers has many important subsets, each with a special name. For instance, the set

$$\{1, 2, 3, 4, \ . \ . \ .\} \qquad \text{A subset of the set of real numbers}$$

is the set of **natural numbers** or **positive integers.** Note that the three dots indicate that the pattern continues. For instance, the set also contains the numbers 5, 6, 7, and so on. Every positive integer is a real number, but there are many real numbers that are not positive integers. For example, the numbers -2, 0, and $\frac{1}{2}$ are real numbers, but they are not positive integers.

Positive integers can be used to describe many things that you encounter in everyday life. For instance, you might be taking four classes this term, or you might be paying $180 a month for rent. But even in everyday life, positive integers cannot describe some concepts accurately. For instance, you could have a zero balance in your checking account, or the temperature could be $-10°$ (ten degrees below zero). To describe such quantities you need to expand the set of positive integers to include **zero** and the **negative integers.** The expanded set is called the set of **integers.**

$$\underbrace{\{. \ . \ . \ , -3, -2, -1,}_{\text{Negative integers}} \overset{\text{Zero}}{0}, \underbrace{1, 2, 3, \ . \ . \ .\}}_{\text{Positive integers}} \qquad \text{Set of integers}$$

The set of integers is also a subset of the set of real numbers.

Even with the set of integers, there are still many quantities in everyday life that you cannot describe accurately. The costs of many items are not in whole-dollar amounts, but in parts of dollars, such as $1.19 or $39.98. You might work $8\frac{1}{2}$ hours, or you might miss the first half of a movie. To describe such quantities, you can expand the set of integers to include **fractions.** The expanded set is called the set of **rational numbers.** In the formal language of mathematics, a real number is **rational** if it can be written as a ratio of two integers. So, $\frac{3}{4}$ is a rational number; so is 0.5 $\left(\text{it can be written as }\frac{1}{2}\right)$; and so is every integer. A real number that is not rational is called **irrational** and cannot be written as the ratio of two integers. One example of an irrational number is $\sqrt{2}$, which is read as the positive square root of 2. Another example is π (the Greek letter pi), which represents the ratio of the circumference of a circle to its diameter. Each of the sets of numbers mentioned—natural numbers, integers, rational numbers, and irrational numbers—is a subset of the set of real numbers, as shown in Figure 1.1.

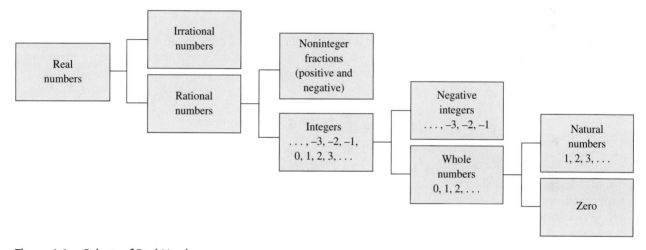

Figure 1.1   *Subsets of Real Numbers*

Study Tip

In *decimal form*, you can recognize rational numbers as decimals that terminate

$$\tfrac{1}{2} = 0.5 \quad \text{or} \quad \tfrac{3}{8} = 0.375$$

or repeat

$$\tfrac{4}{3} = 1.3\overline{3} \quad \text{or} \quad \tfrac{2}{11} = 0.18\overline{18}.$$

Irrational numbers are represented by decimals that neither terminate nor repeat, as in

$$\sqrt{2} = 1.414256237 \ldots$$

or

$$\pi = 3.14159265359 \ldots .$$

Example 1   Classifying Real Numbers

Determine which numbers in the following set are (a) natural numbers, (b) integers, (c) rational numbers, and (d) irrational numbers.

$$\left\{\tfrac{1}{2}, -1, 0, 4, -\tfrac{5}{8}, \tfrac{4}{2}, -\tfrac{3}{1}, 0.86, \sqrt{2}, \sqrt{9}\right\}$$

Solution

a. Natural numbers: $\left\{4, \tfrac{4}{2} = 2, \sqrt{9} = 3\right\}$

b. Integers: $\left\{-1, 0, 4, \tfrac{4}{2} = 2, -\tfrac{3}{1} = -3, \sqrt{9} = 3\right\}$

c. Rational numbers: $\left\{\tfrac{1}{2}, -1, 0, 4, -\tfrac{5}{8}, \tfrac{4}{2}, -\tfrac{3}{1}, 0.86, \sqrt{9} = 3\right\}$

d. Irrational numbers: $\left\{\sqrt{2}\right\}$

e. Real numbers: $\left\{\tfrac{1}{2}, -1, 0, 4, -\tfrac{5}{8}, \tfrac{4}{2}, -\tfrac{3}{1}, 0.86, \sqrt{2}, \sqrt{9}\right\}$

2 Plot numbers on the real number line.

The Real Number Line

The diagram used to represent the real numbers is called the **real number line.** It consists of a horizontal line with a point (the **origin**) labeled 0. Numbers to the left of 0 are **negative** and numbers to the right of 0 are **positive,** as shown in Figure 1.2. The real number zero is neither positive nor negative. Thus, the term **nonnegative** implies that a number may be positive *or* zero.

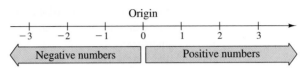

Figure 1.2   *The Real Number Line*

Drawing the point on the real number line that corresponds to a real number is called **plotting** the real number.

Example 2 illustrates the following principle. *Each point on the real number line corresponds to exactly one real number, and each real number corresponds to exactly one point on the real number line.*

Technology: Tip

The Greek letter pi, denoted by the symbol π, is the ratio of the circumference of a circle to its diameter. Because π cannot be written as a ratio of two integers, it is an irrational number. You can get an approximation of π on a scientific or graphing calculator by using the following keystrokes.

Keystroke	Display
$\boxed{\pi}$	3.141592654

Between which two integers would you plot π on the real number line?

Example 2   Plotting Real Numbers

a. In Figure 1.3(a), the point corresponds to the real number $-\frac{1}{2}$.

b. In Figure 1.3(b), the point corresponds to the real number 2.

c. In Figure 1.3(c), the point corresponds to the real number $-\frac{3}{2}$.

d. In Figure 1.3(d), the point corresponds to the real number 1.

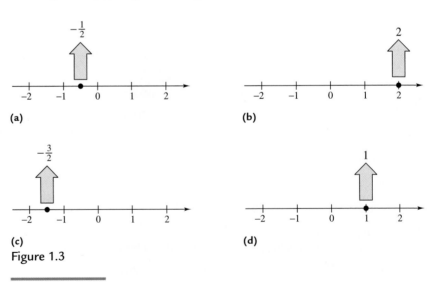

Figure 1.3

Ordering Real Numbers

If you choose any two numbers on the real number line, one of the numbers must be to the left of the other number. The number to the left is **less than** the number to the right, and the number to the right is **greater than** the number to the left. For example, from Figure 1.4 you can see that -3 is less than 2 because -3 lies to the left of 2 on the number line. A "less than" comparison is denoted by the **inequality symbol** <. For instance, "-3 is less than 2" is denoted by $-3 < 2$.

Similarly, the inequality symbol > is used to denote a "greater than" comparison. For instance, "2 is greater than -3" is denoted by $2 > -3$. The inequality symbol ≤ means **less than or equal to,** and the inequality symbol ≥ means **greater than or equal to.**

Figure 1.4 -3 *lies to the left of 2.*

When you are asked to **order** two numbers, you are simply being asked to say which of the two numbers is greater.

Example 3	Ordering Integers

Place the correct inequality symbol (< or >) between the two numbers.

a. 3   5   **b.** -3 -5 **c.** 4   0

d. -2 2   **e.** 1 -4

Solution

See Figure 1.5.

a. $3 < 5$, because 3 lies to the *left* of 5.

b. $-3 > -5$, because -3 lies to the *right* of -5.

c. $4 > 0$, because 4 lies to the *right* of 0.

d. $-2 < 2$, because -2 lies to the *left* of 2.

e. $1 > -4$, because 1 lies to the *right* of -4.

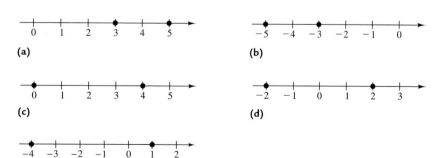

(a)   (b)   (c)   (d)   (e)

Figure 1.5

There are two ways to order fractions: you can write both fractions with the same denominator, or you can rewrite both fractions in decimal form. Here are two examples.

$$\frac{1}{3} = \frac{4}{12} \quad \text{and} \quad \frac{1}{4} = \frac{3}{12} \qquad \Longrightarrow \qquad \frac{1}{3} > \frac{1}{4}$$

$$\frac{11}{131} \approx 0.084 \quad \text{and} \quad \frac{19}{209} \approx 0.091 \qquad \Longrightarrow \qquad \frac{11}{131} < \frac{19}{209}$$

The symbol $\approx$ means "is approximately equal to."

Example 4   Ordering Fractions and Decimals

Place the correct inequality symbol ($<$ or $>$) between the two numbers.

a. $\dfrac{1}{3}$  $\dfrac{1}{5}$

b. $-\dfrac{3}{2}$  $\dfrac{1}{2}$

c. -3.1  2.8

d. -1.09  -1.90

Solution

See Figure 1.6.

a. $\frac{1}{3} > \frac{1}{5}$, because $\frac{1}{3} = \frac{5}{15}$ lies to the *right* of $\frac{1}{5} = \frac{3}{15}$.

b. $-\frac{3}{2} < \frac{1}{2}$, because $-\frac{3}{2}$ lies to the *left* of $\frac{1}{2}$.

c. $-3.1 < 2.8$, because -3.1 lies to the *left* of 2.8.

d. $-1.09 > -1.90$, because -1.09 lies to the *right* of -1.90.

(a)

(b)

(c)

(d)

Figure 1.6

4 Find the absolute value of a number.

Absolute Value

Two real numbers are **opposites** of each other if they lie the same distance from, but on opposite sides of, zero. For example, -2 is the opposite of 2, and 4 is the opposite of -4, as shown in Figure 1.7.

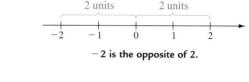

-2 is the opposite of 2.

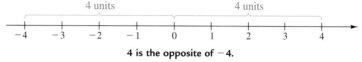

4 is the opposite of -4.

Figure 1.7

Parentheses are useful for denoting the opposite of a negative number. For example, $-(-3)$ means the opposite of -3, which you know to be 3. That is,

$$-(-3) = 3. \qquad \text{The opposite of } -3 \text{ is 3.}$$

For any real number, its distance from zero (on the real number line) is its **absolute value.** A pair of vertical bars, $|\ \ |$, is used to denote absolute value. Here are two examples.

$$|5| = \text{"distance between 5 and 0"} = 5$$

$$|-8| = \text{"distance between } -8 \text{ and 0"} = 8 \qquad \text{See Figure 1.8.}$$

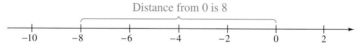

Figure 1.8

Because opposite numbers lie the same distance from 0 on the real number line, they have the same absolute value. Thus,

$$|5| = 5 \qquad \text{and} \qquad |-5| = 5. \qquad \text{See Figure 1.9.}$$

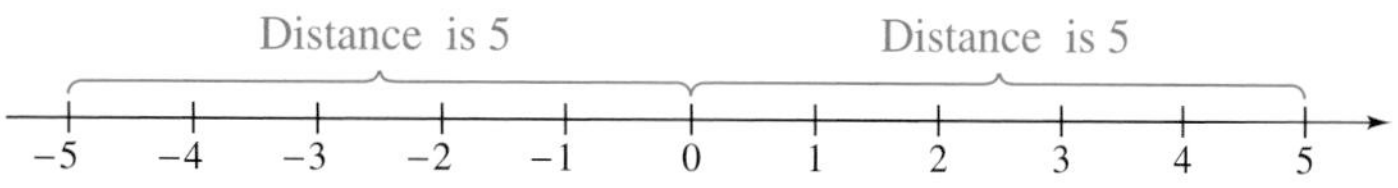

Distance is 5   Distance is 5

Figure 1.9

You can write this more simply as $|5| = |-5| = 5$.

The absolute value of a real number is either positive or zero (never negative). Moreover, zero is the only real number whose absolute value is 0. That is, $|0| = 0$.

The word **expression** means a collection of numbers and symbols such as $3 + 5$ or $|-4|$. When asked to **evaluate** an expression, you are to find the *number* that is equal to the expression.

The concept of absolute value may be difficult for some students. (The formal definition of absolute value is given in Section 1.2.)

Example 5   Evaluating Absolute Value

Evaluate the following expressions.

a. $|-10|$

b. $\left|\dfrac{3}{4}\right|$

c. $|-3.2|$

d. $-|-6|$

Solution

a. $|-10| = 10$, because the distance between -10 and 0 is 10.

b. $\left|\dfrac{3}{4}\right| = \dfrac{3}{4}$, because the distance between $\dfrac{3}{4}$ and 0 is $\dfrac{3}{4}$.

c. $|-3.2| = 3.2$, because the distance between -3.2 and 0 is 3.2.

d. $-|-6| = -(6) = -6$.

Note in Example 6(d) that $-|-6| = -6$ does not contradict the fact that the absolute value of a real number cannot be negative.

Example 6   Comparing Absolute Values

Place the correct symbol ($<$, $>$, or $=$) between the two numbers.

a. $|-9| \quad\quad |9|$

b. $0 \quad\quad |-5|$

c. $-4 \quad\quad -|-4|$

d. $|12| \quad\quad |-15|$

Solution

a. $|-9| = |9|$, because both are equal to 9.

b. $0 < |-5|$, because $|-5| = 5$ and 0 is less than 5.

c. $-4 = -|-4|$, because both numbers are equal to -4.

d. $|12| < |-15|$, because $|12| = 12$ and $|-15| = 15$, and 12 is less than 15.

Discussing the Concept   Interpreting Inequalities

The Discussing the Concept problems can be used for individual or collaborative group work, or for whole class discussion.

Is the statement "$5 \geq 5$" true? Compare your answer with those of the other students in your class. Write an explanation to support your answer.

1.1   Exercises

Developing Skills

In Exercises 1–4, determine which numbers in the set are (a) natural numbers, (b) integers, and (c) rational numbers. Plot the numbers on the real number line. See Examples 1 and 2.

1. $\left\{-3, 2, -\frac{3}{2}, \frac{9}{3}, 4.5\right\}$

2. $\left\{100, -82, -\frac{24}{3}, -8.2\right\}$

3. $\left\{-\frac{5}{2}, 6.5, -4.5, \frac{8}{4}, \frac{3}{4}\right\}$

4. $\left\{8, -1, \frac{4}{3}, -3.25, -\frac{10}{2}\right\}$

In Exercises 5–12, write the real numbers shown by the points on the real number line and place the correct inequality symbol ($<$ or $>$) between the two numbers. See Examples 3 and 4.

5.
```
  +---+---•---+---+---•---+--->
  0   1   2   3   4   5   6
```

6.
```
  •---+---•---+---+---+--->
 -5  -4  -3  -2  -1   0
```

7.
```
  +---•---+---+---•---+--->
 -5  -4  -3  -2  -1   0
```

8.
```
  +---•---+---+---+---•---+--->
 -3  -2  -1   0   1   2   3
```

9.
```
                    3
                    2
  •---+---+---+---•---+--->
 -2  -1   0   1   2
```

10.
```
    -7
     2                        5
                              2
  +---•---+---+---+---+---•---+--->
 -4  -3  -2  -1   0   1   2   3
```

11.
```
    -9
     2
  +---•---+---•---+---+--->
 -5  -4  -3  -2  -1   0
```

12.
```
      50.5        53.5
  +---•---+---+---•---+--->
 49  50  51  52  53  54
```

In Exercises 13–24, show each real number as a point on the real number line and place the correct inequality symbol ($<$ or $>$) between the real numbers. See Examples 3 and 4.

13. 3 ▢ -4

14. 6 ▢ -2

15. 4 ▢ $-\frac{7}{2}$

16. 2 ▢ $\frac{3}{2}$

17. 0 ▢ $-\frac{7}{16}$

18. $-\frac{7}{3}$ ▢ $-\frac{7}{2}$

19. -4.6 ▢ 1.5

20. 28.60 ▢ -3.75

21. $\frac{7}{16}$ ▢ $\frac{5}{8}$

22. $-\frac{3}{8}$ ▢ $-\frac{5}{8}$

23. -2π ▢ -10

24. 2 ▢ π

In Exercises 25–28, on the real number line, what is the distance between a and zero?

25. $a = 2$

26. $a = 5$

27. $a = -4$

28. $a = -10$

In Exercises 29–34, find the opposite of the number. Plot the number and its opposite on the real number line. What is the distance of each from 0?

29. 5

30. 2

31. -3.8

32. -7.5

33. $-\frac{5}{2}$

34. $\frac{3}{4}$

In Exercises 35–38, find the absolute value of the real number and its distance from 0.

35.
```
                            5
                            2
  +---+---+---+---+---•---+--->
 -3  -2  -1   0   1   2   3
```

36.
```
  •---+---+---+---+---+---+--->
 -3  -2  -1   0   1   2   3
```

37.

38.

In Exercises 39–50, evaluate the expression. See Example 5.

39. $|7|$

40. $|-6|$

41. $|-3.4|$

42. $|-16.2|$

43. $\left|-\frac{7}{2}\right|$

44. $\left|-\frac{9}{16}\right|$

45. $-|4.09|$

46. $-|-43.8|$

47. $-|-23.6|$

48. $-|91.3|$

49. $|-3.2|$

50. $|0|$

In Exercises 51–62, place the correct symbol ($<$, $>$, or $=$) between the two real numbers. See Example 6.

51. $|-15|$ ___ $|15|$

52. $|525|$ ___ $|-525|$

53. $|-4|$ ___ $|3|$

54. $|16|$ ___ $|-25|$

55. $|32|$ ___ $|-50|$

56. $|1026|$ ___ $|800|$

57. $\left|\frac{3}{16}\right|$ ___ $\left|\frac{3}{2}\right|$

58. $\left|-\frac{7}{8}\right|$ ___ $\left|\frac{4}{3}\right|$

59. $-|-48.5|$ ___ $|-48.5|$

60. $-|-64|$ ___ $|-50|$

61. $|-\pi|$ ___ $-|-2\pi|$

62. $|-4.9|$ ___ $|-10.2|$

In Exercises 63–66, show the numbers on the real number line.

63. $\frac{5}{2}$, π, -2, $-|-3|$

64. 3.7, $\frac{16}{3}$, $|-1.9|$, $-\frac{1}{2}$

65. -4, $\frac{7}{3}$, $|-3|$, 0

66. $|-2.3|$, 3.2, -2.3, $-|3.2|$

In Exercises 67–70, find all real numbers whose distance from a is given by d.

67. $a = 8$, $d = 12.5$

68. $a = 21.3$, $d = 6$

69. $a = -2$, $d = 3.5$

70. $a = 42.5$, $d = 7$

Explaining Concepts

71. Answer parts (a) to (f) of Motivating the Chapter on page 1.

72. Explain why $\frac{8}{4}$ is a natural number, but $\frac{7}{4}$ is not.

73. How many numbers are 3 units from 0 on the real number line? Explain your answer.

74. Which real number lies farther from 0?

(a) -25 (b) 10

Explain your answer.

75. Which real number lies farther from -7?

(a) 3 (b) -10

Explain your answer.

76. Explain how to determine the smaller of two distinct real numbers.

77. Select the smaller real number and explain your answer.

(a) $\frac{3}{8}$ (b) 0.35

In Exercises 78–83, determine if the statement is true or false. Explain your reasoning.

78. The absolute value of any real number is always positive.

79. The absolute value of a number is equal to the absolute value of its opposite.

80. The absolute value of a rational number is a rational number.

81. A given real number corresponds to exactly one point on the real number line.

82. The opposite of a positive number is a negative number.

83. Every rational number is an integer.

1.2   Operations with Integers

Objectives

1 Add integers with like signs and with different signs.

2 Subtract integers with like signs and with different signs.

3 Multiply integers with like signs and with different signs.

4 Divide integers with like signs and with different signs.

5 Find factors and find prime factors of an integer.

6 Represent the definitions and rules of arithmetic symbolically.

1 Add integers with like signs and with different signs.

Adding Integers

In this section, you will study the four operations of arithmetic (addition, subtraction, multiplication, and division) on the set of integers. There are many examples of these operations in real life. For instance, suppose that your business had a gain of $550 during one week and a loss of $600 the next week. Over the 2-week period, your business would have had a combined profit of

$$550 + (-600) = -50,$$

which means you had a loss of $50.

The number line is a good visual model for demonstrating addition of integers. To add a positive integer, move right, for a negative integer, move left.

Study Tip

As you continue through this chapter, try to capture the overall picture of a *mathematical system,* and note the particular features discussed in each section.

Example 1   Adding Integers Using a Number Line

Addition	*Visual Model*	*Sum*
a. $5 + 2$		$5 + 2 = 7$
b. $5 + (-2)$		$5 + (-2) = 3$
c. $-5 + 2$		$-5 + 2 = -3$
d. $-5 + (-2)$		$-5 + (-2) = -7$
e. $5 + (-5)$		$5 + (-5) = 0$

Example 1 illustrates a *graphical approach* to adding integers. It is more common to use an *analytic approach*, as summarized by the following rules.

▶ **Addition of Integers**

Example

1. To add two integers *with like signs*, add their absolute values and attach the common sign to the result.

$$-3 + (-7) = -(|-3| + |-7|)$$
$$= -(3 + 7)$$
$$= -10$$

2. To add two integers with *different signs*, subtract the smaller absolute value from the larger absolute value and attach the sign of the integer with the larger absolute value.

$$3 + (-7) = -(|-7| - |3|)$$
$$= -(7 - 3)$$
$$= -4$$

The result of an addition problem is called a **sum.**

Example 2 Adding Integers

a. Different signs: $22 + (-17) = 22 - 17 = 5$
b. Different signs: $-84 + 14 = -(84 - 14) = -70$
c. Like signs: $-138 + (-62) = -(138 + 62) = -200$

There are different ways to add three or more integers. You can use the **carrying algorithm** with a vertical format with nonnegative integers, as shown in Figure 1.10, or you can add them two at a time, as illustrated in Example 3.

Example 3 Balance in a Checking Account

Find the balance in the checking account after each of the following transactions.

a. The balance is $28. A deposit of $60 is made and a check is written for $40.
b. The balance is $120. A check is written for $132 and a deposit of $10 is made.

Solution

a. $28 + \$60 + (-\$40) = (\$28 + \$60) + (-\$40)$
$$= \$88 + (-\$40)$$
$$= \$48 \qquad \text{Balance}$$

b. $120 + (-\$132) + \$10 = -\$12 + \$10$
$$= -\$2 \qquad \text{Account is overdrawn.}$$

```
  1 1
  1 4 8
    6 2
+ 5 3 6
-------
  7 4 6
```

Figure 1.10 *Carrying Algorithm*

2 Subtract integers with like signs and with different signs.

Subtracting Integers

Subtraction can be thought of as "taking away." For instance, $8 - 5$ can be thought of as "8 take away 5," which leaves 3. On the number line, you first move 8 units to the right, then 5 units to the left, as shown in Figure 1.11(a). This same result is accomplished by "adding the opposite of 5 to 8," as shown in Figure 1.11(b).

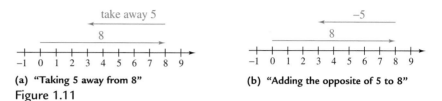

(a) "Taking 5 away from 8"   (b) "Adding the opposite of 5 to 8"

Figure 1.11

> ▶ **Subtraction of Integers**
>
> To **subtract** one integer from another, add the opposite of the integer being subtracted to the other integer. The result is called the **difference** of the two integers.
>
> $$\begin{matrix}\text{First} \\ \text{number}\end{matrix} \;-\; \begin{matrix}\text{Second} \\ \text{number}\end{matrix} \;=\; \begin{matrix}\text{First} \\ \text{number}\end{matrix} \;+\; \begin{matrix}\text{Opposite of} \\ \text{second number}\end{matrix}$$

The **opposite** of an integer is also called its **additive inverse.** For instance, the additive inverse of 5 is -5. The name *additive inverse* comes from the fact that the sum of an integer and its additive inverse is 0. For instance, $5 + (-5) = 0$.

```
   3  10  15
   4   1   5
 - 2   7   6
 ─────────────
   1   3   9
```

Figure 1.12   *Borrowing Algorithm*

Example 4   Subtracting Integers

a. $3 - 8 = 3 + (-8) = -5$ Add opposite of 8.

b. $10 - (-13) = 10 + 13 = 23$ Add opposite of -13.

c. $-5 - 12 = -5 + (-12) = -17$ Add opposite of 12.

d. $-4 - (-17) - 23 = -4 + 17 + (-23) = -10$ Add opposite of -17 and opposite of 23.

Be sure you understand that the terminology involving subtraction is not the same as that used for negative numbers. For instance, -5 is read as "negative 5," but $8 - 5$ is read as "8 subtract 5." It is important to distinguish between the operation and the signs of the numbers involved. For instance, in

$$-3 - 5$$

the operation is subtraction and the numbers are -3 and 5.

For subtraction problems involving only two nonnegative integers, you can use the **borrowing algorithm** shown in Figure 1.12.

Example 5	Temperature Change

The temperature at 4 P.M. was 15°. By midnight, the temperature had decreased by 18°. What was the temperature at midnight?

Solution

To find the temperature at midnight, subtract 18 from 15.

$$15 - 18 = 15 + (-18) = -3$$

The temperature at midnight was $-3°$.

This text includes several examples and exercises that use a calculator. As each new calculator application is encountered, you will be given general instructions for using a calculator. These instructions, however, may not agree precisely with the steps required by *your* calculator, so be sure you are familiar with the use of the keys on your own calculator.

For each of the calculator examples in the text, we will give two possible keystroke sequences: one for a standard *scientific* calculator and one for a *graphing* calculator.

Example 6	Evaluating Expressions with a Calculator

Throughout the text, sample keystrokes are given for scientific and graphing calculators. Urge students to familiarize themselves with the keystrokes appropriate for their own calculators.

Evaluate the following with a calculator.

a. $-4 - 5$ **b.** $2 - (3 - 9)$

	Keystrokes	*Display*	
a.	4 +/− − 5 =	−9	Scientific
	(−) 4 − 5 ENTER	−9	Graphing

	Keystrokes	*Display*	
b.	2 − (3 − 9) =	8	Scientific
	2 − (3 − 9) ENTER	8	Graphing

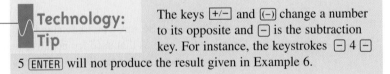

Technology: Tip   The keys +/− and (−) change a number to its opposite and − is the subtraction key. For instance, the keystrokes − 4 − 5 ENTER will not produce the result given in Example 6.

3 Multiply integers with like signs and with different signs.

Multiplying Integers

Multiplication of two integers can be described as repeated addition or subtraction. The result of multiplying one number by another is called a **product.** Here are two examples.

Multiplication	*Repeated Addition*
$3 \times 5 = 15$	$\underbrace{5 + 5 + 5}_{} = 15$
	Add 5 three times.
$4 \times (-2) = -8$	$\underbrace{(-2) + (-2) + (-2) + (-2)}_{} = -8$
	Add -2 four times.

Multiplication is denoted in a variety of ways. For instance,

$$7 \times 3, \quad 7 \cdot 3, \quad 7(3), \quad (7)3, \quad \text{and} \quad (7)(3)$$

all denote the product of "7 times 3," which is 21.

▶ **Rules for Multiplying Integers**

   1. The product of an integer and zero is 0.

   2. The product of two integers with *like* signs is *positive.*

   3. The product of two integers with *different* signs is *negative.*

To find the product of more than two numbers, first find the product of their absolute values. If there is an *even* number of negative factors, then the product is positive. If there is an *odd* number of negative factors, then the product is negative. For instance,

$$5(-3)(-4)(7) = 420.$$ Even number of negative factors

As you move through this section, be sure your students understand the relationship between multiplication and division. This will help them as they learn to solve equations.

Example 7   Multiplying Integers

a. $-6 \cdot 9 = -54$ (Negative) · (positive) = (negative)

b. $(-5)(-7) = 35$ (Negative) · (negative) = (positive)

c. $3(-12) = -36$ (Positive) · (negative) = (negative)

d. $-12 \cdot 0 = 0$ (Negative) · (zero) = (zero)

e. $(-2)(8)(-3)(-1) = -(2 \cdot 8 \cdot 3 \cdot 1)$ Odd number of negative factors

$\qquad\qquad\qquad\qquad = -48$ Answer is negative.

$$
\begin{array}{r}
47 \\
\times \quad 23 \\
\hline
141 \\
94 \\
\hline
1081
\end{array}
$$

141 ⇐ Multiply 3 times 47.

94 ⇐ Multiply 2 times 47.

1081 ⇐ Add columns.

Figure 1.13   *Vertical Multiplication Algorithm*

Be careful to distinguish properly between expressions such as $3(-5)$ and $3 - 5$ or $-3(-5)$ and $-3 - 5$. The first of each pair is a multiplication problem, whereas the second is a subtraction problem.

Multiplication	*Subtraction*
$3(-5) = -15$	$3 - 5 = -2$
$-3(-5) = 15$	$-3 - 5 = -8$

To multiply two integers having two or more digits, we suggest the **vertical multiplication algorithm** demonstrated in Figure 1.13. The sign of the product is determined by the usual multiplication rule.

Example 8   Geometry: Volume of a Box

Find the volume of the rectangular box shown in Figure 1.14.

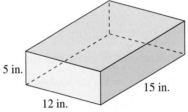

5 in.

15 in.

12 in.

Figure 1.14

Study Tip

Formulas for geometric figures can be found on the inside front cover of this text.

Solution

To find the volume, multiply the length, width, and height of the box.

$$
\begin{aligned}
\text{Volume} &= (\text{Length}) \cdot (\text{Width}) \cdot (\text{Height}) \\
&= (15 \text{ in.}) \cdot (12 \text{ in.}) \cdot (5 \text{ in.}) \\
&= 900 \text{ cubic inches}
\end{aligned}
$$

So, the box has a volume of 900 cubic inches.

---

4 Divide integers with like signs and with different signs.

Dividing Integers

Just as subtraction can be expressed in terms of addition, you can express division in terms of multiplication. Here are some examples.

Division		*Related Multiplication*
$12 \div 4 = 3$	because	$12 = 3 \cdot 4$
$15 \div 3 = 5$	because	$15 = 5 \cdot 3$
$15 \div (-3) = -5$	because	$15 = (-5) \cdot (-3)$
$-15 \div (-3) = 5$	because	$-15 = 5 \cdot (-3)$

The result of dividing one integer by another is called the **quotient** of the integers. Division is denoted by the symbol ÷, or by /, or by a horizontal line. For example,

$$30 \div 6, \quad 30/6, \quad \text{and} \quad \frac{30}{6}$$

all denote the quotient of 30 and 6, which is 5. Using the form $30 \div 6$, 30 is called the **dividend** and 6 is the **divisor**. In the forms 30/6 and $\frac{30}{6}$, 30 is the **numerator** and 6 is the **denominator**.

It is important to know how to use 0 in a division problem. Zero divided by a nonzero integer is always 0. For instance,

$$\frac{0}{13} = 0 \quad \text{because} \quad 0 = 0 \cdot 13.$$

On the other hand, division by zero is *undefined*.

Because division can be described in terms of multiplication, the rules for dividing two integers with like or unlike signs are the same as those for multiplying such integers.

▶ **Rules for Dividing Integers**

1. Zero divided by a nonzero integer is 0, whereas a nonzero integer divided by zero is *undefined*.

2. The quotient of two nonzero integers with *like* signs is *positive*.

3. The quotient of two nonzero integers with *different* signs is *negative*.

Example 9   Dividing Integers

a. $\dfrac{-42}{-6} = 7$ because $-42 = 7(-6)$.

b. $36 \div (-9) = -4$ because $(-4)(-9) = 36$.

c. $\dfrac{0}{-13} = 0$ because $(0)(-13) = 0$.

d. $-105 \div 7 = -15$ because $(-15)(7) = -105$.

When dividing large numbers, the **long division algorithm** can be used. For instance, the long division algorithm shown in Figure 1.15 shows that

$$\frac{351}{13} = 27.$$

Remember that division can be checked by multiplying the answer by the divisor. So it is true that

$$\frac{351}{13} = 27 \quad \text{because} \quad 27(13) = 351.$$

Technology: Discovery

Does $\frac{1}{0} = 0$? Does $\frac{2}{0} = 0$? Write each division above in terms of multiplication. What does this tell you about division by zero? What does your calculator display when you perform the division?

You may want to emphasize the important distinction between division *of* zero by a nonzero number and division *by* zero. For example,

$\frac{0}{4}$ and $\frac{0}{-23}$ are equal to 0.

$\frac{-1}{0}$ and $\frac{8}{0}$ are undefined.

$$\begin{array}{r} 27 \\ 13\overline{)351} \\ \underline{26} \\ 91 \\ \underline{91} \end{array}$$

Figure 1.15   *Long Division Algorithm*

All four operations on integers (addition, subtraction, multiplication, and division) are used in the following real-life example.

Example 10 Stock Purchase

On Monday you bought $500 worth of stock in a company. During the rest of the week, you recorded the following gains and losses in your stock's value.

Tuesday	Wednesday	Thursday	Friday
Gained $15	Lost $18	Lost $23	Gained $10

a. What was the value of the stock at the close of Tuesday?

b. What was the value of the stock at the close of Wednesday?

c. What was the value of the stock at the end of the week?

d. What would the total loss have been if Thursday's loss had occurred each of the four days?

e. What was the average daily gain (or loss) for the four days recorded?

Solution

a. Because the original value of the stock was $500, and the stock gained $15 by the close of Tuesday, its value at the close of Tuesday was

$$500 + 15 = \$515.$$

b. Using the result of part (a), the value at the close of Wednesday was

$$515 - 18 = \$497.$$

c. The value of the stock at the end of the week was

$$500 + 15 - 18 - 23 + 10 = \$484.$$

d. The loss on Thursday was $23. If this loss had occurred each day, the total loss would have been

$$4(23) = \$92.$$

e. To find the average of the four gains and losses, we add and divide by 4. Thus, the average is

$$\text{Average} = \frac{15 + (-18) + (-23) + 10}{4} = \frac{-16}{4} = -4.$$

This means that during the four days, the stock had an average loss of $4 per day.

Study Tip

To find the **average** of n numbers, add the numbers and divide the result by n.

5 Find factors and find prime factors of an integer.

Factors and Prime Numbers

The set of positive integers

$$\{1, 2, 3, \ldots\}$$

is one subset of the real numbers that has intrigued mathematicians for many centuries.

Historically, an important number concept has been *factors* of positive integers. From experience, you know that in a multiplication problem such as $3 \cdot 7 = 21$, the numbers 3 and 7 are called *factors* of 21.

$$3 \cdot 7 = 21$$

Factors   Product

It is also correct to call the numbers 3 and 7 *divisors* of 21, because 3 and 7 each divide evenly into 21.

▶ Factor (or Divisor)

If a and b are positive integers, then a is a **factor** (or **divisor**) of b if and only if there is a positive integer c such that $a \cdot c = b$.

The concept of factors allows you to classify positive integers into three groups: *prime* numbers, *composite* numbers, and the number 1.

▶ Prime and Composite Numbers

1. A positive integer greater than 1 with no factors other than itself and 1 is called a **prime number,** or simply a **prime.**

2. A positive integer greater than 1 with more than two factors is called a **composite number,** or simply a **composite.**

The numbers 2, 3, 5, 7, and 11 are primes because they have only themselves and 1 as factors. The numbers 4, 6, 8, 9, and 10 are composites because each has more than two factors. The number 1 is neither prime nor composite because 1 is its only factor.

Every composite number can be expressed as a *unique* product of prime factors. Here are some examples.

$$6 = 2 \cdot 3, \; 15 = 3 \cdot 5, \; 18 = 2 \cdot 3 \cdot 3, \; 42 = 2 \cdot 3 \cdot 7, \; 124 = 2 \cdot 2 \cdot 31$$

According to the definition of a prime number, is it possible for any negative number to be prime? Consider the number -2. Is it prime? Are its only factors one and itself? No, because

$$-2 = 1(-2),$$

$$-2 = (-1)(2),$$

or $-2 = (-1)(1)(2).$

Pythagoras

(580–500 B.C.)

In the 5th century B.C., the followers of the Greek mathematician Pythagoras believed that numbers revealed the basic structure of the universe. They devoted their lives to the study, discovery, and proof of number patterns. Their works laid the foundation for the field of mathematics now called *number theory.*

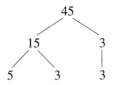

Figure 1.16   *Tree Diagram*

One strategy for factoring a composite number into prime numbers is to begin by finding the smallest prime number that is a factor of the composite number. Dividing this factor into the number yields a *companion* factor. For instance, 3 is the smallest prime number that is a factor of 45 and its companion factor is $15 = 45 \div 3$. Because 15 is also a composite number, continue hunting for factors and companion factors until each factor is prime. As shown in Figure 1.16, a *tree diagram* is a nice way to record your work. From the tree diagram, you can see that the prime factorization of 45 is $45 = 3 \cdot 3 \cdot 5$.

| Example 11 | Prime Factorization |

Find the prime factorization of each of the following.

a. 84   **b.** 78   **c.** 133   **d.** 43

Solution

a. 4 is a recognized divisor of 84. So, $84 = 4 \cdot 21 = 2 \cdot 2 \cdot 3 \cdot 7$.

b. 2 is a recognized divisor of 78. So, $78 = 2 \cdot 39 = 2 \cdot 3 \cdot 13$.

c. If you do not recognize a divisor of 133, you can get started by dividing any of the prime numbers 2, 3, 5, 7, 11, 13, etc., into 133. You will find 7 to be the first prime to divide 133. So, $133 = 7 \cdot 19$ (19 is prime).

d. In this case, none of the primes less than 43 divides 43. So, 43 is prime.

──────────

Other aids to finding prime factors of a number *n* include the following divisibility tests.

▶ **Divisibility Tests**

		Example
1.	A number is divisible by 2 if it is *even*.	364 is divisible by 2 because it is even.
2.	A number is divisible by 3 if the sum of its digits is divisible by 3.	261 is divisible by 3 because $2 + 6 + 1 = 9$.
3.	A number is divisible by 9 if the sum of its digits is divisible by 9.	738 is divisible by 9 because $7 + 3 + 8 = 18$.
4.	A number is divisible by 5 if its units digit is 0 or 5.	325 is divisible by 5 because its units digit is 5.
5.	A number is divisible by 10 if its units digit is 0.	120 is divisible by 10 because its units digit is 0.

When a number is **divisible** by 2, it means that 2 divides into the number without leaving a remainder.

6 Represent the definitions and rules of arithmetic symbolically.

Summary of Definitions and Rules

So far in this chapter, we have described rules and procedures more with words than with symbols. For instance, subtraction is verbally defined as "adding the opposite of the number being subtracted." As you move to higher and higher levels of mathematics, it becomes more and more convenient to use symbols to describe rules and procedures. For instance, subtraction is symbolically defined as $a - b = a + (-b)$.

At its simplest level, algebra is a symbolic form of arithmetic. This arithmetic–algebra connection can be illustrated in the following way.

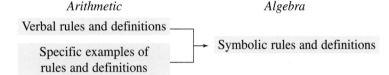

An illustration of this connection is shown in Example 12.

The transition from verbal and numeric descriptions to symbolic descriptions is an important step in a student's progression from arithmetic to algebra.

| **Example 12** | Writing a Rule of Arithmetic in Symbolic Form

Write an example and an algebraic description of the arithmetic rule:
The product of two integers with unlike signs is negative.

Solution

Example

For the integers -3 and 7,

$$(-3) \cdot 7 = 3 \cdot (-7)$$
$$= -(3 \cdot 7)$$
$$= -21.$$

Algebraic Description

If a and b are positive integers, then

$$\underbrace{(-a) \cdot b}_{\substack{\text{Unlike} \\ \text{signs}}} = \underbrace{a \cdot (-b)}_{\substack{\text{Unlike} \\ \text{signs}}} = \underbrace{-(a \cdot b)}_{\substack{\text{Negative} \\ \text{product}}}.$$

The following list summarizes the algebraic versions of important definitions and rules of arithmetic. In each case a specific example is included for clarification.

▶ **Arithmetic Summary**

Definitions: Let a, b, and c be integers.

Encourage students to read and study the definitions and rules on the left and compare them with the examples on the right. Most students need practice in "reading mathematics."

Definition	*Example*

1. Subtraction:

$$a - b = a + (-b)$$

$$5 - 7 = 5 + (-7)$$

2. Multiplication: (a is a positive integer)

$$a \cdot b = \underbrace{b + b + \cdots + b}_{a \text{ terms}}$$

$$3 \cdot 5 = 5 + 5 + 5$$

3. Division: $(b \neq 0)$

$$a \div b = c, \text{ if and only if } a = c \cdot b.$$

$$12 \div 4 = 3 \text{ because } 12 = 3 \cdot 4$$

4. Less than:

$$a < b \text{ if there is a positive real number } c \text{ such that } a + c = b.$$

$$-2 < 1 \text{ because } -2 + 3 = 1$$

5. Absolute value: $|a| = \begin{cases} a, & \text{if } a \geq 0 \\ -a, & \text{if } a < 0 \end{cases}$

$$|-3| = -(-3) = 3$$

6. Divisor:

a is a divisor of b if and only if there is an integer c such that $a \cdot c = b$.

7 is a divisor of 21 because $7 \cdot 3 = 21$

Rules: Let a and b be integers.

Rule	*Example*

1. Addition:

(a) If a and b have *like* signs, evaluate $|a| + |b|$ and attach the common sign to the result.

$$3 + 7 = |3| + |7| = 10$$

(b) If a and b have *different* signs, evaluate which difference, $|a| - |b|$ or $|b| - |a|$, is positive and attach the sign of the integer with the larger absolute value.

$$-5 + 8 = |8| - |-5|$$
$$= 8 - 5$$
$$= 3$$

2. Multiplication:

(a) $a \cdot 0 = 0 = 0 \cdot a$

$$3 \cdot 0 = 0 = 0 \cdot 3$$

(b) Like signs: $a \cdot b > 0$

$$(-2)(-5) = 10$$

(c) Different signs: $a \cdot b < 0$

$$(2)(-5) = -10$$

3. Division:

(a) $\dfrac{0}{a} = 0$

$$\dfrac{0}{4} = 0$$

(b) $\dfrac{a}{0}$ is undefined.

$\dfrac{6}{0}$ is undefined.

(c) Like signs: $\dfrac{a}{b} > 0$

$$\dfrac{-2}{-3} = \dfrac{2}{3}$$

(d) Different signs: $\dfrac{a}{b} < 0$

$$\dfrac{-5}{7} = -\dfrac{5}{7}$$

Example 13   Using Definitions and Rules

a. Use the definition of subtraction to complete the following.

$$4 - 9 = $$

b. Use the definition of multiplication to complete the following.

$$6 + 6 + 6 + 6 = $$

c. Use the definition of absolute value to complete the following.

$$|-9| = $$

d. Use the rule for adding integers with unlike signs to complete the following.

$$-7 + 3 = $$

e. Use the rule for multiplying integers with unlike signs to complete the following.

$$-9 \times 2 = $$

Solution

a. $4 - 9 = 4 + (-9) = -5$

b. $6 + 6 + 6 + 6 = 4 \cdot 6 = 24$

c. $|-9| = -(-9) = 9$

d. $-7 + 3 = -(|-7| - |3|) = -4$

e. $-9 \times 2 = -18$

Discussing the Concept	Finding a Pattern

Complete the patterns below. Decide which rules the patterns demonstrate. Use a calculator to confirm your answers.

$3 \cdot (3)$	$= 9$	$-3 \cdot (3)$	$=$	-9
$3 \cdot (2)$	$= 6$	$-3 \cdot (2)$	$=$	-6
$3 \cdot (1)$	$= 3$	$-3 \cdot (1)$	$=$	-3
$3 \cdot (0)$	$= 0$	$-3 \cdot (0)$	$=$	0
$3 \cdot (-1) =$		$-3 \cdot (-1) =$		
$3 \cdot (-2) =$		$-3 \cdot (-2) =$		
$3 \cdot (-3) =$		$-3 \cdot (-3) =$		

1.2   Exercises

Developing Skills

In Exercises 1–4, find the required sum and demonstrate the addition on the real number line. See Example 1.

1. $2 + 7$

2. $10 + (-3)$

3. $-6 + 4$

4. $(-8) + (-3)$

In Exercises 5–32, find the sum. See Example 2.

5. $-1 + 0$

6. $-3 + 0$

7. $14 + (-14)$

8. $-45 + 45$

9. $(-14) + 13$

10. $(-20) + 19$

11. $-23 + 4$

12. $10 + (-10)$

13. $-18 + (-12)$

14. $-34 + (-16)$

15. $-32 + 16$

16. $-75 + 100$

17. $5 + |-3|$

18. $49 + (-|-17|)$

19. $-|-12| + |-16|$

20. $|-10| + |35|$

21. $-10 + 6 + 34$

22. $-15 + (-3) + 8$

23. $-82 + (-36) + 82$

24. $15 + (-75) + (-75)$

25. $32 + (-32) + (-16)$

26. $-312 + (-564) + (-100)$

27. $1200 + 1300 + (-275)$

28. $104 + 203 + 613 + (-214)$

29. $1875 + (-3143) + 5826$

30. $4365 + (-2145) + (-1873) + 40{,}084$

31. $|-890| + (-|-82|) + 90$

32. $-770 + |492| + (-|-383|)$

In Exercises 33–54, find the difference. See Example 4.

33. $12 - 9$

34. $4 - (-1)$

35. $-4 - (-4)$

36. $9 - (-6)$

37. $55 - 20$

38. $39 - 13$

39. $45 - 35$

40. $27 - 57$

41. $-71 - 32$

42. $-84 - 106$

43. $-10 - (-4)$

44. $2500 - (-600)$

45. $-210 - 400$

46. $-110 - (-30)$

47. $-942 - (-942)$

48. $-12 - (-7)$

49. $|15| - |-7|$

50. $|-100| - |25|$

51. $23 - |15|$

52. $-125 - |165|$

53. $-32 - (-18)$

54. $|515 - 160 - 480|$

55. Find the sum of 250 and -300.

56. Find the sum of -40 and -60.

57. Subtract -120 from 380.

58. Find the absolute value of the sum of -35 and 15.

59. What number must be added to 10 to obtain -5?

60. What number must be subtracted from -12 to obtain 24?

In Exercises 61–64, write each multiplication as repeated addition and find the product.

61. $3 \cdot 2$

62. 4×5

63. $5 \times (-3)$

64. $6(-2)$

In Exercises 65–80, find the product. See Example 7.

65. 7×3

66. $0 \cdot 2$

67. $4(-8)$

68. $10(-5)$

69. $(-6)(-12)$

70. $(-20)(-8)$

71. $(310)(-3)$

72. $(-500)(-6)$

73. $5(-3)(-6)$

74. $-7(3)(-1)$

75. $(-2)(-3)(-5)$

76. $(-10)(-4)(-2)$

77. $|3(-5)(6)|$

78. $|6(20)(4)|$

79. $|(-3)4|$

80. $|8(-9)|$

In Exercises 81–86, use the vertical multiplication algorithm to find the product.

81. 26×13 **82.** $(-14) \times 24$

83. $75(-63)$ **84.** $(-13)(-20)$

85. $(-72)(866)$ **86.** $(-14)(-585)$

In Exercises 87–100, perform the division, if possible. If not possible, state the reason. See Example 9.

87. $27 \div 9$ **88.** $-35 \div (-5)$

89. $72 \div (-12)$ **90.** $(-28) \div 4$

91. $\dfrac{8}{0}$ **92.** $\dfrac{0}{8}$

93. $\dfrac{-81}{-3}$ **94.** $\dfrac{-125}{-25}$

95. $\dfrac{6}{-1}$ **96.** $\dfrac{-12}{1}$

97. $\dfrac{0}{81}$ **98.** $\dfrac{32}{0}$

99. $-180 \div (-45)$ **100.** $(-27) \div (-27)$

In Exercises 101–106, use the long division algorithm to find the quotient.

101. $1440 \div 45$ **102.** $-1312 \div (-16)$

103. $1440 \div (-45)$ **104.** $-1312 \div 16$

105. $2750 \div 25$ **106.** $22{,}010 \div 71$

In Exercises 107–112, use a calculator to perform the specified operation(s).

107. $5(1650) - 3710$ **108.** $516 - (-125)$

109. $\dfrac{44{,}290}{515}$ **110.** $\dfrac{33{,}511}{47}$

111. $\dfrac{169{,}290}{162}$ **112.** $\dfrac{1{,}027{,}500}{250}$

In Exercises 113 and 114, find the product mentally. Explain your strategy.

113. $(-2)(532)(500)$ **114.** $72(8)(25)$

In Exercises 115–124, is the number prime or composite?

115. 240   **116.** 257

117. 643   **118.** 533

119. 3911   **120.** 1281

121. 8324   **122.** 3555

123. 1321   **124.** 1323

In Exercises 125–134, write the prime factorization. See Example 11.

125. 12   **126.** 52

127. 210   **128.** 561

129. 192   **130.** 245

131. 525   **132.** 264

133. 2535   **134.** 1521

Solving Problems

135. *Temperature Change*   The temperature at 6 A.M. was $-10°F$. By noon, the temperature had increased by $22°F$. What was the temperature at noon?

136. *Balance in an Account*   At the beginning of a month, your balance was $2750. During the month you withdrew $350 and $500, deposited $450, and earned interest of $6.42. What was your balance at the end of the month?

137. *Profit*   Your company lost $650,000 during the first 6 months of the year. By the end of the year, you had an overall profit of $362,000. What was your profit during the second 6 months of the year?

138. *Flying Altitude*   An airliner flying at an altitude of 31,000 feet is instructed to descend to an altitude of 24,000 feet (see figure). How many feet must the aircraft descend?

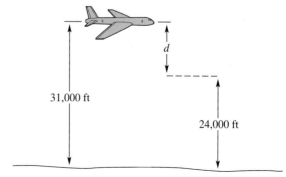

139. *Endowments*   The bar graph gives the market values of Penn State's endowment and similar funds on June 30 in the years 1986 to 1997. (Source: *Penn State Intercom, October 9, 1997*)

(a) Estimate the increase in the market value from 1990 to 1995.

(b) How much greater was the increase from 1996 to 1997 than the increase from 1995 to 1996?

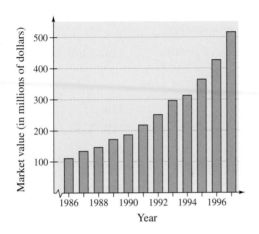

140. *Charitable Giving*   The bar graph gives the sources of charitable giving for the year 1996. (Source: *USA Today*)

(a) How much greater is the giving by individuals than the giving by foundations?

(b) The giving by individuals is approximately (to the nearest integer) how many times greater than the giving by corporations?

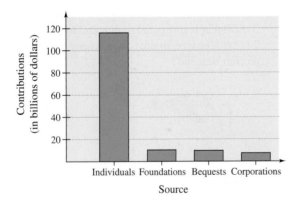

141. *Temperature Change*   The temperature measured by a weather balloon is decreasing approximately 3° for each 1000-foot increase in altitude. The balloon rises 8000 feet. Describe its total temperature change.

142. *Stock Prices*   The Dow Jones average loses 11 points on each of 4 consecutive days. What is the cumulative loss during the 4 days?

143. *Savings Plan*   After you save $50 per month for 10 years, what is the total amount you have saved?

144. *Loss Leaders*   To attract customers, a grocery store runs a sale on bananas. The bananas are *loss leaders*, which means the store loses money on the bananas but hopes to make it up on other items. The store sells 800 pounds at a loss of 26 cents per pound. What is the total loss?

145. *Geometry*   Find the area of the football field.

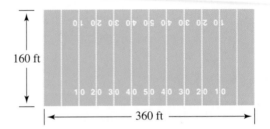

146. *Geometry*   Find the area of the garden.

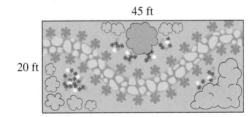

147. *Average Speed*   A commuter train travels a distance of 195 miles between two cities in 3 hours. What is the average speed of the train in miles per hour?

148. *Exam Scores*   A student has a total of 328 points after four 100-point exams.

(a) What is the average number of points scored per exam?

(b) The scores on the four exams are 87, 73, 77, and 91. Plot each of the scores and the average score on the real number line.

(c) Find the difference between each score and the average score. Find the sum of these distances and give a possible explanation of the result.

Geometry   In Exercises 149 and 150, find the volume of the rectangular solid. The volume is found by multiplying the length, width, and height of the solid. See Example 8.

149.

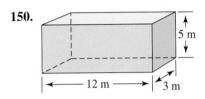

11 in.

9 in.   6 in.

150.

5 m

12 m   3 m

In Exercises 151 and 152, an addition problem is shown visually on the real number line. (a) Write the addition problem and find the sum. (b) State the rule for the addition of integers demonstrated. (c) Suppose the numbers represent the yards gained in two consecutive downs of a football game. How would the sportscasters announce the plays?

151.

-2 -1   0   1   2   3   4   5   6

152.

-3 -2 -1   0   1   2   3   4   5

Explaining Concepts

153. *Writing*   What is the only even prime number? Explain why there are no other even prime numbers.

154. *Investigation*   Twin primes are prime numbers that differ by 2. For instance, 3 and 5 are twin primes. How many other twin primes are less than 100?

155. *Think About It*   The number 1997 is not divisible by a prime number that is less than 45. Explain why this implies that 1997 is a prime number.

156. *The Sieve of Eratosthenes*   Write the integers from 1 through 100 in 10 lines of 10 numbers each.

(a) Cross out the number 1. Cross out all multiples of 2 other than 2 itself. Do the same for 3, 5, and 7.

(b) Of what type are the remaining numbers? Explain why this is the only type of number left.

157. Explain why the sum of two negative numbers is a negative number.

158. Write the rule for adding two numbers of opposite sign. How do you determine the sign of the sum?

159. If a negative number is used as a factor 25 times, what is the sign of the product?

160. If a negative number is used as a factor 16 times, what is the sign of the product?

161. Write a verbal description of what is meant by $3(-5)$.

162. Write the rules for determining the sign of the product or quotient of real numbers.

163. Explain why the product of an even integer and any other integer is even. What can you conclude about the product of two odd integers?

164. Explain how to check the result of a division problem.

165. An integer n is divided by 2 and the quotient is an even integer. What does this tell you about n? Give an example.

166. Which of the following is (are) undefined: $\frac{1}{1}, \frac{0}{1}, \frac{1}{0}, \frac{0}{0}$?

167. The **proper factors** of a number are all its factors less than the number itself. A number is **perfect** if the sum of its proper factors is equal to the number. A number is **abundant** if the sum of its proper factors is greater than the number. Which numbers less than 25 are perfect? Which are abundant? Compare your answers with those in your group and resolve any differences. Try to find the first perfect number greater than 25.

The symbol ✿✿ indicates an exercise that can be used as a discussion problem in place of or in addition to the Discussing the Concept problem given at the end of the section.

Mid-Chapter Quiz

Take this test as you would take a test in class. After you are done, check your work against the answers given in the back of the book.

In Exercises 1–4, show each real number as a point on the real line and place the correct inequality symbol (< or >) between the real numbers.

1. -2.5 ▨ -4

2. $\frac{3}{16}$ ▨ $\frac{3}{8}$

3. -3.1 ▨ 2.7

4. 2π ▨ 6

In Exercises 5 and 6, evaluate the expression.

5. $-|-0.75|$

6. $|25.2|$

In Exercises 7 and 8, place the correct symbol (<, > or =) between the real numbers.

7. $\left|\frac{7}{2}\right|$ ▨ $|-3.5|$

8. $\left|\frac{3}{4}\right|$ ▨ $-|0.75|$

In Exercises 9 and 10, copy the number line, write the opposites of a and b, and plot the opposites on the number line.

9.

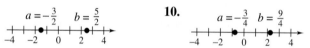

$a = -\frac{3}{2}$ $b = \frac{5}{2}$

10.

$a = -\frac{3}{4}$ $b = \frac{9}{4}$

In Exercises 11–16, evaluate the expression.

11. $-15 - 12$

12. $-15 - (-12)$

13. $25 + |-75|$

14. $-6(10)$

15. $\dfrac{-45}{-3}$

16. $\dfrac{-24}{6}$

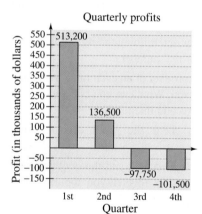

Quarterly profits

Figure for 17

17. A company's quarterly profits are shown in the bar graph at the left. What is the company's total profit for the year?

18. A cord of wood is a pile 8 feet long, 4 feet wide, and 4 feet high. The volume of a rectangular solid is its length times its width times its height. Find the number of cubic feet in a cord of wood.

19. It is necessary to cut a 90-foot rope into six pieces of equal length. What is the length of each piece?

20. Consider the statement, "The sum of two negative integers is positive." Is the statement true or false? If it is false, suggest any change that would make it true.

1.3   Operations with Rational Numbers

Objectives

1 Rewrite fractions as equivalent fractions.

2 Add and subtract fractions.

3 Multiply and divide fractions.

4 Add, subtract, multiply, and divide decimals.

---

1 Rewrite fractions as equivalent fractions.

Rewriting Fractions

A **fraction** is a number that is written as a quotient, with a *numerator* and a *denominator*. The terms *fraction* and *rational number* are related, but are not exactly the same. The term *fraction* refers to a number's form, whereas the term *rational number* refers to its classification. For instance, the number 2 is a fraction when it is written as $\frac{2}{1}$, but it is a rational number regardless of how it is written.

> ▶ **Rules of Signs for Fractions**
>
> **1.** If the numerator and denominator of a fraction have *like* signs, the value of the fraction is *positive*.
>
> **2.** If the numerator and denominator of a fraction have *unlike* signs, the value of the fraction is *negative*.

Study Tip

To find the **greatest common factor** of two natural numbers, list their factors, identify the factors that are common, and then identify the greatest of the common factors. For instance, the greatest common factor of 16 and 24 is 8.

| **Example 1** | Positive and Negative Fractions |

a. All of the following fractions are positive and are equivalent to $\frac{2}{3}$.

$$\frac{2}{3}, \frac{-2}{-3}, -\frac{-2}{3}, -\frac{2}{-3}$$

b. All of the following fractions are negative and are equivalent to $-\frac{2}{3}$.

$$-\frac{2}{3}, \frac{-2}{3}, \frac{2}{-3}, -\frac{-2}{-3}$$

In both arithmetic and algebra, it is often beneficial to write a fraction in **simplest form** or **reduced form,** which means that the numerator and denominator have no common factors (other than 1). By finding the prime factors of the numerator and the denominator, you can determine what common factor(s) to divide out.

> ▶ **Writing a Fraction in Simplest Form**
>
> To write a fraction in simplest form, divide both the numerator and denominator by their greatest common factor (GCF).

You can obtain an **equivalent fraction** by multiplying the numerator and denominator by the same nonzero number or by dividing the numerator and denominator by the same nonzero number. Here are some examples.

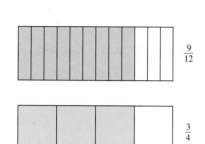

$\dfrac{9}{12}$

$\dfrac{3}{4}$

Figure 1.17 *Equivalent Fractions*

Fraction	*Equivalent Fraction*	*Operation*
$\dfrac{9}{12} = \dfrac{\overset{1}{\cancel{3}} \cdot 3}{\underset{1}{\cancel{3}} \cdot 4}$	$\dfrac{3}{4}$	Divide numerator and denominator by 3. (See Figure 1.17.)
$\dfrac{6}{5} = \dfrac{6 \cdot 2}{5 \cdot 2}$	$\dfrac{12}{10}$	Multiply numerator and denominator by 2.
$\dfrac{-8}{12} = -\dfrac{\overset{1}{\cancel{2}} \cdot \overset{1}{\cancel{2}} \cdot 2}{\underset{1}{\cancel{2}} \cdot \underset{1}{\cancel{2}} \cdot 3}$	$-\dfrac{2}{3}$	Divide numerator and denominator by GCF of 4.

Example 2 Writing Fractions in Simplest Form

Write each fraction in simplest form.

a. $\dfrac{18}{24}$ **b.** $\dfrac{35}{21}$ **c.** $\dfrac{24}{72}$

Solution

a. $\dfrac{18}{24} = \dfrac{\overset{1}{\cancel{2}} \cdot \overset{1}{\cancel{3}} \cdot 3}{2 \cdot 2 \cdot \underset{1}{\cancel{2}} \cdot \underset{1}{\cancel{3}}} = \dfrac{3}{4}$ 　　　Divide out GCF of 6.

b. $\dfrac{35}{21} = \dfrac{5 \cdot \overset{1}{\cancel{7}}}{3 \cdot \underset{1}{\cancel{7}}} = \dfrac{5}{3}$ 　　　Divide out GCF of 7.

c. $\dfrac{24}{72} = \dfrac{\overset{1}{\cancel{2}} \cdot \overset{1}{\cancel{2}} \cdot \overset{1}{\cancel{2}} \cdot \overset{1}{\cancel{3}}}{\underset{1}{\cancel{2}} \cdot \underset{1}{\cancel{2}} \cdot \underset{1}{\cancel{2}} \cdot \underset{1}{\cancel{3}} \cdot 3} = \dfrac{1}{3}$ 　　　Divide out GCF of 24.

Example 3 Writing Equivalent Fractions

Write an equivalent fraction with the indicated denominator.

a. $\dfrac{2}{3} = \dfrac{}{15}$ **b.** $\dfrac{4}{7} = \dfrac{}{42}$ **c.** $\dfrac{9}{15} = \dfrac{}{35}$

Solution

a. $\dfrac{2}{3} = \dfrac{2 \cdot 5}{3 \cdot 5} = \dfrac{10}{15}$ 　　　Multiply numerator and denominator by 5.

b. $\dfrac{4}{7} = \dfrac{4 \cdot 6}{7 \cdot 6} = \dfrac{24}{42}$ 　　　Multiply numerator and denominator by 6.

c. $\dfrac{9}{15} = \dfrac{\cancel{3} \cdot 3}{\cancel{3} \cdot 5} = \dfrac{3 \cdot 7}{5 \cdot 7} = \dfrac{21}{35}$ 　　　Reduce first, then multiply by $\frac{7}{7}$.

Add and subtract fractions.

Adding and Subtracting Fractions

To add fractions with *like* denominators such as $\frac{3}{12}$ and $\frac{4}{12}$, add the numerators and write the sum over the like denominator.

$$\frac{3}{12} + \frac{4}{12} = \frac{3+4}{12} = \frac{7}{12}$$ Add the numbers in the numerator.

To add fractions with *unlike* denominators such as $\frac{1}{4}$ and $\frac{1}{3}$, rewrite the fractions as equivalent fractions with a common denominator.

$$\frac{1}{4} + \frac{1}{3} = \frac{1\cdot3}{4\cdot3} + \frac{1\cdot4}{3\cdot4}$$ Rewrite fractions in equivalent form.

$$= \frac{3}{12} + \frac{4}{12}$$ Rewrite with like denominators.

$$= \frac{7}{12}$$ Add numerators.

To find a common denominator for two or more fractions, find the **least common multiple** (LCM) of their denominators. For instance, the least common multiple of 8 and 12 is 24. To see this, consider all multiples of 8 (8, 16, 24, 32, 40, 48, . . .) and all multiples of 12 (12, 24, 36, 48, . . .). The numbers 24 and 48 are common multiples and the number 24 is the smallest of the common multiples.

$$\frac{3}{8} + \frac{-5}{12} = \frac{3(3)}{8(3)} + \frac{(-5)(2)}{12(2)}$$ LCM of 8 and 12 is 24.

$$= \frac{9}{24} + \frac{-10}{24}$$ Rewrite with like denominators.

$$= \frac{9-10}{24}$$ Add numerators.

$$= \frac{-1}{24}$$ Simplify.

$$= -\frac{1}{24}$$

Study Tip

Adding fractions with unlike denominators is an example of a basic problem-solving strategy that is used in mathematics—rewriting a given problem in a simpler or more familiar form.

▶ **Addition and Subtraction of Fractions**

1. To add two fractions *with like denominators,* add their numerators and write the sum over the like (or common) denominator.

2. To add two fractions *with unlike denominators,* rewrite both fractions so that they have like denominators. Then use the rule for adding fractions with like denominators.

3. To subtract two fractions, add the opposite fraction and proceed as in addition.

> **Example 4** Adding and Subtracting Fractions
>
> **a.** $1\dfrac{4}{5} + \dfrac{11}{15}$ **b.** $\dfrac{7}{9} - \dfrac{11}{12}$

Solution

a. To begin, rewrite the **mixed number** $1\frac{4}{5}$ as a fraction.

$$1\frac{4}{5} = 1 + \frac{4}{5} = \frac{5}{5} + \frac{4}{5} = \frac{9}{5}$$

Then add the two fractions as follows.

$$1\frac{4}{5} + \frac{11}{15} = \frac{9}{5} + \frac{11}{15} \qquad \text{Rewrite } 1\frac{4}{5} \text{ as } \frac{9}{5}.$$

$$= \frac{9(3)}{5(3)} + \frac{11}{15} \qquad \text{LCM of 5 and 15 is 15.}$$

$$= \frac{27}{15} + \frac{11}{15} \qquad \text{Rewrite with like denominators.}$$

$$= \frac{38}{15} \qquad \text{Add numerators.}$$

b.
$$\frac{7}{9} - \frac{11}{12} = \frac{7(4)}{9(4)} + \frac{-11(3)}{12(3)} \qquad \text{LCM of 9 and 12 is 36.}$$

$$= \frac{28}{36} + \frac{-33}{36} \qquad \text{Rewrite with like denominators.}$$

$$= \frac{28 + (-33)}{36} \qquad \text{Add numerators.}$$

$$= \frac{-5}{36} \qquad \text{Simplify.}$$

$$= -\frac{5}{36}$$

Study Tip

In Example 4(a), a common shortcut for writing $1\frac{4}{5}$ as $\frac{9}{5}$ is to multiply 1 by 5, add the result to 4, and then divide by 5, as follows.

$$1\frac{4}{5} = \frac{1(5) + 4}{5} = \frac{9}{5}$$

You can add or subtract *two* fractions, without first finding a common denominator, by using the following rule.

▶ **Alternative Rule for Adding or Subtracting Two Fractions**

If a, b, c, and d are integers with $b \neq 0$ and $d \neq 0$, then

$$\frac{a}{b} + \frac{c}{d} = \frac{ad + bc}{bd} \quad \text{or} \quad \frac{a}{b} - \frac{c}{d} = \frac{ad - bc}{bd}.$$

On page 31, the sum of $\frac{3}{8}$ and $\frac{-5}{12}$ was found using the least common multiple of 8 and 12. Compare those solution steps with the following steps, which use the alternative rule for adding or subtracting two fractions.

$$\frac{3}{8} + \frac{-5}{12} = \frac{3(12) + 8(-5)}{8(12)}$$ Apply alternative rule.

$$= \frac{36 - 40}{96}$$ Simplify.

$$= \frac{-4}{96}$$ Simplify.

$$= -\frac{1}{24}$$ Write in simplest form.

Technology: Tip

When you use a scientific or graphing calculator to add or subtract fractions, your answer may appear in decimal form. An answer such as 0.583333333 is not as exact as $\frac{7}{12}$ and may introduce roundoff error. Refer to the user's manual for your calculator for instructions on adding and subtracting fractions and displaying answers in fraction form.

Example 5   Subtracting Fractions

$$\frac{5}{16} - \left(-\frac{7}{30}\right) = \frac{5}{16} + \frac{7}{30}$$ Add the opposite.

$$= \frac{5(30) + 16(7)}{16(30)} = \frac{150 + 112}{480}$$ Apply alternative rule.

$$= \frac{262}{480}$$ Simplify.

$$= \frac{131}{240}$$ Write in simplest form.

Example 6   Combining Three or More Fractions

Evaluate the following.

$$\frac{5}{6} - \frac{7}{15} + \frac{3}{10} - 1$$

Solution

The least common denominator of 6, 15, and 10 is 30. So, you can rewrite the given expression as follows.

$$\frac{5}{6} - \frac{7}{15} + \frac{3}{10} - 1 = \frac{5(5)}{6(5)} + \frac{(-7)(2)}{15(2)} + \frac{3(3)}{10(3)} + \frac{(-1)(30)}{30}$$

$$= \frac{25}{30} + \frac{-14}{30} + \frac{9}{30} + \frac{-30}{30}$$ Rewrite with like denominators.

$$= \frac{25 - 14 + 9 - 30}{30}$$ Add numerators.

$$= \frac{-10}{30} = -\frac{1}{3}$$ Simplify.

3 Multiply and divide fractions.

Multiplying and Dividing Fractions

The procedure for multiplying fractions is simpler than those for adding and subtracting fractions. Regardless of whether the fractions have like or unlike denominators, you can find the product of two fractions by multiplying the numerators and multiplying the denominators.

> ▶ **Multiplication of Fractions**
>
> To multiply two fractions, multiply the two numerators to form the numerator of the product, and multiply the two denominators to form the denominator of the product.

Example 7 Multiplying Fractions

a. $\dfrac{5}{8} \cdot \dfrac{3}{2} = \dfrac{5(3)}{8(2)}$ Multiply numerators and denominators.

$\qquad = \dfrac{15}{16}$ Simplify.

b. $\left(-\dfrac{7}{9}\right)\left(-\dfrac{5}{21}\right) = \dfrac{7}{9} \cdot \dfrac{5}{21}$ Product of two negatives is positive.

$\qquad = \dfrac{7(5)}{9(21)}$ Multiply numerators and denominators.

Emphasize that only common *factors* can be divided out as a fraction is simplified. For example, discuss

$$\frac{(3)(2)}{(3)(7)} \quad \text{and} \quad \frac{3+2}{(3)(7)}$$

and explain why the first fraction can be reduced but not the second fraction.

$\qquad = \dfrac{7(5)}{9(3)(7)}$ Factor and simplify fraction.

$\qquad = \dfrac{5}{27}$ Write in simplest form.

c. $\left(3\dfrac{1}{5}\right)\left(-\dfrac{7}{6}\right)\left(\dfrac{5}{3}\right) = \left(\dfrac{16}{5}\right)\left(-\dfrac{7}{6}\right)\left(\dfrac{5}{3}\right)$ Rewrite mixed number as a fraction.

$\qquad = -\dfrac{(8)(2)(7)(5)}{(5)(3)(2)(3)}$ Factor and simplify fraction.

$\qquad = -\dfrac{56}{9}$ Write in simplest form.

Technology: Tip

Try verifying some of the products shown in Example 7 with your calculator. Using a *TI-83*, you can verify that $\left(3\frac{1}{5}\right)\left(-\frac{7}{6}\right)\left(\frac{5}{3}\right) = -\frac{56}{9}$ as follows.

⟮ 3 ⊞ 1 ⊟ 5 ⟯ ⊠ ⟮ ⟮ ⟨−⟩ 7 ⊟ 6 ⟯ ⊠
⟮ 5 ⊟ 3 ⟯ (MATH) (▶FRAC) (ENTER)

The **reciprocal** or **multiplicative inverse** of a number is the number by which it must be multiplied to obtain 1. For instance, the reciprocal of 3 is $\frac{1}{3}$ because $3\left(\frac{1}{3}\right) = 1$. Similarly, the reciprocal of $-\frac{2}{3}$ is $-\frac{3}{2}$ because

$$\left(-\frac{2}{3}\right)\left(-\frac{3}{2}\right) = 1.$$

To divide two fractions, multiply the first fraction by the reciprocal of the second fraction. Another way of saying this is "invert the divisor and multiply."

▶ **Division of Fractions**

The quotient of $\dfrac{a}{b}$ and $\dfrac{c}{d}$ is

$$\frac{a}{b} \div \frac{c}{d} = \frac{a}{b} \cdot \frac{d}{c}.$$

You might ask students to write some original exercises involving operations with fractions. Have the students do the operations with pencil and paper and then verify the results on their calculators. This exercise provides excellent practice. (Remind students that the calculator may introduce roundoff error.)

Study Tip

The Division of Fractions Rule works for **complex fractions** (compare to Example 8a).

$$\frac{5}{8} \div \frac{20}{12} = \frac{5/8}{20/12}$$

Invert bottom fraction and multiply. $= \dfrac{5}{8} \cdot \dfrac{12}{20}$

Example 8   Dividing Fractions

Perform the following divisions and write the answers in simplest form.

a. $\dfrac{5}{8} \div \dfrac{20}{12}$ **b.** $\dfrac{6}{13} \div \left(-\dfrac{9}{26}\right)$

Solution

a. $\dfrac{5}{8} \div \dfrac{20}{12} = \dfrac{5}{8} \cdot \dfrac{12}{20}$ Invert divisor and multiply.

$\qquad = \dfrac{(5)(12)}{(8)(20)}$ Multiply numerators and denominators.

$\qquad = \dfrac{(5)(3)(4)}{(8)(4)(5)}$ Factor and simplify fraction.

$\qquad = \dfrac{3}{8}$ Write in simplest form.

b. $\dfrac{6}{13} \div \left(-\dfrac{9}{26}\right) = \dfrac{6}{13} \cdot \left(-\dfrac{26}{9}\right)$ Invert divisor and multiply.

$\qquad = -\dfrac{(6)(26)}{(13)(9)}$ Multiply numerators and denominators.

$\qquad = -\dfrac{(2)(3)(2)(13)}{(13)(3)(3)}$ Factor and simplify fraction.

$\qquad = -\dfrac{4}{3}$ Write in simplest form.

4 Add, subtract, multiply, and divide decimals.

Operations with Decimals

Rational numbers can be represented as **terminating** or **repeating decimals.** Here are some examples.

Terminating Decimals	Repeating Decimals
$\frac{1}{4} = 0.25$	$\frac{1}{6} = 0.1666\ldots$ or $0.1\overline{6}$
$\frac{3}{8} = 0.375$	$\frac{1}{3} = 0.3333\ldots$ or $0.\overline{3}$
$\frac{2}{10} = 0.2$	$\frac{1}{12} = 0.0833\ldots$ or $0.08\overline{3}$
$\frac{5}{16} = 0.3125$	$\frac{8}{33} = 0.2424\ldots$ or $0.\overline{24}$

Note that the *bar* notation is used to indicate the *repeated* digit (or digits) in the decimal notation. You can obtain the decimal representation of any fraction by long division. For instance, the decimal representation of $\frac{5}{12}$ is $0.41\overline{6}$, as can be seen from the following long division algorithm.

$$
\begin{array}{r}
0.4166\ldots = 0.41\overline{6} \\
12\overline{)5.000} \\
\underline{4\,8} \\
20 \\
\underline{12} \\
80 \\
\underline{72} \\
80
\end{array}
$$

For calculations involving decimals such as $0.41666\ldots$, you must **round the decimal.** For instance, rounded to two decimal places, the number $0.41666\ldots$ is 0.42. Similarly, rounded to three decimal places, the number $0.41666\ldots$ is 0.417.

Technology: Tip

You can use a calculator to round decimals. For instance, to round 0.9375 to two decimal places on a scientific calculator, enter

[FIX] [2] .9375 [=].

On a *TI-83* graphing calculator, enter

round (.9375, 2) [ENTER].

Without using a calculator, round -0.88247 to three decimal places. Verify your answer with a calculator. Name the rounding and decision digits.

▶ **Rounding a Decimal**

1. Determine the number of digits of accuracy you wish to keep. The digit in the last position you keep is called the **rounding digit,** and the digit in the first position you discard is called the **decision digit.**

2. If the decision digit is 5 or greater, round up by adding 1 to the rounding digit.

3. If the decision digit is 4 or less, round down by leaving the rounding digit unchanged.

Given decimal	Rounded to three places
0.9763	0.976
0.9768	0.977
0.9765	0.977

Example 9   Operations with Decimals

a. Add 0.583, 1.06, and 2.9104.

b. Multiply -3.57 and 0.032.

Solution

a. To add decimals, align the decimal points and proceed as in integer addition.

$$
\begin{array}{r}
1\ 1 \\
0.583 \\
1.06 \\
+\ \ 2.9104 \\
\hline
4.5534
\end{array}
$$

b. To multiply decimals, use integer multiplication and then place the decimal point (in the product) so that the number of decimal places equals the sum of the decimal places in the two factors.

$$
\begin{array}{r}
-3.57 \qquad \text{Two decimal places} \\
\times \quad 0.032 \qquad \text{Three decimal places} \\
\hline
714 \\
1071 \\
\hline
-0.11424 \qquad \text{Five decimal places}
\end{array}
$$

Example 10   Dividing Decimal Fractions

Divide 1.483 by 0.56.

Solution

To divide 1.483 by 0.56, convert the divisor to an integer by moving its decimal point to the right. Move the decimal point in the dividend an equal number of places to the right. Place the decimal point in the quotient directly above the new decimal point in the dividend and then divide as with integers.

$$
\begin{array}{r}
2.648 \\
56\,\overline{)\,148.3} \\
\underline{112} \\
36\ 3 \\
\underline{33\ 6} \\
2\ 70 \\
\underline{2\ 24} \\
460 \\
\underline{448}
\end{array}
$$

Rounded to two decimal places, the answer is 2.65. This answer can be written as

$$
\frac{1.483}{0.56} \approx 2.65
$$

where the symbol $\approx$ means **is approximately equal to.**

The following example is similar to the stock investment example on page 18. The difference is that this time the gains and losses are given in fractional form.

Example 11   Stock Purchase

On Monday you bought 50 shares of stock at $\$48\frac{1}{2}$ per share. During the week the stock rose and fell, as shown in the table.

Tuesday	Wednesday	Thursday	Friday
Up $\frac{3}{8}$	Up $1\frac{3}{4}$	Down $\frac{1}{2}$	Up $2\frac{7}{8}$

There are three major stock exchanges in the United States: the New York Stock Exchange (NYSE), the American Stock Exchange (AMEX), and the National Association of Securities Dealers Automated Quotations (NASDAQ).

a. What was the value of the stock at the close on Tuesday?

b. What was the value of the stock at the close on Wednesday?

c. What was the value of the stock at the end of the week?

d. What would the total gain have been if Friday's gain had occurred each of the 4 days?

e. What was the average daily gain (loss) for the 4 days recorded?

Solution

a. Because the original value of the stock was $50\left(48\frac{1}{2}\right) = \$2425$, and each of the 50 shares gained $\$\frac{3}{8}$ by the close of Tuesday, the total value of your stock at the close of Tuesday was

$$2425 + 50\left(\frac{3}{8}\right) = 2425 + 18.75 = \$2443.75.$$

b. Using the result of part(a), the value at the close of Wednesday was

$$2443.75 + 50\left(1\frac{3}{4}\right) = 2443.75 + 87.5 = \$2531.25.$$

c. The value of the stock at the end of the week was

$$2425 + 50\left(\frac{3}{8}\right) + 50\left(1\frac{3}{4}\right) + 50\left(-\frac{1}{2}\right) + 50\left(2\frac{7}{8}\right) = \$2650.00.$$

d. The gain on Friday was $2\frac{7}{8}$ per share. If this gain had occurred each day, the total gain would have been

$$4(50)\left(2\frac{7}{8}\right) = \$575.00.$$

e. The total gain for the 4 days was $2650 - 2425 = \$225$. Thus, the average daily gain for the 4 days was $\frac{225}{4} = \$56.25.$

▶ **Summary of Rules for Fractions**

Let a, b, c, and d be real numbers.

Rule	*Example*

1. Addition of fractions:

$$\frac{a}{b} + \frac{c}{d} = \frac{ad + bc}{bd}, \quad b \neq 0, \quad d \neq 0$$

$$\frac{1}{3} + \frac{2}{7} = \frac{1 \cdot 7 + 3 \cdot 2}{3 \cdot 7} = \frac{13}{21}$$

2. Subtraction of fractions:

$$\frac{a}{b} - \frac{c}{d} = \frac{ad - bc}{bd}, \quad b \neq 0, \quad d \neq 0$$

$$\frac{1}{3} - \frac{2}{7} = \frac{1 \cdot 7 - 3 \cdot 2}{3 \cdot 7} = \frac{1}{21}$$

3. Multiplication of fractions:

$$\frac{a}{b} \cdot \frac{c}{d} = \frac{a \cdot c}{b \cdot d}, \quad b \neq 0, \quad d \neq 0$$

$$\frac{1}{3} \cdot \frac{2}{7} = \frac{1(2)}{3(7)} = \frac{2}{21}$$

4. Division of fractions:

$$\frac{a}{b} \div \frac{c}{d} = \frac{a}{b} \cdot \frac{d}{c}, \quad b \neq 0, \quad d \neq 0, \quad c \neq 0$$

$$\frac{1}{3} \div \frac{2}{7} = \frac{1}{3} \cdot \frac{7}{2} = \frac{7}{6}$$

5. Rule of signs for fractions:

$$\frac{a}{b} = \frac{-a}{-b}$$

$$\frac{12}{4} = \frac{-12}{-4}$$

$$\frac{-a}{b} = \frac{a}{-b} = -\frac{a}{b}$$

$$\frac{-12}{4} = \frac{12}{-4} = -\frac{12}{4}$$

6. Equivalent fractions:

$$\frac{a}{b} = \frac{c}{d}, \text{ if and only if } ad = bc; \quad b \neq 0, \quad d \neq 0$$

$$\frac{1}{4} = \frac{3}{12} \text{ because } 1 \cdot 12 = 4 \cdot 3$$

Discussing the Concept   To Round or Not to Round?

When using a calculator to perform operations with decimals, you should try to get in the habit of rounding your answers *only* after all the calculations are done. If you round the answer at a preliminary stage, you can introduce unnecessary roundoff error. Suppose $l = 5.24$, $w = 3.03$, and $h = 2.749$ are the dimensions of a box. Find the volume, $l \cdot w \cdot h$, by multiplying the given numbers and then rounding the answer to one decimal place. Now use a second method, first rounding each dimension to one decimal place and then multiplying the numbers. Compare your answers, and explain which of these techniques produces the more accurate answer.

1.3   Exercises

Developing Skills

In Exercises 1–10, find the greatest common factor.

1. 20, 45   **2.** 45, 90

3. 28, 52   **4.** 48, 64

5. 18, 84, 90   **6.** 84, 98, 192

7. 240, 300, 360   **8.** 117, 195, 507

9. 134, 225, 315, 945   **10.** 80, 144, 214, 504

In Exercises 11–18, write the fraction in simplest form. See Example 2.

11. $\frac{2}{8}$ **12.** $\frac{21}{28}$

13. $\frac{12}{18}$ **14.** $\frac{16}{56}$

15. $\frac{60}{192}$ **16.** $\frac{45}{225}$

17. $\frac{28}{350}$ **18.** $\frac{88}{154}$

In Exercises 19–22, each figure is divided into regions of equal area. Find the sum of the two fractions indicated by the shaded regions of the same color.

19. 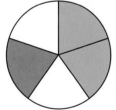   **20.**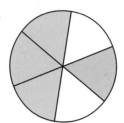

21.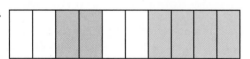

22.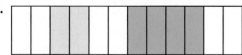

In Exercises 23–34, add or subtract. Write the result in simplest form. See Example 4.

23. $\frac{7}{15} + \frac{2}{15}$ **24.** $\frac{13}{35} + \frac{5}{35}$

25. $\frac{9}{11} + \frac{5}{11}$ **26.** $\frac{5}{6} + \frac{13}{6}$

27. $\frac{9}{16} - \frac{3}{16}$ **28.** $\frac{15}{32} - \frac{7}{32}$

29. $-\frac{23}{11} + \frac{12}{11}$ **30.** $\frac{46}{13} - \frac{20}{13}$

31. $\frac{3}{4} - \frac{5}{4}$ **32.** $\frac{3}{8} - \frac{5}{8}$

33. $\frac{13}{15} + \left|-\frac{11}{15}\right| - \frac{4}{15}$

34. $\frac{5}{8} - \left(-\frac{13}{8}\right) + \frac{3}{8}$

In Exercises 35–38, write an equivalent fraction with the indicated denominator. See Example 3.

35. $\frac{3}{8} = \frac{}{16}$

36. $\frac{4}{5} = \frac{}{15}$

37. $\frac{6}{15} = \frac{}{25}$

38. $\frac{21}{49} = \frac{}{28}$

In Exercises 39–58, add or subtract. Write the result in simplest form. See Examples 4, 5, and 6.

39. $\frac{1}{2} + \frac{1}{3}$ **40.** $\frac{3}{5} + \frac{1}{2}$

41. $\frac{1}{4} - \frac{1}{3}$ **42.** $\frac{2}{3} - \frac{1}{6}$

43. $\frac{3}{16} + \frac{3}{8}$ **44.** $\frac{2}{3} + \frac{4}{9}$

45. $-\frac{1}{8} - \frac{1}{6}$ **46.** $\frac{13}{8} - \frac{3}{4}$

47. $4 - \frac{8}{3}$ **48.** $\frac{17}{25} + 2$

49. $-\frac{7}{8} - \frac{5}{6}$ **50.** $-\frac{5}{12} - \frac{1}{9}$

51. $-\frac{5}{6} - \left(-\frac{3}{4}\right)$ **52.** $\frac{3}{4} - \frac{2}{5}$

53. $\frac{5}{12} - \frac{3}{8} + \frac{5}{16}$ **54.** $-\frac{3}{7} + \frac{5}{14} + \frac{3}{4}$

55. $2 - \frac{25}{6} + \frac{3}{4}$

56. $3 + \frac{12}{3} + \frac{1}{9}$

57. $1 + \frac{2}{3} - \frac{5}{6}$

58. $2 - \frac{15}{16} - \frac{7}{8}$

In Exercises 59–66, write the mixed number as a fraction. See Example 4.

59. $4\frac{3}{5}$

60. $7\frac{2}{3}$

61. $3\frac{7}{10}$

62. $-1\frac{3}{4}$

63. $8\frac{2}{3}$

64. $2\frac{5}{8}$

65. $-10\frac{5}{11}$

66. $3\frac{1}{100}$

In Exercises 67–74, add or subtract. Write the result in simplest form. See Example 4(a).

67. $3\frac{1}{2} + 5\frac{2}{3}$

68. $5\frac{3}{4} + 8\frac{1}{10}$

69. $1\frac{3}{16} - 2\frac{1}{4}$

70. $5\frac{7}{8} - 2\frac{1}{2}$

71. $15\frac{5}{6} - 20\frac{1}{4}$

72. $6 - 3\frac{5}{8}$

73. $-5\frac{2}{3} - 4\frac{5}{12}$

74. $-2\frac{3}{4} - 3\frac{1}{5}$

In Exercises 75 and 76, determine the unknown fractional part of the pie graph.

75.

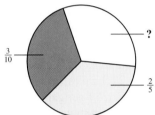

76.

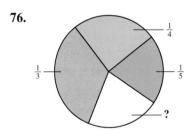

In Exercises 77–94, evaluate the expression. Write the result in simplest form. See Example 7.

77. $\frac{1}{2} \times \frac{3}{4}$

78. $-\frac{2}{3} \times \frac{5}{7}$

79. $\frac{2}{3}\left(-\frac{9}{16}\right)$

80. $\left(-\frac{3}{4}\right)\left(-\frac{4}{9}\right)$

81. $\left(-\frac{7}{16}\right)\left(-\frac{12}{5}\right)$

82. $\left(\frac{5}{3}\right)\left(-\frac{3}{5}\right)$

83. $\left(-\frac{3}{2}\right)\left(-\frac{15}{16}\right)\left(\frac{12}{25}\right)$

84. $\left(\frac{1}{2}\right)\left(-\frac{4}{15}\right)\left(-\frac{5}{24}\right)$

85. $\left(\frac{11}{12}\right)\left(-\frac{9}{44}\right)$

86. $\left(\frac{5}{18}\right)\left(\frac{3}{4}\right)$

87. $9\left(\frac{4}{15}\right)$

88. $24\left(-\frac{7}{18}\right)$

89. $\left(-\frac{3}{11}\right)\left(-\frac{11}{3}\right)$

90. $35\left(\frac{3}{5}\right)\left(\frac{5}{3}\right)$

91. $2\frac{3}{4} \times 3\frac{2}{3}$

92. $-5\frac{2}{3} \times 4\frac{1}{2}$

93. $2\frac{4}{5} \times 6\frac{2}{3}$

94. $-8\frac{1}{2} \times 3\frac{2}{5}$

In Exercises 95–98, find the reciprocal of the number. Show that the product of the number and its reciprocal is 1.

95. 7

96. 14

97. $\frac{4}{7}$

98. $-\frac{5}{9}$

In Exercises 99–114, evaluate the expression and write the result in simplest form. If it is not possible, explain why. See Example 8.

99. $\frac{3}{8} \div \frac{3}{4}$

100. $\frac{5}{16} \div \frac{25}{8}$

101. $-\frac{5}{12} \div \frac{45}{32}$

102. $\left(-\frac{16}{21}\right) \div \left(-\frac{12}{27}\right)$

103. $\frac{3}{5} \div 0$

104. $\frac{3}{5} \div \frac{7}{5}$

105. $-10 \div \frac{1}{9}$

106. $0 \div (-33)$

107. $\dfrac{-\frac{7}{15}}{-\frac{14}{25}}$

108. $\dfrac{-\frac{5}{9}}{0}$

109. $\dfrac{-5}{\frac{15}{16}}$

110. $\dfrac{-\frac{35}{12}}{-14}$

111. $3\frac{3}{4} \div 1\frac{1}{2}$

112. $2\frac{4}{9} \div 5\frac{1}{3}$

113. $3\frac{3}{4} \div 2\frac{5}{8}$

114. $1\frac{5}{6} \div 2\frac{1}{3}$

In Exercises 115–124, write the fraction in decimal form. (Use the bar notation for repeating digits.)

115. $\frac{3}{4}$

116. $\frac{5}{8}$

117. $\frac{9}{16}$

118. $\frac{7}{20}$

119. $\frac{2}{3}$

120. $\frac{5}{6}$

121. $\frac{7}{12}$

122. $\frac{8}{15}$

123. $\frac{5}{11}$

124. $\frac{5}{21}$

In Exercises 125–134, evaluate the expression. Round the answer to two decimal places. See Examples 9 and 10.

125. $1.21 + 4.06 - 3.00$

126. $-3.4 + 1.062 - 5.13$

127. $-0.0005 - 2.01 + 0.111$

128. $132.1 + (-25.45)$

129. $(-6.3)(9.05)$

130. $(-0.05)(-85.95)$

131. $(-0.09)(-0.45)$

132. $3.7(-14.8)$

133. $4.69 \div 0.12$

134. $1.062 \div (-2.1)$

Estimation   In Exercises 135 and 136, estimate the sum to the nearest integer.

135. $\frac{3}{11} + \frac{7}{10}$

136. $\frac{5}{8} + \frac{9}{7}$

Solving Problems

137. *Stock Price*   On Monday, a stock closed at $52\frac{5}{8}$ per share. On Tuesday, it closed at $54\frac{1}{4}$ per share. Determine the increase in the price.

138. *Sewing*   A pattern requires $3\frac{1}{6}$ yards of material to make a skirt and an additional $2\frac{3}{4}$ yards to make a matching jacket. Find the total amount of material required.

139. *Livestock Feed*   During the months of January, February, and March, an animal shelter bought $8\frac{3}{4}$ tons, $7\frac{1}{5}$ tons, and $9\frac{3}{8}$ tons of feed, respectively. Find the total amount of feed purchased during the first quarter of the year.

140. *Recipe*   You are making a batch of cookies. You have placed 2 cups of flour, $\frac{1}{3}$ cup shortening, $\frac{1}{3}$ cup butter, $\frac{1}{2}$ cup brown sugar, and $\frac{1}{3}$ cup granulated sugar in a mixing bowl. How many cups of ingredients are in the mixing bowl?

141. *Volume*   The fuel gauge on a gasoline tank indicates that the tank is $\frac{3}{8}$ full. What fraction of the tank is empty?

142. *Work Progress*   The highway workers have a sign beside a construction project indicating what fraction of the work has been completed. At the beginnings of May and June the fractions of work completed were $\frac{5}{16}$ and $\frac{2}{3}$, respectively. What fraction of the work was completed during the month of May?

143. *Grocery Purchase*   At a convenience store you buy two gallons of milk at $2.23 per gallon and three loaves of bread at $1.23 per loaf. You give the clerk a 20-dollar bill. How much change will you receive? (Assume there is no sales tax.)

144. *Telephone Charge*   A telephone company charges $1.16 for the first minute and $0.85 for each additional minute. Find the cost of a 7-minute phone call.

145. *Making Breadsticks*   You make 60 ounces of dough for breadsticks. If each breadstick requires $\frac{5}{4}$ ounces of dough, how many breadsticks can you make?

146. *Gasoline Price*   The prices per gallon of regular unleaded gasoline at three service stations are $1.259, $1.369, and $1.279, respectively. Find the average price per gallon.

147. *Annual Fuel Cost*   The sticker on a new car gives the fuel efficiency as 22.3 miles per gallon. The average cost of fuel is $1.259 per gallon. Estimate the annual fuel cost for a car that will be driven approximately 12,000 miles per year.

148. *Unit Price*   A $2\frac{1}{2}$-pound can of food costs $4.95. What is the cost per pound?

149. *Stock Purchase*   You buy 200 shares of stock at $23\frac{5}{8}$ per share and 300 shares at $86\frac{1}{4}$ per share.

(a) Estimate the total cost of the stock.

(b) Use a calculator to find the total cost of the stock.

150. *Walking Time*   Your apartment is $\frac{3}{4}$ mile from the subway. If you walk at the rate of $3\frac{1}{4}$ miles per hour, how long does it take you to walk to the subway?

151. *Estimation*   Each day for a week, you practiced the saxophone for $\frac{2}{3}$ hour.

(a) Explain how to use mental math to estimate the number of hours of practice in a week.

(b) Determine the actual number of hours you practiced during the week. Write the result in decimal form, rounding to one decimal place.

152. *Estimation*   Use mental math to determine whether $\left(5\frac{3}{4}\right) \times \left(4\frac{1}{8}\right)$ is less than 20. Explain your reasoning.

Explaining Concepts

153. Answer parts (g) to (l) of Motivating the Chapter on page 1.

154. Is it true that the sum of two fractions of like signs is positive? If not, give an example that shows the statement is false.

155. Is it true that $\frac{2}{3} + \frac{3}{2} = (2 + 3)/(3 + 2) = 1$? Explain your answer.

156. In your own words, describe the rule for determining the sign of the product of two fractions.

157. Two-thirds of a pizza was eaten at dinner.

    (a) How much of the pizza was left?

    (b) For a midnight snack you ate $\frac{1}{2}$ of the pizza that was left. What fraction of the whole pizza did you eat as a midnight snack?

    (c) Make a sketch of the pizza and show how it could be cut to obtain the results of parts (a) and (b).

158. Is it true that $\frac{2}{3} = 0.67$? Explain your answer.

159. Use the figure to determine how many one-fourths are in 3. Explain how to obtain the same result by division.

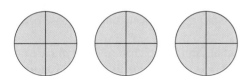

160. Use the figure to determine how many one-sixths are in $\frac{2}{3}$. Explain how to obtain the same result by division.

In Exercises 161–166, determine whether the statement is true or false.

161. The reciprocal of every nonzero integer is an integer.

162. The reciprocal of every nonzero rational number is a rational number.

163. The product of two nonzero rational numbers is a rational number.

164. The product of two positive rational numbers is greater than either factor.

165. If $u > v$, then $u - v > 0$.

166. If $u > 0$ and $v > 0$, then $u - v > 0$.

167. *Think About It*   Determine the placement of the digits 3, 4, 5, and 6 in the following addition problem so that you obtain the specified sum. Use each number only once.

$$\frac{\rule{1cm}{0.4pt}}{\rule{1cm}{0.4pt}} + \frac{\rule{1cm}{0.4pt}}{\rule{1cm}{0.4pt}} = \frac{13}{10}$$

168. If the fractions represented by the points R and P are multiplied, what point on the number line best represents their product: M, S, N, P, or T? (Source: National Council of Teachers of Mathematics)

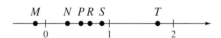

1.4   Exponents, Order of Operations, and Properties of Real Numbers

Objectives

1 Rewrite repeated multiplication in exponential form and evaluate exponential expressions.

2 Evaluate expressions using order of operations.

3 Identify and use the properties of real numbers.

1 Rewrite repeated multiplication in exponential form and evaluate exponential expressions.

Exponents

In Section 1.2, you learned that multiplication by a positive integer can be described as repeated addition.

$$
\begin{array}{cc}
\textit{Repeated Addition} & \textit{Multiplication} \\
7 + 7 + 7 + 7 & 4 \times 7
\end{array}
$$

4 terms of 7

In a similar way, repeated multiplication can be described in **exponential form.**

$$
\begin{array}{cc}
\textit{Repeated Multiplication} & \textit{Exponential Form} \\
7 \cdot 7 \cdot 7 \cdot 7 & 7^4
\end{array}
$$

4 factors of 7

Technology: Discovery

When a negative number is raised to a power, the use of parentheses is very important. To discover why, use a calculator to evaluate $(-5)^4$ and -5^4. Write a statement explaining the results. Then use a calculator to evaluate $(-5)^3$ and -5^3. If necessary, write a new statement explaining your discoveries.

In the exponential form 7^4, 7 is the **base** and it specifies the repeated factor. The number 4 is the **exponent** and it indicates how many times the base occurs as a factor.

When you write the exponential form 7^4, you can say that you are raising 7 to the fourth **power.** When a number is raised to the first power, you usually do not write the exponent 1. For instance, we usually write 5^1 simply as 5. Here are some examples of how exponential expressions are read.

Exponential Expression	Verbal Statement
7^2	"seven to the second power" or "seven squared"
4^3	"four to the third power" or "four cubed"
$(-2)^4$	"negative two to the fourth power"
-2^4	"the opposite of two to the fourth power"

It is important to recognize how exponential forms such as $(-2)^4$ and -2^4 differ.

$$(-2)^4 = (-2)(-2)(-2)(-2) \qquad \text{The negative sign is part of the base.}$$
$$= 16 \qquad \text{The value of the expression is positive.}$$
$$-2^4 = -(2 \cdot 2 \cdot 2 \cdot 2) \qquad \text{The negative sign is not part of the base.}$$
$$= -16 \qquad \text{The value of the expression is negative.}$$

Keep in mind that an exponent applies only to the factor (number) directly preceding it. Parentheses are needed to include a negative sign or other factors as part of the base.

| Example 1 | Evaluating Exponential Expressions |

a. $2^5 = 2 \cdot 2 \cdot 2 \cdot 2 \cdot 2$ Rewrite expression as a product.

    $= 32$ Simplify.

b. $\left(\dfrac{2}{3}\right)^4 = \dfrac{2}{3} \cdot \dfrac{2}{3} \cdot \dfrac{2}{3} \cdot \dfrac{2}{3}$ Rewrite expression as a product.

    $= \dfrac{2 \cdot 2 \cdot 2 \cdot 2}{3 \cdot 3 \cdot 3 \cdot 3}$ Multiply fractions.

    $= \dfrac{16}{81}$ Simplify.

c. $(-3)^3 = (-3)(-3)(-3)$ Rewrite expression as a product.

    $= -27$ Simplify.

d. $(-3)^4 = (-3)(-3)(-3)(-3)$ Rewrite expression as a product.

    $= 81$ Simplify.

e. $-3^4 = -(3 \cdot 3 \cdot 3 \cdot 3)$ Rewrite expression as a product.

    $= -81$ Simplify.

Point out the distinction between $(-3)^4$ and -3^4. The failure to distinguish between such expressions is a common student error.

In parts (c) and (d) of Example 1, note that when a negative number is raised to an *odd* power, the result is *negative*, and when a negative number is raised to an *even* power, the result is *positive*.

| Example 2 | Transporting Capacity |

A truck can transport a load of motor oil that is 6 cases high, 6 cases wide, and 6 cases long. Each case contains 6 quarts of motor oil. How many quarts can the truck transport?

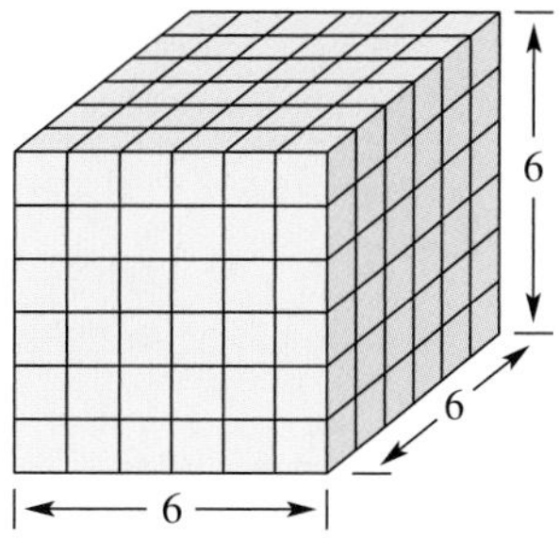

Solution

A sketch can help you solve this problem. From Figure 1.18, you can see that 6 occurs as a factor four times. That is, there are $6 \cdot 6 \cdot 6$ cases of motor oil and each case contains 6 quarts, which implies that the total number of quarts is

$$(6 \cdot 6 \cdot 6) \cdot 6 = 6^4 = 1296.$$

So, the truck can transport 1296 quarts of oil.

Figure 1.18

2 Evaluate expressions using order of operations.

Order of Operations

Up to this point in the text, you have studied five operations of arithmetic— addition, subtraction, multiplication, division, and exponentiation (repeated multiplication). When you use more than one operation in a given problem, you face the question of which operation to do first. For example, without further guidelines, you could evaluate $4 + 3 \cdot 5$ in two ways.

Technology: Discovery

To discover if your calculator performs the established order of operations, evaluate $7 + 5 \cdot 3 - 2^4 \div 4$ exactly as it appears. Does your calculator display 5 or 18? If your calculator performs the established order of operations, it will display 18.

Gottfried Wilhelm von Leibniz (1646–1716)

The symbols used to represent operations were introduced over time. The minus and plus signs were first used in Germany in 1489. The plus sign evolved from the Latin word *et*, meaning "and." The equal sign, the square root notation, and variables were introduced in the 1500s in Europe. In the 1630s, × was introduced to indicate multiplication. Gottfried Wilhelm von Leibniz thought it was easily confused with the variable *x* and proposed the dot symbol (·) in 1698.

Add First	*Multiply First*
$4 + 3 \cdot 5 \overset{?}{=} (4 + 3) \cdot 5$	$4 + 3 \cdot 5 \overset{?}{=} 4 + (3 \cdot 5)$
$= 7 \cdot 5$	$= 4 + 15$
$= 35$	$= 19$

According to the established **order of operations**, the second evaluation is correct. The reason for this is that multiplication has a higher priority than addition. The accepted priorities for order of operations are summarized below.

▶ **Order of Operations**

1. Perform operations inside *symbols of grouping*—( ) or [ ]—or *absolute value symbols*, starting with the innermost symbol.

2. Evaluate all *exponential* expressions.

3. Perform all *multiplications* and *divisions* from left to right.

4. Perform all *additions* and *subtractions* from left to right.

In the priorities for order of operations, note that the highest priority is given to **symbols of grouping** such as parentheses or brackets. This means that when you want to be sure that you are communicating an expression correctly, you can insert symbols of grouping to specify which operations you intend to be performed first. For instance, if you want to make sure that $4 + 3 \cdot 5$ will be evaluated correctly, you can write it as $4 + (3 \cdot 5)$.

Example 3 Order of Operations

a.
$$7 - [(5 \cdot 3) + 2^3] = 7 - [15 + 2^3] \qquad \text{Multiply inside the parentheses.}$$
$$= 7 - [15 + 8] \qquad \text{Evaluate exponential expression.}$$
$$= 7 - 23 \qquad \text{Add inside the brackets.}$$
$$= -16 \qquad \text{Subtract.}$$

b.
$$36 \div (3^2 \cdot 2) - 6 = 36 \div (9 \cdot 2) - 6 \qquad \text{Evaluate exponential expression.}$$
$$= 36 \div 18 - 6 \qquad \text{Multiply inside the parentheses.}$$
$$= 2 - 6 \qquad \text{Divide.}$$
$$= -4 \qquad \text{Subtract.}$$

When you use symbols of grouping in an expression, we suggest that you alternate between parentheses and brackets. For instance, the expression

$$10 - (3 - [4 - (5 + 7)])$$

is easier to understand than $10 - (3 - (4 - (5 + 7)))$.

Study Tip

Often in mathematics, there is no "best way" to solve a problem. For instance, here is a different way to evaluate the expression in Example 4(b) using the Distributive Property. Which way do you prefer?

$$\frac{8}{3}\left(\frac{1}{6} + \frac{1}{4}\right)$$

$$= \frac{8}{3} \cdot \frac{1}{6} + \frac{8}{3} \cdot \frac{1}{4}$$

$$= \frac{8}{18} + \frac{8}{12}$$

$$= \frac{16}{36} + \frac{24}{36}$$

$$= \frac{40}{36}$$

$$= \frac{10}{9}$$

Example 4   Order of Operations

a. $\dfrac{3}{7} \div \dfrac{8}{7} + \left(-\dfrac{3}{5}\right)\left(\dfrac{1}{3}\right) = \dfrac{3}{7} \cdot \dfrac{7}{8} + \left(-\dfrac{3}{5}\right)\left(\dfrac{1}{3}\right)$ Invert divisor and multiply.

$$= \frac{3}{8} + \left(-\frac{1}{5}\right)$$ Multiply fractions.

$$= \frac{15}{40} + \frac{-8}{40}$$ Find common denominator.

$$= \frac{7}{40}$$ Add fractions.

b. $\dfrac{8}{3}\left(\dfrac{1}{6} + \dfrac{1}{4}\right) = \dfrac{8}{3}\left(\dfrac{2}{12} + \dfrac{3}{12}\right)$ Find common denominator.

$$= \frac{8}{3}\left(\frac{5}{12}\right)$$ Add inside the parentheses.

$$= \frac{40}{36}$$ Multiply fractions.

$$= \frac{10}{9}$$ Simplify.

Example 5   Order of Operations

Evaluate the expression $6 + \dfrac{8 + 7}{3^2 - 4} - (-5)$.

Solution

Using the established order of operations, you can evaluate the expression as follows.

$$6 + \frac{8 + 7}{3^2 - 4} - (-5) = 6 + \frac{8 + 7}{9 - 4} - (-5)$$ Evaluate exponential expression.

$$= 6 + \frac{15}{9 - 4} - (-5)$$ Add in numerator.

$$= 6 + \frac{15}{5} - (-5)$$ Subtract in denominator.

$$= 6 + 3 - (-5)$$ Divide.

$$= 9 + 5$$ Add.

$$= 14$$ Add.

In Example 5, note that a fraction bar acts as a symbol of grouping. For instance,

$$\frac{8 + 7}{3^2 - 4} \quad \text{means} \quad (8 + 7) \div (3^2 - 4), \quad \text{not} \quad 8 + 7 \div 3^2 - 4.$$

You might ask students how they would enter these two expressions on their calculators.

3 Identify and use the properties of real numbers.

Properties of Real Numbers

You are now ready for the symbolic versions of the properties that we know are true about operations with real numbers. These properties are referred to as **properties of real numbers.** The table gives a verbal description and an illustrative example for each property. Bear in mind that the letters a, b, c, etc., represent real numbers, even though we have used only rational numbers to this point.

▶ **Properties of Real Numbers:** Let a, b, and c be real numbers.

Property	*Example*

1. Commutative Property of Addition:
Two real numbers can be added in either order.

$$a + b = b + a$$ $3 + 5 = 5 + 3$

2. Commutative Property of Multiplication:
Two real numbers can be multiplied in either order.

$$ab = ba$$ $4 \cdot (-7) = -7 \cdot 4$

3. Associative Property of Addition:
When three real numbers are added, it makes no difference which two are added first.

$$(a + b) + c = a + (b + c)$$ $(2 + 6) + 5 = 2 + (6 + 5)$

4. Associative Property of Multiplication:
When three real numbers are multiplied, it makes no difference which two are multiplied first.

$$(ab)c = a(bc)$$ $(3 \cdot 5) \cdot 2 = 3 \cdot (5 \cdot 2)$

5. Distributive Property:
Multiplication distributes over addition.

$$a(b + c) = ab + ac$$ $3(8 + 5) = 3 \cdot 8 + 3 \cdot 5$

$$(a + b)c = ac + bc$$ $(3 + 8)5 = 3 \cdot 5 + 8 \cdot 5$

6. Additive Identity Property:
The sum of zero and a real number equals the number itself.

$$a + 0 = 0 + a = a$$ $3 + 0 = 0 + 3 = 3$

7. Multiplicative Identity Property:
The product of 1 and a real number equals the number itself.

$$a \cdot 1 = 1 \cdot a = a$$ $4 \cdot 1 = 1 \cdot 4 = 4$

8. Additive Inverse Property:
The sum of a real number and its opposite is zero.

$$a + (-a) = 0$$ $3 + (-3) = 0$

9. Multiplicative Inverse Property:
The product of a nonzero real number and its reciprocal is 1.

$$a \cdot \frac{1}{a} = 1, \ a \neq 0$$ $8 \cdot \frac{1}{8} = 1$

Technology:
Tip

The Multiplicative Inverse Property is one rule listed on page 48: It states that *The product of a nonzero real number and its reciprocal is 1.*

$$a \cdot \frac{1}{a} = 1, \; a \neq 0$$

This property can be illustrated on your calculator by using the reciprocal key $\boxed{1/x}$ or $\boxed{x^{-1}}$. Try doing this with $a = \frac{2}{3}$.

Example 6   Identifying Properties of Real Numbers

Name the property of real numbers that justifies the given statement.

a. $3(a + 2) = 3 \cdot a + 3 \cdot 2$

b. $5 \cdot \dfrac{1}{5} = 1$

c. $7 + (5 + b) = (7 + 5) + b$

d. $(b + 3) + 0 = b + 3$

e. $5(c - 3) = 5 \cdot c - 5 \cdot 3$

Solution

a. This statement is justified by the Distributive Property.

b. This statement is justified by the Multiplicative Inverse Property.

c. This statement is justified by the Associative Property of Addition.

d. This statement is justified by the Additive Identity Property.

e. This statement is justified by the Distributive Property, which works for subtraction also.

Example 7   Using the Properties of Real Numbers

Complete each statement using the specified property of real numbers.

a. Multiplicative Identity Property: **b.** Associative Property of Addition:

    $(3b)1 = $ $(c + 2) + 7 = $

c. Additive Inverse Property: **d.** Distributive Property:

    $0 = 3a + $ $3 \cdot a + 3 \cdot 4 = $

Solution

a. By the Multiplicative Identity Property, you can write

    $(3b)1 = 3b.$

b. By the Associative Property of Addition, you can write

    $(c + 2) + 7 = c + (2 + 7).$

c. By the Additive Inverse Property, you can write

    $0 = 3a + (-3a).$

d. By the Distributive Property, you can write

    $3 \cdot a + 3 \cdot 4 = 3(a + 4).$

One of the distinctive things about algebra is that its rules make sense. You don't have to accept them on "blind faith"—instead, you can learn the reasons that the rules work. For instance, the next example looks at some basic differences among the operations of addition, multiplication, subtraction, and division.

Example 8 Properties of Real Numbers

In the summary of properties of real numbers on page 48, why are all the properties listed in terms of addition and multiplication and not subtraction and division?

Solution

The reason for this is that subtraction and division lack many of the properties listed in the summary. For instance, subtraction and division are not commutative. To see this, consider the following.

$$7 - 5 \neq 5 - 7 \quad \text{and} \quad 12 \div 4 \neq 4 \div 12$$

Similarly, subtraction and division are not associative.

$$9 - (5 - 3) \neq (9 - 5) - 3 \quad \text{and} \quad 12 \div (4 \div 2) \neq (12 \div 4) \div 2$$

Example 9 Geometry: Area

You measure the width of a billboard and find that it is 60 feet. You are told that its height is 22 feet less than its width. Write an expression for the area of the billboard. Use the Distributive Property to rewrite the expression.

Solution

Begin by drawing and labeling a diagram, as shown in Figure 1.19. To find the area of the billboard, multiply the width by the height.

$$\text{Width} \times \text{height} = 60(60 - 22)$$

To rewrite the expression $60(60 - 22)$ using the Distributive Property, distribute 60 over the subtraction.

$$60(60 - 22) = 60(60) - 60(22)$$

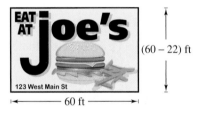

Figure 1.19

Discussing the Concept **Order of Operations**

Using the established order of operations, the value of $7 \cdot 8 + 12$ is

$$7 \cdot 8 + 12 = 56 + 12 = 68.$$

By inserting parentheses into the expression, you can obtain a value of

$$7 \cdot (8 + 12) = 7(20) = 140.$$

Using the established order of operations, which of the following expressions has a value of 72? For those that don't, decide whether you can insert parentheses into the expression so that its value is 72.

a. $4 + 2^3 - 7$ **b.** $4 + 8 \cdot 6$

c. $93 - 25 - 4$ **d.** $70 + 10 \div 5$

e. $60 + 20 \div 2 + 32$ **f.** $35 \cdot 2 + 2$

1.4   Exercises

Developing Skills

In Exercises 1–4, rewrite in exponential form.

1. $2 \cdot 2 \cdot 2 \cdot 2 \cdot 2$

2. $(-5) \cdot (-5) \cdot (-5) \cdot (-5)$

3. $\left(-\frac{1}{4}\right) \cdot \left(-\frac{1}{4}\right) \cdot \left(-\frac{1}{4}\right)$

4. $(1.6) \cdot (1.6) \cdot (1.6) \cdot (1.6) \cdot (1.6)$

In Exercises 5–10, rewrite as a product.

5. $(-3)^6$ **6.** $\left(\frac{3}{8}\right)^5$

7. $(9.8)^3$ **8.** $(0.01)^8$

9. $\left(-\frac{1}{2}\right)^5$ **10.** $\left(\frac{3}{11}\right)^4$

In Exercises 11–14, is the value positive or negative?

11. -2^2 **12.** $(-2)^4$

13. -5^3 **14.** $-(-5)^3$

In Exercises 15–24, evaluate the expression. See Example 1.

15. 3^2 **16.** 4^3

17. 2^6 **18.** 5^3

19. $(-5)^3$ **20.** $-(-3)^2$

21. $\left(\frac{1}{4}\right)^3$ **22.** $\left(\frac{4}{5}\right)^3$

23. $(-1.2)^3$ **24.** $(1.5)^4$

In Exercises 25–64, evaluate the expression. If it is not possible, state the reason. Write fractional answers in simplest form. See Examples 3, 4, and 5.

25. $4 - 6 + 10$ **26.** $5 - (8 - 15)$

27. $-|2 - (6 + 5)|$ **28.** $125 - |10 - (25 - 3)|$

29. $15 + 3 \cdot 4$ **30.** $25 - 32 \div 4$

31. $(16 - 5) \div (3 - 5)$ **32.** $(10 - 16) \cdot (20 - 26)$

33. $(45 \div 10) \cdot 2$ **34.** $[360 - (8 + 12)] \div 10$

35. $5 + (2^2 \cdot 3)$ **36.** $181 - (13 \cdot 3^2)$

37. $(-6)^2 - (5^2 \cdot 4)$ **38.** $(-3)^3 + (12 \div 2^2)$

39. $\left(3 \cdot \frac{5}{9}\right) + 1 - \frac{1}{3}$ **40.** $\frac{2}{3}\left(\frac{3}{4}\right) + 2 - \frac{1}{2}$

41. $4\left(-\frac{2}{3} + \frac{4}{3}\right)$ **42.** $18\left(\frac{1}{2} + \frac{2}{3}\right)$

43. $\frac{3}{2}\left(\frac{2}{3} + \frac{1}{6}\right)$ **44.** $\frac{7}{25}\left(\frac{7}{16} - \frac{1}{8}\right)$

45. $\dfrac{3 \cdot 6 - 4 \cdot 6}{5 + 1}$ **46.** $\dfrac{3 + [15 \div (-3)]}{16}$

47. $\frac{7}{3}\left(\frac{2}{3}\right) \div \frac{28}{15}$ **48.** $\frac{3}{8}\left(\frac{1}{5}\right) \div \frac{25}{32}$

49. $\dfrac{1 - 3^2}{-2}$ **50.** $\dfrac{3^2 + 4^2}{5}$

51. $\dfrac{3^2 - 4^2}{0}$ **52.** $\dfrac{0}{3^2 - 4^2}$

53. $\dfrac{5^2 + 12^2}{13}$ **54.** $\dfrac{4^2 - 2^3}{4}$

55. 2.1×10^2 **56.** 4.85×10^4

57. 5.84×10^3 **58.** 3.28×10^5

59. $\dfrac{8.4}{10^3}$ **60.** $\dfrac{6.23}{10^2}$

61. $\dfrac{732}{10^2}$ **62.** $\dfrac{8235}{10^4}$

63. $\dfrac{0}{5^2 + 1}$ **64.** $\dfrac{3^2 + 1}{0}$

In Exercises 65–68, use a calculator to evaluate the expression. Round your result to two decimal places.

65. $3.4^2 - 6(1.2)^3$ **66.** $300\left(1 + \dfrac{0.1}{12}\right)^{24}$

67. $1000 \div \left(1 + \dfrac{0.09}{4}\right)^8$ **68.** $\dfrac{1.32 + 4(3.68)}{1.5}$

In Exercises 69–72, explain why the statement is true. (The symbol $\neq$ means *is not equal to*.)

69. $4 \cdot 6^2 \neq 24^2$

70. $4 - (6 - 2) \neq 4 - 6 - 2$

71. $-3^2 \neq (-3)(-3)$ **72.** $\dfrac{8 - 6}{2} \neq 4 - 6$

In Exercises 73–92, identify the property of real numbers that justifies the statement. See Example 6.

73. $6(-3) = -3(6)$ **74.** $16 + 10 = 10 + 16$

75. $x + 10 = 10 + x$ **76.** $8x = x(8)$

77. $0 + 15 = 15$ **78.** $1 \cdot 4 = 4$

79. $-16 + 16 = 0$

80. $(2 \cdot 3)4 = 2(3 \cdot 4)$

81. $(10 + 3) + 2 = 10 + (3 + 2)$

82. $25 + (-25) = 0$

83. $4(3 \cdot 10) = (4 \cdot 3)10$

84. $(32 + 8) + 5 = 32 + (8 + 5)$

85. $7\left(\frac{1}{7}\right) = 1$

86. $14 + (-14) = 0$

87. $6(3 + x) = 6 \cdot 3 + 6x$

88. $(14 + 2)3 = 14 \cdot 3 + 2 \cdot 3$

89. $(4 + x)(2 - x) = 4(2 - x) + x(2 - x)$

90. $\frac{1}{a}(3 + y) = \frac{1}{a}(3) + \frac{1}{a}(y)$

91. $x + (y + 3) = (x + y) + 3$

92. $[(x + y)u]v = (x + y)(uv)$

In Exercises 93–96, use the Commutative Property of Addition or Multiplication to rewrite the expression. See Example 7.

93. $5(u + v) = $

94. $y + 5 = $

95. $3 + x = $

96. $10(-3) = $

In Exercises 97–100, use the Distributive Property to rewrite the expression. See Example 7.

97. $6(x + 2) = $

98. $5(u + v) = $

99. $(4 + y)25 = $

100. $x(4 - y) = $

In Exercises 101–104, use the Associative Property of Addition or Multiplication to rewrite the expression. See Example 7.

101. $3x + (2y + 5) = $

102. $12(3 \cdot 4) = $

103. $(6x)y = $

104. $10 + (x + 2y) = $

In Exercises 105–112, find (a) the additive inverse and (b) the multiplicative inverse of the quantity.

105. 50

106. 12

107. -1

108. $-\frac{1}{2}$

109. $2x$

110. $5y$

111. ab

112. uv

In Exercises 113–116, simplify the expression.

113. $3(6 + 10)$

114. $4(8 - 3)$

115. $\frac{2}{3}(9 + 24)$

116. $\frac{1}{2}(4 - 2)$

In Exercises 117–120, explain why the statement is true.

117. $5(x + 3) \neq 5x + 3$

118. $7(x - 2) \neq 7x - 2$

119. $\frac{8}{0} \neq 0$

120. $5\left(\frac{1}{5}\right) \neq 0$

In Exercises 121–124, identify the property of real numbers used to justify each rewritten step.

121. $4(2 + x) = 4(x + 2)$

$\qquad\qquad = 4x + 8$

122. $3 + 10(x + 1) = 3 + 10x + 10$

$\qquad\qquad\qquad = 3 + 10 + 10x$

$\qquad\qquad\qquad = (3 + 10) + 10x$

$\qquad\qquad\qquad = 13 + 10x$

123. $7x + 9 + 2x = 7x + 2x + 9$

$\qquad\qquad\qquad = (7x + 2x) + 9$

$\qquad\qquad\qquad = (7 + 2)x + 9$

$\qquad\qquad\qquad = 9x + 9$

$\qquad\qquad\qquad = 9(x + 1)$

124. $2(x + 3) + x = 2x + 2 \cdot 3 + x$

$\qquad\qquad\qquad = 2x + x + 6$

$\qquad\qquad\qquad = (2 + 1)x + 6$

$\qquad\qquad\qquad = 3x + 6$

$\qquad\qquad\qquad = 3(x + 2)$

Solving Problems

Geometry   In Exercises 125 and 126, find the area.

125.

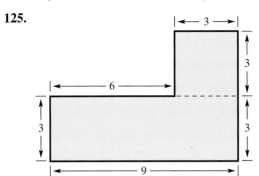

126.

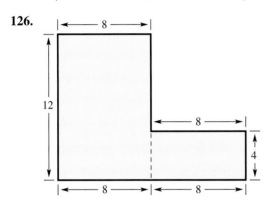

127. *Interpreting a Pie Graph*   The portions of the total expenses for a company are shown in the pie graph. What portion of the total expenses is spent on utilities? If the total expenses are $450,000, how much is spent on utilities?

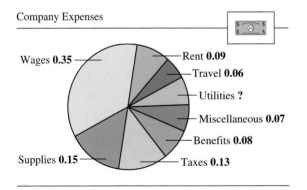

128. *Forecasting*   The projected number of elementary and secondary school teachers for the year 2006 is 3.43×10^6. Evaluate this quantity.   (Source: U.S. National Center for Education Statistics)

129. *Total Cost*   A car is purchased for $750 down and 48 monthly payments of $215 each. What is the total amount paid for the car?

130. *Think About It*   A child suggests the following plan for an allowance during a month with 30 days. The first day of the month she will receive 1 cent, the second day 2 cents, the third day 4 cents, and so on. If the amount continues to double each day, what will her allowance be on day 30?

131. *Sales Tax*   You purchase an item for x dollars. There is a 6% sales tax, which implies that the total amount you must pay is $x + 0.06x$.

    (a) Use the Distributive Property to rewrite the expression.

    (b) How much must you pay if the item costs $25.95?

132. *Geometry*   The width of a movie screen is 30 feet and its height is 8 feet less than the width. Write an expression for the area of the movie screen. Use the Distributive Property to rewrite the expression.

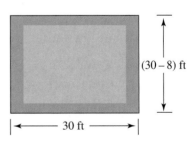

133. *Geometry*   Write an expression for the perimeter of the triangle shown in the figure. Use the properties of real numbers to simplify the expression.

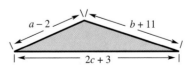

134. *Geometry* Find the area of the yellow rectangle in two ways. Explain how the results are related to the Distributive Property.

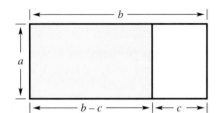

Think About It In Exercises 135 and 136, determine whether the order in which the two activities are performed is "commutative." That is, do you obtain the same result regardless of which activity is performed first?

135. (a) "Drain the used oil from the engine."

(b) "Fill the crankcase with 5 quarts of new oil."

136. (a) "Weed the flower beds."

(b) "Mow the lawn."

Explaining Concepts

137. Consider the expression 3^5.

(a) What is the number 3 called?

(b) What is the number 5 called?

138. Are -6^2 and $(-6)^2$ equal? Explain.

139. Are $2 \cdot 5^2$ and 10^2 equal? Explain.

140. In your own words, describe the priorities for the established order of operations.

141. In the expression $12 + 48 \div 6 - 5$, where would you insert symbols of grouping to help someone understand that the value of the expression is 15?

142. *Error Analysis* Find the error.

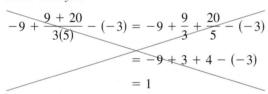

143. In your own words, state the Commutative Properties of Addition and Multiplication. Give an example of each.

144. In your own words, state the Associative Properties of Addition and Multiplication. Give an example of each.

145. Consider the operation of addition.

(a) In your own words, describe the Additive Identity Property. Give an example.

(b) In your own words, describe the Additive Inverse Property. Give an example.

146. Consider the rectangle shown in the figure.

(a) Find the area of the rectangle by adding the areas of regions I and II.

(b) Find the area of the rectangle by multiplying its length by its width.

(c) Explain how the results of parts (a) and (b) relate to the Distributive Property.

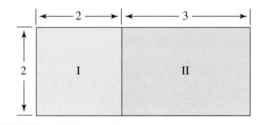

Key Terms

real numbers, *p. 2*
natural numbers, *p. 2*
integers, *p. 2*
rational numbers, *p. 3*
irrational numbers, *p. 3*

real number line, *p. 4*
inequality symbol, *p. 5*
opposites, *p. 7*
absolute value, *p. 7*
expression, *p. 7*

evaluate, *p. 7*
additive inverse, *p. 13*
factor, *p. 19*
prime number, *p. 19*

greatest common factor,
p. 29
reciprocal, *p. 35*
exponent, *p. 44*

Key Concepts

1.1 Ordering of real numbers

Use the real number line and an inequality symbol (<, >, ≤, or ≥) to order real numbers.

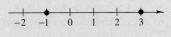

$-1 < 3$

1.1 Absolute value

The absolute value of a number is its distance from zero on the real number line. The absolute value is either positive or zero.

1.2 Addition and subtraction of integers

To add integers with like signs, add their absolute values and attach the common sign to the result.

To add integers with different signs, subtract the smaller absolute value from the larger absolute value and attach the sign of the integer with the larger absolute value.

To subtract one integer from another, add the opposite of the integer being subtracted to the other integer.

1.2 Rules for multiplying and dividing integers

1. The product of an integer and zero is 0.
2. Zero divided by a nonzero integer is 0, whereas a nonzero integer divided by zero is undefined.
3. The product or quotient of two nonzero integers with like signs is positive.
4. The product or quotient of two nonzero integers with different signs is negative.

1.3 Addition and subtraction of fractions

1. To add two fractions with like denominators, add their numerators and write the sum over the like (or common) denominator.
2. To add two fractions with unlike denominators, rewrite both fractions so that they have like denominators. Then use the rule for adding fractions with like denominators.

3. To subtract two fractions, add the opposite fraction and proceed as in addition.

1.3 Multiplication of fractions

To multiply two fractions, multiply the two numerators to form the numerator of the product, and multiply the two denominators to form the denominator of the product.

1.3 Division of fractions

To divide two fractions, invert the divisor and multiply.

1.4 Order of operations

1. Perform operations inside symbols of grouping—( ) or [ ]—or absolute value symbols, starting with the innermost symbol.
2. Evaluate all exponential expressions.
3. Perform all multiplications and divisions from left to right.
4. Perform all additions and subtractions from left to right.

1.4 Properties of real numbers

Commutative Property of Addition $\qquad a + b = b + a$

Commutative Property of Multiplication $\qquad ab = ba$

Associative Property of Addition
$(a + b) + c = a + (b + c)$

Associative Property of Multiplication $\qquad (ab)c = a(bc)$

Distributive Property
$$a(b + c) = ab + ac \qquad a(b - c) = ab - ac$$
$$(a + b)c = ac + bc \qquad (a - b)c = ac - bc$$

Additive Identity Property $\qquad a + 0 = a$

Multiplicative Identity Property $\qquad a \cdot 1 = a$

Additive Inverse Property $\qquad a + (-a) = 0$

Multiplicative Inverse Property $\qquad a \cdot \dfrac{1}{a} = 1, \quad a \neq 0$

REVIEW EXERCISES

Reviewing Skills

1.1 In Exercises 1–4, plot each real number as a point on the real number line and place the correct inequality symbol (< or >) between the real numbers.

1. $-\frac{1}{10}$ ___ 4

2. $\frac{25}{3}$ ___ $\frac{5}{3}$

3. -3 ___ -7

4. 10.6 ___ -3.5

In Exercises 5–8, find the opposite of the number, and determine the distance of the number and its opposite from 0.

5. 152

6. -10.4

7. $-\frac{7}{3}$

8. $\frac{2}{3}$

In Exercises 9–12, evaluate the expression.

9. $|-8.5|$

10. $|3.4|$

11. $-|-8.5|$

12. $|-9.6|$

In Exercises 13–16, place the correct symbol (<, >, or =) between the real numbers.

13. $|-84|$ ___ $|84|$

14. $|-10|$ ___ $|4|$

15. $\left|\frac{3}{10}\right|$ ___ $-\left|\frac{4}{5}\right|$

16. $|2.3|$ ___ $-|2.3|$

1.2 In Exercises 17–36, perform the indicated operations with integers, if possible. If it is not possible, state the reason.

17. $32 + 68$

18. $14 + 54$

19. $16 + (-5)$

20. $-125 + 30$

21. $350 - 125 + 15$

22. $35 - 25 - 10$

23. $-114 + 76 - 230$

24. $-448 - 322 + 100$

25. $|-86| - |124|$

26. $67 + |-53|$

27. 15×3

28. -22×4

29. $-300(-5)$

30. $8(320)$

31. $31(-6)(3)$

32. $(-46)(-5)(-2)$

33. $\frac{-162}{9}$

34. $\frac{-52}{-4}$

35. $815 \div 0$

36. $-48 \div 6$

37. Subtract -549 from 613.

38. Find the absolute value of the sum of 693 and -420.

39. What must you add to 75 to obtain -27?

40. What must you subtract from -83 to obtain 43?

In Exercises 41 and 42, use the long division algorithm to find the quotient.

41. $33{,}768 \div -72$

42. $-144{,}512 \div -32$

In Exercises 43–46, use a calculator to perform the operations.

43. $7(5207) - 52{,}318$

44. $783(1995) + 75(-832)$

45. $\frac{345{,}582}{438}$

46. $\frac{1{,}111{,}521}{89}$

In Exercises 47–50, decide whether the number is prime or composite.

47. 839

48. 909

49. 1764

50. 1847

In Exercises 51–54, write the prime factorization of the number.

51. 378

52. 858

53. 1612

54. 1787

1.3 In Exercises 55–58, find the greatest common factor.

55. 54, 90

56. 154, 220

57. 63, 84, 441

58. 99, 132, 253

In Exercises 59–62, write an equivalent fraction with the indicated denominator.

59. $\frac{2}{3} = \frac{}{15}$

60. $\frac{3}{7} = \frac{}{28}$

61. $\frac{6}{10} = \frac{}{25}$

62. $\frac{9}{12} = \frac{}{16}$

In Exercises 63–74, evaluate the expression. Write the result in simplest form.

63. $\frac{3}{25} + \frac{7}{25}$

64. $\frac{9}{64} + \frac{7}{64}$

65. $\frac{27}{16} - \frac{15}{16}$

66. $-\frac{5}{12} + \frac{1}{12}$

67. $-\frac{5}{9} + \frac{2}{3}$

68. $\frac{7}{15} - \frac{2}{25}$

69. $\frac{25}{32} + \frac{7}{24}$

70. $-\frac{7}{8} - \frac{11}{12}$

71. $5 - \frac{15}{4}$

72. $\frac{12}{5} - 3$

73. $5\frac{3}{4} - 3\frac{5}{8}$

74. $-3\frac{7}{10} + 1\frac{1}{20}$

In Exercises 75–86, evaluate the expression. If it is not possible, explain why.

75. $\frac{5}{8} \cdot \frac{-2}{15}$

76. $\frac{3}{32} \cdot \frac{32}{3}$

77. $35\left(\frac{1}{35}\right)$

78. $-\frac{5}{12}\left(-\frac{4}{25}\right)$

79. $\frac{5}{14} \div \frac{15}{28}$

80. $-\frac{7}{10} \div \frac{4}{15}$

81. $\dfrac{-\frac{3}{4}}{-\frac{7}{8}}$

82. $\dfrac{\frac{15}{32}}{-5}$

83. $\dfrac{\frac{5}{9}}{0}$

84. $\dfrac{0}{12}$

85. $\dfrac{5.25}{0.25}$

86. $(5.2)(16.8)$

In Exercises 87–90, use a calculator to evaluate the expression. Round your answer to two decimal places.

87. $(5.8)^4 - (3.2)^5$

88. $\dfrac{(15.8)^3}{(2.3)^8}$

89. $\dfrac{3000}{(1.05)^{10}}$

90. $500\left(1 + \dfrac{0.07}{4}\right)^{40}$

1.4 In Exercises 91–94, evaluate the exponential expression.

91. 7^3

92. $(-5)^2$

93. $(-7)^3$

94. $-(-2)^4$

In Exercises 95–98, insert the correct symbol ($<$, $>$, or $=$) between the numbers.

95. $2^2 \quad\quad 2^4$

96. $(-3)^2 \quad\quad (-3)^3$

97. $\frac{3}{4} \quad\quad \left(\frac{3}{4}\right)^2$

98. $\left(\frac{2}{3}\right)^3 \quad\quad \left(\frac{2}{3}\right)^2$

In Exercises 99–114, evaluate the expression using the order of operations.

99. $\left(\dfrac{3}{5}\right)^4$

100. $\dfrac{2}{6^3}$

101. $240 - (4^2 \cdot 5)$

102. $5^2 - (625 \cdot 5^2)$

103. $3^2(10 - 2^2)$

104. $-5(16 - 5^2)$

105. $\left(\frac{3}{4}\right)\left(\frac{5}{6}\right) + 4$

106. $75 - 24 \div 2^3$

107. $122 - [45 - (32 + 8) - 23]$

108. $-58 - (48 - 12) - (-30 - 4)$

109. $\dfrac{6 \cdot 4 - 36}{4}$

110. $\dfrac{144}{2 \cdot 3 \cdot 3}$

111. $\dfrac{54 - 4 \cdot 3}{6}$

112. $\dfrac{3 \cdot 5 + 125}{10}$

113. $\dfrac{78 - |-78|}{5}$

114. $\dfrac{300}{15 - |-15|}$

In Exercises 115–122, identify the property of real numbers that justifies the statement.

115. $123 - 123 = 0$

116. $9 \cdot \frac{1}{9} = 1$

117. $14(3) = 3(14)$

118. $5(3x) = (5 \cdot 3)x$

119. $17 \cdot 1 = 17$

120. $10 + 6 = 6 + 10$

121. $-2(7 + x) = -2 \cdot 7 + (-2)x$

122. $2 + (3 + x) = (2 + 3) + x$

Solving Problems

123. *Think About It*   Which is smaller: $\frac{2}{3}$ or 0.6?

124. *Think About It*   An integer n is divisible by 3 and the quotient is also divisible by 3. What does this tell you about n? Give some examples.

125. *True or False?*   The sum of two integers, one negative and one positive, is negative. Explain.

126. *True or False?*   The product of two integers, one negative and one positive, is negative. Explain.

127. *Think About It*   You rotate the tires on your truck, including the spare, so that all five tires are used equally. After 40,000 miles, how many miles has each tire been driven?

128. *Total Cost*   You have purchased a television set. In addition to a down payment of $75 you must make nine monthly payments of $25 each. What is the total amount you will pay for the product?

129. *Reading a Table* The costs of adult and student tickets for a concert are $25 and $10, respectively. The following table gives the numbers of tickets sold the first 4 days of sales.

Day	1	2	3	4
Adult	162	98	148	186
Student	98	64	81	105

(a) Find the revenue from ticket sales each day.

(b) Find the revenue from ticket sales for each type of ticket.

(c) Find the total revenue from ticket sales using part (a). Find the total revenue from ticket sales using part (b). Do your answers agree? Does this provide a sufficient check for your work?

130. *Reading a Graph* The bar graph shows the popular votes (in millions) cast for president in the presidential elections from 1972 through 1996. (Source: U.S. Bureau of the Census)

(a) Estimate the total popular votes cast for the candidates in 1980.

(b) Estimate the difference between the votes cast for the winning candidate and for the independent candidate in 1992.

(c) Estimate the total popular votes cast for each of the elections. Did the number of votes cast increase with time?

(d) Describe how you can use the graph to determine whether the winning candidate received more than one-half of the popular vote. Did this always occur for the elections shown on the graph?

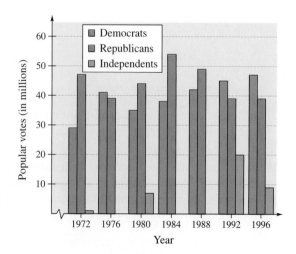

131. *Reading a Table* Initially, a share of stock cost $35\frac{1}{4}$. The daily changes in closing values during the week are shown in the table. Determine the closing price of a share on Friday.

Day	Mon	Tue	Wed	Thu	Fri
Change	$-\frac{3}{8}$	$-\frac{1}{2}$	$-\frac{1}{8}$	$+1\frac{1}{4}$	$+\frac{1}{2}$

132. *Fuel Consumption* The morning and evening readings of the fuel gauge on a car were $\frac{7}{8}$ and $\frac{1}{3}$. What fraction of the tank of fuel was used that day?

133. *Telephone Charge* A telephone call costs $0.64 for the first minute plus $0.72 for each additional minute. Find the cost of a 5-minute call.

134. *Snowfall Rate* During an 8-hour period, $6\frac{3}{4}$ inches of snow fell. What was the average rate of snowfall per hour?

135. *Depreciation* After 3 years, the value of a $16,000 car is given by $16,000\left(\frac{3}{4}\right)^3$.

(a) What is the value of the car after 3 years?

(b) How much has the car depreciated during the 3 years?

136. *Geometry* The volume of water in a hot tub is given by $V = 6^2 \cdot 3$. How many cubic feet of water will the hot tub hold? Find the total weight of the water in the tub. (Use the fact that 1 cubic foot of water weighs 62.4 pounds.)

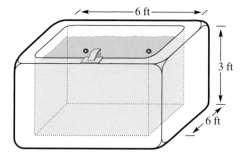

Chapter Test

Take this test as you would take a test in class. After you are done, check your work against the answers given in the back of the book.

1. Which of the following are (a) natural numbers? (b) integers? (c) rational numbers?

$$-10, 8, \frac{3}{4}, \frac{12}{4}, 6.5$$

2. Place the correct inequality symbol ($<$ or $>$) between the real numbers.

$$-\frac{3}{5} \quad\boxed{}\quad -|-2|$$

In Exercises 3–16, evaluate the expression.

3. $16 + (-20)$

4. $-50 - (-60)$

5. $7 + |-3|$

6. $64 - (25 - 8)$

7. $-5(32)$

8. $\dfrac{-72}{-9}$

9. $\dfrac{12 + 9}{7}$

10. $-\dfrac{(-2)(5)}{10}$

11. $\frac{5}{6} - \frac{1}{8}$

12. $-27\left(\frac{5}{6}\right)$

13. $\dfrac{7}{16} \div \dfrac{21}{28}$

14. $\dfrac{-8.1}{0.3}$

15. $-\left(\frac{2}{3}\right)^2$

16. $35 - (50 \div 5^2)$

In Exercises 17–20, state the property of real numbers that justifies the statement.

17. $3(4 + 6) = 3 \cdot 4 + 3 \cdot 6$

18. $5 \cdot \frac{1}{5} = 1$

19. $3 + (4 + 8) = (3 + 4) + 8$

20. $3(x + 2) = (x + 2)3$

21. Write the fraction $\frac{30}{72}$ in simplest form.

22. Explain why -3^4 is not equal to $(-3)^4$.

23. State the order of operations for the expression $32 - 3 \cdot 2^3$.

24. Copy the figure shown below. Then shade two-thirds of the figure. Write two different fractions that are represented by the shaded region.

2 Fundamentals of Algebra

Joseph E. Ramir

Party and special event rentals represent one facet of the equipment rental industry. Today consumers can rent just about any type of equipment from home and garden tools to fine china.

Beachwood Rental

Beachwood Rental is a rental company specializing in equipment for parties and special events. A wedding ceremony is to be held under a canopy that contains 15 rows of 12 chairs.

See Section 2.1, Exercise 89.

a. Let *c* represent the rental cost of a chair. Write an expression that represents the cost of renting all of the chairs under the canopy. The table at the right lists the rental prices for two types of chairs. Use the expression you wrote to find the cost of renting the plastic chairs and the cost of renting the wood chairs.

Chair rental	
Plastic	$1.95
Wood	$2.95

b. The table at the right lists the available canopy sizes. The rental rate for a canopy is $115 + 0.25t$ dollars, where *t* represents the size of the canopy in square feet. Find the cost of each canopy. (*Hint*: The total area under a 20 by 20 foot canopy is $20 \cdot 20 = 400$ square feet.)

Canopy sizes	
Canopy 1	20 by 20 feet
Canopy 2	20 by 30 feet
Canopy 3	30 by 40 feet
Canopy 4	30 by 60 feet
Canopy 5	40 by 60 feet

The figure at the right shows the arrangement of the chairs under the canopy. Beachwood Rental recommends the following.

Width of center aisle—Three times the space between rows
Width of side aisle—Two times the space between rows
Depth of rear aisle—Two times the space between rows
Depth of front region—Seven feet more than three times the space between rows

See Section 2.3, Exercise 80.

c. Let *x* represent the space between rows of chairs. Write an expression for the width of the center aisle. Write an expression for the width of a side aisle.

d. Each chair is 14 inches wide. Convert the width of a chair to feet. Write an expression for the width of the canopy.

e. Write an expression for the depth of the rear aisle. Write an expression for the depth of the front region.

f. Each chair is 12 inches deep. Convert the depth of a chair to feet. Write an expression for the depth of the canopy.

g. If $x = 2$ feet, what is the width of the center aisle? What are the width and depth of the canopy? What size canopy do you need? What is the total rental cost of the canopy and chairs if the wood chairs are used?

h. What could be done to save on the rental cost?

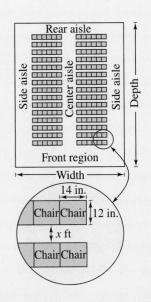

2.1   Writing and Evaluating Algebraic Expressions

Objectives

1 Define and identify terms, variables, and coefficients of an algebraic expression.

2 Define exponential form and interpret exponential expressions.

3 Evaluate algebraic expressions using real numbers.

1 Define and identify terms, variables, and coefficients of an algebraic expression.

Variables and Algebraic Expressions

One of the distinguishing characteristics of algebra is its use of symbols to represent quantities whose numerical values are unknown. Here is a simple example.

Example 1   Writing an Algebraic Expression

You accept a part-time job for $6 per hour. The job offer states that you will be expected to work between 15 and 30 hours a week. Because you don't know how many hours you will work during a week, your total income for a week is unknown. Moreover, your income will probably *vary* from week to week. By representing the variable quantity (the number of hours worked) by the letter x, you can represent the weekly income by the following *algebraic expression*.

$6 per   Number of
hour   hours worked

$$6x$$

In the product $6x$, the number 6 is a *constant* and the letter x is a *variable*.

▶ **Algebraic Expression**

A collection of letters (**variables**) and real numbers (**constants**) combined by using addition, subtraction, multiplication, or division is an **algebraic expression.**

Some examples of algebraic expressions are

$$3x + y, \quad -5a^3, \quad 2W - 7, \quad \frac{x}{y + 3}, \quad \text{and} \quad x^2 - 4x + 5.$$

The **terms** of an algebraic expression are those parts that are separated by *addition*. For example, the expression $x^2 - 4x + 5$ has three terms: x^2, $-4x$, and 5. Note that $-4x$, rather than $4x$, is a term of $x^2 - 4x + 5$ because

$$x^2 - 4x + 5 = x^2 + (-4x) + 5. \qquad \text{To subtract, add the opposite.}$$

For variable terms such as x^2 and $-4x$, the numerical factor is the **coefficient** of the term. Here, the coefficient of x^2 is 1 and the coefficient of $-4x$ is -4.

Example 2   Identifying the Terms of an Algebraic Expression

Identify the terms of each algebraic expression.

a. $x + 2$ **b.** $3x + \dfrac{1}{2}$ **c.** $2y - 5x - 7$

d. $5(x - 3) + 3x - 4$ **e.** $4 - 6x + \dfrac{x + 9}{3}$

Solution

Algebraic Expression	Terms
a. $x + 2$	$x, 2$
b. $3x + \dfrac{1}{2}$	$3x, \dfrac{1}{2}$
c. $2y - 5x - 7$	$2y, -5x, -7$
d. $5(x - 3) + 3x - 4$	$5(x - 3), 3x, -4$
e. $4 - 6x + \dfrac{x + 9}{3}$	$4, -6x, \dfrac{x + 9}{3}$

The terms of an algebraic expression depend on the way the expression is written. Rewriting the expression can (and, in fact, usually does) change its terms. For instance, the expression $2 + 4 - x$ has three terms, but the equivalent expression $6 - x$ has only two terms.

Example 3   Identifying Coefficients

Identify the coefficient of each of the following terms.

a. $-5x^2$ **b.** x^3 **c.** $\dfrac{2x}{3}$ **d.** $-\dfrac{x}{4}$ **e.** $-x^3$

Solution

Term	Coefficient	Comment
a. $-5x^2$	-5	Note that $-5x^2 = (-5)x^2$.
b. x^3	1	Note that $x^3 = 1 \cdot x^3$.
c. $\dfrac{2x}{3}$	$\dfrac{2}{3}$	Note that $\dfrac{2x}{3} = \dfrac{2}{3}(x)$.
d. $-\dfrac{x}{4}$	$-\dfrac{1}{4}$	Note that $-\dfrac{x}{4} = -\dfrac{1}{4}(x)$.
e. $-x^3$	-1	Note that $-x^3 = (-1)x^3$.

2 Define exponential form and
interpret exponential expressions.

Exponential Form

You know from Section 1.4 that a number raised to a power can be evaluated by repeated multiplication. For example, 7^4 represents the product obtained by multiplying 7 by itself four times.

$$\underset{\substack{| \\ \text{Base}}}{7}{\overset{\overset{\text{Exponent}}{\diagup}}{^4}} = \underbrace{7 \cdot 7 \cdot 7 \cdot 7}_{4 \text{ factors}}$$

In general, for any positive integer n and any real number a, you have

$$a^n = \underbrace{a \cdot a \cdot a \cdots a}_{n \text{ factors}}.$$

This rule applies to factors that are *variables* as well as to factors that are *algebraic expressions.*

> ▶ **Definition of Exponential Form**
>
> Let n be a positive integer and let a be a real number, a variable, or an algebraic expression.
>
> $$a^n = \underbrace{a \cdot a \cdot a \cdots a}_{n \text{ factors}}.$$

In this definition remember that the letter a can be a number, a variable, or an algebraic expression. It may be helpful to think of a as a box into which you can place any algebraic expression.

$$\boxed{}^{\,n} = \boxed{} \cdot \boxed{} \cdots \boxed{}$$

The box may contain a number, a variable, or an algebraic expression.

Example 4 Interpreting Exponential Expressions

a. $3^4 = 3 \cdot 3 \cdot 3 \cdot 3$
b. $3x^4 = 3 \cdot x \cdot x \cdot x \cdot x$
c. $(-3x)^4 = (-3x)(-3x)(-3x)(-3x) = (-3)(-3)(-3)(-3) \cdot x \cdot x \cdot x \cdot x$
d. $(y + 2)^3 = (y + 2)(y + 2)(y + 2)$
e. $(5x)^2 y^3 = (5x)(5x)y \cdot y \cdot y = 5 \cdot 5 \cdot x \cdot x \cdot y \cdot y \cdot y$

Be sure you understand the priorities for order of operations involving exponents. Here are two examples that tend to cause problems.

Expression	*Correct Evaluation*	*Incorrect Evaluation*
-3^2	$-(3 \cdot 3) = -9$	$\cancel{(-3)(-3) = 9}$
$3x^2$	$3 \cdot x \cdot x$	$\cancel{(3x)(3x)}$

3 Evaluate algebraic expressions using real numbers.

Evaluating Algebraic Expressions

In applications of algebra, you are often required to **evaluate** an algebraic expression. This means you are to find the *value* of an expression when its variables are replaced by real numbers. For instance, when $x = 2$, the value of the expression $2x + 3$ is as follows.

Expression	*Replace x by 2.*	*Value of Expression*
$2x + 3$	$2(2) + 3$	7

When finding the value of an algebraic expression, be sure to replace every occurrence of the specified variable with the appropriate real number. For instance, when $x = -2$, the value of $x^2 - x + 3$ is

$$(-2)^2 - (-2) + 3 = 4 + 2 + 3 = 9.$$

Example 5   Evaluating Algebraic Expressions

Evaluate each expression when $x = -3$ and $y = 5$.

a. $-x$ **b.** $x - y$ **c.** $3x + 2y$

d. $y - 2(x + y)$ **e.** $y^2 - 3y$

Solution

Encourage students to use parentheses when replacing a variable with a negative number or a fraction.

a. When $x = -3$, the value of $-x$ is

$$-x = -(-3) \qquad \text{Substitute } -3 \text{ for } x.$$
$$= 3. \qquad \text{Simplify.}$$

b. When $x = -3$ and $y = 5$, the value of $x - y$ is

$$x - y = -3 - 5 \qquad \text{Substitute } -3 \text{ for } x \text{ and } 5 \text{ for } y.$$
$$= -8. \qquad \text{Simplify.}$$

c. When $x = -3$ and $y = 5$, the value of $3x + 2y$ is

$$3x + 2y = 3(-3) + 2(5) \qquad \text{Substitute } -3 \text{ for } x \text{ and } 5 \text{ for } y.$$
$$= -9 + 10 \qquad \text{Simplify.}$$
$$= 1. \qquad \text{Simplify.}$$

Study Tip

As shown in parts (a) and (d) of Example 5, it is a good idea to use parentheses when substituting a negative number for a variable.

d. When $x = -3$ and $y = 5$, the value of $y - 2(x + y)$ is

$$y - 2(x + y) = 5 - 2[(-3) + 5] \qquad \text{Substitute } -3 \text{ for } x \text{ and } 5 \text{ for } y.$$
$$= 5 - 2(2) \qquad \text{Simplify.}$$
$$= 1. \qquad \text{Simplify.}$$

e. When $y = 5$, the value of $y^2 - 3y$ is

$$y^2 - 3y = (5)^2 - 3(5) \qquad \text{Substitute } 5 \text{ for } y.$$
$$= 25 - 15 \qquad \text{Simplify.}$$
$$= 10. \qquad \text{Simplify.}$$

**Technology:
Tip**

Absolute value expressions can be evaluated on a graphing calculator using the key $\boxed{\text{ABS}}$. To evaluate $|-3|$, you can use the following keystrokes.

$\boxed{\text{ABS}}$ $\boxed{\text{(-)}}$ 3 $\boxed{\text{ENTER}}$

When evaluating an expression such as $|3 - 6|$, parentheses should surround the entire expression, as shown in the following keystrokes.

$\boxed{\text{ABS}}$ $\boxed{)}$ 3 $\boxed{-}$ 6 $\boxed{)}$ $\boxed{\text{ENTER}}$

Display: 3

Example 6   Evaluating Algebraic Expressions

Evaluate each expression when $x = 4$ and $y = -6$.

a. y^2 **b.** $-y^2$ **c.** $y - x$ **d.** $|y - x|$ **e.** $|x - y|$

Solution

a. When $y = -6$, the value of the expression y^2 is

$$y^2 = (-6)^2 = 36.$$

b. When $y = -6$, the value of the expression $-y^2$ is

$$-y^2 = -(y^2) = -(-6)^2 = -36.$$

c. When $x = 4$ and $y = -6$, the value of the expression $y - x$ is

$$y - x = (-6) - 4 = -6 - 4 = -10.$$

d. When $x = 4$ and $y = -6$, the value of the expression $|y - x|$ is

$$|y - x| = |-6 - 4| = |-10| = 10.$$

e. When $x = 4$ and $y = -6$, the value of the expression $|x - y|$ is

$$|x - y| = |4 - (-6)| = |4 + 6| = |10| = 10.$$

Example 7   Evaluating Algebraic Expressions

Evaluate each expression when $x = -5$, $y = -2$, and $z = 3$.

a. $\dfrac{y + 2z}{5y - xz}$ **b.** $(y + 2z)(z - 3y)$

Solution

Remind students to follow the order of operations when evaluating expressions.

a. When $x = -5$, $y = -2$, and $z = 3$, the value of the expression is

$$\frac{y + 2z}{5y - xz} = \frac{-2 + 2(3)}{5(-2) - (-5)(3)} \qquad \text{Substitute for } x, y, \text{ and } z.$$

$$= \frac{-2 + 6}{-10 + 15} \qquad \text{Simplify.}$$

$$= \frac{4}{5}. \qquad \text{Simplify.}$$

b. When $y = -2$ and $z = 3$, the value of the expression is

$$(y + 2z)(z - 3y) = [(-2) + 2(3)][3 - 3(-2)] \qquad \text{Substitute for } y \text{ and } z.$$

$$= (-2 + 6)(3 + 6) \qquad \text{Simplify.}$$

$$= 4(9) \qquad \text{Simplify.}$$

$$= 36. \qquad \text{Simplify.}$$

On occasion you may need to evaluate an algebraic expression for *several* values of x. In such cases, a table format is a useful way to organize the values of the expression.

Example 8   Repeated Evaluation of an Expression

Complete the following table by evaluating the expression $5x + 2$ for each value of x given in the table.

x	-1	0	1	2
$5x + 2$				

Solution

Begin by substituting each value of x into the expression.

When $x = -1$: $5x + 2 = 5(-1) + 2 = -5 + 2 = -3$
When $x = 0$: $5x + 2 = 5(0) + 2 = 0 + 2 = 2$
When $x = 1$: $5x + 2 = 5(1) + 2 = 5 + 2 = 7$
When $x = 2$: $5x + 2 = 5(2) + 2 = 10 + 2 = 12$

Once you have evaluated the expression for each value of x, fill in the table with the values.

x	-1	0	1	2
$5x + 2$	-3	2	7	12

Technology: Tip

If you have a graphing calculator, try using it to store and evaluate the expression given in Example 8. For instance, here are the steps that will evaluate $-9x + 6$ when $x = 2$ on a *TI-83*.

- Use the Y= key to store the expression as Y_1.
- 2nd QUIT
- Store 2 in X.
  2 STO▶ X,T,Θ,n ENTER
- Display Y_1.
  VARS Y-VARS ENTER
  ENTER

  and then press ENTER again.

Discussing the Concept   Error Analysis

Suppose you are teaching an algebra class and one of your students hands in the following problem. What is the error in this work?

Evaluate $y - 2(x - y)$ when $x = 2$ and $y = -4$.

$$y - 2(x - y) = -4 - 2(2 - 4)$$
$$= -4 - 2(-2)$$
$$= -4 + 4$$
$$= 0$$

What are some possible related errors? Discuss ways of helping students avoid these types of errors.

2.1 Exercises

Integrated Review — Concepts, Skills, and Problem Solving

Keep mathematically in shape by doing these exercises *before* the problems of this section.

Properties and Definitions

In Exercises 1–4, identify the property illustrated by the equation.

1. $x(5) = 5x$

2. $10 - 10 = 0$

3. $3(t + 2) = 3t + 3 \cdot 2$

4. $7 + (8 + z) = (7 + 8) + z$

Simplifying Expressions

In Exercises 5–10, evaluate the expression.

5. $10 - |-7|$ **6.** $6 - (10 - 12)$

7. $\dfrac{3 - (5 - 20)}{4}$

8. $\dfrac{6}{7} - \dfrac{4}{7}$

9. $-\frac{3}{4}\left(\frac{28}{33}\right)$

10. $\frac{5}{8} \div \frac{3}{16}$

Problem Solving

11. You plan to save $50 per month for 10 years. How much money will you set aside during the 10 years?

12. It is necessary to cut a 120-foot rope into eight pieces of equal length. What is the length of each piece?

Developing Skills

In Exercises 1–4, write an algebraic expression for the given statement. See Example 1.

1. The distance traveled in t hours if the average speed is 60 miles per hour

2. The cost of an amusement park ride for a family of n people if the cost per person is $1.25

3. The cost of m pounds of meat if the cost per pound is $2.19

4. The total weight of x 50-pound bags of fertilizer

In Exercises 5–8, identify the variables and constants in the expression.

5. $x + 3$ **6.** $y + 1$

7. $x + z$ **8.** $3^2 + z$

In Exercises 9–22, identify the terms of the expression. See Example 2.

9. $4x + 3$ **10.** $6x - 1$

11. $3x^2 + 5$ **12.** $5 - 3t^2$

13. $\frac{5}{3} - 3y^3$ **14.** $6x - \frac{2}{3}$

15. $2x - 3y + 1$ **16.** $x^2 + 18xy + y^2$

17. $3(x + 5) + 10$ **18.** $16 - (x + 1)$

19. $\dfrac{x}{4} + \dfrac{5}{x}$ **20.** $10 - \dfrac{t}{6}$

21. $\dfrac{3}{x + 2} - 3x + 4$ **22.** $x^2 + \dfrac{3x + 1}{x - 1} + 4$

In Exercises 23–32, identify the coefficient of the term. See Example 3.

23. $-6x$ **24.** $25y$

25. $-\frac{1}{3}y$ **26.** $\frac{1}{8}n$

27. $-\dfrac{3x}{2}$ **28.** $\dfrac{3x}{4}$

29. $2\pi x^2$ **30.** πt^4

31. $4.7u$ **32.** $-5.32b$

In Exercises 33–50, expand the expression as a product of factors. See Example 4.

33. y^5 **34.** x^6

35. $2^2 x^4$ **36.** $5^3 x^2$

37. $4y^2 z^3$ **38.** $3uv^4$

39. $(a^2)^3$ **40.** $(z^3)^3$

41. $4x^3 \cdot x^4$ **42.** $a^2 y^2 \cdot y^3$

43. $(ab)^3$ **44.** $2(xz)^4$

45. $(x + y)^2$ **46.** $(s - t)^5$

47. $\left(\dfrac{a}{3s}\right)^4$ **48.** $\left(\dfrac{2}{x + 1}\right)^3$

49. $[3(r + s)^2][3(r + s)]^2$

50. $[2(a - b)^3][2(a - b)](a - b)^2$

In Exercises 51–60, rewrite the product in exponential form.

51. $2 \cdot u \cdot u \cdot u \cdot u$ **52.** $\frac{1}{3} \cdot x \cdot x \cdot x \cdot x \cdot x$

53. $(2u) \cdot (2u) \cdot (2u) \cdot (2u)$ **54.** $\frac{1}{3}x \cdot \frac{1}{3}x \cdot \frac{1}{3}x \cdot \frac{1}{3}x \cdot \frac{1}{3}x$

55. $a \cdot a \cdot a \cdot b \cdot b$ **56.** $y \cdot y \cdot z \cdot z \cdot z \cdot z$

57. $3 \cdot (x - y) \cdot (x - y) \cdot 3 \cdot 3$

58. $(u - v) \cdot (u - v) \cdot 8 \cdot 8 \cdot 8 \cdot (u - v)$

59. $\left(\dfrac{x^2}{2}\right)\left(\dfrac{x^2}{2}\right)\left(\dfrac{x^2}{2}\right)$

60. $\dfrac{r - s}{5} \cdot \dfrac{r - s}{5} \cdot \dfrac{r - s}{5} \cdot \dfrac{r - s}{5}$

In Exercises 61–78, evaluate the algebraic expression for the given values of the variables. If it is not possible, state the reason. See Examples 5, 6, and 7.

Expression	*Values*
61. $2x - 1$	(a) $x = \frac{1}{2}$ (b) $x = 4$
62. $3x - 2$	(a) $x = \frac{4}{3}$
	(b) $x = -1$
63. $2x^2 - 5$	(a) $x = -2$
	(b) $x = 3$
64. $64 - 16t^2$	(a) $t = 2$ (b) $t = 3$
65. $3x - 2y$	(a) $x = 4, y = 3$
	(b) $x = \frac{2}{3}, y = 1$
66. $10u - 3v$	(a) $u = 3, v = 10$
	(b) $u = -2, v = -7$
67. $x - 3(x - y)$	(a) $x = 3, y = 3$
	(b) $x = 4, y = -4$
68. $-3x + 2(x + y)$	(a) $x = -2, y = 2$
	(b) $x = 0, y = 5$
69. $b^2 - 4ac$	(a) $a = 2, b = -3, c = -1$
	(b) $a = -4, b = 6, c = -2$
70. $a^2 + 2ab$	(a) $a = -2, b = 3$
	(b) $a = -2, b = 4$
71. $\dfrac{x - 2y}{x + 2y}$	(a) $x = 4, y = 2$
	(b) $x = 4, y = -2$

72. $\dfrac{-y}{x^2 + y^2}$ (a) $x = 0, y = 5$

(b) $x = 1, y = -3$

73. $\dfrac{5x}{y - 3}$ (a) $x = 2, y = 4$

(b) $x = 2, y = 3$

74. $\dfrac{2x - y}{y^2 + 1}$ (a) $x = 1, y = 2$

(b) $x = 1, y = 3$

75. *Area of a Triangle*

$\frac{1}{2}bh$ (a) $b = 3, h = 5$

(b) $b = 2, h = 10$

76. *Volume of a Rectangular Prism*

lwh (a) $l = 4, w = 2, h = 9$

(b) $l = 10, w = 5, h = 20$

77. *Distance traveled*

rt (a) $r = 50, t = 3.5$

(b) $r = 35, t = 4$

78. *Simple interest*

Prt (a) $P = 1000, r = 0.08, t = 3$

(b) $P = 500, r = 0.07, t = 5$

79. *Finding a Pattern*

(a) Complete the following table by evaluating the expression $3x - 2$. See Example 8.

x	-1	0	1	2	3	4
$3x - 2$						

(b) Use the table to find the increase in the value of the expression for each 1-unit increase in x.

(c) From the pattern of parts (a) and (b), predict the increase in the algebraic expression $\frac{2}{3}x + 4$ for each 1-unit increase in x. Then verify your prediction.

80. *Finding a Pattern*

(a) Complete the table by evaluating the expression $3 - 2x$. See Example 8.

x	-1	0	1	2	3	4
$3 - 2x$						

(b) Use the table to find the change in the value of the expression for each 1-unit increase in x.

(c) From the pattern of parts (a) and (b), predict the change in the algebraic expression $4 - \frac{3}{2}x$ for each 1-unit increase in x. Then verify your prediction.

Solving Problems

Geometry   In Exercises 81–84, find an expression for the area of the figure. Then evaluate the expression for the given value(s) of the variable(s).

81. $n = 8$

82. $x = 10, y = 3$

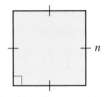

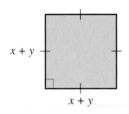

83. $a = 5, b = 4$

84. $x = 9$

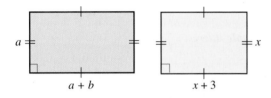

85. *Exploration*   A convex polygon with n sides has

$$\frac{n(n - 3)}{2}, \quad n \geq 4$$

diagonals. Verify the formula for (a) a square (2 diagonals), (b) a pentagon (5 diagonals), and (c) a hexagon (9 diagonals).

86. *Think About It*   Explain why the formula in Exercise 85 will always yield a natural number for the number of diagonals.

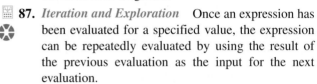 **87.** *Iteration and Exploration*   Once an expression has been evaluated for a specified value, the expression can be repeatedly evaluated by using the result of the previous evaluation as the input for the next evaluation.

(a) The procedure for repeated evaluation of the algebraic expression $\frac{1}{2}x + 3$ can be accomplished on a graphing utility in the following way.

• Clear the display.

• Enter 2 in the display and press ENTER.

• Enter $\frac{1}{2}$ * ANS + 3 and press ENTER.

• Each time ENTER is pressed the utility will evaluate the expression at the value of x obtained in the preceding computation. Continue the process six more times. What value does the expression appear to be approaching?

(b) Repeat part (a) starting with $x = 12$.

88. *Exploration*   Repeat Exercise 87 using the expression $\frac{3}{4}x + 2$.

Explaining Concepts

89. Answer parts (a) and (b) of Motivating the Chapter on page 61.

90. Discuss the difference between terms and factors.

91. Is $3x$ a term of $4 - 3x$? Explain.

92. In the expression $(10x)^3$, what is $10x$ called? What is 3 called?

93. Is it possible to evaluate the expression

$$\frac{x + 2}{y - 3}$$

when $x = 5$ and $y = 3$? Explain.

 The symbol indicates an exercise in which you are instructed to use a graphing utility.

2.2   Simplifying Algebraic Expressions

Objectives

1 Apply the rules of exponents to rewrite exponential expressions.

2 Use the basic rules of algebra to combine like terms of an algebraic expression.

3 Simplify an algebraic expression by rewriting the terms.

4 Use the Distributive Property to remove symbols of grouping.

1 Apply the rules of exponents to rewrite exponential expressions.

Rules of Exponents

To simplify algebraic expressions, you often need to use some rules for operating with exponential expressions. Consider the following illustrations.

1. Multiplying exponential forms with like bases: *Rule*

$$a^3 \cdot a^2 = \underbrace{(a \cdot a \cdot a)}_{\text{3 factors}} \cdot \underbrace{(a \cdot a)}_{\text{2 factors}}$$ Add exponents.

$$= \underbrace{a \cdot a \cdot a \cdot a \cdot a}_{\text{5 factors}} = a^5 = a^{2+3}$$

2. Raising an exponential form to a power: *Rule*

$$(a^3)^2 = \underbrace{a^3 \cdot a^3}_{\text{2 factors of } a^3}$$ Multiply exponents.

$$= \underbrace{(a \cdot a \cdot a)}_{\text{3 factors}} \cdot \underbrace{(a \cdot a \cdot a)}_{\text{3 factors}} = a^6 = a^{2 \cdot 3}$$

3. Raising a product to a power: *Rule*

$$(a \cdot b)^3 = \underbrace{(a \cdot b) \cdot (a \cdot b) \cdot (a \cdot b)}_{\text{3 factors of } (a \cdot b)}$$ Apply exponent to each factor.

$$= \underbrace{(a \cdot a \cdot a)}_{\text{3 factors}} \cdot \underbrace{(b \cdot b \cdot b)}_{\text{3 factors}} = a^3 \cdot b^3$$

These illustrations suggest the following rules for exponential forms.

> ▶ **Rules of Exponents**
>
> Let m and n be positive integers, and let a and b be real numbers, variables, or variable expressions. Then, the following are true.
>
> **1.** $a^m \cdot a^n = a^{m+n}$ **2.** $(a^m)^n = a^{m \cdot n}$ **3.** $(ab)^m = a^m \cdot b^m$

Rules 1 and 3 can be extended to three or more factors such as $a^m \cdot a^n \cdot a^k = a^{m+n+k}$ and $(abc)^m = a^m \cdot b^m \cdot c^m$.

Example 1   Simplifying Products Involving Exponential Forms

Simplify each expression.

a. $5^2 \cdot 5^6 \cdot 5$ **b.** $b^4 b^2 b$ **c.** $3^2 x^3 \cdot x$
d. $(-9x^2)(-3x^5)$ **e.** $(2x^2y)(-xy^4)$

Solution

a. $5^2 \cdot 5^6 \cdot 5 = 5^{2+6+1} = 5^9$

b. $b^4 b^2 b = b^{4+2+1} = b^7$

c. $3^2 x^3 \cdot x = (3^2)(x^{3+1}) = 9x^4$

d. $(-9x^2)(-3x^5) = (-9)(-3)(x^2 \cdot x^5) = 27(x^{2+5}) = 27x^7$

e. $(2x^2y)(-xy^4) = (2)(-1)(x^2 \cdot x)(y \cdot y^4) = -2x^{2+1}y^{1+4} = -2x^3y^5$

Be sure you see the difference between the expressions

$$x^3 \cdot x^4 \text{ and } x^3 + x^4.$$

The first is a *product* of exponential forms, whereas the second is a *sum* of exponential forms. The rule for multiplying exponential forms having the same base can be applied to the first expression, but *not* to the second expression.

Example 2   Applying the Rules of Exponents

Use the rules of exponents to simplify each of the following.

a. $(2^3)^4$ **b.** $(y^2)^3$ **c.** $[(x + 2)^3]^3$ **d.** $(3x)^3$
e. $(-x)^4$ **f.** $(2x^2)^3$ **g.** $x(x^3y^2)^3$

Solution

a. $(2^3)^4 = 2^{3 \cdot 4} = 2^{12} = 4096$

b. $(y^2)^3 = y^{2 \cdot 3} = y^6$

c. $[(x + 2)^3]^3 = (x + 2)^{3 \cdot 3} = (x + 2)^9$

d. $(3x)^3 = 3^3 \cdot x^3 = 27x^3$

e. $(-x)^4 = (-1)^4 x^4 = x^4$

f. $(2x^2)^3 = 2^3(x^2)^3 = 2^3 x^{2 \cdot 3} = 8x^6$

g. $x(x^3y^2)^3 = x(x^{3 \cdot 3}y^{2 \cdot 3}) = x(x^9y^6) = x^{1+9}y^6 = x^{10}y^6$

It is important to recognize that the Rules of Exponents apply to products and not to sums or differences. Note the following illustrations.

Product	*Example*
$x^5 \cdot x^4 = x^{5+4}$	$2^5 \cdot 2^4 \overset{?}{=} 2^{5+4}$
	$512 = 512$

Sum	
$x^5 + x^4 \neq x^{5+4}$	$2^5 + 2^4 \neq 2^{5+4}$
	$48 \neq 512$

2 Use the basic rules of algebra to combine like terms of an algebraic expression.

Basic Rules of Algebra

Knowing the rules of exponents, you are now ready to combine algebraic expressions using the basic rules of algebra. You'll discover as you review the following table of rules that they are the same as the properties of real numbers given on page 48. The only difference is that the *input* for algebra rules can be real numbers, variables, or algebraic expressions.

▶ **Basic Rules of Algebra**

Let a, b, and c represent real numbers, variables, or algebraic expressions.

Property	*Example*
Commutative Property of Addition:	
$a + b = b + a$	$3x + x^2 = x^2 + 3x$
Commutative Property of Multiplication:	
$ab = ba$	$(5 + x)x^3 = x^3(5 + x)$
Associative Property of Addition:	
$(a + b) + c = a + (b + c)$	$(2x + 7) + x^2 = 2x + (7 + x^2)$
Associative Property of Multiplication:	
$(ab)c = a(bc)$	$(2x \cdot 5y) \cdot 7 = 2x \cdot (5y \cdot 7)$
Distributive Property:	
$a(b + c) = ab + ac$	$4x(7 + 3x) = 4x \cdot 7 + 4x \cdot 3x$
$(a + b)c = ac + bc$	$(2y + 5)y = 2y \cdot y + 5 \cdot y$
Additive Identity Property:	
$a + 0 = 0 + a = a$	$3y^2 + 0 = 0 + 3y^2 = 3y^2$
Multiplicative Identity Property:	
$a \cdot 1 = 1 \cdot a = a$	$(-2x^3) \cdot 1 = 1 \cdot (-2x^3) = -2x^3$
Additive Inverse Property:	
$a + (-a) = 0$	$3y^2 + (-3y^2) = 0$
Multiplicative Inverse Property:	
$a \cdot \dfrac{1}{a} = 1, \quad a \neq 0$	$(x^2 + 2) \cdot \dfrac{1}{x^2 + 2} = 1$

Because subtraction is defined as "adding the opposite," the Distributive Property is also true for subtraction. That is,

$$a(b - c) = ab - ac \quad \text{and} \quad (a - b)c = ac - bc.$$

Example 3 Applying the Basic Rules of Algebra

Use the indicated rule to complete the statement.

a. Additive Identity Property: $(x - 2) + \boxed{} = x - 2$

b. Commutative Property of Multiplication: $5(y + 6) = \boxed{}$

c. Commutative Property of Addition: $5(y + 6) = \boxed{}$

d. Distributive Property: $5(y + 6) = \boxed{}$

e. Associative Property of Addition: $(x^2 + 3) + 7 = \boxed{}$

f. Additive Inverse Property: $\boxed{} + 3x^2 = 0$

Solution

a. $(x - 2) + 0 = x - 2$

b. $5(y + 6) = (y + 6)5$

c. $5(y + 6) = 5(6 + y)$

d. $5(y + 6) = 5y + 5(6)$

e. $(x^2 + 3) + 7 = x^2 + (3 + 7)$

f. $-3x^2 + 3x^2 = 0$

Example 4 illustrates some common uses of the Distributive Property. Study this example carefully. Such uses of the Distributive Property are very important in algebra. Applying the Distributive Property as illustrated in Example 4 is called **expanding** an algebraic expression.

Example 4 Using the Distributive Property

Use the Distributive Property to expand each expression.

a. $2(7 - x)$ b. $(10 - 2y)3$ c. $2x(x + 4y)$ d. $-(1 - 2y + x)$

Solution

a. $2(7 - x) = 2 \cdot 7 - 2 \cdot x$

$= 14 - 2x$

b. $(10 - 2y)3 = 10(3) - 2y(3)$

$= 30 - 6y$

c. $2x(x + 4y) = 2x(x) + 2x(4y)$

$= 2x^2 + 8xy$

d. $-(1 - 2y + x) = (-1)(1 - 2y + x)$

$= (-1)(1) - (-1)(2y) + (-1)(x)$

$= -1 + 2y - x$

Study Tip

In Example 4(d) the negative sign is distributed over each term in the parentheses by multiplying each term by -1.

In the next example, note how area can be used to demonstrate the Distributive Property.

Example 5   The Distributive Property and Area

Write the area of each component part of the figure. Then demonstrate the Distributive Property by writing the total area of each figure in two ways.

a.

b.

c.

Solution

a.

The total area is $3(2 + 4) = 3 \cdot 2 + 3 \cdot 4$.

b.

The total area is $a(a + b) = a \cdot a + a \cdot b$.

c.

The total area is $2b(d + 3a + c) = 2bd + 6ab + 2bc$.

Two or more terms of an algebraic expression can be combined only if they are *like terms*.

▶ **Definition of Like Terms**

In an algebraic expression, two terms are said to be **like terms** if they are both constant terms or if they have the same variable factor(s). Factors such as x in $5x$ and ab in $6ab$ are called **variable factors.**

The terms $5x$ and $-3x$ are like terms because they have the same variable factor, x. Similarly, $3x^2y$, $-x^2y$, and $\frac{1}{3}(x^2y)$ are like terms because they have the same variable factor, x^2y.

Study Tip

Notice in Example 6(b) that x^2 and $3x$ are *not* like terms because the variable x is not raised to the same power in both terms.

Example 6   Identifying Like Terms in Expressions

Expression	*Like Terms*
a. $5xy + 1 - xy$	$5xy$ and $-xy$
b. $12 - x^2 + 3x - 5$	12 and -5
c. $7x - 3 - 2x + 5$	$7x$ and $-2x$, -3 and 5

To combine like terms in an algebraic expression, you can simply add their respective coefficients and attach the common variable factor. This is actually an application of the Distributive Property, as shown in Example 7.

Example 7 Using the Distributive Property

Simplify each expression by combining like terms.

a. $5x + 2x - 4$ **b.** $-5 + 8 + 7y - 5y$ **c.** $2y - 3x - 4x$

Solution

a. $5x + 2x - 4 = (5 + 2)x - 4$ Distributive Property

            $= 7x - 4$ Simplest form

b. $-5 + 8 + 7y - 5y = (-5 + 8) + (7 - 5)y$ Distributive Property

            $= 3 + 2y$ Simplest form

c. $2y - 3x - 4x = 2y - x(3 + 4)$ Distributive Property

            $= 2y - x(7)$ Simplify.

            $= 2y - 7x$ Simplest form

Often, you need to use other rules of algebra before you can apply the Distributive Property to combine like terms. This is illustrated in the next example.

Example 8 Using Rules of Algebra to Combine Like Terms

Simplify each expression by combining like terms.

a. $7x + 3y - 4x$ **b.** $12a - 5 - 3a + 7$ **c.** $y - 4x - 7y + 9y$

Solution

a. $7x + 3y - 4x = 3y + 7x - 4x$ Commutative Property

            $= 3y + (7x - 4x)$ Associative Property

            $= 3y + (7 - 4)x$ Distributive Property

            $= 3y + 3x$ Simplest form

b. $12a - 5 - 3a + 7 = 12a - 3a - 5 + 7$ Commutative Property

            $= (12a - 3a) + (-5 + 7)$ Associative Property

            $= (12 - 3)a + (-5 + 7)$ Distributive Property

            $= 9a + 2$ Simplest form

c. $y - 4x - 7y + 9y = -4x + (y - 7y + 9y)$ Collect like terms.

            $= -4x + (1 - 7 + 9)y$ Distributive Property

            $= -4x + 3y$ Simplest form

Study Tip

As you gain experience with the rules of algebra, you may want to combine some of the steps in your work. For instance, you might feel comfortable listing only the following steps to solve part (b) of Example 8.

$12a - 5 - 3a + 7$

$= (12a - 3a) + (-5 + 7)$

$= 9a + 2$

3 Simplify an algebraic expression by rewriting the terms.

Simplifying Algebraic Expressions

Simplifying an algebraic expression by rewriting it in a more usable form is one of the three most frequently used skills in algebra. You will study the other two—solving an equation and sketching the graph of an equation—later in this text.

To "simplify an algebraic expression" generally means to remove symbols of grouping and combine like terms. For instance, the expression $x + (3 + x)$ can be simplified as $2x + 3$.

Example 9   Simplifying Algebraic Expressions

Simplify each expression.

a. $-3(-5x)$

b. $7(-x)$

Solution

a. $-3(-5x) = (-3)(-5)x$ Associative Property

$ = 15x$ Simplest form

b. $7(-x) = 7(-1)(x)$ Coefficient of $-x$ is -1.

$ = -7x$ Simplest form

Example 10   Simplifying Algebraic Expressions

Simplify each expression.

a. $\dfrac{5x}{3} \cdot \dfrac{3}{5} = \left(\dfrac{5}{3} \cdot x\right) \cdot \dfrac{3}{5}$ Coefficient of $\dfrac{5x}{3}$ is $\dfrac{5}{3}$.

$\phantom{\dfrac{5x}{3} \cdot \dfrac{3}{5}} = \left(\dfrac{5}{3} \cdot \dfrac{3}{5}\right) \cdot x$ Commutative and Associative Properties

$\phantom{\dfrac{5x}{3} \cdot \dfrac{3}{5}} = 1 \cdot x$ Multiplicative Inverse

$\phantom{\dfrac{5x}{3} \cdot \dfrac{3}{5}} = x$ Multiplicative Identity

b. $x^2(-2x^3) = (-2)(x^2 \cdot x^3)$ Commutative and Associative Properties

$ = -2x^{2+3}$ Rule of exponents

$ = -2x^5$ Simplest form

c. $(-2x)(4x) = (-2 \cdot 4)(x \cdot x)$ Commutative and Associative Properties

$ = -8(x^{1+1})$ Rule of exponents

$ = -8x^2$ Simplest form

d. $(2rs)(r^2s) = 2(r \cdot r^2)(s \cdot s)$ Commutative and Associative Properties

$ = 2(r^{1+2})(s^{1+1})$ Rule of exponents

$ = 2r^3s^2$ Simplest form

4 Use the Distributive Property to remove symbols of grouping.

Symbols of Grouping

The main tool for removing symbols of grouping is the Distributive Property, as illustrated in Example 11. You may want to review order of operations in Section 1.4.

Study Tip

When a parenthetical expression is preceded by a *plus* sign, you can remove the parentheses without changing the signs of the terms inside.

$$3y + (-2y + 7)$$
$$= 3y - 2y + 7$$

When a parenthetical expression is preceded by a *minus* sign, however, you must change the sign of each term to remove the parentheses.

$$3y - (2y - 7)$$
$$= 3y - 2y + 7$$

Remember that $-(2y - 7)$ is equal to $(-1)(2y - 7)$, and the Distributive Property can be used to "distribute the minus sign."

| **Example 11** | Removing Symbols of Grouping |

Simplify each expression.

a. $-(2y - 7)$ **b.** $5x + (x - 7)2$

c. $-2(4x - 1) + 3x$ **d.** $3(y - 5) - (2y - 7)$

Solution

a. $-(2y - 7) = -2y + 7$ Distributive Property

b. $5x + (x - 7)2 = 5x + 2x - 14$ Distributive Property

$\qquad\qquad\qquad = 7x - 14$ Combine like terms.

c. $-2(4x - 1) + 3x = -8x + 2 + 3x$ Distributive Property

$\qquad\qquad\qquad\qquad = -8x + 3x + 2$ Commutative Property

$\qquad\qquad\qquad\qquad = -5x + 2$ Combine like terms.

d. $3(y - 5) - (2y - 7) = 3y - 15 - 2y + 7$ Distributive Property

$\qquad\qquad\qquad\qquad = (3y - 2y) + (-15 + 7)$ Group like terms.

$\qquad\qquad\qquad\qquad = y - 8$ Combine like terms.

| **Example 12** | Removing Nested Symbols of Grouping |

Simplify each expression.

a. $2[-2(1 - 3x)] = 2[-2 + 6x]$ Distributive Property

$\qquad\qquad\qquad\quad = -4 + 12x$ Distributive Property

b. $5x - 2[4x + 3(x - 1)]$

$\qquad = 5x - 2[4x + 3x - 3]$ Distributive Property

$\qquad = 5x - 2[7x - 3]$ Combine like terms.

$\qquad = 5x - 14x + 6$ Distributive Property

$\qquad = -9x + 6$ Combine like terms.

c. $-7y + 3[2y - (3 - 2y)] - 5y + 4$

$\qquad = -7y + 3[2y - 3 + 2y] - 5y + 4$ Distributive Property

$\qquad = -7y + 3[4y - 3] - 5y + 4$ Combine like terms.

$\qquad = -7y + 12y - 9 - 5y + 4$ Distributive Property

$\qquad = (-7y + 12y - 5y) + (-9 + 4)$ Group like terms.

$\qquad = -5$ Combine like terms.

Example 13   Simplifying Algebraic Expressions

Simplify each expression.

a. $(-3x)(5x^4) + 7x^5 = (-3)(5)x \cdot x^4 + 7x^5$ Commutative and Associative Properties

$$= -15x^5 + 7x^5$$ Rule of exponents

$$= -8x^5$$ Combine like terms.

b. $2x(x + 3y) + 4(5 - xy) = 2x^2 + 6xy + 20 - 4xy$ Distributive Property

$$= 2x^2 + 6xy - 4xy + 20$$ Commutative Property

$$= 2x^2 + 2xy + 20$$ Combine like terms.

The next example illustrates the use of the Distributive Property with fractional expressions.

Example 14   Simplifying Fractional Expressions

Simplify each expression.

a. $\dfrac{3x}{5} - \dfrac{x}{5} = \dfrac{3}{5}x - \dfrac{1}{5}x$ Write with fractional coefficients.

$$= \left(\dfrac{3}{5} - \dfrac{1}{5}\right)x$$ Distributive Property

$$= \dfrac{2}{5}x$$ Subtract fractions.

b. $\dfrac{x}{4} + \dfrac{2x}{7} = \dfrac{1}{4}x + \dfrac{2}{7}x$ Write with fractional coefficients.

$$= \left(\dfrac{1}{4} + \dfrac{2}{7}\right)x$$ Distributive Property

$$= \left[\dfrac{1(7)}{4(7)} + \dfrac{2(4)}{7(4)}\right]x$$ Common denominator

$$= \dfrac{15}{28}x$$ Simplest form

Discussing the Concept   A Mathematical Riddle

What is the largest number that can be written using the three digits 2, 3, and 4? The number 432 seems to be the obvious answer. However, if you allow the digits to be exponents, then you can obtain numbers that are much larger than 432. For instance, consider the numbers

$$(32)^4 = 1,048,576 \quad \text{and} \quad 3^{24} \approx 282,430,000,000.$$

Create the largest number you can using the three digits 2, 3, and 4. Compare your number with those of other students.

2.2   Exercises

Integrated Review   Concepts, Skills, and Problem Solving

Keep mathematically in shape by doing these exercises *before* the problems of this section.

Properties and Definitions

1. Complete the following property of exponents.

   $a^m \cdot a^n = $ ▮

2. Name the property demonstrated by the statement: $\frac{1}{2}(4x + 10) = 2x + 5$.

Simplifying Expressions

In Exercises 3-10, perform the operation.

3. $0 - (-12)$ 4. $60 - (-60)$

5. $-12 - 2 + |-3|$

6. $-730 + 1820 + 3150 + (-10,000)$

7. Find the sum of 72 and -37.

8. Subtract 600 from 250.

9. $\frac{5}{16} - \frac{3}{10}$ 10. $\frac{9}{16} + 2\frac{3}{12}$

Problem Solving

11. *Profit*   A company showed a loss of $1,530,000 during the first 6 months of a given year. If the company ended the year with an overall profit of $832,000, what was the profit during the last two quarters of the year?

12. *Average Speed*   A family on vacation traveled 676 miles in 13 hours. Determine their average speed in miles per hour.

Developing Skills

In Exercises 1-26, simplify the expression. See Examples 1 and 2.

1. $u^2 \cdot u^4$

2. $z^3 \cdot z$

3. $3x^3 \cdot x^4$

4. $4y^3 \cdot y$

5. $5x(x^6)$

6. $(-6x^2)x^4$

7. $(-5z^3)(3z^2)$

8. $(-2x^2)(-4x)$

9. $(-xz)(-2y^2z)$

10. $(6u^2v)(3uv^2)$

11. $2b^4(-ab)(3b^2)$

12. $4xy(-3x^2)(-2y^3)$

13. $(t^2)^4$

14. $(v^3)^2$

15. $5(uv)^5$

16. $3(pq)^4$

17. $(-2s)^3$

18. $(-3z)^2$

19. $(a^2b)^3(ab^2)^4$

20. $(st)^5(s^2t)^4$

21. $(u^2v^3)(-2uv^2)^4$

22. $(-3y^2z)^2(2yz^2)^3$

23. $[(x - 3)^4]^2$

24. $[(t + 1)^2]^5$

25. $(x - 2y)^3(x - 2y)^3$

26. $(x - 3)^2(x - 3)^5$

Think About It   In Exercises 27-30, decide whether the expressions are equal. Explain your reasoning.

27. $x^5 \cdot x^3 \overset{?}{=} x^{15}$

28. $(-2x)^4 \overset{?}{=} -2x^4$

29. $-3x^3 \overset{?}{=} -27x^3$

30. $(xy)^2 \overset{?}{=} xy^2$

In Exercises 31-44, identify the basic rule (or rules) of algebra illustrated by the equation. See Example 3.

31. $x + 2y = 2y + x$

32. $-10(xy^2) = (-10x)y^2$

33. $(9x)y = 9(xy)$

34. $rt + 0 = rt$

35. $(x^2 + y^2) \cdot 1 = x^2 + y^2$

36. $(3x + 2y) + z = 3x + (2y + z)$

37. $2zy = 2yz$

38. $x(y + z) = xy + xz$

39. $(5m + 3) - (5m + 3) = 0$

40. $16xy \cdot \dfrac{1}{16xy} = 1, \quad xy \neq 0$

41. $(x + y) \cdot \dfrac{1}{(x + y)} = 1, \quad x + y \neq 0$

42. $(x + 2)(x + y) = x(x + y) + 2(x + y)$

43. $x^2 + (y^2 - y^2) = x^2$

44. $3y + (z^3 - z^3) = 3y$

In Exercises 45–54, complete the statement. State the rule of algebra that you used. See Example 3.

45. $(x + 10) - \boxed{} = 0$

46. $(-5r)s = -5(\boxed{})$

47. $v(2) = \boxed{}$

48. $(4x - 3y) + \boxed{} = 4x - 3y$

49. $5(t - 2) = 5(\boxed{}) + 5(\boxed{})$

50. $(2z - 3) + \boxed{} = 0$

51. $5x(\boxed{}) = 1, \quad x \neq 0$

52. $(s - 5)(\boxed{}) = s - 5$

53. $12 + (8 - x) = \boxed{} - x$

54. $(2x - y)(-3) = -3\boxed{}$

In Exercises 55–68, use the Distributive Property to expand the expression. See Example 4.

55. $-5(2x - y)$ **56.** $2(16 + 8z)$

57. $(x + 2)(3)$ **58.** $(4 - t)(-6)$

59. $4(x + xy + y^2)$ **60.** $6(r - t + s)$

61. $3(x^2 + x)$ **62.** $4(2y^2 - y)$

63. $-4y(3y - 4)$ **64.** $-z(5 - 2z)$

65. $-(u - v)$ **66.** $-(x + y)$

67. $x(3x - 4y)$ **68.** $r(2r^2 - t)$

In Exercises 69–72, write the area of each component part of the figure. Then demonstrate the Distributive Property by writing the total area of each figure in two ways. See Example 5.

69.

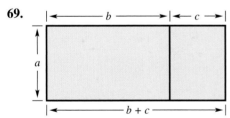

70.

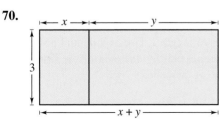

71.

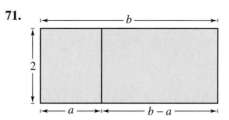

72.

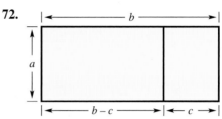

In Exercises 73 and 74, identify the terms of the expression and the coefficient of each term.

73. $6x^2 - 3xy + y^2$ **74.** $-4xy + 2xz - yz$

In Exercises 75–78, identify the like terms. See Example 6.

75. $16t^3 + 4 - 5 + 3t^3$

76. $a^2 + 5ab^2 - 3b^2 + 7a^2b - ab^2 + a^2$

77. $6x^2y + 2xy - 4x^2y$ **78.** $-\frac{1}{4}x^2 - 3x + \frac{3}{4}x^2 + x$

Think About It   In Exercises 79 and 80, state why the two expressions are not like terms.

79. $\frac{1}{2}x^2y, \frac{5}{2}xy^2$ **80.** $-16x^2y^3, 7x^2y$

In Exercises 81–100, simplify the expression by combining like terms. See Examples 7 and 8.

81. $3y - 5y$ **82.** $-16x + 25x$

83. $x + 5 - 3x$ **84.** $7s + 3 - 3s$

85. $2x + 9x + 4$ **86.** $10x - 4 - 5x$

87. $5r + 6 - 2r + 1$ **88.** $2t - 4 + 8t + 9$

89. $x^2 - 2xy + 4 + xy$ **90.** $r^2 + 3rs - 6 - rs$

91. $5z - 5 + 10z + 2z + 16$

92. $7x - 4 + 8 + 3x - 6$

93. $z^3 + 2z^2 + z + z^2 + 2z + 1$

94. $3x^2 - x^2 + 4x + 3x^2 - x + x^2$

95. $2x^2y + 5xy^2 - 3x^2y + 4xy + 7xy^2$

96. $6rt - 3r^2t + 2rt^2 - 4rt - 2r^2t$

97. $3\left(\dfrac{1}{x}\right) - \dfrac{1}{x} + 8$ **98.** $1.2\left(\dfrac{1}{x}\right) + 3.8\left(\dfrac{1}{x}\right) - 4x$

99. $5\left(\dfrac{1}{t}\right) + 6\left(\dfrac{1}{t}\right) - 2t$

100. $16\left(\dfrac{a}{b}\right) - 6\left(\dfrac{a}{b}\right) + \dfrac{3}{2} - \dfrac{1}{2}$

True or False? In Exercises 101–104, decide whether the statement is true or false.

101. $3(x - 4) \overset{?}{=} 3x - 4$

102. $-3(x - 4) \overset{?}{=} -3x - 12$

103. $6x - 4x \overset{?}{=} 2x$

104. $12y^2 + 3y^2 \overset{?}{=} 36y^2$

Mental Math In Exercises 105–108, use the Distributive Property to perform the required arithmetic *mentally.* For example, suppose you work in an industry where the wage is $14 per hour and time-and-one-half for overtime. Thus, your hourly wage for overtime is

$14(1.5) = 14\left(1 + \tfrac{1}{2}\right) = 14 + 7 = \$21.$

105. $8(52) = 8(50 + 2)$

106. $6(29) = 6(30 - 1)$

107. $5(7.98) = 5(8 - 0.02)$

108. $12(11.95) = 12(12 - 0.05)$

In Exercises 109–122, simplify the expression. See Examples 9 and 10.

109. $2(6x)$

110. $7(5a)$

111. $-(-4x)$

112. $-(5t)$

113. $(-2x)(-3x)$

114. $-4(-3y)$

115. $(-5z)(2z^2)$

116. $(10t)(-4t^2)$

117. $\dfrac{18a}{5} \cdot \dfrac{15}{6}$

118. $\dfrac{5x}{8} \cdot \dfrac{16}{5}$

119. $\left(-\dfrac{3x^2}{2}\right)(4x^3)$

120. $\left(\dfrac{4x}{3}\right)\left(\dfrac{3x}{2}\right)$

121. $(12xy^2)(-2x^3y^2)$

122. $(7r^2s^3)(3rs)$

In Exercises 123–142, simplify the expression by removing symbols of grouping and combining like terms. See Examples 11, 12, and 13.

123. $2(x - 2) + 4$

124. $-3(x + 1) - 2$

125. $6(2s - 1) + s + 4$

126. $(2x - 1)(2) + x$

127. $m - 3(m - 5)$

128. $5l - 6(3l - 5)$

129. $-6(1 - 2x) + 10(5 - x)$

130. $3(r - 2s) - 5(3r - 5s)$

131. $\tfrac{2}{3}(12x + 15) + 16$

132. $\tfrac{3}{8}(4 - y) - \tfrac{5}{2} + 10$

133. $3 - 2[6 + (4 - x)]$

134. $10x + 5[6 - (2x + 3)]$

135. $7x(2 - x) - 4x$

136. $-6x(x - 1) + x^2$

137. $4x^2 + x(5 - x)$

138. $-z(z - 2) + 3z^2 + 5$

139. $-3t(4 - t) + t(t + 1)$

140. $-2x(x - 1) + x(3x - 2)$

141. $3t[4 - (t - 3)] + t(t + 5)$

142. $4y[5 - (y + 1)] + 3y(y + 1)$

In Exercises 143–150, use the Distributive Property to simplify the expression. See Example 14.

143. $\dfrac{2x}{3} - \dfrac{x}{3}$

144. $\dfrac{7y}{8} - \dfrac{3y}{8}$

145. $\dfrac{4z}{5} + \dfrac{3z}{5}$

146. $\dfrac{5t}{12} + \dfrac{7t}{12}$

147. $\dfrac{x}{3} - \dfrac{5x}{4}$

148. $\dfrac{5x}{7} + \dfrac{2x}{3}$

149. $\dfrac{3x}{10} - \dfrac{x}{10} + \dfrac{4x}{5}$

150. $\dfrac{3z}{4} - \dfrac{z}{2} - \dfrac{z}{3}$

Solving Problems

Balance in an Account In Exercises 151 and 152, the balance in an account with an initial deposit of P dollars, at an annual interest rate of r for t years, is $P(1 + r)^t$. Find the balance for the given values of P, r, and t.

151. $P = 10,000,$ $\quad r = 0.08,$ $\quad t = 10$

152. $P = 5000,$ $\quad r = 0.06,$ $\quad t = 30$

153. *Geometry* The square and cube shown below have edges of length x. Use exponential notation to write an expression for the area of the square and the volume of the cube.

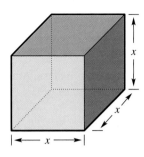

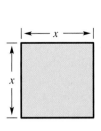

Figure for 153

154. The formulas give the moments of inertia of two solids. Simplify each expression.

(a) $\frac{1}{2}m(2a)^2(2L)$ (b) $k\pi a^2 L\left(\dfrac{a^2}{2}\right)$

155. *Geometry* Write an expression for the perimeter of the triangle shown in the figure. Use the rules of algebra to simplify the expression.

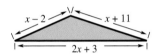

156. *Area of a Trapezoid* The area of a trapezoid with parallel bases of lengths b_1 and b_2 and height h (see figure) is $\frac{1}{2}h(b_1 + b_2)$.

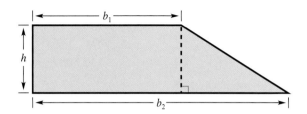

(a) Show that the area can also be expressed as $b_1 h + \frac{1}{2}(b_2 - b_1)h$, and give a geometric explanation for the area represented by each term in this expression.

(b) Find the area of a trapezoid with $b_1 = 7$, $b_2 = 12$, and $h = 3$.

Area of a Trapezoid In Exercises 157 and 158, use the formula for the area of a trapezoid, $\frac{1}{2}h(b_1 + b_2)$, to find the area of the trapezoidal house lot and tile.

157.   **158.**

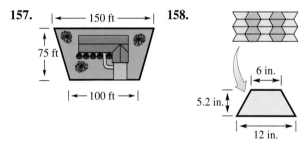

Explaining Concepts

159. Discuss the difference between $(6x)^4$ and $6x^4$.

160. The expressions $4x$ and x^4 each represent repeated operations. What are the operations? Write the expressions showing the repeated operations.

161. Which of the following are equivalent? Explain.

(a) $12x^8$ (b) $12(x^3)^5$ (c) $12x^3x^5$

(d) $3 \cdot 2^2(x^2)^4$ (e) $3 \cdot 5x^8$

162. In your own words, state the definition of like terms. Give an example of like terms and an example of unlike terms.

163. Describe how to combine like terms. What operations are used? Give an example of an expression that can be simplified by combining like terms.

164. Explain why $3(x + 9) \neq 3x + 9$.

165. In your own words, describe the procedure for removing nested symbols of grouping.

166. In your own words, describe the priorities for order of operations.

167. Does the expression $[x - (3 \cdot 4)] \div 5$ change if the parentheses are removed? Does it change if the brackets are removed? Explain.

168. Explain the error in the equation.

$$\frac{x}{3} + \frac{4x}{3} = \frac{5x}{6}$$

Mid-Chapter Quiz

Take this quiz as you would take a quiz in class. After you are done, check your work against the answers given in the back of the book.

In Exercises 1 and 2, evaluate the algebraic expression for the specified values of the variables. If it is not possible, state the reason.

1. $x^2 - 3x$ (a) $x = 3$ (b) $x = -2$ (c) $x = 0$

2. $\dfrac{x}{y - 3}$ (a) $x = 2, y = 4$ (b) $x = 0, y = -1$ (c) $x = 5, y = 3$

3. Identify the coefficients of the terms (a) $-5xy^2$ and (b) $\dfrac{5z}{16}$.

4. Rewrite the expression in exponential form.

(a) $3y \cdot 3y \cdot 3y \cdot 3y$ (b) $2 \cdot (x - 3) \cdot (x - 3) \cdot 2 \cdot 2$

In Exercises 5–10, simplify the expression.

5. $x^4 \cdot x^3$ **6.** $(v^2)^5$ **7.** $(-3y)^2 y^3$

8. $8(x - 4)^2 (x - 4)^4$ **9.** $\dfrac{2z^2}{3y} \cdot \dfrac{5z}{7y^3}$ **10.** $\left(\dfrac{x}{y}\right)^2 \left(\dfrac{x}{y}\right)^5$

In Exercises 11–14, identify the rule of algebra illustrated by the equation.

11. $-3(2y) = (-3 \cdot 2)y$ **12.** $(x + 2)y = xy + 2y$

13. $3y \cdot \dfrac{1}{3y} = 1, \quad y \ne 0$ **14.** $x - x^2 + 2 = -x^2 + x + 2$

In Exercises 15 and 16, use the Distributive Property to expand the expression.

15. $2(3x - 1)$ **16.** $-4(2y - 3)$

In Exercises 17 and 18, simplify the expression by combining like terms.

17. $y^2 - 3xy + y + 7xy$ **18.** $10\left(\dfrac{1}{u}\right) - 7\left(\dfrac{1}{u}\right) + 3u$

In Exercises 19 and 20, simplify the expression by removing symbols of grouping and combining like terms.

19. $5(a - 2b) + 3(a + b)$ **20.** $4x + 3[2 - 4(x + 6)]$

21. Simplify the following expression for the moment of inertia of a cone of height h and radius r (see figure).

$$\left(\tfrac{1}{3}\pi r^2 h\right)\left(\tfrac{3}{10} r^2\right)$$

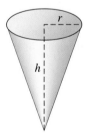

Figure for 21

22. Evaluate the expression $4 \cdot 10^4 + 5 \cdot 10^3 + 7 \cdot 10^2$.

2.3   Algebra and Problem Solving

Objectives

1 Define algebra as a problem-solving language.

2 Construct verbal mathematical models from written statements.

3 Translate verbal phrases into algebraic expressions.

4 Identify hidden operations when constructing algebraic expressions.

5 Use problem-solving strategies to solve an application problem.

1 Define algebra as a problem-solving language.

What Is Algebra?

Algebra is a problem-solving language that is used to solve real-life problems. It has four basic components, which tend to nest within each other, as indicated in Figure 2.1.

1. Symbolic representations and applications of the rules of arithmetic

2. Rewriting (reducing, simplifying, factoring) algebraic expressions into equivalent forms

3. Creating and solving equations

4. Studying relationships among variables by the use of functions and graphs

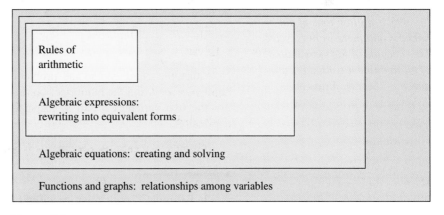

Figure 2.1

Notice that one of the components deals with expressions and another deals with equations. As you study algebra, it is important to understand the difference between simplifying or rewriting an algebraic *expression*, and solving an algebraic *equation*. In general, remember that a mathematical expression *has no equal sign*, whereas a mathematical equation *must have an equal sign*.

When you use an equal sign to *rewrite* an expression, you are merely indicating the *equivalence* of the new expression and the previous one.

Original Expression	*equals*	*Equivalent Expression*
$(a + b)c$	$=$	$ac + bc$

2 Construct verbal mathematical models from written statements.

Constructing a verbal model is a helpful strategy when solving application problems. In class, encourage students to develop verbal models for several exercises before solving them.

Constructing Verbal Models

In the first two sections of this chapter, you studied techniques for rewriting and simplifying algebraic expressions. In this section you will study ways to *construct* algebraic expressions from written statements by first constructing a **verbal mathematical model.**

Let's take another look at Example 1 in Section 2.1 (page 62). In that example you are paid $6 per hour and your weekly pay can be represented by the verbal model

$$\boxed{\text{Pay per hour}} \cdot \boxed{\text{Number of hours}} = 6 \text{ dollars } \cdot x \text{ hours } = 6x.$$

Note the hidden operation of multiplication in this expression. Nowhere in the verbal problem does it say you are to multiply 6 times x. It is *implied* in the problem. This is often the case when algebra is used to solve real-life problems.

In 1995, 1 million tons of aluminum containers were recycled. This accounted for more than 35% of all aluminum containers produced. (Source: Franklin Associates, Ltd.)

Example 1   Constructing an Algebraic Expression

You are paid 5¢ for each aluminum soda can and 3¢ for each glass soda bottle you collect. Write an algebraic expression that represents the total weekly income for this recycling activity.

Solution

Before writing an algebraic expression for the weekly income, it is helpful to construct an informal verbal model. For instance, the following verbal model could be used.

$$\boxed{\text{Pay per can}} \cdot \boxed{\text{Number of cans}} + \boxed{\text{Pay per bottle}} \cdot \boxed{\text{Number of bottles}}$$

Note that the word *and* in the problem indicates addition. Because both the number of cans and the number of bottles can vary from week to week, you can use the two variables c and b, respectively, to write the following algebraic expression.

$$\boxed{5 \text{ cents}} \cdot c \text{ cans } + \boxed{3 \text{ cents}} \cdot b \text{ bottles } = 5c + 3b$$

In Example 1, notice that c is used to represent the number of *cans* and b is used to represent the number of *bottles*. When writing algebraic expressions, choose variables that can be identified with the unknown quantities.

The number of one kind of item can be expressed in terms of the number of another kind of item. Suppose the number of cans in Example 1 was said to be "three times the number of bottles." In this case, only one variable is needed and the model could be written as

$$\boxed{3 \text{ cents}} \cdot b \text{ bottles } + \boxed{5 \text{ cents}} \cdot 3 \cdot b \text{ cans } = 3b + 5(3b)$$
$$= 3b + 15b$$
$$= 18b.$$

3 Translate verbal phrases into algebraic expressions.

Translating Phrases

When translating verbal sentences and phrases into algebraic expressions, it is helpful to watch for key words and phrases that indicate the four different operations of arithmetic. The following list gives several examples.

Translating verbal phrases into algebraic expressions is a helpful first step toward translating application problems into equations.

▶ Translating Phrases into Algebraic Expressions

Key Words and Phrases	*Verbal Description*	*Algebraic Expression*
Addition:		
Sum, plus, greater,	The sum of 6 and x	$6 + x$
increased by, more than,		
exceeds, total of	Eight more than y	$y + 8$
Subtraction:		
Difference, minus,	Five decreased by a	$5 - a$
less, decreased by,		
subtracted from,	Four less than z	$z - 4$
reduced by, the remainder		
Multiplication:		
Product, multiplied by,	Five times x	$5x$
twice, times, percent of		
Division:		$\dfrac{x}{3}$
Quotient, divided by, ratio, per	The ratio of x to 3	

Example 2   Translating Phrases Having Specified Variables

Translate each of the following into an algebraic expression.

a. Three less than m **b.** y decreased by 10

c. The product of 5 and x **d.** The quotient of n and 7

Solution

a. Three less than m

   $m - 3$ Think: 3 subtracted from what?

b. y decreased by 10

   $y - 10$ Think: What is subtracted from y?

c. The product of 5 and x

   $5x$ Think: 5 times what?

d. The quotient of n and 7

   $\dfrac{n}{7}$ Think: n is divided by what?

| Example 3 | Translating Phrases Having Specified Variables |

Translate each of the following into an algebraic expression.

a. Six times the sum of x and 7

b. The product of 4 and x, divided by 3

c. k decreased by the product of 8 and m

Solution

a. Six times the sum of x and 7

$$6(x + 7)$$ Think: 6 multiplied by what?

b. The product of 4 and x, divided by 3

$$\frac{4x}{3}$$ Think: What is divided by 3?

c. k decreased by the product of 8 and m

$$k - 8m$$ Think: What is subtracted from k?

In most applications of algebra, the variables are not specified and it is your task to assign variables to the *appropriate* quantities. Although similar to the translations in Examples 2 and 3, the translations in the next example may seem more difficult because variables have not been assigned to the unknown quantities.

| Example 4 | Translating Phrases Having No Specified Variable |

Translate each of the following into a variable expression.

a. The sum of 3 and a number

b. Five decreased by the product of 3 and a number

c. The difference of a number and 3, divided by 12

Solution

In each case, let x be the unspecified number.

a. The sum of 3 and a number

$$3 + x$$ Think: 3 added to what?

b. Five decreased by the product of 3 and a number

$$5 - 3x$$ Think: What is subtracted from 5?

c. The difference of a number and 3, divided by 12

$$\frac{x - 3}{12}$$ Think: What is divided by 12?

A good way to learn algebra is to do it *forward* and *backward*. In the next example, algebraic expressions are translated into verbal form. Keep in mind that other key words could be used to describe the operations in each expression. Your goal is to use key words or phrases that keep the verbal expressions clear and concise.

Example 5   Translating Algebraic Expressions into Verbal Form

Without using a variable, write a verbal description for each of the following.

a. $7x - 12$ **b.** $7(x - 12)$ **c.** $5 + \dfrac{x}{2}$ **d.** $\dfrac{5 + x}{2}$ **e.** $(3x)^2$

Solution

a. *Algebraic expression:* $7x - 12$
   Primary operation: Subtraction
   Terms: $7x$ and 12
   Verbal description: Twelve less than the product of 7 and a number
b. *Algebraic expression:* $7(x - 12)$
   Primary operation: Multiplication
   Factors: 7 and $(x - 12)$
   Verbal description: Twelve is subtracted from a number and the result is multiplied by 7.

c. *Algebraic expression:* $5 + \dfrac{x}{2}$

   Primary operation: Addition

   Terms: 5 and $\dfrac{x}{2}$

   Verbal description: Five added to the quotient of a number and 2
d. *Algebraic expression:* $\dfrac{5 + x}{2}$

   Primary operation: Division
   Numerator, denominator: Numerator is $5 + x$; denominator is 2
   Verbal description: The sum of 5 and a number, divided by 2
e. *Algebraic expression:* $(3x)^2$
   Primary operation: Raise to a power
   Base, power: $3x$ is the base, 2 is the power
   Verbal description: The product of 3 and x, squared

Translating algebraic expressions into verbal phrases is more difficult than it may appear. It is easy to write a phrase that is ambiguous. For instance, what does the phrase "the sum of 5 and a number times 2" mean? Without further information, this phrase could mean

$$5 + 2x \quad \text{or} \quad 2(5 + x).$$

4 Identify hidden operations when constructing algebraic expressions.

Verbal Models with Hidden Operations

Most real-life problems do not contain verbal expressions that clearly identify all the arithmetic operations involved. You need to rely on past experience and the physical nature of the problem in order to identify the operations hidden in the problem statement. Multiplication is the operation most commonly hidden in real life applications. Watch for *hidden operations* in the next two examples.

Example 6   Discovering Hidden Operations

a. A cash register contains n nickels and d dimes. Write an expression for this amount of money in cents.

b. Write an expression showing how far a person can ride a bicycle in t hours if the person travels at a constant rate of 15 miles per hour.

c. A person paid x dollars plus 6% sales tax for an automobile. Write an expression for the total cost of the automobile.

Solution

a. The amount of money is a sum of products.

Verbal Model: Value of nickel $\cdot$ Number of nickels $+$ Value of dime $\cdot$ Number of dimes

Labels: Value of nickel = 5   (cents)
Number of nickels = n
Value of dime = 10   (cents)
Number of dimes = d

Expression: $5n + 10d$ (cents)

b. The distance traveled is a product.

Verbal Model: Rate of travel $\cdot$ Time traveled

Labels: Rate of travel = 15   (miles per hour)
Time traveled = t (hours)

Expression: $15t$ (miles)

c. The total cost is a sum.

Verbal Model: Cost of automobile $+$ Percent of sales tax $\cdot$ Cost of automobile

Labels: Percent of sales tax = 0.06   (decimal form)
Cost of automobile = x (dollars)

Expression: $x + 0.06x = (1 + 0.06)x$

$$= 1.06x$$

Study Tip

In Example 6(b), the final answer is listed in terms of miles. This makes sense in the following way.

$$15 \frac{\text{miles}}{\text{hours}} \cdot t \text{ hours}$$

Note that the hours "cancel," leaving the answer in terms of miles. This technique, called *unit analysis*, can be very helpful in determining the final unit of measure.

Notice in part (c) of Example 6 that the equal sign is used to denote the equivalence of the three expressions. It is not an equation to be solved.

5 Use problem-solving strategies to solve an application problem.

Encourage students to experiment with each of these four problem-solving strategies. Students should begin to realize that there are *many* correct ways to approach questions in mathematics.

Additional Problem-Solving Strategies

In addition to constructing verbal models, there are other problem-solving strategies that can help you succeed in this course.

▶ Summary of Additional Problem-Solving Strategies

1. **Guess, Check, and Revise** Guess a reasonable solution based on the given data. Check the guess, and revise it, if necessary. Continue guessing, checking, and revising until a correct solution is found.

2. **Make a Table/Look for a Pattern** Make a table using the data in the problem. Look for a number pattern. Then use the pattern to complete the table or find a solution.

3. **Draw a Diagram** Draw a diagram that shows the facts from the problem. Use the diagram to visualize the action of the problem. Use algebra to find a solution. Then check the solution against the facts.

4. **Solve a Simpler Problem** Construct a simpler problem that is similar to the given problem. Solve the simpler problem. Then use the same procedure to solve the given problem.

Example 7   Guess, Check, and Revise

You deposit $500 in an account that earns 6% simple interest. The balance in the account after t years is

$$A = 500(1 + 0.06)^t.$$

How long will it take for your investment to double?

Solution

You can solve this problem using a guess, check, and revise strategy. For instance, you might guess that it takes 10 years for your investment to double. The balance in 10 years is

$$A = 500(1 + 0.06)^{10} \approx \$895.42.$$

Because the amount has not yet doubled, you increase your guess to 15 years.

$$A = 500(1 + 0.06)^{15} \approx \$1198.28$$

Because this amount is more than double the investment, your next guess should be a number between 10 and 15. After trying several more numbers, you can determine that your balance doubles in about 11.9 years.

Another strategy that works well for a problem like Example 7 is to make up a table of data values. Your calculator or graphing utility would work well to create the following table.

t	2	4	6	8	10	12
A	561.80	631.24	709.26	796.92	895.42	1006.10

Example 8   Make a Table/Look for a Pattern

Find the following products. Then describe the pattern and use your description to find the product of 14 and 16.

$$1 \cdot 3, \ 2 \cdot 4, \ 3 \cdot 5, \ 4 \cdot 6, \ 5 \cdot 7, \ 6 \cdot 8, \ 7 \cdot 9$$

Solution

One way to help find a pattern is to organize the results in a table.

Numbers	$1 \cdot 3$	$2 \cdot 4$	$3 \cdot 5$	$4 \cdot 6$	$5 \cdot 7$	$6 \cdot 8$	$7 \cdot 9$
Product	3	8	15	24	35	48	63

From the table, you can see that each of the products is 1 less than a perfect square. For instance, 3 is 1 less than 2^2 or 4, 8 is 1 less than 3^2 or 9, 15 is 1 less than 4^2 or 16, and so on.

If this pattern continues for other numbers, you can hypothesize that the product of 14 and 16 is 1 less than 15^2 or 225. That is,

$$14 \cdot 16 = 15^2 - 1 = 224.$$

You can confirm this result by actually multiplying 14 and 16.

Example 9   Draw a Diagram

The outer dimensions of a rectangular apartment are 25 feet by 40 feet. The combination living-room, dining-room, and kitchen areas occupy two-fifths of the apartment's area. Find the area of the remaining rooms.

Solution

For this problem, it helps to draw a diagram, as shown in Figure 2.2. From the figure, you can see that the total area in the apartment is

$$\text{Area} = (\text{length})(\text{width})$$
$$= (40)(25)$$
$$= 1000 \text{ square feet.}$$

The area occupied by the living room, dining room, and kitchen is

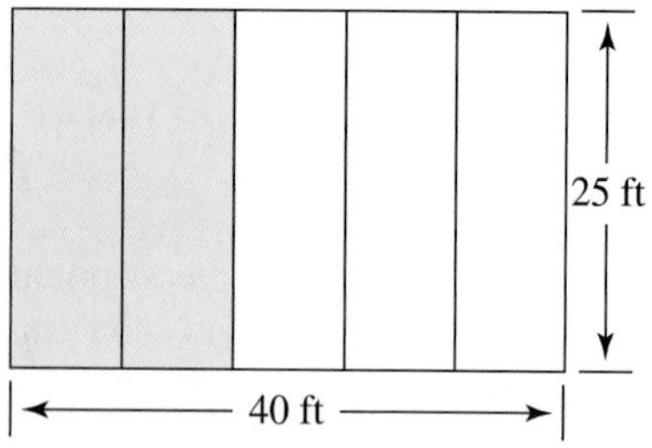

$$\frac{2}{5}(1000) = 400 \text{ square feet.}$$

This implies that the remaining rooms must have a total area of 600 square feet.

Figure 2.2

Example 10	Solve a Simpler Problem

You are driving on an interstate highway and are traveling at an average speed of 60 miles per hour. How far will you travel in $12\frac{1}{2}$ hours?

Solution

Distance and other related formulas can be found on the inside front cover of the text.

One way to solve the problem is to use the formula that relates distance, rate, and time. Suppose, however, that you have forgotten the formula. To help you remember, you could solve some simpler problems.

- If you travel 60 miles per hour for 1 hour, you will travel 60 miles.

- If you travel 60 miles per hour for 2 hours, you will travel 120 miles.

- If you travel 60 miles per hour for 3 hours, you will travel 180 miles.

From these examples, it appears that you can find the total miles traveled by multiplying the rate times the time. So, if you travel 60 miles per hour for $12\frac{1}{2}$ hours, you will travel a distance of

$$(60)(12.5) = 750 \text{ miles.}$$

Hidden operations are often involved when variable names (labels) are assigned to two unknown quantities. A good strategy is to use a *specific* case to help you write a model for the *general* case. For instance, a specific case of finding three consecutive integers

$$3, 3 + 1, \text{ and } 3 + 2$$

may help you write a general case for finding three consecutive integers n, $n + 1$, and $n + 2$. This strategy is illustrated in Examples 11 and 12.

Example 11	Using a Specific Case to Find a General Case

In each of the following, use the given variable to label the unknown quantity.

a. A person's weekly salary is d dollars. What is the annual salary?

b. A person's annual salary is y dollars. What is the monthly salary?

Solution

a. There are 52 weeks in a year.

   Specific case: If the weekly salary is $200, then the annual salary (in dollars) is 52 · 200.

   General case: If the weekly salary is d dollars, then the annual salary (in dollars) is 52 · d or 52d.

b. There are 12 months in a year.

   Specific case: If the annual salary is $24,000, then the monthly salary (in dollars) is 24,000 ÷ 12.

   General case: If the annual salary is y dollars, then the monthly salary (in dollars) is y ÷ 12 or $y/12$.

Example 12   Using a Specific Case to Find a General Case

In each of the following, use the given variable to label the unknown quantity.

a. One person is k inches shorter than another person. The first person is 60 inches tall. How tall is the second person?

b. A consumer buys g gallons of gasoline for a total of d dollars. What is the price per gallon?

c. A person drives on the highway at an average speed of 60 miles per hour for t hours. How far has the person traveled?

Solution

a. The first person is k inches shorter than the second person.

Specific case: If the first person is 10 inches shorter than the second person, then the second person is $60 + 10$ inches tall.

General case: If the first person is k inches shorter than the second person, then the second person is $60 + k$ inches tall.

b. To obtain the price per gallon, divide the price by the number of gallons.

Specific case: If the total price is \$11.50 and the total number of gallons is 10, then the price per gallon is $11.50 \div 10$ dollars per gallon.

General case: If the total price is d dollars and the total number of gallons is g, then the price per gallon is $d \div g$ or d/g dollars per gallon.

c. To obtain the distance driven, multiply the speed by the number of hours.

Specific case: If the person has driven for 2 hours at a speed of 60 miles per hour, then the person has traveled $60 \cdot 2$ miles.

General case: If the person has driven for t hours at a speed of 60 miles per hour, then the person has traveled $60t$ miles.

Discussing the Concept   Enough Information?

Most of the verbal problems you encounter in a mathematics text have precisely the right amount of information necessary to solve the problem. In real life, however, you may need to collect additional information. Decide what additional information would be needed to solve the following problem.

During a given week, a person worked 48 hours for the same employer. The hourly rate for overtime is \$12. Write an expression for the person's gross pay for the week, including any pay received for overtime.

2.3   Exercises

Integrated Review   *Concepts, Skills, and Problem Solving*

Keep mathematically in shape by doing these exercises *before* the problems of this section.

Properties and Definitions

1. The product of two real numbers is -35 and one of the factors is 5. What is the sign of the other factor?

2. Determine the sum of the digits of 744. Since this sum is divisible by 3, the number 744 is divisible by what number?

3. *True or False?* -4^2 is positive.

4. *True or False?* $(-4)^2$ is positive.

Simplifying Expressions

In Exercises 5–10, perform the operation.

5. $(-6)(-13)$

6. $|4(-6)(5)|$

7. $\left(-\frac{4}{3}\right)\left(-\frac{9}{16}\right)$

8. $\frac{7}{8} \div \frac{3}{16}$

9. $\left|-\frac{5}{9}\right| + 2$

10. $-7\frac{3}{5} - 3\frac{1}{2}$

Problem Solving

11. *Buying a Coat*   A coat costs $133.50, including tax. If you can save $30 a week, how many weeks must you save in order to buy the coat? How much money will you have left?

12. *Perimeter*   The length of a rectangle is $1\frac{1}{2}$ times its width. If its width is 8 meters, find its perimeter.

Developing Skills

In Exercises 1–6, match the verbal phrase with the correct algebraic expression.

(a) $11 + \frac{1}{3}x$

(b) $3x - 12$

(c) $3(x - 12)$

(d) $12 - 3x$

(e) $11x + \frac{1}{3}$

(f) $12x + 3$

1. Twelve decreased by 3 times a number

2. Eleven more than $\frac{1}{3}$ of a number

3. Eleven times a number plus $\frac{1}{3}$

4. Three increased by 12 times a number

5. The difference between 3 times a number and 12

6. Three times the difference of a number and 12

In Exercises 7–30, translate the phrase into an algebraic expression. (Let x represent the real number.) See Examples 1, 2, 3, and 4.

7. A number increased by 5

8. 25 more than a number

9. A number decreased by 25

10. A number decreased by 7

11. Six less than a number

12. Ten more than a number

13. Twice a number

14. The product of 30 and a number

15. A number divided by 3

16. A number divided by 100

17. The ratio of a number to 50

18. One-fourth of a number

19. Three-tenths of a number

20. Twenty-five hundredths of a number

21. A number is tripled and the product is increased by 5

22. A number is increased by 5 and the sum is tripled

23. Eight more than 5 times a number

24. The quotient of a number divided by 5 is decreased by 15

25. Ten times the sum of a number and 4

26. Seven more than 5 times a number

27. The absolute value of the sum of a number and 4

28. The absolute value of 4 less than twice a number

29. The square of a number, increased by 1

30. Twice the square of a number, increased by 4

In Exercises 31–42, write a verbal description of the algebraic expression. Use words only—do not use the variable. (There is more than one correct answer.) See Example 5.

31. $x - 10$

32. $x + 9$

33. $3x + 2$

34. $4 - 7x$

35. $7x + 4$

36. $9 - \frac{1}{4}x$

37. $3(2 - x)$

38. $-10(t - 6)$

39. $\dfrac{t + 1}{2}$

40. $\dfrac{1}{2} - \dfrac{t}{5}$

41. $x^2 + 5$

42. $x^3 - 1$

In Exercises 43–50, translate the phrase into a mathematical expression. Simplify the expression.

43. The sum of x and 3 is multiplied by x.

44. The sum of 6 and n is multiplied by 5.

45. The sum of 25 and x is added to x.

46. The sum of 4 and x is added to the sum of x and -8.

47. Nine is subtracted from x and the result is multiplied by 3.

48. The square of x is added to the product of x and $x + 1$.

49. The product of 8 times the sum of x and 24 is divided by 2.

50. Fifteen is subtracted from x and the difference is multiplied by 4.

Problem Solving

51. *Total Amount of Money* A cash register contains d dimes. Write an algebraic expression that represents the total amount of money (in dollars). See Example 6.

52. *Amount of Money* A cash register contains d dimes and q quarters. Write an algebraic expression that represents the total amount of money (in dollars).

53. *Sales Tax* The sales tax on a purchase of L dollars is 6%. Write an algebraic expression that represents the total amount of sales tax. (To find 6% of a quantity, multiply the quantity by 0.06.)

54. *Income Tax* The state income tax on a gross income of I dollars is 2.2%. Write an algebraic expression that represents the total amount of income tax. (To find 2.2% of a quantity, multiply the quantity by 0.022.)

55. *Travel Time* A truck travels 100 miles at an average speed of r miles per hour (see figure). Write an algebraic expression that represents the total travel time.

|← 100 miles →|

56. *Distance Traveled* A plane travels at the rate of r miles per hour for 3 hours. Write an algebraic expression that represents the total distance traveled by the plane.

57. *Camping Fee* A campground charges $15 for adults and $2 for children. Write an algebraic expression that represents the total camping fee for m adults and n children.

58. *Hourly Wage* The hourly wage for an employee is $12.50 per hour plus 75 cents for each of the q units produced during the hour. Write an algebraic expression that represents the total hourly earnings for the employee.

Guess, Check, and Revise In Exercises 59–62, an expression for the balance in an account is given. Guess, check, and revise to determine the time (in years) necessary for the investment of $1000 to double. See Example 7.

59. Interest rate: 7%
$1000(1 + 0.07)^t$

60. Interest rate: 5%
$1000(1 + 0.05)^t$

61. Interest rate: 6%
$1000(1 + 0.06)^t$

62. Interest rate: 8%
$1000(1 + 0.08)^t$

Finding a Pattern   In Exercises 63 and 64, complete the table. The third row in the table is the difference between consecutive entries of the second row. Describe the pattern of the third row. See Example 8.

63.

n	0	1	2	3	4	5
$2n - 1$						
Differences						

64.

n	0	1	2	3	4	5
$7n + 5$						
Differences						

65. *Finding a Pattern*   What would the pattern be in the third row of the table in Exercise 63 if the algebraic expression were $3n + 5$ rather than $2n - 1$?

66. *Finding a Pattern*   What would the pattern be in the third row of the table in Exercise 64 if the algebraic expression were $an + b$ rather than $7n + 5$?

Exploration   In Exercises 67 and 68, find a and b such that the expression $an + b$ yields the table values.

67.

n	0	1	2	3	4	5
$an + b$	4	9	14	19	24	29

68.

n	0	1	2	3	4	5
$an + b$	1	5	9	13	17	21

Geometry   In Exercises 69–72, write an algebraic expression that represents the area of the region. Use the rules of algebra to simplify the expression.

69.

3x

6x − 1

70.

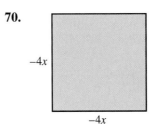

−4x

−4x

71.

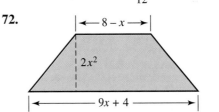

$5x^2 + 2$

12

72.

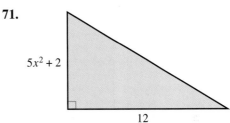

$8 - x$

$2x^2$

$9x + 4$

Drawing a Diagram   In Exercises 73 and 74, draw figures satisfying the specified conditions. See Example 9.

73. The sides of a square have length a centimeters. Draw the square. Draw the rectangle obtained by extending two of the parallel sides of the square 6 centimeters. Find expressions for the perimeter and area of each figure.

74. The dimensions of a rectangular lawn are 150 feet by 250 feet. The property owner has the option of buying a rectangular strip x feet wide along one 250-foot side of the lawn. Draw diagrams representing the lawn before and after the purchase. Write an expression for the area of each.

75. *Geometry*   A computer screen has sides of length s inches (see figure). Write an algebraic expression that represents the area of the screen. Express the area in the correct unit of measure.

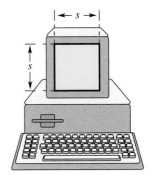

s

s

76. *Geometry*   A rectangle has sides of length $3w$ and w. Write an algebraic expression that represents the perimeter of the rectangle.

77. *Geometry*   Write an algebraic expression that represents the perimeter of the picture frame in the figure.

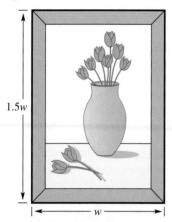

78. *Geometry*   A square has sides of length s. Write an algebraic expression that represents the perimeter of the square.

79. *Fibonacci Sequence*   Each term in the Fibonacci Sequence is the sum of the previous two terms.

   (a) Let m and n represent two consecutive terms in the sequence. Write an algebraic expression for the next term.

   (b) The first three terms in the sequence are 1, 1, and 2. Write the next five terms.

Explaining Concepts

80. Answer parts (c) to (h) of Motivating the Chapter on page 61.

81. The word *difference* indicates what operation?

82. The word *quotient* indicates what operation?

83. Determine which of the following are equivalent to the expression $n + 4$.

   (a) 4 more than n

   (b) the sum of n and 4

   (c) n less than 4

   (d) the ratio of n to 4

   (e) the total of 4 and n

84. Determine whether order is important when translating each of the following phrases into an algebraic expression. Explain.

   (a) x is increased by 10

   (b) 10 is decreased by x

   (c) the product of x and 10

   (d) the quotient of x and 10

85. Give two interpretations of "the quotient of 5 and a number times 3."

2.4   Introduction to Equations

Objectives

1 Distinguish between an algebraic expression and an algebraic equation.

2 Check whether a given value is a solution of an equation.

3 Use properties of equality to solve an equation.

4 Use a verbal model to construct an algebraic equation.

1 Distinguish between an algebraic expression and an algebraic equation.

Equations

An **equation** is a statement in which two mathematical expressions are equal. Here are some examples:

$$x = 3, \quad 5x - 2 = 8, \quad 3x - 12 = 3(x - 4), \quad \text{and} \quad x^2 - 9 = 0.$$

To **solve** an equation involving x means to find all values of x for which the equation is true. Such values are called **solutions,** and solutions **satisfy** the equation. For instance, 3 is a solution of $x = 3$ because $3 = 3$ is a true statement.

The **solution set** of an equation is the set of all solutions of the equation. Sometimes an equation will have the set of all real numbers as its solution set. Such an equation is called an **identity.** For instance, the equation

$$3x - 12 = 3(x - 4) \qquad \text{Identity}$$

is an identity because the equation is true for all real values of x. Try values such as 0, 1, -2, and 5 in this equation to see that each one is a solution.

An equation whose solution set is not the entire set of real numbers is called a **conditional equation.** For instance, the equation

$$x^2 - 9 = 0 \qquad \text{Conditional equation}$$

is a conditional equation because it has only two solutions, 3 and -3.

Be sure that you understand the distinction between an algebraic expression and an algebraic equation. The differences are summarized in the following table.

Algebraic Expression	Algebraic Equations	
	Conditional Equation	Identity
• Example: $4(x - 1)$ • Contains *no* equal sign • Can sometimes be *simplified* to an equivalent form: $4(x - 1)$ simplifies to $4x - 4$ • Can be evaluated for any real number for which the expression is defined	• Example: $4(x - 1) = 12$ • Contains an equal sign and is true for only certain values of the variable • Solution is found by isolating the variable x: $4(x - 1) = 12$ $4x - 4 = 12$ $4x = 16$ $x = 4$	• Example: $3(x - 2) = 3x - 6$ • Contains an equal sign and is true for all real values of the variable • Rewriting one side to be identical to the other shows that every real number is a solution: $3(x - 2) = 3x - 6$ $3x - 6 = 3x - 6$

2 Check whether a given value is a solution of an equation.

Examples 1 and 2 show how to **check** whether a given value of x is a solution of an equation.

Example 1   Checking a Solution of an Equation

Determine whether -2 is a solution of $x^2 - 5 = 4x + 7$.

Solution

$$x^2 - 5 = 4x + 7 \qquad \text{Original equation}$$
$$(-2)^2 - 5 \overset{?}{=} 4(-2) + 7 \qquad \text{Substitute } -2 \text{ for } x.$$
$$4 - 5 \overset{?}{=} -8 + 7 \qquad \text{Simplify.}$$
$$-1 = -1 \qquad \text{Solution checks. } \checkmark$$

Because both sides of the equation turn out to be the same number, you can conclude that -2 is a solution of the original equation.

Just because you have found one solution of an equation, you should not conclude that you have found all of the solutions. For instance, you can check that 6 is also a solution of the equation in Example 1 as follows.

$$x^2 - 5 = 4x + 7 \qquad \text{Original equation}$$
$$(6)^2 - 5 \overset{?}{=} 4(6) + 7 \qquad \text{Substitute 6 for } x.$$
$$36 - 5 \overset{?}{=} 24 + 7 \qquad \text{Simplify.}$$
$$31 = 31 \qquad \text{Solution checks. } \checkmark$$

Example 2   A Trial Solution That Does Not Check

Determine whether 2 is a solution of $x^2 - 5 = 4x + 7$.

Solution

$$x^2 - 5 = 4x + 7 \qquad \text{Original equation}$$
$$(2)^2 - 5 \overset{?}{=} 4(2) + 7 \qquad \text{Substitute 2 for } x.$$
$$4 - 5 \overset{?}{=} 8 + 7 \qquad \text{Simplify.}$$
$$-1 \neq 15 \qquad \text{2 is not a solution. } ✗$$

Because the two sides of the equation turn out to be different, you can conclude that 2 is not a solution of the original equation.

Study Tip

When checking a solution, we suggest that you write a question mark over the equal sign to indicate that you are not sure of the validity of the equation.

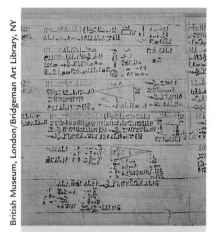

British Museum, London/Bridgeman Art Library, NY

Ahmes Papyrus

An ancient Egyptian papyrus, discovered in 1858, contains one of the earliest examples of mathematical writing in existence. The papyrus itself dates back to about 1650 B.C., but it is actually a copy of writings from two centuries earlier. The algebraic equations on the papyrus were written in words.

3 Use properties of equality to solve an equation.

Forming Equivalent Equations

It is helpful to think of an equation as having two sides that are in balance. Consequently, when you try to solve an equation, you must be careful to maintain that balance by performing the same operation on both sides.

Two equations that have the same set of solutions are called **equivalent.** For instance, the equations $x = 3$ and $x - 3 = 0$ are equivalent because both have only one solution—the number 3. When any one of the operations in the following list is applied to an equation, the resulting equation is equivalent to the original equation.

▶ **Forming Equivalent Equations: Properties of Equality**

An equation can be transformed into an *equivalent equation* using one or more of the following procedures.

	Original Equation	*Equivalent Equation(s)*
1. *Simplify either side:* Remove symbols of grouping, combine like terms, or reduce fractions on one or both sides of the equation.	$3x - x = 8$	$2x = 8$
2. *Apply the Addition Property of Equality:* Add (or subtract) the same quantity to (from) *both* sides of the equation.	$x - 2 = 5$	$x - 2 + 2 = 5 + 2$ $x = 7$
3. *Apply the Multiplication Property of Equality:* Multiply (or divide) *both* sides of the equation by the same *nonzero* quantity.	$3x = 9$	$\dfrac{3x}{3} = \dfrac{9}{3}$ $x = 3$
4. *Interchange the sides of the equation.*	$7 = x$	$x = 7$

The second and third operations in this list can be used to eliminate terms or factors in an equation. For example, to solve the equation $x - 5 = 1$, we need to eliminate the term -5 on the left side. This is accomplished by adding its opposite, 5, to both sides.

$$x - 5 = 1 \qquad \text{Original equation}$$

$$x - 5 + 5 = 1 + 5 \qquad \text{Add 5 to both sides.}$$

$$x + 0 = 6 \qquad \text{Combine like terms.}$$

$$x = 6 \qquad \text{Solution}$$

All four of the equations listed above are equivalent, and we call them the **steps** of the solution.

The next example shows how the properties of equality can be used to solve equations. You will get many more opportunities to practice these skills in the next chapter. For now, your goal should be to understand why each step in the solution is valid. For instance, the second step in part (a) is valid because the Addition Property of Equality states that you can add the same quantity to both sides of an equation.

Example 3   Operations Used to Solve Equations

Identify the property of equality used to solve each equation.

a.

$x - 2 = 3$	Original equation
$x - 2 + 2 = 3 + 2$	Add 2 to both sides.
$x = 5$	Solution

b.

$\dfrac{x}{5} = -2$	Original equation
$\dfrac{x}{5}(5) = -2(5)$	Multiply both sides by 5.
$x = -10$	Solution

c.

$4x = 9$	Original equation
$\dfrac{4x}{4} = \dfrac{9}{4}$	Divide both sides by 4.
$x = \dfrac{9}{4}$	Solution

d.

$\dfrac{5}{3}x = 7$	Original equation
$\dfrac{3}{5} \cdot \dfrac{5}{3}x = \dfrac{3}{5} \cdot 7$	Multiply both sides by $\frac{3}{5}$.
$x = \dfrac{21}{5}$	Solution

Study Tip

In Example 3(c), both sides of the equation are divided by 4 to eliminate the coefficient 4 on the left side. You could just as easily *multiply* both sides by $\frac{1}{4}$. Both techniques are legitimate—which one you decide to use is a matter of personal preference.

Solution

a. The Addition Property of Equality is used to add 2 to both sides of the equation in the second step. Adding 2 eliminates the term -2 from the left side of the equation.

b. The Multiplication Property of Equality is used to multiply both sides of the equation by 5 in the second step. Multiplying by 5 eliminates the denominator from the left side of the equation.

c. The Multiplication Property of Equality is used to divide both sides of the equation by 4 $\left(\text{or multiply both sides by } \frac{1}{4}\right)$ in the second step. Dividing by 4 eliminates the coefficient from the left side of the equation.

d. The Multiplication Property of Equality is used to multiply both sides of the equation by $\frac{3}{5}$ in the second step. Multiplying by the reciprocal of the fraction $\frac{5}{3}$ eliminates the fraction from the left side of the equation.

4 Use a verbal model to construct an algebraic equation.

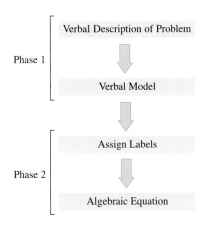

Phase 1

Verbal Description of Problem

Verbal Model

Phase 2

Assign Labels

Algebraic Equation

Verbal models help students organize and picture relationships, which can then be translated into equations.

Constructing Equations

It is helpful to use two phases in constructing equations that model real life. In the first phase, you translate the verbal description into a *verbal model*. In the second phase, you assign labels and translate the verbal model into a *mathematical model* or *algebraic equation*. Here are two examples of verbal models.

1. The sale price of a basketball is $28. The sale price is $7 less than the original price. What is the original price?

   Verbal Model: Sale price = Original price − Discount

   $28 = Original price − $7

2. The original price of a basketball is $35. The original price is discounted by $7. What is the sale price?

   Verbal Model: Sale price = Original price − Discount

   Sale price = $35 − $7

Example 4   Using Verbal Models to Construct Equations

Write an algebraic equation for the problem.

The total income that an employee received in 1998 was $31,550. How much was the employee paid each week? Assume that each weekly paycheck contained the same amount, and that the year consisted of 52 weeks.

Solution

Verbal Model: Income for year = 52 · Weekly pay

Labels: Income for year = 31,550   (dollars)
             Weekly pay = x (dollars)

Algebraic Model: $31{,}550 = 52x$

When you construct an equation, be sure to check that both sides of the equation represent the *same* unit of measure. For instance, in Example 4, both sides of the equation $31{,}550 = 52x$ represent dollar amounts.

Example 5   Using Verbal Models to Construct Equations

Write an algebraic equation for the following problem.

Tickets for a concert cost $15 for each floor seat and $10 for each stadium seat. There were 800 seats on the main floor, and these were sold out. If the total revenue from ticket sales was $52,000, how many stadium seats were sold?

Solution

Verbal Model:

Total revenue	=	Revenue from floor seats	+	Revenue from stadium seats

Labels:

Total revenue = 52,000   (dollars)
Price per floor seat = 15   (dollars per seat)
Number of floor seats = 800   (seats)
Price per stadium seat = 10   (dollars per seat)
Number of stadium seats = x (seats)

Algebraic Model:

$$52,000 = 15(800) + 10x$$

In Example 5, you can use the following *unit analysis* to check that both sides of the equation are measured in dollars.

$$52,000 \text{ dollars} = \left(\frac{15 \text{ dollars}}{\text{seat}}\right)(800 \text{ seats}) + \left(\frac{10 \text{ dollars}}{\text{seat}}\right)(x \text{ seats})$$

In the next chapter, you will study techniques for solving the equations constructed in Examples 4 and 5.

Discussing the Concept   **Red Herring**

When constructing an equation to represent a word problem, you are occasionally given too much information. The unnecessary information in a word problem is sometimes called a "red herring." Find the red herring in the following problem.

Returning to college after spring break, a student travels 3 hours and stops for lunch. If it takes 45 minutes to complete the last 36 miles of the 180-mile trip, find the average speed during the first 3 hours of the trip.

Decide what question to ask that uses all the given information.

In Exercises 27–34, have your students review the examples in Sections 2.1 and 2.2.

Section 2.4   Introduction to Equations   **105**

2.4   Exercises

Integrated Review   *Concepts, Skills, and Problem Solving*

Keep mathematically in shape by doing these exercises *before* the problems of this section.

Properties and Definitions

1. If the numerator and denominator of a fraction have *unlike* signs, the sign of the fraction is .

2. If a negative number is used as a factor eight times, what is the sign of the product? Explain.

3. Complete the Commutative Property:
$6 + 10 =$.

4. Name the property illustrated by $6\left(\frac{1}{6}\right) = 1$.

Simplifying Expressions

In Exercises 5–10, simplify the expression.

5. $t^2 \cdot t^5$

6. $(-3y^3)y^2$

7. $(u^3)^2$

8. $2(ab)^5$

9. $(3a^2)(4ab)$

10. $2(x + 3)^2(x + 3)^3$

Graphs and Models

Geometry   In Exercises 11 and 12, write expressions for the perimeter and area of the figure.

11.
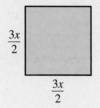

12.
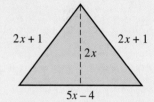

Developing Skills

In Exercises 1–16, determine whether the value of x is a solution of the equation. See Examples 1 and 2.

	Equation		*Values*	
1.	$2x - 6 = 0$	(a) $x = 3$	(b) $x = 1$
2.	$5x - 25 = 0$	(a) $x = 10$	(b) $x = 5$
3.	$2x + 4 = 2$	(a) $x = 0$	(b) $x = -1$
4.	$3x + 10 = 4$	(a) $x = -2$	(b) $x = 2$
5.	$x + 5 = 2x$	(a) $x = -1$	(b) $x = 5$
6.	$2x - 3 = 5x$	(a) $x = 0$	(b) $x = -1$
7.	$x + 3 = 2(x - 4)$	(a) $x = 11$	(b) $x = -5$
8.	$5x - 1 = 3(x + 5)$	(a) $x = 8$	(b) $x = -2$
9.	$2x + 10 = 7(x + 1)$	(a) $x = \frac{3}{5}$	(b) $x = \frac{2}{3}$
10.	$3(3x + 2) = 9 - x$	(a) $x = -\frac{3}{4}$	(b) $x = \frac{3}{10}$
11.	$x^2 - 4 = x + 2$	(a) $x = 3$	(b) $x = -2$
12.	$x^2 = 8 - 2x$	(a) $x = 2$	(b) $x = -4$
13.	$\frac{2}{x} - \frac{1}{x} = 1$	(a) $x = 3$	(b) $x = \frac{1}{3}$

	Equation		*Values*	
14.	$\frac{4}{x} + \frac{2}{x} = 1$	(a) $x = 0$	(b) $x = 6$
15.	$\frac{5}{x - 1} + \frac{1}{x} = 5$	(a) $x = 3$	(b) $x = \frac{1}{6}$
16.	$\frac{3}{x - 2} = x$	(a) $x = -1$	(b) $x = 3$

In Exercises 17–26, use a calculator to determine whether the value of x is a solution of the equation.

	Equation		*Values*	
17.	$x + 3 = 3.5$	(a) $x = 1.2$	(b) $x = 4.8$
18.	$x - 6 = 1.4$	(a) $x = -4.6$	(b) $x = 7.4$
19.	$40x - 490 = 0$	(a) $x = 12.25$	(b) $x = -12.25$
20.	$20x - 560 = 0$	(a) $x = 27.5$	(b) $x = -27.5$
21.	$2x^2 - x - 10 = 0$	(a) $x = \frac{5}{2}$	(b) $x = -1.09$
22.	$22x - 5x^2 = 17$	(a) $x = 1$	(b) $x = 3.4$
23.	$\frac{1}{x} - \frac{9}{x - 4} = 1$	(a) $x = 0$	(b) $x = -2$

Equation   *Values*

24. $x = \dfrac{3}{4x + 1}$ (a) $x = -0.25$ (b) $x = 0.75$

25. $x^3 - 1.728 = 0$ (a) $x = \frac{6}{5}$ (b) $x = -\frac{6}{5}$

26. $4x^2 - 10.24 = 0$ (a) $x = \frac{8}{5}$ (b) $x = -\frac{8}{5}$

In Exercises 27–34, justify each step of the solution. See Example 3.

27.
$$5x + 12 = 22$$
$$5x + 12 - 12 = 22 - 12$$
$$5x = 10$$
$$\frac{5x}{5} = \frac{10}{5}$$
$$x = 2$$

28.
$$14 - 3x = 5$$
$$14 - 3x - 14 = 5 - 14$$
$$14 - 14 - 3x = -9$$
$$-3x = -9$$
$$\frac{-3x}{-3} = \frac{-9}{-3}$$
$$x = 3$$

29.
$$\frac{2}{3}x = 12$$
$$\frac{3}{2}\left(\frac{2}{3}x\right) = \frac{3}{2}(12)$$
$$x = 18$$

30.
$$\frac{4}{5}x = -28$$
$$\frac{5}{4}\left(\frac{4}{5}x\right) = \frac{5}{4}(-28)$$
$$x = -35$$

31.
$$2(x - 1) = x + 3$$
$$2x - 2 = x + 3$$
$$-x + 2x - 2 = -x + x + 3$$
$$x - 2 = 3$$
$$x - 2 + 2 = 3 + 2$$
$$x = 5$$

32.
$$x + 6 = -6(4 - x)$$
$$x + 6 = -24 + 6x$$
$$-x + x + 6 = -x - 24 + 6x$$
$$6 = 5x - 24$$
$$6 + 24 = 5x - 24 + 24$$
$$30 = 5x$$
$$\frac{30}{5} = \frac{5x}{5}$$
$$6 = x$$

33.
$$x = -2(x + 3)$$
$$x = -2x - 6$$
$$2x + x = 2x - 2x - 6$$
$$3x = 0 - 6$$
$$3x = -6$$
$$\frac{3x}{3} = \frac{-6}{3}$$
$$x = -2$$

34.
$$\frac{x}{3} = x + 1$$
$$3\left(\frac{x}{3}\right) = 3(x + 1)$$
$$x = 3x + 3$$
$$-3x + x = -3x + 3x + 3$$
$$-2x = 0 + 3$$
$$-2x = 3$$
$$\frac{-2x}{-2} = \frac{3}{-2}$$
$$x = -\frac{3}{2}$$

In Exercises 35–38, use a property of equality to solve the equation. Check your solution. See Examples 1, 2, and 3.

35. $x + 4 = 6$ **36.** $x - 10 = 5$

37. $3x = 30$ **38.** $\dfrac{x}{4} = 12$

Solving Problems

In Exercises 39–44, write a verbal description of the algebraic equation. Use words only; do not use the variable. (There is more than one correct answer.)

39. $x + 8 = 25$

40. $x - 9 = 52$

41. $10(x - 3) = 8x$

42. $2(x - 5) = 12$

43. $\dfrac{x + 1}{3} = 8$

44. $\dfrac{x - 2}{10} = 6$

In Exercises 45–68, construct an equation for the word problem. Do *not* solve the equation. See Examples 4 and 5.

45. *Test Score*   After your instructor added 6 points to each student's test score, your score is 94. What was your original score?

46. *Rainfall*   With the 1.2-inch rainfall today, the total for the month is 4.5 inches. How much had been recorded for the month before today's rainfall?

47. *Computer Purchase*   You have $3650 saved for the purchase of a new computer that will cost $4532. How much more must you save?

48. *List Price*   The sale price of a coat is $225.98. If the discount is $64, what is the list (original) price?

49. The sum of a number and 12 is 45. What is the number?

50. The sum of 3 times a number and 4 is 16. What is the number?

51. Four times the sum of a number and 6 is 100. What is the number?

52. Find a number such that 6 times the number subtracted from 120 is 96.

53. Find a number such that 2 times the number decreased by 14 equals the number divided by 3.

54. The sum of a number and 8, divided by 4, is 32. What is the number?

55. *Travel Costs*   A company pays its sales representatives 32 cents per mile if they use their personal cars. A sales representative submitted a bill to be reimbursed for $135.36 for driving. How many miles did the sales representative drive?

56. *Pocket Change*   A student has n quarters and seven $1 bills totaling $8.75. How many quarters does the student have?

57. *Dimensions of a Mirror*   The width of a rectangular mirror is one-third its length, as shown in the figure. The perimeter of the mirror is 96 inches.

What are the dimensions of the mirror?

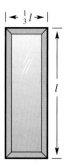

Figure for 57

58. *Height of a Box*   Find the height of a rectangular box if its base is 4 feet by 6 feet and its volume is 72 cubic feet (see figure).

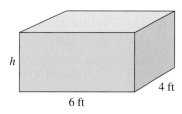

59. *Average Speed*   After traveling for 3 hours, your family is still 25 miles from completing a 160-mile trip (see figure). What was the average speed during the first 3 hours?

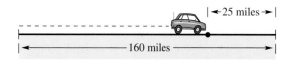

60. *Average Speed*   After traveling for 4 hours, you are still 24 miles from completing a 200-mile trip. If it requires one-half hour to travel the last 24 miles, find the average speed during the first 4 hours of the trip.

61. *Average Speed*   A group of students plans to take two cars to a soccer game. The first car leaves on time, travels at an average speed of 45 miles per hour, and arrives at the destination in 3 hours. Determine the average speed of the students in the second car if they leave one-half hour after the first car and arrive at the game at the same time as the students in the first car.

62. *Dow Jones Average* The Dow Jones average fell 58 points during a week and was 8695 at the close of the market on Friday. What was the average at the close of the market on the previous Friday?

63. *Price of a Product* The price of a product has increased by $45 over the past year. It is now selling for $375. What was the price 1 year ago?

64. *Thunderstorm* You hear thunder 3 seconds after seeing the lightning. How far away is the lightning, if the speed of sound is 1100 feet per second?

65. *Annual Depreciation* A corporation buys equipment with an initial purchase price of $750,000. It is estimated that its useful life will be 3 years and at that time its value will be $75,000. The total depreciation is divided equally among the three years. (Depreciation is the difference between the initial price of an item and its current value.) Determine the amount of depreciation declared each year.

66. *Car Payments* Suppose you make 48 monthly payments of $158 each to buy a used car. The total amount financed is $6000. Find the amount of interest that you paid.

67. *Fund Raising* A student group is selling boxes of greeting cards at a profit of $1.75 each. The group needs $2000 more to have enough money for a trip to Washington, D.C. How many boxes does the group need to sell to earn $2000?

68. *Price of a Product* The price of a product increased $1432 during the past year. The price of the product was $9850 two years ago and $10,120 one year ago. What is its current price?

Unit Analysis In Exercises 69–74, simplify the expression. State the units of the simplified value.

69. $\dfrac{3 \text{ dollars}}{\text{unit}} \cdot (5 \text{ units})$

70. $\dfrac{25 \text{ miles}}{\text{gallon}} \cdot (15 \text{ gallons})$

71. $\dfrac{3 \text{ dollars}}{\text{pound}} \cdot (5 \text{ pounds})$

72. $\dfrac{12 \text{ dollars}}{\text{hour}} \cdot \dfrac{1 \text{ hour}}{60 \text{ minutes}} \cdot (45 \text{ minutes})$

73. $\dfrac{5 \text{ feet}}{\text{second}} \cdot \dfrac{60 \text{ seconds}}{\text{minute}} \cdot (20 \text{ minutes})$

74. $\dfrac{100 \text{ centimeters}}{\text{meter}} \cdot (2.4 \text{ meters})$

Explaining Concepts

75. In your own words, explain the difference between a conditional equation and an identity.

76. Explain how to decide whether a real number is a solution of an equation. Give an example of an equation with a solution that checks and one that does not check.

77. Explain the difference between simplifying an expression and solving an equation. Give an example of each.

78. In your own words, explain what is meant by the term *equivalent equations*.

79. Describe, from memory, the steps that are used to transform an equation into an equivalent equation.

80. Describe a real-life problem that uses the following verbal model.

$$\boxed{\text{Revenue of \$840}} = \boxed{\dfrac{\$35 \text{ per case}}{}} \cdot \boxed{\text{Number of cases}}$$

Key Terms

algebraic expression, *p. 62*
variables, *p. 62*
constants, *p. 62*
terms, *p. 62*
coefficient, *p. 62*

evaluate an algebraic
   expression, *p. 65*
like terms, *p. 75*
simplify an algebraic
   expression, *p. 77*

verbal mathematical
   model, *p. 86*
equation, *p. 99*
solution, *p. 99*
solution set, *p. 99*

identity, *p. 99*
conditional equation,
   p. 99
equivalent equations,
   p. 101

Key Concepts

2.1 Exponential form

Repeated multiplication can be expressed in exponential form using a base a and an exponent n, where a is a real number, variable, or algebraic expression and n is a positive integer.

$$a^n = a \cdot a \cdots a$$

2.1 Evaluating algebraic expressions

To evaluate an algebraic expression, replace every occurrence of the variable in the expression with the appropriate real number and perform the operations.

2.2 Rules of exponents

Let m and n be positive integers, and let a and b be real numbers, variables, or algebraic expressions.

1. $a^m \cdot a^n = a^{m+n}$ 2. $(a^m)^n = a^{m \cdot n}$
3. $(ab)^m = a^m \cdot b^m$

2.2 Basic rules of algebra

Commutative Property:

Addition $a + b = b + a$
Multiplication $ab = ba$

Associative Property:

Addition $(a + b) + c = a + (b + c)$
Multiplication $(ab)c = a(bc)$

Distributive Property:

$a(b + c) = ab + ac$ $a(b - c) = ab - ac$
$(a + b)c = ac + bc$ $(a - b)c = ac - bc$

Identities:

Additive $a + 0 = a$
Multiplicative $a \cdot 1 = a$

Inverses:

Additive $a + (-a) = 0$

Multiplicative $a \cdot \dfrac{1}{a} = 1, \ a \neq 0$

2.2 Combining like terms

To combine like terms, add their respective coefficients and attach the common variable factor.

2.2 Simplifying an algebraic expression

To simplify an algebraic expression, remove symbols of grouping and combine like terms.

2.3 Translating phrases: verbal to algebraic

From the verbal description, write a verbal mathematical model. Assign labels to the known and unknown quantities, and write an algebraic model.

2.3 Other problem-solving strategies

Other problem-solving strategies are (1) guess, check, and revise, (2) make a table/look for a pattern, (3) draw a diagram, and (4) solve a simpler problem.

2.4 Checking solutions of equations

To check a solution, substitute the given solution for each occurrence of the variable in the original equation. Evaluate each side of the equation. If both sides are equivalent, the solution checks.

2.4 Properties of equality

Addition: Add (or subtract) the same quantity to (from) both sides of the equation.

Multiplication: Multiply (or divide) both sides of the equation by the same nonzero quantity.

REVIEW EXERCISES

Reviewing Skills

2.1 In Exercises 1-4, identify the terms and the coefficients of the algebraic expression.

1. $4 - \frac{1}{2}x^3$

2. $5x^2 - 3x + 10$

3. $y^2 - 10yz + \frac{2}{3}z^2$

4. $\dfrac{x + 2y}{3} - \dfrac{4x}{y}$

In Exercises 5-8, rewrite the product in exponential form.

5. $5z \cdot 5z \cdot 5z$

6. $\frac{3}{8}y \cdot \frac{3}{8}y \cdot \frac{3}{8}y \cdot \frac{3}{8}y$

7. $a(b - c) \cdot a(b - c)$

8. $3 \cdot (y - x) \cdot (y - x) \cdot 3 \cdot 3$

In Exercises 9-12, evaluate the algebraic expression for the specified value(s) of the variable(s).

	Expression	*Values*
9.	$x^2 - 2x + 5$	(a) $x = 0$ (b) $x = 2$
10.	$x^3 - 8$	(a) $x = 2$ (b) $x = 4$
11.	$x^2 - x(y + 1)$	(a) $x = 2, y = -1$
		(b) $x = 1, y = 2$
12.	$\dfrac{x + 5}{y}$	(a) $x = -5, y = 3$
		(b) $x = 2, y = -1$

2.2 In Exercises 13-22, simplify the exponential expression.

13. $x^2 \cdot x \cdot x^4$

14. $y^2 \cdot y^3 \cdot y$

15. $(x^3)^2$

16. $(t^4)^3$

17. $t^4(-2t^2)$

18. $u^2(3u^2)$

19. $(xy)(-5x^2y^3)$

20. $(3uv)(-2uv^2)$

21. $(-2y^2)^3(8y)$

22. $(-3x)^2(5x^2)$

In Exercises 23-28, identify the rule of algebra illustrated by the equation.

23. $xy \cdot \dfrac{1}{xy} = 1$

24. $u(vw) = (uv)w$

25. $(x - y)(2) = 2(x - y)$

26. $(a + b) + 0 = a + b$

27. $2x + (3y - z) = (2x + 3y) - z$

28. $x(y + z) = xy + xz$

In Exercises 29-36, use the Distributive Property to expand the expression.

29. $4(x + 3y)$

30. $3(8s - 12t)$

31. $-5(2u - 3v)$

32. $-3(-2x - 8y)$

33. $x(8x + 5y)$

34. $-u(3u - 10v)$

35. $-(-a + 3b)$

36. $(7 - 2j)(-6)$

In Exercises 37-48, simplify the expression by combining like terms.

37. $3a - 5a$

38. $6c - 2c$

39. $3p - 4q + q + 8p$

40. $10x - 4y - 25x + 6y$

41. $\frac{1}{4}s - 6t + \frac{7}{2}s + t$

42. $\frac{2}{3}a + \frac{3}{5}a - \frac{1}{2}b + \frac{2}{3}b$

43. $x^2 + 3xy - xy + 4$

44. $uv^2 + 10 - 2uv^2 + 2$

45. $5x - 5y + 3xy - 2x + 2y$

46. $y^3 + 2y^2 + 2y^3 - 3y^2 + 1$

47. $5\left(1 + \dfrac{r}{n}\right)^2 - 2\left(1 + \dfrac{r}{n}\right)^2$

48. $-7\left(\dfrac{1}{u}\right) + 4\left(\dfrac{1}{u^2}\right) + 3\left(\dfrac{1}{u}\right)$

In Exercises 49-60, simplify the expression by removing symbols of grouping and combining like terms.

49. $5(u - 4) + 10$

50. $16 - 3(v + 2)$

51. $3s - (r - 2s)$

52. $50x - (30x + 100)$

53. $-3(1 - 10z) + 2(1 - 10z)$

54. $8(15 - 3y) - 5(15 - 3y)$

55. $\frac{1}{3}(42 - 18z) - 2(8 - 4z)$

56. $\frac{1}{4}(100 + 36s) - (15 - 4s)$

57. $10 - [8(5 - x) + 2]$

58. $3[2(4x - 5) + 4] - 3$

59. $2[x + 2(y - x)]$

60. $2t[4 - (3 - t)] + 5t$

2.3 In Exercises 61–70, translate the phrase into an algebraic expression. Let x represent the number.

61. Two-thirds of a real number, plus 5

62. One hundred, decreased by 5 times a number

63. Ten less than twice a number

64. The ratio of a number to 10

65. Fifty, increased by the product of 7 and a number

66. Ten decreased by the quotient of a number and 2

67. The sum of a number and 10 divided by 8

68. The product of 15 and a number, decreased by 2

69. The sum of the square of a real number and 64

70. The absolute value of the sum of a number and -10

In Exercises 71–74, write a verbal description of the expression without using the variable. (There is more than one correct answer.)

71. $x + 3$

72. $3x - 2$

73. $\dfrac{y - 2}{3}$

74. $4(x + 5)$

2.4 In Exercises 75–84, check whether each value of x is a solution of the equation.

	Equation		*Values*
75.	$5x + 6 = 36$	(a) $x = 3$	(b) $x = 6$
76.	$17 - 3x = 8$	(a) $x = 3$	(b) $x = -3$
77.	$3x - 12 = x$	(a) $x = -1$	(b) $x = 6$
78.	$8x + 24 = 2x$	(a) $x = 0$	(b) $x = -4$
79.	$4(2 - x) = 3(2 + x)$	(a) $x = \frac{2}{7}$	(b) $x = -\frac{2}{3}$
80.	$5x + 2 = 3(x + 10)$	(a) $x = 14$	(b) $x = -10$
81.	$\dfrac{4}{x} - \dfrac{2}{x} = 5$	(a) $x = -1$	(b) $x = \frac{2}{5}$
82.	$\dfrac{x}{3} + \dfrac{x}{6} = 1$	(a) $x = \frac{2}{9}$	(b) $x = -\frac{2}{9}$
83.	$x(x - 7) = -12$	(a) $x = 3$	(b) $x = 4$
84.	$x(x + 1) = 2$	(a) $x = 1$	(b) $x = -2$

Solving Problems

85. *Depreciation* You pay P dollars for new equipment. Its value after 5 years is given by

$$P\left(\tfrac{9}{10}\right)\left(\tfrac{9}{10}\right)\left(\tfrac{9}{10}\right)\left(\tfrac{9}{10}\right)\left(\tfrac{9}{10}\right).$$

Simplify the expression.

86. *Area* The height of a triangle is $1\frac{1}{2}$ times its base. Its area is given by $\frac{1}{2}b\left(\frac{3}{2}b\right)$. Simplify the expression.

87. *Income Tax* The income tax rate on a taxable income of I dollars is 28%. Write an algebraic expression that represents the total amount of income tax. (To find 28% of a quantity, multiply the quantity by 0.28.)

88. *Total Amount of Money* A person has n nickels and q quarters. Write an algebraic expression that represents the total amount of money in dollars.

89. *Geometry* The face of a tape deck has the dimensions shown in the figure. Find an algebraic expression that represents the area of the face of the tape deck excluding the compartment holding the cassette.

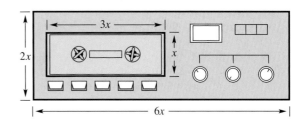

90. *Geometry* Find the perimeter of the figure.

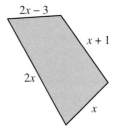

91. *Distance Traveled* A car travels for 10 hours at an average speed of s miles per hour. Write an algebraic expression that represents the total distance traveled.

92. *Sum* Simplify the algebraic expression that represents the sum of three consecutive odd integers, $2n - 1$, $2n + 1$, and $2n + 3$.

93. *Rental Income* Write an expression that represents the rent for n months if the monthly rent is $625.

94. Perform the indicated operations and simplify.

$$7 \cdot 10^4 + 2 \cdot 10^3 + 8 \cdot 10^1$$

95. *Finding a Pattern*

(a) Complete the table. The third row is the difference of consecutive entries of the second row. The fourth row is the difference of consecutive entries of the third row.

n	0	1	2	3	4	5
$n^2 + 3n + 2$						
Differences						
Differences					

(b) Describe the patterns for the third and fourth rows.

96. *Finding a Pattern* Find values for a and b such that the expression $an + b$ agrees with the values given in the table.

n	0	1	2	3	4	5
$an + b$	4	9	14	19	24	29

In Exercises 97–100, write an equation that represents the statement. (Identify the letters you choose as labels.)

97. *Sum* The sum of a number and its reciprocal is $\frac{37}{6}$.

98. *Distance* An automobile travels 135 miles in t hours with an average speed of 45 miles per hour (see figure).

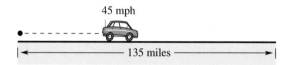

45 mph

135 miles

99. *Geometry* The area of the shaded region in the figure is 24 square inches.

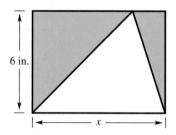

6 in.

x

100. *Geometry* The perimeter of the face of the rectangular traffic light is 72 inches (see figure).

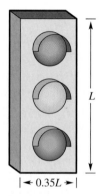

L

$0.35L$

Chapter Test

Take this test as you would take a test in class. After you are done, check your work against the answers given in the back of the book.

1. Identify the terms and coefficients of the expression.

   $2x^2 - 7xy + 3y^3$

2. Rewrite the following product in exponential form.

   $x \cdot (x + y) \cdot x \cdot (x + y) \cdot x$

In Exercises 3-6, identify the rule of algebra demonstrated.

3. $(5x)y = 5(xy)$
4. $2 + (x - y) = (x - y) + 2$
5. $7xy - 7xy = 0$
6. $1 \cdot (x + 5) = (x + 5)$

In Exercises 7 and 8, use the Distributive Property to expand the expression.

7. $3(x + 8)$ 8. $-y(3 - 2y)$

In Exercises 9-14, simplify the expression.

9. $(c^2)^4$ 10. $-5uv(2u^3)$
11. $3b - 2a + a - 10b$ 12. $15(u - v) - 7(u - v)$
13. $3z - (4 - z)$ 14. $2[10 - (t + 1)]$

15. Evaluate the expression when $x = 3$ and $y = -12$.
    (a) $x^3 - 2$ (b) $x^2 + 4(y + 2)$

16. Explain why it is not possible to evaluate $\dfrac{a + 2b}{3a - b}$ when $a = 2$ and $b = 6$.

17. Translate the phrase, "one-fifth of a number, increased by two," into an algebraic expression. Let n represent the number.

18. (a) Write expressions for the perimeter and area of the rectangle at the left.
    (b) Simplify the expressions.
    (c) Identify the unit of measure for each expression.
    (d) Evaluate each expression when $w = 12$ feet.

19. Write an algebraic expression for the income from a concert if the prices of the tickets for adults and children are \$3 and \$2, respectively. Let n represent the number of adults in attendance and let m represent the number of children.

20. Determine whether the values of x are solutions of $6(3 - x) - 5(2x - 1) = 7$.
    (a) $x = -2$ (b) $x = 1$

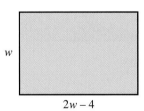

w

$2w - 4$

Figure for 18

3

Linear Equations and Problem Solving

Stewart Cohen/Tony Stone Images

In 1997, the average monthly cellular phone bill was $42.78. (Source: Cellular Telecommunications Industry Association)

Talk Is Cheap?

You plan to purchase a cellular phone with a service contract. For a price of $99, one package includes the phone and 3 months of service. You will be billed a *per minute usage rate* each time you make or receive a call. After 3 months you will be billed a monthly service charge of $19.50 and the per minute usage rate.

A second cellular phone package costs $80, which includes the phone and one month of service. You will be billed a per minute usage rate each time you make or receive a call. After the first month you will be billed a monthly service charge of $24.00 and the per minute usage rate.

See Section 3.3, Exercise 105.

a. Write an equation to find the cost of the phone in the first package. Solve the equation to find the cost of the phone.

b. Write an equation to find the cost of the phone in the second package. Solve the equation to find the cost of the phone. Which phone costs more, the one in the first package or the one in the second package?

c. What percent of the purchase price of $99 goes toward the price of the cellular phone in the first package? Use an equation to answer the question.

d. What percent of the purchase price of $80 goes toward the price of the cellular phone in the second package? Use an equation to answer the question.

e. If the sales tax on your purchase is 5%, what is the total cost of purchasing the first cellular phone package? Use an equation to answer the question.

f. You decide to buy the first cellular phone package. If your total cellular phone bill for the fourth month of use is $92.46 for 3.2 hours of use, what is the per minute usage rate? Use an equation to answer the question.

See Section 3.4, Exercise 87.

g. For the fifth month you were billed the monthly service charge and $47.50 for 125 minutes of use. You estimate that during the next month you spent 150 minutes on calls. Use a proportion to find the charge for 150 minutes of use. (Use the first package.)

See Section 3.6, Exercise 87.

h. You determine that the most you can spend each month on phone calls is $75. Write a compound inequality that describes the number of minutes you can spend talking on the cellular phone each month if the per minute usage rate is $0.35. Solve the inequality. (Use the first package.)

3.1 Solving Linear Equations

Objectives

1 Solve a linear equation in standard form.

2 Solve a linear equation in nonstandard form.

3 Use a linear equation to solve an application problem.

1 Solve a linear equation in standard form.

Linear Equations in the Standard Form $ax + b = c$

This is an important step in your study of algebra. In the first two chapters, you were introduced to the rules of algebra, and you learned to use these rules to rewrite and simplify algebraic expressions. In Sections 2.3 and 2.4, you gained experience in translating verbal expressions and problems into algebraic forms. You are now ready to use these skills and experiences to *solve equations*.

In this section, you will learn how the rules of algebra and the properties of equality can be used to solve the most common type of equation—a linear equation in one variable.

> **Diophantus**
>
> (250 A.D.)
>
> Diophantus, a Greek of Alexandria who lived around 250 A.D., is often called the "Father of Algebra." He was the first to use abbreviated word forms in equations. Diophantus introduced this symbolism in the *Arithmetica*, a collection of problems comprising 13 books.

> ▶ **Definition of Linear Equation**
>
> A **linear equation** in one variable x is an equation that can be written in the standard form
>
> $$ax + b = c$$
>
> where a, b, and c are real numbers with $a \neq 0$.

A linear equation in one variable is also called a **first-degree equation** because its variable has an (implied) exponent of 1. Some examples of linear equations in standard form are

$$2x = 3, \quad x - 7 = 5, \quad 4x + 6 = 0, \quad \text{and} \quad \frac{x}{2} - 1 = \frac{5}{3}.$$

Remember that to *solve* an equation involving x means that you are to find all values of x that satisfy the equation. For the linear equation $ax + b = c$, the goal is to *isolate* x by rewriting the equation in the form

$$x = \boxed{\text{a number}}. \qquad \text{Isolate the variable } x.$$

To obtain this form, you are to use the techniques discussed in Section 2.4. That is, beginning with the original equation, you write a sequence of equivalent equations, each having the same solution as the original equation. For instance, to solve the linear equation $x - 2 = 0$, you can add 2 to both sides of the equation to obtain $x = 2$. As mentioned in Section 2.4, each equivalent equation is called a **step** of the solution.

| Example 1 | Solving a Linear Equation |

Solve $3x - 5 = 10$.

Solution

$$3x - 5 = 10 \qquad \text{Original equation}$$

$$3x - 5 + 5 = 10 + 5 \qquad \text{Add 5 to both sides.}$$

$$3x = 15 \qquad \text{Combine like terms.}$$

$$\frac{3x}{3} = \frac{15}{3} \qquad \text{Divide both sides by 3.}$$

$$x = 5 \qquad \text{Simplify.}$$

It appears that the solution is 5. Here is the check.

Check

$$3x - 5 = 10 \qquad \text{Original equation}$$

$$3(5) - 5 \overset{?}{=} 10 \qquad \text{Substitute 5 for } x.$$

$$15 - 5 \overset{?}{=} 10 \qquad \text{Simplify.}$$

$$10 = 10 \qquad \text{Solution checks. } \checkmark$$

In Example 1, be sure you see that solving an equation has two basic stages. The first stage is to *find* the solution (or solutions). The second stage is to *check* that each solution you find actually satisfies the original equation. You can improve your accuracy in algebra by developing the habit of checking each solution.

A common question in algebra is

"How do I know which step to do *first* to isolate *x*?"

The answer is that you need practice. By solving many linear equations, you will find that your skill will improve. The key thing to remember is that you can "get rid of" terms and factors by using *inverse* operations. Here are some guidelines and examples.

Guideline	*Equation*	*Inverse Operation*
1. Subtract to remove a sum.	$x + 3 = 4$	Subtract 3 from both sides.
2. Add to remove a difference.	$x - 5 = 7$	Add 5 to both sides.
3. Divide to remove a product.	$4x = 20$	Divide both sides by 4.
4. Multiply to remove a quotient.	$\dfrac{x}{8} = 2$	Multiply both sides by 8.

For additional examples, review Example 3 on page 102. In each case of that example, note how inverse operations are used to isolate the variable.

Example 2	Solving a Linear Equation in Standard Form

Solve $2x + 7 = 4$.

Solution

$2x + 7 = 4$	Original equation
$2x + 7 - 7 = 4 - 7$	Subtract 7 from both sides.
$2x = -3$	Combine like terms.
$\dfrac{2x}{2} = -\dfrac{3}{2}$	Divide both sides by 2.
$x = -\dfrac{3}{2}$	Simplify.

Check

$2x + 7 = 4$	Original equation
$2\left(-\dfrac{3}{2}\right) + 7 \overset{?}{=} 4$	Substitute $-\frac{3}{2}$ for x.
$-3 + 7 \overset{?}{=} 4$	Simplify.
$4 = 4$	Solution checks. ✓

So, the solution is $-\frac{3}{2}$.

Example 3	Solving a Linear Equation in Standard Form

Solve $5x - 3 = 9$.

Solution

$5x - 3 = 9$	Original equation
$5x - 3 + 3 = 9 + 3$	Add 3 to both sides.
$5x = 12$	Combine like terms.
$\dfrac{5x}{5} = \dfrac{12}{5}$	Divide both sides by 5.
$x = \dfrac{12}{5}$	Simplify.

Check

$5x - 3 = 9$	Original equation
$5\left(\dfrac{12}{5}\right) - 3 \overset{?}{=} 9$	Substitute $\frac{12}{5}$ for x.
$12 - 3 \overset{?}{=} 9$	Simplify.
$9 = 9$	Solution checks. ✓

So, the solution is $\frac{12}{5}$.

Study Tip

To eliminate a fractional coefficient, it may be easier to multiply both sides by the *reciprocal* of the fraction than to divide by the fraction itself. Here is an example.

$$-\frac{2}{3}x = 4$$

$$\left(-\frac{3}{2}\right)\left(-\frac{2}{3}\right)x = \left(-\frac{3}{2}\right)4$$

$$x = -\frac{12}{2}$$

$$x = -6$$

| **Example 4** | Solving a Linear Equation in Standard Form |

Solve $\dfrac{x}{3} - 1 = -4$.

Solution

$$\frac{x}{3} - 1 = -4 \qquad \text{Original equation}$$

$$\frac{x}{3} - 1 + 1 = -4 + 1 \qquad \text{Add 1 to both sides.}$$

$$\frac{x}{3} = -3 \qquad \text{Combine like terms.}$$

$$3\left(\frac{x}{3}\right) = 3(-3) \qquad \text{Multiply both sides by 3.}$$

$$x = -9 \qquad \text{Simplify.}$$

Check

$$\frac{x}{3} - 1 = -4 \qquad \text{Original equation}$$

$$\frac{-9}{3} - 1 \stackrel{?}{=} -4 \qquad \text{Substitute } -9 \text{ for } x.$$

$$-3 - 1 \stackrel{?}{=} -4 \qquad \text{Simplify.}$$

$$-4 = -4 \qquad \text{Solution checks.} \checkmark$$

So, the solution is -9.

Technology: Tip

Remember to check your solution in the original equation. This can be done efficiently with a graphing utility.

As you gain experience in solving linear equations, you will probably find that you can perform some of the solution steps in your head. For instance, you might solve the equation given in Example 4 by writing only the following steps.

$$\frac{x}{3} - 1 = -4 \qquad \text{Original equation}$$

$$\frac{x}{3} = -3 \qquad \text{Add 1 to both sides.}$$

$$x = -9 \qquad \text{Multiply both sides by 3.}$$

2 Solve a linear equation in nonstandard form.

Solving a Linear Equation in Nonstandard Form

The definition of a linear equation contains the phrase "that can be written in the standard form $ax + b = c$." This suggests that some linear equations may come in nonstandard or disguised form.

A common form of linear equations is one in which the variable terms are not combined into one term. In such cases, you can begin the solution by rewriting the equation in standard form. Note how this is done in the next two examples.

Example 5   Solving a Linear Equation in Nonstandard Form

Solve $3y + 8 - 5y = 4$.

Study Tip

In Example 5, note that the variable in the equation doesn't always have to be x. Any letter can be used.

Solution

$3y + 8 - 5y = 4$	Original equation
$3y - 5y + 8 = 4$	Collect like terms.
$-2y + 8 = 4$	Combine like terms.
$-2y + 8 - 8 = 4 - 8$	Subtract 8 from both sides.
$-2y = -4$	Combine like terms.
$\dfrac{-2y}{-2} = \dfrac{-4}{-2}$	Divide both sides by -2.
$y = 2$	Simplify.

Check

$3y + 8 - 5y = 4$	Original equation
$3(2) + 8 - 5(2) \overset{?}{=} 4$	Substitute 2 for y.
$6 + 8 - 10 \overset{?}{=} 4$	Simplify.
$4 = 4$	Solution checks. ✓

So, the solution is 2.

The solution for Example 5 began by collecting like terms. You can use any of the rules of algebra to attain your goal of "isolating the variable." The next example shows how to solve a linear equation using the Distributive Property.

Study Tip

You can isolate the variable term on either side of the equal sign. For instance, Example 6 could have been solved this way.

$x + 6 = 2(x - 3)$

$x + 6 = 2x - 6$

$x - x + 6 = 2x - x - 6$

$6 = x - 6$

$6 + 6 = x - 6 + 6$

$12 = x$

Example 6   Using the Distributive Property

Solve $x + 6 = 2(x - 3)$.

Solution

$x + 6 = 2(x - 3)$	Original equation
$x + 6 = 2x - 6$	Apply Distributive Property.
$x - 2x + 6 = 2x - 2x - 6$	Subtract $2x$ from both sides.
$-x + 6 = -6$	Combine like terms.
$-x + 6 - 6 = -6 - 6$	Subtract 6 from both sides.
$-x = -12$	Combine like terms.
$(-1)(-x) = (-1)(-12)$	Multiply both sides by -1.
$x = 12$	Simplify.

The solution is 12. Check this in the original equation.

The examples in this section would indicate that an equation that can be written in the standard form $ax + b = c$, where $a \neq 0$, has exactly one solution. Note the following steps in finding the solution.

$$ax + b = c \qquad \text{Original equation}$$

$$ax = c - b \qquad \text{Subtract } b \text{ from both sides.}$$

$$x = \frac{c - b}{a} \qquad \text{Divide both sides by } a.$$

So, the *linear* equation has exactly one solution: $x = (c - b)/a$.

It may not be possible to rewrite some nonstandard forms of linear equations in the form $ax + b = c$, where $a \neq 0$. These types of equations have either no solution or infinitely many solutions.

Study Tip

In the *No Solution* equation the result is not true because $3 \neq 8$. This means that there is no value of x that will make the equation true.

In the *Infinitely Many Solutions* equation the result is true. This means that *any* real number is a solution to the equation.

No Solution	*Infinitely Many Solutions*
$2x + 3 \overset{?}{=} 2(x + 4)$	$2(x + 3) = 2x + 6$
$2x + 3 \overset{?}{=} 2x + 8$	$2x + 6 = 2x + 6$ Identity equation
$2x - 2x + 3 \overset{?}{=} 2x - 2x + 8$	$2x - 2x + 6 - 6 = 2x - 2x + 6 - 6$
$3 \neq 8$	$0 = 0$

Watch out for these types of equations in the exercise set.

3 Use a linear equation to solve an application problem.

Applications

Example 7   Geometry: Dimensions of a Dog Pen

You have 96 feet of fencing to enclose a rectangular pen for your dog. To provide sufficient running space for the dog to exercise, the pen is to be three times as long as it is wide. Find the dimensions of the pen.

Solution

Begin by drawing and labeling a diagram as shown in Figure 3.1. The perimeter of a rectangle is the sum of the widths and lengths.

Verbal Model: Perimeter = 2(width) + 2(length)

Algebraic Model: $96 = 2x + 2(3x)$

You can solve this equation as follows.

$$96 = 2x + 6x \qquad \text{Multiply.}$$

$$96 = 8x \qquad \text{Combine like terms.}$$

$$\frac{96}{8} = \frac{8x}{8} \qquad \text{Divide both sides by 8.}$$

$$12 = x \qquad \text{Simplify.}$$

So, the width of the pen is 12 feet and its length is 36 feet.

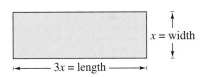

x = width

$3x$ = length

Figure 3.1

| Example 8 | Ticket Sales | |

Tickets for a concert were $40 for each floor seat and $20 for each stadium seat. There were 800 seats on the main floor, and these were sold out. The total revenue from ticket sales was $92,000. How many stadium seats were sold?

Solution

Verbal Model:

| Total revenue | = | Revenue from floor seats | + | Revenue from stadium seats |

Labels:

Total revenue = 92,000 (dollars)
Price per floor seat = 40 (dollars per seat)
Number of floor seats = 800 (seats)
Price per stadium seat = 20 (dollars per seat)
Number of stadium seats = x (seats)

Algebraic Model: $92{,}000 = 40(800) + 20x$

Now that you have written an algebraic equation to represent the problem, you can solve the equation as follows.

$$92{,}000 = 40(800) + 20x \qquad \text{Original equation}$$

$$92{,}000 = 32{,}000 + 20x \qquad \text{Simplify.}$$

$$92{,}000 - 32{,}000 = 32{,}000 - 32{,}000 + 20x \qquad \text{Subtract 32,000 from both sides.}$$

$$60{,}000 = 20x \qquad \text{Combine like terms.}$$

$$\frac{60{,}000}{20} = \frac{20x}{20} \qquad \text{Divide both sides by 20.}$$

$$3000 = x \qquad \text{Simplify.}$$

There were 3000 stadium seats sold. To check this solution, you should go back to the original statement of the problem and substitute 3000 stadium seats and 800 floor seats into the equation. You will find that the total revenue is $92,000.

Two integers are called **consecutive integers** if they differ by 1. Hence, for any integer n, its next two larger consecutive integers are $n + 1$ and $(n + 1) + 1$ or $n + 2$. Thus, you can denote three consecutive integers by n, $n + 1$, and $n + 2$.

▶ **Expressions for Special Types of Integers**

Let n be an integer. Then the following expressions can be used to denote even integers, odd integers, and consecutive integers, respectively.

1. $2n$ denotes an *even* integer.

2. $2n - 1$ and $2n + 1$ denote *odd* integers.

3. The set $\{n, n + 1, n + 2\}$ denotes three *consecutive* integers.

Example 9	Consecutive Integers

Find three consecutive integers whose sum is 48.

Solution

Verbal Model: First integer $+$ Second integer $+$ Third integer $= 48$

Labels:
First integer $= n$
Second integer $= n + 1$
Third integer $= n + 2$

Algebraic Model: $n + (n + 1) + (n + 2) = 48$

You can solve this equation as follows.

$n + (n + 1) + (n + 2) = 48$	Original equation
$3n + 3 = 48$	Combine like terms.
$3n + 3 - 3 = 48 - 3$	Subtract 3 from both sides.
$3n = 45$	Combine like terms.
$\dfrac{3n}{3} = \dfrac{45}{3}$	Divide both sides by 3.
$n = 15$	Simplify.

The solution is $n = 15$. This implies that the three consecutive integers are 15, 16, and 17. Check this in the original statement of the problem.

Discussing the Concept	Solutions That Don't Make Sense

When solving a word problem, be sure to ask yourself whether your solution makes sense. Decide why the following answers don't make sense.

a. A problem asks you to find the volume of an oil drum. The answer you obtain is 20 square feet.

b. A problem asks you to find the price per bar of a packet of candy bars. The answer you obtain is 0.42¢.

c. A problem asks you to find the net weight of a carton of oranges. The answer you obtain is 12.5 liters.

d. A problem asks you to find the height of the ceiling of a room. The answer you obtain is 3 square meters.

3.1 Exercises

Integrated Review — Concepts, Skills, and Problem Solving

Keep mathematically in shape by doing these exercises *before* the problems of this section.

Properties and Definitions

1. Complete the following properties of exponents.

(a) $(ab)^n =$ (b) $(a^m)^n =$

2. Identify the property illustrated by

$(2x + 5) + 8 = 2x + (5 + 8)$.

Simplifying Expressions

In Exercises 3–10, simplify the expression.

3. $(u^2)^4$

4. $(-3a^3)^2$

5. $-3(x - 5)^2(x - 5)^3$

6. $(4rs)(-5r^2)(2s^3)$

7. $\dfrac{2m^2}{3n} \cdot \dfrac{3m}{5n^3}$

8. $\dfrac{5(x + 3)^2}{10(x + 8)}$

9. $-3(3x - 2y) + 5y$

10. $3v - (4 - 5v)$

Problem Solving

11. The length of a relay race is $\frac{3}{4}$ mile. The last change of runners occurs at the $\frac{2}{3}$ mile marker. How far does the last person run?

12. During the months of January, February, and March, a farmer bought $10\frac{1}{3}$ tons, $7\frac{3}{5}$ tons, and $12\frac{5}{6}$ tons of soybeans, respectively. Find the total amount of soybeans purchased during the first quarter of the year.

Developing Skills

In Exercises 1–8, solve the equation mentally.

1. $x + 6 = 14$

2. $u - 3 = 8$

3. $x - 9 = 4$

4. $a + 5 = 11$

5. $7y = 28$

6. $4z = -36$

7. $4s = 12$

8. $6z = 18$

In Exercises 9–12, justify each step of the solution. See Examples 1–6.

9.
$$5x + 15 = 0$$
$$5x + 15 - 15 = 0 - 15$$
$$5x = -15$$
$$\frac{5x}{5} = \frac{-15}{5}$$
$$x = -3$$

10.
$$7x - 14 = 0$$
$$7x - 14 + 14 = 0 + 14$$
$$7x = 14$$
$$\frac{7x}{7} = \frac{14}{7}$$
$$x = 2$$

11.
$$-2x + 5 = 13$$
$$-2x + 5 - 5 = 13 - 5$$
$$-2x = 8$$
$$\frac{-2x}{-2} = \frac{8}{-2}$$
$$x = -4$$

12.
$$22 - 3x = 10$$
$$22 - 3x + 3x = 10 + 3x$$
$$22 = 10 + 3x$$
$$22 - 10 = 10 + 3x - 10$$
$$12 = 3x$$
$$\frac{12}{3} = \frac{3x}{3}$$
$$4 = x$$

In Exercises 13–56, solve the equation and check your solution. (Some equations have no solution.) See Examples 1–6.

13. $5x = 30$

14. $-14x = 42$

15. $9x = -21$

16. $12x = 18$

17. $8x - 4 = 20$

18. $-7x + 24 = 3$

19. $25x - 4 = 46$

20. $15x - 18 = 12$

21. $10 - 4x = -6$

22. $6x + 1 = -11$

23. $6x - 4 = 0$

24. $8z + 10 = 0$

25. $3y - 2 = 2y$

26. $24 - 5x = x$

27. $4 - 7x = 5x$

28. $2s - 13 = 28s$

29. $4 - 5t = 16 + t$

30. $3x + 4 = x + 10$

31. $-3t + 5 = -3t$

32. $4z + 2 = 4z$

33. $15x - 3 = 15 - 3x$

34. $2x - 5 = 7x + 10$

35. $4z = 10$

36. $-6t = 0$

37. $8t - 4 = -6$

38. $4z - 8 = 2$

39. $4x - 6 = 4x - 6$

40. $5 - 3x = 5 - 3x$

41. $2x + 4 = -3x + 6$

42. $4y + 4 = -y + 5$

43. $2x = -3x$

44. $2x = 3x - 3$

45. $2x - 5 + 10x = 3$

46. $-4x + 10 + 10x = 4$

47. $\dfrac{x}{3} = 10$

48. $-\dfrac{x}{2} = 3$

49. $x - \dfrac{1}{3} = \dfrac{4}{3}$

50. $x + \dfrac{5}{2} = \dfrac{9}{2}$

51. $t - \dfrac{1}{3} = \dfrac{1}{2}$

52. $z + \dfrac{2}{5} = -\dfrac{3}{10}$

53. $3t + 1 - 2t = t + 1$

54. $7z - 5z - 8 = 2z - 8$

55. $2y - 18 = -5y - 4$

56. $6 - 21x = 12 - 21x$

Solving Problems

57. *Geometry* The length of a tennis court is 6 feet more than twice the width (see figure). Find the width of the court if the length is 78 feet.

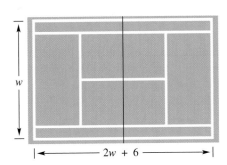

58. *Geometry* The perimeter of a rectangle is 240 inches. Find the dimensions of the rectangle if the length is twice the width.

59. *Geometry* You are asked to cut a 12-foot board into three pieces. Two pieces are to have the same length and the third is to be twice as long as the others. How long are the pieces?

60. *Geometry* The sign below has the shape of an equilateral triangle. The perimeter of the sign is 225 centimeters. Find the length of the sides of the sign. (An equilateral triangle is one whose sides have the same length.)

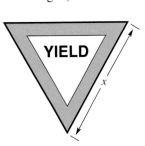

61. *Car Repair* The bill (including parts and labor) for the repair of your car is shown below. Some of the bill is unreadable. From what is given, can you determine how many hours were spent on labor? Explain.

Parts $285.00
Labor ($32 per hour) . . . . $
Total **$357.00**

62. *Car Repair* The bill for the repair of your car was $439. The cost for parts was $265. The cost for labor was $29 per hour. How many hours did the repair work take?

63. *Ticket Sales* Tickets for a community theater are $10 for main floor seats and $8 for balcony seats. There are 400 seats on the main floor, and these were sold out for the evening performance. The total revenue from ticket sales was $5200. How many balcony seats were sold?

64. *Ticket Sales* Tickets for a marching band competition are $5 for 50-yard-line seats and $3 for bleacher seats. Eight hundred 50-yard-line seats were sold. The total revenue from ticket sales was $5500. How many bleacher seats were sold?

65. *Summer Jobs* You have two summer jobs. In the first job, you work 40 hours a week and earn $9.25 an hour. In the second job, you earn $7.50 an hour and can work as many hours as you want. If you want to earn a combined total of $425 a week, how many hours must you work at the second job?

66. *Summer Jobs* You have two summer jobs. In the first job, you work 30 hours a week and earn $8.75 an hour. In the second job, you earn $11.00 an hour and can work as many hours as you want. If you want to earn a combined total of $400 a week, how many hours must you work at the second job?

67. Find a number such that the sum of that number and 45 is 75.

68. Five times the sum of a number and 16 is 100. Find the number.

69. The sum of two consecutive odd integers is 72. Find the two integers.

70. The sum of three consecutive even integers is 192. Find the three integers.

71. *Finding a Pattern* The length of a rectangle is t times its width (see figure). The rectangle has a perimeter of 1200 meters, which implies that

$$2w + 2(tw) = 1200$$

where w is the width of the rectangle.

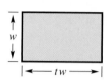

(a) Complete the table.

t	1	1.5	2	3	4	5
Width						
Length						
Area						

(b) Use the completed table to draw a conclusion concerning the area of a rectangle of given perimeter as the length increases relative to its width.

Explaining Concepts

72. Give two examples of linear equations and two examples of nonlinear equations.

73. The scale below is balanced. Each blue box weighs 1 ounce. How much does the red box weigh? If you removed three blue boxes from each side, would the scale still balance? What property of equality does this illustrate?

74. In your own words, describe the steps that can be used to transform an equation into an equivalent equation.

75. Explain how to solve the equation

$x + 5 = 32.$

What property of equality are you using?

76. Explain how to solve the equation

$3x = 5.$

What property of equality are you using?

77. When solving a word problem to determine the average speed of a moving van on a trip from Pittsburgh to Chicago, you obtained an answer of 134.5 kilometers per hour. Can this answer be correct? Explain.

78. *True or False?* Multiplying both sides of an equation by 0 yields an equivalent equation.

79. *True or False?* Subtracting 0 from both sides of an equation yields an equivalent equation.

3.2   Equations That Reduce to Linear Form

Objectives

1 Solve a linear equation containing symbols of grouping.

2 Solve a linear equation involving fractions.

3 Solve a linear equation involving decimals.

1 Solve a linear equation containing symbols of grouping.

Equations Containing Symbols of Grouping

In this section you will continue your study of linear equations by looking at more complicated types of linear equations. To solve a linear equation that contains symbols of grouping, *first remove the symbols of grouping from each side* by the Distributive Property. Then combine like terms and proceed to solve the resulting linear equation in the usual way using properties of equality.

Example 1   Solving a Linear Equation Involving Parentheses

Solve the linear equation (and then display the equation).

Solution

$4(x - 3) = 8$	Original equation
$4 \cdot x - 4 \cdot 3 = 8$	Distributive Property
$4x - 12 = 8$	Simplify.
$4x - 12 + 12 = 8 + 12$	Add 12 to both sides.
$4x = 20$	Combine like terms.
$\dfrac{4x}{4} = \dfrac{20}{4}$	Divide both sides by 4.
$x = 5$	Simplify.

Check

$4(x - 3) = 8$	Original equation
$4(5 - 3) \stackrel{?}{=} 8$	Substitute 5 for x.
$4(2) \stackrel{?}{=} 8$	Simplify.
$8 = 8$	Solution checks. ✓

The solution is 5.

Notice in the check of Example 1 that you do not need to use the Distributive Property to remove the parentheses. Simply evaluate the expression within the parentheses and then multiply.

> **Example 2**   Solving a Linear Equation Involving Parentheses

Solve $3(2x - 1) + x = 11$.

Solution

$3(2x - 1) + x = 11$	Original equation
$3 \cdot 2x - 3 \cdot 1 + x = 11$	Distributive Property
$6x - 3 + x = 11$	Simplify.
$6x + x - 3 = 11$	Collect like terms.
$7x - 3 = 11$	Combine like terms.
$7x - 3 + 3 = 11 + 3$	Add 3 to both sides.
$7x = 14$	Combine like terms.
$\dfrac{7x}{7} = \dfrac{14}{7}$	Divide both sides by 7.
$x = 2$	Simplify.

Check

$3(2x - 1) + x = 11$	Original equation
$3[2(2) - 1] + 2 \stackrel{?}{=} 11$	Substitute 2 for x.
$3(4 - 1) + 2 \stackrel{?}{=} 11$	Simplify.
$3(3) + 2 \stackrel{?}{=} 11$	Simplify.
$9 + 2 \stackrel{?}{=} 11$	Simplify.
$11 = 11$	Solution checks. ✓

The solution is 2.

> **Example 3**   Solving a Linear Equation Involving Parentheses

Solve $5(x + 2) = 2(x - 1)$.

Solution

$5(x + 2) = 2(x - 1)$	Original equation
$5x + 10 = 2x - 2$	Distributive Property
$5x - 2x + 10 = -2$	Subtract $2x$ from both sides.
$3x + 10 = -2$	Combine like terms.
$3x = -2 - 10$	Subtract 10 from both sides.
$3x = -12$	Combine like terms.
$x = -4$	Divide both sides by 3.

The solution is -4. Check this in the original equation.

Example 4 Solving a Linear Equation Involving Parentheses

Solve $2(x - 7) - 3(x + 4) = 4 - (5x - 2)$.

Solution

$$2(x - 7) - 3(x + 4) = 4 - (5x - 2) \qquad \text{Original equation}$$

$$2x - 14 - 3x - 12 = 4 - 5x + 2 \qquad \text{Distributive Property}$$

$$-x - 26 = -5x + 6 \qquad \text{Combine like terms.}$$

$$-x + 5x - 26 = 6 \qquad \text{Add } 5x \text{ to both sides.}$$

$$4x - 26 = 6 \qquad \text{Combine like terms.}$$

$$4x = 6 + 26 \qquad \text{Add 26 to both sides.}$$

$$4x = 32 \qquad \text{Combine like terms.}$$

$$x = 8 \qquad \text{Divide both sides by 4.}$$

The solution is 8. Check this in the original equation.

The linear equation in the next example involves both brackets and parentheses. Watch out for nested symbols of grouping such as these. The innermost symbols of grouping should be removed first.

Technology: Tip

Try using your graphing utility to check the solution found in Example 5. You will need to *nest* some parentheses inside other parentheses. This will give you practice working with nested parentheses on a graphing utility.

Left side

$$5\left(-\frac{1}{3}\right) - 2\left(4\left(-\frac{1}{3}\right)\right.$$

$$\left. + 3\left(\left(-\frac{1}{3}\right) - 1\right)\right)$$

Right side

$$8 - 3\left(-\frac{1}{3}\right)$$

Example 5 An Equation Involving Nested Symbols of Grouping

Solve $5x - 2[4x + 3(x - 1)] = 8 - 3x$.

Solution

$$5x - 2[4x + 3(x - 1)] = 8 - 3x \qquad \text{Original equation}$$

$$5x - 2[4x + 3x - 3] = 8 - 3x \qquad \text{Distributive Property}$$

$$5x - 2[7x - 3] = 8 - 3x \qquad \text{Combine like terms inside brackets.}$$

$$5x - 14x + 6 = 8 - 3x \qquad \text{Distributive Property}$$

$$-9x + 6 = 8 - 3x \qquad \text{Combine like terms.}$$

$$-9x + 3x + 6 = 8 \qquad \text{Add } 3x \text{ to both sides.}$$

$$-6x + 6 = 8 \qquad \text{Combine like terms.}$$

$$-6x = 8 - 6 \qquad \text{Subtract 6 from both sides.}$$

$$-6x = 2 \qquad \text{Combine like terms.}$$

$$x = \frac{2}{-6} \qquad \text{Divide both sides by } -6.$$

$$x = -\frac{1}{3} \qquad \text{Simplify.}$$

The solution is $-\frac{1}{3}$. Check this in the original equation.

2 Solve a linear equation involving fractions.

Equations Involving Fractions or Decimals

To solve a linear equation that contains one or more fractions, it is usually best to first *clear the equation of fractions.*

▶ **Clearing an Equation of Fractions**

An equation such as

$$\frac{x}{a} + \frac{b}{c} = d$$

that contains one or more fractions can be cleared of fractions by multiplying both sides by the least common multiple (LCM) of a and c.

For example, the equation

$$\frac{3x}{2} - \frac{1}{3} = 2$$

can be cleared of fractions by multiplying both sides by 6, the LCM of 2 and 3. Notice how this is done in the next example.

Study Tip

For an equation that contains a *single numerical* fraction such as $2x - \frac{3}{4} = 1$, you can simply add $\frac{3}{4}$ to both sides and then solve for x. You do not need to clear the fraction.

$$2x - \frac{3}{4} + \frac{3}{4} = 1 + \frac{3}{4} \qquad \text{Add } \tfrac{3}{4}.$$

$$2x = \frac{7}{4} \qquad \text{Combine terms.}$$

$$x = \frac{7}{8} \qquad \text{Multiply by } \tfrac{1}{2}.$$

Example 6   Solving a Linear Equation Involving Fractions

Solve $\dfrac{3x}{2} - \dfrac{1}{3} = 2$.

Solution

$$\frac{3x}{2} - \frac{1}{3} = 2 \qquad \text{Original equation}$$

$$6\left(\frac{3x}{2} - \frac{1}{3}\right) = 6 \cdot 2 \qquad \text{Multiply both sides by LCM 6.}$$

$$6 \cdot \frac{3x}{2} - 6 \cdot \frac{1}{3} = 12 \qquad \text{Distributive Property}$$

$$9x - 2 = 12 \qquad \text{Clear fractions.}$$

$$9x = 14 \qquad \text{Add 2 to both sides.}$$

$$x = \frac{14}{9} \qquad \text{Divide both sides by 9.}$$

The solution is $\frac{14}{9}$. Check this in the original equation.

To check a fraction solution like $\frac{14}{9}$ in Example 1, it is helpful to rewrite the variable term as a product.

$$\frac{3}{2} \cdot x - \frac{1}{3} = 2 \qquad \text{Write fraction as a product.}$$

In this form the substitution of $\frac{14}{9}$ for x is easier to calculate.

> ### Example 7   Solving a Linear Equation Involving Fractions

Solve $\dfrac{x}{5} + \dfrac{3x}{4} = 19$.

Solution

$$\frac{x}{5} + \frac{3x}{4} = 19 \qquad \text{Original equation}$$

$$20\left(\frac{x}{5}\right) + 20\left(\frac{3x}{4}\right) = 20(19) \qquad \text{Multiply both sides by LCM 20.}$$

$$4x + 15x = 380 \qquad \text{Simplify.}$$

$$19x = 380 \qquad \text{Combine like terms.}$$

$$x = 20 \qquad \text{Divide both sides by 19.}$$

Check

$$\frac{x}{5} + \frac{3x}{4} = 19 \qquad \text{Original equation}$$

$$\frac{20}{5} + \frac{3(20)}{4} \overset{?}{=} 19 \qquad \text{Substitute 20 for } x.$$

$$4 + 15 \overset{?}{=} 19 \qquad \text{Simplify.}$$

$$19 = 19 \qquad \text{Solution checks. } ✓$$

The solution is 20.

Study Tip

Notice in Example 8 that to clear all fractions in the equation, you multiply by 12 which is the LCM of 3, 4, and 2.

> ### Example 8   Solving a Linear Equation Involving Fractions

Solve $\dfrac{2}{3}\left(x + \dfrac{1}{4}\right) = \dfrac{1}{2}$.

Solution

$$\frac{2}{3}\left(x + \frac{1}{4}\right) = \frac{1}{2} \qquad \text{Original equation}$$

$$\frac{2}{3}x + \frac{2}{12} = \frac{1}{2} \qquad \text{Distributive Property}$$

$$12 \cdot \frac{2}{3}x + 12 \cdot \frac{2}{12} = 12 \cdot \frac{1}{2} \qquad \text{Multiply both sides by LCM 12.}$$

$$8x + 2 = 6 \qquad \text{Simplify.}$$

$$8x = 4 \qquad \text{Subtract 2 from both sides.}$$

$$x = \frac{4}{8} \qquad \text{Divide both sides by 8.}$$

$$x = \frac{1}{2} \qquad \text{Simplify.}$$

The solution is $\frac{1}{2}$. Check this in the original equation.

A common type of linear equation is one that equates two fractions. To solve such equations, consider the fractions to be **equivalent** and use **cross-multiplication.** That is, if

$$\frac{a}{b} = \frac{c}{d}, \quad \text{then} \quad a \cdot d = b \cdot c.$$

Note how cross-multiplication is used in the next example.

You might point out that cross-multiplication would *not* be an appropriate first step in equations such as

$$\frac{x+2}{3} + 4 = \frac{8}{5} \quad \text{and} \quad \frac{x+2}{3} = \frac{8}{5} - 2.$$

Example 9 Using Cross-Multiplication

Use cross-multiplication to solve $\dfrac{x+2}{3} = \dfrac{8}{5}$.

Solution

$\dfrac{x+2}{3} = \dfrac{8}{5}$	Original equation
$5(x+2) = 3(8)$	Cross-multiply.
$5x + 10 = 24$	Distributive Property
$5x = 14$	Subtract 10 from both sides.
$x = \dfrac{14}{5}$	Divide both sides by 5.

Checking solutions may sometimes be challenging for students, but the checking can improve students' accuracy and reinforce their computational skills.

Check

$\dfrac{x+2}{3} = \dfrac{8}{5}$	Original equation
$\dfrac{\left(\frac{14}{5}+2\right)}{3} \stackrel{?}{=} \dfrac{8}{5}$	Substitute $\frac{14}{5}$ for x.
$\dfrac{\left(\frac{14}{5}+\frac{10}{5}\right)}{3} \stackrel{?}{=} \dfrac{8}{5}$	Write 2 as $\frac{10}{5}$.
$\dfrac{\frac{24}{5}}{3} \stackrel{?}{=} \dfrac{8}{5}$	Simplify.
$\dfrac{24}{5}\left(\dfrac{1}{3}\right) \stackrel{?}{=} \dfrac{8}{5}$	Invert and multiply.
$\dfrac{8}{5} = \dfrac{8}{5}$	Solution checks. ✔

The solution is $\frac{14}{5}$.

Bear in mind that cross-multiplication can only be used with equations written in a form that equates two fractions. Try rewriting the equation in Example 6 in this form and then use cross-multiplication to solve for x.

More extensive applications of cross-multiplication will be discussed when you study ratios and proportions later in this chapter.

3 Solve a linear equation involving decimals.

Many real-life applications of linear equations involve decimal coefficients. To solve such an equation, you can clear it of decimals in much the same way you clear an equation of fractions. Multiply both sides by a power of 10 that converts all decimal coefficients to integers, as shown in the next example.

Study Tip

There are other ways to solve the decimal equation in Example 10. You could first clear the equation of decimals by multiplying both sides by 100. Or, you could keep the decimals and use a graphing utility to do the arithmetic operations. The method you choose is a matter of personal preference.

Example 10   Solving a Linear Equation Involving Decimals

Solve $0.3x + 0.2(10 - x) = 0.15(30)$.

Solution

$0.3x + 0.2(10 - x) = 0.15(30)$	Original equation
$0.3x + 2 - 0.2x = 4.5$	Distributive Property
$0.1x + 2 = 4.5$	Combine like terms.
$10(0.1x + 2) = 10(4.5)$	Multiply both sides by 10.
$x + 20 = 45$	Clear decimals.
$x = 25$	Subtract 20 from both sides.

Check

$0.3x + 0.2(10 - x) = 0.15(30)$	Original equation
$0.3(25) + 0.2(10 - 25) \stackrel{?}{=} 0.15(30)$	Substitute 25 for x.
$0.3(25) + 0.2(-15) \stackrel{?}{=} 0.15(30)$	Perform subtraction within parentheses.
$7.5 - 3.0 \stackrel{?}{=} 4.5$	Multiply.
$4.5 = 4.5$	Solution checks. ✓

The solution is 25.

Discussing the Concept   Error Analysis

Suppose you are teaching an algebra class and one of your students hands in the following problem. Find the error in the solution. Write an explanation for the student.

$4(x + 2) - 8 = 3x$	Given equation
$4x + 8 - 8 = 3x$	Distributive Property
$4x = 3x$	Additive inverse
$4 = 3$	Divide both sides by x.

No solution because 4 is not equal to 3.

Explain what happens when you divide both sides of an equation by a variable factor.

3.2   Exercises

Integrated Review   *Concepts, Skills, and Problem Solving*

Keep mathematically in shape by doing these exercises *before* the problems of this section.

Properties and Definitions

1. In your own words, describe how you add the following fractions.

(a) $\frac{1}{5} + \frac{7}{5}$ (b) $\frac{1}{5} + \frac{7}{3}$

2. Make up two examples of algebraic expressions.

Simplifying Expressions

In Exercises 3–10, simplify the expression.

3. $(-2x)^2 x^4$

4. $-y^2(-2y)^3$

5. $5z^3(z^2)^2$

6. $(a + 3)^2(a + 3)^5$

7. $\dfrac{5x}{3} - \dfrac{2x}{3} - 4$

8. $2x^2 - 4 + 5 - 3x^2$

9. $-y^2(y^2 + 4) + 6y^2$

10. $5t(2 - t) + t^2$

Problem Solving

11. At the beginning of the day, a gasoline tank was full. The tank holds 20 gallons. At the end of the day the fuel gauge indicates that the tank is $\frac{5}{8}$ full. How many gallons of gasoline were used?

12. You buy a pickup truck for $1800 down and 36 monthly payments of $625 each.

(a) What is the total amount you will pay?

(b) The final cost of the pickup is $19,999. How much extra did you pay in finance charges and other fees?

Developing Skills

In Exercises 1–52, solve the equation and check your solution. (Some of the equations have no solution.) See Examples 1–8.

1. $-5(t + 3) = 0$

2. $9(y - 7) = 0$

3. $2(y - 4) = 12$

4. $-3(x + 1) = 18$

5. $2(x - 3) = 4$

6. $4(x + 1) = 24$

7. $7(x + 5) = 49$

8. $25(z - 2) = 60$

9. $4 - (z + 6) = 8$

10. $25 - (y + 3) = 15$

11. $3 - (2x - 4) = 3$

12. $16 - (3x - 10) = 5$

13. $-3(t + 5) = 0$

14. $4(z - 2) = 0$

15. $-4(t + 5) = -2(2t + 10)$

16. $4(z - 2) = 2(2z - 4)$

17. $3(x + 4) = 10(x + 4)$

18. $-8(x - 6) = 3(x - 6)$

19. $7 = 3(x + 2) - 3(x - 5)$

20. $24 = 12(z + 1) - 3(4z - 2)$

21. $7x - 2(x - 2) = 12$

22. $15(x + 1) - 8x = 29$

23. $6 = 3(y + 1) - 4(1 - y)$

24. $100 = 4(y - 6) - (y - 1)$

25. $7(2x - 1) = 4(1 - 5x) + 6$

26. $-3(5x + 2) + 5(1 + 3x) = 0$

27. $2[(3x + 5) - 7] = 3(5x - 2)$

28. $6[x - (2x + 3)] = 8 - 5x$

29. $4x + 3[x - 2(2x - 1)] = 4 - 3x$

30. $16 + 4[5x - 4(x + 2)] = 7 - 2x$

31. $\dfrac{x}{2} = \dfrac{3}{2}$

32. $\dfrac{t}{4} = \dfrac{3}{8}$

33. $\dfrac{y}{5} = \dfrac{3}{5}$

34. $\dfrac{z}{3} = -\dfrac{5}{3}$

35. $\dfrac{y}{5} = -\dfrac{3}{10}$

36. $\dfrac{v}{4} = \dfrac{4}{3}$

37. $\dfrac{6x}{25} = \dfrac{3}{5}$

38. $-\dfrac{8x}{9} = \dfrac{2}{3}$

39. $\dfrac{5x}{4} + \dfrac{1}{2} = 0$

40. $\dfrac{y}{4} - \dfrac{5}{8} = 2$

41. $\dfrac{x}{5} - \dfrac{x}{2} = 1$

42. $\dfrac{x}{3} + \dfrac{x}{4} = 1$

43. $2s + \frac{3}{2} = 2s + 2$

44. $\frac{3}{4} + 5s = -2 + 5s$

45. $3x + \frac{1}{4} = \frac{3}{4}$

46. $2x - \frac{3}{8} = \frac{5}{8}$

47. $\frac{1}{5}x + 1 = \frac{3}{10}x - 4$

48. $\frac{1}{8}x + 3 = \frac{1}{4}x + 5$

49. $\frac{2}{3}(z + 5) - \frac{1}{4}(z + 24) = 0$

50. $\frac{3x}{2} + \frac{1}{4}(x - 2) = 10$

51. $\frac{100 - 4u}{3} = \frac{5u + 6}{4} + 6$

52. $\frac{8 - 3x}{2} - 4 = \frac{x}{6}$

In Exercises 53–62, solve the equation by first cross-multiplying. See Example 9.

53. $\frac{t + 4}{6} = \frac{2}{3}$

54. $\frac{x - 6}{10} = \frac{3}{5}$

55. $\frac{x - 2}{5} = \frac{2}{3}$

56. $\frac{2x + 1}{3} = \frac{5}{2}$

57. $\frac{5x - 4}{4} = \frac{2}{3}$

58. $\frac{10x + 3}{6} = \frac{1}{2}$

59. $\frac{x}{4} = \frac{1 - 2x}{3}$

60. $\frac{x + 1}{6} = \frac{3x}{10}$

61. $\frac{10 - x}{2} = \frac{x + 4}{5}$

62. $\frac{2x + 3}{5} = \frac{3 - 4x}{8}$

In Exercises 63–72, solve the equation. Round the solution to two decimal places. See Example 10.

63. $0.2x + 5 = 6$

64. $4 - 0.3x = 1$

65. $0.234x + 1 = 2.805$

66. $275x - 3130 = 512$

67. $0.02x - 0.96 = 1.50$

68. $1.35x + 14.50 = 6.34$

69. $\frac{x}{3.25} + 1 = 2.08$

70. $\frac{3x}{4.5} = \frac{1}{8}$

71. $\frac{x}{3.155} = 2.850$

72. $2x + \frac{1}{3.7} = \frac{3}{4}$

Solving Problems

73. *Time to Complete a Task*   Two people can complete 80% of a task in t hours, where t must satisfy the equation

$$\frac{t}{10} + \frac{t}{15} = 0.8.$$

Solve this equation for t.

74. *Time to Complete a Task*   The time to complete a task is given by the solution of the equation

$$\frac{t}{10} + \frac{t}{15} = 1.$$

Find the required time t.

75. *Course Grade*   To get an A in a course you must have an average of at least 90 points for four tests of 100 points each.

  (a) For the first three tests, your scores are 87, 92, and 84. What must you score on the fourth exam to earn a 90% average for the course?

  (b) Is it possible for you to get an A if your scores on the first three tests are 87, 69, and 89? Explain.

76. *Course Grade*   Repeat Exercise 75 if the fourth test is weighted so that it counts for twice as much as each of the first three tests.

In Exercises 77–80, use the following equation and solve for x.

$$p_1 x + p_2(a - x) = p_3 a$$

77. *Mixture Problem*   Determine the number of quarts of a 10% solution that must be mixed with a 30% solution to obtain 100 quarts of a 25% solution. ($p_1 = 0.1, p_2 = 0.3, p_3 = 0.25,$ and $a = 100$.)

78. *Mixture Problem*   Determine the number of gallons of a 25% solution that must be mixed with a 50% solution to obtain 5 gallons of a 30% solution. ($p_1 = 0.25, p_2 = 0.5, p_3 = 0.3,$ and $a = 5$.)

79. *Mixture Problem*   An 8-quart automobile cooling system is filled with coolant that is 40% antifreeze. Determine the amount that must be withdrawn and replaced with pure antifreeze so that the 8 quarts of coolant will be 50% antifreeze. ($p_1 = 1, p_2 = 0.4,$ $p_3 = 0.5,$ and $a = 8$.)

80. *Mixture Problem*   A grocer mixes two kinds of nuts costing $2.49 per pound and $3.89 per pound to make 100 pounds of a mixture costing $3.19 per pound. How many pounds of the nuts costing $2.49 per pound must be put into the mixture? ($p_1 = 2.49,$ $p_2 = 3.89, p_3 = 3.19,$ and $a = 100$.)

In Exercises 81 and 82, use $W_1 x = W_2(a - x)$.

81. *Balancing a Seesaw*   Find the position of the fulcrum so that the seesaw shown in the figure will balance. ($W_1 = 90$, $W_2 = 60$, and $a = 10$.)

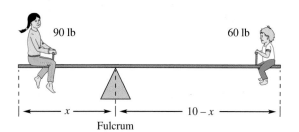

82. *Raising a Weight*   The fulcrum of a 6-foot-long lever is 6 inches from a weight, as shown in the figure. Find the maximum weight that a 190-pound person can lift using this lever. ($W_1 = 190$, $x = 5\frac{1}{2}$, and $a = 6$.)

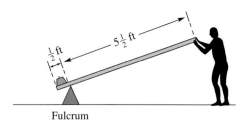

 83. *Fireplace Construction*   A fireplace is 93 inches wide. Each brick in the fireplace has a length of 8 inches and there is $\frac{1}{2}$ inch of mortar between adjoining bricks. Let n be the number of bricks per row.

    (a) Explain why the number of bricks per row is the solution of the equation $8n + \frac{1}{2}(n - 1) = 93$.

    (b) Find the number of bricks per row in the fireplace.

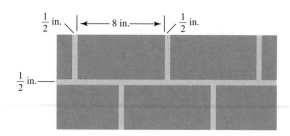

84. *Data Analysis*   The table gives the projected number N (in millions) of persons 65 years of age or older in the United States.   (Source: U.S. Bureau of the Census)

Year	2000	2010	2020	2030
N	34.7	39.4	53.2	69.4

A model for the data is

$$N = 1.2t + 31.5$$

where t represents time in years, with $t = 0$ corresponding to the year 2000. According to the model, in what year will the population of those 65 or older exceed 75 million?

Explaining Concepts

85. In your own words, describe the procedure for removing symbols of grouping. Give some examples.

86. Describe the error in the following.

$$-2(x - 5) = 8$$
$$-2x - 5 = 8$$

87. You could solve $3(x - 7) = 15$ by applying the Distributive Property as the first step. However, there is another way to begin. What is it?

88. What is meant by the least common multiple of the denominators of two or more fractions? Discuss the method for finding the least common multiple of the denominators of fractions.

89. When solving an equation that contains fractions, what is accomplished by multiplying both sides of the equation by the least common multiple of the denominators of the fractions?

 90. When simplifying an algebraic *expression* involving fractions, why can't you simplify the expression by multiplying by the least common multiple of the denominators?

3.3   Problem Solving with Percents

Objectives

1 Convert percents to decimals and fractions and convert decimals and fractions to percents.

2 Solve linear equations involving percents.

3 Solve application problems involving markups and discounts.

---

1 Convert percents to decimals and fractions and convert decimals and fractions to percents.

Percents

In applications involving percents, you usually must convert the percents to decimal (or fraction) form before performing any arithmetic operations. Consequently, you need to be able to convert from percents to decimals (or fractions), and vice versa. The following verbal model can be used to perform the conversions.

$$\boxed{\text{Decimal or fraction}} \cdot \boxed{100\%} = \boxed{\text{Percent}}$$

For example, the decimal 0.38 corresponds to 38 percent. That is,

$$0.38(100\%) = 38\%.$$

Example 1   Converting Decimals and Fractions to Percents

Convert each number to a percent.

a. $\dfrac{3}{5}$ **b.** 1.20

Solution

a. *Verbal Model:* $\boxed{\text{Fraction}} \cdot \boxed{100\%} = \boxed{\text{Percent}}$

Equation: $\dfrac{3}{5}(100\%) = \dfrac{300}{5}\%$

$$= 60\%$$

So, the fraction $\frac{3}{5}$ corresponds to 60%.

b. *Verbal Model:* $\boxed{\text{Decimal}} \cdot \boxed{100\%} = \boxed{\text{Percent}}$

Equation: $(1.20)(100\%) = 120\%$

So, the decimal 1.20 corresponds to 120%.

Note in Example 1(b) that it is possible to have percents that are larger than 100%. It is also possible to have percents that are less than 1% such as $\frac{1}{2}\%$ or 0.78%.

Study Tip

In Examples 1 and 2, there is a quick way to convert between percent form and decimal form.

- To convert from percent form to decimal form, move the decimal point 2 places to the left. For instance,

$$3.5\% = 0.035.$$

- To convert from decimal form to percent form, move the decimal point 2 places to the right. For instance,

$$1.20 = 120\%.$$

- Decimal-to-fraction or fraction-to-decimal conversions can be done on a calculator. Consult your user's guide.

Example 2 Converting Percents to Decimals and Fractions

a. Convert 3.5% to a decimal.

b. Convert 55% to a fraction.

Solution

a. *Verbal Model:* Decimal · 100% = Percent

Label: x = decimal

Equation: $x(100\%) = 3.5\%$

$$x = \frac{3.5\%}{100\%}$$

$$x = 0.035$$

So, 3.5% corresponds to the decimal 0.035.

b. *Verbal Model:* Fraction · 100% = Percent

Label: x = fraction

Equation: $x(100\%) = 55\%$

$$x = \frac{55\%}{100\%}$$

$$x = \frac{11}{20}$$

So, 55% corresponds to the fraction $\frac{11}{20}$.

Some percents occur so commonly that it is helpful to memorize their conversions. For instance, 100% corresponds to 1 and 200% corresponds to 2. The table below shows the decimal and fraction conversions for several percents.

Percent	10%	$12\frac{1}{2}\%$	20%	25%	$33\frac{1}{3}\%$	50%	$66\frac{2}{3}\%$	75%
Decimal	0.1	0.125	0.2	0.25	$0.\overline{3}$	0.5	$0.\overline{6}$	0.75
Fraction	$\frac{1}{10}$	$\frac{1}{8}$	$\frac{1}{5}$	$\frac{1}{4}$	$\frac{1}{3}$	$\frac{1}{2}$	$\frac{2}{3}$	$\frac{3}{4}$

Percent means *per hundred* or *parts of 100*. (The Latin word for 100 is *centum*.) For example, 20% means 20 parts of 100, which is equivalent to the fraction 20/100 or $\frac{1}{5}$. In applications involving percent, many people like to state percent in terms of a portion. For instance, the statement "20% of the population lives in apartments" is often stated as "1 out of every 5 people lives in an apartment."

2 Solve linear equations involving percents.

The Percent Equation

The primary use of percents is to compare two numbers. For example, 2 is 50% of 4, and 5 is 25% of 20. The following model is helpful.

Verbal Model: $a = p$ percent of b

Labels: $b = $ base number
$p = $ percent (in decimal form)
$a = $ number being compared to b

Equation: $a = p \cdot b$

Example 3   Solving Percent Equations

a. What number is 30% of 70?

b. Fourteen is 25% of what number?

c. One hundred thirty-five is what percent of 27?

Solution

a.   *Verbal Model:*   What number $=$ 30% of 70

Label: $a = $ unknown number

Equation: $a = (0.3)(70) = 21$

So, 21 is 30% of 70.

b.   *Verbal Model:*   14 $=$ 25% of what number

Label: $b = $ unknown number

Equation: $14 = 0.25b$

$$\frac{14}{0.25} = b$$

$$56 = b$$

So, 14 is 25% of 56.

c.   *Verbal Model:*   135 $=$ What percent of 27

Label: $p = $ unknown percent (in decimal form)

Equation: $135 = p(27)$

$$\frac{135}{27} = p$$

$$5 = p$$

So, 135 is 500% of 27.

From Example 3, you can see that there are three basic types of percent problems. Each can be solved by substituting the two given quantities into the percent equation and solving for the third quantity.

Question	*Given*	*Percent Equation*
a is what percent of *b*?	*a* and *b*	Solve for *p*.
What number is *p* percent of *b*?	*p* and *b*	Solve for *a*.
a is *p* percent of what number?	*a* and *p*	Solve for *b*.

For instance, part (b) of Example 3 fits the form "*a* is *p* percent of what number?"

In most real-life applications, the base number *b* and the number *a* are much more disguised than they are in Example 3. It sometimes helps to think of *a* as a "new" amount and *b* as the "original" amount.

Example 4 Real Estate Commission

A real estate agency receives a commission of $5167.50 for the sale of a $79,500 house. What percent commission is this?

Solution

Verbal Model: $\boxed{\text{Commission}} = \boxed{\begin{array}{c}\text{Percent (in}\\\text{decimal form)}\end{array}} \cdot \boxed{\text{Sale price}}$

Labels:
Commission = 5167.50 (dollars)
Percent = *p* (in decimal form)
Sale price = 79,500 (dollars)

Equation: $5167.50 = p \cdot (79,500)$

$$\frac{5167.50}{79,500} = p$$

$$0.065 = p$$

So, the real estate agency receives a commission of 6.5%.

Example 5 Cost-of-Living Raise

A union negotiates for a cost-of-living raise of 7%. What is the raise for a union member whose salary is $17,240? What is this person's new salary?

Solution

Verbal Model: $\boxed{\text{Raise}} = \boxed{\begin{array}{c}\text{Percent (in}\\\text{decimal form)}\end{array}} \cdot \boxed{\text{Salary}}$

Labels:
Raise = *a* (dollars)
Percent = 7% = 0.07 (in decimal form)
Salary = 17,240 (dollars)

Equation: $a = 0.07(17,240) = 1206.80$

So, the raise is $1206.80 and the new salary is 17,240.00 + 1206.80 or $18,446.80.

| Example 6 | Course Grade |

You missed an A in your chemistry course by only three points. Your point total for the course is 402. How many points were possible in the course? (Assume that you needed 90% of the course total for an A.)

Solution

Verbal Model:

| Your points | + | 3 points | = | Percent (in decimal form) | · | Total points |

Labels: Your points $= 402$ (points)
             Percent $= 90\% = 0.9$ (in decimal form)
             Total points for course $= b$ (points)

Equation: $402 + 3 = 0.9b$

$$405 = 0.9b$$

$$\frac{405}{0.9} = b$$

$$450 = b$$

Check

$402 + 3 = 0.9b$ Original equation

$402 + 3 \overset{?}{=} 0.9(450)$ Substitute 450 for b.

$405 = 405$ Solution checks. ✓

So, there were 450 total points for the course.

---

3 Solve application problems involving markups and discounts.

Markups and Discounts

You may have had the experience of buying an item at one store and later finding that you could have paid less for the same item at another store. The basic reason for this price difference is **markup,** which is the difference between the **cost** (the amount a retailer pays for the item) and the **price** (the amount at which the retailer sells the item to the consumer). A verbal model for this problem is as follows.

| Selling price | = | Cost | + | Markup |

In such a problem, the markup may be known or it may be expressed as a percent of the cost. This percent is called the **markup rate.**

| Markup | = | Markup rate | · | Cost |

Markup is one of those "hidden products" referred to in Section 2.3.

In business and economics, the terms *cost* and *price* do not mean the same thing. The cost of an item is the amount a business pays for the item. The price of an item is the amount for which the business sells the item.

Example 7   Finding the Selling Price

A sporting goods store uses a markup rate of 55% on all items. The cost of a golf bag is $45. What is the selling price of the bag?

Solution

Verbal Model: $\boxed{\dfrac{\text{Selling}}{\text{price}}} = \boxed{\text{Cost}} + \boxed{\text{Markup}}$

Labels: Selling price $= x$ (dollars)
Cost $= 45$ (dollars)
Markup rate $= 0.55$ (rate in decimal form)
Markup $= (0.55)(45)$ (dollars)

Equation: $x = 45 + (0.55)(45)$

$= 45 + 24.75$

$= \$69.75$

The selling price is $69.75. Check this in the original statement of the problem.

In Example 7, you are given the cost and are asked to find the selling price. Example 8 illustrates the reverse problem. That is, in Example 8 you are given the selling price and asked to find the cost.

Example 8   Finding the Cost of an Item

The selling price of a pair of ski boots is $98. The markup rate is 60%. What is the cost of the boots?

Solution

Verbal Model: $\boxed{\dfrac{\text{Selling}}{\text{price}}} = \boxed{\text{Cost}} + \boxed{\text{Markup}}$

Labels: Selling price $= 98$ (dollars)
Cost $= x$ (dollars)
Markup rate $= 0.60$ (rate in decimal form)
Markup $= 0.60x$ (dollars)

Equation: $98 = x + 0.60x$

$98 = 1.60x$

$\dfrac{98}{1.60} = x$

$\$61.25 = x$

The cost is $61.25. Check this in the original statement of the problem.

Example 9 Finding the Markup Rate

A pair of shoes sells for $60. The cost of the shoes is $24. What is the markup rate?

Solution

Verbal Model: Selling price = Cost + Markup

Labels:
Selling price = 60   (dollars)
Cost = 24   (dollars)
Markup rate = p (rate in decimal form)
Markup = $p(24)$ (dollars)

Equation: $60 = 24 + p(24)$

$$36 = 24p$$

$$\frac{36}{24} = p$$

$$1.5 = p$$

Because $p = 1.5$, it follows that the markup rate is 150%.

The mathematics of a discount is similar to that of a markup. The model for this situation is

Sale price = List price − Discount

where the **discount** is given in dollars, and the **discount rate** is given as a percent of the list price. Notice the "hidden product" in the discount.

Discount = Discount rate · List price

Example 10 Finding the Discount Rate

During a midsummer sale, a lawn mower listed at $199.95 is on sale for $139.95. What is the discount rate?

Solution

Verbal Model: Discount = Discount rate · List price

Labels:
Discount = 199.95 − 139.95 = 60   (dollars)
List price = 199.95   (dollars)
Discount rate = p (rate in decimal form)

Equation: $60 = p(199.95)$

$$0.30 \approx p$$

Because $p \approx 0.30$, it follows that the discount rate is 30%.

| Example 11 | Finding the Sale Price | |

A drug store advertises 40% off the prices of all summer tanning products. A bottle of suntan oil lists for $3.49. What is the sale price?

Solution

Verbal Model:

$$\boxed{\text{Sale price}} = \boxed{\text{List price}} - \boxed{\text{Discount}}$$

Labels:

List price = 3.49	(dollars)
Discount rate = 0.4	(rate in decimal form)
Discount = 0.4(3.49)	(dollars)
Sale price = x	(dollars)

Equation:

$$x = 3.49 - (0.4)(3.49)$$
$$\approx \$2.09$$

The sale price is $2.09. Check this in the original statement of the problem.

The following guidelines summarize the problem-solving strategy that we recommend for word problems.

▶ **Guidelines for Solving Word Problems**

1. Write a *verbal model* that describes the problem.

2. Assign *labels* to fixed quantities and variable quantities.

3. Rewrite the verbal model as an *algebraic equation* using the assigned labels.

4. *Solve* the algebraic equation.

5. *Check* to see that your solution satisfies the word problem as stated.

Discussing the Concept   **Comparing Growth Patterns**

In the year 2000, your starting annual salary is $28,000. You are given two options for an 8-year contract. In the first option, you will be given a $1500 raise each year. In the second option, you will be given a 5% raise each year.

a. Make a table showing your salaries and raises for both options for each of the 8 years of the contract. Which option would you choose for an 8-year contract?

b. Which option would you choose if it were a 3-year contract? a 4-year contract? Explain.

c. In which year would the raise for the second option surpass the raise for the first option? Why do you think this happens?

3.3 Exercises

Integrated Review   *Concepts, Skills, and Problem Solving*

Keep mathematically in shape by doing these exercises *before* the problems of this section.

Properties and Definitions

1. Explain how to put the two numbers 63 and -28 in order.

2. For any real number, its distance from ____ on the real number line is its absolute value.

Simplifying Expressions

In Exercises 3–6, evaluate the expression.

3. $8 - |-7 + 11| + (-4)$

4. $34 - [54 - (-16 + 4) + 6]$

5. Subtract 230 from -300.

6. Find the absolute value of the difference of 17 and -12.

In Exercises 7 and 8, use the Distributive Property to expand the expression.

7. $4(2x - 5)$

8. $-z(xz - 2y^2)$

In Exercises 9 and 10, evaluate the algebraic expression for the specified values of the variables. (If not possible, state the reason.)

9. $x^2 - y^2$

(a) $x = 4, y = 3$

(b) $x = -5, y = 3$

10. $\dfrac{z^2 + 2}{x^2 - 1}$

(a) $x = 1, z = 1$

(b) $x = 2, z = 2$

Problem Solving

11. A telephone company charges \$1.37 for the first minute and \$0.95 for each additional minute. Find the cost of a 15-minute phone call.

12. A train travels at the rate of r miles per hour for 5 hours. Write an algebraic expression that represents the total distance traveled by the train.

Developing Skills

In Exercises 1–12, complete the table showing the equivalent forms of a percent. See Examples 1 and 2.

	Percent	Parts out of 100	Decimal	Fraction
1.	40%			
2.	15%			
3.	7.5%			
4.	75%			
5.		63		
6.		10.5		
7.			0.155	
8.			0.80	
9.				$\frac{3}{5}$
10.				$\frac{3}{20}$
11.	150%			
12.			1.25	

In Exercises 13–20, change the decimal to a percent. See Example 1.

13. 0.62

14. 0.57

15. 0.20

16. 0.38

17. 0.075

18. 0.005

19. 2.5

20. 1.75

In Exercises 21–28, change the percent to a decimal. See Example 2.

21. 12.5%

22. 95%

23. 125%

24. 8.5%

25. 250%

26. 0.3%

27. $\frac{3}{4}$%

28. $33\frac{1}{3}$%

In Exercises 29–36, change the fraction to a percent. See Example 1.

29. $\frac{4}{5}$ **30.** $\frac{1}{4}$

31. $\frac{5}{4}$ **32.** $\frac{6}{5}$

33. $\frac{5}{6}$ **34.** $\frac{2}{3}$

35. $\frac{7}{20}$ **36.** $\frac{3}{2}$

In Exercises 37–40, what percent of the figure is shaded? (There are a total of 360° in a circle.)

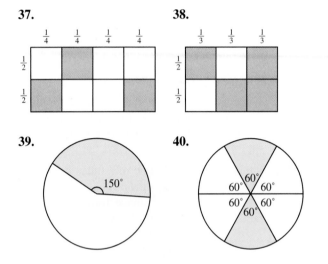

37.   **38.**

39.   **40.**

In Exercises 41–64, solve the percent equation. See Example 3.

41. What number is 30% of 150?

42. What number is 62% of 1200?

43. What number is 9.5% of 816?

44. What number is $33\frac{1}{3}\%$ of 516?

45. What number is $\frac{3}{4}\%$ of 56?

46. What number is 0.2% of 100,000?

47. What number is 200% of 88?

48. What number is 325% of 450?

49. 903 is 43% of what number?

50. 425 is 85% of what number?

51. 275 is $12\frac{1}{2}\%$ of what number?

52. 210 is 250% of what number?

53. 594 is 450% of what number?

54. 814 is $66\frac{2}{3}\%$ of what number?

55. 2.16 is 0.6% of what number?

56. 51.2 is 0.08% of what number?

57. 576 is what percent of 800?

58. 1950 is what percent of 5000?

59. 45 is what percent of 360?

60. 38 is what percent of 5700?

61. 22 is what percent of 800?

62. 110 is what percent of 110?

63. 1000 is what percent of 200?

64. 148.8 is what percent of 960?

In Exercises 65–74, find the missing quantities. See Examples 7, 8, and 9.

	Cost	Selling Price	Markup	Markup Rate
65.	$26.97	$49.95		
66.		$224.87	$75.08	
67.		$74.38		81.5%
68.	$680.00			$33\frac{1}{3}\%$
69.		$125.98	$56.69	
70.	$71.97	$119.95		
71.		$15,900.00	$2650.00	
72.		$350.00	$80.77	
73.	$107.97			85.2%
74.		$69.99		55.5%

In Exercises 75–84, find the missing quantities. See Examples 10 and 11.

	List Price	Sale Price	Discount	Discount Rate
75.	$39.95	$29.95		
76.	$18.95		$8.00	
77.		$18.95		20%
78.		$259.97	$135.00	
79.	$189.99		$30.00	
80.	$50.99	$45.99		
81.	$119.96			50%
82.	$84.95			65%
83.		$695.00	$300.00	
84.		$189.00		40%

Solving Problems

85. *Rent Payment* You spend 17% of your monthly income of $3200 for rent. What is your monthly payment?

86. *Cost of Housing* You budget 30% of your annual after-tax income for housing. If your after-tax income is $38,500, what amount can you spend on housing?

87. *Retirement Plan* You budget $7\frac{1}{2}$% of your gross income for an individual retirement plan. Your annual gross income is $45,800. How much will you put in your retirement plan each year?

88. *Enrollment* Thirty-five percent of the students enrolled in a college are freshmen. The enrollment of the college is 2800. Find the number of freshmen.

89. *Snowfall* During the winter, there was 120 inches of snow. Of that amount, 86 inches fell in December. What percent of the snow fell in December?

90. *Layoff* Because of slumping sales, a small company laid off 30 of its 153 employees.

(a) What percent of the work force was laid off?

(b) Complete the statement: "About 1 out of every ▭ workers was laid off."

91. *Unemployment Rate* During a recession, 72 out of 1000 workers in the population were unemployed. Find the unemployment rate (as a percent).

92. *Inflation Rate* You purchase a lawn tractor for $3750 and 1 year later you note that the cost has increased to $3900. Determine the inflation rate (as a percent) for the tractor.

93. *Original Price* A coat sells for $250 during a 20% off storewide clearance sale. What was the original price of the coat?

94. *Membership Drive* Because of a membership drive for a public television station, the current membership is 125% of what it was a year ago. The current number of members is 7815. How many members did the station have last year?

95. *Price* The price of a new van is approximately 110% of what it was 3 years ago. The current price is $26,850. What was the approximate price 3 years ago?

96. *Decision Making* A new car you want to buy costs $17,800. If you wait another month to buy the car, the price will increase by 6%. However, to buy it now you will have to pay an interest penalty of $450 for the early withdrawal of a certificate of deposit. Should you buy the car now or wait another month? Explain.

97. *Eligible Voters* The news media reported that 6432 votes were cast in the last election and that this represented 63% of the eligible voters of a district. How many eligible voters are in the district?

98. *Defective Parts* A quality control engineer tested several parts and found two to be defective. The engineer reported that 2.5% were defective. How many were tested?

99. *Course Grade* You were six points shy of a B in your mathematics course. Your point total for the course is 394. How many points were possible in the course? (Assume that you needed 80% of the course total for a B.)

100. *Target Size* A circular target is attached to a rectangular board, as shown in the figure. The radius of the circle is $4\frac{1}{2}$ inches, and the measurements of the board are 12 inches by 15 inches. What percentage of the board is covered by the target? (The area of a circle is $A = \pi r^2$, where r is the radius of the circle.)

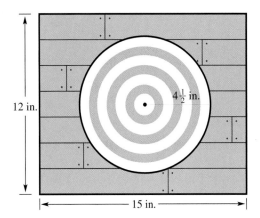

101. *Analyzing Data*   In 1995 there were 697.1 million visits to office-based physicians. The figure classifies the age groups of those making the visits. Approximate the number of Americans in each of the classifications.   (Source: U.S. National Center for Health Statistics)

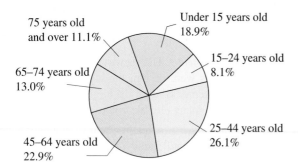

102. *Graphical Estimation*   The graph shows the number (in thousands) of criminal cases commenced in the United States District Courts from 1990 through 1996.   (Source: Administrative Office of the U.S. Courts)

(a) Determine the percent increase in cases from 1991 to 1992.

(b) Determine the percent decrease in cases from 1992 to 1995.

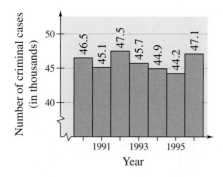

103. *Interpreting a Table*   The table shows the numbers of women scientists and the percents of women scientists in the United States in three fields for the years 1983 and 1996.   (Source: U.S. Bureau of Labor Statistics)

(a) Find the total number of mathematicians and computer scientists (men and women) in 1996.

(b) Find the total number of chemists (men and women) in 1983.

(c) Explain how the number of women in biology can increase while the percent of women in biology decreases.

Field	1983		1996	
	Number	%	Number	%
Math/Computer	137,000	29.6%	411,600	30.6%
Chemistry	22,800	23.3%	42,600	30.6%
Biology	22,400	40.8%	45,200	39.0%

104. *Population Analysis*   The table gives the approximate population (in millions) of Bangladesh for each decade from 1950 through 1990. Approximate the percent growth rate for each decade. If the growth rate of the 1980s continued until the year 2010, approximate the population in 2010.   (Source: U.S. Bureau of the Census, International Data Base)

Year	1950	1960	1970	1980	1990
Population	45.6	54.6	67.4	88.1	110.1

Explaining Concepts

105. Answer parts (a)–(f) of Motivating the Chapter on page 115.

106. Explain the meaning of the word "percent."

107. Explain the concept of "rate."

108. In your own words, explain how to change a percent to a fraction. Give an example.

109. In your own words, explain how to change a decimal to a percent. Give an example.

110. In your own words, explain how to change a fraction to a percent. Give an example.

111. Can any positive decimal be written as a percent? Explain.

112. Is it true that $\frac{1}{2}\% = 50\%$? Explain.

3.4   Ratios and Proportions

Objectives

1️⃣ Compare relative sizes using ratios.

2️⃣ Find the unit price of a consumer item.

3️⃣ Solve a proportion that equates two ratios.

4️⃣ Solve application problems using the Consumer Price Index.

1️⃣ Compare relative sizes using ratios.

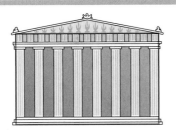

The Golden Ratio

In ancient Greek art and architecture, rectangles can be found in which the ratio of the longer side to the shorter side is

$$\frac{\sqrt{5} + 1}{2} \approx 1.618.$$

This ratio is known as the Golden Ratio. The ancient Greeks were not the only ones to use this ratio. Leonardo DaVinci used the Golden Ratio in his paintings. And the Golden Ratio has also been discovered in nature in the growth patterns of living things such as plants and seashells.

Setting Up Ratios

A **ratio** is a comparison of one number to another by division. For example, in a class of 29 students made up of 16 women and 13 men, the ratio of women to men is 16 to 13 or $\frac{16}{13}$. Some other ratios for this class are as follows.

$$\text{Men to women: } \frac{13}{16} \qquad \text{Men to students: } \frac{13}{29} \qquad \text{Students to women: } \frac{29}{16}$$

Note the order implied by a ratio. The ratio of a to b means a/b, whereas the ratio of b to a means b/a.

▶ **Definition of Ratio**

The **ratio** of the real number a to the real number b is given by

$$\frac{a}{b}.$$

The ratio of a to b is sometimes written as $a : b$.

Example 1   Writing Ratios in Fractional Form

a. The ratio of 7 to 5 is given by $\frac{7}{5}$.

b. The ratio of 12 to 8 is given by $\frac{12}{8} = \frac{3}{2}$.

   Note that the fraction $\frac{12}{8}$ can be written in reduced form as $\frac{3}{2}$.

c. The ratio of $3\frac{1}{2}$ to $5\frac{1}{4}$ is given by

$$\frac{3\frac{1}{2}}{5\frac{1}{4}} = \frac{\frac{7}{2}}{\frac{21}{4}} \qquad \text{Rewrite mixed numbers as fractions.}$$

$$= \frac{7}{2} \cdot \frac{4}{21} \qquad \text{Invert divisor and multiply.}$$

$$= \frac{2}{3}. \qquad \text{Simplify.}$$

There are many real-life applications of ratios. For instance, ratios are used to describe opinion surveys (for/against), populations (male/female, unemployed/employed), and mixtures (oil/gasoline, water/alcohol).

When comparing two *measurements* by a ratio, you should use the same unit of measurement in both the numerator and the denominator. For example, to find the ratio of 4 feet to 8 inches, you could convert 4 feet to 48 inches (by multiplying by 12) to obtain

$$\frac{4\text{ feet}}{8\text{ inches}} = \frac{48\text{ inches}}{8\text{ inches}} = \frac{48}{8} = \frac{6}{1}.$$

Or you could convert 8 inches to $\frac{8}{12}$ feet (by dividing by 12) to obtain

$$\frac{4\text{ feet}}{8\text{ inches}} = \frac{4\text{ feet}}{\frac{8}{12}\text{ feet}} = 4 \cdot \frac{12}{8} = \frac{6}{1}.$$

If you use different units of measurement in the numerator and denominator, then you *must* include the units. If you use the same units of measurement in the numerator and denominator, then it is not necessary to write the units. A list of common conversion factors is given on the inside back cover.

Example 2   Comparing Measurements

Find a ratio to compare the relative sizes of the following.

a. 5 gallons to 7 gallons   **b.** 3 meters to 40 centimeters

c. 200 cents to 3 dollars   **d.** 30 months to $1\frac{1}{2}$ years

Solution

a. Because the units of measurement are the same, the ratio is $\frac{5}{7}$.

b. Because the units of measurement are different, begin by converting meters to centimeters *or* centimeters to meters. Here, it is easier to convert meters to centimeters by multiplying by 100.

$$\frac{3\text{ meters}}{40\text{ centimeters}} = \frac{3(100)\text{ centimeters}}{40\text{ centimeters}} \qquad \text{Convert meters to centimeters.}$$

$$= \frac{300}{40} \qquad \text{Multiply numerator.}$$

$$= \frac{15}{2} \qquad \text{Simplify.}$$

c. Because 200 cents is the same as 2 dollars, the ratio is

$$\frac{200\text{ cents}}{3\text{ dollars}} = \frac{2\text{ dollars}}{3\text{ dollars}} = \frac{2}{3}.$$

d. Because $1\frac{1}{2}$ years $= 18$ months, the ratio is

$$\frac{30\text{ months}}{1\frac{1}{2}\text{ years}} = \frac{30\text{ months}}{18\text{ months}} = \frac{30}{18} = \frac{5}{3}.$$

2 Find the unit price of a consumer item.

Unit Prices

As a consumer, you must be able to determine the unit prices of items you buy in order to make the best use of your money. The **unit price** of an item is given by the ratio of the total price to the total units.

$$\frac{\text{Unit}}{\text{price}} = \frac{\text{Total price}}{\text{Total units}}$$

To state unit prices, we usually use the word *per.* For instance, the unit price for a particular brand of coffee might be 4.69 dollars *per* pound, or $4.69 per pound.

Example 3   Finding a Unit Price

Find the unit price (in dollars per ounce) for a 5-pound, 4-ounce box of detergent that sells for $4.62.

Solution

Begin by writing the weight in ounces. That is,

$$5 \text{ pounds} + 4 \text{ ounces} = 5 \text{ pounds}\left(\frac{16 \text{ ounces}}{1 \text{ pound}}\right) + 4 \text{ ounces}$$

$$= 80 \text{ ounces} + 4 \text{ ounces}$$

$$= 84 \text{ ounces}.$$

Next, determine the unit price as follows.

Verbal Model: $\dfrac{\text{Unit}}{\text{price}} = \dfrac{\text{Total price}}{\text{Total units}}$

Unit Price: $\dfrac{\$4.62}{84 \text{ ounces}} = \$0.055 \text{ per ounce}$

Example 4   Comparing Unit Prices

Which has the lower unit price: a 12-ounce box of breakfast cereal for $2.69 or a 16-ounce box of the same cereal for $3.49?

Solution

The unit price for the smaller box is

$$\text{Unit price} = \frac{\text{total price}}{\text{total units}} = \frac{\$2.69}{12 \text{ ounces}} \approx \$0.224 \text{ per ounce}.$$

The unit price for the larger box is

$$\text{Unit price} = \frac{\text{total price}}{\text{total units}} = \frac{\$3.49}{16 \text{ ounces}} \approx \$0.218 \text{ per ounce}.$$

So, the larger box has a slightly lower unit price.

3 Solve a proportion that equates two ratios.

Solving Proportions

A **proportion** is a statement that equates two ratios. For example, if the ratio of a to b is the same as the ratio of c to d, we can write the proportion as

$$\frac{a}{b} = \frac{c}{d}.$$

In typical applications, you know the values for three of the letters (quantities) and are required to find the value of the fourth. To solve such a fractional equation, you can use the *cross-multiplication* procedure introduced in Section 3.2.

▶ **Solving a Proportion**

If $\dfrac{a}{b} = \dfrac{c}{d}$, then $ad = bc$. The quantities a and d are called the **extremes** of the proportion, whereas b and c are called the **means** of the proportion.

Example 5   Solving Proportions

Solve the following proportions for x.

a. $\dfrac{50}{x} = \dfrac{2}{28}$

b. $\dfrac{x}{3} = \dfrac{10}{6}$

Solution

a.

$$\frac{50}{x} = \frac{2}{28} \qquad \text{Proportion}$$

$$50(28) = 2x \qquad \text{Cross-multiply.}$$

$$\frac{1400}{2} = x \qquad \text{Divide both sides by 2.}$$

$$700 = x \qquad \text{Simplify.}$$

So, the ratio of 50 to 700 is the same as the ratio of 2 to 28.

b. $\dfrac{x}{3} = \dfrac{10}{6} \qquad \text{Proportion}$

$$x = \frac{30}{6} \qquad \text{Multiply both sides by 3.}$$

$$x = 5 \qquad \text{Simplify.}$$

So, the ratio of 5 to 3 is the same as the ratio of 10 to 6.

To solve an equation, you want to isolate the variable. In Example 5(b) this was done by multiplying both sides by 3 instead of cross-multiplying. In this case, multiplying both sides by 3 was the only step needed to isolate the x-variable. However, either method is valid for solving the equation.

| Example 6 | Geometry: Similar Triangles |

A triangular lot has perpendicular sides of lengths 100 feet and 210 feet. You are to make a proportional sketch of this lot using 8 inches as the length of the shorter side. How long should you make the other side?

Solution

This is a case of similar triangles in which the ratios of the corresponding sides are equal. The triangles are shown in Figure 3.2.

$$\frac{\text{Shorter side of lot}}{\text{Longer side of lot}} = \frac{\text{shorter side of sketch}}{\text{longer side of sketch}} \qquad \text{Proportion for similar triangles}$$

$$\frac{100}{210} = \frac{8}{x} \qquad \text{Substitute.}$$

$$x \cdot 100 = 210 \cdot 8 \qquad \text{Cross-multiply.}$$

$$x = \frac{1680}{100} = 16.8 \qquad \text{Divide both sides by 100.}$$

So, the length of the longer side of the sketch should be 16.8 inches.

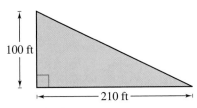

Triangular lot

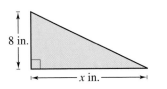

Sketch

Figure 3.2

| Example 7 | Resizing a Picture | |

You have a 7-by-8-inch picture of a graph that you want to paste into a term paper, but you have only a 6-by-6-inch space in which to put it. You go to the copier that has five options for resizing your graph: 64%, 78%, 100%, 121%, and 129%.

a. Which option should you choose?

b. What are the measurements of the resized picture?

Solution

a. Because the longest side must be *reduced* from 8 inches to no more than 6 inches, consider the proportion

$$\frac{\text{New length}}{\text{Old length}} = \frac{\text{new percent}}{\text{old percent}} \qquad \text{Proportion}$$

$$\frac{6}{8} = \frac{x}{100} \qquad \text{Substitute.}$$

$$\frac{6}{8} \cdot 100 = x \qquad \text{Multiply both sides by 100.}$$

$$75 = x.$$

To guarantee a fit, you should choose the 64% option, because 78% is greater than the required 75%.

b. To find the measurements of the resized picture, multiply by 64% or 0.64.

$$\text{Length} = 0.64(8) = 5.12 \text{ inches}$$

$$\text{Width} = 0.64(7) = 4.48 \text{ inches}$$

The size of the reduced picture is 5.12 inches by 4.48 inches.

4 Solve application problems using the Consumer Price Index.

The Consumer Price Index

The rate of inflation is important to all of us. Simply stated, *inflation* is an economic condition in which the price of a fixed amount of goods or services increases. So, a fixed amount of money buys less in a given year than in previous years.

The most widely used measurement of inflation in the United States is the *Consumer Price Index* (CPI), often called the *Cost-of-Living Index*. The table below shows the "All Items" or general index for the years 1950 to 1997. (Source: U.S. Bureau of Labor Statistics)

Year	CPI	Year	CPI	Year	CPI	Year	CPI
1950	24.1	1962	30.2	1974	49.3	1986	109.6
1951	26.0	1963	30.6	1975	53.8	1987	113.6
1952	26.5	1964	31.0	1976	56.9	1988	118.3
1953	26.7	1965	31.5	1977	60.6	1989	124.0
1954	26.9	1966	32.4	1978	65.2	1990	130.7
1955	26.8	1967	33.4	1979	72.6	1991	136.2
1956	27.2	1968	34.8	1980	82.4	1992	140.3
1957	28.1	1969	36.7	1981	90.9	1993	144.5
1958	28.9	1970	38.8	1982	96.5	1994	148.2
1959	29.1	1971	40.5	1983	99.6	1995	152.4
1960	29.6	1972	41.8	1984	103.9	1996	156.9
1961	29.9	1973	44.4	1985	107.6	1997	160.5

To determine (from the CPI) the change in the buying power of a dollar from one year to another, use the following proportion.

$$\frac{\text{Price in year } n}{\text{Price in year } m} = \frac{\text{index in year } n}{\text{index in year } m}$$

For instance, if you paid $15,000 for a house in 1950, then the amount you could expect to pay for the same house in 1990 is given by the following proportion.

$$\frac{\text{Price in 1990}}{\text{Price in 1950}} = \frac{\text{index in 1990}}{\text{index in 1950}}$$

$$\frac{x}{15,000} = \frac{130.7}{24.1} \implies x \approx \$81,350$$

$$x = \frac{130.7}{24.1} \cdot 15,000$$

$$x \approx \$81,350$$

| Example 8 | Using the Consumer Price Index |

You purchased a piece of jewelry for $750 in 1990. What would you expect the replacement value of the jewelry to have been in 1996?

Solution

To answer this question, you can use the Consumer Price Index, as follows.

Verbal
Model: $\dfrac{\text{Price in 1996}}{\text{Price in 1990}} = \dfrac{\text{index in 1996}}{\text{index in 1990}}$

Labels: Price in 1996 = x (dollars)
             Price in 1990 = 750   (dollars)
             Index in 1996 = 156.9
             Index in 1990 = 130.7

Proportion: $\dfrac{x}{750} = \dfrac{156.9}{130.7}$

$$x = 750 \cdot \dfrac{156.9}{130.7}$$

$$x \approx 900$$

You should expect the replacement value of the jewelry to have been approximately $900 in 1996. Check this solution in the original statement of the problem.

| Discussing the Concept | **The Value of Pi** |

One of the best known ratios in mathematics is denoted by the Greek letter π, pronounced "pie." This number represents the ratio of the circumference of *any* circle to its diameter. To estimate the value of π, try the following experiment.

Measure the diameter of a circular cylinder (such as a soda can), and then measure the circumference of the cylinder, as shown in the figure at the left. Then use your graphing utility to approximate the value of π as follows.

$$\pi = \dfrac{\text{Circumference}}{\text{Diameter}}$$

Try to find this ratio for several different sizes of circular objects. Does the ratio depend on the size of the circumference of the circle?

In examples such as Example 8, you might point out that an "approximate" answer will not check "exactly" in the original statement of the problem. However, the process of checking solutions is still important.

Discussing the Concept problems are flexible. For example, you might suggest that each student try the activity below for circular objects of three different sizes. Alternatively, you might organize this as a class activity wherein you assign small groups to report calculations for one or more object(s). The results from all groups can then be collected, organized, and analyzed by the class.

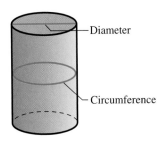

Diameter

Circumference

3.4   Exercises

Integrated Review   *Concepts, Skills, and Problem Solving*

Keep mathematically in shape by doing these exercises *before* the problems of this section.

Properties and Definitions

1. Explain how to write $\frac{15}{12}$ in reduced form.

2. Explain how to divide $\frac{3}{5}$ by $\frac{x}{2}$.

3. Complete the Associative Property: $(3x)y =$
.

4. Name the property illustrated by $x^2 + 0 = x^2$.

Simplifying Expressions

In Exercises 5–10, evaluate the expression.

5. $3^2 - (-4)$

6. $(-5)^3 + 3$

7. 9.3×10^6

8. $\dfrac{-|7 + 3^2|}{4}$

9. $(-4)^2 - (30 \div 50)$ **10.** $(8 \cdot 9) + (-4)^3$

Writing Models

In Exercises 11 and 12, translate the sentence into an algebraic expression.

11. A number is decreased by 10 and the difference is doubled.

12. The area of a triangle with base b and height $\frac{1}{2}(b + 6)$

Developing Skills

In Exercises 1–8, write the ratio as a fraction in simplest form. See Example 1.

1. 36 to 9

2. 24 to 32

3. 27 to 54

4. 50 to 15

5. 14 : 21

6. 60 : 45

7. 144 : 16

8. 12 : 30

In Exercises 9–26, find a ratio to compare the relative sizes. (Use the same units of measurement for both quantities.) See Example 2.

9. Thirty-six inches to 24 inches

10. Fifteen feet to 12 feet

11. Forty dollars to $60

12. Twenty-four pounds to 30 pounds

13. One quart to 1 gallon

14. Three inches to 2 feet

15. Seven nickels to 3 quarters

16. Twenty-four ounces to 3 pounds

17. Three hours to 90 minutes

18. Twenty-one feet to 35 yards

19. Seventy-five centimeters to 2 meters

20. Two meters to 75 centimeters

21. Sixty milliliters to 1 liter

22. Fifty cubic centimeters to 1 liter

23. Ninety minutes to 2 hours

24. Five and one-half pints to 2 quarts

25. Three thousand pounds to 5 tons

26. Twelve thousand pounds to 2 tons

In Exercises 27–30, find the unit price (in dollars per ounce). See Example 3.

27. A 20-ounce can of pineapple for 79¢

28. An 18-ounce box of cereal for $3.19

29. A 1-pound, 4-ounce loaf of bread for $1.29

30. A 1-pound package of cheese for $2.89

In Exercises 31–36, which product has the smaller unit price? See Example 4.

31. (a) A $27\frac{3}{4}$-ounce can of spaghetti sauce for $1.19

(b) A 32-ounce jar of spaghetti sauce for $1.45

32. (a) A 16-ounce package of margarine quarters for $1.29

(b) A 3-pound tub of margarine for $3.29

33. (a) A 10-ounce package of frozen green beans for 59¢

(b) A 16-ounce package of frozen green beans for 89¢

34. (a) An 18-ounce jar of peanut butter for $1.39

(b) A 28-ounce jar of peanut butter for $2.19

35. (a) A 2-liter bottle (67.6 ounces) of soft drink for $1.09

(b) Six 12-ounce cans of soft drink for $1.69

36. (a) A 1-quart container of oil for $1.29

(b) A 2.5-gallon container of oil for $11.20

In Exercises 37–52, solve the proportion. See Example 5.

37. $\dfrac{5}{3} = \dfrac{20}{y}$

38. $\dfrac{9}{x} = \dfrac{18}{5}$

39. $\dfrac{4}{t} = \dfrac{2}{25}$

40. $\dfrac{y}{25} = \dfrac{12}{10}$

41. $\dfrac{5}{x} = \dfrac{3}{2}$

42. $\dfrac{z}{35} = \dfrac{5}{14}$

43. $\dfrac{8}{3} = \dfrac{t}{6}$

44. $\dfrac{12}{7} = \dfrac{6}{x}$

45. $\dfrac{0.5}{0.8} = \dfrac{n}{0.3}$

46. $\dfrac{2}{4.5} = \dfrac{t}{0.5}$

47. $\dfrac{x+1}{5} = \dfrac{3}{10}$

48. $\dfrac{z-3}{8} = \dfrac{3}{16}$

49. $\dfrac{x+6}{3} = \dfrac{x-5}{2}$

50. $\dfrac{x-2}{4} = \dfrac{x+10}{10}$

51. $\dfrac{x+2}{8} = \dfrac{x-1}{3}$

52. $\dfrac{x-4}{5} = \dfrac{x}{6}$

Solving Problems

In Exercises 53–62, express the statement as a ratio in simplest form. (Use the same units of measurement for both quantities.)

53. *Study Hours*   You study 6 hours per day and are in class 3 hours per day. Find the ratio of the number of study hours to class hours.

54. *Income Tax*   You have $16.50 of state tax withheld from your paycheck per week when your gross pay is $750. Find the ratio of tax to gross pay.

55. *Price-Earnings Ratio*   The ratio of the price of a stock to its earnings is called the *price-earnings ratio*. A certain stock sells for $78 per share and earns $6.50 per share. What is the price-earnings ratio of this stock?

56. *Student-Teacher Ratio*   There are 2921 students and 127 faculty members at your school. Find the ratio of the number of students to the number of faculty members.

57. *Compression Ratio*   The *compression ratio* of an engine is the ratio of the expanded volume of gas in one of its cylinders to the compressed volume of gas in the cylinder (see figure). A cylinder in a certain diesel engine has an expanded volume of 345 cubic centimeters and a compressed volume of 17.25 cubic centimeters. What is the compression ratio of this engine?

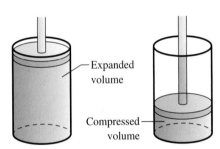

Figure for 57

58. *Turn Ratio*   The *turn ratio* of a transformer is the ratio of the number of turns on the secondary winding to the number of turns on the primary winding (see figure). A transformer has a primary winding with 250 turns and a secondary winding with 750 turns. What is its turn ratio?

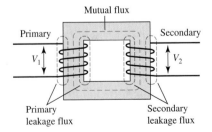

59. *Gear Ratio* The *gear ratio* of two gears is the ratio of the number of teeth on one gear to the number of teeth on the other gear. Find the gear ratio of the larger gear to the smaller gear for the gears in the figure.

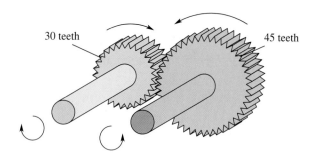

30 teeth   45 teeth

60. *Gear Ratio* On a five-speed bicycle, the ratio of the pedal gear to the axle gear depends on which axle gear is engaged. Use the table to find the gear ratios for the five different gears. For which gear is it easiest to pedal? Why?

Gear	1st	2nd	3rd	4th	5th
Teeth on Pedal Gear	52	52	52	52	52
Teeth on Axle Gear	28	24	20	17	14

61. *Geometry* Find the ratio of the area of the larger pizza to the area of the smaller pizza in the figure. (*Note:* The area of a circle is $A = \pi r^2$.)

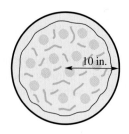

10 in.   7 in.

62. *Specific Gravity* The *specific gravity* of a substance is the ratio of its weight to the weight of an equal volume of water. Kerosene weighs 0.82 grams per cubic centimeter and water weighs 1 gram per cubic centimeter. What is the specific gravity of kerosene?

63. *Gasoline Cost* A car uses 20 gallons of gasoline for a trip of 500 miles. How many gallons would be used on a trip of 400 miles?

64. *Amount of Fuel* A tractor requires 4 gallons of diesel fuel to plow for 90 minutes. How many gallons of fuel would be required to plow for 8 hours?

65. *Building Material* One hundred cement blocks are required to build a 16-foot wall. How many blocks are needed to build a 40-foot wall?

66. *Force on a Spring* A force of 50 pounds stretches a spring 4 inches. How much force is required to stretch the spring 6 inches?

67. *Real Estate Taxes* The tax on a property with an assessed value of $65,000 is $825. Find the tax on a property with an assessed value of $90,000.

68. *Real Estate Taxes* The tax on a property with an assessed value of $65,000 is $1100. Find the tax on a property with an assessed value of $90,000.

69. *Polling Results* In a poll, 624 people from a sample of 1100 indicated they would vote for a certain candidate. How many votes can the candidate expect to receive from 40,000 votes cast?

70. *Quality Control* A quality control engineer found two defective units in a sample of 50. At this rate, what is the expected number of defective units in a shipment of 10,000 units?

71. *Pumping Time* A pump can fill a 750-gallon tank in 35 minutes. How long will it take to fill a 1000-gallon tank with this pump?

72. *Increasing a Recipe* Two cups of flour are required to make one batch of cookies. How many cups are required for $2\frac{1}{2}$ batches?

73. *Amount of Gasoline* The gasoline-to-oil ratio for a two-cycle engine is 40 to 1. How much gasoline is required to produce a mixture that contains one-half pint of oil?

74. *Pounds of Sand* The ratio of cement to sand in an 80-pound bag of dry mix is 1 to 4. Find the number of pounds of sand in the bag. (*Note:* Dry mix is composed of only cement and sand.)

75. *Map Scale* Use the map to approximate the distance between Philadelphia and Pittsburgh.

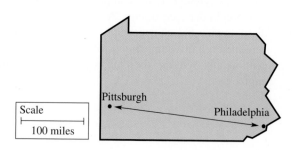

Pittsburgh
Philadelphia

Scale
100 miles

76. *Map Scale*   On a map, $1\frac{1}{2}$ inches represents 40 miles. Estimate the distance between two cities that are 4 inches apart on the map.

Similar Triangles   In Exercises 77 and 78, find the length *x* of the side of the larger triangle. (Assume that the two triangles are similar, and use the fact that corresponding sides of similar triangles are proportional.)

77.

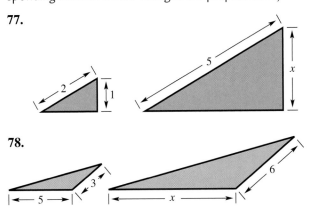

78.

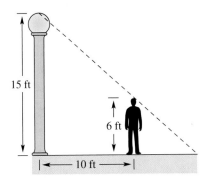

79. *Shadow Length*   In the figure, how long is the man's shadow? (*Hint:* Use similar triangles to create a proportion.)

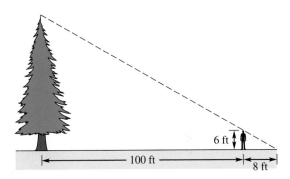

80. *Shadow Length*   A man who is 6 feet tall walks directly toward the tip of the shadow of a tree (see figure). When the man is 100 feet from the tree, he starts forming his own shadow beyond the shadow of the tree. The length of the shadow of the tree beyond this point is 8 feet. Find the height of the tree. (*Hint:* Use similar triangles to create a proportion.)

81. *Resizing a Picture*   You have an 8-by-10-inch photo that must be reduced to a size of 1.6 by 2 inches for the school yearbook. What percent does the photo need to be reduced by in order to fit the allotted space?

82. *Resizing a Picture*   You have a 7-by-5-inch photo of the math club that must be reduced to a size of 5.6 by 4 inches for the school yearbook. What percent does the photo need to be reduced by in order to fit the allotted space?

In Exercises 83–86, use the Consumer Price Index table on page 154 to estimate the price of the item in the indicated year.

83. The 1988 price of a lawn tractor that cost $2875 in 1978

84. The 1993 price of a watch that cost $58 in 1960

85. The 1960 price of a gallon of milk that cost $2.75 in 1996

86. The 1970 price of a coat that cost $225 in 1992

Explaining Concepts

87. Answer part (g) of Motivating the Chapter on page 115.

88. In your own words, describe the term *ratio*.

89. You are told that the ratio of men to women in a class is 2 to 1. Does this information tell you the total number of people in the class? Explain.

90. Explain the following statement. "When setting up a ratio, be sure you are comparing apples to apples and not apples to oranges."

91. In your own words, describe the term *proportion*.

92. Create a proportion problem. Exchange problems with another student and solve the problem you receive.

Mid-Chapter Quiz

Take this quiz as you would take a quiz in class. After you are done, check your work against the answers given in the back of the book.

In Exercises 1–10, solve the equation.

1. $120 - 3y = 0$

2. $10(y - 8) = 0$

3. $3x + 1 = x + 20$

4. $6x + 8 = 8 - 2x$

5. $-10x + \dfrac{2}{3} = \dfrac{7}{3} - 5x$

6. $\dfrac{x}{5} + \dfrac{x}{8} = 1$

7. $\dfrac{9 + x}{3} = 15$

8. $4 - 0.3(1 - x) = 7$

9. $\dfrac{x + 3}{6} = \dfrac{4}{3}$

10. $\dfrac{x + 7}{5} = \dfrac{x + 9}{7}$

In Exercises 11 and 12, solve the equation. Round the solution to two decimal places. In your own words, explain how to check the solution.

11. $32.86 - 10.5x = 11.25$

12. $\dfrac{x}{5.45} + 3.2 = 12.6$

13. What number is 62% of 25?

14. What number is $\frac{1}{2}$% of 8400?

15. 300 is what percent of 150?

16. 145.6 is 32% of what number?

17. The perimeter of a rectangle is 60 meters. Find the measurements of the rectangle if the length is $1\frac{1}{2}$ times the width.

18. You have two jobs. In the first job, you work 40 hours a week and earn $7.50 per hour. In the second job, you earn $6.00 per hour and can work as many hours as you want. If you want to earn $360 a week, how many hours must you work at the second job?

19. A region has an area of 42 square meters. It must be divided into three subregions so that the second has twice the area of the first, and the third has twice the area of the second. Determine the area of each subregion.

20. To get an A in a course, you must have an average of at least 90 points for three tests of 100 points each. For the first two tests, your scores are 84 and 93. What must you score on the third test to earn a 90% average for the course?

21. The price of a television set is approximately 108% of what it was 2 years ago. The current price is $535. What was the approximate price 2 years ago?

22. The figure at the left shows where charitable giving went for the year 1996. What percent of the total giving went to religious organizations?   (Source: *USA Today*)

23. A large round pizza has a radius of $r = 15$ inches and a small round pizza has a radius of $r = 8$ inches. Find the ratio of the area of the large pizza to the area of the small pizza. (*Hint:* The area of a circle is $A = \pi r^2$.)

Where Contributions Went (in billions of dollars)

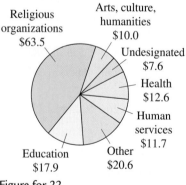

Religious organizations $63.5

Arts, culture, humanities $10.0

Undesignated $7.6

Health $12.6

Human services $11.7

Education $17.9

Other $20.6

Figure for 22

3.5   Geometric and Scientific Applications

Objectives

1 Use a common formula to solve an application problem.

2 Solve a mixture problem involving hidden products.

3 Solve a work-rate problem.

---

1 Use a common formula to solve an application problem.

Using Formulas

Some formulas occur so frequently in problem solving that it is to your benefit to memorize them. For instance, the following formulas for area, perimeter, and volume are often used to create verbal models for word problems. In the geometry formulas below, *A* represents area, *P* represents perimeter, *C* represents circumference, and *V* represents volume.

Study Tip

When solving problems involving perimeter, area, or volume, be sure you list the units of measurement for your answers.

▶ **Common Formulas for Area, Perimeter, and Volume**

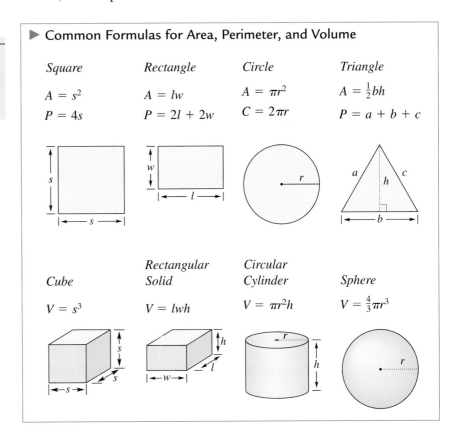

Square

$A = s^2$

$P = 4s$

Rectangle

$A = lw$

$P = 2l + 2w$

Circle

$A = \pi r^2$

$C = 2\pi r$

Triangle

$A = \frac{1}{2}bh$

$P = a + b + c$

Cube

$V = s^3$

Rectangular Solid

$V = lwh$

Circular Cylinder

$V = \pi r^2 h$

Sphere

$V = \frac{4}{3}\pi r^3$

- *Perimeter* is always measured in linear units, such as inches, feet, miles, centimeters, meters, and kilometers.
- *Area* is always measured in square units, such as square inches, square feet, square centimeters, and square meters.
- *Volume* is always measured in cubic units, such as cubic inches, cubic feet, cubic centimeters, and cubic meters.

Example 1 Using a Geometric Formula

A sailboat has a triangular sail with an area of 96 square feet and a base that is 16 feet long, as shown in Figure 3.3. What is the height of the sail?

Solution

Because the sail is triangular, and you are given its area, you should begin with the formula for the area of a triangle.

$$A = \frac{1}{2}bh \qquad \text{Area of a triangle}$$

$$96 = \frac{1}{2}(16)h \qquad \text{Substitute 96 for } A \text{ and 16 for } b.$$

$$96 = 8h \qquad \text{Simplify.}$$

$$12 = h \qquad \text{Divide both sides by 8.}$$

The height of the sail is 12 feet.

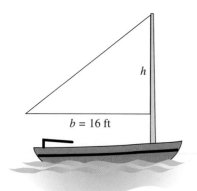

Figure 3.3

In Example 1, notice that b and h are measured in feet. When they are multiplied in the formula $\frac{1}{2}bh$, the resulting area is measured in *square* feet.

$$A = \frac{1}{2}(16 \text{ feet})(12 \text{ feet}) = 96 \text{ feet}^2$$

Note that square feet can be written as feet^2.

Example 2 Using a Geometric Formula

The local municipality is planning to develop the street along which you own a rectangular lot that is 500 feet deep and has an area of 100,000 square feet. To help pay for the new sewer system, each lot owner will be assessed $5.50 per foot of lot frontage.

a. Find the length of the frontage of your lot.

b. How much will you be assessed for the new sewer system?

Solution

a. To solve this problem, it helps to begin by drawing a diagram such as the one shown in Figure 3.4. In the diagram, label the depth of the property as $l = 500$ feet and the unknown frontage as w.

$$A = lw \qquad \text{Area of a rectangle}$$

$$100{,}000 = 500(w) \qquad \text{Substitute 100,000 for } A \text{ and 500 for } l.$$

$$200 = w \qquad \text{Divide both sides by 500 and simplify.}$$

The frontage of the rectangular plot is 200 feet.

b. If each foot of frontage costs $5.50, then your total assessment will be $200(5.50) = \$1100$.

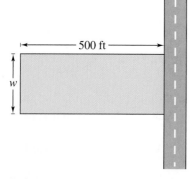

Figure 3.4

▶ Miscellaneous Common Formulas

Temperature: F = degrees Fahrenheit, C = degrees Celsius

$$F = \frac{9}{5}C + 32$$

Simple Interest: I = interest, P = principal, r = interest rate, t = time

$$I = Prt$$

Distance: d = distance traveled, r = rate, t = time

$$d = rt$$

In some applications, it helps to rewrite a common formula by solving for a different variable. For instance, you can obtain a formula for C (degrees Celsius) in terms of F (degrees Fahrenheit) as follows.

$$F = \frac{9}{5}C + 32 \qquad \text{Temperature formula}$$

$$F - 32 = \frac{9}{5}C \qquad \text{Subtract 32 from both sides.}$$

$$\frac{5}{9}(F - 32) = C \qquad \text{Multiply both sides by } \tfrac{5}{9}.$$

$$C = \frac{5}{9}(F - 32) \qquad \text{Formula}$$

Example 3   **Simple Interest**

An amount of \$5000 is deposited in an account paying simple interest. After 6 months, the account has earned \$162.50 in interest. What is the annual interest rate for this account?

Solution

$$I = Prt \qquad \text{Simple interest formula}$$

$$162.50 = 5000(r)\left(\tfrac{1}{2}\right) \qquad \text{Substitute for } I, P, \text{ and } t.$$

$$162.50 = 2500r \qquad \text{Simplify.}$$

$$\frac{162.50}{2500} = r \qquad \text{Divide both sides by 2500.}$$

$$0.065 = r \qquad \text{Simplify.}$$

The annual interest rate is r = 0.065 (or 6.5%). Check this solution in the original statement of the problem.

One of the most familiar rate problems and most often used formulas in real life is the one that relates distance, rate (or speed), and time: $d = rt$. For instance, if you are traveling at a constant (or average) rate of 50 miles per hour for 45 minutes, the total distance traveled is given by

$$\left(50 \, \frac{\text{miles}}{\text{hour}}\right) \cdot \left(\frac{45}{60} \, \text{hour}\right) = 37.5 \text{ miles.}$$

As with all problems involving applications, be sure to check that the units in the model make sense. For instance, in this problem the rate is given in *miles per hour*. Therefore, in order for the solution to be given in *miles*, we must convert the time (from minutes) to *hours*. In the model, you can think of canceling the two "hours," as follows.

$$\left(50 \, \frac{\text{miles}}{\text{hour}}\right) \cdot \left(\frac{45}{60} \, \text{hour}\right) = 37.5 \text{ miles}$$

Example 4   A Distance-Rate-Time Problem

You can jog at an average rate of 8 kilometers per hour. How long will it take you to jog 14 kilometers?

Solution

Verbal Model: Distance $=$ Rate $\cdot$ Time

Labels:
Distance $= 14$ (kilometers)
Rate $= 8$ (kilometers per hour)
Time $= t$ (hours)

Equation: $14 = 8(t)$

$$\frac{14}{8} = t$$

$$1.75 = t$$

It will take you 1.75 hours (or 1 hour and 45 minutes). Check this in the original statement of the problem.

If you are having trouble solving a distance-rate-time problem, consider making a table such as that shown below for Example 4.

Distance $=$ Rate $\cdot$ Time

Rate (km/hr)	8	8	8	8	8	8	8	8
Time (hours)	0.25	0.50	0.75	1.00	1.25	1.50	1.75	2.00
Distance (kilometers)	2	4	6	8	10	12	14	16

2 Solve a mixture problem involving hidden products.

Solving Mixture Problems

Many real-world problems involve combinations of two or more quantities that make up a new or different quantity. Such problems are called **mixture problems.** They are usually composed of the sum of two or more "hidden products" that involve *rate factors.* Here is the generic form of the verbal model for mixture problems.

$$\underbrace{\boxed{\begin{array}{c}\text{First}\\\text{rate}\end{array}} \cdot \boxed{\text{Amount}}}_{\text{First component}} + \underbrace{\boxed{\begin{array}{c}\text{Second}\\\text{rate}\end{array}} \cdot \boxed{\text{Amount}}}_{\text{Second component}} = \underbrace{\boxed{\begin{array}{c}\text{Final}\\\text{rate}\end{array}} \cdot \boxed{\begin{array}{c}\text{Final}\\\text{amount}\end{array}}}_{\text{Final mixture}}$$

The rate factors are usually expressed as *percents* or *percent of measure* such as dollars per pound, jobs per hour, or gallons per minute.

Example 5   A Nut Mixture Problem

A grocer wants to mix cashew nuts worth $7 per pound with 15 pounds of peanuts worth $2.50 per pound. To obtain a nut mixture worth $4 per pound, how many pounds of cashews are needed? How many pounds of mixed nuts will be produced for the grocer to sell?

Solution

In this problem, the rates are the *unit prices* for the nuts.

Verbal Model: $\boxed{\begin{array}{c}\text{Total cost}\\\text{of cashews}\end{array}} + \boxed{\begin{array}{c}\text{Total cost}\\\text{of peanuts}\end{array}} = \boxed{\begin{array}{c}\text{Total cost of}\\\text{mixed nuts}\end{array}}$

Labels:
    Unit price of cashews $= 7$ (dollars per pound)
    Unit price of peanuts $= 2.5$ (dollars per pound)
    Unit price of mixed nuts $= 4$ (dollars per pound)
    Amount of cashews $= x$ (pounds)
    Amount of peanuts $= 15$ (pounds)
    Amount of mixed nuts $= x + 15$ (pounds)

Equation:
$$7(x) + 2.5(15) = 4(x + 15)$$
$$7x + 37.5 = 4x + 60$$
$$3x = 22.5$$
$$x = \frac{22.5}{3}$$
$$x = 7.5$$

The grocer needs 7.5 pounds of cashews. This will result in $7.5 + 15$ or 22.5 pounds of mixed nuts. You can check these results as follows.

$$\overbrace{(\$7.00/\text{lb})(7.5 \text{ lb})}^{\text{Cashews}} + \overbrace{(\$2.50/\text{lb})(15 \text{ lb})}^{\text{Peanuts}} = \overbrace{(\$4.00/\text{lb})(22.5 \text{ lb})}^{\text{Mixed Nuts}}$$

$$\$52.50 + \$37.50 = \$90.00$$

$$\$90.00 = \$90.00 \qquad \text{Solution checks.} \checkmark$$

In Chapter 7, similar mixture problems
will be solved using a system of linear
equations.

| Example 6 | A Solution Mixture Problem |

A pharmacist needs to strengthen a 15% alcohol solution so that it contains 32% alcohol. How much pure alcohol should be added to 100 milliliters of the 15% solution? (See Figure 3.5.)

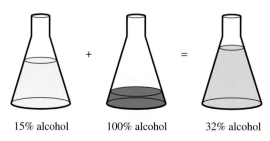

15% alcohol   100% alcohol   32% alcohol

Figure 3.5

Solution

In this problem, the rates are the alcohol *percents* of the solutions.

Verbal Model:

| Amount of alcohol in original solution | + | Amount of alcohol in pure solution | = | Amount of alcohol in final solution |

Labels:

Alcohol percent of original solution = 0.15	(% in decimal form)
Alcohol amount of original solution = 100	(milliliters)
Alcohol percent of pure solution = 1.00	(% in decimal form)
Alcohol amount of pure solution = x	(milliliters)
Alcohol percent of final solution = 0.32	(% in decimal form)
Alcohol amount of final solution = $x + 100$	(milliliters)

Equation:

$$0.15(100) + 1.00(x) = 0.32(100 + x)$$

$$15 + x = 32 + 0.32x$$

$$0.68x = 17$$

$$x = \frac{17}{0.68}$$

$$x = 25 \text{ ml}$$

The pharmacist should add 25 milliliters of pure alcohol to the original solution. You can check this in the original statement of the problem as follows.

$$\overbrace{0.15(100)}^{\text{Original}} + \overbrace{1.00(25)}^{\text{Pure}} = \overbrace{0.32(125)}^{\text{Final}}$$

$$15 + 25 = 40$$

$$40 = 40 \qquad \text{Solution checks.} \checkmark$$

Remember that mixture problems are sums of two or more hidden products that involve different rates. Watch for such problems in the exercises.

3 Solve a work-rate problem.

Solving Work-Rate Problems

Although not generally referred to as such, most **work-rate problems** are actually *mixture* problems because they involve two or more rates. In work-rate problems, the work rate is the *reciprocal* of the time needed to do the entire job. For instance, if it takes 7 hours to complete a job, the per-hour work rate is

$$\frac{1}{7} \text{ job per hour.}$$

Similarly, if it takes $4\frac{1}{2}$ minutes to complete a job, the per-minute rate is

$$\frac{1}{4\frac{1}{2}} = \frac{1}{\frac{9}{2}} = \frac{2}{9} \text{ job per minute.}$$

Example 7   A Work-Rate Problem

Consider two machines in a paper manufacturing plant. Machine 1 can produce 2000 pounds of paper in 3 hours. Machine 2 is newer and can produce 2000 pounds of paper in $2\frac{1}{2}$ hours. How long will it take the two machines working together to produce 2000 pounds of paper?

Solution

Remind students that the work rate is the reciprocal of the time required to do the entire job. Machine 1, which requires 3 hours, has a work rate of $\frac{1}{3}$ job per hour. Machine 2, which requires $2\frac{1}{2}$ hours, has a work rate that is the reciprocal of $2\frac{1}{2}$; this work rate is

$$\frac{1}{2\frac{1}{2}} = \frac{1}{\frac{5}{2}} = \frac{2}{5} \text{ job per hour.}$$

Verbal Model:

$$\boxed{\text{Work done}} = \boxed{\text{Portion done by machine 1}} + \boxed{\text{Portion done by machine 2}}$$

Labels:

Work done = 1	(job)
Rate (machine 1) = $\frac{1}{3}$	(job per hour)
Time (machine 1) = t	(hours)
Rate (machine 2) = $\frac{2}{5}$	(job per hour)
Time (machine 2) = t	(hours)

Equation:

$$1 = \left(\frac{1}{3}\right)(t) + \left(\frac{2}{5}\right)(t)$$

$$1 = \left(\frac{1}{3} + \frac{2}{5}\right)(t)$$

$$1 = \left(\frac{11}{15}\right)(t)$$

$$\frac{15}{11} = t$$

It would take $\frac{15}{11}$ hours (or about 1.36 hours) for the machines to complete the job working together. Check this solution in the original statement of the problem.

Note in Example 7 that the "2000 pounds" of paper was unnecessary information. We simply represented the 2000 pounds as "one complete job." This unnecessary information was a red herring.

Example 8 A Fluid-Rate Problem

An above-ground swimming pool has a capacity of 15,600 gallons, as shown in Figure 3.6. A drain pipe can empty the pool in $6\frac{1}{2}$ hours. At what rate (in gallons per minute) does the water flow through the drain pipe?

Solution

To begin, change the time from hours to minutes by multiplying by 60. That is, $6\frac{1}{2}$ hours is equal to $(6.5)(60)$ or 390 minutes.

Verbal Model: $\dfrac{\text{Volume}}{\text{of pool}} = \boxed{\text{Rate}} \cdot \boxed{\text{Time}}$

Labels: Volume = 15,600 (gallons)
Rate = r (gallons per minute)
Time = 390 (minutes)

Equation: $15,600 = r(390)$

$$\frac{15,600}{390} = r$$

$$40 = r$$

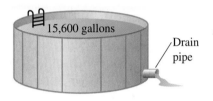

15,600 gallons

Drain pipe

Figure 3.6

The water is flowing through the drain pipe at the rate of 40 gallons per minute. You can check this as follows.

$$\left(\frac{40 \text{ gallons}}{\text{minute}}\right)(390 \text{ minutes}) = 15,600 \text{ gallons}$$

Discussing the Concept   **Creating a Formula**

You are to design a package from a rectangular piece of material measuring 9 inches by 12 inches by cutting out a square from each corner and folding up the sides, as shown in the figure. Calculate the volumes of the different boxes formed by cutting out 1-inch, 2-inch, and 3-inch squares. Create a formula for the volume of a box made in this manner.

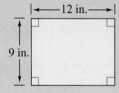

12 in.

9 in.

3.5   Exercises

Integrated Review   *Concepts, Skills, and Problem Solving*

Keep mathematically in shape by doing these exercises *before* the problems of this section.

Properties and Definitions

1. If n is an integer, distinguish between $2n$ and $2n + 1$.

2. Demonstrate the Addition Property of Equality for the equation

   $2x - 3 = 10$.

Simplifying Expressions

In Exercises 3–10, simplify the expression.

3. $(-3.5y^2)(8y)$

4. $(-3x^2)^4$

5. $\left(\dfrac{24u}{15}\right)\left(\dfrac{25u^2}{6}\right)$

6. $12\left(\dfrac{3y}{18}\right)$

7. $5x(2 - x) + 3x$

8. $3t - 4(2t - 8)$

9. $3(v - 4) + 7(v - 4)$

10. $5[6 - 2(x - 3)]$

Problem Solving

11. *Sales Tax*   You buy a computer for $2750 and your total bill is $2915. Find the sales tax rate.

12. *Comparing Prices*   A mail-order catalog lists an area rug for $109.95, plus a shipping charge of $14.25. A local store has a sale on the same rug with 20% off a list price of $139.99. Which is the better bargain?

Developing Skills

In Exercises 1–16, solve for the specified variable.

1. Solve for h: $A = \frac{1}{2}bh$

2. Solve for L: $P = 2L + 2W$

3. Solve for R: $E = IR$

4. Solve for r: $C = 2\pi r$

5. Solve for l: $V = lwh$

6. Solve for h: $V = \pi r^2 h$

7. Solve for r: $A = P + Prt$

8. Solve for L: $S = L - RL$

9. Solve for C: $S = C + RC$

10. Solve for P: $A = P\left(1 + \dfrac{r}{n}\right)^{nt}$

11. Solve for b: $A = \frac{1}{2}(a + b)h$

12. Solve for m_2: $F = \alpha\dfrac{m_1 m_2}{r^2}$

13. Solve for r: $V = \frac{1}{3}\pi h^2(3r - h)$

14. Solve for b: $V = \frac{4}{3}\pi a^2 b$

15. Solve for a: $h = v_0 t + \frac{1}{2}at^2$

16. Solve for a: $S = \dfrac{n}{2}[2a + (n - 1)d]$

In Exercises 17 and 18, evaluate the formula for the specified values of the variables. (List the *units* of the answer.)

17. *Volume of a Right Circular Cylinder:* $V = \pi r^2 h$
    $r = 5$ meters, $h = 4$ meters

18. *Electric Power:* $I = \dfrac{P}{V}$

    $P = 1500$ watts, $V = 110$ volts

In Exercises 19–24, find the missing distance, rate, or time. See Example 4.

	Distance, d	Rate, r	Time, t
19.		55 mi/hr	3 hr
20.		32 ft/sec	10 sec
21.	500 km	90 km/hr	
22.	128 ft	16 ft/sec	
23.	5280 ft		$\frac{5}{2}$ sec
24.	432 mi		9 hr

Solving Problems

In Exercises 25–32, use a common geometric formula to solve the problem. See Examples 1 and 2.

25. *Geometry* Each room in the floor plan of a house is square (see figure). The perimeter of the bathroom is 32 feet. The perimeter of the kitchen is 80 feet. Find the area of the living room.

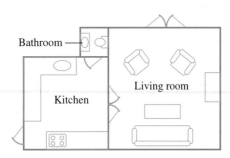

26. *Geometry* A rectangle has a perimeter of 10 feet and a width of 2 feet. Find the length of the rectangle.

27. *Geometry* A triangle has an area of 48 square meters and a height of 12 meters. Find the length of the base.

28. *Geometry* The perimeter of a square is 48 feet. Find its area.

29. *Geometry* The circumference of the wheel in the figure is 30π inches. Find the diameter of the wheel.

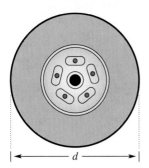

30. *Geometry* A circle has a circumference of 15 meters. What is the radius of the circle? Round your result to two decimal places.

31. *Geometry* A circle has a circumference of 25 meters. Find the radius and area of the circle. Round your results to two decimal places.

32. *Geometry* The volume of a right circular cylinder is $V = \pi r^2 h$. Find the volume of a right circular cylinder that has a radius of 2 meters and a height of 3 meters. List the units of measurement for your result.

Geometry In Exercises 33–36, use the closed rectangular box shown in the figure to answer the question.

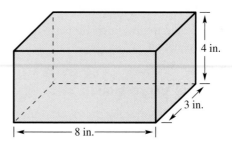

33. Find the area of the base.

34. Find the perimeter of the base.

35. Find the volume of the box.

36. Find the surface area of the box. (*Note:* This is the combined area of the six surfaces.)

Simple Interest In Exercises 37–46, use the formula for simple interest. See Example 3.

37. Find the interest on a $1000 bond paying an annual rate of 9% for 6 years.

38. A $1000 corporate bond pays an annual rate of $7\frac{1}{2}\%$. Find the interest on the bond if it matures in $3\frac{1}{2}$ years.

39. You borrow $15,000 for $\frac{1}{2}$ year. You promise to pay back the principal and the interest in one lump sum. The annual interest rate is 13%. What is your payment?

40. You have a balance of $650 on your credit card that you cannot pay this month. The annual interest rate on an unpaid balance is 19%. Find the lump sum of principal and interest due in 1 month.

41. Find the annual rate on a savings account that earns $110 interest in 1 year on a principal of $1000.

42. Find the annual interest rate on a certificate of deposit that earned $128.98 interest in 1 year on a principal of $1500.

43. Find the principal required to earn $408 interest in 4 years, if the annual interest rate is $8\frac{1}{2}\%$.

44. How long must $1000 be invested at an annual interest rate of $7\frac{1}{2}\%$ to earn $225 interest?

45. *Mixture Problem*   Six thousand dollars is divided between two investments earning 7% and 9% simple interest. (There is more risk in the 9% fund.) Your goal is to have a total annual interest income of $500. What is the smallest amount you can invest at 9% in order to meet your objective?

46. *Mixture Problem*   An inheritance of $30,000 is divided into two investments earning 8.5% and 10% simple interest, respectively. (There is more risk in the 10% fund.) Your goal is to have a total annual interest income of $2700. What is the smallest amount you can invest at 10% in order to meet your objective?

In Exercises 47–56, use the distance formula to solve the problem. See Example 4.

47. *Space Shuttle Time*   The speed of the space shuttle is 17,000 miles per hour (see figure). How long will it take the shuttle to travel a distance of 3000 miles?

48. *Speed of Light*   The speed of light is 670,616,625.6 miles per hour, and the distance between the earth and the sun is 93,000,000 miles. How long does it take light from the sun to reach the earth?

49. *Distance*   Two cars start at a given point and travel in the same direction at average speeds of 45 miles per hour and 52 miles per hour (see figure). How far apart will they be in 4 hours?

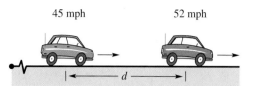

45 mph   52 mph

Figure for 49

50. *Distance*   Two planes leave an airport at approximately the same time and fly in opposite directions (see figure). Their speeds are 510 miles per hour and 600 miles per hour. How far apart will the planes be after $1\frac{1}{2}$ hours?

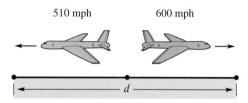

510 mph   600 mph

51. *Speed*   Determine the average speed of an experimental plane that can travel 3000 miles in 2.6 hours.

52. *Speed*   Determine the average speed of an Olympic runner who completes the 10,000-meter race in 27 minutes and 45 seconds.

53. *Time*   Two cars start at the same point and travel in the same direction at average speeds of 40 miles per hour and 55 miles per hour. How much time must elapse before the two cars are 5 miles apart?

54. *Time*   Suppose that on the first part of a 225-mile automobile trip you averaged 55 miles per hour. On the last part of the trip you averaged 48 miles per hour because of increased traffic congestion. The total trip took 4 hours and 15 minutes. Find the amount of time at each speed.

55. *Think About It*   A truck traveled at an average speed of 60 miles per hour on a 200-mile trip to pick up a load of freight. On the return trip, with the truck fully loaded, the average speed was 40 miles per hour.

(a) Guess the average speed for the round trip.

(b) Calculate the average speed for the round trip. Is the result the same as in part (a)? Explain.

56. *Time* A jogger leaves a given point on a fitness trail running at a rate of 4 miles per hour. Ten minutes later a second jogger leaves from the same location running at 5 miles per hour. How long will it take the second runner to overtake the first? How far will each have run at that point?

In Exercises 57–60, determine the numbers of units of solutions 1 and 2 required to obtain the desired amount and percent concentration of the final solution. See Example 6.

	Concentration Solution 1	Concentration Solution 2	Concentration Final Solution	Amount of Final Solution
57.	10%	30%	25%	100 gal
58.	25%	50%	30%	5 L
59.	15%	45%	30%	10 qt
60.	70%	90%	75%	25 gal

61. *Number of Stamps* You have 100 stamps that have a total value of $27.80. Some of the stamps are worth 20¢ each and the others are worth 33¢ each. How many stamps of each type do you have?

62. *Number of Stamps* You have 20 stamps that have a total value of $6.08. Some of the stamps are worth 20¢ each and others are worth 33¢ each. How many stamps of each type do you have?

63. *Number of Coins* A person has 20 coins in nickels and dimes with a combined value of $1.60. Determine the number of coins of each type.

64. *Number of Coins* A person has 50 coins in dimes and quarters with a combined value of $7.70. Determine the number of coins of each type.

65. *Nut Mixture* A grocer mixes two kinds of nuts that cost $2.49 and $3.89 per pound to make 100 pounds of a mixture that costs $3.47 per pound. How many pounds of each kind of nut are put into the mixture? See Example 5.

66. *Flower Order* A floral shop receives an order for flowers that totals $384. The prices per dozen for the roses and carnations are $18 and $12, respectively. The order contains twice as many roses as carnations. How many of each type of flower are in the order?

67. *Antifreeze* The cooling system in a truck contains 4 gallons of coolant that is 30% antifreeze. How much must be withdrawn and replaced with 100% antifreeze to bring the coolant in the system to 50% antifreeze?

68. *Ticket Sales* Ticket sales for a play total $1700. The number of tickets sold to adults is three times the number sold to children. The prices of the tickets for adults and children are $5 and $2, respectively. How many of each type were sold?

69. *Interpreting a Table* An agricultural corporation must purchase 100 tons of cattle feed. The feed is to be a mixture of soybeans, which cost $200 per ton, and corn, which costs $125 per ton. Complete the following table, where x is the number of tons of corn in the mixture.

Corn, x	Soybeans, $100 - x$	Price per ton of the mixture
0		
20		
40		
60		
80		
100		

(a) How does an increase in the number of tons of corn affect the number of tons of soybeans in the mixture?

(b) How does an increase in the number of tons of corn affect the price per ton of the mixture?

(c) If there were equal weights of corn and soybeans in the mixture, how would the price of the mixture relate to the price of each component?

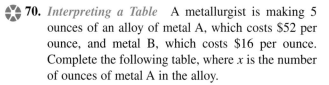 **70.** *Interpreting a Table*   A metallurgist is making 5 ounces of an alloy of metal A, which costs $52 per ounce, and metal B, which costs $16 per ounce. Complete the following table, where x is the number of ounces of metal A in the alloy.

Metal A, x	Metal B, $5 - x$	Price per ounce of the alloy
0		
1		
2		
3		
4		
5		

(a) How does an increase in the number of ounces of metal A in the alloy affect the number of ounces of metal B in the alloy?

(b) How does an increase in the number of ounces of metal A in the alloy affect the price of the alloy?

(c) If there were equal amounts of metal A and metal B in the alloy, how would the price of the alloy relate to the price of each of the components?

71. *Work Rate*   You can mow a lawn in 2 hours using a riding mower, and in 3 hours using a push mower. Using both machines together, how long will it take you and a friend to mow the lawn? See Example 7.

72. *Work Rate*   One person can complete a typing project in 6 hours, and another can complete the same project in 8 hours. If they both work on the project, in how many hours can it be completed?

73. *Work Rate*   One worker can complete a task in h hours while a second can complete the task in $3h$ hours. Show that by working together they can complete the task in $t = \frac{3}{4}h$ hours.

74. *Age Problem*   Your age is three times that of one of your cousins. What is the age of your cousin if your combined ages total 32?

75. *Age Problem*   A mother was 30 years old when her son was born. How old will the son be when his age is $\frac{1}{3}$ his mother's age?

76. *Age Problem*   The difference in age between a father and daughter is 32 years. Determine the age of the father when his age is twice that of his daughter.

77. *Poll Results*   One thousand people were surveyed in an opinion poll. Candidates A and B received approximately the same number of votes. Candidate C received twice as many votes as each of the other two candidates. How many votes did each candidate receive?

78. *Poll Results*   One thousand people were surveyed in an opinion poll. The numbers of votes for candidates A, B, and C had ratios 5 to 3 to 2, respectively. How many people voted for each candidate?

Explaining Concepts

79. In your own words, describe the units of measure used for perimeter, area, and volume. Give some examples of each.

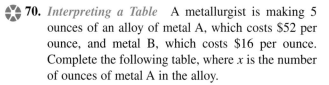 **80.** If the height of a triangle is doubled, does the area of the triangle double? Explain.

81. If the radius of a circle is doubled, does its circumference double? Does its area double? Explain.

82. It takes you 4 hours to drive 180 miles. Explain how to use mental math to find your average speed. Then explain how your method is related to the formula $d = rt$.

83. It takes you 5 hours to complete a job. What portion do you complete each hour?

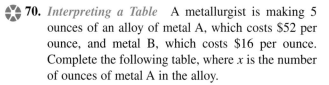 **84.** Create a mixture problem. Exchange problems with another student and solve the problem you receive.

3.6   Linear Inequalities

Objectives

1 Graph the solution set of an inequality on the real number line.

2 Become familiar with the properties of inequalities.

3 Solve a linear inequality and graph its solution set.

4 Solve a compound inequality and graph its solution set.

5 Translate a verbal statement into a linear inequality and solve the application problem.

---

1 Graph the solution set of an inequality on the real number line.

Remind students that the following pairs of inequalities are equivalent.

$$x < 7 \quad \text{and} \quad 7 > x$$
$$b > -4 \quad \text{and} \quad -4 < b$$
$$c \geq 9 \quad \text{and} \quad 9 \leq c$$
$$-3 \leq y \leq 5 \quad \text{and} \quad 5 \geq y \geq -3$$

Inequalities and Their Graphs

In this section you will study **algebraic inequalities,** which are inequalities that contain one or more variable terms. Here are some examples.

$$x \leq 3, \quad x \geq -2, \quad x - 5 < 2, \quad \text{and} \quad 5x - 7 < 3x + 9$$

Each of these inequalities is a **linear inequality** in the variable x because the (implied) exponent of x is 1.

As with an equation, you can **solve an inequality** in the variable x by finding all values of x for which the inequality is true. Such values are **solutions** and are said to **satisfy** the inequality. The **solution set** of an inequality is the set of all real numbers that are solutions of the inequality.

Often, the solution set of an inequality will consist of infinitely many real numbers. To get a visual image of the solution set, it is helpful to sketch its **graph** on the real number line. For instance, the graph of the solution set of $x < 2$ consists of all points on the real number line that are to the left of 2. A parenthesis is used to *exclude* an endpoint from the solution interval. A square bracket is used to *include* an endpoint in the solution interval. This is illustrated in the next example.

Example 1   Graphs of Inequalities

Inequality	*Graph of Solution Set*	*Verbal Description*
a. $x < 2$		x is less than 2.
b. $x \geq -2$		x is greater than or equal to -2.
c. $-1 \leq x \leq 2$		x is greater than or equal to -1 *and* less than or equal to 2.
d. $2 \leq x < 5$		x is greater than or equal to 2 *and* less than 5.
e. $-3 < x \leq -1$		x is greater than -3 *and* less than or equal to -1.

2 Become familiar with the properties of inequalities.

Properties of Inequalities

The procedures for solving linear inequalities in one variable are much like those for solving linear equations. To isolate the variable, you can use the **properties of inequalities.** These properties are similar to the properties of equality, but there are two important exceptions. *When both sides of an inequality are multiplied or divided by a negative number, the direction of the inequality symbol must be reversed.* Here is an example.

$$-2 < 5 \qquad \text{Original inequality}$$

$$(-3)(-2) > (-3)(5) \qquad \text{Multiply both sides by } -3 \text{ and reverse inequality.}$$

$$6 > -15 \qquad \text{Simplify.}$$

Two inequalities that have the same solution set are called **equivalent.** The following list describes operations that can be used to create equivalent inequalities.

▶ Properties of Inequalities

Let a, b, and c be real numbers, variables, or algebraic expressions.

Property	*Verbal and Algebraic Descriptions*
Addition:	Add the same quantity to both sides.
	If $a < b$, then $a + c < b + c$.
Subtraction:	Subtract the same quantity from both sides.
	If $a < b$, then $a - c < b - c$.
Multiplication:	Multiply both sides by a *positive* quantity.
	If $a < b$ and c is positive, then $ac < bc$.
	Multiply both sides by a *negative* quantity and reverse the inequality symbol.
	If $a < b$ and c is negative, then $ac > bc$.
Division:	Divide both sides by a *positive* quantity.
	If $a < b$ and c is positive, then $\dfrac{a}{c} < \dfrac{b}{c}$.
	Divide both sides by a *negative* quantity and reverse the inequality symbol.
	If $a < b$ and c is negative, then $\dfrac{a}{c} > \dfrac{b}{c}$.
Transitive:	If $a < b$ and $b < c$, then $a < c$.

Each of the properties above is true if the symbol $<$ is replaced by $\leq$ and the symbol $>$ is replaced by $\geq$. Moreover, the letters a, b, and c can be real numbers, variables, or algebraic expressions. Note that you cannot multiply or divide both sides of an inequality by zero.

Technology: Tip

Linear inequalities can be graphed using a graphing utility. The inequality $x > -2$ is shown in the graph below. Notice that the graph appears above the x-axis. Consult the user's manual of your graphing utility for directions.

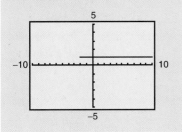

3 Solve a linear inequality and graph its solution set.

Solving Inequalities

The solution set of a linear inequality can be written in set notation. For the solution $x > 1$, the set notation is $\{x \mid x > 1\}$ and is read "the set of all x such that x is greater than 1."

In Examples 4 and 5, pay special attention to the steps in which the inequality symbol is reversed. Remember that when you multiply or divide an inequality by a negative number, you must reverse the inequality symbol.

Study Tip

Checking the solution set of an inequality is not as simple as checking the solution set of an equation. (There are usually too many x-values to substitute back into the original inequality.) You can, however, get an indication of the validity of a solution set by substituting a few convenient values of x. For instance, in Example 2, the solution of $x + 5 < 8$ was found to be $x < 3$. Try checking that $x = 0$ satisfies the original inequality, whereas $x = 4$ does not.

Example 2 Solving a Linear Inequality

Solve and graph the inequality $x + 5 < 8$.

Solution

$x + 5 < 8$	Original inequality
$x + 5 - 5 < 8 - 5$	Subtract 5 from both sides.
$x < 3$	Solution set

The solution set is $x < 3$ or, in set notation, $\{x \mid x < 3\}$. The graph of the solution set is shown in Figure 3.7.

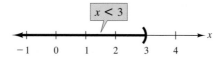

$x < 3$

Figure 3.7 *All real numbers that are less than 3*

Ask students to compare the solving of this inequality with the solving of the equation $3y - 1 = -7$.

Example 3 Solving a Linear Inequality

Solve and graph the inequality $3y - 1 \le -7$.

Solution

$3y - 1 \le -7$	Original inequality
$3y - 1 + 1 \le -7 + 1$	Add 1 to both sides.
$3y \le -6$	Combine like terms.
$\dfrac{3y}{3} \le \dfrac{-6}{3}$	Divide both sides by (positive) 3.
$y \le -2$	Solution set

The solution set is $y \le -2$ or, in set notation, $\{y \mid y \le -2\}$. The graph of the solution set is shown in Figure 3.8.

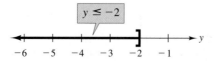

$y \le -2$

Figure 3.8 *All real numbers that are less than or equal to -2*

Example 4　Solving a Linear Inequality

Solve and graph the inequality $12 - 2x > 10$.

Solution

Forgetting to reverse the inequality symbol is a common student error in solving inequalities.

$$12 - 2x > 10 \qquad \text{Original inequality}$$

$$12 - 12 - 2x > 10 - 12 \qquad \text{Subtract 12 from both sides.}$$

$$-2x > -2 \qquad \text{Combine like terms.}$$

$$\frac{-2x}{-2} < \frac{-2}{-2} \qquad \text{Divide both sides by } -2 \text{ and reverse inequality.}$$

$$x < 1 \qquad \text{Solution set}$$

The solution set is $x < 1$ or, in set notation, $\{x \mid x < 1\}$. The graph of the solution set is shown in Figure 3.9.

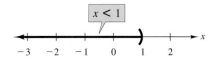

Figure 3.9　*All real numbers that are less than 1*

Example 5　Solving a Linear Inequality

Solve and graph the inequality $1 - \dfrac{3x}{2} \geq x - 4$.

Solution

$$1 - \frac{3x}{2} \geq x - 4 \qquad \text{Original inequality}$$

$$2 - 3x \geq 2x - 8 \qquad \text{Multiply both sides by 2.}$$

$$-3x \geq 2x - 10 \qquad \text{Subtract 2 from both sides.}$$

$$-5x \geq -10 \qquad \text{Subtract } 2x \text{ from both sides.}$$

$$x \leq 2 \qquad \text{Divide both sides by } -5 \text{ and reverse inequality.}$$

The solution set is $x \leq 2$ or, in set notation, $\{x \mid x \leq 2\}$. The graph of the solution set is shown in Figure 3.10.

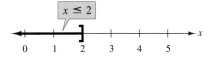

Figure 3.10　*All real numbers that are less than or equal to 2*

4 Solve a compound inequality and graph its solution set.

Solving a Compound Inequality

Two inequalities joined by the word *and* or *or* constitute a **compound inequality.** When the two inequalities are joined by the word *and*, the solution set consists of all real numbers that satisfy *both* inequalities. The solution set for the compound inequality

$$x \geq -2 \quad \text{and} \quad x \leq 3 \qquad \text{Compound inequality}$$

is all real numbers greater than or equal to -2 *and* less than or equal to 3. This compound inequality can be written more simply as the **double inequality**

$$-2 \leq x \leq 3. \qquad \text{Double inequality}$$

The graph of the solution set is shown in Figure 3.11.

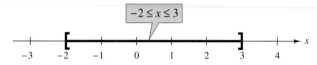

Figure 3.11

Study Tip

Compound inequalities formed by the word *and* are called **conjunctive** and they are the only kind that have the potential to form a double inequality. Compound inequalities joined by the word *or* are called **disjunctive** and they cannot be reformed into double inequalities.

When the two inequalities are joined by the word *or*, the solution set consists of all real numbers that satisfy *either* inequality. The solution set for the compound inequality

$$x < -1 \quad \text{or} \quad x \geq 4 \qquad \text{Compound inequality}$$

is all real numbers less than -1 *or* greater than or equal to 4. The graph of the solution set is shown in Figure 3.12.

Figure 3.12

Example 6   Solving a Double Inequality

Solve the compound inequality $5 < 2x \leq 8$.

Solution

$$5 < 2x \leq 8 \qquad \text{Original inequality}$$

$$\frac{5}{2} < \frac{2}{2}x \leq \frac{8}{2} \qquad \text{Divide all parts by 2.}$$

$$\frac{5}{2} < x \leq 4 \qquad \text{Solution set}$$

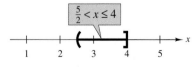

Figure 3.13   *All real numbers that are greater than $\frac{5}{2}$ and less than or equal to 4*

The solution set is $\frac{5}{2} < x \leq 4$ or, in set notation, $\{x \mid \frac{5}{2} < x \leq 4\}$. The graph of the solution set is shown in Figure 3.13.

Compound inequalities can be written using *set notation.* In set notation, the word *and* is represented by the symbol ∩, which is read as **intersection.** The word *or* is represented by the symbol ∪, which is read as **union.** A graphical representation is shown in Figure 3.14.

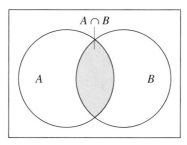
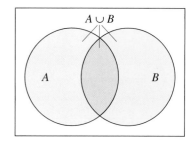

Intersection of two sets   *Union of two sets*
Figure 3.14

If *A* and *B* are sets, then *x* is in $A \cap B$ if it is in both *A and B.* Similarly, *x* is in $A \cup B$ if it is in *A or B*, or possibly in both.

Example 7   Writing a Compound Inequality Using Union

A solution set is shown on the number line in Figure 3.15.

Figure 3.15

a. Write the solution set as a compound inequality.

b. Write the solution set using set notation and union.

Solution

a. As a compound inequality, you can write the solution set as $x \le -2 \ or \ x > 1$.

b. Using set notation, you can write the left interval as $A = \{x \mid x \le -2\}$ and the right interval as $B = \{x \mid x > 1\}$. So, using the union symbol, the entire solution set can be written as $A \cup B$.

Example 8   Writing a Compound Inequality Using Intersection

Write the compound inequality $1 \le x \le 5$ using set notation and intersection.

Solution

Consider the two sets $A = \{x \mid x \le 5\}$ and $B = \{x \mid x \ge 1\}$. These two sets overlap, as shown on the number line in Figure 3.16. The compound inequality $1 \le x \le 5$ consists of all numbers that are in $x \le 5$ *and* $x \ge 1$, which means that it can be written as $A \cap B$.

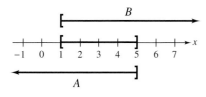

Figure 3.16

Example 9   Solving a Conjunctive Inequality

Solve the compound inequality $-3 \le 6x - 1$ and $6x - 1 < 3$.

Solution

Begin by rewriting the compound inequality as $-3 \le 6x - 1 < 3$.

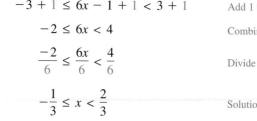

$-3 \le 6x - 1 < 3$	Double inequality
$-3 + 1 \le 6x - 1 + 1 < 3 + 1$	Add 1 to all three parts.
$-2 \le 6x < 4$	Combine like terms.
$\dfrac{-2}{6} \le \dfrac{6x}{6} < \dfrac{4}{6}$	Divide each part by 6.
$-\dfrac{1}{3} \le x < \dfrac{2}{3}$	Solution set

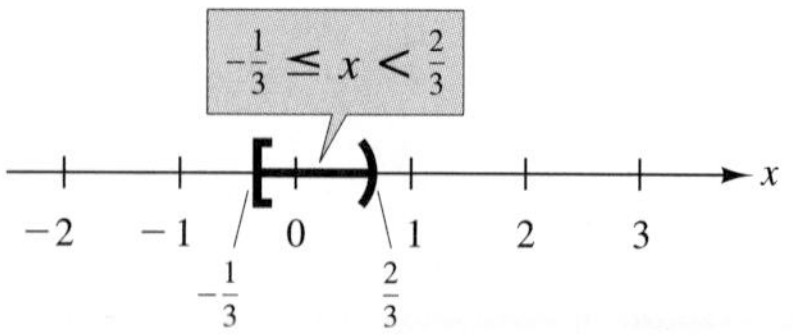

Figure 3.17 *All real numbers that are greater than or equal to $-\frac{1}{3}$ and less than $\frac{2}{3}$*

The solution set is $-\frac{1}{3} \le x < \frac{2}{3}$ or, in set notation, $\{x \mid -\frac{1}{3} \le x < \frac{2}{3}\}$. The graph of the solution set is shown in Figure 3.17.

The double inequality in Example 9 could have been solved in two parts as follows.

$$-3 \le 6x - 1 \qquad \text{and} \qquad 6x - 1 < 3$$
$$-2 \le 6x \qquad\qquad\qquad 6x < 4$$
$$-\frac{1}{3} \le x \qquad\qquad\qquad x < \frac{2}{3}$$

The solution set consists of all real numbers that satisfy *both* inequalities. In other words, the solution set is the set of all values of x for which $-\frac{1}{3} \le x < \frac{2}{3}$.

Example 10   Solving a Disjunctive Inequality

Solve the compound inequality

$$-2x + 3 < -5 \quad \text{or} \quad -2x + 3 > 5.$$

Solution

$-2x + 3 < -5$	or	$-2x + 3 > 5$	Original inequality
$-2x + 3 - 3 < -5 - 3$		$-2x + 3 - 3 > 5 - 3$	Subtract 3 from all parts.
$-2x < -8$		$-2x > 2$	Simplify.
$\dfrac{-2x}{-2} > \dfrac{-8}{-2}$		$\dfrac{-2x}{-2} < \dfrac{2}{-2}$	Divide all parts by -2 and reverse both inequality symbols.
$x > 4$		$x < -1$	Simplify.

Figure 3.18 *All real numbers that are less than -1 or greater than 4*

The solution set is $x < -1$ *or* $x > 4$ or, in set notation, $\{x \mid x < -1 \text{ or } x > 4\}$. The graph of the solution set is shown in Figure 3.18.

5 Translate a verbal statement into a linear inequality and solve the application problem.

Applications

Before looking at applications, we give some examples of the translations of verbal statements into inequalities. Study the meanings of the key phrases in the next example.

Example 11   Translating Verbal Statements

Students frequently need to translate such phrases into inequalities when they are solving application problems.

Verbal Statement	*Inequality*
a. x is at most 2.	$x \leq 2$
b. x is no more than 2.	$x \leq 2$
c. x is at least 2.	$x \geq 2$
d. x is more than 2.	$x > 2$
e. x is less than 2.	$x < 2$

When translating inequalities, remember that "at most" means "less than or equal to," and "at least" means "greater than or equal to." Also, be sure to distinguish between the *sum* "2 more than a number" $(x + 2)$ and the *inequality* "2 is more than a number" $(2 > x)$. It is generally preferable to read an inequality from left to right.

Example 12   Course Grade

Suppose you are taking a college course in which your grade is based on six 100-point exams. To earn an A in the course, you must have a total of at least 90% of the points. On the first five exams, your scores were 85, 92, 88, 96, and 87. How many points do you have to obtain on the sixth test in order to earn an A in the course?

Solution

Verbal Model: Total points $\geq$ 90% of 600

Labels: Score for sixth exam $= x$ (points)
Total points $= (85 + 92 + 88 + 96 + 87) + x$ (points)

Inequality: $(85 + 92 + 88 + 96 + 87) + x \geq 0.9(600)$

$$448 + x \geq 540$$

$$x \geq 540 - 448$$

$$x \geq 92$$

You must get at least 92 points on the sixth exam to earn an A in the course. Check this solution in the original statement of the problem.

In 1996, $14.5 billion was spent on passenger car rentals in the United States. (Source: U.S. Bureau of the Census)

| Example 13 | Car Rental | |

A subcompact car can be rented from Company A for $190 per week with no extra charge for mileage. A similar car can be rented from Company B for $100 per week, plus 20¢ for each mile driven. How many miles must you drive in a week to make the rental fee for Company A less than that for Company B?

Solution

Verbal Model:

| Weekly cost for A | $<$ | Weekly cost for B |

Labels:

Number of miles driven in 1 week $= m$	(miles)
Weekly cost for A $= 190$	(dollars)
Weekly cost for B $= 100 + 0.2m$	(dollars)

Inequality:

$$190 < 100 + 0.2m$$

$$90 < 0.2m$$

$$450 < m$$

Note that the inequality $450 < m$ is equivalent to writing $m > 450$. So, the car from Company A is cheaper if you plan to drive more than 450 miles in a week. The table confirms this conclusion.

Miles driven	447	448	449	450	451	452	453
Company A	$190.00	$190.00	$190.00	$190.00	$190.00	$190.00	$190.00
Company B	$189.40	$189.60	$189.80	$190.00	$190.20	$190.40	$190.60

Discussing the Concept   Misuse of a Compound Inequality

Suppose you are to find the solution set of an inequality that says: "$x - 2$ is greater than 3 and less than -3." Determine if it is appropriate to write this inequality in the form

$$3 < x - 2 < -3.$$

If not, explain why. Then find the solution set using appropriate steps.

3.6　Exercises

Integrated Review　　*Concepts, Skills, and Problem Solving*

Keep mathematically in shape by doing these exercises *before* the problems of this section.

Properties and Definitions

1. Name the property illustrated by $3x(x + 1) = 3x^2 + 3x$.

2. Complete the Associative Property: $(x + 2) - 4 = $ _____ .

3. If $a < 0$, then $|a| = $ _____ .

4. If $a < 0$ and $b > 0$, then $a \cdot b$ _____ 0.

In Exercises 5–8, place the correct inequality symbol between the two real numbers.

5. $-\frac{1}{2}$ ____ -7 6. $-\frac{1}{3}$ ____ $-\frac{1}{6}$

7. $-\pi$ ____ -3 8. -6 ____ $-\frac{13}{2}$

Graphs and Models

In Exercises 9 and 10, write expressions for the perimeter and area of the triangle. Then simplify the expressions.

9.

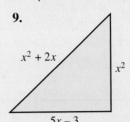

10.

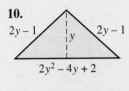

Problem Solving

11. A company had a first-quarter loss of $312,500, a second-quarter profit of $275,500, a third-quarter profit of $297,750, and a fourth-quarter profit of $71,300. What was the profit for the year?

12. A family on vacation traveled 371 miles in 7 hours. Determine their average speed.

Developing Skills

In Exercises 1–6, describe the inequality verbally and sketch its graph. See Example 1.

1. $x \geq 3$ 2. $z > 8$

3. $x \leq 10$ 4. $-3 < x < 4$

5. $-\frac{3}{2} < y \leq 5$ 6. $-3 \geq t > -3.8$

In Exercises 7–14, determine whether the value of x is a solution of the inequality.

Inequality	*Values*	
7. $5x - 12 > 0$	(a) $x = 3$	(b) $x = -3$
	(c) $x = \frac{5}{2}$	(d) $x = \frac{3}{2}$
8. $2x + 1 < 3$	(a) $x = 0$	(b) $x = 4$
	(c) $x = -4$	(d) $x = -3$
9. $3 - \frac{1}{2}x > 0$	(a) $x = 10$	(b) $x = 6$
	(c) $x = -\frac{3}{4}$	(d) $x = 0$

Inequality	*Values*	
10. $\frac{2}{3}x + 4 < 6$	(a) $x = 7$	(b) $x = 0$
	(c) $x = -\frac{1}{2}$	(d) $x = 3$
11. $0 < \dfrac{x - 2}{4} < 2$	(a) $x = 4$	(b) $x = 10$
	(c) $x = 0$	(d) $x = \frac{7}{2}$
12. $-1 < \dfrac{3 - x}{2} \leq 1$	(a) $x = 0$	(b) $x = 3$
	(c) $x = 1$	(d) $x = 5$
13. $-12 \leq 3(x + 4) \leq 6$	(a) $x = -5$	(b) $x = -1$
	(c) $x = -7$	(d) $x = \frac{2}{3}$
14. $0 \leq 2(x - 4) \leq 12$	(a) $x = 0$	(b) $x = 15$
	(c) $x = 5$	(d) $x = 10$

In Exercises 15–20, match the inequality with its graph. [The graphs are labeled (a), (b), (c), (d), (e), and (f).]

(a)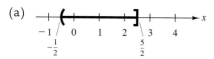

(b)

(c)

(d)

(e)

(f)

15. $x < 4$

16. $x \geq 6$

17. $-3 \leq x < 2$

18. $-\frac{1}{2} < x \leq \frac{5}{2}$

19. $8 > x > \frac{3}{2}$

20. $5 \geq x \geq -5$

In Exercises 21–58, solve and graph the inequality. See Examples 2–6, 9, and 10.

21. $t - 3 \geq 2$

22. $t + 1 < 6$

23. $x + 4 \leq 6$

24. $z - 2 > 0$

25. $4x < 12$

26. $2x > 3$

27. $-10x < 40$

28. $-6x > 18$

29. $\frac{2}{3}x \leq 12$

30. $-\frac{5}{8}x \geq 10$

31. $2x - 5 > 7$

32. $3x + 2 \leq 14$

33. $4 - 2x < 3$

34. $14 - 3x > 5$

35. $2x - 5 > -x + 6$

36. $25x + 4 \leq 10x + 19$

37. $6 < 3(y + 1) - 4(1 - y)$

38. $8 > 2(3x - 1) - (7x - 3)$

39. $-2(z + 1) \geq 3(z + 1)$

40. $8(t - 3) < 4(t - 3)$

41. $10(1 - y) < -4(y - 2)$

42. $6(3 - z) \geq 5(3 + z)$

43. $\frac{x}{4} + \frac{1}{2} > 0$

44. $\frac{y}{4} - \frac{5}{8} < 2$

45. $\frac{x}{5} - \frac{x}{2} \leq 1$

46. $\frac{x}{3} + \frac{x}{4} \geq 1$

47. $1 < 2x + 3 < 9$

48. $-9 \leq -3x + 6 < 12$

49. $-4 < 2x - 3 < 4$

50. $0 \leq 4x + 3 < 5$

51. $6 > \frac{x - 2}{-3} > -2$

52. $-2 < \frac{x - 4}{-2} \leq 3$

53. $\frac{3}{4} > x + 1 > \frac{1}{4}$

54. $-\frac{1}{3} < x - 2 < \frac{1}{4}$

55. $-5 < 2x + 3$ and $2x + 3 \leq 9$

56. $-1 \leq 5x - 11$ and $5x - 11 < 4$

57. $4 - 3x < -8$ or $4 - 3x > 7$

58. $2x - 7 \leq -12$ or $2x - 7 > -1$

In Exercises 59–66, write the compound inequality using set notation and intersection or union. See Examples 7 and 8.

59. $x < -5$ or $x > 3$

60. $x \leq 1$ or $x \geq 2$

61. $x < 6$ and $x > 0$

62. $x > 4$ and $x < 10$

63. $-3 \leq x \leq 7$

64. $12 > x > 6$

65. $x < 7$ or $x > 8$

66. $x \geq -4$ or $x \leq -10$

In Exercises 67–76, translate the verbal statement into a linear inequality. See Example 11.

67. x is nonnegative.

68. P is no more than 2.

69. y is more than -6.

70. z is at least 3.

71. x is at least 4.

72. t is less than 8.

73. y is no more than 25.

74. x is greater than or equal to -2 and less than 5.

75. x is greater than 0 and less than or equal to 6.

76. x is greater than -4 and less than or equal to 3.

Solving Problems

77. *Planet Distances* Mars is farther from the sun than Venus, and Venus is farther from the sun than Mercury. What can be said about the relationship between the distances of Mars and Mercury from the sun? Identify the property of inequalities that is demonstrated.

78. *Budgets* Department A's budget is less than Department B's budget, and Department B's budget is less than Department C's budget. What can you say about the relationship between the budgets of Departments A and C? Identify the property of inequalities that is demonstrated.

79. *Cellular Phone Cost*   The cost of a cellular phone call is \$0.46 for the first minute and \$0.31 for each additional minute. The total cost of the call cannot exceed \$4. Find the interval of time that is available for the call.

80. *Budget for a Trip*   You have \$2500 budgeted for a trip. The transportation for the trip will cost \$900. To stay within your budget, all other costs must be no more than what amount?

81. *Annual Operating Budget*   A utility company has a fleet of vans. The annual operating cost C (in dollars) per van is $C = 0.45m + 3200$ where m is the number of miles traveled by a van in a year. What number of miles will yield an annual operating cost per van that is less than \$12,000?

82. *Profit*   The revenue for selling x units of a product is $R = 115.95x$. The cost of producing x units is $C = 95x + 750$. In order to obtain a profit, the revenue must be greater than the cost. For what values of x will this product produce a profit?

83. *Geometry*   The lengths of the sides of the triangle in the figure are a, b, and c. Find the inequality that relates $a + b$ and c.

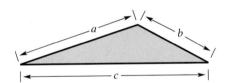

84. *Cargo Weight*   The weight of a truck is 4350 pounds. The legal gross weight of the loaded truck is 6000 pounds. Find an interval for the number of bushels of grain that the truck can haul if each bushel weighs 48 pounds.

85. *Distance*   The minimum and maximum speeds on an interstate highway are 45 miles per hour and 65 miles per hour. You travel nonstop for 4 hours on this highway. Assuming that you stay within the speed limits, give an interval for the distance you traveled.

86. *Comparing Distances*   You live 3 miles from college and 2 miles from the business where you work (see figure). Let d represent the distance between your work and the college. Write an inequality involving d.

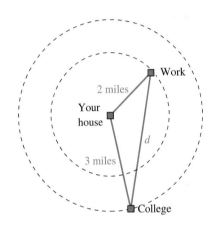

Explaining Concepts

87. Answer part (h) of Motivating the Chapter on page 115.

88. Give a verbal description of each of the symbols $<$, $\leq$, $>$, $\geq$, and $=$.

89. Is adding -5 to both sides of an inequality the same as subtracting 5 from both sides? Explain.

90. Is dividing both sides of an inequality by 5 the same as multiplying both sides by $\frac{1}{5}$? Explain.

91. How many numbers are in the solution set of a linear inequality? Give an example.

92. Explain the effect on an inequality when both sides are multiplied or divided by a negative number. Give examples demonstrating your explanation.

93. Compare solving linear equations to solving linear inequalities.

94. Write an inequality symbol equivalent to $\not<$.

95. Write an inequality symbol equivalent to $\not\geq$.

In Exercises 96–99, determine whether the statement is true or false. Explain your answer.

96. The inequality $x + 6 > 0$ is equivalent to $x > -6$.

97. The inequality $-\frac{1}{2}x + 6 > 0$ is equivalent to $x > 12$.

98. The statement that z is nonnegative is equivalent to the inequality $z > 0$.

99. The statement that u is at least 10 is equivalent to the inequality $u \geq 10$.

3.7 Absolute Value Equations and Inequalities

Objectives

1 Solve an equation involving absolute value.

2 Solve an inequality involving absolute value.

1 Solve an equation involving absolute value.

Solving Equations Involving Absolute Value

Consider the **absolute value equation**

$$|x| = 4.$$

The only solutions of this equation are -4 and 4, because these are the only two real numbers whose distance from zero is 4. (See Figure 3.19.) In other words, the absolute value equation $|x| = 4$ has exactly two solutions: $x = -4$ and $x = 4$.

Study Tip

Recall from Section 1.1 that the absolute value of a difference, $|a - b|$, denotes the distance between the real numbers a and b. So, $|x|$ can be written as $|x - 0|$ and means the distance between x and 0. Similarly, $|x - 2|$ denotes the distance between x and 2.

Figure 3.19

> ▶ **Solving an Absolute Value Equation**
>
> Let x be a variable or a variable expression and let a be a real number such that $a \geq 0$. The solutions of the equation $|x| = a$ are given by $x = -a$ and $x = a$. That is,
>
> $$|x| = a \implies x = -a \quad \text{and} \quad x = a.$$

Study Tip

The strategy for solving absolute value equations is to *rewrite* the equation in *equivalent forms* that can be solved by previously learned methods. This is a common strategy in mathematics. That is, when you encounter a new type of problem, you try to rewrite the problem so that it can be solved by techniques you already know.

Example 1 Solving Absolute Value Equations

Solve each absolute value equation.

a. $|x| = 8$ **b.** $|x| = 0$ **c.** $|y| = -2$

Solution

a. This equation is equivalent to the two linear equations

$$x = -8 \quad \text{and} \quad x = 8. \qquad \text{Equivalent linear equations}$$

So, the absolute value equation has two solutions: -8 and 8.

b. This equation is equivalent to the two linear equations

$$x = 0 \quad \text{and} \quad x = 0. \qquad \text{Equivalent linear equations}$$

Because both equations are the same, you can conclude that the absolute value equation has only one solution: 0.

c. This absolute value equation has *no solution* because it is not possible for the absolute value of a real number to be negative.

| Example 2 | Solving an Absolute Value Equation |

Solve $|4x - 5| = 15$.

Solution

$$|4x - 5| = 15 \qquad \text{Original equation}$$
$$4x - 5 = -15 \quad \text{or} \quad 4x - 5 = 15 \qquad \text{Equivalent equations}$$
$$4x = -10 \qquad\qquad 4x = 20 \qquad \text{Add 5 to both sides.}$$
$$x = -\frac{5}{2} \qquad\qquad x = 5 \qquad \text{Divide both sides by 4.}$$

Check

$$|4x - 5| = 15 \qquad |4x - 5| = 15 \qquad \text{Original equation}$$
$$\left|4\left(-\tfrac{5}{2}\right) - 5\right| = 15 \qquad |4(5) - 5| = 15 \qquad \text{Substitute } -\tfrac{5}{2} \text{ and 5 for } x.$$
$$|-15| = 15 \qquad |15| = 15 \qquad \text{Simplify.}$$
$$15 = 15 \qquad\qquad 15 = 15 \qquad \text{Solutions check.}$$

The solutions are $x = -\frac{5}{2}$ and $x = 5$.

When solving absolute value equations, remember that it is possible that they have no solution. For instance, the equation $|4x - 5| = -15$ has no solution because the absolute value of a real number cannot be negative. Do not make the mistake of trying to solve such an equation by writing the "equivalent" linear equations as $4x - 5 = -15$ and $4x - 5 = 15$. These equations have solutions, but they are both extraneous.

The equation in the next example is not given in the **standard form**

$$|ax + b| = c, \quad c \geq 0.$$

Notice that the first step in solving such an equation is to write it in standard form.

| Example 3 | An Absolute Value Equation in Nonstandard Form |

Solve $|2x + 4| + 2 = 6$.

Solution

$$|2x + 4| + 2 = 6 \qquad \text{Original equation}$$
$$|2x + 4| = 4 \qquad \text{Standard form}$$
$$2x + 4 = -4 \quad \text{or} \quad 2x + 4 = 4 \qquad \text{Equivalent equations}$$
$$2x = -8 \qquad\qquad 2x = 0 \qquad \text{Subtract 4 from both sides.}$$
$$x = -4 \qquad\qquad x = 0 \qquad \text{Divide both sides by 2.}$$

The solutions are $x = -4$ and $x = 0$. Check these in the original equation.

2 Solve an inequality involving absolute value.

Solving Inequalities Involving Absolute Value

To see how to solve inequalities involving absolute value, consider the following comparisons.

$|x| = 1$	$|x| < 1$	$|x| > 1$
$x = -1$ and $x = 1$	$-1 < x < 1$	$x < -1$ or $x > 1$

Notice that an **absolute value inequality** can be rewritten as a compound inequality. These comparisons suggest the following rules for solving inequalities involving absolute value.

▶ **Solving an Absolute Value Inequality**

Let x be a variable or an algebraic expression and let a be a real number such that $a > 0$.

1. The solutions of $|x| < a$ are all values of x that lie *between* $-a$ and a. That is,

$$|x| < a \quad \text{if and only if} \quad -a < x < a.$$

2. The solutions of $|x| > a$ are all values of x that are *less than* $-a$ or *greater than* a. That is,

$$|x| > a \quad \text{if and only if} \quad x < -a \text{ or } x > a.$$

These rules are also valid if $<$ is replaced by $\leq$ and $>$ is replaced by $\geq$.

Study Tip

- A "less than" inequality $|ax + b| < c$ is a *conjunction* and can be solved as the double inequality

$$-c < ax + b < c.$$

- A "greater than" inequality $|ax + b| > c$ is a *disjunction* and must be solved as a compound inequality.

Example 4 Solving a Conjunctive Absolute Value Inequality

Solve $|x + 3| \leq 6$.

Solution

$|x + 3| \leq 6$	Original inequality
$-6 \leq x + 3 \leq 6$	Equivalent double inequality
$-6 - 3 \leq x + 3 - 3 \leq 6 - 3$	Subtract 3 from all three parts.
$-9 \leq x \leq 3$	Combine like terms.

The solution set consists of all real numbers greater than or equal to -9 and less than or equal to 3. The set notation for this solution set is $\{x \mid -9 \leq x \leq 3\}$. The graph of this solution set is shown in Figure 3.20.

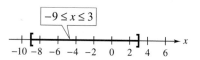

Figure 3.20

Keep in mind that a conjunctive ($\leq$) absolute value inequality can be solved as a double inequality where a disjunctive ($\geq$) one must be solved as a compound inequality.

| Example 5 | Solving a Disjunctive Absolute Value Inequality |

Solve $|4x - 5| > 13$.

Solution

$$|4x - 5| > 13 \qquad \text{Original inequality}$$

$$4x - 5 < -13 \quad \text{or} \quad 4x - 5 > 13 \qquad \text{Equivalent compound inequality}$$

$$4x - 5 + 5 < -13 + 5 \qquad 4x - 5 + 5 > 13 + 5 \qquad \text{Add 5 to all parts.}$$

$$4x < -8 \qquad\qquad 4x > 18 \qquad \text{Combine like terms.}$$

$$\frac{4x}{4} < \frac{-8}{4} \qquad\qquad \frac{4x}{4} > \frac{18}{4} \qquad \text{Divide all parts by 4.}$$

$$x < -2 \qquad\qquad x > \frac{9}{2} \qquad \text{Simplify.}$$

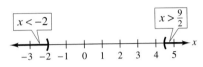

Figure 3.21

The solution set consists of all real numbers less than -2 or greater than $\frac{9}{2}$ or in set notation $\{x \mid x < -2 \text{ or } x > \frac{9}{2}\}$. (See Figure 3.21.)

| Example 6 | Solving a Conjunctive Absolute Value Inequality |

Solve $\left|3.6 - \dfrac{x}{2}\right| \leq 0.5$.

Solution

$$\left|3.6 - \frac{x}{2}\right| \leq 0.5 \qquad \text{Original inequality}$$

$$-0.5 \leq 3.6 - \frac{x}{2} \leq 0.5 \qquad \text{Equivalent double inequality}$$

$$-4.1 \leq -\frac{x}{2} \leq -3.1 \qquad \text{Subtract 3.6 from all three parts.}$$

$$8.2 \geq x \geq 6.2 \qquad \text{Multiply all three parts by } -2 \text{ and reverse both inequality symbols.}$$

$$6.2 \leq x \leq 8.2 \qquad \text{Solution set in standard form}$$

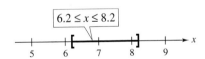

Figure 3.22

The solution set consists of all real numbers greater than or equal to 6.2 and less than or equal to 8.2 or in set notation $\{x \mid 6.2 \leq x \leq 8.2\}$. (See Figure 3.22.)

Discussing the Concept   Solution Sets

Without doing any calculations, which of the following absolute value equations and inequalities do not have a solution? Explain. Find the solution set for the remaining equations and inequalities.

a. $|3x + 7| = 5$ b. $|3 - x| = -3$ c. $\left|\dfrac{x}{4} + 2\right| = 0$

d. $|-x + 1| \leq 4$ e. $|5x - 9| > -1$ f. $\left|\dfrac{x}{3} - \dfrac{2}{3}\right| < -5$

3.7   Exercises

Integrated Review   Concepts, Skills, and Problem Solving

Keep mathematically in shape by doing these exercises *before* the problems of this section.

Properties and Definitions

1. If n is an integer, how do the numbers $2n$ and $2n - 1$ differ? Explain.

2. Are $-3x^2$ and $(-3x)^2$ equal? Explain.

3. Explain how to write $\frac{27}{12}$ in reduced form.

4. Explain how to divide $\frac{2}{3}$ by $\frac{5}{3}$.

Order of Real Numbers

In Exercises 5–10, place the correct inequality symbol ($<$ or $>$) between the two real numbers.

5. 3 _____ -2 **6.** -3 _____ -2

7. $-\frac{1}{2}$ _____ -3 **8.** $-\frac{1}{3}$ _____ $-\frac{2}{3}$

9. $\frac{1}{2}$ _____ $\frac{5}{16}$ **10.** 4 _____ $\frac{45}{11}$

Problem Solving

In Exercises 11 and 12, determine whether there is more than a $500 difference between the budgeted amount and the actual expense.

11. Wages
    Budgeted: $76,300
    Actual: $75,926

12. Taxes
    Budgeted: $37,800
    Actual: $39,632

Developing Skills

In Exercises 1–4, determine whether the value is a solution of the equation.

Equation	Value
1. $\lvert x + 3 \rvert = 10$	$x = -13$
2. $\lvert x - 12 \rvert = 10$	$x = 18$
3. $\lvert 3 - 2y \rvert = 2$	$y = 1$
4. $\left\lvert \frac{1}{3}z + 11 \right\rvert = 14$	$z = 9$

In Exercises 5–8, transform the absolute value equation into two linear equations.

5. $\lvert u - 3 \rvert = 7$ **6.** $\lvert m + 4 \rvert = 3$

7. $\left\lvert \frac{1}{2}x + 7 \right\rvert = \frac{3}{2}$ **8.** $\lvert 3k - 5 \rvert = 7$

In Exercises 9–34, solve the equation. (Some of the equations have no solution.) See Examples 1–3.

9. $\lvert x \rvert = 7$ **10.** $\lvert y \rvert = 6$

11. $\lvert v \rvert = 15$ **12.** $\lvert z \rvert = 3$

13. $\lvert m \rvert = -3$ **14.** $\lvert a \rvert = -8$

15. $\lvert 3x \rvert = 18$ **16.** $\left\lvert \frac{3}{2}x \right\rvert = 12$

17. $\lvert x - 12 \rvert = 4$ **18.** $\lvert y - 10 \rvert = 25$

19. $\lvert s + 3 \rvert = 11$ **20.** $\lvert a + 6 \rvert = 2$

21. $\lvert 16 - y \rvert = 3$ **22.** $\lvert 3 - x \rvert = 2$

23. $\lvert 2x + 4 \rvert = -8$ **24.** $\lvert 20 - 5t \rvert = 0$

25. $\lvert 2x - 3 \rvert = 21$ **26.** $\lvert 3x + 5 \rvert = 17$

27. $\lvert 3x + 2 \rvert = 5$ **28.** $\lvert 4 - 3x \rvert = 16$

29. $\lvert 5x - 9 \rvert - 4 = 0$ **30.** $\lvert 4x + 3 \rvert + 1 = 12$

31. $\left\lvert 5 - \frac{2}{3}x \right\rvert = 3$ **32.** $\left\lvert \frac{1}{2}x + 3 \right\rvert = 9$

33. $\lvert 0.25x - 2 \rvert = 4$ **34.** $\lvert 3.2 - 1.5x \rvert = 2$

Think About It   In Exercises 35 and 36, write a single equation that is equivalent to the two equations.

35. $x + 3 = 8, x + 3 = -8$

36. $3t - 5 = 7, 3t - 5 = -7$

Think About It   In Exercises 37 and 38, write a single equation that is equivalent to the statement.

37. The distance between x and 4 is 2.

38. The distance between t and 10 is 4.

In Exercises 39–46, determine whether the *x*-values are solutions of the inequality.

Inequality		*Values*
39. $|x| < 2$	(a) $x = 1$	(b) $x = -3$
	(c) $x = 5$	(d) $x = -\frac{1}{2}$
40. $|x| \leq 10$	(a) $x = -12$	(b) $x = -6$
	(c) $x = 15$	(d) $x = 4$
41. $|x| \geq 5$	(a) $x = 2$	(b) $x = -7$
	(c) $x = 25$	(d) $x = -3$
42. $|x| > 8$	(a) $x = 12$	(b) $x = -6$
	(c) $x = 7.9$	(d) $x = 8.1$
43. $|x - 4| < 2$	(a) $x = 2$	(b) $x = 1.5$
	(c) $x = 0$	(d) $x = 5$
44. $|x + 1| \leq 4$	(a) $x = 10$	(b) $x = -10$
	(c) $x = -2$	(d) $x = 3$
45. $|x + 5| \geq 3$	(a) $x = -8$	(b) $x = -5$
	(c) $x = -2$	(d) $x = -4$
46. $|x - 4| > 6$	(a) $x = 9$	(b) $x = 10$
	(c) $x = 11$	(d) $x = -1$

In Exercises 47–50, transform the absolute value inequality into a double inequality or two separate inequalities.

47. $|z + 2| < 1$ **48.** $|x - 7| \leq 3$

49. $|5 - h| \geq 2$ **50.** $|8 - x| > 10$

In Exercises 51–54, sketch a graph that shows the real numbers that satisfy the statement.

51. All real numbers greater than -3 *and* less than 3

52. All real numbers greater than or equal to 2 *and* less than 8

53. All real numbers less than or equal to 5 *or* greater than 10

54. All real numbers less than -2 *or* greater than or equal to 4

In Exercises 55–70, solve the inequality and sketch the solution on the real number line. See Examples 4 and 5.

55. $|y| < 3$ **56.** $|x| < 5$

57. $|y| \geq 2$ **58.** $|x| \geq 5$

59. $|t| > 5$ **60.** $|y| > 7$

61. $|y - 2| \leq 2$ **62.** $|u - 3| \leq 4$

63. $|x + 1| < 4$ **64.** $|z + 3| < 5$

65. $|2x| < 12$ **66.** $|4z| \leq 16$

67. $|y - 5| > 2$ **68.** $|v - 4| > 4$

69. $|m + 2| \geq 3$ **70.** $|s + 3| \geq 5$

In Exercises 71–74, match the inequality with its graph. [The graphs are labeled (a), (b), (c), and (d).]

71. $|x - 3| \leq 2$ **72.** $|x - 3| < 4$

73. $|x - 3| > 2$ **74.** $|x - 3| \geq 3$

(a)

(b)

(c)

(d)

In Exercises 75–78, write an absolute value inequality that represents the interval.

75.

76.

77.

78.

In Exercises 79–84, write an absolute value inequality that represents the verbal statement.

79. The set of all real numbers x whose distance from 0 is less than 2.

80. The set of all real numbers x whose distance from 0 is more than 2.

81. The set of all real numbers x whose distance from 0 is more than 5.

82. The set of all real numbers x whose distance from 0 is at least 5.

83. The set of all real numbers x whose distance from 4 is more than 2.

84. The set of all real numbers x whose distance from 6 is no more than 2.

Solving Problems

85. *Temperature*   The temperature of a room satisfies the inequality

$$|t - 72| < 1.5$$

where t is in degrees Fahrenheit. Sketch the graph of the solution set of the inequality.

86. *Time Study*   A time study was conducted to determine the length of the useful life of a car battery. Approximately two-thirds of the batteries had lifetimes satisfying the inequality

$$|L - 52| < 4$$

where L is time in months. Sketch the graph of the solution set of the inequality.

87. *Accuracy of Measurements*   In a machine shop, the diameter of a machined part must be within 0.005 centimeter of specifications. Let $(s - x)$ represent the difference between the specification s and the measured diameter x of the machined part.

  (a) Write an absolute value inequality that describes the values of x that are within specifications.

  (b) The diameter of a part is specified to be $s = 3.5$ centimeters. Describe the acceptable diameters for this piece.

 88. *Think About It*   When you buy a 16-ounce bag of chips, you expect to get *precisely* 16 ounces. Suppose the actual weight w (in ounces) of a "16-ounce" bag of chips is given by $|w - 16| \leq \frac{1}{2}$. If you buy four 16-ounce bags, what is the greatest amount you can expect to get? What is the least? Explain.

Explaining Concepts

89. Give a graphical description of the absolute value of a real number.

90. Give an example of an absolute value equation that has only one solution.

91. In your own words, explain how to solve an absolute value equation. Illustrate your explanation with an example.

92. Give a verbal description of the solution of the inequality $|x| > 3$.

Key Terms

linear equation, *p. 116*
consecutive integers,
  p. 122
cross-multiplication,
  p. 132
markup, *p. 141*

discount, *p. 143*
ratio, *p. 149*
unit price, *p. 151*
proportion, *p. 152*
mixture problems, *p. 165*

work-rate problems,
  p. 167
linear inequality, *p. 174*
solution set, *p. 174*
compound inequality,
  p. 178

absolute value equation,
  p. 186
absolute value inequality,
  p. 188

Key Concepts

3.1 Solving a linear equation

Solve a linear equation using inverse operations to isolate the variable.

3.1 Expressions for special types of integers

1. $2n$ denotes an *even* integer.
2. $2n - 1$ and $2n + 1$ denote *odd* integers.
3. The set $\{n, n + 1, n + 2\}$ denotes three *consecutive* integers.

3.2 Equations containing symbols of grouping

Solve a linear equation by first removing the symbols of grouping using the Distributive Property.

3.2 Equations involving fractions or decimals

1. Clear an equation of fractions by multiplying both sides by the least common multiple (LCM) of the denominators.
2. Use cross-multiplication to solve a linear equation that equates two fractions. That is, if
   $\frac{a}{b} = \frac{c}{d}$, then $a \cdot d = b \cdot c$.
3. To solve a linear equation with decimal coefficients, multiply both sides by a power of 10 that converts all decimal coefficients to integers.

3.3 The percent equation

The percent equation $a = p \cdot b$ compares two numbers.

b is the base number.
p is the percent in decimal form.
a is the number being compared to b.

3.3 Markups and discounts

1. A markup is the difference between the cost (what the retailer pays) and the price (what the consumer pays).
2. A discount is the amount off the list price (what the consumer pays).

3.3 Guidelines for solving word problems

1. Write a *verbal model* that describes the problem.

2. Assign *labels* to fixed quantities and variable quantities.
3. Rewrite the verbal model as an *algebraic equation* using the assigned labels.
4. *Solve* the algebraic equation.
5. *Check* to see that your solution satisfies the word problem as stated.

3.4 Solving a proportion

A proportion equates two ratios.
  If $\frac{a}{b} = \frac{c}{d}$, then $ad = bc$.

3.6 Properties of inequalities

Let a, b, and c be real numbers, variables, or algebraic expressions.
Addition: If $a < b$, then $a + c < b + c$.
Subtraction: If $a < b$, then $a - c < b - c$.
Multiplication: If $a < b$ and $c > 0$, then $ac < bc$.
  If $a < b$ and $c < 0$, then $ac > bc$.

Division: If $a < b$ and $c > 0$, then $\frac{a}{c} < \frac{b}{c}$.

  If $a < b$ and $c < 0$, then $\frac{a}{c} > \frac{b}{c}$.

Transitive: If $a < b$ and $b < c$, then $a < c$.

3.6 Solving a linear inequality or a compound inequality

Solve a linear inequality or a compound inequality by performing inverse operations on all parts of the inequality.

3.7 Solving an absolute value equation

Solve an absolute value equation by rewriting as two linear equations.

3.7 Solving an absolute value inequality

Solve an absolute value inequality by rewriting as a compound inequality.

193

REVIEW EXERCISES

Reviewing Skills

3.1 In Exercises 1–4, solve the equation mentally.

1. $y - 25 = 10$

2. $z + 5 = 12$

3. $\frac{x}{4} = 7$

4. $6u = 30$

In Exercises 5 and 6, justify each step of the solution.

5.
$$10x - 12 = 18$$
$$10x - 12 + 12 = 18 + 12$$
$$10x = 30$$
$$\frac{10x}{10} = \frac{30}{10}$$
$$x = 3$$

6.
$$\frac{t}{4} + \frac{t}{3} = 1$$
$$3t + 4t = 12$$
$$7t = 12$$
$$\frac{7t}{7} = \frac{12}{7}$$
$$t = \frac{12}{7}$$

In Exercises 7–20, solve the linear equation and check your solution.

7. $x + 10 = 13$

8. $x - 3 = 8$

9. $5 - x = 2$

10. $3 = 8 - x$

11. $10x = 50$

12. $-3x = 21$

13. $8x + 7 = 39$

14. $12x - 5 = 43$

15. $24 - 7x = 3$

16. $13 + 6x = 61$

17. $15x - 4 = 16$

18. $3x - 8 = 2$

19. $\frac{x}{5} = 4$

20. $-\frac{x}{14} = \frac{1}{2}$

3.2 In Exercises 21–30, solve the linear equation and check your solution.

21. $3x - 2(x + 5) = 10$

22. $4x + 2(7 - x) = 5$

23. $2x + 3 = 5x - 2$

24. $8(x - 2) = 3(x + 2)$

25. $\frac{2}{3}x - \frac{1}{6} = \frac{9}{2}$

26. $\frac{1}{8}x + \frac{3}{4} = \frac{5}{2}$

27. $\frac{x}{3} - \frac{1}{9} = 2$

28. $\frac{1}{2} - \frac{x}{8} = 7$

29. $\frac{u}{10} + \frac{u}{5} = 6$

30. $\frac{x}{3} + \frac{x}{5} = 1$

In Exercises 31–34, solve the equation. Round your result to two decimal places.

31. $516x - 875 = 3250$

32. $2.825x + 3.125 = 12.5$

33. $\frac{x}{4.625} = 48.5$

34. $5x + \frac{1}{4.5} = 18.125$

3.3 In Exercises 35 and 36, complete the table.

35.

Percent	Parts out of 100	Decimal	Fraction
35%			

36.

Percent	Parts out of 100	Decimal	Fraction
			$\frac{4}{5}$

37. What number is 125% of 16?

38. What number is 0.8% of 3250?

39. 150 is $37\frac{1}{2}\%$ of what number?

40. 323 is 95% of what number?

41. 150 is what percent of 250?

42. 130.6 is what percent of 3265?

3.4 In Exercises 43–46, find a ratio that compares the relative sizes of the quantities. (Use the same units of measurement for both quantities.)

43. Eighteen inches to 4 yards

44. One pint to 2 gallons

45. Two hours to 90 minutes

46. Four meters to 150 centimeters

In Exercises 47–52, solve the proportion.

47. $\frac{7}{16} = \frac{z}{8}$

48. $\frac{x}{12} = \frac{5}{4}$

49. $\dfrac{x+2}{4} = -\dfrac{1}{3}$ **50.** $\dfrac{x-4}{1} = \dfrac{9}{4}$

51. $\dfrac{x-3}{2} = \dfrac{x+6}{5}$ **52.** $\dfrac{x+1}{3} = \dfrac{x+2}{4}$

3.5 In Exercises 53 and 54, solve the formula for the specified variable.

53. Solve for θ: $A = \dfrac{r^2\theta}{2}$

54. Solve for n: $S = a + (n-1)d$

In Exercises 55–60, find the missing distance, rate, or time.

	Distance, d	Rate, r	Time, t
55.		65 mi/hr	8 hr
56.		4.7 m/sec	3 sec
57.	400 mi	50 mi/hr	
58.	855 m	5 m/min	
59.	3000 mi		50 hr
60.	1000 km		25 hr

3.6 In Exercises 61–64, write the linear inequality symbolically.

61.
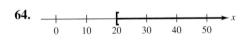

62.

63.

64.

In Exercises 65–80, solve and graph the linear inequality.

65. $x + 5 \geq 7$ **66.** $x - 2 \leq 1$

67. $3x - 8 < 1$ **68.** $4x + 3 > 15$

69. $-11x \leq -22$ **70.** $-7x \geq 21$

71. $\frac{4}{5}x > 8$ **72.** $\frac{2}{3}n < -4$

73. $14 - \frac{1}{2}t < 12$ **74.** $32 + \frac{7}{8}k > 11$

75. $3 - 3y \geq 2(4 + y)$ **76.** $4 - 3y \leq 8(10 - y)$

77. $-2 < 2x + 6 \leq 2$ **78.** $-5 \leq 3 - 4x < 5$

79. $3 > \dfrac{x+1}{-2} > 0$ **80.** $5 \geq \dfrac{x-3}{3} > 2$

In Exercises 81–88, write the compound inequality using set notation and intersection or union.

81. $x < -3$ or $x > 7$ **82.** $x \leq -2$ or $x \geq -1$

83. $x < 0$ and $x > -6$ **84.** $x > -3$ and $x < 4$

85. $-8 \leq x \leq -5$ **86.** $5 > x > -1$

87. $x < 2$ or $x > 3$ **88.** $x \geq 6$ or $x \leq -1$

In Exercises 89–94, write a linear inequality that represents the statement.

89. z is at least 10.

90. x is nonnegative.

91. y is more than 8 but less than 12.

92. The area A is no more than 100 square feet.

93. The volume V is less than 12 cubic feet.

94. The perimeter P is at least 24 inches.

3.7 In Exercises 95–100, solve the absolute value equation.

95. $|x - 25| = 5$ **96.** $|x - 150| = 100$

97. $|7t| = 42$ **98.** $\left|\frac{3}{2}z\right| = 72$

99. $|3u + 24| = 0$ **100.** $|4x - 3| - 13 = 0$

In Exercises 101–106, solve the absolute value inequality and sketch the solution on the real number line.

101. $\left|\frac{1}{2}v\right| \leq 3$ **102.** $|3u| \geq 12$

103. $|y - 4| > 3$ **104.** $|k + 4| < 6$

105. $|2n - 3| < 5$ **106.** $|1 - 3n| \geq 5$

Solving Problems

107. *Driving Distances* On a 1200-mile trip, you drive about $1\frac{1}{2}$ times as much as your friend. Approximate the number of miles each of you drive.

108. *Hourly Wage* Your hourly wage is $8.30 per hour plus 60 cents for each unit you produce. How many units must you produce in an hour so that your hourly wage is $15.50?

109. *Geometry* The length of a rectangle is 30 meters greater than its width. Find the measurements of the rectangle if its perimeter is 260 meters.

110. *Geometry* A 10-foot board is cut so that one piece is 4 times as long as the other. Find the length of each piece.

111. *Revenue* The revenues for a corporation (in millions of dollars) in the years 1997 and 1998 were $4521.4 and $4679.0, respectively. Determine the percent increase in revenue from 1997 to 1998.

112. *Price Increase* The manufacturer's suggested retail price for a car is $18,459. Estimate the price of a comparably equipped car for the next model year if the price will increase by $4\frac{1}{2}\%$.

113. *Analyzing Data* The figure gives the living arrangements for women 65 years old or older for the year 1995. Find the number of women in each category if there were approximately 19,844,000 women who were at least 65 in 1995. (Source: U.S. Bureau of the Census)

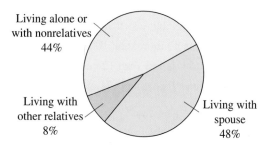

114. *Analyzing Data* The figure gives the living arrangements for men 65 years old or older for the year 1995. Find the number of men in each category if there were approximately 13,689,000 men who were at least 65 in 1995. (Source: U.S. Bureau of the Census)

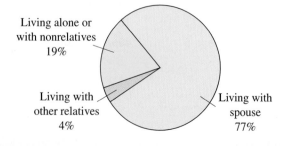

In Exercises 115–118, use a proportion to solve the problem.

115. *Real Estate Tax* The tax on a property with an assessed value of $75,000 is $1150. Find the tax on a property with an assessed value of $110,000.

116. *Recipe Proportions* One and one-half cups of milk are needed to make one batch of pudding. How much is required to make three batches?

117. *Map Distance* The scale on the map in the figure represents 100 miles on the map. Use the map to approximate the distance between St. Petersburg and Tallahassee.

118. *Geometry* Solve for the length x in the figure. Assume that the two triangles are similar, and use the fact that corresponding sides of similar triangles are proportional.

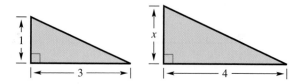

119. *Time* A train's average speed is 60 miles per hour. How long will it take the train to travel 562 miles?

120. *Distance* An airplane has an average speed of 475 miles per hour. How far will it travel in $2\frac{1}{3}$ hours?

121. *Speed* You can walk 20 kilometers in 3 hours and 47 minutes. What is your average speed?

122. *Speed* For the first hour of a 350-mile trip, your average speed is 40 miles per hour. Determine the average speed that must be maintained for the remainder of the trip if you want the average speed for the entire trip to be 50 miles per hour.

123. *Number of Coins*   You have 30 coins in dimes and quarters with a combined value of $5.55. Determine the number of coins of each type.

124. *Poll Results*   Thirteen hundred people were surveyed in an opinion poll. Candidates A and B received the same number of votes. Candidate C received $1\frac{1}{4}$ times as many votes as each of the other two candidates. How many votes did each candidate receive?

125. *Measurements of a Swimming Pool*   The width of a rectangular swimming pool is 4 feet less than its length. The perimeter of the pool is 112 feet. Find the measurements of the pool.

126. *Measurements of a Triangle*   The perimeter of an isosceles triangle is 65 centimeters. Find the length of the two equal sides if each is 10 centimeters longer than the third side. (An isosceles triangle has two sides of equal length.)

Simple Interest   In Exercises 127–130, use the simple interest formula.

127. Find the total interest you will earn on a $1000 corporate bond that matures in 5 years and has an annual interest rate of 9.5%.

128. Find the annual interest rate on a certificate of deposit that pays $60 per year in interest on a principal of $750.

129. Find the principal required to have an annual interest income of $25,000 if the annual interest rate is 8.75%.

130. You invest $2500 in a certificate of deposit that has an annual interest rate of 7%. After 6 months, the interest is computed and added to the principal. During the second 6 months the interest is computed using the original investment plus the interest earned during the first 6 months. What is the total interest earned during the first year of the investment?

131. *Work Rate*   Find the time for two people working together to complete a task that, if they worked individually, would take them 5 hours and 6 hours, respectively.

132. *Work Rate*   Suppose the person in Exercise 131 who can complete the task in 5 hours has already worked 1 hour when the second person starts. How long will they work together to complete the task?

Chapter Test

Take this test as you would take a test in class. After you are done, check your work against the answers given in the back of the book.

In Exercises 1–6, solve the equation and check your solution.

1. $4x - 3 = 18$

2. $10 - (2 - x) = 2x + 1$

3. $\dfrac{3x}{4} = \dfrac{5}{2} + x$

4. $\dfrac{t + 2}{3} = \dfrac{2t}{5}$

5. $|x - 5| = 2$

6. $|3x - 4| = 5$

7. Solve $4.08(x + 10) = 9.50(x - 2)$. Round the result to two decimal places.

8. The bill (including parts and labor) for the repair of a home appliance is $142. The cost for parts is $62. How many hours were spent repairing the appliance if the cost of labor is $32 per hour?

9. Express the fraction $\frac{3}{8}$ as a percent and as a decimal.

10. 324 is 27% of what number?

11. 90 is what percent of 250?

12. Express the ratio of 40 inches to 2 yards as a fraction in simplest form. Use the same units for both quantities, and explain how you made this conversion.

13. Solve the proportion $\dfrac{2x}{3} = \dfrac{x + 4}{5}$.

14. On the map at the left, 1 centimeter represents 55 miles. Approximate the distance between Akron and Columbus.

15. You traveled 264 miles in $5\frac{1}{2}$ hours. What was your average speed?

16. You can paint a building in 9 hours. Your friend would require 12 hours. Working together, how long will it take the two of you to paint the building?

17. Solve for R in the formula $S = C + RC$.

18. How much must you deposit to earn $500 per year at 8% simple interest?

In Exercises 19–24, solve and graph the inequality.

19. $x + 3 \le 7$

20. $-\dfrac{2x}{3} > 4$

21. $-3 < 2x - 1 \le 3$

22. $2 \ge \dfrac{3 - x}{2} > -1$

23. $|x + 4| \le 3$

24. $|2x - 1| > 3$

SCALE

| 0 | 55 | 110 | 165 miles |

| 0 | 1 | 2 | 3 cm |

Figure for 14

Cumulative Test: Chapters 1–3

Cumulative Tests provide a useful progress check for students to assess how well they are retaining various algebraic skills and concepts.

Take this test as you would take a test in class. After you are done, check your work against the answers given in the back of the book.

1. Place the correct symbol (< or >) between the numbers: $-\frac{3}{4}$ ⬜ $\left|-\frac{7}{8}\right|$.

In Exercises 2–7, evaluate the expression.

2. $(-200)(2)(-3)$ 3. $\frac{3}{8} - \frac{5}{6}$ 4. $-\frac{2}{9} \div \frac{8}{75}$

5. $-(-2)^3$ 6. $3 + 2(6) - 1$ 7. $24 + 12 \div 3$

In Exercises 8 and 9, evaluate the expression when $x = -2$ and $y = 3$.

8. $2x + y^2$ 9. $4y - x^3$

10. Use exponential form to write the product $3 \cdot (x + y) \cdot (x + y) \cdot 3 \cdot 3$.

11. Use the Distributive Property to expand $-2x(x - 3)$.

12. Identify the rule of algebra illustrated by $2 + (3 + x) = (2 + 3) + x$.

In Exercises 13–15, simplify the expression.

13. $(3x^3)(5x^4)$ 14. $(a^3b^2)(ab)^5$

15. $2x^2 - 3x + 5x^2 - (2 + 3x)$

In Exercises 16–18, solve the equation and check your solution.

16. $12x - 3 = 7x + 27$ 17. $2x - \dfrac{5x}{4} = 13$

18. $2(x - 3) + 3 = 12 - x$

19. Solve and graph the inequality

$$-1 \le \frac{x + 3}{2} < 2.$$

20. The sticker on a new car gives the fuel efficiency as 28.3 miles per gallon. In your own words, explain how to estimate the annual fuel cost for the buyer if the car will be driven approximately 15,000 miles per year and the fuel cost is $1.179 per gallon.

21. Express the ratio "24 ounces to 2 pounds" as a fraction in reduced form.

22. The sum of two consecutive even integers is 494. Find the two numbers.

23. The suggested retail price of a camcorder is $1150. The camcorder is on sale for "20% off" the list price. Find the sale price.

24. The figure at the left shows two pieces of property. The assessed values of the properties are proportional to their areas. The value of the larger piece is $95,000. What is the value of the smaller piece?

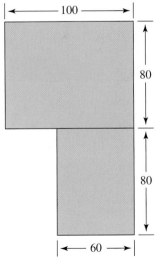

Figure for 24

4

Graphs and Functions

Rudi Von Briel/PhotoEdit

In 1996, $30.7 billion was spent on advertising. Of that, advertising agencies received $21.4 billion.   (Source: U.S. Bureau of the Census)

Motivating the Chapter

 ## Salary Plus Commission

You work as a sales representative for an advertising agency. You are paid a weekly salary, plus a commission on all ads placed by your accounts. The table shows your sales and your total weekly earnings.

	Week 1	Week 2	Week 3	Week 4
Weekly sales	$24,000	$7000	$0	$36,000
Weekly earnings	$980	$640	$500	$1220

See Section 4.3, Exercise 72

a. Rewrite the data as a set of ordered pairs.

b. Does the table represent a function? If so, identify the dependent and independent variables.

c. Describe what you consider to be appropriate domain and range values.

See Section 4.5, Exercise 108

d. Explain how to determine whether the function is linear or not.

e. Determine the slope of this function. What is the *rate* at which the weekly pay increases for each unit increase in ad sales? What is the rate called in the context of the problem?

f. Write an equation that describes the linear relationship between weekly sales and weekly earnings.

g. Sketch a graph of the equation. Identify the *y*-intercept and explain its meaning in the context of the problem. Identify the *x*-intercept. Does the *x*-intercept have any meaning in the context of the problem? If so, what is it?

See Section 4.6, Exercise 70

h. What amount of ad sales is needed to guarantee a weekly pay of at least $840?

4.1	Ordered Pairs and Graphs

Objectives

1 Plot and find the coordinates of a point on a rectangular coordinate system.

2 Construct a table of values for an equation and determine whether an ordered pair is a solution point of the equation.

3 Use the verbal problem-solving method to plot points on a rectangular coordinate system.

---

1 Plot and find the coordinates of a point on a rectangular coordinate system.

Corbis-Bettmann

René Descartes

(1596–1650)

Descartes made many contributions to philosophy, science, and mathematics. The idea of representing points in the plane by pairs of real numbers and representing curves in the plane by equations was described by Descartes in his book *La Géométrie*, published in 1637.

The Rectangular Coordinate System

Just as you can represent real numbers by points on the real number line, you can represent ordered pairs of real numbers by points in a plane. This plane is called a **rectangular coordinate system** or the **Cartesian plane,** after the French mathematician René Descartes (1596–1650).

A rectangular coordinate system is formed by two real lines intersecting at right angles, as shown in Figure 4.1. The horizontal number line is usually called the **x-axis** and the vertical number line is usually called the **y-axis.** (The plural of axis is *axes*.) The point of intersection of the two axes is the **origin,** and the axes separate the plane into four regions called **quadrants.**

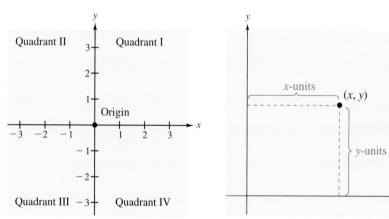

Figure 4.1   Figure 4.2

Each point in the plane corresponds to an **ordered pair** (x, y) of real numbers x and y, called the **coordinates** of the point. The first number (or **x-coordinate**) tells how far to the left or right the point is from the vertical axis, and the second number (or **y-coordinate**) tells how far up or down the point is from the horizontal axis, as shown in Figure 4.2.

A positive x-coordinate implies that the point lies to the *right* of the vertical axis; a negative x-coordinate implies that the point lies to the *left* of the vertical axis; and an x-coordinate of zero implies that the point lies *on* the vertical axis. Similar statements can be made about y-coordinates. A positive y-coordinate implies that the point lies *above* the horizontal axis, and a negative y-coordinate implies that the point lies *below* the horizontal axis.

Locating a point in a plane is called **plotting** the point. This procedure is demonstrated in Example 1.

Example 1   Plotting Points on a Rectangular Coordinate System

Plot the points $(-1, 2)$, $(3, 0)$, $(2, -1)$, $(3, 4)$, $(0, 0)$, and $(-2, -3)$ on a rectangular coordinate system.

Solution

The point $(-1, 2)$ is 1 unit to the *left* of the vertical axis and 2 units *above* the horizontal axis.

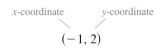

Similarly, the point $(3, 0)$ is 3 units to the *right* of the vertical axis and *on* the horizontal axis. (It is on the horizontal axis because the y-coordinate is zero.) The other four points can be plotted in a similar way, as shown in Figure 4.3.

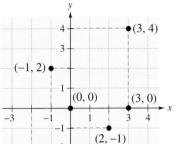

Figure 4.3

In Example 1 you were given the coordinates of several points and asked to plot the points on a rectangular coordinate system. Example 2 looks at the reverse problem. That is, you are given points on a rectangular coordinate system and asked to determine their coordinates.

Example 2   Finding Coordinates of Points

Determine the coordinates for each of the points shown in Figure 4.4.

Solution

Point A lies 3 units to the *left* of the vertical axis and 2 units *above* the horizontal axis. So, point A must be given by the ordered pair $(-3, 2)$. The coordinates of the other four points can be determined in a similar way, and we summarize the results as follows.

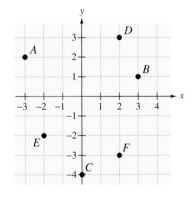

Figure 4.4

Point	Position	Coordinates
A	3 units *left*, 2 units *up*	$(-3, 2)$
B	3 units *right*, 1 unit *up*	$(3, 1)$
C	0 units *left* (or *right*), 4 units *down*	$(0, -4)$
D	2 units *right*, 3 units *up*	$(2, 3)$
E	2 units *left*, 2 units *down*	$(-2, -2)$
F	2 units *right*, 3 units *down*	$(2, -3)$

In Example 2, note that point A $(-3, 2)$ and point F $(2, -3)$ are different points. The order in which the numbers appear in an ordered pair is important.

Each year since 1967, the winners of the American Football Conference and the National Football Conference have played in the Super Bowl. The first Super Bowl was played between the Green Bay Packers and the Kansas City Chiefs.

Example 3   Super Bowl Scores

The scores of the winning and losing football teams for the Super Bowl games from 1981 through 1999 are given in the table below. Plot these points on a rectangular coordinate system.   (Source: National Football League)

Year	1981	1982	1983	1984	1985	1986	1987
Winning score	27	26	27	38	38	46	39
Losing score	10	21	17	9	16	10	20

Year	1988	1989	1990	1991	1992	1993	1994
Winning score	42	20	55	20	37	52	30
Losing score	10	16	10	19	24	17	13

Year	1995	1996	1997	1998	1999
Winning score	49	27	35	31	34
Losing score	26	17	21	24	19

Solution

Plot the years on the *x*-axis and the winning and losing scores on the *y*-axis. In Figure 4.5, the winning scores are shown as black dots, and the losing scores are shown as blue dots. Note that the break in the *x*-axis indicates that the numbers between 0 and 1981 have been omitted.

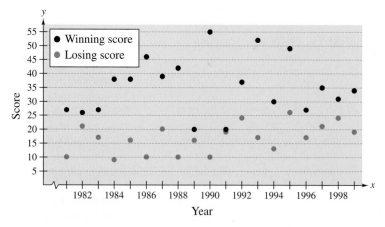

Figure 4.5

2 Construct a table of values for an equation and determine whether an ordered pair is a solution point of the equation.

Ordered Pairs as Solutions of Equations

In Example 3, the relationship between the year and the Super Bowl scores was given by a **table of values.** In mathematics, the relationship between the variables x and y is often given by an equation. From the equation, you must then construct your own table of values. For instance, consider the equation

$$y = 2x + 1.$$

To construct a table of values for this equation, choose several x-values and then calculate the corresponding y-values. For example, if you choose $x = 1$, the corresponding y-value is

$$y = 2(1) + 1 \qquad\qquad \text{Substitute 1 for } x.$$

$$y = 3. \qquad\qquad \text{Simplify.}$$

The corresponding ordered pair $(x, y) = (1, 3)$ is a **solution point** (or simply a **solution**) of the equation. The table below is a table of values (and the corresponding solution points) using x-values of -3, -2, -1, 0, 1, 2, and 3. These x-values are arbitrary. You should try to use x-values that are convenient and simple to use.

Choose x	Calculate y	Solution Points
$x = -3$	$y = 2(-3) + 1 = -5$	$(-3, -5)$
$x = -2$	$y = 2(-2) + 1 = -3$	$(-2, -3)$
$x = -1$	$y = 2(-1) + 1 = -1$	$(-1, -1)$
$x = 0$	$y = 2(0) + 1 = 1$	$(0, 1)$
$x = 1$	$y = 2(1) + 1 = 3$	$(1, 3)$
$x = 2$	$y = 2(2) + 1 = 5$	$(2, 5)$
$x = 3$	$y = 2(3) + 1 = 7$	$(3, 7)$

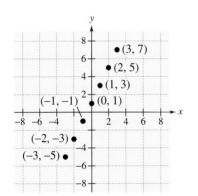

Figure 4.6

Once you have constructed a table of values, you can get a visual idea of the relationship between the variables x and y by plotting the solution points on a rectangular coordinate system. For instance, the solution points shown in the table are plotted in Figure 4.6.

In many places throughout this course, you will see that approaching a problem in different ways can help you understand the problem better. For instance, the discussion above looks at solutions of an equation in three ways.

▶ **Three Approaches to Problem Solving**

1. **Algebraic Approach** Use algebra to find several solutions.

2. **Numerical Approach** Construct a table that shows several solutions.

3. **Graphical Approach** Draw a graph that shows several solutions.

When making up a table of values for an equation, it is helpful first to solve the equation for y. For instance, the equation $4x + 2y = -8$ can be solved for y as follows.

$$4x + 2y = -8 \qquad \text{Original equation}$$

$$4x - 4x + 2y = -8 - 4x \qquad \text{Subtract } 4x \text{ from both sides.}$$

$$2y = -8 - 4x \qquad \text{Combine like terms.}$$

$$\frac{2y}{2} = \frac{-8 - 4x}{2} \qquad \text{Divide both sides by 2.}$$

$$y = -4 - 2x \qquad \text{Simplify.}$$

This procedure is further demonstrated in Example 4.

Example 4 Making Up a Table of Values

Make up a table of values showing five solution points for the equation

$$6x - 2y = 4.$$

Then plot the solution points on a rectangular coordinate system. (Choose x-values of $-2, -1, 0, 1,$ and 2.)

Solution

$$6x - 2y = 4 \qquad \text{Original equation}$$

$$6x - 6x - 2y = 4 - 6x \qquad \text{Subtract } 6x \text{ from both sides.}$$

$$-2y = -6x + 4 \qquad \text{Combine like terms.}$$

$$\frac{-2y}{-2} = \frac{-6x + 4}{-2} \qquad \text{Divide both sides by } -2.$$

$$y = 3x - 2 \qquad \text{Simplify.}$$

Now, using the equation $y = 3x - 2$, you can construct a table of values, as shown below.

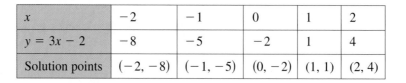

x	-2	-1	0	1	2
$y = 3x - 2$	-8	-5	-2	1	4
Solution points	$(-2, -8)$	$(-1, -5)$	$(0, -2)$	$(1, 1)$	$(2, 4)$

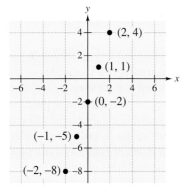

Figure 4.7

Finally, from the table you can plot the five solution points on a rectangular coordinate system, as shown in Figure 4.7.

> ▶ **Guidelines for Verifying Solutions**
>
> To verify that an ordered pair (x, y) is a solution to an equation with variables x and y, use the following steps.
>
> 1. Substitute the values of x and y into the equation.
>
> 2. Simplify both sides of the equation.
>
> 3. If both sides simplify to the same number, the ordered pair is a solution. If the two sides yield different numbers, the ordered pair is not a solution.

Example 5   Verifying Solutions of an Equation

Determine which of the following ordered pairs is a solution of $x + 3y = 6$.

a. $(1, 2)$ **b.** $\left(-2, \frac{8}{3}\right)$ **c.** $(-6, 0)$ **d.** $(0, 2)$ **e.** $\left(\frac{8}{3}, \frac{10}{9}\right)$

Solution

a. For the ordered pair $(x, y) = (1, 2)$, substitute $x = 1$ and $y = 2$ into the original equation.

$$x + 3y = 6 \qquad\qquad \text{Original equation}$$

$$1 + 3(2) \overset{?}{=} 6 \qquad\qquad \text{Substitute } x = 1 \text{ and } y = 2.$$

$$7 \neq 6 \qquad\qquad \text{Simplify.}$$

Because the substitution does not satisfy the original equation, the ordered pair $(1, 2)$ *is not* a solution of the equation.

b. For the ordered pair $(x, y) = \left(-2, \frac{8}{3}\right)$, substitute $x = -2$ and $y = \frac{8}{3}$ into the original equation.

$$x + 3y = 6 \qquad\qquad \text{Original equation}$$

$$(-2) + 3\left(\tfrac{8}{3}\right) \overset{?}{=} 6 \qquad\qquad \text{Substitute } x = -2 \text{ and } y = \tfrac{8}{3}.$$

$$-2 + 8 = 6 \qquad\qquad \text{Simplify.}$$

$$6 = 6 \qquad\qquad \text{Simplify.}$$

Because the substitution satisfies the original equation, the ordered pair $\left(-2, \frac{8}{3}\right)$ *is* a solution of the equation.

c. The ordered pair $(-6, 0)$ *is not* a solution of the original equation because

$$-6 + 3(0) = -6 \neq 6.$$

d. The ordered pair $(0, 2)$ *is* a solution of the original equation because

$$0 + 3(2) = 6.$$

e. The ordered pair $\left(\frac{8}{3}, \frac{10}{9}\right)$ *is* a solution of the original equation because

$$\frac{8}{3} + 3\left(\frac{10}{9}\right) = \frac{8}{3} + \frac{10}{3} = \frac{18}{3} = 6.$$

3 Use the verbal problem-solving method to plot points on a rectangular coordinate system.

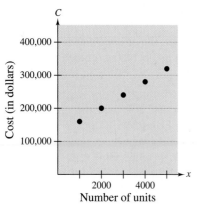

Figure 4.8

Application

Example 6   A Business Application

You are setting up a small business to assemble computer keyboards. Your initial cost is $120,000, and your unit cost to assemble each keyboard is $40. Write an equation that relates your total cost to the number of keyboards produced. Then plot the total costs of producing 1000, 2000, 3000, 4000, and 5000 keyboards.

Solution

The total cost equation must represent both the unit cost and the initial cost. A verbal model for this problem is as follows.

Verbal Model: Cost = Unit cost · Number of keyboards + Initial cost

Labels: Cost = C (dollars)
Unit cost = 40   (dollars per keyboard)
Number of keyboards = x (keyboards)
Initial cost = 120,000   (dollars)

Algebraic Model: $C = 40x + 120,000$

Using this equation, you can construct the following table of values.

x	1000	2000	3000	4000	5000
$C = 40x + 120,000$	160,000	200,000	240,000	280,000	320,000

From the table you can plot the ordered pairs, as shown in Figure 4.8.

Discussing the Concept   Misleading Graphs

Although graphs can help us visualize relationships between two variables, they can also be misleading. The graphs shown below represent the same data points. Which graph is misleading? Why?

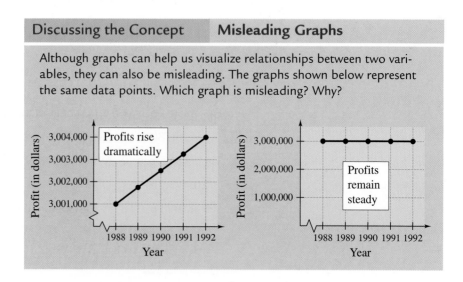

4.1   Exercises

Integrated Review   *Concepts, Skills, and Problem Solving*

Keep mathematically in shape by doing these exercises *before* the problems of this section.

Properties and Definitions

1. Is $3x = 7$ a linear equation? Explain. Is $x^2 + 3x = 2$ a linear equation? Explain.

2. Explain how to check whether $x = 3$ is a solution to the equation $5x - 4 = 11$.

Solving Equations

In Exercises 3–10, solve the equation.

3. $-y = 10$

4. $10 - t = 6$

5. $3x - 42 = 0$

6. $64 - 16x = 0$

7. $125(r - 1) = 625$

8. $2(3 - y) = 7y + 5$

9. $20 - \frac{1}{9}x = 4$

10. $0.35x = 70$

Problem Solving

11. The total cost of a lot and house is $154,000. The cost of constructing the house is 7 times the cost of the lot. What is the cost of the lot?

12. You have two summer jobs. In the first job, you work 40 hours a week and earn $9.50 an hour. In the second job, you work as many hours as you want and earn $8 an hour. If you plan to earn $450 a week, how many hours a week should you work at the second job?

Developing Skills

In Exercises 1–10, plot the points on a rectangular coordinate system. See Example 1.

1. $(3, 2), (-4, 2), (2, -4)$

2. $(-1, 6), (-1, -6), (4, 6)$

3. $(-10, -4), (4, -4), (4, 3)$

4. $(-6, 4), (0, 0), (3, -2)$

5. $(-3, 4), (0, -1), (2, -2), (5, 0)$

6. $(-1, 3), (0, 2), (-4, -4), (-1, 0)$

7. $\left(\frac{3}{2}, -1\right), \left(-3, \frac{3}{4}\right), \left(\frac{1}{2}, -\frac{1}{2}\right)$

8. $\left(-\frac{2}{3}, 4\right), \left(\frac{1}{2}, -\frac{5}{2}\right), \left(-4, -\frac{5}{4}\right)$

9. $(3, -4), \left(\frac{5}{2}, 0\right), (0, 3)$ **10.** $\left(\frac{5}{2}, 2\right), \left(-3, \frac{4}{3}\right), \left(\frac{3}{4}, \frac{9}{4}\right)$

In Exercises 11–14, determine the coordinates of the points. See Example 2.

11.

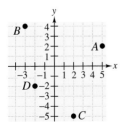

12.

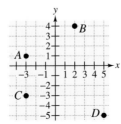

13.

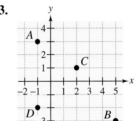

14.

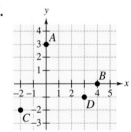

In Exercises 15–20, determine the quadrant in which the point is located.

15. $(-3, 1)$

16. $(4, -3)$

17. $\left(-\frac{1}{8}, -\frac{2}{7}\right)$

18. $\left(\frac{3}{11}, \frac{7}{8}\right)$

19. $(-100, -365.6)$

20. $(-157.4, 305.6)$

In Exercises 21–26, determine the quadrant or quadrants in which the point must be located.

21. $(-5, y)$, y is a real number.

22. $(6, y)$, y is a real number.

23. $(x, -2)$, x is a real number.

24. $(x, 3)$, x is a real number.

25. $(x, y), xy < 0$

26. $(x, y), xy > 0$

In Exercises 27–30, find the coordinates of the point.

27. The point is on the y-axis and 3 units above the x-axis.

28. The point is on the x-axis and 2 units to the left of the y-axis.

29. The point is 5 units to the left of the y-axis and 10 units below the x-axis.

30. The point is 12 units to the right of the y-axis and 4 units below the x-axis.

In Exercises 31–38, plot the points and connect them with line segments to form the figure.

31. Triangle: $(-1, 1)$, $(2, -1)$, $(3, 4)$

32. Triangle: $(0, 3)$, $(-1, -2)$, $(4, 8)$

33. Square: $(2, 4)$, $(5, 1)$, $(2, -2)$, $(-1, 1)$

34. Rectangle: $(2, 1)$, $(4, 2)$, $(-1, 7)$, $(1, 8)$

35. Parallelogram: $(5, 2)$, $(7, 0)$, $(1, -2)$, $(-1, 0)$

36. Parallelogram: $(-1, 1)$, $(0, 4)$, $(4, -2)$, $(5, 1)$

37. Rhombus: $(0, 0)$, $(3, 2)$, $(2, 3)$, $(5, 5)$

38. Rhombus: $(0, 0)$, $(1, 2)$, $(2, 1)$, $(3, 3)$

In Exercises 39–44, complete the table. Plot the results on a rectangular coordinate system. See Example 4.

39.

x	-2	0	2	4	6
$y = 3x - 4$					

40.

x	-2	0	2	4	6
$y = \frac{1}{4}x + 1$					

41.

x		-4	-2	4	6	8
$y = -\frac{3}{2}x + 5$						

42.

x	-4	-2	0	2	4
$y = -\frac{1}{2}x + 3$					

43.

x	-2	-1	0	1	2
$y = 2x - 1$					

44.

x	-2	0	$\frac{1}{2}$	2	4
$y = -\frac{7}{2}x + 3$					

In Exercises 45–50, solve the equation for y. See Example 4.

45. $6x - 3y = 3$ **46.** $2x + y = 1$ **47.** $x + 4y = 8$

48. $x - 2y = -6$ **49.** $4x - 5y = 3$ **50.** $4y - 3x = 7$

In Exercises 51–58, determine whether each ordered pair is a solution of the equation. See Example 5.

51. $y = 2x + 4$ (a) $(3, 10)$ (b) $(-1, 3)$
                        (c) $(0, 0)$ (d) $(-2, 0)$

52. $y = 5x - 2$ (a) $(2, 0)$ (b) $(-2, -12)$
                        (c) $(6, 28)$ (d) $(1, 1)$

53. $2y - 3x + 1 = 0$ (a) $(1, 1)$ (b) $(5, 7)$
                        (c) $(-3, -1)$ (d) $(-3, -5)$

54. $x - 8y + 10 = 0$ (a) $(-2, 1)$ (b) $(6, 2)$
                        (c) $(0, -1)$ (d) $(2, -4)$

55. $y = \frac{2}{3}x$ (a) $(6, 6)$ (b) $(-9, -6)$
                        (c) $(0, 0)$ (d) $\left(-1, \frac{2}{3}\right)$

56. $y = 5x - 2$ (a) $\left(-\frac{4}{5}, 1\right)$ (b) $(0, 0)$
                        (c) $\left(-\frac{2}{5}, -4\right)$ (d) $\left(\frac{3}{5}, 1\right)$

57. $y = 3 - 4x$ (a) $\left(-\frac{1}{2}, 5\right)$ (b) $(1, 7)$
                        (c) $(0, 0)$ (d) $\left(-\frac{3}{4}, 0\right)$

58. $y = \frac{3}{2}x + 1$ (a) $\left(0, \frac{3}{2}\right)$ (b) $(4, 7)$
                        (c) $\left(\frac{2}{3}, 2\right)$ (d) $(-2, -2)$

Solving Problems

59. *Organizing Data* The distance y (in centimeters) a spring is compressed by a force x (in kilograms) is given by $y = 0.066x$. Complete a table for $x = 20$, 40, 60, 80, and 100 to determine the distance the spring is compressed for each of the specified forces. Plot the results on a rectangular coordinate system.

60. *Organizing Data* A company buys a new copier for $9500. Its value y after x years is given by $y = -800x + 9500$. Complete a table for $x = 0, 2$, 4, 6, and 8 to determine the value of the copier at the specified times. Plot the results on a rectangular coordinate system.

61. *Organizing Data* With an initial cost of $5000, a company will produce *x* units at $35 per unit. Write an equation that relates the total cost of producing *x* units to the number of units produced. Plot the cost for producing 100, 150, 200, 250, and 300 units.

62. *Organizing Data* An employee earns $10 plus $0.50 for every *x* units produced per hour. Write an equation that relates the employee's total hourly wage to the number of units produced. Plot the hourly wage for producing 2, 5, 8, 10, and 20 units per hour.

63. *Organizing Data* The table gives the normal temperature *y* (in degrees Fahrenheit) for Anchorage, Alaska for each month *x* of the year. The months are numbered 1 through 12, with *x* = 1 corresponding to January. (Source: National Oceanic and Atmospheric Administration)

x	1	2	3	4	5	6
y	13	18	24	35	46	54
x	7	8	9	10	11	12
y	58	56	48	35	22	14

(a) Plot the data given in the table.

(b) Did you use the same scale on both axes? Explain.

(c) Using the graph, find the three consecutive months when the normal temperature changes the least.

64. *Organizing Data* The table gives the speed of a car *x* (in kilometers per hour) and the approximate stopping distance *y* (in meters).

x	50	70	90	110	130
y	20	35	60	95	148

(a) Plot the data given in the table.

(b) The *x*-coordinates increase at equal increments of 20 kilometers per hour. Describe the pattern for the *y*-coordinates. What are the implications for the driver?

65. *Graphical Interpretation* The table gives the numbers of hours *x* that a student studied for five different algebra exams and the resulting scores *y*.

x	3.5	1	8	4.5	0.5
y	72	67	95	81	53

(a) Plot the data given in the table.

(b) Use the graph to describe the relationship between the number of hours studied and the resulting exam score.

66. *Graphical Interpretation* The table gives the net income *y* per share of common stock of the H. J. Heinz Company for the years 1988 through 1997. The year is represented by *x*. (Source: H. J. Heinz Company 1997 Annual Report)

x	1988	1989	1990	1991	1992
y	$0.97	$1.11	$1.26	$1.42	$1.60
x	1993	1994	1995	1996	1997
y	$1.02	$1.57	$1.59	$1.75	$0.81

(a) Plot the data given in the table.

(b) Use the graph to find the year that had the greatest increase and the year that had the greatest decrease in the income per share.

Graphical Estimation In Exercises 67–70, use the scatter plot showing new privately-owned housing unit starts (in thousands) in the United States from 1985 through 1997. (Source: U.S. Bureau of the Census)

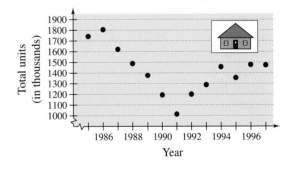

67. Estimate the number of new housing starts in 1986.

68. Estimate the number of new housing starts in 1991.

69. Estimate the increase and the percent increase in housing starts from 1993 to 1994.

70. Estimate the decrease and the percent decrease in housing starts from 1994 to 1995.

Graphical Estimation In Exercises 71–74, use the scatter plot showing the per capita personal income in the United States from 1990 through 1997. (Source: U.S. Bureau of Economic Analysis)

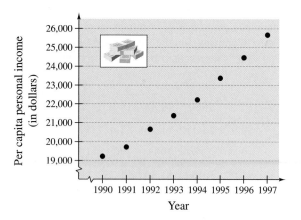

71. Estimate the personal income in 1992.

72. Estimate the personal income in 1995.

73. Estimate the percent increase in personal income from 1996 to 1997.

74. Estimate the percent increase in personal income from 1980 to 1990 if the per capita income in 1980 was $11,892.

Graphical Estimation In Exercises 75 and 76, use the bar graph, which compares the percents of gross domestic product spent on health care in several countries in 1995. (Source: Organization for Economic Cooperation and Development)

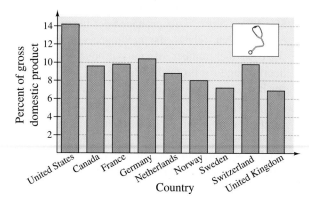

75. Estimate the percent of gross domestic product spent on health care in Sweden.

76. Estimate the percent of gross domestic product spent on health care in the United States.

Explaining Concepts

77. (a) Plot the points $(3, 2)$, $(-5, 4)$, and $(6, -4)$ on a rectangular coordinate system.

   (b) Change the sign of the x-coordinate of each point. Plot the three new points on the same axes.

   (c) What can you infer about the location of a point when the sign of the x-coordinate is changed?

78. (a) Plot the points $(3, 2)$, $(-5, 4)$, and $(6, -4)$ on a rectangular coordinate system.

   (b) Change the sign of the y-coordinate of each point. Plot the three new points on the same axes.

   (c) What can you infer about the location of a point when the sign of the y-coordinate is changed?

79. Discuss the significance of the word "ordered" when referring to an ordered pair (x, y).

80. When the point (x, y) is plotted, what does the x-coordinate measure? What does the y-coordinate measure?

81. What is the x-coordinate of any point on the y-axis? What is the y-coordinate of any point on the x-axis?

82. Describe the signs of the x- and y-coordinates of points that lie in the first and second quadrants.

83. Describe the signs of the x- and y-coordinates of points that lie in the third and fourth quadrants.

84. In a rectangular coordinate system, must the scales on the x-axis and y-axis be the same? If not, give an example in which the scales differ.

85. Review the tables in Exercises 39–44 and observe that in some cases the y-coordinates of the solution points increase and in others the y-coordinates decrease. What factor in the equation causes this? Explain.

4.2   Graphs of Equations in Two Variables

Objectives

1 Sketch the graph of an equation using the point-plotting method.

2 Find and use *x*- and *y*-intercepts as aids to sketching graphs.

3 Use the verbal problem-solving method to write an equation and sketch its graph.

---

1 Sketch the graph of an equation using the point-plotting method.

x	$y = 2x - 1$
-3	-7
-2	-5
-1	-3
0	-1
1	1
2	3
3	5

The Graph of an Equation

You have already seen that the solutions of an equation involving two variables can be represented by points on a rectangular coordinate system. The set of all such points is called the **graph** of the equation.

To see how to sketch a graph, let's begin with an example. For instance, consider the equation

$$y = 2x - 1.$$

To begin sketching the graph of this equation, construct a table of values, as shown at the left. Next, plot the solution points on a rectangular coordinate system, as shown in Figure 4.9(a). Finally, find a pattern for the plotted points and use the pattern to connect the points with a smooth curve or line, as shown in Figure 4.9(b).

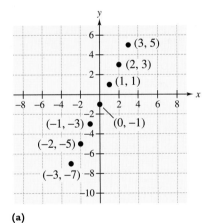

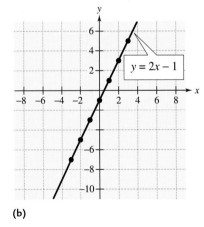

(a)   (b)

Figure 4.9

> ▶ **The Point-Plotting Method of Sketching a Graph**
>
> **1.** If possible, rewrite the equation by isolating one of the variables.
>
> **2.** Make up a table of values showing several solution points.
>
> **3.** Plot these points on a rectangular coordinate system.
>
> **4.** Connect the points with a smooth curve or line.

| Example 1 | Sketching the Graph of an Equation |

Sketch the graph of $3x + y = 5$.

Solution

To begin, rewrite the equation so that y is isolated on the left.

$$3x + y = 5 \qquad \text{Original equation}$$

$$3x - 3x + y = -3x + 5 \qquad \text{Subtract } 3x \text{ from both sides.}$$

$$y = -3x + 5 \qquad \text{Simplify.}$$

Next, create a table of values, as shown below.

x	-2	-1	0	1	2	3
$y = -3x + 5$	11	8	5	2	-1	-4
Solution	$(-2, 11)$	$(-1, 8)$	$(0, 5)$	$(1, 2)$	$(2, -1)$	$(3, -4)$

Plot the six solution points, as shown in Figure 4.10(a). It appears that all six points lie on a line, so you can complete the sketch by drawing a line through the six points, as shown in Figure 4.10(b).

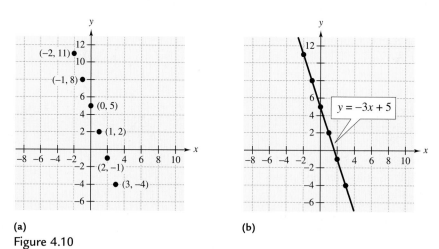

(a)   (b)

Figure 4.10

When creating a table of values, you are generally free to choose any x-values. When doing this, however, remember that the more x-values you choose, the easier it will be to recognize a pattern.

The equation in Example 1 is an example of a **linear equation** in two variables—the variables are raised to the first power and the graph of the equation is a straight line. As shown in the next two examples, graphs of nonlinear equations are not straight lines.

Technology: Discovery

Most graphing utilities have the following standard viewing window.

Xmin = -10
Xmax = 10
Xscl = 1
Ymin = -10
Ymax = 10
Yscl = 1

What happens when the equation $x + y = 12$ is graphed in a standard viewing window?

To see where the equation crosses the x- and y-axes, you need to change the viewing window. What changes would you make to the viewing window to see where the line intersects the axes?

Graph each of the following equations on a graphing utility and describe the viewing window used.

a. $y = \left| \frac{1}{2}x + 6 \right|$

b. $y = 2x^2 + 5x + 10$

c. $y = 10 - x$

d. $y = -3x^3 + 5x + 8$

Example 2   Sketching the Graph of a Nonlinear Equation

Sketch the graph of $x^2 + y = 4$.

Solution

To begin, rewrite the equation so that y is isolated on the left.

$$x^2 + y = 4 \qquad \text{Original equation}$$

$$x^2 - x^2 + y = -x^2 + 4 \qquad \text{Subtract } x^2 \text{ from both sides.}$$

$$y = -x^2 + 4 \qquad \text{Simplify.}$$

Next, create a table of values, as shown below. Be careful with the signs of the numbers when creating a table. For instance, when $x = -3$, the value of y is

$$y = -(-3)^2 + 4$$

$$= -9 + 4$$

$$= -5.$$

x	-3	-2	-1	0	1	2	3
$y = -x^2 + 4$	-5	0	3	4	3	0	-5
Solution	$(-3, -5)$	$(-2, 0)$	$(-1, 3)$	$(0, 4)$	$(1, 3)$	$(2, 0)$	$(3, -5)$

Plot the seven solution points, as shown in Figure 4.11(a). Finally, connect the points with a smooth curve, as shown in Figure 4.11(b).

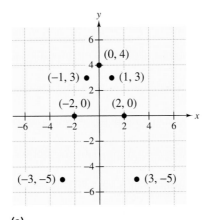

(a)

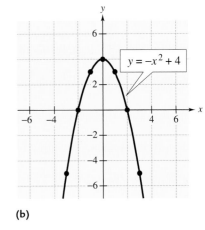

(b)

Figure 4.11

The graph of the equation in Example 2 is called a **parabola.** You will study this type of graph in a later chapter.

Example 3 examines the graph of an equation that involves an absolute value. Remember that to find the absolute value of a number, you disregard the sign of the number. For instance, $|-5| = 5$, $|2| = 2$, and $|0| = 0$.

> **Example 3**   The Graph of an Equation Having an Absolute Value

Sketch the graph of $y = |x - 1|$.

Solution

This equation is already written in a form with y isolated on the left. You can begin by creating a table of values, as shown below. Be sure to check the values in this table to make sure that you understand how the absolute value is working. For instance, when $x = -2$, the value of y is

$$y = |-2 - 1|$$
$$= |-3|$$
$$= 3.$$

Similarly, when $x = 2$, the value of y is $|2 - 1|$ or 1.

x	-2	-1	0	1	2	3	4
$y = |x - 1|$	3	2	1	0	1	2	3
Solution	$(-2, 3)$	$(-1, 2)$	$(0, 1)$	$(1, 0)$	$(2, 1)$	$(3, 2)$	$(4, 3)$

Plot the seven solution points, as shown in Figure 4.12(a). It appears that the points lie in a "V-shaped" pattern, with the point $(1, 0)$ lying at the bottom of the "V." Following this pattern, you can connect the points to form the graph shown in Figure 4.12(b).

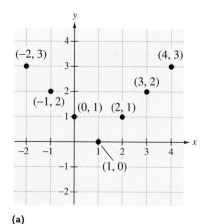

(a)

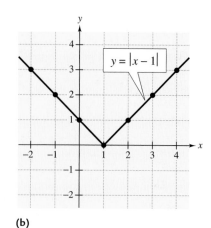

(b)

Figure 4.12

2 Find and use x- and y-intercepts as aids to sketching graphs.

Intercepts: An Aid to Sketching Graphs

Two types of solution points that are especially useful are those having zero as either the x- or y-coordinate. Such points are called **intercepts** because they are the points at which the graph intersects the x- or y-axis.

> ▶ **Definition of Intercepts**
>
> The point $(a, 0)$ is called an **x-intercept** of the graph of an equation if it is a solution point of the equation. To find the x-intercept(s), let y be zero and solve the equation for x.
>
> The point $(0, b)$ is called a **y-intercept** of the graph of an equation if it is a solution point of the equation. To find the y-intercept(s), let x be zero and solve the equation for y.

> **Example 4**   Finding the Intercepts of a Graph

Find the intercepts and sketch the graph of

$$y = 2x - 5.$$

Solution

To find any x-intercepts, let $y = 0$ and solve the resulting equation for x.

$$y = 2x - 5 \qquad \text{Original equation}$$

$$0 = 2x - 5 \qquad \text{Let } y = 0.$$

$$\frac{5}{2} = x \qquad \text{Solve equation for } x.$$

So, the graph has one x-intercept, which occurs at the point $\left(\frac{5}{2}, 0\right)$. To find any y-intercepts, let $x = 0$ and solve the resulting equation for y.

$$y = 2x - 5 \qquad \text{Original equation}$$

$$y = 2(0) - 5 \qquad \text{Let } x = 0.$$

$$y = -5 \qquad \text{Solve equation for } y.$$

So, the graph has one y-intercept, which occurs at the point $(0, -5)$. To sketch the graph of the equation, create a table of values (as follows). Then plot the points and connect the points with a line, as shown in Figure 4.13.

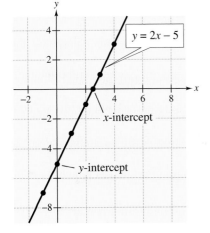

Figure 4.13

x	-1	0	1	2	$\frac{5}{2}$	3	4
$y = 2x - 5$	-7	-5	-3	-1	0	1	3
Solution	$(-1, -7)$	$(0, -5)$	$(1, -3)$	$(2, -1)$	$\left(\frac{5}{2}, 0\right)$	$(3, 1)$	$(4, 3)$

When you create a table of values, include any intercepts you have found. You should also include points to the left and to the right of the intercepts.

3 Use the verbal problem-solving method to write an equation and sketch its graph.

Application

| Example 5 | Depreciation | |

The value of a $25,500 van depreciates over 10 years. At the end of the 10 years, the salvage value is expected to be $1500. Find an equation that relates the value of the van to the number of years. Then sketch the graph of the equation. (The depreciation is the same each year.)

Solution

The total depreciation over the 10 years is $25,500 - 1500 = \$24,000$. Because the same amount is depreciated each year, it follows that the annual depreciation is $24,000/10 = \$2400$.

Verbal Model:

| Value after t years | = | Original value | − | Annual depreciation | · | Number of years |

Labels:

Value after t years = y	(dollars)
Original value = 25,500	(dollars)
Annual depreciation = 2400	(dollars per year)
Number of years = t	(years)

Algebraic Model:

$$y = 25,500 - 2400t$$

A sketch of the graph of this equation is shown in Figure 4.14. Note that the y-intercept (0, 25,500) corresponds to the original value of the van.

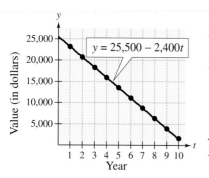

$y = 25,500 - 2,400t$

Figure 4.14

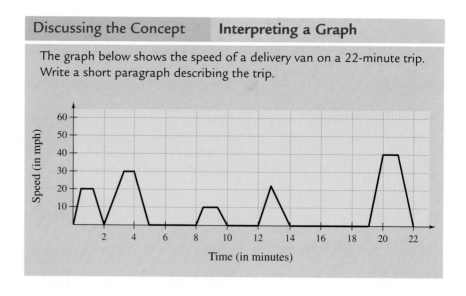

Discussing the Concept   Interpreting a Graph

The graph below shows the speed of a delivery van on a 22-minute trip. Write a short paragraph describing the trip.

4.2   Exercises

Integrated Review   *Concepts, Skills, and Problem Solving*

Keep mathematically in shape by doing these exercises *before* the problems of this section.

Properties and Definitions

1. If $x - 2 > 5$ and c is an algebraic expression, then what is the relationship between $x - 2 + c$ and $5 + c$?

2. If $x - 2 < 5$ and $c < 0$, then what is the relationship between $(x - 2)c$ and $5c$?

3. Complete the Multiplicative Inverse Property: $x(1/x) = $ _____ .

4. Name the property illustrated by $x + y = y + x$.

Simplifying Expressions

In Exercises 5–10, simplify the expression.

5. $-3(3x - 2y) + 5y$ **6.** $3z - (4 - 5z)$

7. $-y^2(y^2 + 4) + 6y^2$ **8.** $5t(2 - t) + t^2$

9. $3[6x - 5(x - 2)]$ **10.** $5(t - 2) - 5(t - 2)$

Problem Solving

11. A company pays its sales representatives $30 per day plus 32 cents per mile for the use of their personal cars. A sales representative submits a bill for $50.80 for driving her own car.

(a) How many miles did she drive?

(b) How many days did she drive? Explain.

(c) Suppose the bill had been submitted for $96.80. Could you determine how many days and miles were claimed? Explain.

12. The width of a rectangular mirror is $\frac{3}{5}$ its length. The perimeter of the mirror is 80 inches. What are the measurements of the mirror?

Developing Skills

In Exercises 1–8, match the equation with its graph. [The graphs are labeled (a), (b), (c), (d), (e), (f), (g), and (h).]

(a)

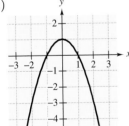

(b)
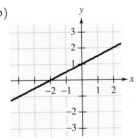

(c)
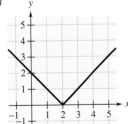

(d)
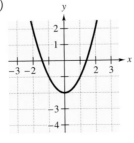

(e)
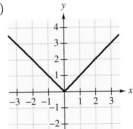

(f)
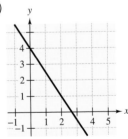

(g)
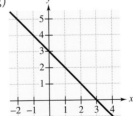

(h)
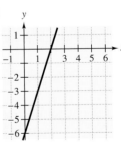

1. $y = 3 - x$ **2.** $y = \frac{1}{2}x + 1$

3. $y = -x^2 + 1$ **4.** $y = |x|$

5. $y = 3x - 6$ **6.** $y = |x - 2|$

7. $y = x^2 - 2$ **8.** $y = 4 - \frac{3}{2}x$

In Exercises 9–16, complete the table and use the results to sketch a graph of the equation. See Examples 1–3.

9. $y = 9 - x$

x	-2	-1	0	1	2
y					

10. $y = x - 1$

x	-2	-1	0	1	2
y					

11. $y = 4x - 2$

x	-2	-1	0	1	2
y					

12. $y = 7 - \frac{3}{2}x$

x	-2	0	2	4	6
y					

13. $x + 2y = 4$

x	-2	0	2	4	6
y					

14. $3x - 2y = 6$

x	-2	0	2	4	6
y					

15. $y = |x + 1|$

x	-3	-2	-1	0	1
y					

16. $y = (x - 1)^2$

x	-1	0	1	2	3
y					

In Exercises 17–24, estimate the x- and y-intercepts from the graph. Check your results algebraically.

17. $4x - 2y = -8$

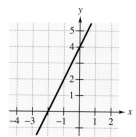

18. $5y - 2x = 10$

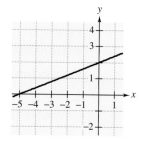

19. $x + 3y = 6$

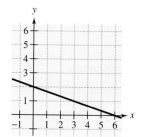

20. $4x + 3y = 12$

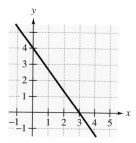

21. $y = |x| - 3$

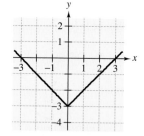

22. $y = 4 - |x|$

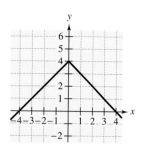

23. $y = 16 - x^2$

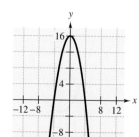

24. $y = x^2 - 4$

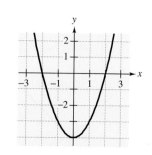

In Exercises 25–36, find the x- and y-intercepts (if any) of the graph of the equation. See Example 4.

25. $y = 6x + 2$

26. $y = -3x + 5$

27. $y = \frac{1}{2}x - 1$

28. $y = -\frac{1}{2}x + 3$

29. $x - y = 1$

30. $x + y = 10$

31. $2x + y = 4$

32. $3x - 2y = 1$

33. $2x + 6y - 9 = 0$

34. $2x - 5y + 50 = 0$

35. $\frac{3}{4}x - \frac{1}{2}y = 3$

36. $\frac{1}{2}x + \frac{2}{3}y = 1$

In Exercises 37–62, sketch the graph of the equation and label the coordinates of at least three solution points.

37. $y = 2 - x$

38. $y = x + 3$

39. $y = x - 1$

40. $y = 5 - x$

41. $y = 3x$

42. $y = -2x$

43. $2x - y = 4$

44. $2x + y = -2$

45. $10x + 5y = 20$

46. $7x - 7y = 14$

47. $4x + y = 2$

48. $y - 2x = 3$

49. $y = \frac{3}{8}x + 15$

50. $y = 14 - \frac{2}{3}x$

51. $y = \frac{2}{3}x - 5$

52. $y = \frac{3}{2}x + 3$

53. $y = x^2$

54. $y = -x^2$

55. $y = -x^2 + 9$

56. $y = x^2 - 1$

57. $y = (x - 3)^2$

58. $y = -(x + 2)^2$

59. $y = |x - 5|$

60. $y = |x + 3|$

61. $y = 5 - |x|$

62. $y = |x| - 3$

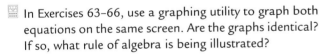 In Exercises 63–66, use a graphing utility to graph both equations on the same screen. Are the graphs identical? If so, what rule of algebra is being illustrated?

63. $y_1 = \frac{1}{3}x - 1$

  $y_2 = -1 + \frac{1}{3}x$

64. $y_1 = 3\left(\frac{1}{4}x\right)$

  $y_2 = \left(3 \cdot \frac{1}{4}\right)x$

65. $y_1 = 2(x - 2)$

  $y_2 = 2x - 4$

66. $y_1 = 2 + (x + 4)$

  $y_2 = (2 + x) + 4$

In Exercises 67–74, use a graphing utility to graph the equation. (Use a standard setting.)

67. $y = 4x$

68. $y = -2x$

69. $y = -\frac{1}{3}x$

70. $y = \frac{1}{2}x$

71. $y = -2x^2 + 5$

72. $y = x^2 - 7$

73. $y = |x + 1| - 2$

74. $y = 4 - |x - 2|$

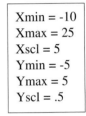 In Exercises 75–78, use a graphing utility to graph the equation. Use the viewing window given.

75. $y = 25 - 5x$

76. $y = 8x + 20$

```
Xmin = -5
Xmax = 7
Xscl = 1
Ymin = -5
Ymax = 30
Yscl = 5
```

```
Xmin = -5
Xmax = 5
Xscl = 1
Ymin = -10
Ymax = 30
Yscl = 5
```

77. $y = 2.3x - 4.1$

78. $y = 1.7 - 0.1x$

```
Xmin = -5
Xmax = 5
Xscl = 1
Ymin = -10
Ymax = 5
Yscl = 1
```

```
Xmin = -10
Xmax = 25
Xscl = 5
Ymin = -5
Ymax = 5
Yscl = .5
```

 In Exercises 79–82, use a graphing utility to graph the equation and find a viewing window that yields a graph that matches the one shown.

79. $y = \frac{1}{2}x + 2$

80. $y = 2x - 1$

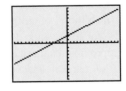

81. $y = \frac{1}{4}x^2 - 4x + 12$

82. $y = 16 - 4x - x^2$

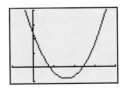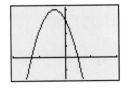

Solving Problems

83. *Creating a Model* Let y represent the distance traveled by a car that is moving at a constant speed of 35 miles per hour. Let t represent the number of hours the car has traveled. Write an equation that relates y to t and sketch its graph.

84. *Creating a Model* The cost of printing a book is $500, plus $5 per book. Let C represent the total cost and let x represent the number of books. Write an equation that relates C and x and sketch its graph.

85. *Modeling Data* The table gives the life expectancy (in years) in the United States for a child at birth for various years. A model for the life expectancy during this period is $y = 0.2t + 66.7$, with $t = 0$ corresponding to 1950. (Source: U.S. Bureau of the Census)

t	-10	0	10	20	30	40	45
y	62.9	68.2	69.7	70.8	73.7	75.4	75.8

(a) Graph the data and the model.

(b) Predict the life expectancy for a child born in 2010.

86. *Modeling Data* The table gives the number of passengers x (in millions) in the U.S. scheduled airline industry and the revenue y (in billions of dollars) generated by the passengers for the years 1990 through 1996. A model that approximates these data is $y = 0.1344x - 3.7122$. (Source: Air Transport Association of America)

Year	1990	1991	1992	1993	1994	1995	1996
x	465.6	452.3	475.1	488.5	528.8	547.8	581.2
y	58.5	57.1	59.8	63.9	65.4	69.6	75.3

(a) Plot the points that represent the actual data.

(b) On the same axes, graph the model.

(c) Predict passenger-generated revenue for a year when there are 600 million passengers.

87. *Graphical Comparisons* The graphs of two types of depreciation are shown. In one type, called *straight-line depreciation,* the value depreciates by the same amount each year. In the other type, called *declining balances,* the value depreciates by the same percent each year. Which is which?

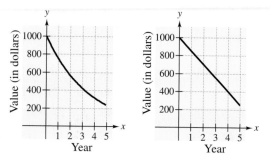

Figures for 87

88. *Graphical Interpretation* In Exercise 87, what is the original cost of the equipment that is being depreciated?

89. *Writing* Compare the benefits and disadvantages of the two types of depreciation shown in Exercise 87.

90. *Interpreting Intercepts* The model $5F - 9C = 160$ relates the temperature in degrees Celsius C and degrees Fahrenheit F.

(a) Graph the equation where F is measured on the horizontal axis.

(b) Explain what the intercepts represent.

Explaining Concepts

91. In your own words, define what is meant by the *graph* of an equation.

92. How many solution points can an equation in two variables have? How many points do you need to plot the general shape of the graph?

93. In your own words, describe the point-plotting method of sketching the graph of an equation.

94. In your own words, describe how you can check that an ordered pair (x, y) is a solution of an equation.

95. Explain how to find the x- and y-intercepts of a graph.

96. You are walking toward an object. Let x represent the time (in seconds) and let y represent the distance (in feet) between you and the object. Sketch a possible graph that shows how x and y are related.

97. *Research Project* Use a newspaper or a weekly news magazine to find examples of misleading graphs and explain why they are misleading.

4.3   Relations, Functions, and Graphs

Objectives

1 Identify the domain and range of a relation.

2 Determine if a relation is a function by inspection or by using the Vertical Line Test.

3 Use function notation and evaluate a function.

1 Identify the domain and range of a relation.

Relations

Many everyday occurrences involve pairs of quantities that are matched with each other by some rule of correspondence. For instance, each person is matched with a birth month (person, month); the number of hours worked is matched with a paycheck (hours, pay); an instructor is matched with a course (instructor, course); and the time of day is matched with the outside temperature (time, temperature). In each instance, sets of ordered pairs can be formed. Such sets of ordered pairs are called **relations.**

▶ **Definition of a Relation**

A **relation** is any set of ordered pairs. The set of first components in the ordered pairs is the **domain** of the relation. The set of second components is the **range** of the relation.

In mathematics, relations are commonly described by ordered pairs of *numbers*. The set of *x*-coordinates is the domain and the set of *y*-coordinates is the range. In the relation

$$\{(3, 5), (1, 2), (4, 4), (0, 3)\}$$

the domain D and range R are the sets

$$D = \{3, 1, 4, 0\} \quad \text{and} \quad R = \{5, 2, 4, 3\}.$$

Example 1   Analyzing a Relation

Find the domain and range of the relation

$$\{(0, 1), (1, 3), (2, 5), (3, 5), (0, 3)\}.$$

Then sketch a graphic representation of the relation.

Solution

The domain and range are

$$D = \{0, 1, 2, 3\} \quad \text{and} \quad R = \{1, 3, 5\}.$$

A graphic representation is shown in Figure 4.15.

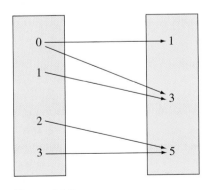

Figure 4.15

Functions

In the study of mathematics and its applications, the focus is mainly on a special type of relation, called a **function.**

> ▶ **Definition of a Function**
>
> A **function** is a relation in which no two ordered pairs have the same first component and a different second component.

This definition means that a given first component cannot be paired with two different second components. For instance, the pairs $(1, 3)$ and $(1, -1)$ cannot be part of a function.

Consider the relations described at the beginning of this section.

Relation	Ordered Pairs	Sample Relation
1	(person, month)	{(A, May), (B, Dec), (C, Oct), . . .}
2	(hours, pay)	{(12, 84), (4, 28), (6, 42), (15, 105), . . .}
3	(instructor, course)	{(A, MATH001), (A, MATH002), . . .}
4	(time, temperature)	{(8, 70°), (10, 78°), (12, 78°), . . .}

The first relation *is* a function because each person has only one birth month. The second relation *is* a function because the given number of hours worked at a particular job can yield only *one* paycheck amount. The third relation *is not* a function because an instructor can teach more than one course. The fourth relation *is* a function. Note that the ordered pairs $(10, 78°)$ and $(12, 78°)$ do not violate the definition of a function.

Study Tip

The ordered pairs of a relation can be thought of in the form (input, output). For a *function*, a given input cannot yield two different outputs. For instance, if the input is a person's name and the output is that person's month of birth, then your name as the input can yield only your month of birth as the output.

Example 2 Testing Whether a Relation Is a Function

Which of the relations are functions?

a. Input: a, b, c
Output: 2, 3, 4
{(a, 2), (b, 3), (c, 4)}

b.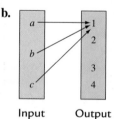
Input   Output

c.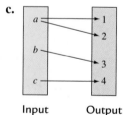
Input   Output

Solution

a. No first component has two different second components, so the relation *is* a function.

b. No first component has two different second components, so the relation *is* a function.

c. Because the first component a is paired with two different second components, this relation *is not* a function.

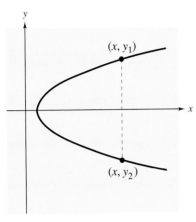

Figure 4.16

In algebra, it is common to represent functions by equations in two variables rather than by ordered pairs. For instance, the equation $y = x^2$ represents the variable y as a function of x. The variable x is the **independent variable** (the input) and y is the **dependent variable** (the output). In this context, the domain of the function is the set of all *allowable* values for x, and the range is the *resulting* set of all values taken on by the dependent variable y.

From the graph of an equation, it is easy to determine whether the equation represents y as a function of x. For instance, the graph in Figure 4.16 *does not* represent a function of x because the indicated value of x is paired with two y-values. Graphically, this means that a vertical line intersects the graph more than once. See Figure 4.16.

▶ **Vertical Line Test**

A graph is not the graph of a function if a vertical line can be drawn that intersects the graph at more than one point.

Example 3   Using the Vertical Line Test for Functions

Determine if the relation is a function using the Vertical Line Test.

a.

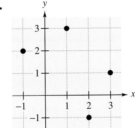

b.

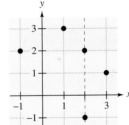

c.

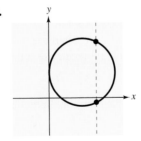

d.

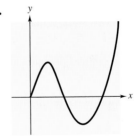

Solution

a. This relation *is* a function. No vertical line intersects more than one point on the graph.

b. This relation *is not* a function. A vertical line intersects more than one point on the graph.

c. This relation *is not* a function. A vertical line intersects more than one point on the graph.

d. This relation *is* a function. No vertical line intersects more than one point on the graph.

3 Use function notation and evaluate a function.

Function Notation

To discuss functions represented by equations, it is often convenient to give them names using **function notation.** For instance, the function

$$y = 2x - 6$$

can be given the name "f" and written in function notation as

$$f(x) = 2x - 6.$$

The Granger Collection

Leonhard Euler

(1707–1783)

Leonhard Euler, a Swiss mathematician, is considered to have been the most prolific and productive mathematician in history. One of his greatest influences on mathematics was his use of symbols, or notation. The notation $y = f(x)$ was introduced by Euler.

Remind students to use the order of operations as they evaluate functions.

▶ **$f(x)$ Notation**

In the notation $f(x)$:

f is the **name** of the function.

x is a **domain** value.

$f(x)$ is a **range** value y for a given x.

The symbol $f(x)$ is read as **the value of f at x** or simply **f of x.**

The process of finding $f(x)$ for a given value of x is called **evaluating the function.** This is accomplished by substituting the given x-value (input) into the equation and obtaining the value of $f(x)$ (output). Here's an illustration.

Function	*x-Values (input)*	*f(x)-Values (output)*
$f(x) = 4 - 3x$	$x = -2$	$f(-2) = 4 - 3(-2) = 4 + 6 = 10$
	$x = -1$	$f(-1) = 4 - 3(-1) = 4 + 3 = 7$
	$x = 0$	$f(0) = 4 - 3(0) = 4 - 0 = 4$
	$x = 2$	$f(2) = 4 - 3(2) = 4 - 6 = -2$
	$x = 3$	$f(3) = 4 - 3(3) = 4 - 9 = -5$

Although f and x are often used as a convenient function name and independent (input) variable, you can use other letters. For instance, the equations

$$f(x) = x^2 - 3x + 5, \quad f(t) = t^2 - 3t + 5, \quad \text{and} \quad g(s) = s^2 - 3s + 5$$

all describe the same function. In fact, the letters used are just "place holders" and the same function is well described by the form

$$f(\quad) = (\quad)^2 - 3(\quad) + 5.$$

You can evaluate $f(-2)$ as

$$f(-2) = (-2)^2 - 3(-2) + 5$$

$$= 4 + 6 + 5$$

$$= 15.$$

It is important to put parentheses around the x-value (input) and then simplify the result.

Example 4   Evaluating a Function

Given $f(x) = x^2 + 1$ and $g(x) = 3x - x^2$, find the following.

a. $f(-2)$ **b.** $f(0)$ **c.** $g(2)$ **d.** $g(0)$

Solution

a. $f(x) = x^2 + 1$ Given function

$f(-2) = (-2)^2 + 1$ Substitute -2 for x.

$= 4 + 1 = 5$ Simplify.

b. $f(x) = x^2 + 1$ Given function

$f(0) = (0)^2 + 1$ Substitute 0 for x.

$= 0 + 1 = 1$ Simplify.

c. $g(x) = 3x - x^2$ Given function

$g(2) = 3(2) - (2)^2$ Substitute 2 for x.

$= 6 - 4 = 2$ Simplify.

d. $g(x) = 3x - x^2$ Given function

$g(0) = 3(0) - (0)^2$ Substitute 0 for x.

$= 0 - 0 = 0$ Simplify.

The domain of a function may be explicitly described along with the function, or it may be *implied* by the context in which the function is used. For instance, if weekly pay is a function of hours worked, the implied domain is typically the interval $0 \le x \le 40$. Certainly x cannot be negative in this context.

Example 5   Finding the Range of a Function

Determine the range R for the specified domain D of the function. Graph the function over the given domain.

$$f(x) = 2 - x^2, \qquad D = \{-2, -1, 0, 1\}$$

Solution

To find the range, substitute the values of the domain into the function.

$$f(-2) = 2 - (-2)^2 = 2 - 4 = -2$$
$$f(-1) = 2 - (-1)^2 = 2 - 1 = 1$$
$$f(0) = 2 - (0)^2 = 2 - 0 = 2$$
$$f(1) = 2 - (1)^2 = 2 - 1 = 1$$

The range of the function over the given domain is $R = \{-2, 1, 2\}$. The graph of the function is shown in Figure 4.17.

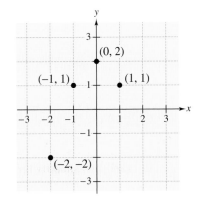

Figure 4.17

Example 6   Finding an Equation to Represent a Function

Is the area of a square a *function* of the length of one of its sides? If so, find an equation that represents this function.

Solution

Figure 4.18 shows a square.

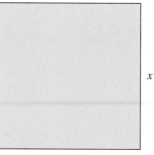

x

x

Figure 4.18

For this square, let the variable A represent the area of the square, and let the variable x represent the length of any one of its sides. (Remember that, by definition, all sides of a square have the same length.) Because the area of a square is completely determined by the lengths of its sides, you can see that A *is* a function of x. The equation that represents the function is

$$A(x) = x^2.$$

Discussing the Concept   Matching Equations with Graphs

Match the equations with their graphs. Discuss which equations are easier to graph using a graphing utility. Which equations represent y as a function of x? What can you conclude?

a.

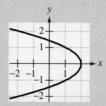

b.

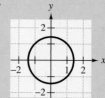

c.

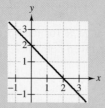

d.

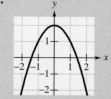

1. $2x^2 + 2y^2 = 4$

2. $2x^2 + 2y = 4$

3. $2x + 2y^2 = 4$

4. $2x + 2y = 4$

4.3   Exercises

Integrated Review   Concepts, Skills, and Problem Solving

Keep mathematically in shape by doing these exercises *before* the problems of this section.

Properties and Definitions

1. If $a < b$ and $b < c$, then what is the relationship between a and c? Name this property.

2. Demonstrate the Multiplicative Property of Equality for the equation $7x = 21$.

Simplifying Expressions

In Exercises 3–6, simplify the expression.

3. $4s - 6t + 7s + t$ **4.** $2x^2 - 4 + 5 - 3x^2$

5. $\frac{5}{3}x - \frac{2}{3}x - 4$

6. $3x^2y + xy - xy^2 - 6xy$

Solving Equations

In Exercises 7–10, solve the equation.

7. $3x + 9 = 0$ **8.** $\frac{x}{4} + \frac{x}{3} = \frac{1}{3}$

9. $\frac{2x - 3}{4} = \frac{3}{2}$ **10.** $-(4 - 3x) = 2(x - 1)$

Problem Solving

11. An inheritance of $7500 is invested in a mutual fund and at the end of 1 year the value of the investment is $8190. What simple interest rate would yield the same growth?

12. Determine the average speed of an aircraft that can travel 2500 miles in 3 hours.

Developing Skills

In Exercises 1–6, find the domain and range of the relation. See Example 1.

1. $\{(-4, 3), (2, 5), (1, 2), (4, -3)\}$

2. $\{(-1, 5), (8, 3), (4, 6), (-5, -2)\}$

3. $\left\{(2, 16), (-9, -10), \left(\frac{1}{2}, 0\right)\right\}$

4. $\left\{\left(\frac{2}{3}, -4\right), \left(-6, \frac{1}{4}\right), (0, 0)\right\}$

5. $\{(-1, 3), (5, -7), (-1, 4), (8, -2), (1, -7)\}$

6. $\{(1, 1), (2, 4), (3, 9), (-2, 4), (-1, 1)\}$

In Exercises 7–24, is the relation a function? See Example 2.

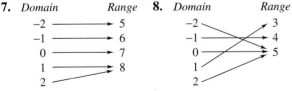

7. *Domain* → *Range*
-2 → 5
-1 → 6
0 → 7
1 → 8
2 →

8. *Domain* → *Range*
-2 → 3
-1 → 4
0 → 5
1 →
2 →

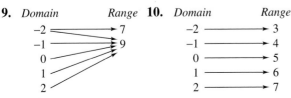

9. *Domain* → *Range*
-2 → 7
-1 → 9
0 →
1 →
2 →

10. *Domain* → *Range*
-2 → 3
-1 → 4
0 → 5
1 → 6
2 → 7

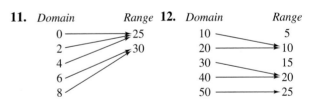

11. *Domain* → *Range*
0 → 25
2 → 30
4 →
6 →
8 →

12. *Domain* → *Range*
10 → 5
20 → 10
30 → 15
40 → 20
50 → 25

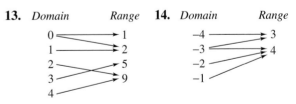

13. *Domain* → *Range*
0 → 1
1 → 2
2 → 5
3 → 9
4 →

14. *Domain* → *Range*
-4 → 3
-3 → 4
-2 →
-1 →

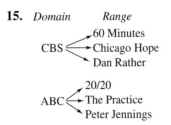

15. *Domain*   *Range*
CBS → 60 Minutes
     → Chicago Hope
     → Dan Rather

ABC → 20/20
     → The Practice
     → Peter Jennings

16. Domain   Range

60 Minutes
Chicago Hope → CBS
Dan Rather

20/20
The Practice → ABC
Peter Jennings

17. Domain   Range

	Single women in the labor force
Year	(in percent)
1993 →	66.2
1994 →	66.7
1995 →	66.8
1996 →	67.1

(Source: U.S. Bureau of Labor Statistics)

18. Domain   Range

U.S. RDA
of vitamin C
per serving   Cereal

Corn Flakes
25% → Wheaties
100% → Cheerios
Total

19.

Input value	0	1	2	3	4
Output value	2	4	6	8	10

20.

Input value	0	1	2	1	0
Output value	2	4	6	8	10

21.

Input value	1	3	5	3	1
Output value	1	2	3	4	5

22.

Input value	2	4	6	8	10
Output value	1	1	1	1	1

23. {(0, 25), (2, 25), (4, 30), (6, 30), (8, 30)}
24. {(10, 5), (20, 10), (30, 15), (40, 20), (50, 25)}

In Exercises 25–36, use the Vertical Line Test to determine whether y is a function of x. See Example 3.

25.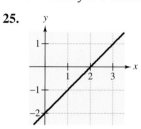

26.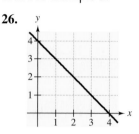

27.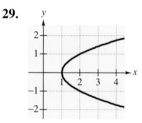

28.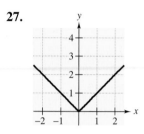

29.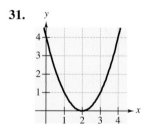

30.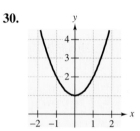

31.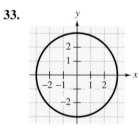

32.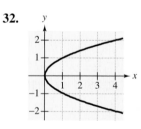

33.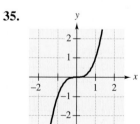

34.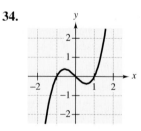

35.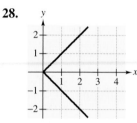

36.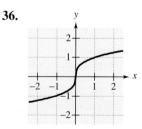

In Exercises 37–52, evaluate the function. See Example 4.

37. $f(x) = \frac{1}{2}x$ (a) $f(2)$ (b) $f(5)$
   (c) $f(-4)$ (d) $f\left(-\frac{2}{3}\right)$

38. $g(x) = -\frac{4}{5}x$ (a) $g(5)$ (b) $g(0)$
   (c) $g(-3)$ (d) $g\left(-\frac{5}{4}\right)$

39. $f(x) = 2x - 1$ (a) $f(0)$ (b) $f(3)$
   (c) $f(-3)$ (d) $f\left(-\frac{1}{2}\right)$

40. $f(t) = 3 - 4t$ (a) $f(0)$ (b) $f(1)$
   (c) $f(-2)$ (d) $f\left(\frac{3}{4}\right)$

41. $f(x) = 4x + 1$ (a) $f(1)$ (b) $f(-1)$
   (c) $f(-4)$ (d) $f\left(-\frac{4}{3}\right)$

42. $g(t) = 5 - 2t$ (a) $g\left(\frac{5}{2}\right)$ (b) $g(-10)$
   (c) $g(0)$ (d) $g\left(\frac{3}{4}\right)$

43. $h(t) = \frac{1}{4}t - 1$ (a) $h(200)$ (b) $h(-12)$
   (c) $h(8)$ (d) $h\left(-\frac{5}{2}\right)$

44. $f(s) = 4 - \frac{2}{3}s$ (a) $f(60)$ (b) $f(-15)$
   (c) $f(-18)$ (d) $f\left(\frac{1}{2}\right)$

45. $f(v) = \frac{1}{2}v^2$ (a) $f(-4)$ (b) $f(4)$
   (c) $f(0)$ (d) $f(2)$

46. $g(u) = -2u^2$ (a) $g(0)$ (b) $g(2)$
   (c) $g(3)$ (d) $g(-4)$

47. $g(x) = 2x^2 - 3x + 1$ (a) $g(0)$ (b) $g(-2)$
   (c) $g(1)$ (d) $g\left(\frac{1}{2}\right)$

48. $h(x) = x^2 + 4x - 1$ (a) $h(0)$ (b) $h(-4)$
   (c) $h(10)$ (d) $h\left(\frac{3}{2}\right)$

49. $g(u) = |u + 2|$ (a) $g(2)$ (b) $g(-2)$
   (c) $g(10)$ (d) $g\left(-\frac{5}{2}\right)$

50. $h(s) = |s| + 2$ (a) $h(4)$ (b) $h(-10)$
   (c) $h(-2)$ (d) $h\left(\frac{3}{2}\right)$

51. $h(x) = x^3 - 1$ (a) $h(0)$ (b) $h(1)$
   (c) $h(3)$ (d) $h\left(\frac{1}{2}\right)$

52. $f(x) = 16 - x^4$ (a) $f(-2)$ (b) $f(2)$
   (c) $f(1)$ (d) $f(3)$

In Exercises 53–60, determine the range R of the function for the specified domain D. Graph the function over the given domain. See Example 5.

53. $g(x) = 4 - x$
   $D = \{0, 1, 2, 3, 4\}$

54. $g(x) = x + 1$
   $D = \{-2, -1, 0, 1, 2\}$

55. $h(t) = 100$
   $D = \{-1, 0, 1, 2, 3\}$

56. $f(x) = x^2$
   $D = \{-2, -1, 0, 1, 2\}$

57. $f(x) = x^3$
   $D = \{-2, -1, 0, 1, 2\}$

58. $h(t) = t^3 - 3t^2 + 3t - 1$
   $D = \{-1, 0, 1, 2, 3\}$

59. $g(s) = |s|$
   $D = \{-2, -1, 0, 1, 2\}$

60. $g(u) = |u + 2| - |u|$
   $D = \{-3, -1, 1, 3, 5\}$

Solving Problems

61. *Demand Function* The demand for a product is a function of its price. Consider the demand function $f(p) = 20 - 0.5p$, where p is the price in dollars.

   (a) Find $f(10)$ and $f(15)$.

   (b) Describe the effect a price increase has on demand.

62. *Maximum Load* The maximum safe load L (in pounds) for a wooden beam 2 inches wide and d inches high is $L(d) = 100d^2$.

d	2	4	6	8
$L(d)$				

   (a) Complete the table.

   (b) Describe the effect of an increase in height on the maximum safe load.

63. *Distance* The function $d(t) = 50t$ gives the distance (in miles) that a car will travel in t hours at an average speed of 50 miles per hour. Find the distance traveled for (a) $t = 2$, (b) $t = 4$, and (c) $t = 10$.

64. *Speed of Sound* The function $S(h) = 1116 - 4.04h$ approximates the speed of sound (in feet per second) at altitude h (in thousands of feet). Use the function to approximate the speed of sound for (a) $h = 0$, (b) $h = 10$, and (c) $h = 30$.

Interpreting a Graph   In Exercises 65–68, use the information in the graph.   (Source: National Center for Education Statistics)

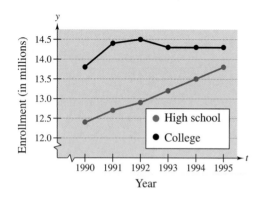

65. Is the high school enrollment a function of the year?

66. Is the college enrollment a function of the year?

67. Let $f(t)$ represent the number of high school students in year t. Find $f(1992)$.

68. Let $g(t)$ represent the number of college students in year t. Find $g(1990)$.

69. *Geometry*   Write the formula for the perimeter P of a square with sides of length s. Is P a function of s? Explain.

70. *Geometry*   Write the formula for the volume V of a cube with sides of length t. Is V a function of t? Explain.

71. *Time Between Sunrise and Sunset*   The graph approximates the length of time L (in hours) between sunrise and sunset in Erie, Pennsylvania over a period of 1 year. The variable t represents the day of the year.

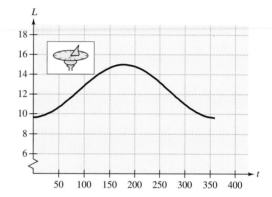

(a) Is L a function of t?

(b) Estimate the range for this relation.

Explaining Concepts

72. Answer parts (a)–(c) of Motivating the Chapter on page 201.

73. Explain the difference between a relation and a function. Give an example of a relation that is not a function.

74. Is it possible to find a function that is not a relation? If it is, find one.

75. Explain the meaning of the terms *domain* and *range* in the context of a function.

76. Give an example of a function defined by an equation in two variables. Give an example of a function that is not defined by an equation in two variables.

77. State the Vertical Line Test. Explain how this test can be used to determine if a relation is a function.

78. Describe some advantages of using function notation.

79. Is it possible for the number of elements in the domain to be greater than the number of elements in the range? Explain.

80. *Terminology*   Do the statements use the word *function* in a way that is mathematically correct? Explain your reasoning.

(a) The amount of money in your savings account is a function of your salary.

(b) The speed at which a free-falling baseball strikes the ground is a function of the height from which it is dropped.

Mid-Chapter Quiz

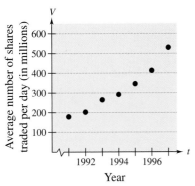

Figure for 4

Take this quiz as you would take a quiz in class. After you are done, check your work against the answers given in the back of the book.

1. Plot the points $(4, -2)$ and $\left(-1, -\frac{5}{2}\right)$ on a rectangular coordinate system.

2. Determine the quadrants in which the points $(x, 5)$ must be located. (x is a real number.)

3. Decide whether the ordered pairs are solutions of the equation $y = 9 - |x|$.

    (a) $(2, 7)$ (b) $(-3, 12)$ (c) $(-9, 0)$ (d) $(0, -9)$

4. The scatter plot at the left shows the average number (in millions) of shares traded per day on the New York Stock Exchange for the years 1991 through 1997. Estimate the average number of shares traded per day for each year from 1991 to 1997. (Source: The New York Stock Exchange)

In Exercises 5 and 6, find the x- and y-intercepts of the graph of the equation.

5. $x - 3y = 12$ **6.** $y = 6 - 4x$

In Exercises 7–12, graph the equation.

7. $y = x - 1$ **8.** $y = 5 - 2x$

9. $y = 4 - x^2$ **10.** $y = (x + 2)^2$

11. $y = |x + 3|$ **12.** $y = 1 - |x|$

13. Does the table below represent y as a function of x? Explain.

x	0	1	2	3	4
y	-1	2	5	8	11

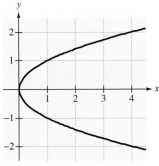

Figure for 14

14. Does the graph at the left represent y as a function of x? Explain.

In Exercises 15 and 16, evaluate the function at the given values of x and t.

15. $f(x) = 3x - 2$ (a) $f(-2)$ (b) $f(0)$ (c) $f(5)$ (d) $f\left(-\frac{1}{3}\right)$

16. $g(t) = 2t^2 - |t|$ (a) $g(-2)$ (b) $g(2)$ (c) $g(0)$ (d) $g\left(-\frac{1}{2}\right)$

17. Find the range of $f(x) = x^2 - x$ for the domain $D = \{-2, -1, 0, 1, 2\}$.

18. Find the domain for the area of a square with side s. $(A = s^2)$

19. Use a graphing utility to graph $h(x) = 3x^2 - 4x - 7$. Graphically estimate the intercepts of the graph. Explain how to verify your estimates algebraically.

20. A new computer system sells for approximately $3000 and depreciates at the rate of $500 per year for 4 years. Write the value V of the computer as a function of time t in years. What is the domain of the function? Graph the function over its domain.

4.4 Slope and Graphs of Linear Equations

Objectives

1 Determine the slope of a line through two points.

2 Write a linear equation in slope-intercept form and use it to sketch the graph of the line.

3 Use slope to determine whether lines are parallel, perpendicular, or neither.

---

1 Determine the slope of a line through two points.

The Slope of a Line

The **slope** of a nonvertical line is the number of units the line rises or falls vertically for each unit of horizontal change from left to right. For example, the line in Figure 4.19 rises 2 units for each unit of horizontal change from left to right, and we say that this line has a slope of $m = 2$.

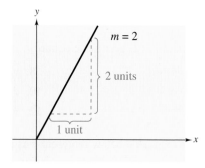

Figure 4.19   Figure 4.20

> ▶ **Definition of the Slope of a Line**
>
> The **slope** m of a nonvertical line passing through the points (x_1, y_1) and (x_2, y_2) is
>
> $$m = \frac{y_2 - y_1}{x_2 - x_1} = \frac{\text{change in } y}{\text{change in } x} = \frac{\text{rise}}{\text{run}}$$
>
> where $x_1 \neq x_2$ (see Figure 4.20).

When the formula for slope is used, the *order of subtraction* is important. Given two points on a line, you are free to label either one of them as (x_1, y_1) and the other as (x_2, y_2). However, once this is done, you must form the numerator and denominator using the same order of subtraction.

$$m = \frac{y_2 - y_1}{x_2 - x_1} \qquad m = \frac{y_1 - y_2}{x_1 - x_2} \qquad m = \frac{y_2 - y_1}{x_1 - x_2}$$

Correct   Correct   Incorrect

Example 1   Finding the Slope of a Line Through Two Points

Find the slope of the line passing through each pair of points.

a. $(-2, 0)$ and $(3, 1)$ **b.** $(-1, 2)$ and $(2, 2)$ **c.** $(0, 0)$ and $(1, -1)$

Solution

a. Let $(x_1, y_1) = (-2, 0)$ and $(x_2, y_2) = (3, 1)$.

You might point out that the subtraction could be done in the opposite order for *both* x-coordinates and y-coordinates, and the result would be the same.

$$m = \frac{0 - 1}{-2 - 3} = \frac{-1}{-5} = \frac{1}{5}$$

$$m = \frac{y_2 - y_1}{x_2 - x_1}$$

$$= \frac{1 - 0}{3 - (-2)} \qquad \text{Difference in } y\text{-values}$$
$$\qquad\qquad\qquad \text{Difference in } x\text{-values}$$

$$= \frac{1}{5} \qquad \text{Simplify.}$$

b. The slope of the line through $(-1, 2)$ and $(2, 2)$ is

$$m = \frac{2 - 2}{2 - (-1)} \qquad \begin{array}{l} \text{Difference in } y\text{-values} \\ \text{Difference in } x\text{-values} \end{array}$$

$$= \frac{0}{3} = 0. \qquad \text{Simplify.}$$

c. The slope of the line through $(0, 0)$ and $(1, -1)$ is

The slope of a nonvertical line can be described as the *ratio* of vertical change to horizontal change between any two points on the line.

$$m = \frac{-1 - 0}{1 - 0} \qquad \begin{array}{l} \text{Difference in } y\text{-values} \\ \text{Difference in } x\text{-values} \end{array}$$

$$= \frac{-1}{1} = -1. \qquad \text{Simplify.}$$

The graphs of the three lines are shown in Figure 4.21.

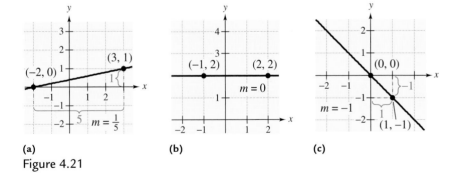

(a)   (b)   (c)

Figure 4.21

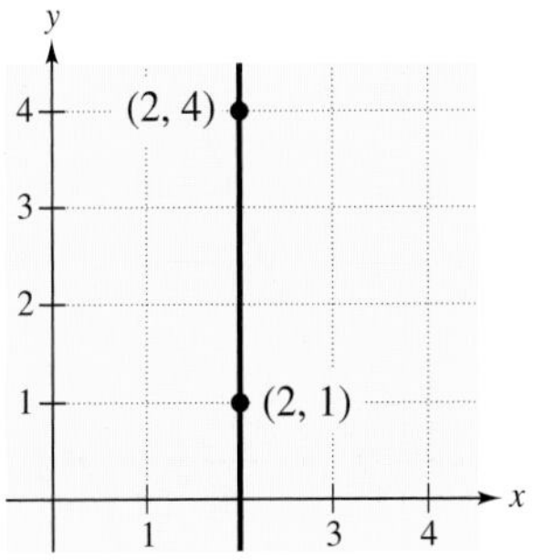

The definition of slope does not apply to vertical lines. For instance, consider the points $(2, 4)$ and $(2, 1)$ on the vertical line shown in Figure 4.22. Applying the formula for slope, you have

$$\frac{4 - 1}{2 - 2} = \frac{3}{0}. \qquad \text{Undefined division by zero}$$

Because division by zero is not defined, the slope of a vertical line is not defined.

Figure 4.22   *Slope is undefined.*

Students may have difficulty distinguishing between the zero slope of a horizontal line and the undefined slope of a vertical line.

From the slopes of the lines shown in Figures 4.21 and 4.22, you can make several generalizations about the slope of a line.

▶ **Slope of a Line**

1. A line with positive slope ($m > 0$) *rises* from left to right.

2. A line with negative slope ($m < 0$) *falls* from left to right.

3. A line with zero slope ($m = 0$) is *horizontal.*

4. A line with undefined slope is *vertical.*

Example 2 **Using Slope to Describe Lines**

Describe the lines through the pairs of points.

a. $(3, -2), (3, 3)$ **b.** $(-2, 5), (1, 4)$ **c.** $(-4, -3), (0, -3)$ **d.** $(1, 0), (4, 6)$

Solution

a. Because the slope is undefined, the line is vertical.

$$m = \frac{3 - (-2)}{3 - 3} = \frac{5}{0} \qquad \text{Undefined slope (See Figure 4.23a.)}$$

b. Because the slope is negative, the line falls from left to right.

$$m = \frac{4 - 5}{1 - (-2)} = -\frac{1}{3} < 0 \qquad \text{Negative slope (See Figure 4.23b.)}$$

c. Because the slope is zero, the line is horizontal.

$$m = \frac{-3 - (-3)}{0 - (-4)} = \frac{0}{4} = 0 \qquad \text{Zero slope (See Figure 4.23c.)}$$

d. Because the slope is positive, the line rises from left to right.

$$m = \frac{6 - 0}{4 - 1} = \frac{6}{3} = 2 > 0 \qquad \text{Positive slope (See Figure 4.23d.)}$$

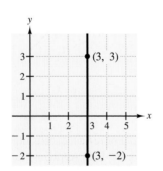

(a) Vertical line:
    undefined slope

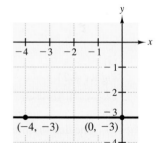

(b) Line falls:
    negative slope

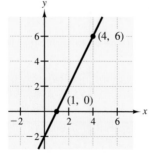

(c) Horizontal line:
    zero slope

(d) Line rises:
    positive slope

Figure 4.23

Any two points on a nonvertical line can be used to calculate its slope. This is demonstrated in the next two examples.

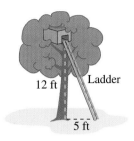

Figure 4.24

| Example 3 | Finding the Slope of a Ladder |

Find the slope of the ladder leading up to the tree house in Figure 4.24.

Solution

Consider the tree trunk as the y-axis and the level ground as the x-axis. The endpoints of the ladder are $(0, 12)$ and $(5, 0)$. So, the slope of the ladder is

$$m = \frac{y_2 - y_1}{x_2 - x_1} = \frac{0 - 12}{5 - 0} = -\frac{12}{5}.$$

| Example 4 | Finding the Slope of a Line |

Sketch the graph of the line $3x - 2y = 4$. Then find the slope of the line. (Choose two different pairs of points on the line and show that the same slope is obtained using either pair.)

Solution

Begin by solving the equation for y.

$$y = \frac{3}{2}x - 2 \qquad \text{\small y is a function of x.}$$

Then, construct a table of values as shown below.

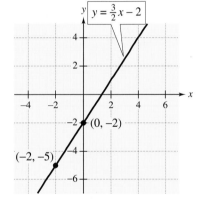

x	-2	0	2	4
$y = \frac{3}{2}x - 2$	-5	-2	1	4
Solution points	$(-2, -5)$	$(0, -2)$	$(2, 1)$	$(4, 4)$

From the solution points shown in the table, sketch the graph of the line, as shown in Figure 4.25. To calculate the slope of the line using two different sets of points, first use the points $(-2, -5)$ and $(0, -2)$ to obtain a slope of

$$m = \frac{-2 - (-5)}{0 - (-2)} = \frac{3}{2}.$$

Next, use the points $(2, 1)$ and $(4, 4)$ to obtain a slope of

$$m = \frac{4 - 1}{4 - 2} = \frac{3}{2}.$$

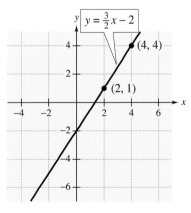

Figure 4.25

Try some other pairs of points on the line to see that you obtain a slope of $m = \frac{3}{2}$ regardless of which two points you use.

2 Write a linear equation in slope-intercept form and use it to sketch the graph of the line.

Slope as a Graphing Aid

You have seen in Section 4.1 that before creating a table of values for an equation, it is helpful first to solve the equation for y. When doing this for a linear equation, you obtain some very useful information. Consider the results of Example 4.

$$3x - 2y = 4 \qquad \text{Original equation}$$

$$3x - 3x - 2y = -3x + 4 \qquad \text{Subtract } 3x \text{ from both sides.}$$

$$-2y = -3x + 4 \qquad \text{Simplify.}$$

$$\frac{-2y}{-2} = \frac{-3x + 4}{-2} \qquad \text{Divide both sides by } -2.$$

$$y = \frac{3}{2}x - 2 \qquad \text{Simplify.}$$

Observe that the coefficient of x is the slope of the graph for this equation (see Example 4). Moreover, the constant term, -2, gives the y-intercept of the graph.

$$y = \boxed{\frac{3}{2}} x + \boxed{-2}$$

slope y-intercept $(0, -2)$

This form is called the **slope-intercept form** of the equation of the line.

> ▶ **Slope-Intercept Form of the Equation of a Line**
>
> The graph of the equation
>
> $$y = mx + b \qquad \text{y is a linear function of x.}$$
>
> is a line whose slope is m and whose y-intercept is $(0, b)$. (See Figure 4.26.)

Study Tip

Remember that slope is a *rate of change*. In the slope-intercept equation

$$y = mx + b$$

the slope m is the rate of change of y with respect to x.

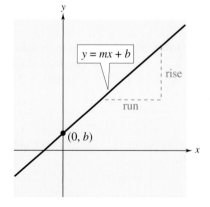

Figure 4.26

The slope-intercept form of the equation of a line identifies y as a function of x. So, the term **linear function** is often used as an alternative description of the slope-intercept form of the equation of a line.

So far, you have been plotting several points to sketch the equation of a line. However, now that you can recognize equations of lines (linear functions), you don't have to plot as many points—two points are enough. (You might remember from geometry that *two points are all that are necessary to determine a line.*) The next example shows how to use the slope to help sketch a line.

Example 5   Using the Slope and *y*-Intercept to Sketch a Line

Use the slope and *y*-intercept to sketch the graph of

$$x - 3y = -6.$$

Point out that the larger *the* positive *slope of a line, the more steeply the line rises from left to right.*

Solution

First, write the equation in slope-intercept form.

$x - 3y = -6$	Original equation
$-3y = -x - 6$	Subtract x from both sides.
$y = \dfrac{-x - 6}{-3}$	Divide both sides by -3.
$y = \dfrac{1}{3}x + 2$	Simplify to slope-intercept form.

So, the slope of the line is $m = \frac{1}{3}$ and the *y*-intercept is $(0, b) = (0, 2)$. Now you can sketch the graph of the equation. First, plot the *y*-intercept, as shown in Figure 4.27(a). Then, using a slope of $\frac{1}{3}$,

$$m = \frac{1}{3} = \frac{\text{change in } y}{\text{change in } x}$$

locate a second point on the line by moving 3 units to the right and 1 unit up (or 1 unit up and 3 units to the right), also shown in Figure 4.27(a). Finally, obtain the graph by drawing a line through the two points [Figure 4.27(b)].

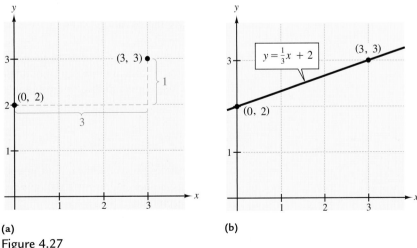

(a)

(b)

Figure 4.27

3 Use slope to determine whether lines are parallel, perpendicular, or neither.

Parallel and Perpendicular Lines

You know from geometry that two lines in a plane are **parallel** if they do not intersect. What this means in terms of their slopes is shown in Example 6.

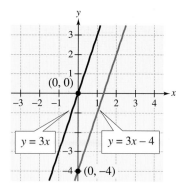

Figure 4.28

| Example 6 | Lines That Have the Same Slope |

On the same set of axes, sketch the lines $y = 3x$ and $y = 3x - 4$.

Solution

For the line

$$y = 3x$$

the slope is $m = 3$ and the y-intercept is $(0, 0)$. For the line

$$y = 3x - 4$$

the slope is also $m = 3$ and the y-intercept is $(0, -4)$. The graphs of these two lines are shown in Figure 4.28.

In Example 6, notice that the two lines have the same slope *and* that the two lines appear to be parallel. The following rule states that this is always the case. That is, two (nonvertical) lines are parallel *if and only if* they have the same slope.

> ▶ **Parallel Lines**
>
> Two distinct nonvertical lines are parallel if and only if they have the same slope.

The phrase "if and only if" in this rule is used in mathematics as a way to write two statements in one. The first statement says that *if two distinct nonvertical lines have the same slope, they must be parallel.* The second (or reverse) statement says that *if two distinct nonvertical lines are parallel, they must have the same slope.*

Another rule resulting from geometry is that two lines in a plane are **perpendicular** if they intersect at right angles. In terms of their slopes, this means that two nonvertical lines are perpendicular if their slopes are negative reciprocals of each other.

> ▶ **Perpendicular Lines**
>
> Consider two nonvertical lines whose slopes are m_1 and m_2. The two lines are perpendicular if and only if their slopes are *negative reciprocals* of each other. That is,
>
> $$m_1 = -\frac{1}{m_2}, \text{ or equivalently, } m_1 \cdot m_2 = -1.$$

Point out that the negative slope indicates that the line falls from left to right.

Example 7 Parallel or Perpendicular?

Determine whether the pairs of lines are parallel, perpendicular, or neither.

a. $y = -3x - 2$, $y = \frac{1}{3}x + 1$

b. $y = \frac{1}{2}x + 1$, $y = \frac{1}{2}x - 1$

Solution

a. The first line has a slope of $m_1 = -3$ and the second line has a slope of $m_2 = \frac{1}{3}$. Because these slopes are negative reciprocals of each other, the two lines must be perpendicular, as shown in Figure 4.29.

b. Both lines have a slope of $m = \frac{1}{2}$. So, the two lines must be parallel, as shown in Figure 4.30.

Consider this additional pair of equations: Line 1: $y = 3x + 1$ and Line 2: $y = -3x + 2$. Because the slopes are not the same and are not negative reciprocals, the lines are neither parallel nor perpendicular. Because they are not parallel, the lines must intersect, but they do not intersect at right angles.

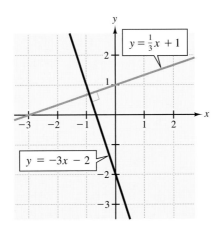

Figure 4.29

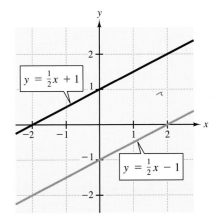

Figure 4.30

Discussing the Concept   Creating a Linear Equation

Plot the following data points for a telephone call.

Minutes	1	3	8	15
Cost of call	$1.22	$1.66	$2.76	$4.30

Decide if these data points fit a straight line. If so, what are the slope and y-intercept? If not, why not?

4.4 Exercises

Integrated Review   *Concepts, Skills, and Problem Solving*

Keep mathematically in shape by doing these exercises *before* the problems of this section.

Properties and Definitions

1. Two equations that have the same set of solutions are called _____ .

2. Use the Addition Property of Equality to fill in the blank.

    $5x - 2 = 6$

    $5x = 6 +$ ☐

Simplifying Expressions

In Exercises 3–10, simplify the expression.

3. $(x^2)^3 \cdot x^3$

4. $(y^2z^3)(z^2)$

5. $(u^4v^2)^2$

6. $(ab)^4$

7. $(25x^3)(2x^2)$

8. $(3yz)^2(6yz^3)$

9. $x^2 - 2x - x^2 + 3x + 2$

10. $x^2 - 5x - 2 + x$

Problem Solving

11. A builder must cut a 10-foot board into three pieces. Two are to have the same length and the third is to be three times as long as the two of equal length. Find the lengths of the three pieces.

12. The bill for the repair of your dishwasher was $113. The cost for parts was $65. The cost for labor was $32 per hour. How many hours did the repair work take?

Developing Skills

In Exercises 1–10, estimate the slope (if it exists) of the line from its graph.

1.
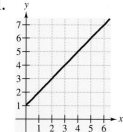

2.
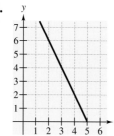

3.
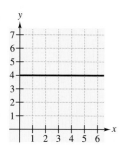

4.
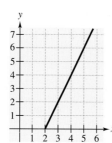

5.
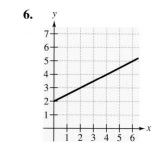

6.

7.
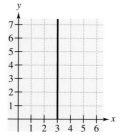

8.
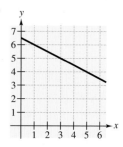

9.

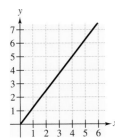

10.

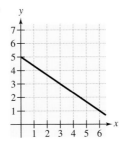

In Exercises 11 and 12, match the line in the figure with its slope.

11. (a) $m = \frac{3}{2}$

(b) $m = 0$

(c) $m = -\frac{2}{3}$

(d) $m = -2$

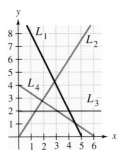

12. (a) $m = -\frac{3}{4}$

(b) $m = \frac{1}{2}$

(c) m is undefined.

(d) $m = 3$

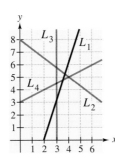

In Exercises 13–32, plot the points and find the slope (if possible) of the line passing through the pair of points. State whether the line rises, falls, is horizontal, or is vertical. See Examples 1 and 2.

13. $(0, 0), (4, 5)$

14. $(0, 0), (-3, 6)$

15. $(0, 0), (8, -4)$

16. $(0, 0), (-1, -3)$

17. $(0, 6), (8, 0)$

18. $(0, -6), (8, 0)$

19. $(-3, -2), (1, 6)$

20. $(2, 4), (4, -4)$

21. $(-6, -1), (-6, 4)$

22. $(-4, -10), (-4, 0)$

23. $(3, -4), (8, -4)$

24. $(1, 2), (-2, -2)$

25. $\left(\frac{1}{4}, \frac{3}{2}\right), \left(\frac{9}{2}, -3\right)$

26. $\left(-\frac{5}{4}, -\frac{1}{4}\right), \left(\frac{7}{8}, \frac{3}{4}\right)$

27. $(3.2, -1), (-3.2, 4)$

28. $(1.4, 0), (1.4, 3)$

29. $(3.5, -1), (5.75, 4.25)$

30. $(0, 6.4), (5, 6.4)$

31. $(a, 3), (4, 3), \ a \neq 4$

32. $(4, a), (4, 2), \ a \neq 2$

In Exercises 33 and 34, complete the table. Use two different pairs of solution points to show that the same slope is obtained using either pair.

x		-2	0	2	4
y					
Solution points					

33. $y = -2x - 2$

34. $y = 3x + 4$

In Exercises 35–38, use the slope formula to find the value of y such that the line through the two points will have the given slope.

35. Points: $(3, -2), (0, y)$

Slope: $m = -8$

36. Points: $(-3, y), (8, 2)$

Slope: $m = 2$

37. Points: $(-4, y), (7, 6)$

Slope: $m = \frac{5}{2}$

38. Points: $(0, 10), (6, y)$

Slope: $m = -\frac{1}{3}$

In Exercises 39–50, a point on a line and the slope of the line are given. Plot the point and use the slope to find two additional points on the line. (There are many correct answers.)

39. $(2, 1)$

$m = 0$

40. $(-3, 4)$

m is undefined.

41. $(1, -6)$

$m = 2$

42. $(-2, -4)$

$m = 1$

43. $(0, 1)$

$m = -2$

44. $(-2, 4)$

$m = -3$

45. $(-4, 0)$

$m = \frac{2}{3}$

46. $(-1, -1)$

$m = -\frac{1}{4}$

47. $(3, 5)$

$m = -\frac{1}{2}$

48. $(1, 3)$

$m = \frac{4}{3}$

49. $(-8, 1)$

m is undefined.

50. $(-3, -1)$

$m = 0$

In Exercises 51–56, sketch the graph of a line through the point $(0, 2)$ having the given slope.

51. $m = 0$

52. m is undefined.

53. $m = 3$

54. $m = -1$

55. $m = -\frac{2}{3}$

56. $m = \frac{3}{4}$

In Exercises 57–62, plot the x- and y-intercepts and sketch the graph of the line.

57. $2x - 3y + 6 = 0$ **58.** $3x + 4y + 12 = 0$

59. $-5x + 2y - 10 = 0$ **60.** $3x - 7y - 21 = 0$

61. $6x - 4y + 12 = 0$ **62.** $5y - 2x - 20 = 0$

In Exercises 63–76, write the equation in slope-intercept form. Use the slope and y-intercept to graph the line. See Example 5.

63. $x + y = 0$ **64.** $x - y = 0$

65. $\frac{1}{2}x + y = 0$ **66.** $3x - y = 0$

67. $2x - y - 3 = 0$ **68.** $x - y + 2 = 0$

69. $x - 3y + 6 = 0$ **70.** $3x - 2y - 2 = 0$

71. $x + 2y - 2 = 0$ **72.** $10x + 6y - 3 = 0$

73. $3x - 4y + 2 = 0$ **74.** $2x + 3y = 0$

75. $y + 5 = 0$ **76.** $y - 3 = 0$

In Exercises 77–80, determine if the lines L_1 and L_2 passing through the given pairs of points are parallel, perpendicular, or neither.

77. L_1: $(0, -1), (5, 9)$ **78.** L_1: $(-2, -1), (1, 5)$
    L_2: $(0, 3), (4, 1)$ L_2: $(1, 3), (5, -5)$

79. L_1: $(3, 6), (-6, 0)$ **80.** L_1: $(4, 8), (-4, 2)$
    L_2: $(0, -1), \left(5, \frac{7}{3}\right)$ L_2: $(3, -5), \left(-1, \frac{1}{3}\right)$

In Exercises 81–84, sketch the graphs of the two lines on the same rectangular coordinate system. Determine whether the lines are parallel, perpendicular, or neither. Use a graphing utility to verify your result. (Use a square setting.) See Examples 6 and 7.

81. $y_1 = 2x - 3$ **82.** $y_1 = -\frac{1}{3}x - 3$
    $y_2 = 2x + 1$ $y_2 = -\frac{1}{3}x + 1$

83. $y_1 = 2x - 3$ **84.** $y_1 = -\frac{1}{3}x - 3$
    $y_2 = -\frac{1}{2}x + 1$ $y_2 = 3x + 1$

Solving Problems

85. *Roof Pitch*   Determine the slope (pitch) of the roof of the house in the figure.

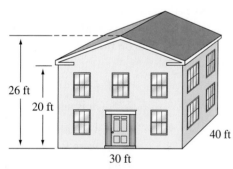

26 ft

20 ft

40 ft

30 ft

86. *Slope of a Ladder*   Find the slope of the ladder in the figure.

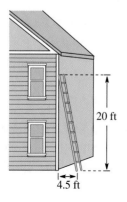

20 ft

4.5 ft

87. *Sketching a Diagram*   A subway track rises 3 feet over a 200-foot horizontal distance.

(a) Sketch a diagram of the track and label the rise and run.

(b) Find the slope of the track.

(c) Would the slope be steeper if the track rose 3 feet over a distance of 100 feet? Explain.

88. *Estimating Slope*   An airplane leaves an airport. As it flies over a town, its altitude is 4 miles. The town is about 20 miles from the airport. Approximate the slope of the linear path followed during takeoff.

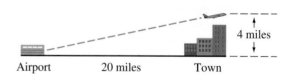

Airport   20 miles   Town

4 miles

89. *Graphical Interpretation*   The graph gives the net sales (in billions of dollars) for Wal-Mart for 1993 through 1997. (Source: 1997 Wal-Mart Annual Report)

(a) Find the slopes of the four line segments.

(b) Find the slope of the line segment connecting the first and last points of the line graph. Explain the meaning of this slope.

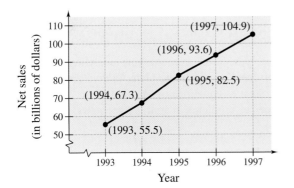

90. *Comparing Models*   Based on different assumptions, the marketing department of a company develops two models to predict the annual profit of the company over the next 10 years. The models are

$$P_1 = 0.2t + 2.4 \quad \text{and} \quad P_2 = 0.3t + 2.4$$

where P_1 and P_2 represent profit in millions of dollars and t is time in years ($0 \le t \le 10$).

(a) Interpret the slopes of the two linear models.

(b) Which model predicts a faster increase in profits?

(c) Use each model to predict profits when $t = 10$.

(d) Use a graphing utility to graph the models on the same screen. Use the following viewing window.

Xmin = 0
Xmax = 10
Xscl = 1
Ymin = 0
Ymax = 7
Yscl = 1

91. *Misleading Graphs*   Use a graphing utility to graph the line $y = 0.75x - 2$ for each viewing window.

Xmin = -10	Xmin = 0
Xmax = 10	Xmax = 1
Xscl = 2	Xscl = 0.5
Ymin = -100	Ymin = -2
Ymax = 100	Ymax = -1.5
Yscl = 10	Yscl = 0.1

(a) Do the lines appear to have the same slope?

(b) Does either of the lines appear to have a slope of 0.75? If not, find a setting that will make the line appear to have a slope of 0.75.

(c) Describe real-life situations in which it would be to your advantage to use the two given settings.

92. *Rate of Change*   The following are the slopes of lines representing annual sales y in terms of time t in years. Use the slopes to determine any change in annual sales for a 1-year increase in time t.

(a) $m = 76$ (b) $m = 0$ (c) $m = -14$

Explaining Concepts

93. Is the slope of a line a ratio? Explain.

94. Explain how you can visually determine the sign of the slope of a line by observing the graph of the line.

95. *True or False?*   If both the x- and y-intercepts of a line are positive, then the slope of the line is positive.

96. Which slope is steeper: -5 or 2? Explain.

97. Is it possible to have two perpendicular lines with positive slopes? Explain.

98. The slope of a line is $\frac{3}{2}$. If x is increased by 8 units, how much will y change? Explain.

99. When a quantity y is increasing or decreasing at a constant rate over time t, the graph of y versus t is a line. What is another name for the rate of change?

100. Is it possible to use a graphing utility in function mode to graph the equation $x - 5 = 0$? Explain.

101. Explain how to use slopes to determine if the points $(-2, -3)$, $(1, 1)$, and $(3, 4)$ lie on the same line.

102. When determining the slope of the line through two points, does the order of subtracting coordinates of the points matter? Explain.

4.5   Equations of Lines

Objectives

1 Write an equation of a line using the point-slope form.

2 Write the equations of horizontal and vertical lines.

3 Use a linear model to solve an application problem.

1 Write an equation of a line using the point-slope form.

The Point-Slope Equation of a Line

In Sections 4.1 through 4.4, you have been studying analytic (or coordinate) geometry. Analytic geometry uses a coordinate plane to give visual representations of algebraic concepts, such as equations or functions.

There are two basic types of problems in analytic geometry.

1. Given an equation, sketch its graph.

Algebra ⟹ Geometry

2. Given a graph, write its equation.

Geometry ⟹ Algebra

In Section 4.4, you worked primarily with the first type of problem. In this section, you will study the second type. Specifically, you will learn how to write the equation of a line when you are given its slope and a point on the line. Before we give a general formula for doing this, consider the following example.

Example 1   Writing an Equation of a Line

A line has a slope of $\frac{5}{3}$ and passes through the point (2, 1). Find its equation.

Solution

Begin by sketching the line, as shown in Figure 4.31. The slope of a line is the same through any two points on the line. So, to find an equation of the line, let (x, y) represent *any* point on the line. Now, using the representative point (x, y) and the given point (2, 1), it follows that the slope of the line is

$$m = \frac{y - 1}{x - 2}.$$

⟸ Difference in y-coordinates
⟸ Difference in x-coordinates

By substituting $\frac{5}{3}$ for m, you obtain the equation of the line.

$$\frac{5}{3} = \frac{y - 1}{x - 2} \qquad \text{Slope formula}$$

$$5(x - 2) = 3(y - 1) \qquad \text{Cross-multiply.}$$

$$5x - 10 = 3y - 3 \qquad \text{Distributive Property}$$

$$5x - 3y = 7 \qquad \text{Equation of line}$$

So, an equation for the line is $5x - 3y = 7$.

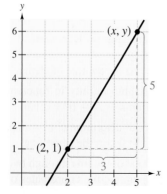

Figure 4.31

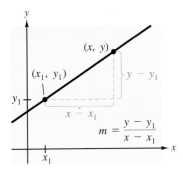

Figure 4.32

Point out the relationship between the point-slope form of the equation of a line and the definition of slope.

The procedure in Example 1 can be used to derive a *formula* for the equation of a line given its slope and a point on the line. In Figure 4.32, let (x_1, y_1) be a given point on a line whose slope is m. If (x, y) is any *other* point on the line, it follows that

$$\frac{y - y_1}{x - x_1} = m.$$

This equation in variables x and y can be rewritten in the form

$$y - y_1 = m(x - x_1)$$

which is called the **point-slope form** of the equation of a line.

▶ **Point-Slope Form of the Equation of a Line**

The **point-slope form** of the equation of a line with slope m and passing through the point (x_1, y_1) is

$$y - y_1 = m(x - x_1).$$

Example 2   The Point-Slope Form of the Equation of a Line

Find an equation of the line with slope 3 and passing through the point $(1, -2)$.

Solution

Use the point-slope form with $(x_1, y_1) = (1, -2)$ and $m = 3$.

$$y - y_1 = m(x - x_1) \qquad \text{Point-slope form}$$

$$y - (-2) = 3(x - 1) \qquad \text{Substitute } -2 \text{ for } y_1, 1 \text{ for } x_1, \text{ and } 3 \text{ for } m.$$

$$y + 2 = 3x - 3 \qquad \text{Simplify.}$$

$$y = 3x - 5 \qquad \text{Equation of line}$$

So, an equation of the line is $y = 3x - 5$. Note that this is the slope-intercept form of the equation. The graph of this line is shown in Figure 4.33.

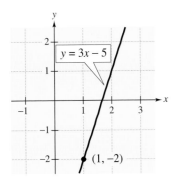

Figure 4.33

In Example 2, note that we concluded that $y = 3x - 5$ is "an" equation of the line rather than saying it is "the" equation of the line. The reason for this is that every equation can be written in many equivalent forms. For instance,

$$y = 3x - 5, \quad 3x - y = 5, \quad \text{and} \quad 3x - y - 5 = 0$$

are all equations of the line in Example 2. The first of these equations ($y = 3x - 5$) is in the slope-intercept form

$$y = mx + b \qquad \text{Slope-intercept form}$$

and it provides the most information about the line. The last of these equations ($3x - y - 5 = 0$) is in the general form of the equation of a line.

$$ax + by = 0 \qquad \text{General form}$$

The point-slope form can be used to find an equation of a line passing through any two points (x_1, y_1) and (x_2, y_2). First, use the formula for the slope of a line passing through these two points.

$$m = \frac{y_2 - y_1}{x_2 - x_1}$$

Then, knowing the slope, use the point-slope form to obtain the equation

$$y - y_1 = \frac{y_2 - y_1}{x_2 - x_1}(x - x_1). \qquad \text{Two-point form}$$

This is sometimes called the **two-point form** of an equation of a line.

Example 3   A Line Passing Through Two Points

Find an equation of the line that passes through the points $(3, 1)$ and $(-3, 4)$.

Solution

Let $(x_1, y_1) = (3, 1)$ and $(x_2, y_2) = (-3, 4)$. The slope of a line passing through these points is

$$m = \frac{y_2 - y_1}{x_2 - x_1} \qquad \text{Formula for slope}$$

$$= \frac{4 - 1}{-3 - 3} \qquad \text{Substitute for } x_1, y_1, x_2, \text{ and } y_2.$$

$$= \frac{3}{-6} \qquad \text{Simplify.}$$

$$= -\frac{1}{2}. \qquad \text{Simplify.}$$

Now, use the point-slope form to find an equation of the line.

$$y - y_1 = m(x - x_1) \qquad \text{Point-slope form}$$

$$y - 1 = -\frac{1}{2}(x - 3) \qquad \text{Substitute 1 for } y_1, 3 \text{ for } x_1, \text{ and } -\frac{1}{2} \text{ for } m.$$

$$y - 1 = -\frac{1}{2}x + \frac{3}{2} \qquad \text{Simplify.}$$

$$y = -\frac{1}{2}x + \frac{5}{2} \qquad \text{Equation of line}$$

The graph of this line is shown in Figure 4.34.

In Example 3, it does not matter which of the two points is labeled (x_1, y_1) and which is labeled (x_2, y_2). Try switching these labels to $(x_1, y_1) = (-3, 4)$ and $(x_2, y_2) = (3, 1)$ and reworking the problem to see that you obtain the same equation.

Technology: Tip

A program that uses the two-point form to find the equation of a line is available at our website *www.hmco.com.* Programs for several models of calculators are available.

The program prompts for the coordinates of the two points and then outputs the slope and the *y*-intercept of the line that passes through the two points. Verify Example 3 using this program.

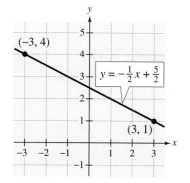

Figure 4.34

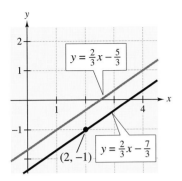

Figure 4.35

Example 4   Equations of Parallel Lines

Find an equation of the line that passes through the point $(2, -1)$ and is parallel to the line

$$2x - 3y = 5,$$

as shown in Figure 4.35.

Solution

To begin, write the given equation in slope-intercept form.

$$2x - 3y = 5 \qquad \text{Given equation}$$

$$-3y = -2x + 5 \qquad \text{Subtract } 2x \text{ from both sides.}$$

$$y = \frac{2}{3}x - \frac{5}{3} \qquad \text{Divide both sides by } -3.$$

Because the line has a slope of $m = \frac{2}{3}$, it follows that any parallel line must have the same slope. So, an equation of the line through $(2, -1)$, parallel to the given line is

$$y - y_1 = m(x - x_1) \qquad \text{Point-slope form}$$

$$y - (-1) = \frac{2}{3}(x - 2) \qquad \text{Substitute } -1 \text{ for } y_1, 2 \text{ for } x_1, \text{ and } \frac{2}{3} \text{ for } m.$$

$$y + 1 = \frac{2}{3}x - \frac{4}{3} \qquad \text{Distributive Property}$$

$$y = \frac{2}{3}x - \frac{7}{3}. \qquad \text{Equation of line}$$

Example 5   Equations of Perpendicular Lines

Find an equation of the line that passes through the point $(2, -1)$ and is perpendicular to the line

$$2x - 3y = 5,$$

as shown in Figure 4.36.

Solution

From Example 4, the given line has a slope of $\frac{2}{3}$. Hence, any line perpendicular to this line must have a slope of $-\frac{3}{2}$. So, the equation of the required line through $(2, -1)$ has the following form.

$$y - y_1 = m(x - x_1) \qquad \text{Point-slope form}$$

$$y - (-1) = -\frac{3}{2}(x - 2) \qquad \text{Substitute } -1 \text{ for } y_1, 2 \text{ for } x_1, \text{ and } -\frac{3}{2} \text{ for } m.$$

$$y + 1 = -\frac{3}{2}x + 3 \qquad \text{Distributive Property}$$

$$y = -\frac{3}{2}x + 2 \qquad \text{Equation of line}$$

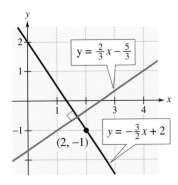

Figure 4.36

2 Write the equations of horizontal and vertical lines.

Equations of Horizontal and Vertical Lines

From the slope-intercept form of the equation of a line, you can see that a horizontal line ($m = 0$) has an equation of the form

$$y = (0)x + b \quad \text{or} \quad y = b. \qquad \text{Horizontal line}$$

This is consistent with the fact that each point on a horizontal line through $(0, b)$ has a y-coordinate of b.

Students may have difficulty recognizing equations of horizontal and vertical lines.

$x = 8$	Vertical
$y = -3$	Horizontal
$x + 7 = 0$	Vertical
$y - 9 = 9$	Horizontal

In a similar way, each point on a vertical line through $(a, 0)$ has an x-coordinate of a. So, a vertical line has an equation of the form

$$x = a. \qquad \text{Vertical line}$$

The equation of a vertical line cannot be written in slope-intercept form because the slope of a vertical line is undefined. However, *every* line has an equation that can be written in the **general form**

$$ax + by + c = 0 \qquad \text{General form}$$

where a and b are not *both* zero.

Example 6 Writing Equations of Horizontal and Vertical Lines

Write an equation for each of the following lines.

a. Vertical line through $(-3, 2)$

b. Line passing through $(-1, 2)$ and $(4, 2)$

c. Line passing through $(0, 2)$ and $(0, -2)$

d. Horizontal line through $(0, -4)$

Solution

a. Because the line is vertical and passes through the point $(-3, 2)$, every point on the line has an x-coordinate of -3. So, the equation of the line is

$$x = -3. \qquad \text{Vertical line}$$

b. Because both points have the same y-coordinate, the line through $(-1, 2)$ and $(4, 2)$ is horizontal. So, its equation is

$$y = 2. \qquad \text{Horizontal line}$$

c. Because both points have the same x-coordinate, the line through $(0, 2)$ and $(0, -2)$ is vertical. So, its equation is

$$x = 0. \qquad \text{Vertical line } (y\text{-axis})$$

d. Because the line is horizontal and passes through the point $(0, -4)$, every point on the line has a y-coordinate of -4. So, the equation of the line is

$$y = -4. \qquad \text{Horizontal line}$$

The graphs of the lines are shown in Figure 4.37.

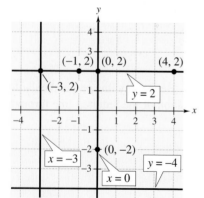

Figure 4.37

In Example 6(c), note that the equation $x = 0$ represents the y-axis. In a similar way, you can show that the equation $y = 0$ represents the x-axis.

3 Use a linear model to solve an application problem.

Application

| Example 7 | Total Sales |

During the first year of operation, a company had sales of $146 million. During the second year, the company had sales of $154 million. Using this information only and assuming this trend continues, what would you estimate the sales to be during the third year? the fifth year?

Solution

To solve this problem, use a *linear model,* with y representing the total sales and t representing the year. That is, in Figure 4.38, let $(1, 146)$ and $(2, 154)$ be two points on the line representing the sales for the company. The slope of this line is

$$m = \frac{154 - 146}{2 - 1} = 8.$$

With this slope, you can use the point-slope form to find an equation of the line.

$y - y_1 = m(t - t_1)$	Point-slope form
$y - 146 = 8(t - 1)$	Substitute 146 for y_1, 1 for t_1, and 8 for m.
$y - 146 = 8t - 8$	Distributive Property
$y = 8t + 138$	Equation of line

Using this model, an estimate of the sales during the third year $(t = 3)$ is

$$y = 8(3) + 138 = \$162 \text{ million.}$$

An estimate of the sales during the fifth year $(t = 5)$ is found similarly.

$$y = 8(5) + 138 = \$178 \text{ million.}$$

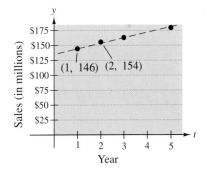

Figure 4.38

The estimation method illustrated in Example 7 is called **linear extrapolation.** Note in Figure 4.39 that for linear extrapolation, the estimated point lies *to the right* of the given points. When the estimated point lies *between* two given points, the method is called **linear interpolation.**

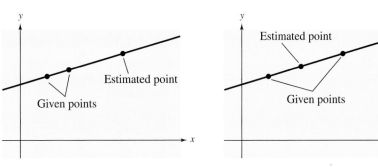

Linear Extrapolation

Linear Interpolation

Figure 4.39

You have now studied several formulas that relate to equations of lines. In the summary below, remember that the formulas that deal with slope cannot be applied to vertical lines. For instance, the lines $x = 2$ and $y = 3$ are perpendicular, but they do not follow the "negative reciprocal property" of perpendicular lines because the line $x = 2$ is vertical (and has no slope).

A discussion of the summary highlighted here could lead to the Discussing the Concept feature below.

▶ **Summary of Equations of Lines**

1. Slope of the line through (x_1, y_1) and (x_2, y_2):

$$m = \frac{y_2 - y_1}{x_2 - x_1}$$

2. General form of an equation of a line:

$$ax + by + c = 0$$

3. Equation of a vertical line:

$$x = a$$

4. Equation of a horizontal line:

$$y = b$$

5. Slope-intercept form of an equation of a line:

$$y = mx + b$$

6. Point-slope form of an equation of a line:

$$y - y_1 = m(x - x_1)$$

7. Parallel lines have *equal* slopes:

$$m_1 = m_2$$

8. Perpendicular lines have *negative reciprocal* slopes:

$$m_1 = -\frac{1}{m_2}$$

Discussing the Concept   **Versatility of $y = mx + b$**

In this chapter, it has been shown that, of the forms of the equation of a line, $y = mx + b$ is better suited for *sketching the graph* of a given equation. On the other hand, $y - y_1 = m(x - x_1)$ is better suited for *creating the equation* of a line, given its slope and a point on the line. Show how $y = mx + b$ can be used to determine the equation of a line that passes through $(-3, 2)$ and has slope of -2. Compare this procedure with the use of the point-slope form. Which procedure do you prefer? Explain why.

4.5   Exercises

Integrated Review   Concepts, Skills, and Problem Solving

Keep mathematically in shape by doing these exercises *before* the problems of this section.

Properties and Definitions

1. Find the greatest common factor of 180 and 300 and explain how you arrived at your answer.

2. Find the least common multiple of 180 and 300 and explain how you arrived at your answer.

Simplifying Expressions

In Exercises 3–6, simplify the expression.

3. $4(3 - 2x)$

4. $x^2(xy^3)$

5. $3x - 2(x - 5)$

6. $u - [3 + (u - 4)]$

Solving Equations

In Exercises 7–10, solve for y in terms of x.

7. $3x + y = 4$

8. $4 - y + x = 0$

9. $4x - 5y = -2$

10. $3x + 4y - 5 = 0$

Developing Skills

In Exercises 1–14, find an equation for the line that passes through the point and has the specified slope. Sketch the line. See Example 1.

1. $(0, 0), m = -2$

2. $(0, -2), m = 3$

3. $(6, 0), m = \frac{1}{2}$

4. $(0, 10), m = -\frac{1}{4}$

5. $(-2, 1), m = 2$

6. $(3, -5), m = -1$

7. $(-8, -1), m = -\frac{1}{4}$

8. $(12, 4), m = -\frac{2}{3}$

9. $\left(\frac{1}{2}, -3\right), m = 0$

10. $\left(-\frac{5}{4}, 6\right), m = 0$

11. $\left(0, \frac{3}{2}\right), m = \frac{2}{3}$

12. $\left(0, -\frac{5}{2}\right), m = \frac{3}{4}$

13. $(2, 4), m = -0.8$

14. $(6, -3), m = 0.67$

In Exercises 15–26, use the point-slope form to write an equation of the line passing through the point and having the specified slope. (Write your answer in slope-intercept form.) See Example 2.

15. $(0, -4), m = 3$

16. $(0, 7), m = -1$

17. $(-3, 6), m = -2$

18. $(-1, 4), m = 4$

19. $(9, 0), m = -\frac{1}{3}$

20. $(0, -2), m = \frac{4}{3}$

21. $(-10, 4), m = 0$

22. $(-2, -5), m = 0$

23. $(8, 1), m = -\frac{3}{4}$

24. $(-3, 2), m = \frac{1}{3}$

25. $(-2, 1), m = \frac{2}{3}$

26. $(1, 3), m = -\frac{1}{2}$

In Exercises 27–38, find the slope of the line. If it is not possible, explain why.

27. $y = \frac{3}{8}x - 4$

28. $y = -3x + 10$

29. $y - 2 = 5(x + 3)$

30. $y + 3 = -2(x - 6)$

31. $y + \frac{5}{6} = \frac{2}{3}(x + 4)$

32. $y - \frac{1}{4} = \frac{5}{8}\left(x - \frac{13}{5}\right)$

33. $3x + y = 0$

34. $y - 6 = 0$

35. $2x - y = 0$

36. $x + 5 = 0$

37. $3x - 2y + 10 = 0$

38. $5x + 4y - 8 = 0$

In Exercises 39–42, write the slope-intercept form of the line.

39.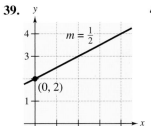

40.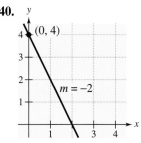

41.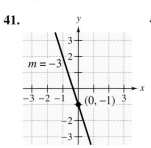

42.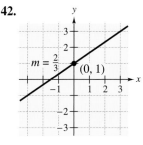

In Exercises 43–46, write the point-slope form of the equation of the line.

43.

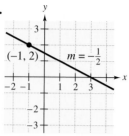

44.

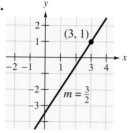

45.

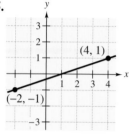

46.

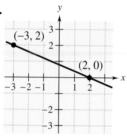

In Exercises 47–58, write an equation of the line through the points. Sketch a graph of the line. See Example 3.

47. $(0, 0), (4, 4)$
48. $(0, 0), (-2, 4)$
49. $(0, 0), (2, -4)$
50. $(6, -1), (3, 3)$
51. $(2, 3), (6, 5)$
52. $(-4, 6), (-2, 3)$
53. $(-6, 2), (3, 5)$
54. $(-9, 7), (-4, 4)$
55. $(5, -1), (3, 2)$
56. $(0, 3), (5, 3)$
57. $\left(\frac{5}{2}, -1\right), \left(\frac{9}{2}, 7\right)$
58. $\left(4, \frac{5}{3}\right), \left(-1, \frac{2}{3}\right)$

In Exercises 59–72, write an equation of the line passing through the points. (Write your answer in general form.)

59. $(0, 3), (3, 0)$
60. $(0, 1), (-2, 0)$
61. $(5, -1), (-5, 5)$
62. $(4, 3), (-4, 5)$
63. $(5, 4), (1, -4)$
64. $(-5, 7), (-2, 1)$
65. $(5, -1), (7, -4)$
66. $(3, 5), (1, 6)$
67. $(-3, 8), (2, 5)$
68. $(9, -9), (7, -5)$
69. $\left(2, \frac{1}{2}\right), \left(\frac{1}{2}, \frac{5}{2}\right)$
70. $\left(\frac{1}{4}, 1\right), \left(-\frac{3}{4}, -\frac{2}{3}\right)$
71. $(1, 0.6), (2, -0.6)$
72. $(-8, 0.6), (2, -2.4)$

In Exercises 73–82, write an equation of the line through the indicated point (a) parallel to the given line and (b) perpendicular to the given line. See Examples 4 and 5.

73. $(2, 1)$
  $x - y = 3$
74. $(-3, 2)$
  $x + y = 7$
75. $(-12, 4)$
  $3x + 4y = 7$
76. $(15, -2)$
  $5x + 3y = 0$
77. $(1, 3)$
  $2x + y = 0$
78. $(5, -2)$
  $x + 5y = 3$
79. $(-1, 0)$
  $y + 3 = 0$
80. $(2, 5)$
  $x - 4 = 0$
81. $(4, -1)$
  $3y - 2x = 7$
82. $(-6, 5)$
  $4x - 5y = 2$

In Exercises 83–90, write an equation for each line. See Example 6.

83. Vertical line through $(-2, 4)$
84. Horizontal line through $(7, 3)$
85. Horizontal line through $\left(\frac{1}{2}, \frac{2}{3}\right)$
86. Vertical line through $\left(\frac{1}{4}, 0\right)$
87. Line passing through $(4, 1)$ and $(4, 8)$
88. Line passing through $(-1, 5)$ and $(6, 5)$
89. Line passing through $(1, -8)$ and $(7, -8)$
90. Line passing through $(3, 0)$ and $(3, 5)$

Graphical Exploration In Exercises 91–94, use a graphing utility to graph the lines. Use the square setting. Are the lines parallel, perpendicular, or neither?

91. $y = -0.4x + 3$
  $y = \frac{5}{2}x - 1$
92. $y = \frac{2x - 3}{3}$
  $y = \frac{4x + 3}{6}$
93. $y = 0.4x + 1$
  $y = x + 2.5$
94. $y = \frac{3}{4}x - 5$
  $y = -\frac{3}{4}x + 2$

95. *Graphical Exploration* Use a graphing utility to graph the following equations on the same screen. Use the square setting. What can you conclude?
  (a) $y = \frac{1}{3}x + 2$
  (b) $y = 4x + 2$
  (c) $y = -3x + 2$
  (d) $y = -\frac{1}{4}x + 2$

Solving Problems

96. *Writing a Linear Model*   A sales representative receives a salary of $2000 per month plus a commission of 2% of the total monthly sales. Write the wages W as a linear function of sales S.

97. *Writing a Linear Model*   A sales representative is reimbursed $225 per day for lodging and meals plus $0.28 per mile driven. Write the daily cost C to the company as a function of x, the number of miles driven.

98. *Writing a Linear Model*   A sales representative is reimbursed $250 per day for lodging and meals plus $0.43 per mile driven. Write the daily cost C to the company as a function of x, the number of miles driven.

99. *Writing a Linear Model*   A sales representative receives a salary of $2300 per month plus a commission of 3% of the total monthly sales. Write the wages W as a linear function of sales S.

100. *Writing and Graphing a Linear Model*   A car travels for t hours at an average speed of 50 miles per hour. Write the distance d as a linear function of t. Graph the function for $0 \le t \le 5$.

101. *Writing and Using a Linear Model*   A store is offering a 20% discount on all items in its inventory.

  (a) Write the sale price S for an item as a linear function of its list price L.

  (b) Use a graphing utility to graph the model.

  (c) Use the graph to estimate the sale price of an item whose list price is $49.98. Confirm your estimate algebraically.

102. *Writing and Using a Linear Model*   A small business purchased a plain paper copier for $5400. After 1 year, its depreciated value is $4300. The depreciation is linear. See Example 7.

  (a) Write the value V of the copier as a linear function of time t in years.

  (b) Use the model to estimate the value after 3 years.

103. *Writing and Using a Linear Model*   A business purchased a new machine for $200,000. After 1 year, its depreciated value is $170,000. The depreciation is linear.

  (a) Write the value V of the machine as a linear function of time t in years.

  (b) Use the model to estimate the value after 5 years.

104. *Writing and Using a Linear Model*   A real estate office handles an apartment complex with 50 units. When the rent per unit is $480 per month, all 50 units are occupied. However, when the rent is $525 per month, the average number of occupied units drops to 47. Assume that the relationship between the monthly rent p and the demand x is linear.

  (a) Represent the given information as two ordered pairs of the form (x, p). Plot these ordered pairs.

  (b) Write the rent p as a linear function of the demand x. Graph the line and describe the relationship between the rent and the demand.

  (c) (*Linear Extrapolation*) Predict the number of units occupied if the rent is raised to $555.

  (d) (*Linear Interpolation*) Predict the number of units occupied if the rent is lowered to $495.

105. *Writing and Using a Linear Model*   A small liberal arts college had an enrollment of 1200 students in 1990. During the next 10 years the enrollment increased by approximately 50 students per year.

  (a) Write the enrollment N as a function of the year t. (Let $t = 0$ represent 1990.)

  (b) (*Linear Interpolation*) Use the model to predict the enrollment in the year 2004.

  (c) (*Linear Interpolation*) Use the model to estimate the enrollment in 1998.

106. *Think About It*   Find the slope of the line for the equation $5x + 7y - 21 = 0$. Use the same process to find a formula for the slope of the line $ax + by + c = 0$ where $b \ne 0$.

107. *Graphical Interpretation* Match each situation labeled (a), (b), (c), and (d) with one of the graphs labeled (e), (f), (g), and (h). Then find the slope of the line and write a verbal description of the slope in the context of the real-life situation.

(a) A friend is paying you $10 per week to repay a $100 loan.

(b) An employee is paid $12.50 per hour plus $1.50 for each unit produced per hour.

(c) A sales representative receives $40 per day for food plus $0.32 for each mile traveled.

(d) A typewriter purchased for $600 depreciates $100 per year.

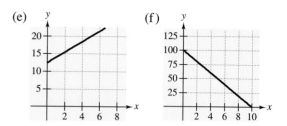

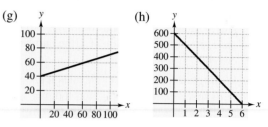

Explaining Concepts

108. Answer parts (d)–(g) of Motivating the Chapter on page 201.

109. Can any pair of points on a line be used to calculate the slope of the line? Explain.

110. Can the equation of a vertical line be written in slope-intercept form? Explain.

111. In the equation $y = mx + b$, what do m and b represent?

112. In the equation $y - y_1 = m(x - x_1)$, what do x_1 and y_1 represent?

113. Explain how to find analytically the x-intercept of the line given by $y = mx + b$.

114. What is implied about the graphs of the lines $a_1x + b_1y + c_1 = 0$ and $a_2x + b_2y + c_2 = 0$ if $a_1/b_1 = a_2/b_2$?

115. *Research Project* In a news magazine or newspaper, find an example of data that are *increasing* linearly with time. Write a linear function that models the data. Repeat the project for data that are *decreasing*.

4.6   Graphs of Linear Inequalities

Objectives

1 Determine whether an ordered pair is a solution of a linear inequality in two variables.

2 Sketch the graph of a linear inequality in two variables.

1 Determine whether an ordered pair is a solution of a linear inequality in two variables.

Linear Inequalities in Two Variables

A **linear inequality** in two variables x and y is an inequality that can be written in one of the following forms.

$$ax + by < c, \quad ax + by > c, \quad ax + by \leq c, \quad \text{and} \quad ax + by \geq c$$

Here are some examples.

$$x - y > 2, \quad 3x - 2y \leq 6, \quad x \geq 5, \quad \text{and} \quad y < -1$$

An ordered pair (x_1, y_1) is a **solution** of a linear inequality in x and y if the inequality is true when x_1 and y_1 are substituted for x and y, respectively. For instance, the ordered pair $(3, 2)$ is a solution of the inequality $x - y > 0$ because $3 - 2 > 0$ is a true statement.

Example 1   Verifying Solutions of Linear Inequalities

Decide whether the points are solutions of $3x - y \geq -1$.

a. $(0, 0)$ **b.** $(1, 4)$ **c.** $(-1, 2)$

Solution

a. $3x - y \geq -1$ Original inequality

$$3(0) - 0 \overset{?}{\geq} -1$$ Substitute 0 for x and 0 for y.

$$0 \geq -1$$ Inequality is satisfied. ✓

Because the inequality is satisfied, the point $(0, 0)$ *is* a solution.

b. $3x - y \geq -1$ Original inequality

$$3(1) - 4 \overset{?}{\geq} -1$$ Substitute 1 for x and 4 for y.

$$-1 \geq -1$$ Inequality is satisfied. ✓

Because the inequality is satisfied, the point $(1, 4)$ *is* a solution.

c. $3x - y \geq -1$ Original inequality

$$3(-1) - 2 \overset{?}{\geq} -1$$ Substitute -1 for x and 2 for y.

$$-5 \ngeq -1$$ Inequality is not satisfied. ✗

Because the inequality is not satisfied, the point $(-1, 2)$ *is not* a solution.

2 Sketch the graph of a linear inequality in two variables.

The Graph of a Linear Inequality

The **graph** of an inequality is the collection of all solution points of the inequality. To sketch the graph of a linear inequality such as

$$3x - 2y < 6 \qquad \text{Original inequality}$$

begin by sketching the graph of the *corresponding linear equation*

$$3x - 2y = 6. \qquad \text{Corresponding equation}$$

Use a *dashed* line for the inequalities $<$ and $>$ and a *solid* line for the inequalities $\leq$ and $\geq$. The graph of the equation separates the plane into two **half-planes.** In each half-plane, one of the following must be true.

1. All points in the half-plane are solutions of the inequality.

2. No point in the half-plane is a solution of the inequality.

So, you can determine whether the points in an entire half-plane satisfy the inequality by simply testing *one* point in the region.

> **Example 2**   Sketching the Graph of a Linear Inequality

Sketch the graphs of the linear inequalities.

a. $x > -2$ **b.** $y \leq 3$

Solution

a. The graph of the corresponding equation $x = -2$ is a vertical line. The points (x, y) that satisfy the inequality $x > -2$ are those lying to the right of this line, as shown in Figure 4.40.

b. The graph of the corresponding equation $y = 3$ is a horizontal line. The points (x, y) that satisfy the inequality $y \leq 3$ are those lying below (or on) this line, as shown in Figure 4.41.

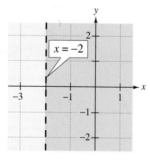

Figure 4.40

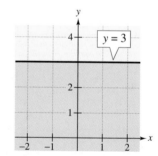

Figure 4.41

Notice that a dashed line is used for the graph of $x > -2$ and a solid line is used for the graph of $y \leq 3$.

Some guidelines for sketching the graph of a linear inequality in two variables are listed below.

▶ **Guidelines for Graphing a Linear Inequality**

1. Replace the inequality sign by an equal sign and sketch the graph of the resulting equation. (Use a dashed line for < and > and a solid line for ≤ and ≥.)

2. Test one point in each of the half-planes formed by the graph in Step 1. If the point satisfies the inequality, then shade the entire half-plane to denote that every point in the region satisfies the inequality.

Study Tip

You can use any point that is not on the line as a test point. However, the origin is often the most convenient because it is easy to evaluate expressions in which 0 is substituted for each variable.

Technology: Tip

Many graphing utilities are capable of graphing linear inequalities. Consult the user's guide of your graphing utility for specific instructions.

The graph of $y \le -x + 2$ is shown below.

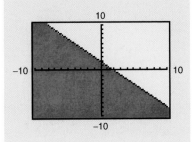

Example 3   Sketching the Graph of a Linear Inequality

Sketch the graph of the linear inequality

$$x - y < 2. \qquad \text{Original inequality}$$

Solution

The graph of the corresponding equation

$$x - y = 2 \qquad \text{Corresponding equation}$$

is a line, as shown in Figure 4.42. Because the origin $(0, 0)$ does not lie on the line, use it as the test point.

$$x - y < 2 \qquad \text{Original inequality}$$
$$0 - 0 \overset{?}{<} 2 \qquad \text{Substitute 0 for } x \text{ and 0 for } y.$$
$$0 < 2 \qquad \text{Inequality is satisfied.} \checkmark$$

Because $(0, 0)$ satisfies the inequality, the graph consists of the half-plane lying above the line. Try checking a point below the line. Regardless of the point you choose, you will see that it is not a solution.

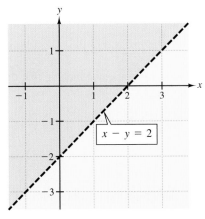

Figure 4.42

For a linear inequality in two variables, you can sometimes simplify the graphing procedure by writing the inequality in *slope-intercept* form. For instance, by writing $x - y < 2$ in the form $y > x - 2$, you can see that the solution points lie *above* the line $y = x - 2$, as shown in Figure 4.42. Similarly, by writing the inequality $3x - 2y > 5$ in the form

$$y < \frac{3}{2}x - \frac{5}{2}$$

you can see that the solutions lie *below* the line $y = \frac{3}{2}x - \frac{5}{2}$, as shown in Figure 4.43.

Study Tip

The solution of the inequality

$$y < \frac{3}{2}x - \frac{5}{2}$$

is a half-plane with the line

$$y = \frac{3}{2}x - \frac{5}{2}$$

as its boundary. The y-values that are less than this equation make the inequality true. So, you want to shade the half-plane with the smaller y-values, as shown in Figure 4.43.

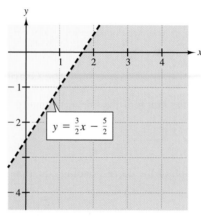

$$y = \frac{3}{2}x - \frac{5}{2}$$

Figure 4.43

| Example 4 | Sketching the Graph of a Linear Inequality |

Use the slope-intercept form of a linear equation as an aid in sketching the graph of the inequality $5x + 4y \leq 12$.

Solution

To begin, rewrite the inequality in slope-intercept form.

$$5x + 4y \leq 12 \qquad \text{Original inequality}$$

$$4y \leq -5x + 12 \qquad \text{Subtract } 5x \text{ from both sides.}$$

$$y \leq -\frac{5}{4}x + 3 \qquad \text{Slope-intercept form}$$

From this form, you can conclude that the solution is the half-plane lying *on* or *below* the line

$$y = -\frac{5}{4}x + 3.$$

The graph is shown in Figure 4.44. You can verify this by testing the solution point $(0, 0)$.

$$5x + 4y \leq 12 \qquad \text{Original inequality}$$

$$5(0) + 4(0) \overset{?}{\leq} 12 \qquad \text{Substitute 0 for } x \text{ and 0 for } y.$$

$$0 \leq 12 \qquad \text{Inequality is satisfied. } \checkmark$$

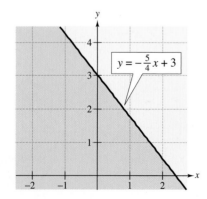

$$y = -\frac{5}{4}x + 3$$

Figure 4.44

Example 5   Writing a Model

You have two part-time jobs. One is at a fast-food restaurant, which pays $6 per hour, and the other is babysitting for $4 per hour. Between the two jobs, you want to earn at least $100 a week. Write an inequality that shows the number of hours that you need to work. Then sketch a graph of the inequality.

Solution

To write the inequality, use the problem-solving method.

Verbal Model:	Hourly pay job 1	·	Number of hours job 1	+	Hourly pay job 2	·	Number of hours job 2	≥	Earnings in a week

Labels: Hourly pay job 1 $= 6$ (dollars per hour)
Number of hours job 1 $= x$ (hours)
Hourly pay job 2 $= 4$ (dollars per hour)
Number of hours job 2 $= y$ (hours)
Earnings in a week $= 100$ (dollars)

Algebraic Inequality: $6x + 4y \geq 100$

To sketch the graph, rewrite the inequality in slope-intercept form.

$$6x + 4y \geq 100 \qquad \text{Original inequality}$$

$$4y \geq -6x + 100 \qquad \text{Subtract } 6x \text{ from both sides.}$$

$$y \geq \frac{-6x + 100}{4} \qquad \text{Divide both sides by 4.}$$

$$y \geq -\frac{3}{2}x + 25 \qquad \text{Slope-intercept form}$$

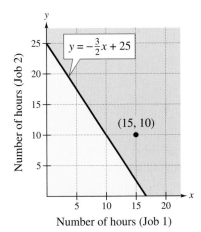

$y = -\frac{3}{2}x + 25$

(15, 10)

Number of hours (Job 2)

Number of hours (Job 1)

Figure 4.45

From the graph of the inequality, shown in Figure 4.45, you can see that the point (15, 10) is one solution point. This means that if you work 15 hours at the restaurant and babysit for 10 hours, you will earn at least $100.

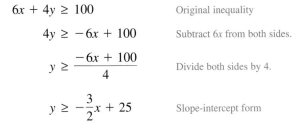

Discussing the Concept   A Double Inequality

Determine how to use a graphing utility to find the solution set to the double inequality

$$2x \leq y \leq x + 2.$$

Choose a point in the region shaded by the utility, and show that it satisfies the double inequality.

4.6   Exercises

Integrated Review   Concepts, Skills, and Problem Solving

Keep mathematically in shape by doing these exercises *before* the problems of this section.

Properties and Definitions

In Exercises 1–4, complete the property of inequalities by inserting the correct inequality symbol. (Consider a, b, and c to be real numbers, variables, or algebraic expressions.)

1. If $a < b$, then $a + 5$ ___ $b + 5$.

2. If $a < b$, then $2a$ ___ $2b$.

3. If $a < b$, then $-3a$ ___ $-3b$.

4. If $a < b$ and $b < c$, then a ___ c.

Solving Inequalities

In Exercises 5–10, solve the inequality and graph it on the real number line.

5. $x + 3 > 0$

6. $2 - x \geq 0$

7. $2t - 11 \leq 5$

8. $\frac{3}{2}y + 8 < 20$

9. $5 < 2x + 3 < 15$

10. $-2 < -\dfrac{x}{4} < 1$

Problem Solving

11. Assume the sales commission rate is 4.5%. Determine the sales of an employee who earned $544.50 as a sales commission.

12. One person can complete a typing project in 3 hours, and another can complete the same project in 4 hours. If they both work on the project, in how many hours can it be completed?

Developing Skills

In Exercises 1–8, which points are solutions? See Example 1.

Inequality		*Points*	
1. $x + y > 5$	(a) $(0, 0)$	(b) $(3, 6)$
	(c) $(-6, 20)$	(d) $(3, 2)$
2. $2x - y > 3$	(a) $(3, 0)$	(b) $(2, 6)$
	(c) $(-6, -20)$	(d) $(3, 3)$
3. $-3x + 5y \leq 12$	(a) $(1, 2)$	(b) $(2, -3)$
	(c) $(1, 3)$	(d) $(2, 8)$
4. $5x + 3y < 100$	(a) $(25, 10)$	(b) $(6, 10)$
	(c) $(0, -12)$	(d) $(4, 5)$
5. $3x - 2y < 2$	(a) $(1, 3)$	(b) $(2, 0)$
	(c) $(0, 0)$	(d) $(3, -5)$
6. $y - 2x > 5$	(a) $(4, 13)$	(b) $(8, 1)$
	(c) $(0, 7)$	(d) $(1, -3)$
7. $5x + 4y \geq 6$	(a) $(-2, 4)$	(b) $(5, 5)$
	(c) $(7, 0)$	(d) $(-2, 5)$
8. $5y + 8x \leq 14$	(a) $(-3, 8)$	(b) $(7, -6)$
	(c) $(1, 1)$	(d) $(3, 0)$

In Exercises 9–12, state whether the boundary of the graph of the inequality should be dashed or solid.

9. $2x + 3y < 6$

10. $2x + 3y \leq 6$

11. $2x + 3y \geq 6$

12. $2x + 3y > 6$

In Exercises 13–16, match the inequality with its graph. [The graphs are labeled (a), (b), (c), and (d).]

(a)

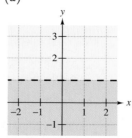

(b)

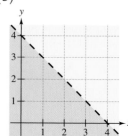

(c)

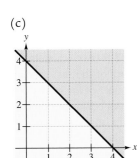

(d)

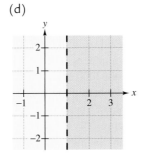

13. $x + y < 4$

14. $x + y \geq 4$

15. $x > 1$

16. $y < 1$

In Exercises 17–20, match the inequality with its graph. [The graphs are labeled (a), (b), (c), and (d).]

(a)

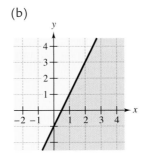

(b)

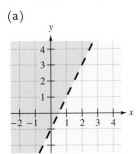

(c)

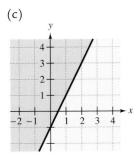

(d)

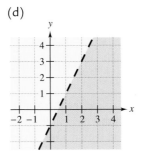

17. $2x - y \leq 1$

18. $2x - y < 1$

19. $2x - y \geq 1$

20. $2x - y > 1$

In Exercises 21–50, graph the inequality. See Examples 2–4.

21. $y \geq 3$

22. $x \leq 0$

23. $x > \frac{3}{2}$

24. $y < -2$

25. $y < \frac{1}{2}x$

26. $y > -\frac{2}{3}x$

27. $x - y < 0$

28. $x + y > 0$

29. $y \leq 2x - 1$

30. $y \geq -x + 3$

31. $y \leq x - 2$

32. $y \geq 0.6x + 1$

33. $y > x - 2$

34. $y < -x + 3$

35. $y > -2x + 10$

36. $y < 3x + 1$

37. $y \geq \frac{2}{3}x + \frac{1}{3}$

38. $y \leq -\frac{3}{4}x + 2$

39. $2x + y - 3 \geq 3$

40. $x - 2y + 6 \leq 0$

41. $-3x + 2y - 6 < 0$

42. $x + 4y + 2 \geq 2$

43. $5x + 2y < 5$

44. $5x + 2y > 5$

45. $x \geq 3y - 5$

46. $x > -2y + 10$

47. $y - 3 < \frac{1}{2}(x - 4)$

48. $y + 1 < -2(x - 3)$

49. $\frac{x}{3} + \frac{y}{4} < 1$

50. $\frac{x}{-2} + \frac{y}{2} > 1$

In Exercises 51–58, use a graphing utility to graph the inequality.

51. $y \geq 2x - 1$

52. $y \leq 4 - 0.5x$

53. $y \leq -2x + 4$

54. $y \geq x - 3$

55. $y \geq \frac{1}{2}x + 2$

56. $y \leq -\frac{2}{3}x + 6$

57. $6x + 10y - 15 \leq 0$

58. $3x - 2y + 4 \geq 0$

In Exercises 59–64, write an inequality that represents the graph.

59.

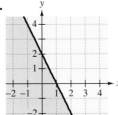

60.

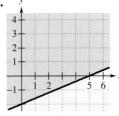

61.

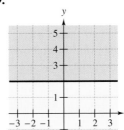

62.

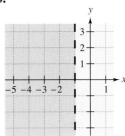

63.

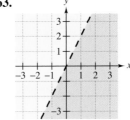

64.

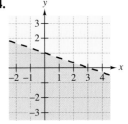

Solving Problems

65. *Writing a Model* You have two part-time jobs. One is at a grocery store, which pays $7 per hour, and the other is mowing lawns, which pays $5 per hour. Between the two jobs, you want to earn at least $140 a week. Write an inequality that shows the different numbers of hours you can work at each job, and sketch the graph of the inequality. From the graph, find several ordered pairs with positive integer coordinates that are solutions of the inequality.

66. *Writing a Model* A cash register must have at least $25 in change consisting of d dimes and q quarters. Write an inequality that shows the different numbers of coins that can be in the cash register, and sketch the graph of the inequality. From the graph, find several ordered pairs with positive integer coordinates that are solutions of the inequality.

67. *Writing a Model* Each table produced by a furniture company requires 1 hour in the assembly center. The matching chair requires $1\frac{1}{2}$ hours in the assembly center. A total of 12 hours per day is available in the assembly center. Write an inequality that shows the different numbers of hours that can be spent assembling tables and chairs, and sketch a graph of the inequality. From the graph, find several ordered pairs with positive integer coordinates that are solutions of the inequality.

68. *Writing a Model* A store sells two models of computers. The costs to the store of the two models are $2000 and $3000, and the owner of the store does not want more than $30,000 invested in the inventory for these two models. Write an inequality that represents the different numbers of each model that can be held in inventory. Sketch a graph of the inequality. From the graph, find several ordered pairs with positive integer coordinates that are solutions of the inequality.

69. *Dietetics* A dietitian is asked to design a special diet supplement using two foods. Each ounce of food X contains 20 units of calcium and each ounce of food Y contains 10 units of calcium. The minimum daily requirement in the diet is 300 units of calcium. Write an inequality that shows the different numbers of units of food X and food Y required. Sketch the graph of the inequality. From the graph, find several ordered pairs with positive integer coordinates that are solutions of the inequality.

Explaining Concepts

70. Answer part (h) of Motivating the Chapter on page 201.

71. List the four forms of a linear inequality in variables x and y.

72. What is meant by saying that (x_1, y_1) is a solution of a linear inequality in x and y?

73. Explain the difference between graphs that have dashed lines and those that have solid lines.

74. After graphing the boundary, explain how you determine which half-plane is the graph of a linear inequality.

75. Explain the difference between graphing the solution to the inequality $x \geq 1$ (a) on the real number line and (b) on a rectangular coordinate system.

76. Write the inequality whose graph consists of all points above the x-axis.

77. Does $2x < 2y$ have the same graph as $y > x$? Explain.

78. Write an inequality whose graph has no points in the first quadrant.

Key Terms

rectangular coordinate
  system, *p. 202*
ordered pair, *p. 202*
x-coordinate, *p.202*
y-coordinate, *p. 202*
solution point, *p. 205*

x-intercept, *p. 217*
y-intercept, *p. 217*
relation, *p. 223*
domain, *p. 223*
range, *p. 223*
function, *p. 224*

independent variable,
  p. 225
dependent variable, *p. 225*
slope, *p. 234*
slope-intercept form,
  p. 238

parallel lines, *p. 240*
perpendicular lines, *p. 240*
point-slope form, *p. 247*
half-plane, *p. 258*

Key Concepts

4.1 Rectangular coordinate system

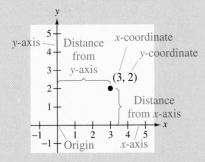

4.2 Point-plotting method of sketching the graph of an equation

1. If possible, rewrite the equation by isolating one of the variables.
2. Make up a table of values showing several solution points.
3. Plot these points on a rectangular coordinate system.
4. Connect the points with a smooth curve or line.

4.2 Finding *x*- and *y*-intercepts

1. To find the *x*-intercept(s), let $y = 0$ and solve the resulting equation for *x*.
2. To find the *y*-intercept(s), let $x = 0$ and solve the resulting equation for *y*.

4.3 Vertical Line Test

A graph is not the graph of a function if a vertical line can be drawn that intersects the graph at more than one point.

4.3 Function notation

In the notation $f(x)$:

    f is the name of the function.

    x is a domain value.

$f(x)$ is a range value *y* for a given *x*.

The symbol $f(x)$ is read as "the value of *f* at *x*" or simply "*f* of *x*."

4.4 Slope of a line

The slope of a nonvertical line passing through points (x_1, y_1) and (x_2, y_2) is

$$m = \frac{y_2 - y_1}{x_2 - x_1} = \frac{\text{change in } y}{\text{change in } x} = \frac{\text{rise}}{\text{run}}$$

where $x_1 \neq x_2$.

1. If $m > 0$, the line rises from left to right.
2. If $m < 0$, the line falls from left to right.
3. If $m = 0$, the line is horizontal.
4. If *m* is undefined ($x_1 = x_2$), the line is vertical.

4.4 Slope-intercept form

The slope-intercept form of the equation of a line is

$$y = mx + b,$$

where the slope of the line is *m* and the *y*-intercept is $(0, b)$.

4.5 Point-slope form

The point-slope form of the equation of a line with slope *m* and passing through the point (x_1, y_1) is

$$y - y_1 = m(x - x_1).$$

4.6 Graphing a linear inequality

1. Replace the inequality sign by an equal sign and sketch the graph of the corresponding equation. (Use a dashed line for < and > and a solid line for ≤ and ≥.)
2. Test one point in each of the half-planes formed by the graph in Step 1. If the point satisfies the inequality, then shade the entire half-plane to denote that every point in the region satisfies the inequality.

REVIEW EXERCISES

Reviewing Skills

4.1 In Exercises 1–4, plot the points on a rectangular coordinate system.

1. $(-1, 6), (4, -3), (-2, 2), (3, 5)$
2. $(0, -1), (-4, 2), (5, 1), (3, -4)$
3. $(-2, 0), (\frac{3}{2}, 4), (-1, -3)$
4. $(3, -\frac{5}{2}), (-5, 2\frac{3}{4}), (4, 6)$

In Exercises 5–12, determine the quadrant(s) in which the point must be located or the axis on which the point is located.

5. $(-5, 3)$
6. $(4, -6)$
7. $(4, 0)$
8. $(0, -3)$
9. $(x, 5)$, $x < 0$
10. $(-3, y)$, $y > 0$
11. $(-6, y)$, y is a real number.
12. $(x, -1)$, x is a real number.

In Exercises 13–16, solve the equation for y.

13. $3x + 4y = 12$
14. $2x + 3y = 6$
15. $x - 2y = 8$
16. $-x - 3y = 9$

In Exercises 17 and 18, construct a table of values for the equation that shows four solution points. Use x-values of $-1, 0, 1$, and 2.

17. $2x - y = 1$
18. $6x + 3y = -3$

In Exercises 19–22, determine whether the ordered pairs are solution points of the equation.

19. $x - 3y = 4$
    (a) $(1, -1)$ (b) $(0, 0)$
    (c) $(2, 1)$ (d) $(5, -2)$
20. $y - 2x = -1$
    (a) $(3, 7)$ (b) $(0, -1)$
    (c) $(-2, -5)$ (d) $(-1, 0)$
21. $y = \frac{2}{3}x + 3$
    (a) $(3, 5)$ (b) $(-3, 1)$
    (c) $(-6, 0)$ (d) $(0, 3)$
22. $y = \frac{1}{4}x + 2$
    (a) $(-4, 1)$ (b) $(-8, 0)$
    (c) $(12, 5)$ (d) $(0, 2)$

4.2 In Exercises 23–34, sketch the graph of the equation using the point-plotting method, and label any x- and y-intercepts of the graph.

23. $y = 7$
24. $x = -2$
25. $y = 3x$
26. $y = -2x$
27. $y = 4 - \frac{1}{2}x$
28. $y = \frac{3}{2}x - 3$
29. $y - 2x - 4 = 0$
30. $3x + 2y + 6 = 0$
31. $y = 2x - 1$
32. $y = 5 - 4x$
33. $y = \frac{1}{4}x + 2$
34. $y = -\frac{2}{3}x - 2$

In Exercises 35–38, use a graphing utility to graph the equation. (Use a standard setting.)

35. $y = \frac{7}{8}x + 1$
36. $y = 5 - 2x$
37. $y = -\frac{1}{4}x^2 + x$
38. $y = x(x^2 - 4)$

In Exercises 39–42, graph the equation using a graphing utility.

39. $y = 250 - 50x$
40. $y = 800 + 9x$

```
Xmin = -5
Xmax = 5
Xscl = 1
Ymin = 0
Ymax = 500
Yscl = 25
```

```
Xmin = 0
Xmax = 100
Xscl = 10
Ymin = 500
Ymax = 2000
Yscl = 200
```

41. $y = -2x^2 + 112x + 50$
42. $y = |x - 3| + |x - 6|$

```
Xmin = -10
Xmax = 75
Xscl = 5
Ymin = -200
Ymax = 2000
Yscl = 200
```

```
Xmin = -2
Xmax = 11
Xscl = 1
Ymin = 0
Ymax = 12
Yscl = 1
```

4.3 In Exercises 43–46, identify the domain and range of the relation.

43. $\{(8, 3), (-2, 7), (5, 1), (3, 8)\}$

44. $\{(0, 1), (-1, 3), (4, 6), (-7, 5)\}$

45. $\{(2, -3), (-2, 3), (7, 0), (-4, -2)\}$

46. $\{(1, 7), (-3, 4), (6, 5), (-2, -9)\}$

In Exercises 47–50, determine if the relation is a function.

47.

Input value	0	2	4	6	2
Output value	0	1	1	2	3

48.

Input value	−6	−3	0	3	6
Output value	1	0	1	4	2

49. *Domain   Range*

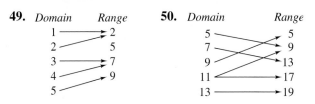

50. *Domain   Range*

In Exercises 51–56, determine whether the relation represents y as a function of x.

51. $x = y^2 - 4$

52. $y = x^3 - 3x + 2$

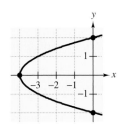

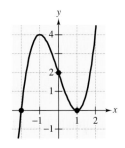

53. $y = x^2 - 4x$

54. $x = y^3 - y$

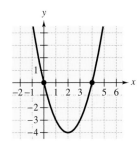

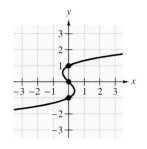

55.

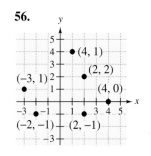

56.

In Exercises 57–62, evaluate the function.

57. $f(x) = |2x + 3|$ (a) $f(0)$ (b) $f(5)$
(c) $f(-4)$ (d) $f\left(-\frac{3}{2}\right)$

58. $g(t) = -16t^2 + 64$ (a) $g(0)$ (b) $g\left(\frac{1}{4}\right)$
(c) $g(1)$ (d) $g(2)$

59. $h(u) = u(u - 3)^2$ (a) $h(0)$ (b) $h(3)$
(c) $h(-1)$ (d) $h\left(\frac{3}{2}\right)$

60. $f(x) = 25$ (a) $f(-1)$ (b) $f(7)$
(c) $f(10)$ (d) $f\left(-\frac{4}{3}\right)$

61. $f(x) = 2x - 7$ (a) $f(-1)$ (b) $f(3)$
(c) $f\left(\frac{1}{2}\right)$ (d) $f(-4)$

62. $f(x) = |x| - 4$ (a) $f(-1)$ (b) $f(1)$
(c) $f(-4)$ (d) $f(2)$

In Exercises 63–70, use a graphing utility to graph the function. Identify any intercepts of the graph.

63. $f(x) = \frac{3}{2}x + 2$ **64.** $f(x) = 5 - \frac{1}{2}x$

65. $g(x) = \frac{1}{5}(25 - x^2)$ **66.** $f(x) = x^2 + 2x - 15$

67. $g(x) = x^2(x - 4)$ **68.** $h(x) = x(x^2 - 4)$

69. $f(x) = 4 - \frac{1}{2}|x|$ **70.** $h(x) = |x^2 - 9|$

4.4 In Exercises 71 and 72, estimate the slope of the line from its graph.

71.

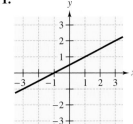

72.

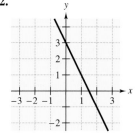

In Exercises 73–76, match the equation with its graph. [The graphs are labeled (a), (b), (c), and (d).]

(a)

(b)
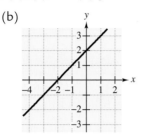

(c)
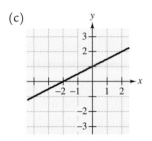

(d)
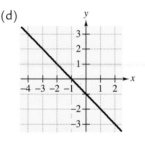

73. $y = \frac{1}{2}x + 1$ **74.** $y = \frac{1}{2}x - 1$

75. $y = x + 2$ **76.** $y = -x - 1$

In Exercises 77–88, determine the slope of the line through the points.

77. $(2, 1), (14, 6)$ **78.** $(-2, 2), (3, -10)$

79. $(-1, 0), (6, 2)$ **80.** $(1, 6), (4, 2)$

81. $(4, 0), (4, 6)$ **82.** $(1, 3), (4, 3)$

83. $(-2, 5), (1, 1)$ **84.** $(-6, 1), (10, 5)$

85. $(1, -4), (5, 10)$ **86.** $(-3, 3), (8, 6)$

87. $\left(0, \frac{5}{2}\right), \left(\frac{5}{6}, 0\right)$ **88.** $(0, 0), \left(3, \frac{4}{5}\right)$

In Exercises 89–92, write the linear equation in slope-intercept form and graph the line.

89. $3x + 6y = 12$ **90.** $2x - y = -1$

91. $5y - 2x = 5$ **92.** $7x + 21y = -14$

In Exercises 93–96, use the slope to determine whether the lines are parallel, perpendicular, or neither.

93. $y = 4x - 8, \ y = -\frac{1}{4}x + 2$

94. $y = x + 3, \ y = 5 - x$

95. $4x - y = 7, \ 8x - 2y = 3$

96. $2x - 3y = 7, \ 3y - 2x = 5$

In Exercises 97–102, a point on a line and the slope of the line are given. Find two additional points on the line. (There are many correct answers.)

97. $(3, -1), \ m = -2$ **98.** $(-2, 5), \ m = 3$

99. $(2, 3), \ m = \frac{3}{4}$ **100.** $(-3, 1), \ m = -\frac{2}{3}$

101. $\left(\frac{4}{3}, 4\right), \ m = 0$ **102.** $\left(6, \frac{7}{2}\right), \ m$ is undefined.

4.5 In Exercises 103–112, write an equation of the line passing through the point and with the specified slope using the point-slope form if possible. (Write your answer in general form.)

103. $(4, -1), \ m = 2$ **104.** $(-5, 2), \ m = 3$

105. $(1, 2), \ m = -4$ **106.** $(7, -3), \ m = -1$

107. $(-5, -2), \ m = \frac{4}{5}$ **108.** $(12, -4), \ m = -\frac{1}{6}$

109. $(-1, 3), \ m = -\frac{8}{3}$ **110.** $(4, -2), \ m = \frac{8}{5}$

111. $(3, 8), \ m$ is undefined.

112. $(-4, 6), \ m = 0$

In Exercises 113–116, determine the slope of the line. If it is not possible, explain why.

113. $y = 5x + 3$ **114.** $y = 6$

115. $y + 10 = \frac{4}{3}(x - 4)$ **116.** $x + 5 = 0$

In Exercises 117–124, find an equation of the line passing through the points. (Write your answer in general form.)

117. $(-4, 0), (0, -2)$ **118.** $(-4, -2), (4, 6)$

119. $(0, 8), (6, 8)$ **120.** $(2, -6), (2, 5)$

121. $(-1, 2), (4, 7)$ **122.** $\left(0, \frac{4}{3}\right), (3, 0)$

123. $(2.4, 3.3), (6, 7.8)$ **124.** $(-1.4, 0), (3.2, 9.2)$

In Exercises 125–128, find an equation of the line through the point (a) parallel to the given line and (b) perpendicular to the given line.

125. $(-6, 3), \ 2x + 3y = 1$

126. $\left(\frac{1}{5}, -\frac{4}{5}\right), \ 5x + y = 2$

127. $\left(\frac{3}{8}, 4\right), \ 4x + 3y = 16$

128. $(-2, 1), \ 5x = 2$

⬚ *Graphical Exploration*   In Exercises 129–132, use a graphing utility to graph the lines. Use the square setting. Are the lines parallel, perpendicular, or neither?

129. $y = -0.5x + 4$
$y = 2x - 3$

130. $y = \frac{1}{4}(x - 4)$
$y = \frac{1}{8}(2x + 15)$

131. $y = 2.5x + 1$
$y = \frac{1}{2}(5x - 4)$

132. $y = 3x - 7$
$y = -2.5x + 6$

4.6 In Exercises 133 and 134, determine whether the ordered pair is a solution of the inequality.

133. $x - y > 4$
   (a) $(-1, -5)$ (b) $(0, 0)$
   (c) $(3, -2)$ (d) $(8, 1)$

134. $y - 2x \le -1$
   (a) $(0, 0)$ (b) $(-2, 1)$
   (c) $(-3, 4)$ (d) $(-1, -6)$

In Exercises 135–140, sketch the graph of the linear inequality.

135. $x - 2 \ge 0$

136. $y + 3 < 0$

137. $2x + y < 1$

138. $3x - 4y > 2$

139. $x \le 4y - 2$

140. $x \ge 3 - 2y$

In Exercises 141–144, write an inequality that represents the graph.

141.
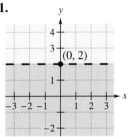

142.
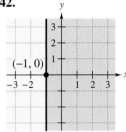

143.
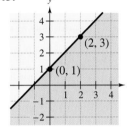

144.
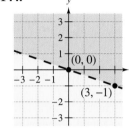

Solving Problems

145. *Organizing Data*   The data from a study measuring the relationship between the wattage x of a standard light bulb and the energy rate y (in lumens) are given in the table.   (Source: Standard Handbook for Mechanical Engineers)

x	25	40	60	100	150	200
y	266	470	840	1750	2700	4000

(a) Plot the data given in the table.

(b) Describe the relationship between x and y.

(c) Estimate the value of y when $x = 125$. Is it easier to use the table or the graph to estimate this value? Explain your reasoning.

146. *Graphical Interpretation*   The line graph shows the average salaries (in thousands of dollars) for professional players in baseball, basketball, and football in the United States for the years 1990 through 1995.   (Source: Major League Baseball Players Association, National Basketball Association, National Football League Players Association)

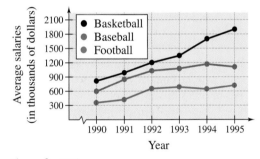

Figure for 146

(a) Approximate the average salary for professional basketball players in 1991.

(b) In what year did the average salary of professional baseball players first exceed 1 million dollars?

(c) Approximate the percentage increase in average salaries for football players from 1990 to 1991.

147. *Writing a Model*   The cost of sending a package is $2.25 plus $0.75 per pound. Write the total cost C as a function of the weight x. Use a graphing utility to graph the function for $0 < x \le 20$.

148. *Geometry* The volume V of the segment of a sphere of radius 5 is a function of the height h of the segment (see figure). The formula for the function is

$$V(h) = \pi\left(5h^2 - \frac{h^3}{3}\right), \quad 0 < h \le 5.$$

Use a graphing utility to graph the function over the specified interval.

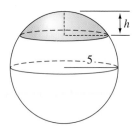

149. *Geometry* A wire 24 inches long is cut into four pieces to form a rectangle (see figure). Express the area A of the rectangle as a function of x.

150. *Business Expense* A company reimburses its sales representatives $150 per day for lodging and meals plus $0.30 per mile driven. Write the daily cost y to the company as a function of x, the number of miles driven. Graph the function.

151. *Graphical Estimation* A person who weighs 180 pounds begins a diet of 1500 calories per day. The person's weight y after dieting for x weeks is approximated by

$$y = 0.014x^2 - 1.218x + 180, \quad 0 \le x \le 26.$$

(a) Use a graphing utility to graph the function.

(b) Approximate the person's weight after 26 weeks.

(c) Approximate the time required for the person to lose 5 pounds.

152. *Slope of a Ramp* The floor of a truck is 4 feet above ground level. The end of the ramp used in loading the truck rests on the ground 6 feet behind the truck. Determine the slope of the ramp.

153. *Slope of a Path* An aircraft is on its approach to an airport. Radar shows its altitude to be 15,000 feet when it is 10 miles from touchdown. Approximate the slope of the linear path followed during landing.

154. *Graphical Interpretation* The velocity (in feet per second) of a ball thrown vertically upward from ground level is modeled by $v = -32t + 48$, where t is time in seconds.

(a) Graph the expression for the velocity.

(b) Interpret the slope of the line in the context of this real-life setting.

(c) Find the velocity when $t = 0$ and $t = 1$.

(d) Find the time when the ball reaches its maximum height. (*Hint:* Find the time when $v = 0$.)

155. *Writing a Model* A company produces a product for which the variable cost is $5.35 per unit and the fixed cost is $16,000. The product is sold for $8.20 per unit. (Let x represent the number of units produced and sold.)

(a) Write an equation that represents the total cost C as a linear function of x.

(b) Write an equation that represents the profit P as a linear function of x.

156. *Writing a Model* Each week a company produces x VCRs and y camcorders. The assembly times for the two types of units are 2 and 3 hours, respectively. The time available in a week is 120 hours. Write an inequality that shows the different numbers of VCRs and camcorders that can be produced. Sketch a graph of the inequality. From the graph, find several ordered pairs that are solutions of the inequality.

Chapter Test

Take this test as you would take a test in class. After you are done, check your work against the answers given in the back of the book.

1. Plot the points $(-1, 2)$, $(1, 4)$, and $(2, -1)$ on a rectangular coordinate system. Connect the points with line segments to form a right triangle.

2. Which ordered pairs are solutions of $y = |x| + |x - 2|$?
   (a) $(0, -2)$ (b) $(0, 2)$ (c) $(-4, 10)$ (d) $(-2, -2)$

3. What is the y-coordinate of any point on the x-axis?

4. Find the x- and y-intercepts of the graph of $3x - 4y + 12 = 0$.

x	0	1	2	1	0
y	4	5	8	-3	-1

Table for 5

5. Does the table at the left represent y as a function of x? Explain your reasoning.

6. Does the graph at the left represent y as a function of x? Explain.

7. Evaluate $f(x) = x^3 - 2x^2$ at the indicated values.
   (a) $f(0)$ (b) $f(2)$ (c) $f(-2)$ (d) $f\left(\dfrac{1}{2}\right)$

Figure for 6

8. Find the slope of the line passing through the points $(-5, 0)$ and $\left(2, \dfrac{3}{2}\right)$.

9. A line with slope $m = -2$ passes through the point $(-3, 4)$. Find two additional points on the line. (The problem has many correct answers.)

10. Find the slope of a line *perpendicular* to the line $3x - 5y + 2 = 0$.

In Exercises 11–14, graph the equation.

11. $x - 2y = 6$

12. $y = \dfrac{1}{4}x - 1$

13. $y = |x + 2|$

14. $y = (x - 3)^2$

15. Find an equation of the line that passes through the point $(0, 6)$ with slope $m = -\dfrac{3}{8}$.

16. Which points are solutions of the inequality $3x + 5y \leq 16$?
    (a) $(2, 2)$ (b) $(6, -1)$ (c) $(-2, 4)$ (d) $(7, -1)$

In Exercises 17–20, graph the inequality.

17. $y \geq -2$

18. $y < 5 - 2x$

19. $x \geq 2$

20. $y \leq 5$

21. The sales y of a product are modeled by $y = 230x + 5000$, where x is time in years. Interpret the meaning of the slope in this model.

5 Exponents and Polynomials

John Madere/The Stock Market

FedEx receives an average of more than 3.2 million packages daily worldwide. (Source: FedEx)

Motivating the Chapter

 Packaging Restrictions

A shipping company has the following restrictions on the dimensions and weight of packages.

1. The maximum weight is 150 pounds.
2. The maximum length is 108 inches.
3. The sum of the length and girth can be at most 130 inches.

The girth of a package is the distance around the package, as shown in the figure.

Girth = 2(Height + Width)

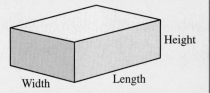

You are shipping a package that has a height of x inches. The length of the package is twice the square of the height and the width is 5 inches more than 3 times the height.

See Section 5.1, Exercise 111

a. Write an expression for the length of the package in terms of the height x. Write an expression for the width of the package in terms of the height x.

b. Write an expression for the *perimeter* of the base of the package. Simplify the expression.

c. Write an expression for the *girth* of the package. Simplify the expression. Write an expression for the sum of the length and the girth. If the height of the package is 5 inches, does the package meet the second and third restrictions? Explain.

See Section 5.2, Exercise 135

d. Write an expression for the *surface area* of the package. Simplify the expression. (The surface area is the sum of the areas of the six sides of the package.)

e. The length of the package is changed to match its width (5 inches more than 3 times its height). Write an expression for the area of the base. Simplify the expression.

f. Write an expression for the *volume* of the package. Simplify the expression.

See Section 5.4, Exercise 94

g. Suppose the width of the package is the same as in part (a) and the area of the base is known to be $6x^2 + 7x - 5$. What is the new length of the package?

273

5.1 Adding and Subtracting Polynomials

Objectives

1 Determine the degree and leading coefficient of a polynomial.

2 Add polynomials using a horizontal or vertical format.

3 Subtract polynomials using a horizontal or vertical format.

1 Determine the degree and leading coefficient of a polynomial.

Basic Definitions

To work with polynomials, you need to know the following rules for exponents, which were discussed in Section 2.2.

1. $a^m \cdot a^n = a^{m+n}$ Multiply factors having the same base.

2. $(a^m)^n = a^{m \cdot n}$ Raise a power to a power.

3. $(ab)^m = a^m b^m$ Raise a product to a power.

Additional rules for exponents will be introduced later in this chapter.

Remember that the *terms* of an algebraic expression are those parts separated by addition. An algebraic expression whose terms are all of the form ax^k, where a is any real number and k is a nonnegative integer, is called a **polynomial in one variable,** or simply a **polynomial.** Here are some examples of polynomials in one variable.

$$2x + 5, \quad x^2 - 3x + 7, \quad \text{and} \quad x^3 + 8$$

In the term ax^k, a is the **coefficient** of the term and k is the **degree** of the term. Because a polynomial is an algebraic sum, the coefficients take on the signs between the terms. For instance,

$$x^4 + 2x^3 - 5x^2 + 7 = (1)x^4 + 2x^3 + (-5)x^2 + (0)x + 7$$

has coefficients 1, 2, -5, 0, and 7. For this polynomial, the last term, 7, is the **constant term.** Polynomials are usually written in the order of descending powers of the variable. This is called **standard form.** Here are two examples.

Nonstandard Form	*Standard Form*
$4 + x$	$x + 4$
$3x^2 - 5 - x^3 + 2x$	$-x^3 + 3x^2 + 2x - 5$

The **degree of a polynomial** is the degree of the term with the highest power, and the coefficient of this term is the **leading coefficient** of the polynomial. For instance, the polynomial

Leading coefficient
$$-3x^4 + 4x^2 + x + 7$$

is of fourth degree, and its leading coefficient is -3. The reasons why the degree of a polynomial is important will become clear as you study factoring and problem solving in Chapter 6.

Encourage students to continue building their mathematical vocabularies.

▶ **Definition of a Polynomial in x**

Let $a_n, a_{n-1}, \ldots, a_2, a_1, a_0$ be real numbers and let n be a *nonnegative integer.* A **polynomial in x** is an expression of the form

$$a_n x^n + a_{n-1}x^{n-1} + \cdots + a_2 x^2 + a_1 x + a_0$$

where $a_n \neq 0$. The polynomial is of **degree** n, and the number a_n is the **leading coefficient.** The number a_0 is the **constant term.**

Example 1   Identifying Polynomials

Identify which of the following are polynomials, and for any that are not polynomials, state why.

a. $3x^4 - 8x + x^{-1}$ **b.** $x^2 - 3x + 1$

c. $x^3 + 3x^{1/2}$ **d.** $-\dfrac{1}{3}x + \dfrac{x^3}{4}$

Solution

a. $3x^4 - 8x + x^{-1}$ is *not* a polynomial because the third term, x^{-1}, has a negative exponent.

b. $x^2 - 3x + 1$ is a polynomial of degree 2 with integer coefficients.

c. $x^3 + 3x^{1/2}$ is *not* a polynomial because the exponent in the second term, $3x^{1/2}$, is not an integer.

d. $-\dfrac{1}{3}x + \dfrac{x^3}{4}$ is a polynomial of degree 3 with rational coefficients.

Example 2   Determining Degrees and Leading Coefficients

Write the polynomial in standard form and determine the degree and leading coefficient.

Polynomial	Standard Form	Degree	Leading Coefficient
a. $4x^2 - 5x^7 - 2 + 3x$	$-5x^7 + 4x^2 + 3x - 2$	7	-5
b. $4 - 9x^2$	$-9x^2 + 4$	2	-9
c. 8	8	0	8
d. $2 + x^3 - 5x^2$	$x^3 - 5x^2 + 2$	3	1

In part (c), note that a polynomial with *only* a constant term has a degree of zero.

A polynomial with only one term is called a **monomial.** Polynomials with two *unlike* terms are called **binomials,** and those with three *unlike* terms are called **trinomials.** For example, $3x^2$ is a *monomial*, $-3x + 1$ is a *binomial*, and $4x^3 - 5x + 6$ is a *trinomial.*

2 Add polynomials using a horizontal or vertical format.

Study Tip

When you use the vertical arrangement to add polynomials, be sure that you line up the *like terms*.

Technology: Tip

You can use a graphing utility to check the results of adding or subtracting polynomials. For instance, try graphing

$$y = (2x + 1) + (-3x - 4)$$

and

$$y = -x - 3$$

on the same screen, as shown below. Because both graphs are the same, you can reason that

$$(2x + 1) + (-3x - 4) = -x - 3.$$

This graphing technique is called "graph the left side and graph the right side."

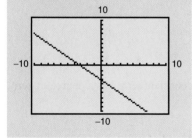

Adding Polynomials

As with algebraic expressions, the key to adding two polynomials is to recognize *like* terms—those having the *same degree*. By the Distributive Property, you can then combine the like terms using either a horizontal or a vertical arrangement of terms. For instance, the polynomials $2x^2 + 3x + 1$ and $x^2 - 2x + 2$ can be added horizontally to obtain

$$(2x^2 + 3x + 1) + (x^2 - 2x + 2) = (2x^2 + x^2) + (3x - 2x) + (1 + 2)$$
$$= (2 + 1)x^2 + (3 - 2)x + (1 + 2)$$
$$= 3x^2 + x + 3$$

or they can be added vertically to obtain the same result.

$$2x^2 + 3x + 1$$ Vertical arrangement
$$\underline{x^2 - 2x + 2}$$
$$3x^2 + x + 3$$

Example 3   Adding Polynomials Horizontally

Use a horizontal arrangement to find the sum.

a. $(2x^2 + 4x - 1) + (x^2 - 3)$ Original polynomials

   $= (2x^2 + x^2) + (4x) + (-1 - 3)$ Group like terms.

   $= 3x^2 + 4x - 4$ Combine like terms.

b. $(x^3 + 2x^2 + 4) + (3x^2 - x + 5)$ Original polynomials

   $= (x^3) + (2x^2 + 3x^2) + (-x) + (4 + 5)$ Group like terms.

   $= x^3 + 5x^2 - x + 9$ Combine like terms.

c. $(2x^2 - x + 3) + (4x^2 - 7x + 2) + (-x^2 + x - 2)$ Original polynomials

   $= (2x^2 + 4x^2 - x^2) + (-x - 7x + x) + (3 + 2 - 2)$ Group like terms.

   $= 5x^2 - 7x + 3$ Combine like terms.

Example 4   Adding Polynomials Vertically

Use a vertical arrangement to find the sum.

a. $(-4x^3 - 2x^2 + x - 5) + (2x^3 + 3x + 4)$

b. $(5x^3 + 2x^2 - x + 7) + (3x^2 - 4x + 7) + (-x^3 + 4x^2 - 2x - 8)$

Solution

a. $-4x^3 - 2x^2 + x - 5$

$\underline{ 2x^3 + 3x + 4}$

$-2x^3 - 2x^2 + 4x - 1$

b. $5x^3 + 2x^2 - x + 7$

$3x^2 - 4x + 7$

$\underline{-x^3 + 4x^2 - 2x - 8}$

$4x^3 + 9x^2 - 7x + 6$

3 Subtract polynomials using a horizontal or vertical format.

Subtracting Polynomials

To subtract one polynomial from another, you *add the opposite* by changing the sign of each term of the polynomial that is being subtracted and then adding the resulting like terms. Note how $(x^2 - 1)$ is subtracted from $(2x^2 - 4)$.

$$(2x^2 - 4) - (x^2 - 1) = 2x^2 - 4 - x^2 + 1 \qquad \text{Distributive Property}$$

$$= (2x^2 - x^2) + (-4 + 1) \qquad \text{Group like terms.}$$

$$= x^2 - 3 \qquad \text{Combine like terms.}$$

Recall from the Distributive Property that

$$-(x^2 - 1) = (-1)(x^2 - 1) = -x^2 + 1.$$

Example 5   Subtracting Polynomials Horizontally

Perform the following operations.

a. $(2x^2 + 3) - (3x^2 - 4)$

b. $(4x^4 - x^2 + 1) - (x^4 - 2x^3 - x^2)$

c. $(3x^3 - 4x^2 + 3) - (x^3 + 3x^2 - x - 4)$

d. $(x^2 - 2x + 1) - [(x^2 + x - 3) + (-2x^2 - 4x)]$

Solution

a. $(2x^2 + 3) - (3x^2 - 4) = 2x^2 + 3 - 3x^2 + 4 \qquad$ Distributive Property

$$= (2x^2 - 3x^2) + (3 + 4) \qquad \text{Group like terms.}$$

$$= -x^2 + 7 \qquad \text{Combine like terms.}$$

b. $(4x^4 - x^2 + 1) - (x^4 - 2x^3 - x^2) \qquad$ Original polynomials

$$= 4x^4 - x^2 + 1 - x^4 + 2x^3 + x^2 \qquad \text{Distributive Property}$$

$$= (4x^4 - x^4) + (2x^3) + (-x^2 + x^2) + (1) \qquad \text{Group like terms.}$$

$$= 3x^4 + 2x^3 + 1 \qquad \text{Combine like terms.}$$

c. $(3x^3 - 4x^2 + 3) - (x^3 + 3x^2 - x - 4) \qquad$ Original polynomials

$$= 3x^3 - 4x^2 + 3 - x^3 - 3x^2 + x + 4 \qquad \text{Distributive Property}$$

$$= (3x^3 - x^3) + (-4x^2 - 3x^2) + (x) + (3 + 4) \qquad \text{Group like terms.}$$

$$= 2x^3 - 7x^2 + x + 7 \qquad \text{Combine like terms.}$$

d. $(x^2 - 2x + 1) - [(x^2 + x - 3) + (-2x^2 - 4x)] \qquad$ Original polynomials

$$= (x^2 - 2x + 1) - [(x^2 - 2x^2) + (x - 4x) + (-3)] \qquad \text{Group like terms.}$$

$$= (x^2 - 2x + 1) - [-x^2 - 3x - 3] \qquad \text{Combine like terms.}$$

$$= x^2 - 2x + 1 + x^2 + 3x + 3 \qquad \text{Distributive Property}$$

$$= (x^2 + x^2) + (-2x + 3x) + (1 + 3) \qquad \text{Group like terms.}$$

$$= 2x^2 + x + 4 \qquad \text{Combine like terms.}$$

Students may be able to omit some of these steps. However, point out that changing signs incorrectly is one of the most common algebraic errors.

Be especially careful to use the correct signs when subtracting one polynomial from another. One of the most common mistakes in algebra is to forget to change signs correctly when subtracting one expression from another. Here is an example.

Wrong sign
↓

$$(x^2 + 3) - (x^2 + 2x - 2) \neq x^2 + 3 - x^2 + 2x - 2 \qquad \text{Common error}$$

↑
Wrong sign

Note that the error is forgetting to change all of the signs in the polynomial that is being subtracted. Here is the correct way to perform the subtraction.

Correct sign
↓

$$(x^2 + 3) - (x^2 + 2x - 2) = x^2 + 3 - x^2 - 2x + 2 \qquad \text{Correct}$$

↑
Correct sign

Just as you did for addition, you can use a vertical arrangement to subtract one polynomial from another. (The vertical arrangement doesn't work well with subtractions involving three or more polynomials.) When using a vertical arrangement, write the polynomial being subtracted underneath the one it is being subtracted from. Be sure to align like terms in vertical columns.

Example 6 Subtracting Polynomials Vertically

Use a vertical arrangement to perform the following operations.

a. $(3x^2 + 7x - 6) - (3x^2 + 7x)$
b. $(5x^3 - 2x^2 + x) - (4x^2 - 3x + 2)$
c. $(4x^4 - 2x^3 + 5x^2 - x + 8) - (3x^4 - 2x^3 + 3x - 4)$

Solution

a. $(3x^2 + 7x - 6)$ ⟹ $3x^2 + 7x - 6$

  $-(3x^2 + 7x \quad)$ ⟹ $-3x^2 - 7x$ Change signs and add.

  $\qquad\qquad\qquad\qquad\qquad -6$ Combine like terms.

b. $(5x^3 - 2x^2 + x \quad)$ ⟹ $5x^3 - 2x^2 + x$

  $-(\quad 4x^2 - 3x + 2)$ ⟹ $-4x^2 + 3x - 2$ Change signs and add.

  $\qquad\qquad\qquad\qquad 5x^3 - 6x^2 + 4x - 2$ Combine like terms.

c. $(4x^4 - 2x^3 + 5x^2 - x + 8)$ ⟹ $4x^4 - 2x^3 + 5x^2 - x + 8$

  $-(3x^2 - 2x^3 \quad + 3x - 4)$ ⟹ $-3x^4 + 2x^3 \qquad - 3x + 4$

  $\qquad\qquad\qquad\qquad\qquad x^4 \qquad + 5x^2 - 4x + 12$

In Example 6, try using a horizontal arrangement to perform the subtractions.

Example 7   Combining Polynomials

Perform the indicated operations.

a. $(3x^2 - 7x + 2) - (4x^2 + 6x - 1) + (-x^2 + 4x + 5)$

b. $(-2x^2 + 4x - 3) - [(4x^2 - 5x + 8) - (-x^2 + x + 3)]$

c. $3(x^2 - 2x + 1) - 2(x^2 + x - 3)$

Solution

Remind students that they can use graphing utilities to verify these results.

a. $(3x^2 - 7x + 2) - (4x^2 + 6x - 1) + (-x^2 + 4x + 5)$

$$= 3x^2 - 7x + 2 - 4x^2 - 6x + 1 - x^2 + 4x + 5$$

$$= (3x^2 - 4x^2 - x^2) + (-7x - 6x + 4x) + (2 + 1 + 5)$$

$$= -2x^2 - 9x + 8$$

b. $(-2x^2 + 4x - 3) - [(4x^2 - 5x + 8) - (-x^2 + x + 3)]$

$$= (-2x^2 + 4x - 3) - [4x^2 - 5x + 8 + x^2 - x - 3]$$

$$= (-2x^2 + 4x - 3) - [(4x^2 + x^2) + (-5x - x) + (8 - 3)]$$

$$= (-2x^2 + 4x - 3) - [5x^2 - 6x + 5]$$

$$= -2x^2 + 4x - 3 - 5x^2 + 6x - 5$$

$$= (-2x^2 - 5x^2) + (4x + 6x) + (-3 - 5)$$

$$= -7x^2 + 10x - 8$$

c. $3(x^2 - 2x + 1) - 2(x^2 + x - 3) = 3x^2 - 6x + 3 - 2x^2 - 2x + 6$

$$= (3x^2 - 2x^2) + (-6x - 2x) + (3 + 6)$$

$$= x^2 - 8x + 9$$

Example 8   Geometry: Area of a Region

Find a polynomial that represents the area of the shaded region in Figure 5.1.

Solution

Area of shaded region	=	Area of outer rectangle	−	Area of inner rectangle

$$\text{Area } = 3x(x) - 8\left(\frac{1}{4}x\right) = 3x^2 - 2x$$

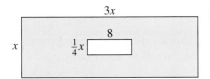

Figure 5.1

Discussing the Concept   Adding Polynomials

Write a paragraph that explains how the adage "You can't add apples and oranges" might relate to adding two polynomials. Include several examples to illustrate the applicability of this statement. Share your paragraph and examples with fellow students to see if they make sense to others.

5.1 Exercises

Integrated Review   *Concepts, Skills, and Problem Solving*

Keep mathematically in shape by doing these exercises *before* the problems of this section.

Properties and Definitions

1. In your own words, state the definition of an algebraic expression.

2. State the definition of a term of an algebraic expression.

Simplifying Expressions

In Exercises 3–6, use the Distributive Property to expand the expression.

3. $10(x - 1)$ **4.** $4(3 - 2z)$

5. $-\frac{1}{2}(4 - 6x)$ **6.** $-25(2x - 3)$

In Exercises 7–10, simplify the expression.

7. $8y - 2x + 7x - 10y$

8. $\frac{5}{6}x - \frac{2}{3}x + 8$

9. $10(x - 1) - 3(x + 2)$

10. $-3[x + (2 + 3x)]$

Graphs

In Exercises 11 and 12, graph the function. Use a graphing utility to verify your graph.

11. $g(x) = 2 + \frac{3}{2}x$ **12.** $h(t) = (t + 1)(t - 3)$

Developing Skills

In Exercises 1–8, determine whether the expression is a polynomial. If it is not, explain why. See Example 1.

1. $9 - z$ **2.** $t^2 - 4$

3. $x^{2/3} + 8$ **4.** $9 - z^{1/2}$

5. $6x^{-1}$ **6.** $1 - 4x^{-2}$

7. $z^{-1} + z^2 - 2$ **8.** $t^3 - 3t + 4$

In Exercises 9–18, write the polynomial in standard form. Then determine its degree and leading coefficient. See Example 2.

9. $5 - 32x$ **10.** $2x - 3$

11. $x^3 - 4x^2 + 9$ **12.** $9 - 2y^4$

13. $8x + 2x^5 - x^2 - 1$ **14.** $5x^3 - 3x^2 + 10$

15. 10 **16.** -32

17. $v_0 t - 16t^2$ **18.** $64 - \frac{1}{2}at^2$

    (v_0 is a constant.)   (a is a constant.)

In Exercises 19–24, determine whether the polynomial is a monomial, a binomial, or a trinomial.

19. $x^2 - 2x + 3$ **20.** $-6y$

21. $x^3 - 4$ **22.** $u^2 - 3u + 5$

23. 5 **24.** $16 - z^2$

In Exercises 25–30, give an example of a polynomial that fits the description. (*Note:* There are many correct answers.)

25. A binomial of degree 3

26. A trinomial of degree 4

27. A monomial of degree 2

28. A binomial of degree 5

29. A trinomial of degree 6

30. A monomial of degree 0

In Exercises 31–44, use a horizontal arrangement to perform the polynomial addition. See Example 3.

31. $(11x - 2) + (3x + 8)$

32. $(-2x + 4) + (x - 6)$

33. $(3z^2 - z + 2) + (z^2 - 4)$

34. $(6x^4 + 8x) + (4x - 6)$

35. $b^2 + (b^3 - 2b^2 + 3) + (b^3 - 3)$

36. $(3x^2 - x) + 5x^3 + (-4x^3 + x^2 - 8)$

37. $(12 - 3t - 7t^2) + (1 + 3t - t^2)$

38. $(3 + 6x + 8x^2 + 9x^3) + (3 - 2x + 4x^2 - 5x^3)$

39. $(2ab - 3) + (a^2 - 2ab) + (4b^2 - a^2)$

40. $(uv - 3) + (4uv + 1)$

41. $\left(\frac{2}{3}y^2 - \frac{3}{4}\right) + \left(\frac{5}{6}y^2 + 2\right)$

42. $\left(\frac{3}{4}x^3 - \frac{1}{2}\right) + \left(\frac{1}{8}x^3 + 3\right)$

43. $(0.1t^3 - 3.4t^2) + (1.5t^3 - 7.3)$

44. $(0.7x^2 - 0.2x + 2.5) + (7.4x - 3.9)$

In Exercises 45–60, use a vertical arrangement to perform the polynomial addition. See Example 4.

45. $2x + 5$
    $\underline{3x + 8}$

46. $10x - 7$
    $\underline{6x + 4}$

47. $-2x + 10$
    $\underline{x - 38}$

48. $4x^2 + 13$
    $\underline{3x^2 - 11}$

49. $-x^3 + 3$
    $\underline{3x^3 + 2x^2 + 5}$

50. $2z^3 + 3z - 2$
    $\underline{ z^2 - 2z}$

51. $3x^4 - 2x^3 - 4x^2 + 2x - 5$
    $\underline{ x^2 - 7x + 5}$

52. $x^5 - 4x^3 + x + 9$
    $\underline{ 2x^4 + 3x^3 - 3}$

53. $(x^2 - 4) + (2x^2 + 6)$

54. $(x^3 + 2x - 3) + (4x + 5)$

55. $(2 - 3y) + (y^4 + 3y + 2)$

56. $(a^2 + 3a - 2) + (5a - a^2 - 6a) + (a^2 + 2)$

57. $(x^2 - 2x + 2) + (x^2 + 4x) + 2x^2$

58. $(5y + 10) + (y^2 - 3y - 2) + (2y^2 + 4y - 3)$

59. Add $8y^3 + 7$ to $5 - 3y^3$.

60. Add $2z - 8z^2 - 3$ to $z^2 + 5z$.

Comparing Two Formats   In Exercises 61 and 62, add the two polynomials using the horizontal arrangement and the vertical arrangement. Which format do you prefer? Explain.

61. $(6x^2 + 5) + (3 - 2x^2)$

62. $(0.5x^4 - 6.2x^2 + 7.1) +$
    $(3.2x^4 + 8x^3 - 16x + 10.5)$

In Exercises 63–72, use a horizontal arrangement to perform the polynomial subtraction. See Example 5.

63. $(11x - 8) - (2x + 3)$

64. $(9x + 2) - (15x - 4)$

65. $(x^2 - x) - (x - 2)$

66. $(x^2 - 4) - (x^2 - 4)$

67. $(4 - 2x - x^3) - (3 - 2x + 2x^3)$

68. $(t^4 - 2t^2) - (3t^2 - t^4 - 5)$

69. $10 - (u^2 + 5)$

70. $(z^3 + z^2 + 1) - z^2$

71. $(x^5 - 3x^4 + x^3 - 5x + 1) - (4x^5 - x^3 + x - 5)$

72. $(t^4 + 5t^3 - t^2 + 8t - 10) -$
    $(t^4 + t^3 + 2t^2 + 4t - 7)$

In Exercises 73–86, use a vertical arrangement to perform the polynomial subtraction. See Example 6.

73. $2x - 2$
    $\underline{-(x - 1)}$

74. $9x + 7$
    $\underline{-(3x + 9)}$

75. $2x^2 - x + 2$
    $\underline{-(3x^2 + x - 1)}$

76. $y^4 - 2$
    $\underline{-(y^4 + 2)}$

77. $ -3x^3 - 4x^2 + 2x - 5$
    $\underline{-(2x^4 + 2x^3 - 4x + 5)}$

78. $ 12x^3 + 25x^2 - 15$
    $\underline{-(-2x^3 + 18x^2 - 3x)}$

79. $(2 - x^3) - (2 + x^3)$

80. $(4z^3 - 6) - (-z^3 + z - 2)$

81. $(4t^3 - 3t + 5) - (3t^2 - 3t - 10)$

82. $(-s^2 - 3) - (2s^2 + 10s)$

83. $(6x^3 - 3x^2 + x) - [(x^3 + 3x^2 + 3) + (x - 3)]$

84. $(y^2 - y) - [(2y^2 + y) - (4y^2 - y + 2)]$

85. Subtract $7x^3 - 4x + 5$ from $10x^3 + 15$.

86. Subtract $y^5 - y^4$ from $y^2 + 3y^4$.

In Exercises 87–100, perform the operations. See Example 7.

87. $(6x - 5) - (8x + 15)$

88. $(2x^2 + 1) + (x^2 - 2x + 1)$

89. $-(x^3 - 2) + (4x^3 - 2x)$

90. $-(5x^2 - 1) - (-3x^2 + 5)$

91. $2(x^4 + 2x) + (5x + 2)$

92. $(z^4 - 2z^2) + 3(z^4 + 4)$

93. $(15x^2 - 6) - (-8x^3 - 14x^2 - 17)$

94. $(15x^4 - 18x - 19) - (-13x^4 - 5x + 15)$

95. $5z - [3z - (10z + 8)]$

96. $(y^3 + 1) - [(y^2 + 1) + (3y - 7)]$

97. $2(t^2 + 5) - 3(t^2 + 5) + 5(t^2 + 5)$

98. $-10(u + 1) + 8(u - 1) - 3(u + 6)$

99. $8v - 6(3v - v^2) + 10(10v + 3)$

100. $3(x^2 - 2x + 3) - 4(4x + 1) - (3x^2 - 2x)$

Solving Problems

Geometry In Exercises 101 and 102, find the perimeter of the figure.

101.

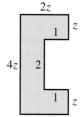

2z

4z   2   1   z
          1   z

102.

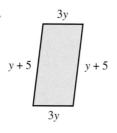

3y

y + 5   y + 5

3y

In Exercises 103–108, write a polynomial that represents the area of the shaded portion of the figure. See Example 8.

103.

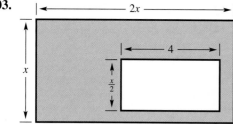

2x

4

x

$\frac{x}{2}$

104.

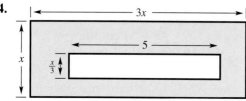

3x

5

x

$\frac{x}{3}$

105.

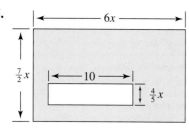

6x

10

$\frac{7}{2}x$ $\frac{4}{5}x$

106.

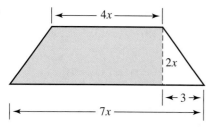

4x

2x

3

7x

107.

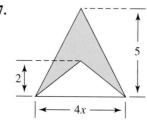

5

2

4x

108.

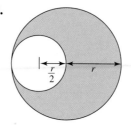

$\frac{r}{2}$ r

109. *Comparing Models* From 1990 through 1995, the per capita consumption (in pounds) of beef B and chicken C in the United States can be modeled by

$$B = 0.29t^2 - 1.43t + 64.11, \quad 0 \le t \le 5$$

and

$$C = -0.32t^2 + 2.98t + 42.17, \quad 0 \le t \le 5$$

where $t = 0$ represents 1990. (Source: U.S. Department of Agriculture)

(a) Add the polynomials to find a model for the total per capita consumption T of beef and chicken.

(b) Use a graphing utility to graph the models B, C, and T.

(c) Use the graphs in part (b) to determine whether the consumption represented by the model T is increasing or decreasing.

110. *Comparing Business Models* The cost of producing x units of a product is $C = 100 + 30x$. The revenue for selling x units is $R = 90x - x^2$, where $0 \le x \le 40$. The profit is given by the revenue minus the cost.

(a) Perform the subtraction required to find the polynomial representing profit.

(b) Use a graphing utility to graph the polynomial representing profit.

(c) Determine the profit when $x = 30$ units are produced and sold. Use the graph in part (b) to predict the change in profit if x is some value other than 30.

Explaining Concepts

111. Answer parts (a)–(c) of Motivating the Chapter on page 273.

112. Explain the difference between the degree of a term of a polynomial and the degree of a polynomial.

113. Determine which of the two statements is always true. Is the statement not selected always false? Explain.

(a) "A polynomial is a trinomial."

(b) "A trinomial is a polynomial."

114. In your own words, define "like terms." What is the only factor of like terms that can differ?

115. Describe how to combine like terms. What operations are used?

116. Is a polynomial an algebraic expression? Explain.

117. In your own words, explain how to subtract polynomials. Give an example.

118. Is the sum of two binomials always a binomial? Explain.

5.2 Multiplying Polynomials: Special Products

Objectives

1 Find a product with monomial multipliers.

2 Multiply binomials using the Distributive Property and the FOIL Method.

3 Multiply polynomials using a horizontal or vertical format.

4 Identify and use special binomial products.

---

1 Find a product with monomial multipliers.

Monomial Multipliers

To multiply polynomials, you use many of the rules for simplifying algebraic expressions. You may want to review these rules from Section 2.2.

1. Properties of exponents

2. The Distributive Property

3. Combining like terms

4. Symbols of grouping

The simplest type of polynomial multiplication involves a monomial multiplier. The product is obtained by direct application of the Distributive Property. For instance, to multiply the monomial x by the polynomial $(2x + 5)$, multiply *each* of the terms of the polynomial by x.

$$(x)(2x + 5) = (x)(2x) + (x)(5) = 2x^2 + 5x$$

Here is another example.

$$(2x)(3x^2 - 4x + 1) = (2x)(3x^2) - (2x)(4x) + (2x)(1)$$
$$= 6x^3 - 8x^2 + 2x$$

Blaise Pascal

(1623–1662)

Pascal was a French mathematician, scientist, and philosopher. In addition to his religious and philosophical writings, he made many invaluable contributions to mathematics and physics. Perhaps his most important contribution to mathematics was the invention and construction of the first calculating machine. He invented the machine when he was only nineteen years old.

Example 1 Finding Products with Monomial Multipliers

Find each product.

a. $(3x - 7)(-2x)$ **b.** $3x^2(5x - x^3 + 2)$ **c.** $(-x)(2x^2 - 3x)$

Solution

a. $(3x - 7)(-2x) = 3x(-2x) - 7(-2x)$ Distributive Property

$= -6x^2 + 14x$ Standard form

b. $3x^2(5x - x^3 + 2)$

$= (3x^2)(5x) - (3x^2)(x^3) + (3x^2)(2)$ Distributive Property

$= 15x^3 - 3x^5 + 6x^2$ Properties of exponents

$= -3x^5 + 15x^3 + 6x^2$ Standard form

c. $(-x)(2x^2 - 3x) = (-x)(2x^2) - (-x)(3x)$ Distributive Property

$= -2x^3 + 3x^2$ Standard form

2 Multiply binomials using the Distributive Property and the FOIL Method.

Multiplying Binomials

To multiply two binomials, you can use both (left and right) forms of the Distributive Property. For example, if you treat the binomial $(5x + 7)$ as a single quantity, you can multiply $(3x - 2)$ by $(5x + 7)$ as follows.

$$(3x - 2)(5x + 7) = 3x(5x + 7) - 2(5x + 7)$$

$$= (3x)(5x) + (3x)(7) - (2)(5x) - 2(7)$$

$$= 15x^2 + 21x - 10x - 14$$

Product of First terms	Product of Outer terms	Product of Inner terms	Product of Last terms

$$= 15x^2 + 11x - 14$$

With practice you should be able to multiply two binomials without writing out all of the steps above. In fact, the four products in the boxes above suggest that you can write the product of two binomials in just one step. This is referred to as the **FOIL Method.** Note that the words *first, outer, inner,* and *last* refer to the positions of the terms in the original product.

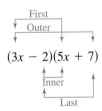

$$(3x - 2)(5x + 7)$$

Technology: Tip

Remember that you can use a graphing utility to check whether you have performed a polynomial operation correctly. For instance, to check if

$$(x - 1)(x + 5) = x^2 + 4x - 5$$

you can "graph the left side and graph the right side" on the same screen, as shown below. Because both graphs are the same, you can reason that the multiplication was performed correctly.

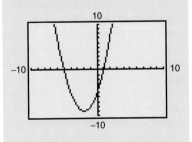

Example 2   Multiplying with the Distributive Property

Use the Distributive Property to find the product.

a. $(x - 1)(x + 5)$ **b.** $(2x + 3)(x - 2)$

Solution

a. $(x - 1)(x + 5) = x(x + 5) - (1)(x + 5)$ Right Distributive Property

$$= x^2 + 5x - x - 5$$ Left Distributive Property

$$= x^2 + (5x - x) - 5$$ Group like terms.

$$= x^2 + 4x - 5$$ Combine like terms.

b. $(2x + 3)(x - 2) = 2x(x - 2) + 3(x - 2)$ Right Distributive Property

$$= 2x^2 - 4x + 3x - 6$$ Left Distributive Property

$$= 2x^2 + (-4x + 3x) - 6$$ Group like terms.

$$= 2x^2 - x - 6$$ Combine like terms.

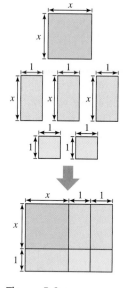

Figure 5.2

| Example 3 | Multiplying Binomials Using the FOIL Method |

Use the FOIL Method to find the product.

a. $(x - 4)(x + 4)$ **b.** $(3x + 5)(2x + 1)$

Solution

$$ \text{F} \quad \text{O} \quad \text{I} \quad \text{L}$$

a. $(x - 4)(x + 4) = x^2 + 4x - 4x - 16$

$$= x^2 - 16 \qquad\qquad \text{Combine like terms.}$$

$$ \text{F} \quad \text{O} \quad \text{I} \quad \text{L}$$

b. $(3x + 5)(2x + 1) = 6x^2 + 3x + 10x + 5$

$$= 6x^2 + 13x + 5 \qquad\qquad \text{Combine like terms.}$$

In Example 3(a), note that the outer and inner products add up to zero.

| Example 4 | A Geometric Model of a Polynomial Product |

What polynomial product is represented in Figure 5.2?

Solution

On the top you have the sum $x^2 + (x + x + x) + (1 + 1)$, or $x^2 + 3x + 2$. On the bottom you have the product $(x + 1)(x + 2)$, which represents the area of the rectangular figure. So, the display shows that

$$x^2 + 3x + 2 = (x + 1)(x + 2).$$

| Example 5 | Simplifying Polynomial Expressions |

Simplify each expression and write the result in standard form.

a. $(4x + 5)^2$ **b.** $(3x^2 - 2)(4x + 7) - (4x)^2$

Solution

a. $(4x + 5)^2 = (4x + 5)(4x + 5)$ \qquad Repeated multiplication

$$= 16x^2 + 20x + 20x + 25 \qquad \text{Multiply binomials.}$$

$$= 16x^2 + 40x + 25 \qquad \text{Combine like terms.}$$

b. $(3x^2 - 2)(4x + 7) - (4x)^2$

$$= 12x^3 + 21x^2 - 8x - 14 - (4x)^2 \qquad \text{Multiply binomials.}$$

$$= 12x^3 + 21x^2 - 8x - 14 - 16x^2 \qquad \text{Square monomial.}$$

$$= 12x^3 + 5x^2 - 8x - 14 \qquad \text{Combine like terms.}$$

3 Multiply polynomials using a horizontal or vertical format.

Multiplying Polynomials

The FOIL Method for multiplying two binomials is simply a device for guaranteeing that *each term of one binomial is multiplied by each term of the other binomial.*

$$(ax + b)(cx + d) = ax(cx) + ax(d) + b(cx) + b(d)$$

F   O   I   L

This same rule applies to the product of two polynomials: *each term of one polynomial must be multiplied by each term of the other polynomial.* This can be accomplished using either a horizontal or vertical format.

Example 6   Multiplying Polynomials (Horizontal Format)

Use a horizontal format to find the product.

a. $(x - 4)(x^2 - 4x + 2)$ **b.** $(2x^2 - 7x + 1)(4x + 3)$

Solution

You could show students that Example 6(b) could also be written as

$2x^2(4x + 3) - 7x(4x + 3) + 1(4x + 3)$

$= 8x^3 + 6x^2 - 28x^2 - 21x + 4x + 3$

$= 8x^3 - 22x^2 - 17x + 3.$

a. $(x - 4)(x^2 - 4x + 2)$

$= x(x^2 - 4x + 2) - 4(x^2 - 4x + 2)$ Distributive Property

$= x^3 - 4x^2 + 2x - 4x^2 + 16x - 8$ Distributive Property

$= x^3 - 8x^2 + 18x - 8$ Combine like terms.

b. $(2x^2 - 7x + 1)(4x + 3)$

$= (2x^2 - 7x + 1)(4x) + (2x^2 - 7x + 1)(3)$ Distributive Property

$= 8x^3 - 28x^2 + 4x + 6x^2 - 21x + 3$ Distributive Property

$= 8x^3 - 22x^2 - 17x + 3$ Combine like terms.

Example 7   Multiplying Polynomials (Vertical Format)

Use a vertical format to find the product: $(3x^2 + x - 5)(2x - 1).$

Solution

With a vertical format, line up like terms in the same vertical columns, just as you align digits in whole number multiplication.

$$
\begin{array}{r}
3x^2 + x - 5 \\
\times 2x - 1 \\
\hline
-3x^2 - x + 5 \\
6x^3 + 2x^2 - 10x \\
\hline
6x^3 - x^2 - 11x + 5
\end{array}
$$

Place polynomial with most terms on top.

$-1(3x^2 + x - 5)$

$2x(3x^2 + x - 5)$

Combine like terms in columns.

When multiplying two polynomials, it is best to write each in standard form before using either the horizontal or vertical format. This is illustrated in the next example.

Example 8 Multiplying Polynomials

Multiply the polynomials.

$$(x + 3x^2 - 4)(5 + 3x - x^2)$$

Solution

$$
\begin{array}{r}
3x^2 + x - 4 \\
\times \quad -x^2 + 3x + 5 \\
\hline
15x^2 + 5x - 20 \\
9x^3 + 3x^2 - 12x \\
-3x^4 - x^3 + 4x^2 \\
\hline
-3x^4 + 8x^3 + 22x^2 - 7x - 20
\end{array}
$$

Standard form
Standard form
$5(3x^2 + x - 4)$
$3x(3x^2 + x - 4)$
$-x^2(3x^2 + x - 4)$
Combine like terms.

Example 9 Multiplying Polynomials

Find the product.

$$(x - 3)^3$$

Solution

To raise $(x - 3)$ to the third power, you can use two steps. First, because $(x - 3)^3 = (x - 3)^2(x - 3)$, find the product $(x - 3)^2$.

$$
\begin{aligned}
(x - 3)^2 &= (x - 3)(x - 3) \\
&= x^2 - 3x - 3x + 9 \\
&= x^2 - 6x + 9
\end{aligned}
$$

Repeated multiplication
FOIL
Combine like terms.

Now, using a vertical arrangement, find $(x - 3)^3$.

$$
\begin{array}{r}
x^2 - 6x + 9 \\
\times \quad\quad x - 3 \\
\hline
-3x^2 + 18x - 27 \\
x^3 - 6x^2 + 9x \\
\hline
x^3 - 9x^2 + 27x - 27
\end{array}
$$

$(x - 3)^2$

$-3(x^2 - 6x + 9)$
$x(x^2 - 6x + 9)$
Combine like terms.

So, $(x - 3)^3 = x^3 - 9x^2 + 27x - 27$.

Use a graphing utility to graph $y = (x - 3)^3$ and $y = x^3 - 9x^2 + 27x - 27$ and verify that these two expressions are equal.

4 Identify and use special binomial products.

Special Products

Some binomial products such as those in Examples 3(a) and 5(a) have special forms that occur frequently in algebra. Let's look at those products again. The product $(x + 4)(x - 4)$ is called a **product of the sum and difference of two terms.** With such products, the two middle terms cancel, as follows.

$$(x + 4)(x - 4) = x^2 - 4x + 4x - 16 \qquad \text{Sum and difference of two terms}$$

$$= x^2 - 16 \qquad \text{Product has no middle term.}$$

Another common type of product is the **square of a binomial.** With this type of product, the middle term is always twice the product of the terms in the binomial.

$$(4x + 5)^2 = (4x + 5)(4x + 5) \qquad \text{Square of a binomial}$$

$$= 16x^2 + 20x + 20x + 25$$

$$= 16x^2 + 40x + 25 \qquad \text{Middle term is twice the product of the terms of the binomial.}$$

You should learn to recognize the patterns of these two special products. We give the general form of these special products in the following statements. The FOIL Method can be used to verify each rule.

Emphasize the importance of these special products.

▶ **Special Products**

Let a and b be real numbers, variables, or algebraic expressions.

Special Product	*Example*
Sum and Difference of Two Terms:	
$(a + b)(a - b) = a^2 - b^2$	$(2x - 5)(2x + 5) = 4x^2 - 25$
Square of a Binomial:	
$(a + b)^2 = a^2 + 2ab + b^2$	$(3x + 4)^2 = 9x^2 + 2(3x)(4) + 16$
	$= 9x^2 + 24x + 16$
$(a - b)^2 = a^2 - 2ab + b^2$	$(x - 7)^2 = x^2 - 2(x)(7) + 49$
	$= x^2 - 14x + 49$

When a binomial is squared, the resulting middle term is always *twice* the product of the two terms.

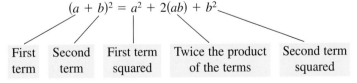

$$(a + b)^2 = a^2 + 2(ab) + b^2$$

First term | Second term | First term squared | Twice the product of the terms | Second term squared

Be sure to include the middle term. For instance, $(a + b)^2$ is *not* equal to $a^2 + b^2$.

> **Example 10**   Finding Sum and Difference Products

Find each product.

a. $(x + 2)(x - 2)$ **b.** $(5x - 6)(5x + 6)$ **c.** $(2 + 3x)(2 - 3x)$

Solution

$$\overset{\text{Sum}}{} \overset{\text{Difference}}{} \quad \overset{(\text{1st term})^2}{} \overset{(\text{2nd term})^2}{}$$

a. $(x + 2)(x - 2) = (x)^2 - (2)^2$

$$= x^2 - 4$$

$$\overset{\text{Difference}}{} \overset{\text{Sum}}{} \quad \overset{(\text{1st term})^2}{} \overset{(\text{2nd term})^2}{}$$

b. $(5x - 6)(5x + 6) = (5x)^2 - (6)^2$

$$= 25x^2 - 36$$

$$\overset{\text{Sum}}{} \overset{\text{Difference}}{} \quad \overset{(\text{1st term})^2}{} \overset{(\text{2nd term})^2}{}$$

c. $(2 + 3x)(2 - 3x) = (2)^2 - (3x)^2$

$$= 4 - 9x^2$$

> **Example 11**   Squaring a Binomial

Find each product.

a. $(4x - 9)^2$ **b.** $(3x + 7)^2$ **c.** $(6 - 5x^2)^2$

Solution

$$\overset{\text{1st term}}{} \overset{\text{2nd term}}{} \quad \overset{(\text{1st term})^2}{} \overset{\text{Twice the product of the terms}}{} \overset{(\text{2nd term})^2}{}$$

a. $(4x - 9)^2 = (4x)^2 - 2(4x)(9) + (9)^2$

$$= 16x^2 - 72x + 81$$

$$\overset{\text{1st term}}{} \overset{\text{2nd term}}{} \quad \overset{(\text{1st term})^2}{} \overset{\text{Twice the product of the terms}}{} \overset{(\text{2nd term})^2}{}$$

b. $(3x + 7)^2 = (3x)^2 + 2(3x)(7) + (7)^2$

$$= 9x^2 + 42x + 49$$

$$\overset{\text{1st term}}{} \overset{\text{2nd term}}{} \quad \overset{(\text{1st term})^2}{} \overset{\text{Twice the product of the terms}}{} \overset{(\text{2nd term})^2}{}$$

c. $(6 - 5x^2)^2 = (6)^2 - 2(6)(5x^2) + (5x^2)^2$

$$= 36 - 60x^2 + (5)^2(x^2)^2$$

$$= 36 - 60x^2 + 25x^4$$

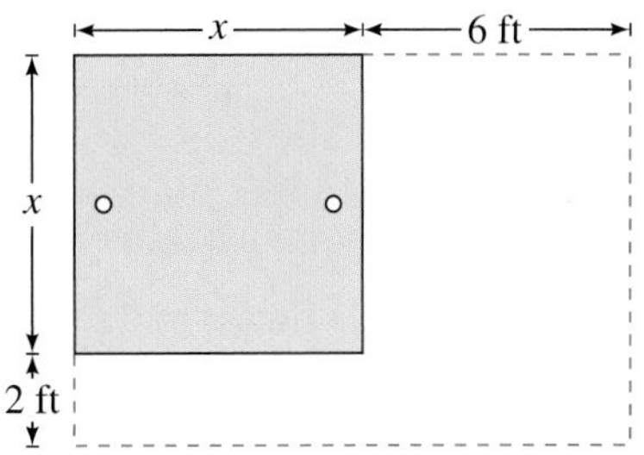

Example 12   Finding the Measurements of a Golf Tee

A landscaper wants to reshape a square tee area for the 9th hole of a golf course. The new tee area is to have one side 2 feet longer and the adjacent side 6 feet longer than the original tee. (See Figure 5.3.) If the new tee has 204 square feet more area than the original tee, what are the measurements of the original 9th hole tee?

Figure 5.3

Solution

Verbal Model: New area = Old area + 204

Labels: Original length = original width = x (feet)
New length = $x + 6$ (feet)
New width = $x + 2$ (feet)

Equation: $(x + 6)(x + 2) = x^2 + 204$ x^2 is original area.

$x^2 + 8x + 12 = x^2 + 204$ Multiply factors.

$8x + 12 = 204$ Subtract x^2 from both sides.

$8x = 192$ Subtract 12 from both sides.

$x = 24$ Simplify.

The original tee measured 24 feet by 24 feet.

Discussing the Concept   Pascal's Triangle

The following triangular pattern of numbers on the left shows the first seven rows of **Pascal's Triangle,** named after the French mathematician Blaise Pascal (1623–1662). Try to discover the pattern formed by the numbers in the triangle. Then use the pattern on the right to write out the expansion of $(x + 1)^7$.

$$1$$
$$1 \quad 1$$
$$1 \quad 2 \quad 1$$
$$1 \quad 3 \quad 3 \quad 1$$
$$1 \quad 4 \quad 6 \quad 4 \quad 1$$
$$1 \quad 5 \quad 10 \quad 10 \quad 5 \quad 1$$
$$1 \quad 6 \quad 15 \quad 20 \quad 15 \quad 6 \quad 1$$

$$(x + 1)^0 = 1$$
$$(x + 1)^1 = x + 1$$
$$(x + 1)^2 = x^2 + 2x + 1$$
$$(x + 1)^3 = x^3 + 3x^2 + 3x + 1$$
$$(x + 1)^4 = x^4 + 4x^3 + 6x^2 + 4x + 1$$
$$(x + 1)^5 = x^5 + 5x^4 + 10x^3 + 10x^2 + 5x + 1$$
$$(x + 1)^6 = x^6 + 6x^5 + 15x^4 + 20x^3 + 15x^2 + 6x + 1$$

Discuss how to determine the number of terms in the expansion of $(x + 1)^{14}$.

5.2 Exercises

Integrated Review   *Concepts, Skills, and Problem Solving*

Keep mathematically in shape by doing these exercises *before* the problems of this section.

Properties and Definitions

1. Relative to the x- and y-axes, explain the meaning of each coordinate of the point $(3, -2)$.

2. A point lies 4 units from the x-axis and 3 units from the y-axis. Give the ordered pair for such a point in each quadrant.

Simplifying Expressions

In Exercises 3–8, simplify the expression.

3. $\frac{3}{4}x - \frac{5}{2} + \frac{3}{2}x$ 4. $4 - 2(3 - x)$

5. $2(x - 4) + 5x$ 6. $4(3 - y) + 2(y + 1)$

7. $-3(z - 2) - (z - 6)$

8. $(u - 2) - 3(2u + 1)$

Problem Solving

9. Your sales commission rate is 5.5%. Your commission is $1600. How much did you sell?

10. A jogger leaves a location on a fitness trail running at a rate of 4 miles per hour. Fifteen minutes later, a second jogger leaves from the same location running at 5 miles per hour. How long will it take the second runner to overtake the first and how far will each have run at that point? Use a diagram to help answer the question.

Graphs and Models

In Exercises 11 and 12, use a graphing utility to graph the function. Identify any intercepts.

11. $g(x) = 4 - \frac{1}{2}x$ 12. $f(x) = x(x - 4)$

Developing Skills

In Exercises 1–50, multiply and simplify. See Examples 1–3 and 5.

1. $x(-2x)$ 2. $y(-3y)$ 3. $t^2(4t)$ 4. $3u(u^4)$

5. $\left(\frac{x}{4}\right)(10x)$ 6. $9x\left(\frac{x}{12}\right)$

7. $(-2b^2)(-3b)$ 8. $(-4m)(3m^2)$

9. $y(3 - y)$ 10. $z(z - 3)$

11. $-x(x^2 - 4)$ 12. $-t(10 - 3t)$

13. $3t(2t - 5)$ 14. $-5u(u^2 + 4)$

15. $-4x(3 + 3x^2 - 6x^3)$ 16. $5v(5 - 4v + 5v^2)$

17. $3x(x^2 - 2x + 1)$ 18. $y(4y^2 + 2y - 3)$

19. $2x(x^2 - 2x + 8)$ 20. $-3x(x - 3)$

21. $4t^3(t - 3)$ 22. $-2t^4(t + 6)$

23. $x^2(4x^2 - 3x + 1)$ 24. $y^2(2y^2 + y - 5)$

25. $-3x^3(4x^2 - 6x + 2)$ 26. $5u^4(2u^3 - 3u + 3)$

27. $-2x(-3x)(5x + 2)$ 28. $4x(-2x)(x^2 - 1)$

29. $2x(6x^4) - 3x^2(2x^2)$ 30. $-8y(-5y^4) - 2y^2(5y^3)$

31. $(x + 3)(x + 4)$ 32. $(x - 5)(x + 10)$

33. $(3x - 5)(2x + 1)$ 34. $(7x - 2)(4x - 3)$

35. $(2x - y)(x - 2y)$ 36. $(x + y)(x + 2y)$

37. $(2x + 4)(x + 1)$ 38. $(4x + 3)(2x - 1)$

39. $(6 - 2x)(4x + 3)$ 40. $(8x - 6)(5 - 4x)$

41. $(3x - 2y)(x - y)$ 42. $(7x + 5y)(x + y)$

43. $(3x^2 - 4)(x + 2)$ 44. $(5x^3 - 2)(x - 1)$

45. $(2x^3 + 4)(x^2 + 6)$ 46. $(7x^2 - 3)(2x^2 - 4)$

47. $(3s + 1)(3s + 4) - (3s)^2$

48. $(2t + 5)(4t - 2) - (2t)^2$

49. $(4x^2 - 1)(2x + 8) + (-x)^3$

50. $(3 - 3x^2)(4 - 5x^2) - (-x^2)^2$

In Exercises 51–64, multiply using a horizontal format. See Example 6.

51. $(x + 10)(x + 2)$ 52. $(x - 1)(x + 3)$

53. $(2x - 5)(x + 2)$ 54. $(3x - 2)(2x - 3)$

55. $(x + 1)(x^2 + 2x - 1)$ 56. $(x - 3)(x^2 - 3x + 4)$

57. $(x^3 - 2x + 1)(x - 5)$ 58. $(x + 1)(x^2 - x + 1)$

59. $(x - 2)(x^2 + 2x + 4)$ 60. $(x + 9)(x^2 - x - 4)$

61. $(x^2 + 3)(x^2 - 6x + 2)$ 62. $(x^2 + 3)(x^2 - 2x + 3)$

63. $(3x^2 + 1)(x^2 - 4x - 2)$

64. $(x^2 + 2x + 5)(4x^3 - 2)$

In Exercises 65–80, multiply using a vertical format. See Examples 7–9.

65. $x + 3$
         $\times \, x - 2$

66. $2x - 1$
         $\times \, 5x + 1$

67. $x^2 - 3x + 9$
         $\times \qquad x + 3$

68. $4x^4 - 6x^2 + 9$
         $\times \qquad 2x \, + 3$

69. $(x^2 - x + 2)(x^2 + x - 2)$

70. $(x^2 + 2x + 5)(2x^2 - x - 1)$

71. $(x^3 + x + 3)(x^2 + 5x - 4)$

72. $(x^2 + x + 1)(x^2 - x - 1)$

73. $(x - 2)^3$

74. $(x + 3)^3$

75. $(x - 1)^2(x - 1)^2$

76. $(x + 4)^2(x + 4)^2$

77. $(x + 2)^2(x - 4)$

78. $(x - 4)^2(x - 1)$

79. $(u - 1)(2u + 3)(2u + 1)$

80. $(2x + 5)(x - 2)(5x - 3)$

In Exercises 81–110, use a special product pattern to find the product. See Examples 10 and 11.

81. $(x + 3)(x - 3)$

82. $(x - 5)(x + 5)$

83. $(x + 4)(x - 4)$

84. $(y + 9)(y - 9)$

85. $(2u + 3)(2u - 3)$

86. $(3z + 4)(3z - 4)$

87. $(4t - 6)(4t + 6)$

88. $(3u + 7)(3u - 7)$

89. $(2x + 3y)(2x - 3y)$

90. $(5u + 12v)(5u - 12v)$

91. $(4u - 3v)(4u + 3v)$

92. $(8a - 5b)(8a + 5b)$

93. $(2x^2 + 5)(2x^2 - 5)$

94. $(4t^2 + 6)(4t^2 - 6)$

95. $(x + 6)^2$

96. $(a - 2)^2$

97. $(t - 3)^2$

98. $(x + 10)^2$

99. $(3x + 2)^2$

100. $(2x - 8)^2$

101. $(8 - 3z)^2$

102. $(1 - 5t)^2$

103. $(2x - 5y)^2$

104. $(4s + 3t)^2$

105. $(6t + 5s)^2$

106. $(3u - 8v)^2$

107. $[(x + 1) + y]^2$

108. $[(x - 3) - y]^2$

109. $[u - (v - 3)]^2$

110. $[2u + (v + 1)]^2$

In Exercises 111 and 112, perform the multiplication and simplify.

111. $(x + 2)^2 - (x - 2)^2$

112. $(u + 5)^2 + (u - 5)^2$

Think About It   In Exercises 113 and 114, is the equation an identity? Explain.

113. $(x + y)^3 = x^3 + 3x^2y + 3xy^2 + y^3$

114. $(x - y)^3 = x^3 - 3x^2y + 3xy^2 - y^3$

In Exercises 115 and 116, use the results of Exercises 113 and 114 to find the product.

115. $(x + 2)^3$

116. $(x + 1)^3$

Solving Problems

117. *Finding a Pattern*   Perform each multiplication.

(a) $(x - 1)(x + 1)$

(b) $(x - 1)(x^2 + x + 1)$

(c) $(x - 1)(x^3 + x^2 + x + 1)$

(d) Use the pattern formed in the first three products to guess the product

$(x - 1)(x^4 + x^3 + x^2 + x + 1)$.

Verify your guess by multiplying.

118. *Geometry*   The base of a triangular sail is $2x$ feet and its height is $x + 10$ feet (see figure). Find the area A of the sail.

119. *Geometry*   The height of a rectangular sign is twice its width w (see figure). Find (a) the perimeter and (b) the area of the rectangle.

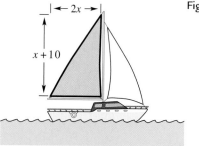

Figure for 118

Figure for 119

SPEED LIMIT **65**

Geometry In Exercises 120–123, what polynomial product is represented? Explain. See Example 4.

120.

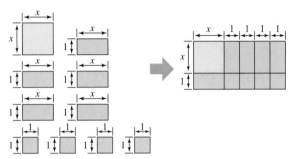

121.

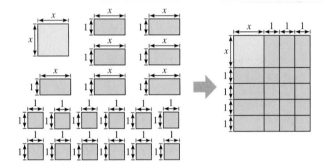

122.

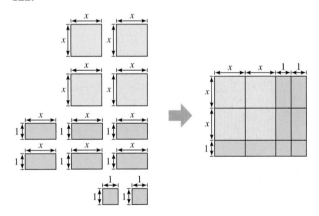

123.

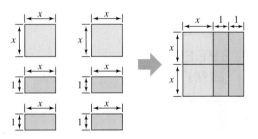

124. *Geometry* Add the areas of the four rectangular regions shown in the figure. What special product does the geometric model represent?

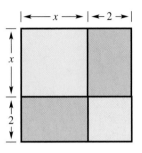

125. *Geometry* Add the areas of the four rectangular regions shown in the figure. Notice how this demonstrates the FOIL Method for finding the product $(x + a)(x + b)$.

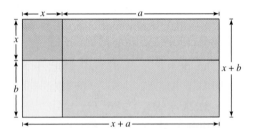

Geometry In Exercises 126 and 127, find a polynomial product that represents the area of the region. Then simplify the product.

126.

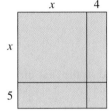

127.

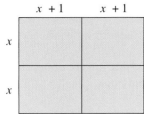

Geometry   In Exercises 128 and 129, find two different expressions that represent the area of the shaded portion of the figure.

128.   **129.**

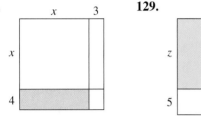

130. *Measurements of a Living Room*   A contractor plans to enlarge a living room by enclosing the wrap-around porch and knocking out the walls between the porch and the living room (see figure). If the enlarged living room is 112 square feet larger than the original living room, what are the measurements of the enlarged living room?

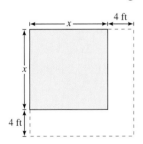

 131. *Using Mathematical Models*   For the years 1980 through 1996, each American's share S of the debt of the federal government is modeled by

$$S = 16.99t^2 + 767.47t + 3525.39, \quad 0 \le t \le 16$$

where $t = 0$ represents 1980. The population P (in millions) during the same period can be modeled by

$$P = 2.37t + 226.94, \quad 0 \le t \le 16.$$

(Source: U.S. Bureau of the Census)

(a) Use a graphing utility to graph the model of the per capita debt S.

(b) Multiply the polynomials representing the population P and the per capita debt S.

(c) Use the product in part (b) to estimate the total federal debt for 1990. (*Note*: The answer will be in millions of dollars.)

132. *Interpreting Graphs*   When x units of a product are sold, the revenue R is given by $R = x(900 - 0.5x)$.

(a) Use a graphing utility to graph the expression.

(b) Multiply the factors in the expression for revenue and use a graphing utility to graph the product. Verify that the graph is the same as in part (a).

(c) Find the revenue if 500 units are sold. Use the graph to determine if revenue would increase or decrease if more units were sold.

133. *Compound Interest*   After 2 years, a $500 investment compounded annually at interest rate r, will yield an amount $500(1 + r)^2$. Find this product.

134. *Compound Interest*   Repeat Exercise 133 if $1200 is invested.

Explaining Concepts

135. Answer parts (d)–(f) of Motivating the Chapter on page 273.

136. Explain why an understanding of the Distributive Property is essential in multiplying polynomials. Illustrate your explanation with an example.

137. Describe the properties of exponents that are used to multiply polynomials. Give examples.

138. Discuss any differences between the expressions $(3x)^2$ and $3x^2$.

139. Explain the meaning of each letter of "FOIL" as it relates to multiplying two binomials.

140. What is the degree of the product of two polynomials of degrees m and n? Explain.

141. A polynomial with m terms is multiplied by a polynomial with n terms. How many *monomial-by-monomial* products must be found? Explain.

142. *True or False?*   Because the product of two monomials is a monomial, it follows that the product of two binomials is a binomial.

143. *True or False?* $(x + 2)^2 = x^2 + 4$

Mid-Chapter Quiz

Take this quiz as you would take a quiz in class. After you are done, check your work against the answers given in the back of the book.

1. Explain why $x^2 + 2x - 3x^{-1}$ is not a polynomial.

2. Determine the degree and the leading coefficient of the polynomial $-3x^4 + 2x^2 - x$.

3. Give an example of a trinomial in one variable of degree 5.

4. *True or False?*   The product of two binomials is a binomial. If false, give an example to show it is false.

In Exercises 5–14, perform the indicated operation and simplify.

5. $(y^2 + 3y - 1) + (4 + 3y)$ **6.** $(3v^2 - 5) - (v^3 + 2v^2 - 6v)$

7. $9s - [6 - (s - 5) + 7s]$ **8.** $-3(4 - x) + 4(x^2 + 2) - (x^2 - 2x)$

9. $2r^2(5r)$ **10.** $m^3(-2m)$

11. $(2y - 3)(y + 5)$ **12.** $(x + 4)(2x^2 - 3x - 2)$

13. $(4 - 3x)^2$ **14.** $(2u - 3)(2u + 3)$

In Exercises 15–18, perform the indicated operation using a vertical format.

15. $5x^4 \quad + 2x^2 \quad + \ x \ - 3$ **16.** $2x^3 + \quad x^2 \qquad - 8$
$+ \quad 3x^3 - 2x^2 \ - 3x \ + 5$ $- \qquad (5x^2 - 3x - 9)$

17. $3x^2 + 7x \ + \ 1$ **18.** $5x^3 - 6x^2 + \ 3$
$\times \qquad 2x \ - \ 5$ $\times \qquad x^2 - 3x$

19. Find the perimeter of the figure.

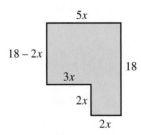

20. Find the area of the figure.

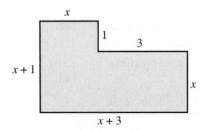

5.3   Negative Exponents and Scientific Notation

Objectives

1 Use the negative exponent rule to rewrite exponential expressions.

2 Use rules of exponents to rewrite expressions without negative exponents.

3 Write numbers in scientific notation.

1 Use the negative exponent rule to rewrite exponential expressions.

Negative Exponents

This section extends the properties of exponents to include **negative exponents.** Consider the property

$$a^m \cdot a^n = a^{m+n}, \quad a \neq 0.$$

If this property is to hold for negative exponents, then the statement

$$a^2 \cdot a^{-2} = a^{2+(-2)} = a^0 = 1$$

implies that a^{-2} is the *reciprocal* of a^2. In other words, it must be true that

$$a^{-2} = \frac{1}{a^2}.$$

Informally, you can think of this property as allowing you to "move" powers from the numerator to the denominator (or vice versa) by changing the sign of the exponent.

> ▶ **Negative Exponent Rule**
>
> Let n be an integer and let a be a real number, variable, or algebraic expression such that $a \neq 0$.
>
> $$a^{-n} = \frac{1}{a^n}$$

Study Tip

Be sure you see that the negative exponent rule allows you to move only *factors* in a numerator (or denominator), *not terms.* For example,

$$\frac{x^{-2} \cdot y}{4} = \frac{y}{4x^2}$$

whereas the following is not true.

~~$$\frac{x^{-2} + y}{4} = \frac{y}{4x^2}$$~~

Example 1   Monomials Involving Negative Exponents

a. $6^{-2} = \dfrac{1}{6^2} = \dfrac{1}{36}$ Move 6^{-2} to denominator and change the sign of the exponent.

b. $x^{-7} = \dfrac{1}{x^7}$ Move x^{-7} to denominator and change the sign of the exponent.

c. $5x^{-4} = \dfrac{5}{x^4}$ Move x^{-4} to denominator and change the sign of the exponent.

d. $\dfrac{1}{2x^{-3}} = \dfrac{x^3}{2}$ Move x^{-3} to numerator and change the sign of the exponent.

e. $x^{-2}y^3 = \dfrac{y^3}{x^2}$ Move x^{-2} to denominator and change the sign of the exponent.

2 Use rules of exponents to rewrite expressions without negative exponents.

Rules of Exponents

All of the rules of exponents apply to negative exponents. For convenience, these rules are summarized below. Remember that these rules apply to real numbers, variables, or algebraic expressions.

▶ **Rules of Exponents**

Let m and n be integers, and let a and b be real numbers, variables, or algebraic expressions such that $a \neq 0$ and $b \neq 0$.

Property	*Example*
1. $a^m a^n = a^{m+n}$	$y^2 \cdot y^4 = y^{2+4} = y^6$
2. $\dfrac{a^m}{a^n} = a^{m-n}$	$\dfrac{x^7}{x^4} = x^{7-4} = x^3$
3. $(ab)^m = a^m b^m$	$(5x)^4 = 5^4 x^4$
4. $\left(\dfrac{a}{b}\right)^m = \dfrac{a^m}{b^m}$	$\left(\dfrac{2}{x}\right)^3 = \dfrac{2^3}{x^3}$
5. $(a^m)^n = a^{mn}$	$(y^3)^{-4} = y^{3(-4)} = y^{-12}$
6. $a^{-n} = \dfrac{1}{a^n}$	$y^{-4} = \dfrac{1}{y^4}$
7. $a^0 = 1$	$(x^2 + 1)^0 = 1$

Study Tip

There is more than one way to solve problems such as those in Example 2. For instance, you might prefer to write Example 2(c) as

$$\frac{y^{-2}}{3y^{-5}} = \frac{y^5}{3y^2} = \frac{y^{5-2}}{3} = \frac{y^3}{3}.$$

Example 2 Using Rules of Exponents

a. $x^3(2x^{-4}) = 2(x^3)(x^{-4})$ Regroup factors.

$\qquad\qquad = 2x^{3+(-4)}$ Apply rules of exponents.

$\qquad\qquad = 2x^{-1}$ Simplify.

$\qquad\qquad = \dfrac{2}{x}$ Simplify.

b. $(-3ab^4)(4ab^{-3}) = (-3)(4)(a)(a)(b^4)(b^{-3})$ Regroup factors.

$\qquad\qquad\qquad = (-12)(a^{1+1})(b^{4-3})$ Apply rules of exponents.

$\qquad\qquad\qquad = -12a^2b$ Simplify.

c. $\dfrac{y^{-2}}{3y^{-5}} = \dfrac{1}{3}y^{-2-(-5)}$ Apply rules of exponents.

$\qquad\quad = \dfrac{1}{3}y^3$ Simplify.

$\qquad\quad = \dfrac{y^3}{3}$ Simplify.

Example 3   Using Rules of Exponents

You could ask students to compare these examples.

$5^0 = 1$ $5x^0 = 5$
$-5^0 = -1$ $-(5x)^0 = -1$
$(-5)^0 = 1$ $(-5x^3)^0 = 1$

Use rules of exponents to rewrite each expression without negative exponents. (Assume that no variable is equal to zero.)

a. $3x^{-1}(-4x^2y)^0$ **b.** $\left(\dfrac{5x^3}{y^{-1}}\right)^2$ **c.** $\left(\dfrac{a^2}{3}\right)^{-2}$ **d.** $\left(\dfrac{x^{-2}y^3}{2}\right)^{-3}$

Solution

a. This problem is a little tricky. Note that the factor $(-4x^2y)$ is raised to the *zero* power. Because any nonzero number raised to the zero power is 1, you can write

$$3x^{-1}(-4x^2y)^0 = 3x^{-1}(1) = \frac{3}{x}.$$

Assure students that there is more than one way to solve these problems. Encourage students to justify each step mentally by the rules of exponents.

b. This problem can also be tricky. The important thing to realize is that the *entire fraction* $(5x^3/y^{-1})$ is raised to the second power. This means that you must apply the exponent 2 to each factor of the numerator and denominator, as follows.

$$\left(\frac{5x^3}{y^{-1}}\right)^2 = \frac{(5x^3)^2}{(y^{-1})^2} = \frac{5^2(x^3)^2}{y^{-2}} = \frac{25x^6}{y^{-2}} = 25x^6y^2$$

c. In this problem, note that the *entire expression* $(a^2/3)$ is raised to the -2 power.

$$\left(\frac{a^2}{3}\right)^{-2} = \frac{a^{-4}}{3^{-2}} = \frac{3^2}{a^4} = \frac{9}{a^4}$$

d. In this problem, note that the *entire expression* $(x^{-2}y^3/2)$ is raised to the -3 power.

$$\left(\frac{x^{-2}y^3}{2}\right)^{-3} = \frac{x^6y^{-9}}{2^{-3}} \qquad \text{Property of exponents}$$

$$= \frac{2^3x^6}{y^9} = \frac{8x^6}{y^9} \qquad \text{Convert to positive exponent.}$$

Technology: Tip

Calculators and Negative Exponents
The keystrokes used to evaluate expressions with negative exponents vary. For instance, to evaluate 13^{-2} on a calculator, you can try one of the following keystroke sequences.

Keystrokes

13 $\boxed{x^y}$ 2 $\boxed{+/-}$ $\boxed{=}$ Scientific

13 $\boxed{\wedge}$ $\boxed{(-)}$ 2 $\boxed{\text{ENTER}}$ Graphing

With either of these sequences, your calculator should display .00591716. If it doesn't, consult the user's guide for your calculator to find the correct keystrokes.

3 Write numbers in scientific notation.

Scientific Notation

Exponents provide an efficient way of writing and computing with the very large (or very small) numbers used in science. For instance, a drop of water contains more than 33 billion billion molecules. That is 33 followed by 18 zeros. It is convenient to write such numbers in **scientific notation.** This notation has the form $c \times 10^n$, where $1 \le c < 10$ and n is an integer. So, the number of molecules in a drop of water can be written in scientific notation as follows.

$$33{,}000{,}000{,}000{,}000{,}000{,}000 = 3.3 \times 10^{19}$$

19 places

The *positive* exponent 19 indicates that the number is large (10 or more) and that the decimal point has been moved 19 places.

A *negative* exponent in scientific notation indicates that the number is *small* (less than 1). For instance, the mass (in grams) of one electron is approximately as follows.

$$9.0 \times 10^{-28} = 0.00000000000000000000000000009$$

28 places

Example 4   Converting from Decimal to Scientific Notation

Write the decimal number in scientific notation.

a. 1,260,000   **b.** 0.0000782   **c.** 836,100,000.0

Solution

a. $1{,}260{,}000. = 1.26 \times 10^6$ Large number yields positive exponent.

Six places

b. $0.0000782 = 7.82 \times 10^{-5}$ Small number yields negative exponent.

Five places

c. $836{,}100{,}000.0 = 8.361 \times 10^8$ Large number yields positive exponent.

Eight places

Example 5   Converting from Scientific to Decimal Notation

The storage capacity of a 6-gigabyte computer is

$$6 \times 10^9 = 6{,}000{,}000{,}000 \text{ bytes.}$$ Positive exponent yields large number.

Nine places

The probability of being dealt a royal flush in poker is

$$1.54 \times 10^{-6} = 0.00000154.$$ Negative exponent yields small number.

Six places

Technology: Tip

Calculators and Scientific Notation
Most scientific calculators automatically switch to scientific notation when they are displaying large (or small) numbers that exceed the display range. Try multiplying $98,900,000 \times 5000$. If your calculator follows standard conventions, its display should show

| 4.945   11 | or | 4.945 E 11 |.

This means that $c = 4.945$ and the exponent of 10 is $n = 11$, which implies that the number is 4.945×10^{11}. For *entering* numbers in scientific notation, your calculator should have an exponential entry key labeled [EE] or [EXP].

Example 6   Using Scientific Notation

Use a calculator to evaluate $78,000 \times 2,400,000,000$.

Solution
Because $78,000 = 7.8 \times 10^4$ and $2,400,000,000 = 2.4 \times 10^9$, you can evaluate the product as follows.

7.8 [EXP] 4 [×] 2.4 [EXP] 9 [=]   Scientific

7.8 [EE] 4 [×] 2.4 [EE] 9 [ENTER]   Graphing

After these keystrokes have been entered, the calculator display should show
| 1.872   14 |. So, the product of the two numbers is

$$(7.8 \times 10^4)(2.4 \times 10^9) = 1.872 \times 10^{14} = 187,200,000,000,000.$$

Use a calculator to evaluate $(7.8)(2.4) \times (10^4)(10^9)$. Your answer should be the same as in Example 6. This illustrates the commutative property of multiplication.

Discussing the Concept   **Exponential Expressions**

Find as many equivalent pairs as possible among the following exponential expressions.

$$\frac{2}{x^{-3}}, \quad \frac{1}{2x^3}, \quad 2x^{-3}, \quad \frac{1}{(2x)^{-3}}, \quad 2x^3, \quad \frac{x^3}{8}, \quad \frac{1}{8x^3}, \quad \frac{x^{-3}}{2}, \quad 8x^3, \quad (2x)^{-3}$$

Next, use a calculator, with $x = 3$, to illustrate the equivalence of each pair. Organize your work into a table with four columns—an expression, the equivalent expression, and each expression evaluated at $x = 3$. Compare your results with those of other students in your class.

5.3 Exercises

Integrated Review   *Concepts, Skills, and Problem Solving*

Keep mathematically in shape by doing these exercises *before* the problems of this section.

Properties and Definitions

1. In your own words, define the graph of the function $y = f(x)$.

2. Describe the point-plotting method of sketching a graph for $y = f(x)$.

3. Find the coordinates of two points on the graph of $g(x) = \sqrt{x}$.

4. Describe the procedure for finding the x- and y-intercepts of the graph of $f(x) = 3(x - 2)$.

Simplifying Expressions

In Exercises 5–8, simplify the expression. (Assume that no denominator is zero.)

5. $x^2 \cdot x^3$ **6.** $(y^2 z^3)(z^2)^4$

7. $\left(\dfrac{x^2}{y}\right)^3$ **8.** $\dfrac{a^2 b^3}{c} \cdot \dfrac{2a}{3}$

Graphing Equations

In Exercises 9–12, use a graphing utility to graph the function. Identify any intercepts.

9. $f(x) = 4 - 3x$ **10.** $g(x) = |2x + 1|$

11. $g(x) = x^2 - 2x + 1$ **12.** $h(x) = \sqrt{x + 4}$

Developing Skills

In Exercises 1–12, rewrite with positive exponents. See Example 1.

1. 3^{-3} **2.** 4^{-2}

3. y^{-5} **4.** z^{-2}

5. $8x^{-7}$ **6.** $6x^{-2}y^{-3}$

7. $7x^{-4}y^{-1}$ **8.** $9u^{-5}v^{-2}$

9. $\dfrac{1}{2z^{-4}}$ **10.** $\dfrac{7x^2}{y^{-3}}$

11. $\dfrac{2x}{3y^{-2}}$ **12.** $\dfrac{5u^2}{6v^{-4}}$

In Exercises 13–22, rewrite with negative exponents.

13. $\dfrac{1}{4}$ **14.** $\dfrac{1}{3^2}$

15. $\dfrac{1}{x^2}$ **16.** $\dfrac{7}{y^3}$

17. $\dfrac{10}{t^5}$ **18.** $\dfrac{3}{z^n}$

19. $\dfrac{5}{x^n}$ **20.** $\dfrac{9}{y^n}$

21. $\dfrac{2x^2}{y^4}$ **22.** $\dfrac{5x^3}{y^6}$

In Exercises 23–36, rewrite with positive exponents. Then evaluate the expression.

23. 3^{-2} **24.** 5^{-3}

25. $(-4)^{-3}$ **26.** $(-6)^{-2}$

27. $\dfrac{1}{4^{-2}}$ **28.** $\dfrac{1}{16^{-1}}$

29. $\dfrac{2}{3^{-4}}$ **30.** $\dfrac{4}{3^{-2}}$

31. $\dfrac{2^{-4}}{3^{-2}}$ **32.** $\dfrac{4^{-3}}{2}$

33. $\dfrac{4^{-2}}{3^{-4}}$ **34.** $\left(\dfrac{3}{4}\right)^{-3}$

35. $\left(\dfrac{2}{3}\right)^{-2}$ **36.** $\left(\dfrac{5}{4}\right)^{-3}$

In Exercises 37–40, use a calculator to evaluate the expression.

37. 3.8^{-4} **38.** 6.2^{-3}

39. $100(1.06)^{-15}$ **40.** $500(1.08)^{-20}$

In Exercises 41–82, simplify using rules of exponents. Write your answer with positive exponents. (Assume that no variable is zero.) See Examples 2 and 3.

41. $4^{-2} \cdot 4^3$

42. $5^{-3} \cdot 5^2$

43. $x^{-4} \cdot x^6$

44. $a^{-5} \cdot a^2$

45. $u^{-6} \cdot u^3$

46. $t^{-2} \cdot t^2$

47. $xy^{-3} \cdot y^2$

48. $u^{-2}v \cdot u^2$

49. $\dfrac{x^2}{x^{-3}}$

50. $\dfrac{z^4}{z^{-2}}$

51. $\dfrac{y^{-5}}{y}$

52. $\dfrac{x^{-3}}{x^2}$

53. $\dfrac{x^{-4}}{x^{-2}}$

54. $\dfrac{t^{-5}}{t^{-1}}$

55. $(y^{-3})^2$

56. $(z^{-2})^3$

57. $(s^2)^{-1}$

58. $(a^3)^{-3}$

59. $(2x^{-2})^0$

60. $(2x^{-5})^0$

61. $\dfrac{b^2 \cdot b^{-3}}{b^4}$

62. $\dfrac{c^{-3} \cdot c^4}{c^{-1}}$

63. $(3x^2y)^{-2}$

64. $(4x^{-3}y^2)^{-3}$

65. $(4a^{-2}b^3)^{-3}$

66. $(-2s^{-1}t^{-2})^{-1}$

67. $(-2x^2)(4x^{-3})$

68. $(4y^{-2})(3y^4)$

69. $\left(\dfrac{x}{10}\right)^{-1}$

70. $\left(\dfrac{4}{z}\right)^{-2}$

71. $\left(\dfrac{3z^2}{x}\right)^{-2}$

72. $\left(\dfrac{x^{-3}y^4}{5}\right)^{-3}$

73. $\dfrac{(2y)^{-4}}{(2y)^{-4}}$

74. $\dfrac{(3z)^{-2}}{(3z)^{-2}}$

75. $\dfrac{3}{2} \cdot \left(\dfrac{-2}{3}\right)^{-3}$

76. $\dfrac{3}{8} \cdot \left(\dfrac{-5}{2}\right)^{-3}$

77. $\dfrac{(-2x)^{-3}}{-4x^{-2}}$

78. $\dfrac{2x^{-3}}{(5x)^{-1}}$

79. $(5x^2y^4z^6)^3(5x^2y^4z^6)^{-3}$

80. $(8x^3y^2z^5)^6(8x^3y^2z^5)^{-6}$

81. $(x+y)^{-8}(x+y)^8$

82. $(u^2-v)^4(u^2-v)^{-4}$

In Exercises 83–92, write in scientific notation. See Example 4.

83. 93,000,000

84. 900,000,000

85. 1,637,000,000

86. 67.8

87. 0.000435

88. 0.008367

89. 0.004392

90. 0.00000045

91. 16,000,000

92. 0.00082

In Exercises 93–102, write in decimal form. See Example 5.

93. 1.09×10^6

94. 2.345×10^8

95. 8.67×10^{-2}

96. 9.4675×10^4

97. 8.52×10^{-3}

98. 7.021×10^{-5}

99. 6.21×10^0

100. 4.73×10^0

101. $(8 \times 10^3) + (3 \times 10^0) + (5 \times 10^{-2})$

102. $(6 \times 10^4) + (9 \times 10^3) + (4 \times 10^{-1})$

In Exercises 103–114, use a calculator to evaluate the expression. See Example 6.

103. $8{,}000{,}000 \times 623{,}000$

104. $93{,}200{,}000 \times 1{,}657{,}000$

105. $0.000345 \times 8{,}980{,}000{,}000$

106. $345{,}000 \times 0.000086$

107. $3{,}200{,}000^5$

108. $75{,}000{,}000^6$

109. $(3.28 \times 10^{-6})^4$

110. $(4.5 \times 10^{-5})^3$

111. $\dfrac{848{,}000{,}000}{1{,}620{,}000}$

112. $\dfrac{67{,}000{,}000}{0.0052}$

113. $(4.85 \times 10^5)(2.04 \times 10^8)$

114. $\dfrac{8.6 \times 10^4}{3.9 \times 10^7}$

Solving Problems

115. *Time for Light to Travel*   Light travels from the sun to the earth in approximately

$$\frac{9.3 \times 10^7}{1.1 \times 10^7}$$

minutes. Write this time in decimal form.

116. *Distance to a Star*   The star Beta Andromeda is approximately 76 light-years from the earth (see figure). (A light-year is the distance light can travel in 1 year.) Estimate the distance to this star if a light-year is approximately 5.8746×10^{12} miles.

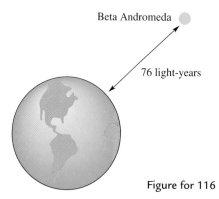

Beta Andromeda

76 light-years

Figure for 116

117. *Solar System*   One astronomical unit AU is the mean distance between the sun and the earth (approximately 149,503,000 kilometers). The table gives the mean distances between selected planets and the sun in astronomical units. Approximate each distance in kilometers and give the answer in scientific notation.

Planet	Mercury	Saturn	Neptune	Pluto
AU	0.39	9.56	30.13	39.47

118. *Numerical and Graphical Analysis*   A new car is purchased for $24,000. Its value V after t years is

$$V = 24{,}000(1.2)^{-t}.$$

(a) Use the model to complete the table.

t	0	2	4	6	8
$24{,}000(1.2)^{-t}$					

(b) Graph the data in the table.

(c) *Guess, Check, and Revise*   When will the car be valued at less than $1000?

119. *Numerical and Graphical Analysis*

(a) Complete the table by evaluating the indicated powers of 2.

x	-1	-2	-3	-4	-5
2^x					

(b) Graph the data in the table.

(c) Use the table or the graph to describe the value of 2^{-n} when n is very large. Will the value of 2^{-n} ever be negative?

120. *Hydraulic Compression*   A hydraulic cylinder in a large press (see figure) contains 2 gallons of oil. When the cylinder is under full pressure, the actual volume of oil is decreased by

$$2(150)(20 \times 10^{-6})$$

gallons. Write this volume in decimal form.

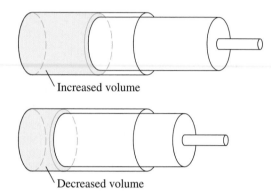

Increased volume

Decreased volume

121. *Boltzmann's Constant*   The study of the kinetic energy of an ideal gas uses Boltzmann's constant. This constant k is given by

$$k = \frac{8.31 \times 10^7}{6.02 \times 10^{23}}.$$

Perform the division, leaving your result in scientific notation.

Explaining Concepts

True or False?   In Exercises 122–127, state whether the equation is true or false. If it is false, find values of x and y that show it to be false.

122. $x^3y^3 = xy^3$

123. $x^{-1}y^{-1} = \dfrac{1}{xy}$

124. $x^{-1} + y^{-1} = \dfrac{1}{x + y}$

125. $\dfrac{x^{-4}}{x^{-3}} = x$

126. $(x \times 10^3)^4 = x^4 \times 10^{12}$

127. $\dfrac{2x \times 10^{-5}}{x \times 10^{-3}} = 2 \times 10^{-2}$

128. Without looking back at page 298, state as many of the seven rules of exponents as you can.

129. Give examples of large and small numbers written in scientific notation.

130. Find the reciprocal of 4×10^{-3}.

131. Justify each step.

$$
\begin{aligned}
(3 \times 10^5)(4 \times 10^6) &= (3 \times 10^5)(10^6 \times 4) \\
&= 3(10^5 \times 10^6)(4) \\
&= 3(10^{5+6})(4) \\
&= (3 \cdot 4)10^{11} \\
&= 12 \times 10^{11} = 1.2 \times 10^{12}
\end{aligned}
$$

5.4   Dividing Polynomials

Objectives

1 Use the properties of exponents to divide a monomial expression by a monomial expression.

2 Divide a polynomial expression by a monomial expression.

3 Divide a polynomial expression by a binomial expression.

4 Use synthetic division to divide a polynomial expression by a binomial expression.

---

1 Use the properties of exponents to divide a monomial expression by a monomial expression.

Dividing a Monomial by a Monomial

In this section, you will learn how to divide a polynomial by a monomial or a binomial. In all cases, assume that the divisor (denominator) is nonzero.

To begin, let's consider division problems in which both the numerator *and* the denominator are monomials. To divide a monomial by a monomial, you make use of the *subtraction* property of exponents illustrated in the following examples. (In each of the following, assume that the variable is *not zero*.)

By Reducing	*By Subtracting Exponents*
$\dfrac{x^4}{x^2} = \dfrac{x \cdot x \cdot x \cdot x}{x \cdot x} = x^2$	$\dfrac{x^4}{x^2} = x^{4-2} = x^2$
$\dfrac{y^3}{y^3} = \dfrac{y \cdot y \cdot y}{y \cdot y \cdot y} = 1$	$\dfrac{y^3}{y^3} = y^{3-3} = y^0 = 1$
$\dfrac{5y^7}{2y^5} = \dfrac{5 \cdot y \cdot y \cdot y \cdot y \cdot y \cdot y \cdot y}{2 \cdot y \cdot y \cdot y \cdot y \cdot y} = \dfrac{5y^2}{2}$	$\dfrac{5y^7}{2y^5} = \dfrac{5y^{7-5}}{2} = \dfrac{5y^2}{2}$
$\dfrac{2x^2}{x^5} = \dfrac{2 \cdot x \cdot x}{x \cdot x \cdot x \cdot x \cdot x} = \dfrac{2}{x^3}$	$\dfrac{2x^2}{x^5} = 2x^{2-5} = 2x^{-3} = \dfrac{2}{x^3}$

The examples above show that you can divide one monomial by another by subtracting exponents.

Study Tip

If you remember the first rule at the right, you can use it to derive the second rule. That is,

$$1 = \frac{a^n}{a^n} = a^{n-n} = a^0,$$

$a \neq 0$.

▶ Properties of Exponents

Let m and n be positive integers and let a represent a real number, a variable, or an algebraic expression.

1. $\dfrac{a^m}{a^n} = a^{m-n}$

2. $\dfrac{a^n}{a^n} = 1 = a^0$

Note the special definition for raising a *nonzero* quantity to the zero power. That is, if $a \neq 0$, then $a^0 = 1$.

| Example 1 | Dividing a Monomial by a Monomial |

Perform each division. (In each case, assume that $x \neq 0$ and $y \neq 0$.)

a. $2y^8 \div y^5$ **b.** $16x^4 \div 4x^2$

c. $16x^4 \div 3x$ **d.** $32y^3 \div 8y^5$

e. $8x^3 \div \frac{1}{2}x^3$ **f.** $12x^3 \div 4x^4$

g. $3x^3y \div 4x$

Solution

a. $\dfrac{2y^8}{y^5} = 2 \cdot y^{8-5} = 2y^3$

b. $\dfrac{16x^4}{4x^2} = \dfrac{16}{4} \cdot \dfrac{x^4}{x^2} = \dfrac{16}{4} \cdot x^{4-2} = 4x^2$

c. $\dfrac{16x^4}{3x} = \dfrac{16}{3} \cdot \dfrac{x^4}{x} = \dfrac{16}{3} \cdot x^{4-1} = \dfrac{16}{3}x^3$

d. $\dfrac{32y^3}{8y^5} = \dfrac{32}{8} \cdot \dfrac{y^3}{y^5} = \dfrac{32}{8} \cdot y^{3-5} = 4 \cdot y^{-2} = \dfrac{4}{y^2}$

e. $\dfrac{8x^3}{\frac{1}{2}x^3} = \dfrac{8}{\frac{1}{2}} \cdot \dfrac{x^3}{x^3} = 8\left(\dfrac{2}{1}\right)(1) = 16$

f. $\dfrac{12x^3}{4x^4} = \dfrac{12}{4} \cdot \dfrac{x^3}{x^4} = 3 \cdot x^{3-4} = 3 \cdot x^{-1} = \dfrac{3}{x}$

g. $\dfrac{3x^3y}{4x} = \dfrac{3}{4} \cdot x^{3-1} \cdot y = \dfrac{3}{4} \cdot x^2 \cdot y = \dfrac{3x^2y}{4}$

Study Tip

The subtraction property of exponents works only for division of monomials with the *same variable* for a base. For instance, the subtraction property does not apply to x^5/y^3 because no cancellations can occur. So, for the fraction

$$\frac{x^5}{y^3} = \frac{x \cdot x \cdot x \cdot x \cdot x}{y \cdot y \cdot y}$$

no simplifying is possible.

Although the division problems in Example 1 are straightforward, you should study them carefully. Be sure you can justify each step. Also remember that there are often several ways to solve a given problem in algebra. As you gain practice and confidence, you will discover that you like some techniques better than others. For instance, which one of the following techniques seems best to you?

Point out that there can be *many* correct ways to solve an algebraic problem.

1. $\dfrac{6x^3}{2x} = \dfrac{3 \cdot 2 \cdot x \cdot x \cdot \cancel{x}}{2 \cdot \cancel{x}} = 3x^2, \quad x \neq 0$

2. $\dfrac{6x^3}{2x} = \left(\dfrac{6}{2}\right)\left(\dfrac{x^3}{x}\right) = (3)(x^{3-1}) = 3x^2, \quad x \neq 0$

3. $\dfrac{6x^3}{2x} = \dfrac{3x^3}{x} = 3x^{3-1} = 3x^2, \quad x \neq 0$

When two different people (even math instructors) are writing out the steps of a solution, rarely will the steps be the same, so don't worry if your steps don't look exactly like someone else's. If you feel comfortable with writing more steps, then you should write more steps. Just be sure that each step can be justified by the rules of algebra.

2 Divide a polynomial expression by a monomial expression.

Caution students to avoid these common errors.

$\dfrac{x + 6}{x} \neq 6$ and $\dfrac{x + 6}{3} \neq x + 2$

Instead, $\dfrac{x + 6}{x} = \dfrac{x}{x} + \dfrac{6}{x} = 1 + \dfrac{6}{x}$,

and $\dfrac{x + 6}{3} = \dfrac{x}{3} + \dfrac{6}{3} = \dfrac{x}{3} + 2$.

Dividing a Polynomial by a Monomial

The preceding examples show how to divide a *monomial* by a monomial. To divide a *polynomial* by a monomial, use the reverse form of the rule for adding two fractions with a common denominator. In Section 1.3, you added two fractions with like denominators using the rule

$$\frac{a}{c} + \frac{b}{c} = \frac{a + b}{c}. \qquad \text{Adding fractions}$$

Here you can use the rule in the *reverse* order and divide a polynomial by a monomial by dividing each term of the polynomial by the monomial. That is,

$$\frac{a + b}{c} = \frac{a}{c} + \frac{b}{c}. \qquad \text{Dividing by a monomial}$$

Here is an example.

$$\frac{x^3 - 5x^2}{x^2} = \frac{x^3}{x^2} - \frac{5x^2}{x^2} = x - 5, \quad x \neq 0$$

The essence of this problem is to separate the original division problem into *two* division problems, each involving the division of a monomial by a monomial.

Technology: Tip

As with other types of operations with polynomials, you can use a graphing utility to help check division problems. For instance, graph

$$y = \frac{6x - 5}{3} \quad \text{and} \quad y = 2x - \frac{5}{3}$$

on the same screen, as shown below. Because both graphs are the same, you can reason that

$$\frac{6x - 5}{3} = 2x - \frac{5}{3}.$$

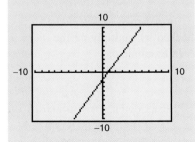

Example 2   Dividing a Polynomial by a Monomial

a. $\dfrac{6x + 5}{3} = \dfrac{6x}{3} + \dfrac{5}{3} = 2x + \dfrac{5}{3}$

b. $\dfrac{4x^2 - 3x}{3x} = \dfrac{4x^2}{3x} - \dfrac{3x}{3x} = \dfrac{4x}{3} - 1, \quad x \neq 0$

c. $\dfrac{8x^3 - 6x^2 + 10x}{2x} = \dfrac{8x^3}{2x} - \dfrac{6x^2}{2x} + \dfrac{10x}{2x} = 4x^2 - 3x + 5, \quad x \neq 0$

Example 3   Dividing a Polynomial by a Monomial

Perform the division. (Assume $x \neq 0$.)

a. $(5x^3 - 4x^2 - x + 6) \div 2x$

b. $(8x^4 + 6x^3 + 3x^2 - 2x) \div 3x^2$

Solution

a. $\dfrac{5x^3 - 4x^2 - x + 6}{2x} = \dfrac{5x^3}{2x} - \dfrac{4x^2}{2x} - \dfrac{x}{2x} + \dfrac{6}{2x}$ Divide each term separately.

$\qquad = \dfrac{5x^2}{2} - 2x - \dfrac{1}{2} + \dfrac{3}{x}$ Use properties for dividing monomials.

b. $\dfrac{8x^4 + 6x^3 + 3x^2 - 2x}{3x^2} = \dfrac{8x^4}{3x^2} + \dfrac{6x^3}{3x^2} + \dfrac{3x^2}{3x^2} - \dfrac{2x}{3x^2}$ Divide each term separately.

$\qquad = \dfrac{8x^2}{3} + 2x + 1 - \dfrac{2}{3x}$ Use properties for dividing monomials.

3 Divide a polynomial expression by a binomial expression.

Dividing a Polynomial by a Binomial

To divide a polynomial by a *binomial*, follow the *long division* pattern used for dividing whole numbers. Recall that you divide 6982 by 27 as follows.

Think $\frac{69}{27} \approx 2$

Think $\frac{158}{27} \approx 5$

Think $\frac{232}{27} \approx 8$

$$
\begin{array}{r}
258 \\
27 \overline{)\, 6982} \\
\underline{54} \\
158 \\
\underline{135} \\
232 \\
\underline{216} \\
16
\end{array}
$$

Multiply 2 by 27.

Subtract and bring down 8.

Multiply 5 by 27.

Subtract and bring down 2.

Multiply 8 by 27.

Remainder

You can express the result as $\frac{6982}{27} = 258\frac{16}{27}$ or $258 + \frac{16}{27}$.

Example 4   Dividing a Polynomial by a Binomial

Divide $(x^2 + 3x + 5)$ by $(x + 1)$.

Solution

Think $\frac{x^2}{x} = x$

Think $\frac{2x}{x} = 2$

$$
\begin{array}{r}
x + 2 \\
x + 1 \overline{)\, x^2 + 3x + 5} \\
\underline{x^2 + x} \\
2x + 5 \\
\underline{2x + 2} \\
3
\end{array}
$$

Multiply $x(x + 1)$.

Subtract and bring down 5.

Multiply $2(x + 1)$.

Remainder.

Considering the remainder as a fractional part of the divisor, you can write

$$
\underbrace{\frac{\overbrace{x^2 + 3x + 5}^{\text{Dividend}}}{\underbrace{x + 1}_{\text{Divisor}}}}_{} = \overbrace{x + 2}^{\text{Quotient}} + \frac{\overset{\text{Remainder}}{3}}{\underbrace{x + 1}_{\text{Divisor}}}.
$$

Remember that a division problem can be checked by multiplying the *quotient* (answer) by the *divisor* to obtain the *dividend*. In Example 4,

$$
\overbrace{(x + 1)}^{\text{Divisor}}\overbrace{\left(x + 2 + \frac{3}{x + 1} \right)}^{\text{Quotient}} = (x + 1)(x + 2) + (x + 1)\left(\frac{3}{x + 1} \right)
$$

$$
= (x^2 + 3x + 2) + 3 = \underbrace{x^2 + 3x + 5}_{\text{Dividend}}.
$$

Example 5   A Binomial Divisor

Divide $(6x^3 - 19x^2 + 16x - 4)$ by $(x - 2)$.

Solution

$$
\begin{array}{r}
\text{Think } \frac{6x^3}{x} = 6x^2. \\
\text{Think } -\frac{7x^2}{x} = -7x. \\
\text{Think } \frac{2x}{x} = 2.
\end{array}
$$

$$
\begin{array}{r}
6x^2 - 7x + 2 \\
x - 2 \overline{)\, 6x^3 - 19x^2 + 16x - 4} \\
\underline{6x^3 - 12x^2} \\
-\;\; 7x^2 + 16x \\
\underline{-\;\; 7x^2 + 14x} \\
2x - 4 \\
\underline{2x - 4} \\
0
\end{array}
$$

Multiply $6x^2(x - 2)$.
Subtract and bring down $16x$.
Multiply $-7x(x - 2)$.
Subtract and bring down -4.
Multiply $2(x - 2)$.
Remainder

So, $\overbrace{6x^3 - 19x^2 + 16x - 4}^{\text{Dividend}} \div \overbrace{x - 2}^{\text{Divisor}} = \overbrace{6x^2 - 7x + 2}^{\text{Quotient}}, \quad x \neq 2.$

Check this division by multiplying $6x^2 - 7x + 2$ by the divisor $x - 2$.

In Example 5, the remainder is zero. In such cases, the denominator (or divisor) is said to **divide evenly** into the numerator (or dividend).

Example 6   A Binomial Divisor

Divide $(-13x^3 + 10x^4 + 8x - 7x^2 + 4)$ by $(3 - 2x)$.

Solution

First write the divisor and dividend in standard polynomial form.

You might advise students that errors in long division problems frequently occur in the *subtraction* steps. In this example, notice that

$-13x^3 - (-15x^3) = -13x^3 + 15x^3 = 2x^3.$

$$
\begin{array}{r}
-5x^3 - x^2 + 2x - 1 \\
-2x + 3 \overline{)\, 10x^4 - 13x^3 - 7x^2 + 8x + 4} \\
\underline{10x^4 - 15x^3} \\
2x^3 - 7x^2 \\
\underline{2x^3 - 3x^2} \\
-4x^2 + 8x \\
\underline{-4x^2 + 6x} \\
2x + 4 \\
\underline{2x - 3} \\
7
\end{array}
$$

Multiply $-5x^3(-2x + 3)$.
Subtract and bring down $-7x^2$.
Multiply $-x^2(-2x + 3)$.
Subtract and bring down $8x$.
Multiply $2x(-2x + 3)$.
Subtract and bring down 4.
Multiply $-1(-2x + 3)$.
Remainder

Using the fractional form of the remainder, you can write

$$
\underbrace{\frac{\overbrace{10x^4 - 13x^3 - 7x^2 + 8x + 4}^{\text{Dividend}}}{-2x + 3}}_{\text{Divisor}} = \overbrace{-5x^3 - x^2 + 2x - 1}^{\text{Quotient}} + \overbrace{\frac{7}{-2x + 3}}^{\text{Remainder}}.
$$

Study Tip

You should always check two things when you begin a long division problem.

1. The divisor and the dividend should be written in standard form—that is, in decreasing powers of the variable.

2. Zero coefficients or spaces should be inserted for any "missing" terms in the dividend.

Example 7 A Binomial Divisor

Use the long division algorithm to simplify

$$\frac{x^3 - 1}{x - 1}.$$

Solution

Because there are no x^2- or x-terms in the dividend, you can line up the subtractions by using *zero* coefficients (or by leaving spaces) for the missing terms.

$$
\begin{array}{r}
x^2 + x + 1 \\
x - 1 \overline{)\, x^3 + 0x^2 + 0x - 1} \\
\underline{x^3 - x^2} \\
x^2 \\
\underline{x^2 - x} \\
x - 1 \\
\underline{x - 1} \\
0
\end{array}
$$

Multiply $x^2(x - 1)$.

Subtract.

Multiply $x(x - 1)$.

Subtract and bring down -1.

Multiply $1(x - 1)$.

Remainder

So, $x - 1$ divides evenly into $x^3 - 1$ and you can write

$$\frac{x^3 - 1}{x - 1} = x^2 + x + 1, \quad x \neq 1.$$

4 Use synthetic division to divide a polynomial expression by a binomial expression.

Synthetic Division

There is a nice shortcut for long division of polynomials by divisors of the form $x - k$. The shortcut is called **synthetic division.** We summarize the pattern for synthetic division of a cubic polynomial as follows. (The pattern for higher-degree polynomials is similar.)

> ▶ **Synthetic Division (for a Cubic Polynomial)**
>
> To divide $ax^3 + bx^2 + cx + d$ by $x - k$, use the following pattern.
>
>
> *Vertical pattern:* Add terms.
> *Diagonal pattern:* Multiply by k.

Synthetic division works *only* for divisors of the form $x - k$. [Remember that $x + k = x - (-k)$.] You cannot use synthetic division to divide a polynomial by a quadratic such as $x^2 - 3$.

Example 8 Using Synthetic Division

Use synthetic division to divide $x^3 + 5x^2 + 4x - 2$ by $x + 2$.

Solution

You should set up the division as follows.

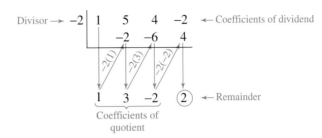

The bottom row of the table shows the coefficients of the quotient and the remainder. So the quotient is

$$(1)x^2 + (3)x + (-2)$$

and the remainder is 2. The result of the division problem is

$$\frac{x^3 + 5x^2 + 4x - 2}{x + 2} = x^2 + 3x - 2 + \frac{2}{x + 2}.$$

You can check the result by multiplying.

Try using synthetic division to perform the divisions in Examples 4, 5, and 7.

Discussing the Concept   Creating Practice Problems

You are tutoring a friend in algebra and you want to create some division problems for practice. You want to find several division problems that involve third-degree polynomials that are evenly divisible by first-degree polynomials. For instance, in Example 7, $x^3 - 1$ is evenly divisible by $x - 1$ because the remainder is 0.

$$\frac{x^3 - 1}{x - 1} = x^2 + x + 1$$

Develop a method for finding a third-degree polynomial that is evenly divisible by a first-degree polynomial. Demonstrate your method by finding a third-degree polynomial that is evenly divisible by $2x - 1$.

5.4   Exercises

Integrated Review   *Concepts, Skills, and Problem Solving*

Keep mathematically in shape by doing these exercises *before* the problems of this section.

Properties and Definitions

1. Explain how to write the fraction $\dfrac{24x}{18}$ in reduced form.

2. The point $(-1, 4)$ lies in what quadrant? Explain.

Simplifying Expressions

In Exercises 3–6, simplify the fraction.

3. $\dfrac{8}{12}$

4. $\dfrac{18}{144}$

5. $\dfrac{60}{150}$

6. $\dfrac{175}{42}$

In Exercises 7–10, find the product and simplify.

7. $-2x^2(5x^3)$

8. $(2z + 1)(2z - 1)$

9. $(x + 7)^2$

10. $(x + 4)(2x - 5)$

Creating a Model and Problem Solving

11. Write an algebraic expression that represents the product of two consecutive odd integers, the first of which is $2n + 1$.

12. After traveling for 3 hours, you are still 24 miles from completing a 180-mile trip. It takes you one-half hour to travel the last 24 miles. Find your average speed during the trip.

Developing Skills

In Exercises 1–14, perform the division by cancellation *and* by subtracting exponents. (Assume that no denominator is zero.)

1. $\dfrac{x^5}{x^2}$

2. $\dfrac{y^7}{y^3}$

3. $\dfrac{x^2}{x^5}$

4. $\dfrac{y^3}{y^7}$

5. $\dfrac{z^4}{z^7}$

6. $\dfrac{y^8}{y^3}$

7. $\dfrac{3u^4}{u^3}$

8. $\dfrac{z^6}{5z^4}$

9. $\dfrac{2^3 y^4}{2^2 y^2}$

10. $\dfrac{3^5 x^7}{3^3 x^4}$

11. $\dfrac{4^5 x^3}{4x^5}$

12. $\dfrac{6z^5}{6z^5}$

13. $\dfrac{3^4(ab)^2}{3(ab)^3}$

14. $\dfrac{8^2 u^4 v^5}{8^3 u^4 v^2}$

In Exercises 15–32, simplify the expression. (Assume that no denominator is zero.) See Example 1.

15. $\dfrac{-3x^2}{x}$

16. $\dfrac{-4a^6}{-a^2}$

17. $\dfrac{4}{x^3}$

18. $\dfrac{-16}{v^2}$

19. $\dfrac{-12z^3}{-3z}$

20. $\dfrac{16y^5}{8y^3}$

21. $\dfrac{32b^4}{12b^3}$

22. $\dfrac{-7c^2}{8c^5}$

23. $\dfrac{-22y^2}{4y}$

24. $\dfrac{54x^2}{-24x^4}$

25. $\dfrac{-18s^4}{-12r^2 s}$

26. $\dfrac{-21v^3}{12u^2 v}$

27. $\dfrac{(-3z)^2}{18z^3}$

28. $\dfrac{4a^3}{(-8a)^2}$

29. $\dfrac{(2x^2 y)^3}{(4y^2)^2 x^4}$

30. $\dfrac{15(uv^4)^2}{(-3u^3)^3 v^5}$

31. $\dfrac{24u^2 v^4}{18u^2 v^6}$

32. $\dfrac{15x^3 y^0}{27x^3}$

In Exercises 33–72, perform the division and simplify. (Assume that no denominator is zero.) See Examples 2–7.

33. $\dfrac{3z + 3}{3}$

34. $\dfrac{7x + 7}{7}$

35. $\dfrac{4z - 12}{4}$

36. $\dfrac{8u - 24}{8}$

37. $\dfrac{9x - 5}{3}$

38. $\dfrac{3 - 10x}{5}$

39. $\dfrac{b^2 - 2b}{b}$

40. $\dfrac{3x + 2x^3}{x}$

41. $(5x^2 - 2x) \div x$

42. $(16a^2 + 5a) \div a$

43. $\dfrac{25z^3 + 10z^2}{-5z}$

44. $\dfrac{12c^4 - 36c}{-6c}$

45. $\dfrac{8z^3 + 3z^2 - 2z}{2z}$

46. $\dfrac{3x^3 + 5x^2 - 4x}{3x}$

47. $\dfrac{m^3 + 3m - 4}{m}$

48. $\dfrac{l^2 - 4l + 8}{l}$

49. $\dfrac{4x^2 - 12x}{4x^2}$

50. $\dfrac{14y^4 + 21y^3}{-7y^3}$

51. $\dfrac{6x^4 - 2x^3 + 3x^2 - x + 4}{2x^3}$

52. $\dfrac{9x^5 - 12x^3 + 3x^2 - 5x}{-3x^2}$

53. $\dfrac{x^2 - x - 2}{x + 1}$

54. $\dfrac{x^2 - 5x + 6}{x - 2}$

55. $\dfrac{x^2 + 9x + 20}{x + 4}$

56. $\dfrac{x^2 - 7x - 30}{x - 10}$

57. $\dfrac{3y^2 + 4y - 4}{3y - 2}$

58. $\dfrac{7t^2 - 10t - 8}{7t + 4}$

59. $(18t^2 - 21t - 4) \div (3t - 4)$

60. $(20t^2 + 32t - 16) \div (2t + 4)$

61. $(x^3 - 4x^2 + 9x - 7) \div (x - 2)$

62. $(2x^3 - 2x^2 + 3x + 9) \div (x + 1)$

63. $(7x + 3) \div (x + 2)$

64. $(8x - 5) \div (2x + 1)$

65. $\dfrac{x^3 - 8}{x - 2}$

66. $\dfrac{x^3 + 27}{x + 3}$

67. $\dfrac{x^2 + 9}{x + 3}$

68. $\dfrac{y^2 + 3}{y + 3}$

69. Divide $9x^2 - 1$ by $3x + 1$.

70. Divide $25y^2 - 4$ by $5y - 2$.

71. Divide $x^4 - 1$ by $x - 1$.

72. Divide x^4 by $x - 1$.

In Exercises 73–78, use synthetic division. See Example 8.

73. Divide $4x^2 + 3x + 1$ by $x + 1$.

74. Divide $7x^2 + 4x + 3$ by $x + 2$.

75. $\dfrac{x^3 - 7x + 6}{x - 2}$

76. $\dfrac{x^3 - 28x - 48}{x + 4}$

77. $\dfrac{3t^3 + 7t^2 + 3t - 2}{t + 2}$

78. $\dfrac{2x^3 + 5x^2 - 2x + 3}{x + 3}$

In Exercises 79–84, simplify the expression. (Assume that no denominator is zero.)

79. $\dfrac{4x^3}{x^2} - \dfrac{8x}{4}$

80. $\dfrac{25x^2}{10x} + \dfrac{3x}{2}$

81. $\dfrac{8u^2v}{2u} + \dfrac{(uv)^2}{uv}$

82. $\dfrac{9x^5y}{3x^4} - \dfrac{(x^2y)^3}{x^5y^2}$

83. $\dfrac{x^2 + 2x + 1}{x + 1} - (3x - 4)$

84. $\dfrac{x^2 - 3x + 2}{x - 1} + (4x - 3)$

In Exercises 85–88, determine whether the cancellation is valid.

85. $\dfrac{3 + 4}{3} = \dfrac{\cancel{3} + 4}{\cancel{3}} = 4$

86. $\dfrac{4 + 7}{4 + 11} = \dfrac{\cancel{4} + 7}{\cancel{4} + 11} = \dfrac{7}{11}$

87. $\dfrac{7 \cdot 12}{19 \cdot 7} = \dfrac{\cancel{7} \cdot 12}{19 \cdot \cancel{7}} = \dfrac{12}{19}$

88. $\dfrac{24}{43} = \dfrac{2\cancel{4}}{\cancel{4}3} = \dfrac{2}{3}$

Solving Problems

89. *Exploration* Consider the equation

$$(x + 3)(x^2 + 2x - 1) = x^3 + 5x^2 + 5x - 3.$$

(a) Use a graphing utility to verify that the equation is an identity by graphing both the left side and the right side of the equation. Are the graphs the same?

(b) Verify the identity equation by multiplying the polynomials on the left side of the equation.

(c) Verify the identity equation by performing the long division

$$\frac{x^3 + 5x^2 + 5x - 3}{x + 3}.$$

90. *Exploration* Consider the equation

$$2x^3 - 5x^2 + 2x - 5 = (2x - 5)(x^2 + 1).$$

(a) Using a graphing utility to verify that the equation is an identity by graphing both the left side and the right side of the equation. Are the graphs the same?

(b) Verify the identity equation by multiplying the polynomials on the right side of the equation.

(c) Verify the identity equation by performing the long division

$$\frac{2x^3 - 5x^2 + 2x - 5}{2x - 5}.$$

91. *Comparing Ages* You have two children: one is 18 years old and the other is 8 years old. In t years, their ages will be $t + 18$ and $t + 8$.

(a) Use long division to rewrite the ratio of your older child's age to your younger child's age.

(b) Complete the table.

t	0	10	20	30	40	50	60
$\dfrac{t + 18}{t + 8}$							

(c) What happens to the values of the ratio as t increases? Use the result of part (a) to explain your conclusion.

92. *Geometry* The area of a rectangle is $x^2 + 5x - 6$. Find the length of the rectangle if its width is $x - 1$.

93. *Geometry* The area of a rectangle is $x^2 + 2x - 15$. Find the width of the rectangle if its length is $x + 5$.

Explaining Concepts

94. Answer part (g) of Motivating the Chapter on page 273.

95. Match each part of the equation with its name:

$$\frac{x^2 + 2}{x - 3} = x + 3 + \frac{11}{x - 3}.$$

(a) Dividend   (b) Divisor

(c) Quotient   (d) Remainder

96. Explain how you can check the result of a division problem algebraically *and* graphically.

97. Give an example of using the subtraction property of exponents to divide a monomial by a monomial.

98. Describe the method of dividing a polynomial by a monomial.

99. What does it mean when the divisor divides *evenly* into the dividend?

100. If the degree of the dividend is 5 and the degree of the divisor is 3, what is the degree of the quotient? Generalize this result if the degree of the numerator is m and the degree of the denominator is n, where $m > n$.

Key Terms

polynomial, *p. 274*
constant term, *p. 274*
standard form of a
  polynomial, *p. 274*

degree of a polynomial,
  p. 274
leading coefficient, *p. 274*
monomial, *p. 275*

binomial, *p. 275*
trinomial, *p. 275*
FOIL Method, *p. 285*
negative exponents, *p. 297*

scientific notation, *p. 300*
synthetic division, *p. 310*

Key Concepts

5.1 Polynomial in *x*

Let $a_n, a_{n-1}, \ldots, a_2, a_1$ be real numbers and let n be a nonnegative integer. A polynomial in x is an expression of the form

$$a_n x^n + a_{n-1} x^{n-1} + \cdots + a_2 x^2 + a_1 x + a_0$$

where $a_n \neq 0$. The polynomial is of degree n, and the number a_n is the leading coefficient. The number a_0 is the constant term.

5.1 Adding polynomials

To add polynomials, you combine like terms (those having the same degree) by using the Distributive Property.

5.1 Subtracting polynomials

To subtract polynomials, you add the opposite by changing the sign of each term of the polynomial being subtracted and then adding the resulting like terms.

5.2 Multiplying polynomials

1. To multiply a polynomial by a monomial, apply the Distributive Property.
2. To multiply two binomials, use the FOIL Method. Find the product of the **F**irst terms, the product of the **O**uter terms, the product of the **I**nner terms, and the product of the **L**ast terms.
3. To multiply two polynomials, use the Distributive Property to multiply each term of one polynomial by each term of the other polynomial.

5.2 Special Products

Sum and Difference of Two Terms:
$$(a + b)(a - b) = a^2 - b^2$$

Square of a Binomial:
$$(a + b)^2 = a^2 + 2ab + b^2$$
$$(a - b)^2 = a^2 - 2ab + b^2$$

5.3 Rules of Exponents

1. $a^m a^n = a^{m+n}$
2. $\dfrac{a^m}{a^n} = a^{m-n}$
3. $(ab)^m = a^m b^m$
4. $\left(\dfrac{a}{b}\right)^m = \dfrac{a^m}{b^m}$
5. $(a^m)^n = a^{mn}$
6. $a^{-n} = \dfrac{1}{a^n}$
7. $a^0 = 1$

5.4 Dividing Polynomials

1. To divide a monomial by a monomial, use the properties of exponents.
2. To divide a polynomial by a monomial, divide each term of the polynomial by the monomial.
3. To divide a polynomial by a binomial, follow the long division pattern used for dividing whole numbers.
4. Use synthetic division to divide a polynomial by a binomial of the form $x - k$. [Remember that $x + k = x - (-k)$.]

REVIEW EXERCISES

Reviewing Skills

5.1 In Exercises 1–8, write the polynomial in standard form. Then determine its degree and leading coefficient.

1. $10x - 4 - 5x^3$ **2.** $2x^2 + 9$

3. $4x^3 - 2x + 5x^4 - 7x^2$ **4.** $6 - 3x + 6x^2 - x^3$

5. $7x^4 - 1$ **6.** $12x^2 + 2x - 8x^5 + 1$

7. -2 **8.** $\frac{1}{4}t^2$

In Exercises 9–12, give an example of a polynomial that satisfies the given conditions. (*Note:* There are many correct answers.)

9. A trinomial of degree 4

10. A monomial of degree 2

11. A binomial of degree 1

12. A trinomial of degree 5

In Exercises 13–32, perform the operations and simplify.

13. $(2x + 3) + (x - 4)$ **14.** $\left(\frac{1}{2}x + \frac{2}{3}\right) + \left(4x + \frac{1}{3}\right)$

15. $(t - 5) - (3t - 1)$ **16.** $(y + 3) - (y - 9)$

17. $(2x^3 - 4x^2 + 3) + (x^3 + 4x^2 - 2x)$

18. $(6x^2 - 9x - 5) - (4x^2 - 6x + 1)$

19. $3(2x^2 - 4) - (2x^2 - 5)$

20. $-4(6 - x + x^2) + (3x^2 + x)$

21. $(5x^4 - 7x^3 + x) - (4x^3 + 2x^2 - 4) +$
     $(4x + 8x^3 - 2x^4)$

22. $(6x^3 - 4x^2 + 3) + (x^2 - 2x) - (6x^3 - 4x + 6)$

23. $(4 - x^2) + 2(x - 2)$

24. $(z^2 + 6z) - 3(z^2 + 2z)$

25. $(-x^3 - 3x) - 2(2x^3 + x + 1)$

26. $(3u + 4u^2) + 5(u + 1) + 3u^2$

27. $4y^2 - [y - 3(y^2 + 2)]$

28. $(6a^3 + 3a) - 2[a + (a^3 - 2)]$

29. $-x^4 - 2x^2 + 3$ **30.** $5z^3 \quad\quad - 4z - 7$
     $\underline{+ (3x^4 - 5x^2 \quad\quad)}$ $\underline{+ (z^2 - 2z \quad\quad)}$

31. $5x^2 + 2x - 27$ **32.** $12y^4 - 15$
     $\underline{- (2x^2 - 2x - 13)}$ $\underline{- (18y^4 - \; 9)}$

5.2 In Exercises 33–46, multiply the polynomials using the Distributive Property or the FOIL Method.

33. $2x(x + 4)$ **34.** $3y(y + 1)$

35. $(x - 4)(x + 6)$ **36.** $(u + 5)(u - 2)$

37. $(x + 3)(2x - 4)$ **38.** $(y + 2)(4y - 3)$

39. $(4x - 3)(3x + 4)$ **40.** $(6 - 2x)(7x + 10)$

41. $(x^2 + 5x + 2)(2x + 3)$

42. $(s^3 + 4s - 3)(s - 3)$

43. $(2t - 1)(t^2 - 3t + 3)$

44. $(4x + 2)(x^2 + 6x - 5)$

45. $2u(u - 5) - (u + 1)(u - 5)$

46. $(3v - 2)(-2v) + 2v(3v - 2)$

In Exercises 47–60, use a special binomial product to expand the expression.

47. $(x + 3)^2$ **48.** $(x - 5)^2$

49. $(4x - 7)^2$ **50.** $(9 - 2x)^2$

51. $\left(\frac{1}{2}x - 4\right)^2$ **52.** $(4 + 3b)^2$

53. $(u - 6)(u + 6)$ **54.** $(r + 3)(r - 3)$

55. $(3t - 1)(3t + 1)$ **56.** $(3a + 8)(3a - 8)$

57. $(2x - y)^2$ **58.** $(3a + b)^2$

59. $(2x - 4y)(2x + 4y)$

60. $(4u + 5v)(4u - 5v)$

5.3 In Exercises 61–76, evaluate the expression.

61. 4^{-2} **62.** 3^{-4}

63. $6^{-4}6^2$ **64.** $(2^2 \cdot 3^2)^{-1}$

65. $\dfrac{1}{3^{-2}}$ **66.** $\dfrac{1}{5^{-3}}$

67. $\dfrac{4}{4^{-2}}$ **68.** $\dfrac{7}{3^{-3}}$

69. $\left(\dfrac{3}{5}\right)^{-3}$ **70.** $\left(\dfrac{2^{-2}}{3}\right)^2$

71. $\left(-\dfrac{2}{5}\right)^3\left(\dfrac{5}{2}\right)^2$ **72.** $\dfrac{2^2 \cdot 3^{-2}}{2^{-2} \cdot 3^{-1}}$

73. $(3 \times 10^3)^2$ **74.** $(4 \times 10^{-3})(5 \times 10^7)$

75. $\dfrac{1.85 \times 10^9}{5 \times 10^4}$ **76.** $\dfrac{1}{(4 \times 10^{-2})^3}$

In Exercises 77–100, use the rules of exponents to write the expression without negative exponents. (Assume that no variable is zero.)

77. y^{-4}

78. x^{-5}

79. $6t^{-2}$

80. $-4u^{-3}$

81. $\dfrac{1}{7x^{-6}}$

82. $\dfrac{1}{2y^{-4}}$

83. $2x^{-1}y^{-3}$

84. $5u^{-2}v^{-4}$

85. $t^{-4} \cdot t^2$

86. $x^5 \cdot x^{-8}$

87. $4x^{-6}y^2 \cdot x^6$

88. $-2u^5v^{-4} \cdot v^4$

89. $(-3a^2)^{-2}$

90. $(3u^{-3})(9u^6)$

91. $(x^2y^{-3})^2$

92. $5(x+3)^0$

93. $\dfrac{t^{-4}}{t^{-1}}$

94. $\dfrac{a^3 \cdot a^{-2}}{a^{-1}}$

95. $\dfrac{u^5 \cdot u^{-8}}{u^{-3}}$

96. $\dfrac{x^9 \cdot x^{-6}}{x^{-3}}$

97. $\left(\dfrac{y}{5}\right)^{-2}$

98. $\left(\dfrac{7}{x^4}\right)^{-1}$

99. $(2u^{-2}v)^3(4u^{-5}v^4)^{-1}$

100. $(3x^2y^4)^3(3x^2y^4)^{-3}$

 5.4 In Exercises 101–112, divide the polynomials.

101. $\dfrac{8x^3 - 12x}{4x^2}$

102. $\dfrac{18 - 3x + 9x^2}{12x^2}$

103. $(5x^2 + 15x) \div (5x)$

104. $(8u^3 + 4u^2) \div (2u)$

105. $\dfrac{x^2 - x - 6}{x - 3}$

106. $\dfrac{x^2 + x - 20}{x + 5}$

107. $\dfrac{24x^2 - x - 8}{3x - 2}$

108. $\dfrac{21x^2 + 4x + 7}{3x - 2}$

109. $\dfrac{2x^3 + 2x^2 - x + 2}{x - 1}$

110. $\dfrac{6x^4 - 4x^3 - 27x^2 + 18x}{3x - 2}$

111. $\dfrac{x^4 - 3x^2 + 2}{x^2 - 1}$

112. $\dfrac{3x^4}{x^2 - 1}$

Solving Problems

Geometry In Exercises 113–116, find a polynomial that represents the area of the shaded portion of the figure.

113.

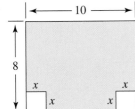

114.

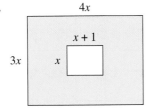

115.

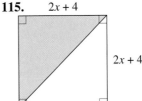

116.

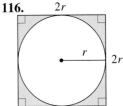

117. *Geometry* The length of a rectangular wall is x units, and its height is $x - 3$ units (see figure). Find (a) the perimeter and (b) the area of the wall.

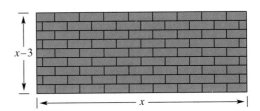

118. *Graphical Interpretation* The cost of producing x units of a product is

$$C = 15 + 26x.$$

The revenue for selling x units is

$$R = 40x - \frac{1}{2}x^2, \quad 0 \le x \le 20.$$

The profit is the difference between revenue and cost.

(a) Perform the subtraction required to find the polynomial representing profit.

(b) Use a graphing utility to graph the polynomial representing profit.

(c) Determine the profit when $x = 14$ units. Use the graph in part (b) to describe the profit when x is less than or greater than 14.

119. *Geometry* The area of a rectangle is

$$2x^2 - 5x - 12.$$

Find the length, if the width is $x - 4$.

120. *Geometry* The area of a rectangle is

$$3x^2 + 5x - 3.$$

Find the width, if the length is $x + 3$.

121. *Metal Expansion* When the temperature of a 150-foot iron steam pipe is increased by 100°C, the length of the pipe, as shown in the figure, increases by $100(150)(10 \times 10^{-6})$ feet. Write the amount of increase in decimal form.

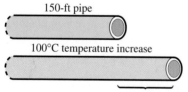

150-ft pipe

100°C temperature increase

Length increased by
$100(150)(10 \times 10^{-6})$ ft

122. *Comparing Models* The table gives population projections (in millions) for the United States for selected years from 2000 to 2050. It gives three series of projections: lowest P_L, middle P_M, and highest P_H. (Source: U.S. Bureau of the Census)

Year	2000	2010	2020	2030	2040	2050
P_L	271.2	281.5	288.8	291.1	287.7	282.5
P_M	274.6	297.7	322.7	347.0	370.0	393.9
P_H	278.1	314.6	357.7	405.1	458.4	518.9

In the following models for the data, $t = 0$ corresponds to the year 2000.

$$P_L = -0.022t^2 + 1.33t + 270.71$$

$$P_M = 2.386t + 274.857$$

$$P_H = 0.028t^2 + 3.40t + 278.18$$

(a) Use a graphing utility to plot the data and graph the models on the same screen.

(b) Find $(P_L + P_H)/2$. Use a graphing utility to graph this polynomial and state which graph from part (a) it most resembles. Does this seem reasonable? Explain.

(c) Find $P_H - P_L$ and sketch its graph. Explain why it is increasing.

123. *Special Product* What special product does the figure illustrate? Explain your reasoning.

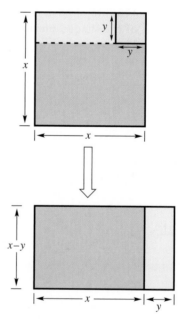

Chapter Test

Take this test as you would take a test in class. After you are done, check your work against the answers given in the back of the book.

1. Explain how to determine the degree and the leading coefficient of $-3x^4 - 5x^2 + 2x - 10$.

2. Give an example of a trinomial in one variable of degree 4.

In Exercises 3–14, perform the indicated operation and simplify. (Assume that no variable or denominator is zero.)

3. $(3z^2 - 3z + 7) + (8 - z^2)$

4. $(8u^3 + 3u^2 - 2u - 1) - (u^3 + 3u^2 - 2u)$

5. $6y - [2y - (3 + 4y - y^2)]$

6. $-5(x^2 - 1) + 3(4x + 7) - (x^2 + 26)$

7. $(5b + 3)(2b - 1)$

8. $4x\left(\dfrac{3x}{2}\right)^2$

9. $(z + 2)(2z^2 - 3z + 5)$

10. $(x - 5)^2$

11. $(2x - 3)(2x + 3)$

12. $\dfrac{15x + 25}{5}$

13. $\dfrac{x^3 - x - 6}{x - 2}$

14. $\dfrac{4x^3 + 10x^2 - 2x - 5}{2x + 1}$

In Exercises 15 and 16, simplify the expression. (Assume that no variable is zero.)

15. $\dfrac{-6a^2b}{-9ab}$

16. $(3x^{-2}y^3)^{-2}$

17. Evaluate the expression *without* using a calculator. Show your work.

   (a) 4^{-3} (b) $\dfrac{2^{-3}}{3^{-1}}$ (c) $(1.5 \times 10^5)^2$

18. Find the polynomial that represents the area of the shaded region (see figure).

19. Write an expression that represents the area of the triangle (see figure). Explain your reasoning.

20. The mean distance from earth to the moon is 3.84×10^8 meters. Write this distance in decimal form.

21. The standard atmospheric pressure is 101,300 newtons per square meter. Write this pressure in scientific notation.

22. The area of a rectangle is $x^2 - 2x - 3$. Find the width, if the length is $x + 1$.

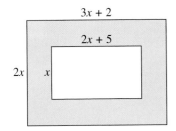

$3x + 2$

$2x + 5$

$2x$ x

Figure for 18

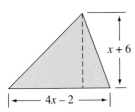

$x + 6$

$4x - 2$

Figure for 19

6 Factoring and Solving Equations

David Frazier/Tony Stone Images

In 1997, approximately 46 billion pounds of potatoes were produced in the United States. (Source: U.S. Department of Agriculture)

Dimensions of a Potato Storage Bin

A bin used to store potatoes has the form of a rectangular solid with a volume (in cubic feet) given by the polynomial $12x^3 + 64x^2 - 48x$.

See Section 6.3, Exercise 109

a. The height of the bin is $4x$ feet. Write an expression for the area of the base of the bin.

b. Factor the expression for the area of the base of the bin. Use the result to write expressions for the length and width of the bin.

See Section 6.5, Exercise 102

c. The area of the base is 32 square feet. What are the dimensions of the bin?

d. If you were told that the bin has a volume of 256 cubic feet, could you find the dimensions of the bin? Explain your reasoning.

e. A polynomial that represents the volume of the truck bin in cubic feet is $6x^3 + 32x^2 - 24x$. How many truck loads does it take to fill the bin? Explain your reasoning.

6.1   Factoring Polynomials with Common Factors

Objectives

1 Find the greatest common factor of two expressions.

2 Factor out the greatest common monomial factor from a polynomial.

3 Factor a polynomial by grouping.

---

1 Find the greatest common factor of two expressions.

Greatest Common Factor

In Chapter 5, you used the Distributive Property to multiply polynomials. In this chapter, you will study the *reverse* process, which is **factoring.**

$$\underset{\text{Factor}\quad\text{Factor}}{2x\,(7 - 3x)} \implies \underset{\text{Product}}{14x - 6x^2}\qquad \underset{\text{Product}}{14x - 6x^2} \implies \underset{\text{Factor}\quad\text{Factor}}{2x\,(7 - 3x)}$$

$$\textit{Multiplying Polynomials}\qquad\qquad \textit{Factoring Polynomials}$$

To factor an expression efficiently, you need to understand the concept of the *greatest common factor* of two (or more) integers or terms. In Section 1.3, you learned that the **greatest common factor** of two or more integers is the greatest integer that is a factor of each integer. For example, the greatest common factor of $12 = 2 \cdot 2 \cdot 3$ and $30 = 2 \cdot 3 \cdot 5$ is $2 \cdot 3 = 6$.

Example 1   Finding the Greatest Common Factor

Find the greatest common factor of $5x^2y^2$ and $30x^3y$.

Solution

From the factorizations

$$5x^2y^2 = 5 \cdot x \cdot x \cdot y \cdot y = (5x^2y)(y)$$

$$30x^3y = 2 \cdot 3 \cdot 5 \cdot x \cdot x \cdot x \cdot y = (5x^2y)(6x)$$

you can conclude that the greatest common factor is $5x^2y$.

Example 2   Finding the Greatest Common Factor

Find the greatest common factor of $8x^5$, $20x^3$, and $16x^4$.

Solution

From the factorizations

$$8x^5 = 2 \cdot 2 \cdot 2 \cdot x \cdot x \cdot x \cdot x \cdot x = (4x^3)(2x^2)$$

$$20x^3 = 2 \cdot 2 \cdot 5 \cdot x \cdot x \cdot x = (4x^3)(5)$$

$$16x^4 = 2 \cdot 2 \cdot 2 \cdot 2 \cdot x \cdot x \cdot x \cdot x = (4x^3)(4x)$$

you can conclude that the greatest common factor is $4x^3$.

2 Factor out the greatest common monomial factor from a polynomial.

Common Monomial Factors

Consider the three terms listed in Example 2 as terms of the polynomial

$$8x^5 + 16x^4 + 20x^3.$$

The greatest common factor, $4x^3$, of these terms is the **greatest common monomial factor** of the polynomial. When you use the Distributive Property to remove this factor from each term of the polynomial, you are **factoring out** the common monomial factor.

$$8x^5 + 16x^4 + 20x^3 = 4x^3(2x^2) + 4x^3(4x) + 4x^3(5) \qquad \text{Factor each term.}$$

$$= 4x^3(2x^2 + 4x + 5) \qquad \text{Factor out common monomial factor.}$$

Study Tip

To find the greatest common monomial factor of a polynomial, answer these two questions.

1. What is the greatest integer factor common to each coefficient of the polynomial?

2. What is the highest–powered variable factor common to each term of the polynomial?

| Example 3 | Greatest Common Monomial Factor |

Factor out the greatest common monomial factor from $6x - 18$.

Solution

The greatest common integer factor of $6x$ and 18 is 6. There is no common variable factor.

$$6x - 18 = 6(x) - 6(3) \qquad \text{Greatest common monomial factor is 6.}$$

$$= 6(x - 3) \qquad \text{Factor 6 out of each term.}$$

| Example 4 | Greatest Common Monomial Factor |

Factor out the greatest common monomial factor from

$$10y^3 - 25y^2.$$

Solution

For the terms $10y^3$ and $25y^2$, 5 is the greatest common integer factor and y^2 is the highest–powered common variable factor.

$$10y^3 - 25y^2 = (5y^2)(2y) - (5y^2)(5) \qquad \text{Greatest common factor is } 5y^2.$$

$$= 5y^2(2y - 5) \qquad \text{Factor } 5y^2 \text{ out of each term.}$$

| Example 5 | Greatest Common Monomial Factor |

Factor out the greatest common monomial factor from

$$45x^3 - 15x^2 - 15.$$

Solution

The greatest common integer factor of $45x^3$, $15x^2$, and 15 is 15. There is no common variable factor.

$$45x^3 - 15x^2 - 15 = 15(3x^3) - 15(x^2) - 15(1)$$

$$= 15(3x^3 - x^2 - 1)$$

| Example 6 | Common Monomial Factors |

Factor each polynomial.

a. $35y^3 - 7y^2 - 14y$

b. $6y^5 + 3y^3 - 2y^2$

c. $3xy^2 - 15x^2y + 12xy$

Solution

a. $35y^3 - 7y^2 - 14y = 7y(5y^2) - 7y(y) - 7y(2)$ $7y$ is common factor.

$\qquad\qquad\qquad\quad = 7y(5y^2 - y - 2)$ Factor $7y$ out of each term.

b. $6y^5 + 3y^3 - 2y^2 = y^2(6y^3) + y^2(3y) - y^2(2)$ y^2 is common factor.

$\qquad\qquad\qquad\quad = y^2(6y^3 + 3y - 2)$ Factor y^2 out of each term.

c. $3xy^2 - 15x^2y + 12xy = 3xy(y) - 3xy(5x) + 3xy(4)$ $3xy$ is common factor.

$\qquad\qquad\qquad\qquad\quad = 3xy(y - 5x + 4)$ Factor $3xy$ out of each term.

The greatest common monomial factor of the terms of a polynomial is usually considered to have a positive coefficient. However, sometimes it is convenient to factor a negative number out of a polynomial.

| Example 7 | A Negative Common Monomial Factor |

Factor the polynomial $-2x^2 + 8x - 12$ in two ways.

a. Factor out a common monomial factor of 2.

b. Factor out a common monomial factor of -2.

Solution

a. To factor out the common monomial factor of 2, write the following.

$$-2x^2 + 8x - 12 = 2(-x^2) + 2(4x) - 2(6)$$

$$= 2(-x^2 + 4x - 6)$$

b. To factor -2 out of the polynomial, write the following.

$$-2x^2 + 8x - 12 = -2(x^2) + (-2)(-4x) + (-2)(6)$$

$$= -2(x^2 - 4x + 6)$$

Check this result by multiplying $(x^2 - 4x + 6)$ by -2. When you do, you will obtain the original polynomial.

With experience, you should be able to omit writing the first step shown in Examples 6 and 7. For instance, to factor -2 out of $-2x^2 + 8x - 12$, you could simply write

$$-2x^2 + 8x - 12 = -2(x^2 - 4x + 6).$$

3 Factor a polynomial by grouping.

Factoring by Grouping

There are occasions when the common factor of a polynomial is not simply a monomial. For instance, the polynomial

$$x^2(x - 2) + 3(x - 2)$$

has the common *binomial* factor $(x - 2)$. Factoring out this common factor produces

$$x^2(x - 2) + 3(x - 2) = (x - 2)(x^2 + 3).$$

Example 8   Common Binomial Factors

Factor each polynomial.

a. $5x^2(7x - 1) - 3(7x - 1)$ **b.** $2x(3x - 4) + (3x - 4)$

c. $3y^2(y - 3) + 4(3 - y)$

Solution

a. Each of the terms of this polynomial has a binomial factor of $(7x - 1)$.

$$5x^2(7x - 1) - 3(7x - 1) = (7x - 1)(5x^2 - 3)$$

Students may find it helpful to write $2x(3x - 4) + (3x - 4)$ as $2x(3x - 4) + 1(3x - 4)$ before factoring it as $(3x - 4)(2x + 1)$.

b. Each of the terms of this polynomial has a binomial factor of $(3x - 4)$.

$$2x(3x - 4) + (3x - 4) = (3x - 4)(2x + 1)$$

Be sure you see that when $(3x - 4)$ is factored out of itself, you are left with the factor 1. This follows from the fact that $(3x - 4)(1) = (3x - 4)$.

c. $3y^2(y - 3) + 4(3 - y) = 3y^2(y - 3) - 4(y - 3)$ Write $4(3 - y)$ as $-4(y - 3)$.

$$= (y - 3)(3y^2 - 4)$$ Common factor is $(y - 3)$.

In Example 8, the polynomials were already grouped so that it was easy to determine the common binomial factors. In practice, you will have to do the grouping as well as the factoring. To see how this works, consider the expression

$$x^3 + 2x^2 + 3x + 6$$

and try to *factor* it. Note first that there is no common monomial factor to take out of all four terms. But suppose you *group* the first two terms together and the last two terms together.

$$x^3 + 2x^2 + 3x + 6 = (x^3 + 2x^2) + (3x + 6)$$ Group terms.

$$= x^2(x + 2) + 3(x + 2)$$ Distributive Property

$$= (x + 2)(x^2 + 3)$$ Distributive Property

This process is called **factoring by grouping.** Try grouping the polynomial as

$$(x^3 + 3x) + (2x^2 + 6).$$

Show how this grouping is used to factor the polynomial.

Example 9	Factoring by Grouping

Factor $x^3 - 2x^2 + x - 2$.

Solution

$$
\begin{aligned}
x^3 - 2x^2 + x - 2 &= (x^3 - 2x^2) + (x - 2) && \text{Group terms.} \\
&= x^2(x - 2) + (x - 2) && \text{Distributive Property} \\
&= (x - 2)(x^2 + 1) && \text{Distributive Property}
\end{aligned}
$$

Example 10	Factoring by Grouping

Factor $3x^2 + 12x - 5x - 20$.

Solution

$$
\begin{aligned}
3x^2 + 12x - 5x - 20 &= (3x^2 + 12x) - (5x + 20) && \text{Group terms.} \\
&= 3x(x + 4) - 5(x + 4) && \text{Distributive Property} \\
&= (x + 4)(3x - 5) && \text{Distributive Property}
\end{aligned}
$$

You can always check to see that you have factored an expression correctly by multiplying and comparing the result with the original expression. Try using multiplication to check the results of Examples 9 and 10.

Example 11	Geometry: Area of a Rectangle

The area of the rectangle in Figure 6.1 can be represented by the polynomial $2x^3 + 4x - x^2 - 2$. Factor the polynomial to find the dimensions of the rectangle.

Solution

$$
\begin{aligned}
2x^3 + 4x - x^2 - 2 &= (2x^3 + 4x) - (x^2 + 2) && \text{Group terms.} \\
&= 2x(x^2 + 2) - (x^2 + 2) && \text{Distributive Property} \\
&= (x^2 + 2)(2x - 1) && \text{Distributive Property}
\end{aligned}
$$

The dimensions of the rectangle are $(x^2 + 2)$ by $(2x - 1)$.

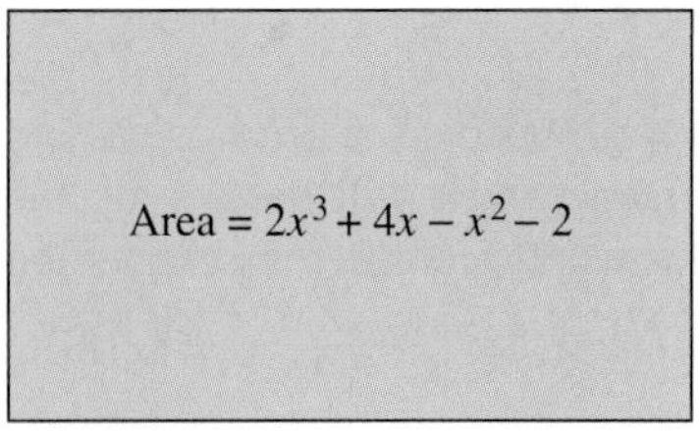

Study Tip

Notice in Example 11 that the polynomial is not written in standard form. You could have rewritten the polynomial before factoring and still obtained the same result.

$$
\begin{aligned}
2x^3 &+ 4x - x^2 - 2 \\
&= 2x^3 - x^2 + 4x - 2 \\
&= (2x^3 - x^2) + (4x - 2) \\
&= x^2(2x - 1) + 2(2x - 1) \\
&= (2x - 1)(x^2 + 2)
\end{aligned}
$$

Area $= 2x^3 + 4x - x^2 - 2$

Figure 6.1

Discussing the Concept	Factoring by Grouping

Suppose you are tutoring someone in algebra and you want to create several polynomials for your student to factor. Develop a procedure for creating polynomials that contain a common factor or that can be factored by the grouping method of this section. Create a list of practice problems and have another member of your class factor them.

6.1   Exercises

Integrated Review   *Concepts, Skills, and Problem Solving*

Keep mathematically in shape by doing these exercises *before* the problems of this section.

Properties and Definitions

1. In your own words, define a function of x.

2. State the definitions of the domain and range of a function of x.

3. Bearing in mind the Vertical Line Test, sketch a graph for which y is not a function of x.

4. Bearing in mind the Vertical Line Test, sketch a graph for which y is a function of x.

Evaluating Functions

In Exercises 5–8, evaluate the function.

5. $f(x) = \frac{1}{2}x + 1$ (a) $f(0)$ (b) $f(4)$
                                   (c) $f(-3)$ (d) $f\left(-\frac{3}{2}\right)$

6. $g(t) = t(t - 4)$ (a) $g(0)$ (b) $g(4)$
                             (c) $g(-2)$ (d) $g\left(-\frac{5}{2}\right)$

7. $F(x) = \sqrt{2x + 1}$ (a) $F(0)$ (b) $F(4)$
                                  (c) $F\left(-\frac{1}{2}\right)$ (d) $F(10)$

8. $h(s) = |s - 3|$ (a) $h(0)$ (b) $h(4)$
                           (c) $h(2)$ (d) $h(-3)$

Problem Solving

9. Determine the commission rate for an employee who earned $1620 in commissions on sales of $54,000.

10. One person can complete a typing project in 10 hours, and another can complete the same project in 6 hours. Working together, how long will they take to complete the project?

Graphs

In Exercises 11–14, graph the function and show the coordinates of at least three solution points, including any intercepts.

11. $h(x) = 8 - 4x$ **12.** $g(x) = 3x - 6$

13. $f(x) = -\frac{1}{2}x^2$ **14.** $H(x) = |x + 2|$

Developing Skills

In Exercises 1–16, find the greatest common factor. See Examples 1 and 2.

1. 24, 90

2. 20, 45

3. 18, 150, 100

4. 60, 80, 90

5. $z^2, -z^6$

6. t^4, t^7

7. $2x^2, 12x$

8. $36x^4, 18x^3$

9. u^2v, u^3v^2

10. $r^6s^4, -rs$

11. $9yz^2, -12y^2z^3$

12. $-15x^6y^3, 45xy^3$

13. $14x^2, 1, 7x^4$

14. $5y^4, 10x^2y^2, 15xy$

15. $28a^4b^2, 14a^3b^3, 42a^2b^5$

16. $16x^2y, 12xy^2, 36x^2y^2$

In Exercises 17–60, factor the polynomial. (*Note:* Some of the polynomials have no common factor.) See Examples 3–6.

17. $3x + 3$

18. $5y + 5$

19. $6z - 6$

20. $3x - 3$

21. $8t - 16$

22. $3u + 12$

23. $-25x - 10$

24. $-14y - 7$

25. $24y^2 - 18$

26. $7z^3 + 21$

27. $x^2 + x$

28. $-s^3 - s$

29. $25u^2 - 14u$

30. $36t^4 + 24t^2$

31. $2x^4 + 6x^3$

32. $9z^6 + 27z^4$

33. $7s^2 + 9t^2$

34. $12x^2 - 5y^3$

35. $12x^2 - 2x$

36. $12u + 9u^2$

37. $-10r^3 - 35r$

38. $-144a^2 + 24a$

39. $16a^3b^3 + 24a^4b^3$

40. $6x^4y + 12x^2y$

41. $10ab + 10a^2b$

42. $21x^2z - 35xz$

43. $12x^2 + 16x - 8$

44. $9 - 3y - 15y^2$

45. $100 + 75z - 50z^2$

46. $42t^3 - 21t^2 + 7$

47. $9x^4 + 6x^3 + 18x^2$

48. $32a^5 - 2a^3 + 6a$

49. $5u^2 + 5u^2 + 5u$

50. $11y^3 - 22y^2 + 11y^2$

51. $x(x - 3) + 5(x - 3)$

52. $x(x + 6) + 3(x + 6)$

53. $t(s + 10) - 8(s + 10)$

54. $y(q - 5) - 10(q - 5)$

55. $a^2(b + 2) - b(b + 2)$

56. $x^3(y + 4) + y(y + 4)$

57. $z^3(z + 5) + z^2(z + 5)$

58. $x^3(x - 2) + x(x - 2)$

59. $(a + b)(a - b) + a(a + b)$

60. $(x + y)(x - y) - x(x - y)$

In Exercises 61–68, factor a negative real number from the polynomial and write the polynomial factor with a positive leading coefficient. See Example 7.

61. $5 - 10x$

62. $3 - x$

63. $3000 - 3x$

64. $9 - 2x^2$

65. $4 + 2x - x^2$

66. $18 - 12x - 6x^2$

67. $4 + 12x - 2x^2$

68. $x - 2x^2 - x^4$

In Exercises 69–84, factor the polynomial by grouping. See Examples 8–10.

69. $x^2 + 10x + x + 10$

70. $x^2 - 5x + x - 5$

71. $a^2 - 4a + a - 4$

72. $x^2 + 25x + x + 25$

73. $ky^2 - 4ky + 2y - 8$

74. $ay^2 + 3ay + 3y + 9$

75. $t^3 - 3t^2 + 2t - 6$

76. $3s^3 + 6s^2 + 2s + 4$

77. $x^3 + 2x^2 + x + 2$

78. $x^3 - 5x^2 + x - 5$

79. $6z^3 + 3z^2 - 2z - 1$

80. $4u^3 - 2u^2 - 6u + 3$

81. $x^3 - 3x - x^2 + 3$

82. $x^3 + 7x - 3x^2 - 21$

83. $4x^2 - x^3 - 8 + 2x$

84. $5x^2 + 10x^3 + 4 + 8x$

In Exercises 85–90, complete the factorization.

85. $\frac{1}{4}x + \frac{3}{4} = \frac{1}{4}(\quad)$

86. $\frac{5}{6}x - \frac{1}{6} = \frac{1}{6}(\quad)$

87. $2y - \frac{1}{5} = \frac{1}{5}(\quad)$

88. $3z + \frac{3}{4} = \frac{1}{4}(\quad)$

89. $\frac{7}{8}x + \frac{5}{16}y = \frac{1}{16}(\quad)$

90. $\frac{5}{12}u - \frac{5}{8}v = \frac{1}{24}(\quad)$

In Exercises 91–94, use a graphing utility to graph both functions on the same screen. Use the graphs to verify the factorization.

91. $y_1 = 9 - 3x$
$y_2 = -3(x - 3)$

92. $y_1 = x^2 - 4x$
$y_2 = x(x - 4)$

93. $y_1 = 6x - x^2$
$y_2 = x(6 - x)$

94. $y_1 = x(x + 2) - 3(x + 2)$
$y_2 = (x + 2)(x - 3)$

Solving Problems

In Exercises 95 and 96, factor the polynomial to find the length of the rectangle.

95. Area $= 2x^2 + 2x$

96. Area $= x^2 + 2x + 10x + 20$

Geometry   In Exercises 97–100, write an expression for the area of the shaded region and factor the expression if possible.

97.

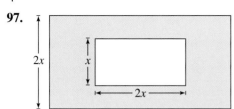

98.

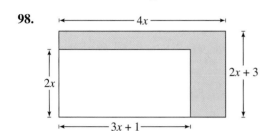

99.

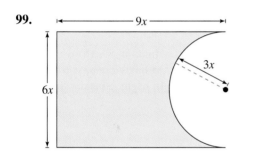

100.

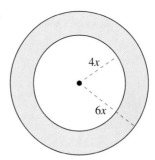

101. *Geometry*   The surface area of a right circular cylinder is

$$S = 2\pi r^2 + 2\pi rh.$$

Factor the expression for the surface area.

102. *Simple Interest*   The amount after t years when a principal of P dollars is invested at $r\%$ simple interest is given by $P + Prt$. Factor the expression for simple interest.

103. *Chemical Reaction*   The rate of change in a chemical reaction is $kQx - kx^2$, where Q is the original amount, x is the new amount, and k is a constant of proportionality. Factor the expression.

104. *Unit Price*   The revenue R for selling x units of a product at a price of p dollars per unit is given by $R = xp$. For a particular commodity, the revenue is

$$900x - 0.1x^2.$$

Factor the revenue model and determine an expression that represents the price p in terms of x.

Explaining Concepts

105. Give an example of a polynomial that is written in factored form.

106. Give an example of a trinomial whose greatest common monomial factor is $3x$.

107. In your own words, describe a method for finding the greatest common factor of a polynomial.

108. How do you check your result when factoring a polynomial?

109. Explain how the word *factor* can be used as a noun and as a verb.

110. Give several examples of the use of the Distributive Property in factoring.

111. Give an example of a polynomial with four terms that can be factored by grouping. Explain the steps you used to construct the polynomial.

6.2   Factoring Trinomials

Objectives

1 Factor a trinomial of the form $x^2 + bx + c$.

2 Factor a trinomial in two variables.

3 Factor a trinomial completely.

---

1 Factor a trinomial of the form $x^2 + bx + c$.

Factoring Trinomials of the Form $x^2 + bx + c$

From Section 5.2, you know that the product of two binomials is often a trinomial. Here are some examples.

Factored Form   F   O   I   L   *Trinomial Form*

$$(x - 1)(x + 5) = x^2 + 5x - x - 5 = x^2 + 4x - 5$$
$$(x - 3)(x - 3) = x^2 - 3x - 3x + 9 = x^2 - 6x + 9$$
$$(x + 5)(x + 1) = x^2 + x + 5x + 5 = x^2 + 6x + 5$$
$$(x - 2)(x - 4) = x^2 - 4x - 2x + 8 = x^2 - 6x + 8$$

Try covering the factored forms in the left-hand column above. Can you determine the factored forms from the trinomial forms? In this section, you will learn how to factor trinomials of the form $x^2 + bx + c$. To begin, consider the following factorization.

$$(x + m)(x + n) = x^2 + nx + mx + mn$$
$$= x^2 + (n + m)x + mn$$

Sum of terms   Product of terms

$$= x^2 + \quad b \quad x + \quad c$$

So, to *factor* a trinomial $x^2 + bx + c$ into a product of two binomials, you must find two numbers m and n whose product is c and whose sum is b.

There are many different techniques that people use to factor trinomials. The most common is to use *Guess, Check, and Revise* with mental math.

Example 1   Factoring a Trinomial

Factor $x^2 + 5x + 6$.

Solution

You need to find two numbers whose product is 6 and whose sum is 5. Using mental math, you can determine that the numbers are 2 and 3.

The product of 2 and 3 is 6.

$$x^2 + 5x + 6 = (x + 2)(x + 3)$$

The sum of 2 and 3 is 5.

Study Tip

With *any* factoring problem, remember that you can check your result by multiplying. For instance, in Example 1, you can check the result by multiplying $(x + 2)$ by $(x + 3)$ to see that you obtain $x^2 + 5x + 6$.

| Example 2 | Factoring Trinomials |

Factor each trinomial.

a. $x^2 + 5x - 6$ **b.** $x^2 - x - 6$ **c.** $x^2 - 5x + 6$ **d.** $14 + 5x - x^2$

Solution

a. You need to find two numbers whose product is -6 and whose sum is 5.

The product of -1 and 6 is -6.

$$x^2 + 5x - 6 = (x - 1)(x + 6)$$

The sum of -1 and 6 is 5.

b. You need to find two numbers whose product is -6 and whose sum is -1.

The product of -3 and 2 is -6.

$$x^2 - x - 6 = (x - 3)(x + 2)$$

The sum of -3 and 2 is -1.

c. You need to find two numbers whose product is 6 and whose sum is -5.

The product of -2 and -3 is 6.

$$x^2 - 5x + 6 = (x - 2)(x - 3)$$

The sum of -2 and -3 is -5.

d. It is helpful to first factor out -1. So,

$$14 + 5x - x^2 = -1(x^2 - 5x - 14).$$

Now you need two numbers -7 and 2 whose product is -14 and whose sum is -5. So,

$$14 + 5x - x^2 = -(x^2 - 5x - 14) = -(x - 7)(x + 2).$$

If you have trouble factoring a trinomial, it helps to make a list of all the distinct pairs of factors and then check each sum. For instance, consider the trinomial

$$x^2 - 5x - 24.$$

For this trinomial, you need to find two numbers whose product is -24 and whose sum is -5.

Factors of -24	Sum	
$1, -24$	-23	
$-1, 24$	23	
$2, -12$	-10	
$-2, 12$	10	
$3, -8$	-5	Correct choice
$-3, 8$	5	
$4, -6$	-2	
$-4, 6$	2	

So, $x^2 - 5x - 24 = (x + 3)(x - 8)$.

Study Tip

Use a list to help you find the two numbers with the required product and sum. For Example 2(b):

Factors of -6	Sum
$1, -6$	-5
$-1, 6$	5
$2, -3$	-1
$-2, 3$	1

Because -1 is the required sum, the correct factorization is

$$x^2 - x - 6 = (x + 2)(x - 3).$$

With experience, you will be able to narrow the list of possible factors *mentally* to only two or three possibilities whose sums can then be tested to determine the correct factorization. Here are some suggestions for narrowing the list.

> ▶ **Guidelines for Factoring $x^2 + bx + c$**
>
> To factor $x^2 + bx + c$, you need to find two numbers m and n whose product is c and whose sum is b.
>
> $$x^2 + bx + c = (x + m)(x + n)$$
>
> 1. If c is *positive*, then m and n have like signs that match the sign of b.
> 2. If c is *negative*, then m and n have unlike signs.
> 3. If $|b|$ is small relative to $|c|$, first try those factors of c that are closest to each other in absolute value.

Example 3 Factoring Trinomials

Factor the following trinomials.

a. $x^2 - 2x - 15$

b. $x^2 + 20x + 36$

c. $x^2 + 7x - 30$

Solution

a. You need to find two numbers whose product is -15 and whose sum is -2.

The product of -5 and 3 is -15.

$$x^2 - 2x - 15 = (x - 5)(x + 3)$$

The sum of -5 and 3 is -2.

b. You need to find two numbers whose product is 36 and whose sum is 20.

The product of 2 and 18 is 36.

$$x^2 + 20x + 36 = (x + 2)(x + 18)$$

The sum of 2 and 18 is 20.

c. You need to find two numbers whose product is -30 and whose sum is 7.

The product of -3 and 10 is -30.

$$x^2 + 7x - 30 = (x - 3)(x + 10)$$

The sum of -3 and 10 is 7.

Study Tip

Notice that factors may be written in any order. For example,
$(x - 5)(x + 3) =$
$(x + 3)(x - 5)$ and
$(x + 2)(x + 18) =$
$(x + 18)(x + 2)$ because of the Commutative Property of Multiplication.

Not all trinomials are factorable using integer factors. For instance,

$$x^2 - 2x - 6$$

is not factorable using integer factors. (List the factors and test them.) Such nonfactorable trinomials are called **prime polynomials.**

Factoring Trinomials in Two Variables

2 Factor a trinomial in two variables.

The first three examples each involved trinomials of the form

$$x^2 + bx + c. \qquad \text{Trinomial in one variable}$$

The next two examples show how to factor trinomials of the form

$$x^2 + bxy + cy^2. \qquad \text{Trinomial in two variables}$$

Note that this trinomial has two variables, x and y. However, from the factorization

$$x^2 + bxy + cy^2 = (x + my)(x + ny)$$
$$= x^2 + (m + n)xy + mny^2$$

you can see that you still need to find two factors of c whose sum is b.

Example 4   Factoring a Trinomial in Two Variables

Factor the trinomial $x^2 - xy - 12y^2$.

Solution

You need to find two numbers whose product is -12 and whose sum is -1.

The product of -4 and 3 is -12.

$$x^2 - xy - 12y^2 = (x - 4y)(x + 3y)$$

The sum of -4 and 3 is -1.

Check this result by multiplying $(x - 4y)$ by $(x + 3y)$.

Example 5   Factoring a Trinomial in Two Variables

Factor the following trinomials.

a. $y^2 - 6xy + 8x^2$ **b.** $x^2 + 11xy + 10y^2$

Solution

a. You need to find two numbers whose product is 8 and whose sum is -6.

The product of -2 and -4 is 8.

$$y^2 - 6xy + 8x^2 = (y - 2x)(y - 4x)$$

The sum of -2 and -4 is -6.

Check this result by multiplying $(y - 2x)$ by $(y - 4x)$.

b. You need to find two numbers whose product is 10 and whose sum is 11.

The product of 1 and 10 is 10.

$$x^2 + 11xy + 10y^2 = (x + y)(x + 10y)$$

The sum of 1 and 10 is 11.

Check this result by multiplying $(x + y)$ by $(x + 10y)$.

Encourage students to play detective and put together the clues leading to the correct factors. These problems, like other puzzle-solving challenges, can be intriguing.

3 Factor a trinomial completely.

Factoring Completely

Some trinomials have a common monomial factor. In such cases you should first factor out the common monomial factor. Then you can try to factor the resulting trinomial by the methods of this section. This "multiple-stage factoring process" is called **factoring completely.** For instance, the trinomial

$$2x^2 - 4x - 6 = 2(x^2 - 2x - 3)$$ Factor out common monomial factor 2.

$$= 2(x - 3)(x + 1)$$ Factor trinomial.

is factored completely.

Example 6   Factoring Completely

Factor each trinomial completely.

a. $2x^2 - 12x + 10$

b. $3x^3 - 27x^2 + 54x$

c. $4y^4 + 32y^3 + 28y^2$

Remind students to include the common monomial factor in the final result.

Solution

a. $2x^2 - 12x + 10 = 2(x^2 - 6x + 5)$ Factor out common monomial factor 2.

$$= 2(x - 5)(x - 1)$$ Factor trinomial.

b. $3x^3 - 27x^2 + 54x = 3x(x^2 - 9x + 18)$ Factor out common monomial factor 3x.

$$= 3x(x - 3)(x - 6)$$ Factor trinomial.

c. $4y^4 + 32y^3 + 28y^2 = 4y^2(y^2 + 8y + 7)$ Factor out common monomial factor $4y^2$.

$$= 4y^2(y + 1)(y + 7)$$ Factor trinomial.

Check these results by multiplying the factors to see that you obtain the original trinomials.

Discussing the Concept   Factoring Polynomials

Discuss this question in your class. "Is it possible to factor a polynomial such as

$$x^3 + 5x^2 - 3x - 15$$

by the method used for trinomials in this section?" Try this method on

$$x^3 + 5x^2 - 3x - 15$$

and

$$x^3 - 7x^2 + 2x - 14,$$

and then factor these polynomials by grouping. Which method do you prefer? Explain your preference.

6.2   Exercises

Integrated Review   *Concepts, Skills, and Problem Solving*

Keep mathematically in shape by doing these exercises *before* the problems of this section.

Properties and Definitions

1. Explain why a function of x cannot have two y-intercepts.

2. What is the leading coefficient of the polynomial $3x - 7x^2 + 4x^3 - 4$?

Rewriting Algebraic Expressions

In Exercises 3–8, find the product.

3. $y(y + 2)$

4. $-a^2(a - 1)$

5. $(x - 2)(x - 5)$

6. $(v - 4)(v + 7)$

7. $(2x + 5)(2x - 5)$

8. $x^2(x + 1) - 5(x^2 - 2)$

Problem Solving

9. A company showed a loss of \$2,500,000 during the first 6 months of a given year. If the company ended the year with an overall profit of \$1,475,000, what was the profit during the second 6 months of the year?

10. Computer printer ribbons cost \$11.95 per ribbon. If there are 12 ribbons per box and five boxes were ordered, determine the total cost of the order.

11. The revenue from selling x units of a product is $R = 75x$. The cost of producing x units is

$C = 62.5x + 570.$

In order to obtain a profit, the revenue must be greater than the cost. For what values of x will this product produce a profit?

12. The minimum and maximum speeds on an interstate highway are 40 miles per hour and 65 miles per hour. You travel nonstop for $3\frac{1}{2}$ hours on this highway. Assuming that you stay within the speed limits, give an interval for the distance you travel.

Developing Skills

In Exercises 1–8, find the missing factor. Then check your answer by multiplying the factors.

1. $x^2 + 4x + 3 = (x + 3)(\quad)$

2. $x^2 + 5x + 6 = (x + 3)(\quad)$

3. $a^2 + a - 6 = (a + 3)(\quad)$

4. $c^2 + 2c - 3 = (c + 3)(\quad)$

5. $y^2 - 2y - 15 = (y + 3)(\quad)$

6. $y^2 - 4y - 21 = (y + 3)(\quad)$

7. $z^2 - 5z + 6 = (z - 3)(\quad)$

8. $z^2 - 4z + 3 = (z - 3)(\quad)$

In Exercises 9–12, find all possible products of the form $(x + m)(x + n)$ where $m \cdot n$ is the specified product. (Assume that m and n are integers.)

9. $m \cdot n = 11$

10. $m \cdot n = 10$

11. $m \cdot n = 12$

12. $m \cdot n = 18$

In Exercises 13–42, factor the trinomial. (*Note:* Some of the trinomials may be prime.) See Examples 1–5.

13. $x^2 + 6x + 8$

14. $x^2 + 13x + 12$

15. $x^2 - 13x + 40$

16. $x^2 - 9x + 14$

17. $z^2 - 7z + 12$

18. $x^2 + 10x + 24$

19. $y^2 + 5y + 11$

20. $s^2 - 7s - 25$

21. $x^2 - x - 6$

22. $x^2 + x - 6$

23. $x^2 + 2x - 15$

24. $b^2 - 2b - 15$

25. $y^2 - 6y + 10$

26. $c^2 - 6c + 10$

27. $u^2 - 22u - 48$

28. $x^2 - x - 36$

29. $x^2 + 19x + 60$

30. $x^2 + 3x - 70$

31. $x^2 - 17x + 72$

32. $x^2 + 21x + 108$

33. $x^2 - 8x - 240$ **34.** $r^2 - 30r + 216$

35. $x^2 + xy - 2y^2$ **36.** $x^2 - 5xy + 6y^2$

37. $x^2 + 8xy + 15y^2$ **38.** $u^2 - 4uv - 5v^2$

39. $x^2 - 7xz - 18z^2$ **40.** $x^2 + 15xy + 50y^2$

41. $a^2 + 2ab - 15b^2$ **42.** $y^2 + 4yz - 60z^2$

In Exercises 43–60, factor the trinomial completely. (*Note:* Some of the trinomials may be prime.) See Example 6.

43. $3x^2 + 21x + 30$ **44.** $4x^2 - 32x + 60$

45. $4y^2 - 8y - 12$ **46.** $5x^2 - 20x - 25$

47. $3z^2 + 5z + 6$ **48.** $7x^2 + 5x + 10$

49. $9x^2 + 18x - 18$ **50.** $6x^2 - 24x - 6$

51. $x^3 - 13x^2 + 30x$ **52.** $x^3 + x^2 - 2x$

53. $x^4 - 5x^3 + 6x^2$ **54.** $x^4 + 3x^3 - 10x^2$

55. $-3y^2x - 9yx + 54x$ **56.** $-5x^2z + 15xz + 50z$

57. $x^3 + 5x^2y + 6xy^2$ **58.** $x^2y - 6xy^2 + y^3$

59. $2x^3y + 4x^2y^2 - 6xy^3$

60. $x^4y^2 + 3x^3y^3 + 2x^2y^4$

In Exercises 61–66, find all integer values of b such that the trinomial can be factored.

61. $x^2 + bx + 15$ **62.** $x^2 + bx + 10$

63. $x^2 + bx - 21$ **64.** $x^2 + bx - 18$

65. $x^2 + bx + 36$ **66.** $x^2 + bx - 48$

In Exercises 67–72, find two integer values of c such that the trinomial can be factored. (There are many correct answers.)

67. $x^2 + 3x + c$ **68.** $x^2 + 5x + c$

69. $x^2 - 6x + c$ **70.** $x^2 - 15x + c$

71. $x^2 - 9x + c$ **72.** $x^2 + 12x + c$

Graphical Verification In Exercises 73–76, use a graphing utility to graph the two functions in the same viewing rectangle. What can you conclude?

73. $y_1 = x^2 - x - 6$

$y_2 = (x + 2)(x - 3)$

74. $y_1 = x^2 - 10x + 16$

$y_2 = (x - 2)(x - 8)$

75. $y_1 = x^3 + x^2 - 20x$

$y_2 = x(x - 4)(x + 5)$

76. $y_1 = 2x - x^2 - x^3$

$y_2 = x(1 - x)(2 + x)$

Geometric Model of Factoring In Exercises 77–80, factor the trinomial and draw a geometric model of the result. [The sample shows a geometric model for factoring $x^2 + 3x + 2 = (x + 1)(x + 2)$.]

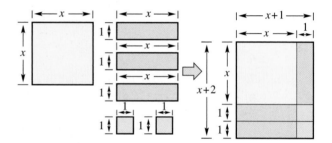

77. $x^2 + 4x + 3$ **78.** $x^2 + 5x + 4$

79. $x^2 + 5x + 6$ **80.** $x^2 + 6x + 5$

Solving Problems

81. *Exploration* An open box is to be made from a 4-foot-by-6-foot sheet of metal by cutting equal squares from the corners and turning up the sides (see figure). The volume of the box can be modeled by

$V = 4x^3 - 20x^2 + 24x, \quad 0 < x < 2.$

(a) Factor the trinomial modeling the volume of the box. Use the factored form to explain how the model was found.

(b) Use a graphing utility to graph the trinomial over the specified interval. Use the graph to approximate the size of the squares to be cut from the corners so that the volume of the box is greatest.

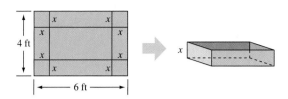

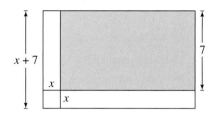

Figure for 81

82. *Geometry*   The area of the rectangle in the figure is $x^2 + 30x + 200$. What is the area of the shaded region?

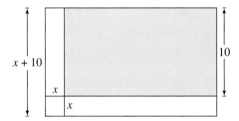

83. *Geometry*   The area of the rectangle in the figure is $x^2 + 17x + 70$. What is the area of the shaded region?

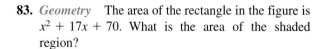

Explaining Concepts

84. State which of the following are factorizations of $2x^2 + 6x - 20$. For each correct factorization, state whether or not it is complete.

   (a) $(2x - 4)(x + 5)$ (b) $(2x - 4)(2x + 10)$

   (c) $(x - 2)(x + 5)$ (d) $2(x - 2)(x + 5)$

85. In factoring $x^2 - 4x + 3$, why is it unnecessary to test $(x - 1)(x + 3)$ and $(x + 1)(x - 3)$?

86. In your own words, explain how to factor a trinomial of the form $x^2 + bx + c$. Give examples with your explanation.

87. What is meant by a prime trinomial?

88. Can you completely factor a trinomial into two different sets of prime factors? Explain.

89. In factoring the trinomial $x^2 + bx + c$, is the process easier if c is a prime number such as 5 or a composite number such as 120? Explain.

6.3   More About Factoring Trinomials

Objectives

1 Factor a trinomial of the form $ax^2 + bx + c$.

2 Factor a trinomial completely.

3 Factor a trinomial by grouping.

---

1 Factor a trinomial of the form $ax^2 + bx + c$.

Factoring Trinomials of the Form $ax^2 + bx + c$

In this section you will learn how to factor a trinomial whose leading coefficient is *not* 1. To see how this works, consider the following.

Factors of a

$$ax^2 + bx + c = (x +)(x +)$$

Factors of c

The goal is to find a combination of factors of a and c such that the outer and inner products add up to the middle term bx.

Example 1   Factoring a Trinomial of the Form $ax^2 + bx + c$

Factor $4x^2 - 4x - 3$.

Solution

In this trinomial, $a = 4$ and $c = -3$. You need to find a combination of the factors of 4 and -3 such that the outer and inner products add up to $-4x$. The possible combinations are as follows.

Factors	$O + I$	
Inner product $= 4x$ $(x + 1)(4x - 3)$ Outer product $= -3x$	$-3x + 4x = x$	x does not equal $-4x$.
Inner product $= -4x$ $(x - 1)(4x + 3)$ Outer product $= 3x$	$3x - 4x = -x$	$-x$ does not equal $-4x$.
$(x + 3)(4x - 1)$	$-x + 12x = 11x$	$11x$ does not equal $-4x$.
$(x - 3)(4x + 1)$	$x - 12x = -11x$	$-11x$ does not equal $-4x$.
$(2x + 1)(2x - 3)$	$-6x + 2x = -4x$	$-4x$ equals $-4x$. ✓
$(2x - 1)(2x + 3)$	$6x - 2x = 4x$	$4x$ does not equal $-4x$.

So, the correct factorization is

$$4x^2 - 4x - 3 = (2x + 1)(2x - 3).$$

| Example 2 | Factoring a Trinomial of the Form $ax^2 + bx + c$ |

Factor $6x^2 + 5x - 4$.

Solution

In this trinomial, $a = 6$ and $c = -4$. You need to find a combination of the factors of 6 and -4 such that the outer and inner products add up to $5x$.

Study Tip

If the original trinomial has no common monomial factors, then its binomial factors can't have common monomial factors. So, in Example 2, you don't have to test factors such as $(6x - 4)$ that have a common monomial factor of 2.

Factors	$O + I$	
$(x + 1)(6x - 4)$	$-4x + 6x = 2x$	$2x$ does not equal $5x$.
$(x - 1)(6x + 4)$	$4x - 6x = -2x$	$-2x$ does not equal $5x$.
$(x + 4)(6x - 1)$	$-x + 24x = 23x$	$23x$ does not equal $5x$.
$(x - 4)(6x + 1)$	$x - 24x = -23x$	$-23x$ does not equal $5x$.
$(x + 2)(6x - 2)$	$-2x + 12x = 10x$	$10x$ does not equal $5x$.
$(x - 2)(6x + 2)$	$2x - 12x = -10x$	$-10x$ does not equal $5x$.
$(2x + 1)(3x - 4)$	$-8x + 3x = -5x$	$-5x$ does not equal $5x$.
$(2x - 1)(3x + 4)$	$8x - 3x = 5x$	$5x$ equals $5x$. ✓
$(2x + 4)(3x - 1)$	$-2x + 12x = 10x$	$10x$ does not equal $5x$.
$(2x - 4)(3x + 1)$	$2x - 12x = -10x$	$-10x$ does not equal $5x$.
$(2x + 2)(3x - 2)$	$-4x + 6x = 2x$	$2x$ does not equal $5x$.
$(2x - 2)(3x + 2)$	$4x - 6x = -2x$	$-2x$ does not equal $5x$.

So, the correct factorization is $6x^2 + 5x - 4 = (2x - 1)(3x + 4)$.

The following guidelines can help shorten the list of possible factorizations.

> ▶ **Guidelines for Factoring $ax^2 + bx + c$ ($a > 0$)**
>
> 1. First, factor out any common monomial factor.
>
> 2. Because the resulting trinomial has no common monomial factors, you don't have to test any binomial factors that have a common monomial factor.
>
> 3. If the middle-term test ($O + I$) yields the opposite of b, switch the signs of the factors of c.

Using these guidelines, you can shorten the list in Example 2 to the following.

$(x + 4)(6x - 1) = 6x^2 + 23x - 4$

$(x - 4)(6x + 1) = 6x^2 - 23x - 4$

$(2x + 1)(3x - 4) = 6x^2 - 5x - 4$

$(2x - 1)(3x + 4) = 6x^2 + 5x - 4$ Correct factorization

Do you see why you can cut the list from 12 possible factorizations to only four?

As with other types of factoring, you can use a graphing utility to check your results. For instance, graph

$$y = 2x^2 + x - 15 \text{ and}$$

$$y = (2x - 5)(x + 3)$$

on the same screen, as shown below. Because both graphs are the same, you can reason that

$$2x^2 + x - 15$$

$$= (2x - 5)(x + 3).$$

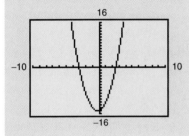

| Example 3 | Factoring a Trinomial of the Form $ax^2 + bx + c$ |

Factor $2x^2 + x - 15$.

Solution

In this trinomial, $a = 2$, which factors as $(1)(2)$, and $c = -15$, which factors as $(1)(-15), (-1)(15), (3)(-5),$ and $(-3)(5)$.

$$(2x + 1)(x - 15) = 2x^2 - 29x - 15$$

$$(2x + 15)(x - 1) = 2x^2 + 13x - 15$$

$$(2x + 3)(x - 5) = 2x^2 - 7x - 15$$

$$(2x + 5)(x - 3) = 2x^2 - x - 15 \qquad \text{Middle term has incorrect sign.}$$

$$(2x - 5)(x + 3) = 2x^2 + x - 15 \qquad \text{Correct factorization}$$

So, the correct factorization is

$$2x^2 + x - 15 = (2x - 5)(x + 3).$$

Notice in Example 3 that when the middle term has the incorrect sign, you need only to swap the signs of the second term of each factor.

Factoring Completely

Remember that if a trinomial has a common monomial factor, the common monomial factor should be factored out first. The complete factorization then shows all monomial and binomial factors.

2 Factor a trinomial completely.

| Example 4 | Factoring Completely |

Factor $4x^2 - 30x + 14$.

Solution

Begin by factoring out the common monomial factor.

$$4x^2 - 30x + 14 = 2(2x^2 - 15x + 7)$$

Now, for the trinomial $2x^2 - 15x + 7$, $a = 2$ and $c = 7$. The possible factorizations of this trinomial are listed below.

$$(2x - 7)(x - 1) = 2x^2 - 9x + 7$$

$$(2x - 1)(x - 7) = 2x^2 - 15x + 7 \qquad \text{Correct factorization}$$

So, the complete factorization of the original trinomial is

$$4x^2 - 30x + 14 = 2(2x^2 - 15x + 7)$$

$$= 2(2x - 1)(x - 7).$$

In factoring a trinomial with a negative leading coefficient, we suggest that you first factor -1 out of the trinomial.

Example 5   A Negative Leading Coefficient

Factor $-5x^2 + 7x + 6$.

Solution

Begin by factoring -1 out of the trinomial.

$$-5x^2 + 7x + 6 = (-1)(5x^2 - 7x - 6)$$

Now, for the trinomial $5x^2 - 7x - 6$, $a = 5$ and $c = -6$. After testing the possible factorizations, you can conclude that

$$(x - 2)(5x + 3) = 5x^2 - 7x - 6. \qquad \text{Correct factorization}$$

So, a correct factorization is

$$-5x^2 + 7x + 6 = (-1)(x - 2)(5x + 3)$$

$$= (-x + 2)(5x + 3).$$

Another correct factorization is $(x - 2)(-5x - 3)$.

---

3 Factor a trinomial by grouping.

Factoring by Grouping

The examples in this and the preceding section have shown how to use *Guess, Check, and Revise* to factor trinomials. An alternative technique that some people like to use is factoring by grouping. Recall from Section 6.1 that the polynomial

$$x^3 + 2x^2 + 3x + 6$$

was factored by first grouping terms and then applying the Distributive Property.

$$x^3 + 2x^2 + 3x + 6 = (x^3 + 2x^2) + (3x + 6) \qquad \text{Group terms.}$$

$$= x^2(x + 2) + 3(x + 2) \qquad \text{Distributive Property}$$

$$= (x + 2)(x^2 + 3) \qquad \text{Distributive Property}$$

By rewriting the middle term of the trinomial $2x^2 + x - 15$ as

$$2x^2 + x - 15 = 2x^2 + 6x - 5x - 15$$

you can group the first two terms and the last two terms and factor the trinomial as shown.

$$2x^2 + x - 15 = 2x^2 + (6x - 5x) - 15 \qquad \text{Rewrite middle term.}$$

$$= (2x^2 + 6x) - (5x + 15) \qquad \text{Group terms.}$$

$$= 2x(x + 3) - 5(x + 3) \qquad \text{Distributive Property}$$

$$= (x + 3)(2x - 5) \qquad \text{Distributive Property}$$

The key to this method of factoring is knowing how to rewrite the middle term. In general, *to factor a trinomial $ax^2 + bx + c$ by grouping, choose factors of the product ac that add up to b and use these factors to rewrite the middle term.*

Example 6   Factoring a Trinomial by Grouping

Use factoring by grouping to factor the trinomial

$$2x^2 + 5x - 3.$$

Solution

In the trinomial $2x^2 + 5x - 3$, $ac = 2(-3) = -6$, which has factors 6 and -1 that add up to 5. So, rewrite the middle term as $5x = 6x - x$. This produces the following.

$$\begin{aligned}
2x^2 + 5x - 3 &= 2x^2 + 6x - x - 3 && \text{Rewrite middle term.} \\
&= (2x^2 + 6x) - (x + 3) && \text{Group terms.} \\
&= 2x(x + 3) - (x + 3) && \text{Distributive Property} \\
&= (x + 3)(2x - 1) && \text{Distributive Property}
\end{aligned}$$

So, the trinomial factors as

$$2x^2 + 5x - 3 = (x + 3)(2x - 1).$$

Example 7   Factoring a Trinomial by Grouping

Use factoring by grouping to factor the trinomial

$$6x^2 - 11x - 10.$$

Solution

In the trinomial $6x^2 - 11x - 10$, $ac = 6(-10) = -60$, which has the factors -15 and 4 that add up to -11. So, rewrite the middle term as $-11x = -15x + 4x$. This produces the following.

$$\begin{aligned}
6x^2 - 11x - 10 &= 6x^2 - 15x + 4x - 10 && \text{Rewrite middle term.} \\
&= (6x^2 - 15x) + (4x - 10) && \text{Group terms.} \\
&= 3x(2x - 5) + 2(2x - 5) && \text{Distributive Property} \\
&= (2x - 5)(3x + 2) && \text{Distributive Property}
\end{aligned}$$

So, the trinomial factors as

$$6x^2 - 11x - 10 = (2x - 5)(3x + 2).$$

Discussing the Concept   Factoring Trinomials

What do you think of the technique of factoring a trinomial by grouping? Many people think it is more efficient than the *Guess, Check, and Revise* strategy, especially when the coefficients a and c have many factors. Try factoring $6x^2 - 13x + 6$, $2x^2 + 5x - 12$, and $3x^2 + 11x - 4$ using both methods. Which method do you prefer? Explain the advantages and disadvantages of each method.

6.3   Exercises

Integrated Review   *Concepts, Skills, and Problem Solving*

Keep mathematically in shape by doing these exercises *before* the problems of this section.

Properties and Definitions

1. Is 29 prime or composite?

2. Without dividing 255 by 3, how can you tell whether it is divisible by 3?

Simplifying Expressions

In Exercises 3–6, write the prime factorization.

3. 500   **4.** 315   **5.** 792   **6.** 2275

In Exercises 7 and 8, multiply and simplify.

7. $(2x - 5)(x + 7)$ **8.** $(3x - 2)^2$

Graphs and Models

In Exercises 9 and 10, graph the function and identify any intercepts.

9. $f(x) = (3 + x)(3 - x)$

10. $g(t) = 2t - 1$

11. An equation for the distance y (in inches) a spring is stretched from its equilibrium when a force of x pounds is applied is modeled by $y = 0.066x$.

(a) Graph the model.

(b) Estimate y when a force of 100 pounds is applied.

Developing Skills

In Exercises 1–8, find the missing factor.

1. $5x^2 + 18x + 9 = (x + 3)(\quad)$

2. $5x^2 + 19x + 12 = (x + 3)(\quad)$

3. $5a^2 + 12a - 9 = (a + 3)(\quad)$

4. $5c^2 + 11c - 12 = (c + 3)(\quad)$

5. $2y^2 - 3y - 27 = (y + 3)(\quad)$

6. $3y^2 - y - 30 = (y + 3)(\quad)$

7. $4z^2 - 13z + 3 = (z - 3)(\quad)$

8. $6z^2 - 23z + 15 = (z - 3)(\quad)$

In Exercises 9–12, find all possible products of the form $(5x + m)(x + n)$, where $m \cdot n$ is the specified product. (Assume that m and n are integers.)

9. $m \cdot n = 3$ **10.** $m \cdot n = 21$

11. $m \cdot n = 12$ **12.** $m \cdot n = 36$

In Exercises 13–40, factor the polynomial. (*Note:* Some of the trinomials may be prime.) See Examples 1–3.

13. $2x^2 + 5x + 3$ **14.** $3x^2 + 7x + 2$

15. $4y^2 + 5y + 1$ **16.** $3x^2 + 5x - 2$

17. $2y^2 - 3y + 1$ **18.** $3a^2 - 5a + 2$

19. $2x^2 - x - 3$ **20.** $3z^2 - z - 2$

21. $5x^2 - 2x + 1$ **22.** $4z^2 - 8z + 1$

23. $2x^2 + x + 3$ **24.** $6x^2 - 10x + 5$

25. $5s^2 - 10s + 6$ **26.** $6v^2 + v - 2$

27. $4x^2 + 13x - 12$ **28.** $6y^2 - 7y - 20$

29. $9x^2 - 18x + 8$ **30.** $4a^2 - 16a + 15$

31. $18u^2 - 9u - 2$ **32.** $24s^2 + 37s - 5$

33. $15a^2 + 14a - 8$ **34.** $12x^2 - 8x - 15$

35. $10t^2 - 3t - 18$ **36.** $10t^2 + 43t - 9$

37. $15m^2 + 16m - 15$ **38.** $21b^2 - 40b - 21$

39. $16z^2 - 34z + 15$ **40.** $12x^2 - 41x + 24$

In Exercises 41–50, factor the trinomial. (*Note:* The leading coefficient is negative.) See Example 5.

41. $-2x^2 + x + 3$ **42.** $-5x^2 + x + 4$

43. $4 - 4x - 3x^2$ **44.** $-4x^2 + 17x + 15$

45. $-6x^2 + 7x + 10$ **46.** $2 + x - 6x^2$

47. $1 - 4x - 60x^2$ **48.** $2 + 5x - 12x^2$

49. $16 - 8x - 15x^2$ **50.** $20 + 17x - 10x^2$

In Exercises 51–72, factor the polynomial completely. (*Note:* Some of the polynomials may be prime.) See Examples 4 and 5.

51. $6x^2 - 3x$

52. $3a^4 - 9a^3$

53. $15y^2 + 18y$

54. $24y^3 - 16y$

55. $u(u - 3) + 9(u - 3)$

56. $x(x - 8) - 2(x - 8)$

57. $2v^2 + 8v - 42$

58. $4z^2 - 12z - 40$

59. $-3x^2 - 3x - 60$

60. $5y^2 + 40y + 35$

61. $9z^2 - 24z + 15$

62. $6x^2 + 8x - 8$

63. $4x^2 + 4x + 2$

64. $6x^2 - 6x - 36$

65. $-15x^4 - 2x^3 + 8x^2$

66. $15y^2 - 7y^3 - 2y^4$

67. $3x^3 + 4x^2 + 2x$

68. $5x^3 - 3x^2 - 4x$

69. $6x^3 + 24x^2 - 192x$

70. $35x + 28x^2 - 7x^3$

71. $18u^4 + 18u^3 - 27u^2$

72. $12x^5 - 16x^4 + 8x^3$

In Exercises 73–78, find all integers b such that the trinomial can be factored.

73. $3x^2 + bx + 10$

74. $4x^2 + bx + 3$

75. $2x^2 + bx - 6$

76. $5x^2 + bx - 6$

77. $6x^2 + bx + 20$

78. $8x^2 + bx - 18$

In Exercises 79–84, find two integer values of c such that the trinomial can be factored. (There are many correct answers.)

79. $4x^2 + 3x + c$

80. $2x^2 + 5x + c$

81. $3x^2 - 10x + c$

82. $8x^2 - 3x + c$

83. $6x^2 - 5x + c$

84. $4x^2 - 9x + c$

In Exercises 85–100, factor the trinomial by grouping. See Examples 6 and 7.

85. $3x^2 + 7x + 2$

86. $2x^2 + 5x + 2$

87. $2x^2 + x - 3$

88. $5x^2 - 14x - 3$

89. $6x^2 + 5x - 4$

90. $12y^2 + 11y + 2$

91. $15x^2 - 11x + 2$

92. $12x^2 - 13x + 1$

93. $3a^2 + 11a + 10$

94. $3z^2 - 4z - 15$

95. $16x^2 + 2x - 3$

96. $20c^2 + 19c - 1$

97. $12x^2 - 17x + 6$

98. $10y^2 - 13y - 30$

99. $6u^2 - 5u - 14$

100. $12x^2 + 28x + 15$

Geometric Model of Factoring   In Exercises 101 and 102, factor the trinomial and draw a geometric model of the result. [This sample geometric model illustrates the factorization of $2x^2 + 3x + 1$ as $(2x + 1)(x + 1)$.]

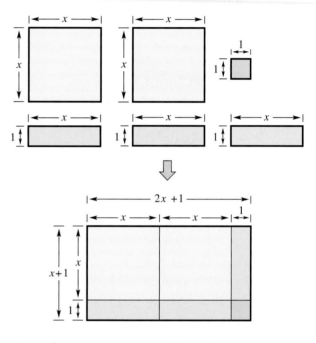

101. $2x^2 + 5x + 2$

102. $3x^2 + 4x + 1$

Solving Problems

103. *Geometry*   The sandbox shown in the figure has a height of x and a width of $x + 2$. The volume of the box is $2x^3 + 7x^2 + 6x$. Find the length of the box.

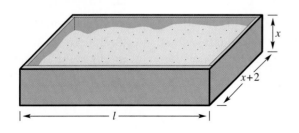

104 *Geometry*   The pool shown in the figure has a depth of d and a length of $5d + 2$. The volume of the pool is $15d^3 - 14d^2 - 8d$. Find the width of the pool.

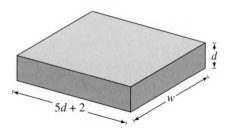

105. *Geometry*   The area of the rectangle in the figure is $2x^2 + 9x + 10$. What is the area of the shaded region?

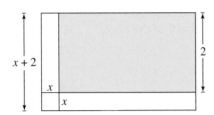

106. *Geometry*   The area of the rectangle in the figure is $3x^2 + 10x + 3$. What is the area of the shaded region?

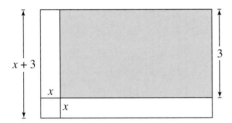

107. *Graphical Exploration*   Consider the functions $y_1 = 2x^3 + 3x^2 - 5x$ and $y_2 = x(2x + 5)(x - 1)$.

(a) Factor the trinomial represented by y_1. What is the relationship between y_1 and y_2?

(b) Demonstrate your answer to part (a) graphically by using a graphing utility to graph y_1 and y_2.

(c) Identify the x- and y-intercepts of the graphs of y_1 and y_2.

108. *Beam Deflection*   A cantilever beam of length l is fixed at the origin. A load weighing W pounds is attached to the end of the beam (see figure). The deflection y of the beam x units from the origin is given by

$$y = -\frac{1}{10}x^2 - \frac{1}{120}x^3, \quad 0 \le x \le 3.$$

(a) Factor the expression for the deflection. (Write the binomial factor with positive integer coefficients.)

(b) Use a graphing utility to graph the expression for deflection over the specified interval.

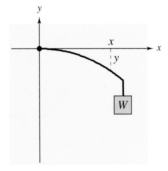

Explaining Concepts

109. Answer parts (a) and (b) of Motivating the Chapter on page 321.

110. Explain the meaning of each letter of FOIL.

111. Without multiplying, why is $(2x + 3)(x + 5)$ not a factorization of $2x^2 + 7x - 15$?

112. Find the error.

$$9x^2 - 9x - 54 = (3x + 6)(3x - 9)$$
$$= 3(x + 2)(x - 3)$$

113. In factoring $ax^2 + bx + c$, how many possible factorizations must be tested if a and c are prime? Explain your reasoning.

114. Give an example of a prime trinomial that is of the form $ax^2 + bx + c$.

115. Give an example of a trinomial of the form $ax^3 + bx^2 + cx$ that has a common monomial factor of $2x$.

116. Can a trinomial with its leading coefficient not equal to 1 have two identical factors? If so, give an example.

Mid-Chapter Quiz

Take this test as you would take a test in class. After you are done, check your work against the answers given in the back of the book.

In Exercises 1–4, find the missing factor.

1. $\frac{2}{3}x - 1 = \frac{1}{3}(\quad)$
2. $x^2y - xy^2 = xy(\quad)$
3. $y^2 + y - 42 = (y + 7)(\quad)$
4. $2x^2 - x - 1 = (x - 1)(\quad)$

In Exercises 5–16, factor the polynomial.

5. $10x^2 + 70$ 6. $2a^3b - 4a^2b^2$

7. $x(x + 2) - 3(x + 2)$ 8. $t^3 - 3t^2 + t - 3$

9. $y^2 + 11y + 30$ 10. $u^2 + u - 30$

11. $x^3 - x^2 - 30x$ 12. $2x^2y + 8xy - 64y$

13. $3v^2 - 4v - 2$ 14. $6 - 13z - 5z^2$

15. $6x^2 - x - 2$ 16. $10s^4 - 14s^3 + 2s^2$

17. Find all integer values of b such that the polynomial

    $x^2 + bx + 12$

    can be factored. Describe the method you used.

18. Find two values of c such that

    $x^2 - 10x + c$

    can be factored. Describe the method you used.

19. Find all possible products of the form

    $(3x + m)(x + n)$

    such that $mn = 6$. Describe the method you used.

20. The area of the rectangle in the figure is $3x^2 + 38x + 80$. What is the area of the shaded region?

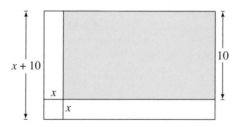

21. Use a graphing utility to graph $y_1 = -2x^2 + 11x - 12$ and $y_2 = (3 - 2x)(x - 4)$ on the same screen. What can you conclude?

6.4   Factoring Polynomials with Special Forms

Objectives

1 Factor the difference of two squares.

2 Recognize repeated factorization.

3 Identify and factor a perfect square trinomial.

4 Factor the sum and difference of two cubes.

1 Factor the difference of two squares.

Difference of Two Squares

One of the easiest special polynomial forms to recognize and to factor is the form $a^2 - b^2$. It is called a **difference of two squares,** and it factors according to the following pattern.

▶ **Difference of Two Squares**

Let a and b be real numbers, variables, or algebraic expressions.

$$a^2 - b^2 = (a + b)(a - b)$$

       Difference   Opposite signs

Technology: Discovery

Use your calculator to verify the special polynomial form called the "difference of two squares." To do so, evaluate the equation when $a = 16$ and $b = 9$. Try more values, including negative values. What can you conclude?

This pattern can be illustrated geometrically, as shown in Figure 6.2. The area of the shaded region on the left is represented by $a^2 - b^2$ (the area of the larger square minus the area of the smaller square). On the right, the *same* area is represented by a rectangle whose width is $a + b$ and whose length is $a - b$.

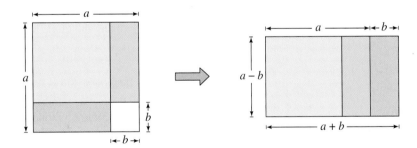

Figure 6.2

To recognize perfect squares, look for coefficients that are squares of integers and for variables raised to *even* powers. Here are some examples.

Original Polynomial		*Difference of Squares*		*Factored Form*
$x^2 - 1$	⟹	$(x)^2 - (1)^2$	⟹	$(x + 1)(x - 1)$
$4x^2 - 9$	⟹	$(2x)^2 - (3)^2$	⟹	$(2x + 3)(2x - 3)$
$25 - 64x^4$	⟹	$(5)^2 - (8x^2)^2$	⟹	$(5 + 8x^2)(5 - 8x^2)$

Study Tip

When factoring a polynomial, remember that you can check your result by multiplying the factors. For instance, you can check the factorization in Example 1(a) as follows.

$$(x + 6)(x - 6) = x^2 - 36$$

Example 1   Factoring the Difference of Two Squares

Factor each polynomial.

a. $x^2 - 36$ **b.** $x^2 - \frac{4}{25}$ **c.** $81x^2 - 49$

Solution

a. $x^2 - 36 = x^2 - 6^2$ Write as a difference of squares.

     $= (x + 6)(x - 6)$ Factored form

b. $x^2 - \frac{4}{25} = x^2 - \left(\frac{2}{5}\right)^2$ Write as a difference of squares.

     $= \left(x + \frac{2}{5}\right)\left(x - \frac{2}{5}\right)$ Factored form

c. $81x^2 - 49 = (9x)^2 - 7^2$ Write as a difference of squares.

     $= (9x + 7)(9x - 7)$ Factored form

Check your results by using the FOIL Method.

The rule $u^2 - v^2 = (u + v)(u - v)$ applies to polynomials or expressions in which u and v are themselves expressions.

Students may find this problem challenging. Compare

$k^2 - 49 = (k + 7)(k - 7)$

with

$(k + m)^2 - 49$

$= [(k + m) + 7][(k + m) - 7]$

$= (k + m + 7)(k + m - 7).$

You could also compare

$a^2 - 64 = (a + 8)(a - 8)$

with

$(a + 3)^2 - 64$

$= [(a + 3) + 8][(a + 3) - 8]$

$= (a + 3 + 8)(a + 3 - 8)$

$= (a + 11)(a - 5).$

Example 2   Factoring the Difference of Two Squares

Factor $(x + 1)^2 - 4$.

Solution

$(x + 1)^2 - 4 = (x + 1)^2 - 2^2$ Write as a difference of squares.

     $= [(x + 1) + 2][(x + 1) - 2]$ Factored form

     $= (x + 3)(x - 1)$ Simplify.

Check your result by using the FOIL Method.

Sometimes the difference of two squares can be hidden by the presence of a common monomial factor. Remember that with all factoring techniques, you should first remove any common monomial factors.

Example 3   Removing a Common Monomial Factor First

Factor $20x^3 - 5x$.

Solution

$20x^3 - 5x = 5x(4x^2 - 1)$ Factor out common monomial factor $5x$.

     $= 5x[(2x)^2 - 1^2]$ Write as a difference of squares.

     $= 5x(2x + 1)(2x - 1)$ Factored form

2 Recognize repeated factorization.

Repeated Factorization

To factor a polynomial completely, you should always check to see whether the factors obtained might themselves be factorable. That is, can any of the factors be factored? For instance, after factoring the polynomial $(x^4 - 1)$ once as the difference of two squares

$$x^4 - 1 = (x^2)^2 - 1^2 \qquad \text{Write as a difference of squares.}$$

$$= (x^2 + 1)(x^2 - 1) \qquad \text{Factored form}$$

You might explain that $x^2 + 1$ *cannot* be factored (using real numbers). Students frequently attempt to factor the sum of two squares.

you can see that the second factor is itself the difference of two squares. So, to factor the polynomial *completely*, you must continue the factoring process.

$$x^4 - 1 = (x^2 + 1)(x^2 - 1) \qquad \text{Factor as a difference of squares.}$$

$$= (x^2 + 1)(x + 1)(x - 1) \qquad \text{Factor completely.}$$

Another example of repeated factoring is shown in the next example.

Study Tip

Note in Example 4 that no attempt was made to factor the *sum of two squares*. A second-degree polynomial that is the sum of two squares cannot be factored as the product of binomials (using integer coefficients). For instance, the second-degree polynomials

$$x^2 + 4$$

and

$$4x^2 + 9$$

cannot be factored using integer coefficients. In general, *the sum of two squares is not factorable.*

| **Example 4** | Factoring Completely |

Factor $x^4 - 16$ completely.

Solution

Recognizing $x^4 - 16$ as a difference of two squares, you can write

$$x^4 - 16 = (x^2)^2 - 4^2 \qquad \text{Write as a difference of squares.}$$

$$= (x^2 + 4)(x^2 - 4). \qquad \text{Factored form}$$

Note that the second factor $(x^2 - 4)$ is itself a difference of two squares and so

$$x^4 - 16 = (x^2 + 4)(x^2 - 4) \qquad \text{Factor as a difference of squares.}$$

$$= (x^2 + 4)(x + 2)(x - 2). \qquad \text{Factor completely.}$$

| **Example 5** | Factoring Completely |

Factor $48x^4 - 3$ completely.

Solution

Start by removing the common monomial factor.

$$48x^4 - 3 = 3(16x^4 - 1) \qquad \text{Remove common monomial factor 3.}$$

Recognizing $16x^4 - 1$ as the difference of two squares, you can write

$$48x^4 - 3 = 3(16x^4 - 1) \qquad \text{Factor monomial.}$$

$$= 3[(4x^2)^2 - 1^2] \qquad \text{Write as a difference of squares.}$$

$$= 3(4x^2 + 1)(4x^2 - 1) \qquad \text{Recognize } 4x^2 - 1 \text{ as a difference of squares.}$$

$$= 3(4x^2 + 1)[(2x)^2 - 1^2] \qquad \text{Write as a difference of squares.}$$

$$= 3(4x^2 + 1)(2x + 1)(2x - 1). \qquad \text{Factor completely.}$$

3 Identify and factor a perfect square trinomial.

Perfect Square Trinomials

A **perfect square trinomial** is the square of a binomial. For instance,

$$x^2 + 4x + 4 = (x + 2)^2$$

is the square of the binomial $(x + 2)$. Perfect square trinomials come in two patterns, one in which the middle term is positive and the other in which the middle term is negative. In both cases, the first and last terms are perfect squares and positive.

▶ **Perfect Square Trinomials**

Let a and b be real numbers, variables, or algebraic expressions.

1. $a^2 + 2ab + b^2 = (a + b)^2$ **2.** $a^2 - 2ab + b^2 = (a - b)^2$

Same sign   Same sign

Study Tip

To recognize a perfect square trinomial, remember that the first and last terms must be perfect squares and positive, and the middle term must be twice the product of a and b. (The middle term can be positive or negative.) Watch for squares of fractions.

$4x^2 - \frac{4}{3}x + \frac{1}{9}$

$(2x)^2 \qquad \left(\frac{1}{3}\right)^2$

$2(2x)\left(\frac{1}{3}\right)$

Example 6 Identifying Perfect Square Trinomials

Which of the following are perfect square trinomials?

a. $m^2 - 4m + 4$ **b.** $4x^2 - 2x + 1$

c. $y^2 + 6y - 9$ **d.** $x^2 + x + \frac{1}{4}$

Solution

a. This polynomial *is* a perfect square trinomial. It factors as $(m - 2)^2$.

b. This polynomial *is not* a perfect square trinomial because the middle term is not twice the product of $2x$ and 1.

c. This polynomial *is not* a perfect square trinomial because the last term, -9, is not positive.

d. This polynomial *is* a perfect square trinomial. The first and last terms are perfect squares, x^2 and $\left(\frac{1}{2}\right)^2$, and it factors as $\left(x + \frac{1}{2}\right)^2$.

Example 7 Factoring Perfect Square Trinomials

a. $y^2 - 6y + 9 = y^2 - 2(3y) + 3^2$ Recognize the pattern.

$= (y - 3)^2$ Write in factored form.

b. $16x^2 + 40x + 25 = (4x)^2 + 2(4x)(5) + 5^2$ Recognize the pattern.

$= (4x + 5)^2$ Write in factored form.

c. $9x^2 - 24xy + 16y^2 = (3x)^2 - 2(3x)(4y) + (4y)^2$ Recognize the pattern.

$= (3x - 4y)^2$ Write in factored form.

4 Factor the sum and difference of two cubes.

Sum and Difference of Two Cubes

The last type of special factoring that you will study in this section is the sum and difference of two *cubes*. The patterns for these two special forms are summarized below.

▶ **Sum and Difference of Two Cubes**

Let a and b be real numbers, variables, or algebraic expressions.

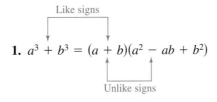

Like signs

1. $a^3 + b^3 = (a + b)(a^2 - ab + b^2)$

Unlike signs

Like signs

2. $a^3 - b^3 = (a - b)(a^2 + ab + b^2)$

Unlike signs

When using either of these factoring patterns, pay special attention to the signs, as indicated above. Remembering the "like" and "unlike" patterns for the signs is helpful.

Study Tip

It is easy to make arithmetic errors when applying the patterns for factoring the sum or difference of two cubes. When you use these patterns, be sure to check your work by multiplying the two factors. For instance, you can check the factorization in Example 8(a) as shown.

$$\begin{array}{r} y^2 - 3y + 9 \\ y + 3 \\ \hline 3y^2 - 9y + 27 \\ y^3 - 3y^2 + 9y \quad\quad\quad \\ \hline y^3 \quad\quad\quad\quad\quad + 27 \end{array}$$

Example 8   Factoring Sums and Differences of Two Cubes

Factor the polynomials.

a. $y^3 + 27$ **b.** $64 - x^3$ **c.** $2x^3 - 16$

Solution

a. $y^3 + 27 = y^3 + 3^3$ Write as sum of two cubes.

$\quad\quad\quad = (y + 3)[y^2 - (y)(3) + 3^2]$ Factored form

$\quad\quad\quad = (y + 3)(y^2 - 3y + 9)$ Simplify.

b. $64 - x^3 = 4^3 - x^3$ Write as difference of two cubes.

$\quad\quad\quad = (4 - x)(4^2 + 4x + x^2)$ Factored form

$\quad\quad\quad = (4 - x)(16 + 4x + x^2)$ Simplify.

c. $2x^3 - 16 = 2(x^3 - 8)$ Factor out common monomial factor 2.

$\quad\quad\quad = 2(x^3 - 2^3)$ Write as a difference of two cubes.

$\quad\quad\quad = 2(x - 2)[x^2 + (x)(2) + 2^2]$ Factored form

$\quad\quad\quad = 2(x - 2)(x^2 + 2x + 4)$ Simplify.

The following guidelines are steps for applying the various procedures involved in factoring polynomials.

▶ Guidelines for Factoring Polynomials

1. Factor out any common factors.

2. Factor according to one of the special polynomial forms: difference of two squares, sum or difference of two cubes, or perfect square trinomials.

3. Factor trinomials, $ax^2 + bx + c$, with $a = 1$ or $a \neq 1$.

4. Factor by grouping—for polynomials with four terms.

5. Check to see whether the factors themselves can be factored.

6. Check the results by multiplying the factors.

Discussing the Concept	A Three-Dimensional View of a Special Product

The figure below shows two cubes: a large cube whose volume is a^3 and a smaller cube whose volume is b^3. If the smaller cube is removed from the larger, the remaining solid has a volume of $a^3 - b^3$ and is composed of three rectangular boxes, labeled Box 1, Box 2, and Box 3. Find the volume of each box and describe how these results are related to the following special product pattern.

$$a^3 - b^3 = (a - b)(a^2 + ab + b^2)$$
$$= (a - b)a^2 + (a - b)ab + (a - b)b^2$$

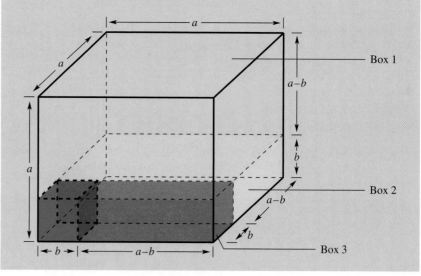

6.4   Exercises

Integrated Review   *Concepts, Skills, and Problem Solving*

Keep mathematically in shape by doing these exercises *before* the problems of this section.

Properties and Definitions

In Exercises 1 and 2, determine the quadrant or quadrants in which the point must be located.

1. $(-5, 2)$

2. $(x, 3)$, x is a real number.

3. Find the coordinates of the point on the x-axis and 4 units to the left of the y-axis.

4. Find the coordinates of the point 9 units to the right of the y-axis and 6 units below the x-axis.

Solving Equations

In Exercises 5–10, solve the equation and check your result.

5. $7 + 5x = 7x - 1$

6. $2 - 5(x - 1) = 2[x + 10(x - 1)]$

7. $2(x + 1) = 0$

8. $\frac{3}{4}(12x - 8) = 10$

9. $\frac{x}{5} + \frac{1}{5} = \frac{7}{10}$

10. $\frac{3x}{4} + \frac{1}{2} = 8$

Problem Solving

11. Because of a membership drive for a public television station, the current membership is 120% of what it was a year ago. The current number is 8345. How many members did the station have last year?

12. Suppose you budget 26% of your annual after-tax income for housing. If your after-tax income is $46,750, what amount can you spend on housing?

Developing Skills

In Exercises 1–18, factor the difference of two squares. See Examples 1 and 2.

1. $x^2 - 36$

2. $y^2 - 49$

3. $u^2 - 64$

4. $x^2 - 4$

5. $49 - x^2$

6. $81 - x^2$

7. $u^2 - \frac{1}{4}$

8. $v^2 - \frac{4}{9}$

9. $t^2 - \frac{1}{16}$

10. $u^2 - \frac{25}{81}$

11. $16y^2 - 9$

12. $9z^2 - 25$

13. $100 - 49x^2$

14. $16 - 81x^2$

15. $(x - 1)^2 - 4$

16. $(t + 2)^2 - 9$

17. $25 - (z + 5)^2$

18. $(a - 2)^2 - 16$

In Exercises 19–30, factor completely. See Examples 3–5.

19. $2x^2 - 72$

20. $3x^2 - 27$

21. $8 - 50x^2$

22. $a^3 - 16a$

23. $y^4 - 81$

24. $z^4 - 16$

25. $1 - x^4$

26. $256 - u^4$

27. $3x^4 - 48$

28. $18 - 2x^4$

29. $81x^4 - 16$

30. $81x^4 - 1$

In Exercises 31–48, factor the perfect square trinomial. See Examples 6 and 7.

31. $x^2 - 4x + 4$

32. $x^2 + 10x + 25$

33. $z^2 + 6z + 9$

34. $a^2 - 12a + 36$

35. $4t^2 + 4t + 1$

36. $9x^2 - 12x + 4$

37. $25y^2 - 10y + 1$

38. $16z^2 + 24z + 9$

39. $b^2 + b + \frac{1}{4}$

40. $x^2 + \frac{2}{5}x + \frac{1}{25}$

41. $4x^2 - x + \frac{1}{16}$

42. $4t^2 - \frac{4}{3}t + \frac{1}{9}$

43. $x^2 - 6xy + 9y^2$

44. $16x^2 - 8xy + y^2$

45. $4y^2 + 20yz + 25z^2$

46. $u^2 + 8uv + 16v^2$

47. $9a^2 - 12ab + 4b^2$

48. $49m^2 - 28mn + 4n^2$

Think About It   In Exercises 49–54, find two values of b such that the expression is a perfect square trinomial.

49. $x^2 + bx + 1$

50. $x^2 + bx + 100$

51. $x^2 + bx + \frac{16}{25}$

52. $y^2 + by + \frac{1}{9}$

53. $4x^2 + bx + 81$

54. $4x^2 + bx + 9$

Think About It In Exercises 55-58, find a number c such that the expression is a perfect square trinomial.

55. $x^2 + 6x + c$

56. $x^2 + 10x + c$

57. $y^2 - 4y + c$

58. $z^2 - 14z + c$

In Exercises 59-66, factor the sum or difference of two cubes. See Example 8.

59. $x^3 - 8$

60. $x^3 - 27$

61. $y^3 + 64$

62. $z^3 + 125$

63. $1 + 8t^3$

64. $27s^3 + 1$

65. $27u^3 + 8$

66. $64v^3 - 125$

In Exercises 67-108, factor the expression completely. (*Note:* Some of the polynomials may be prime.)

67. $6x - 36$

68. $8t + 48$

69. $u^2 + 3u$

70. $x^3 - 4x^2$

71. $5y^2 - 25y$

72. $12a^2 - 24a$

73. $5y^2 - 125$

74. $6x^2 - 54$

75. $y^4 - 25y^2$

76. $y^4 - 49y^2$

77. $1 - 4x + 4x^2$

78. $9x^2 - 6x + 1$

79. $x^2 - 2x + 1$

80. $16 + 6x - x^2$

81. $9x^2 + 10x + 1$

82. $4x^3 + 3x^2 + x$

83. $2x^2 + 4x - 2x^3$

84. $2y^3 - 7y^2 - 15y$

85. $9t^2 - 16$

86. $16t^2 - 144$

87. $36 - (z + 6)^2$

88. $(t - 4)^2 - 9$

89. $(t - 1)^2 - 121$

90. $(x - 3)^2 - 100$

91. $u^3 + 2u^2 + 3u$

92. $u^3 + 2u^2 - 3u$

93. $x^2 + 81$

94. $x^2 + 16$

95. $2t^3 - 16$

96. $24x^3 - 3$

97. $2 - 16x^3$

98. $54 - 2x^3$

99. $x^4 - 81$

100. $2x^4 - 32$

101. $1 - x^4$

102. $81 - y^4$

103. $x^3 - 4x^2 - x + 4$

104. $y^3 + 3y^2 - 4y - 12$

105. $x^4 + 3x^3 - 16x^2 - 48x$

106. $36x + 18x^2 - 4x^3 - 2x^4$

107. $64 - y^6$

108. $1 - y^8$

Graphical Verification In Exercises 109-112, use a graphing utility to graph the two functions on the same screen. What can you conclude?

109. $y_1 = x^2 - 36$
$y_2 = (x + 6)(x - 6)$

110. $y_1 = x^2 - 8x + 16$
$y_2 = (x - 4)^2$

111. $y_1 = x^3 - 6x^2 + 9x$
$y_2 = x(x - 3)^2$

112. $y_1 = x^3 + 27$
$y_2 = (x + 3)(x^2 - 3x + 9)$

Mental Math In Exercises 113-116, evaluate the quantity mentally using the two samples as models.

$29^2 = (30 - 1)^2$
$= 30^2 - 2 \cdot 30 \cdot 1 + 1^2$
$= 900 - 60 + 1 = 841$

$48 \cdot 52 = (50 - 2)(50 + 2)$
$= 50^2 - 2^2 = 2496$

113. 21^2

114. 49^2

115. $59 \cdot 61$

116. $28 \cdot 32$

Solving Problems

117. *Geometry* An annulus is the region between two concentric circles. The area of the annulus in the figure is $\pi R^2 - \pi r^2$. Give the complete factorization of the expression for the area.

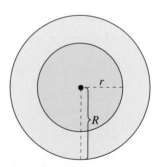

Figure for 117

In Exercises 118 and 119, write the polynomial as the difference of two squares. Use the result to factor the polynomial.

118. $x^2 + 6x + 8 = (x^2 + 6x + 9) - 1$

$$= \boxed{}^2 - \boxed{}^2$$

119. $x^2 + 8x + 12 = (x^2 + 8x + 16) - 4$

$$= \boxed{}^2 - \boxed{}^2$$

Geometric Factoring Models In Exercises 120 and 121, write the factoring problem represented by the geometric factoring model.

120.

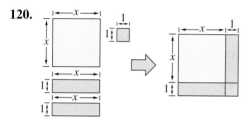

121.

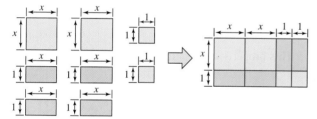

122. *Conjecture*

(a)

$5 \times 5 =$	$8 \times 8 =$	$11 \times 11 =$
$6 \times 4 =$	$9 \times 7 =$	$12 \times 10 =$

(b) Use the pattern of part (a) to fill in the blanks.

$$12 \times 12 = 144$$

$$\boxed{} \times \boxed{} = 143$$

(c) Use the pattern of parts (a) and (b) to make a conjecture. If possible, prove your conjecture.

123. *Think About It*   You design a square flower garden, but later change it to a rectangular shape by increasing one pair of opposite sides by 1 foot and decreasing the other pair of sides by 1 foot. The area of the rectangle is 224 square feet. Use the result of Exercise 122 to determine the dimensions of the square in the original design.

124. *Geometry*   From the eight vertices of a cube of dimension x, cubes of dimension y are removed (see figure).

(a) Write an expression for the volume of the solid that remains after the eight cubes at the vertices are removed. (*Hint:* The volume of a rectangular solid is length times width times height.)

(b) Factor the expression for the volume in part (a).

(c) In the context of this problem, y must be less than what multiple of x? Explain your answer geometrically and from the result of part (b).

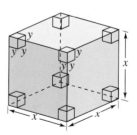

Explaining Concepts

125. Explain how to identify and factor the difference of two squares.

126. Explain how to identify and factor a perfect square trinomial.

127. Is the expression $x(x + 2) - 2(x + 2)$ in factored form? If not, rewrite it in factored form.

128. Is $x^2 + 4$ equal to $(x + 2)^2$? Explain.

129. *True or False?*   Because the sum of two squares cannot be factored, it follows that the sum of two cubes cannot be factored. Explain your reasoning.

130. In your own words, state guidelines for factoring polynomials.

6.5 Polynomial Equations and Applications

Objectives

1 Use the Zero-Factor Property to solve an equation.

2 Use factoring to solve a quadratic equation.

3 Solve a polynomial equation by factoring.

4 Solve an application problem by factoring.

1 Use the Zero-Factor Property to solve an equation.

The Zero-Factor Property

You have spent nearly two chapters developing skills for *rewriting* (simplifying and factoring) polynomials. You are now ready to use these skills together with the **Zero-Factor Property** to *solve* polynomial equations.

Study Tip

The Zero-Factor Property is just another way of saying that the only way the product of two or more factors can be zero is if one or more of the factors is zero.

▶ **Zero-Factor Property**

Let a and b be real numbers, variables, or algebraic expressions. If a and b are factors such that

$$ab = 0$$

then $a = 0$ or $b = 0$. This property also applies to three or more factors.

The Zero-Factor Property is the primary property for solving equations in algebra. For instance, to solve the equation

$$(x - 1)(x + 2) = 0 \qquad \text{Original equation}$$

you can use the Zero-Factor Property to conclude that either $(x - 1)$ or $(x + 2)$ must be zero. Setting the first factor equal to zero implies that $x = 1$ is a solution.

$$x - 1 = 0 \quad \Longrightarrow \quad x = 1 \qquad \text{First solution}$$

Similarly, setting the second factor equal to zero implies that $x = -2$ is a solution.

$$x + 2 = 0 \quad \Longrightarrow \quad x = -2 \qquad \text{Second solution}$$

So, the equation $(x - 1)(x + 2) = 0$ has exactly two solutions: 1 and -2. You can check these solutions by substituting them into the original equation.

Check

$$(x - 1)(x + 2) = 0 \qquad \text{Original equation}$$

$$(1 - 1)(1 + 2) \overset{?}{=} 0 \qquad \text{Substitute 1 for } x.$$

$$(0)(3) = 0 \qquad \text{First solution checks. } \checkmark$$

$$(-2 - 1)(-2 + 2) \overset{?}{=} 0 \qquad \text{Substitute } -2 \text{ for } x.$$

$$(-3)(0) = 0 \qquad \text{Second solution checks. } \checkmark$$

2 Use factoring to solve a quadratic equation.

Solving Quadratic Equations by Factoring

A **quadratic equation** is an equation of the form $ax^2 + bx + c = 0$. Here are some examples.

$$x^2 - 2x - 3 = 0, \quad 2x^2 + x - 1 = 0, \quad \text{and} \quad x^2 - 5x = 0$$

In the next four examples, note how you can combine your factoring skills with the Zero-Factor Property to solve quadratic equations.

| Example 1 | Using Factoring to Solve a Quadratic Equation |

Solve $x^2 - x - 6 = 0$.

Solution

First, check to see that the right side of the equation is zero. Next, factor the left side of the equation. Finally, apply the Zero-Factor Property to find the solutions.

$x^2 - x - 6 = 0$	Original equation
$(x + 2)(x - 3) = 0$	Factor left side of equation.
$x + 2 = 0$	Set 1st factor equal to 0.
$x = -2$	Solve for x.
$x - 3 = 0$	Set 2nd factor equal to 0.
$x = 3$	Solve for x.

Check

$x^2 - x - 6 = 0$	Original equation
$(-2)^2 - (-2) - 6 \overset{?}{=} 0$	Substitute -2 for x.
$4 + 2 - 6 \overset{?}{=} 0$	Simplify.
$0 = 0$	Solution checks. ✓
$x^2 - x - 6 = 0$	Original equation
$(3)^2 - 3 - 6 \overset{?}{=} 0$	Substitute 3 for x.
$9 - 3 - 6 \overset{?}{=} 0$	Simplify.
$0 = 0$	Solution checks. ✓

The equation has two solutions: -2 and 3.

Study Tip

In Section 3.1, you learned that the general strategy for solving a linear equation is to *isolate the variable.* Notice in Example 1 that the general strategy for solving a quadratic equation is to factor the equation into linear factors.

Factoring and the Zero-Factor Property allow you to solve a quadratic equation by converting it into two *linear* equations, which you already know how to solve. This is a common strategy of algebra—to break down a given problem into simpler parts, each solved by previously learned methods.

In order for the Zero-Factor Property to be used, a polynomial equation *must* be written in **general form.** That is, the polynomial must be on one side of the equation and zero must be the only term on the other side of the equation. To write $x^2 - 2x = 3$ in general form, subtract 3 from both sides of the equation.

$$x^2 - 2x = 3 \qquad \text{Original equation}$$

$$x^2 - 2x - 3 = 3 - 3 \qquad \text{Subtract 3 from both sides.}$$

$$x^2 - 2x - 3 = 0 \qquad \text{General form}$$

To solve this equation, factor the left side as $(x - 3)(x + 1)$, then form the linear equations $x - 3 = 0$ and $x + 1 = 0$. The solutions of these two linear equations are 3 and -1, respectively. The general strategy for solving a quadratic equation by factoring is summarized in the following guidelines.

▶ **Guidelines for Solving Quadratic Equations**

1. Write the quadratic equation in general form.

2. Factor the left side of the equation.

3. Set each factor with a variable equal to zero.

4. Solve each linear equation.

5. Check each solution in the original equation.

Example 2 Solving a Quadratic Equation by Factoring

Solve $2x^2 + 5x = 12$.

Solution

$$2x^2 + 5x = 12 \qquad \text{Original equation}$$

$$2x^2 + 5x - 12 = 0 \qquad \text{Write in general form.}$$

$$(2x - 3)(x + 4) = 0 \qquad \text{Factor left side of equation.}$$

$$2x - 3 = 0 \qquad \text{Set 1st factor equal to 0.}$$

$$x = \tfrac{3}{2} \qquad \text{Solve for } x.$$

$$x + 4 = 0 \qquad \text{Set 2nd factor equal to 0.}$$

$$x = -4 \qquad \text{Solve for } x.$$

The solutions are $\tfrac{3}{2}$ and -4. Check these solutions in the original equation.

You might tell students that Chapter 10 will introduce methods for solving quadratic equations that can't be solved by factoring.

Be sure you see that the Zero-Factor Property can be applied only to a product that is equal to *zero*. For instance, you cannot conclude from the equation $x(x - 3) = 10$ that $x = 10$ and $x - 3 = 10$ yield solutions. Instead, you must first write the equation in general form and then factor the left side, as follows.

$$x^2 - 3x - 10 = 0 \quad \Longrightarrow \quad (x - 5)(x + 2) = 0$$

Now, from the factored form, you can see that the solutions are 5 and -2.

In Examples 1 and 2, the original equations each involved a second-degree (quadratic) polynomial and each had *two different* solutions. You will sometimes encounter second-degree polynomial equations that have only one (repeated) solution. This occurs when the left side of the equation is a perfect square trinomial, as shown in Example 3.

Technology: Discovery

Write the function in Example 3 in general form. Graph this function on your graphing utility.

$$y = x^2 - 8x + 16$$

What are the x-intercepts of the function?

Write the function in Example 4 in general form. Graph this function on your graphing utility.

$$y = x^2 + 9x + 14$$

What are the x-intercepts of the function?

How do the x-intercepts relate to the solutions of the equations? What can you conclude about the solutions to the equations and the x-intercepts?

Example 3   A Quadratic Equation with a Repeated Solution

Solve $x^2 - 8x + 20 = 4$.

Solution

$x^2 - 8x + 20 = 4$	Original equation
$x^2 - 8x + 16 = 0$	Write in general form.
$(x - 4)^2 = 0$	Factor.
$x - 4 = 0$	Set factor equal to 0.
$x = 4$	Solve for x.

Note that even though the left side of this equation has two factors, the factors are the same. Thus, the only solution of the equation is 4.

$x^2 - 8x + 20 = 4$	Original equation
$(4)^2 - 8(4) + 20 \stackrel{?}{=} 4$	Substitute 4 for x.
$16 - 32 + 20 \stackrel{?}{=} 4$	Simplify.
$4 = 4$	Solution checks. ✓

Example 4   Solving a Polynomial Equation

Solve $(x + 3)(x + 6) = 4$.

Solution

Begin by multiplying the factors on the left side.

$(x + 3)(x + 6) = 4$	Original equation
$x^2 + 9x + 18 = 4$	Multiply factors.
$x^2 + 9x + 14 = 0$	General form
$(x + 2)(x + 7) = 0$	Factor left side of equation.
$x + 2 = 0$	Set 1st factor equal to 0.
$x = -2$	Solve for x.
$x + 7 = 0$	Set 2nd factor equal to 0.
$x = -7$	Solve for x.

A common error is setting $x + 3 = 4$ or $x + 6 = 4$. Emphasize the necessity of having a product equal to *zero* before applying the Zero-Factor Property.

The equation has two solutions: -2 and -7. Check these in the original equation.

3 Solve a polynomial equation by factoring.

Niels Henrik Abel

(1802–1829)

In the exploration of algebra, general solutions were found for second-, third-, and fourth-degree polynomial equations. (You will study the Quadratic Formula for second-degree equations in Chapter 10.) Attempts to find an algebraic solution for a fifth-degree polynomial equation met with failure.

In 1824, Niels Henrik Abel published a proof that showed that for any degree greater than four, the general polynomial equation could not be solved algebraically. His work included the concept of a group. Subsequent research in group theory gave mathematicians new ways to explore and describe algebraic structures. This marked the beginning of the modern theory of equations.

Solving Polynomial Equations by Factoring

Example 5   Solving a Polynomial Equation with Three Factors

Solve $3x^3 = 12x^2 + 15x$.

Solution

$3x^3 = 12x^2 + 15x$	Original equation
$3x^3 - 12x^2 - 15x = 0$	General form
$3x(x^2 - 4x - 5) = 0$	Factor out $3x$.
$3x(x - 5)(x + 1) = 0$	Factor completely.
$3x = 0 \implies x = 0$	Set 1st factor equal to 0.
$x - 5 = 0 \implies x = 5$	Set 2nd factor equal to 0.
$x + 1 = 0 \implies x = -1$	Set 3rd factor equal to 0.

There are three solutions: 0, 5, and -1. Check these in the original equation.

Notice that the equation in Example 5 is a third-degree equation and has three solutions. This is not a coincidence. In general, a polynomial equation can have *at most* as many solutions as its degree. For instance, a second-degree equation can have zero, one, or two solutions, but it cannot have three or more solutions. Notice that the equation in Example 6 is a fourth-degree equation and has four solutions.

Example 6   Solving a Polynomial Equation with Four Factors

Solve $x^4 + x^3 - 4x^2 - 4x = 0$.

Solution

$x^4 + x^3 - 4x^2 - 4x = 0$	Original equation
$x(x^3 + x^2 - 4x - 4) = 0$	Factor out x.
$x[x^2(x + 1) - 4(x + 1)] = 0$	Distributive Property
$x[(x + 1)(x^2 - 4)] = 0$	Factor by grouping.
$x(x + 1)(x + 2)(x - 2) = 0$	Factor completely.
$x = 0 \implies x = 0$	Set 1st factor equal to 0.
$x + 1 = 0 \implies x = -1$	Set 2nd factor equal to 0.
$x + 2 = 0 \implies x = -2$	Set 3rd factor equal to 0.
$x - 2 = 0 \implies x = 2$	Set 4th factor equal to 0.

There are four solutions: 0, -1, -2, and 2. Check these in the original equation.

---

4 Solve an application problem by factoring.

Applications

Example 7   Consecutive Integers

The product of two consecutive positive integers is 56. What are the integers?

Solution

Verbal Model: First integer · Second integer = 56

Labels: First integer $= n$
Second integer $= n + 1$

Equation: $n(n + 1) = 56$ Original equation

$n^2 + n - 56 = 0$ General form

$(n + 8)(n - 7) = 0$ Factor left side of equation.

$n = -8 \text{ or } 7$ Solutions

Because the problem states that the integers are positive, discard -8 as a solution and choose $n = 7$. So, the two integers are $n = 7$ and $n + 1 = 8$.

Example 8   A Falling Object Model

A rock is dropped from the top of a 256-foot river gorge, as shown in Figure 6.3. The height (in feet) of the rock is modeled by the equation

$$\text{Height} = -16t^2 + 256$$

where t is the time measured in seconds. How long will it take the rock to hit the bottom of the gorge?

Solution

From Figure 6.3, note that the bottom of the gorge corresponds to a height of 0 feet. So, substitute a height of 0 into the model and solve for t.

$$0 = -16t^2 + 256$$ Set height equal to 0.

$$16t^2 - 256 = 0$$ General form

$$16(t^2 - 16) = 0$$ Factor out 16.

$$16(t + 4)(t - 4) = 0$$ Factor left side of equation.

$$t + 4 = 0 \implies t = -4$$ Set 1st factor equal to 0.

$$t - 4 = 0 \implies t = 4$$ Set 2nd factor equal to 0.

Because a time of -4 seconds doesn't make sense in this problem, choose the positive solution and conclude that the rock hits the bottom of the gorge 4 seconds after it is dropped.

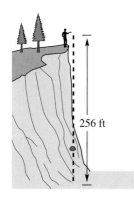

256 ft

Figure 6.3

In Example 8, the equation is a second-degree equation and, as such, cannot have more than two solutions, 4 and -4. The factor 16 in the equation

$$16(t + 4)(t - 4) = 0$$

does not give us another solution. Setting this factor equal to zero yields the *false* statement $16 = 0$.

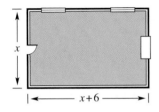

Figure 6.4

Example 9   An Application from Geometry

A rectangular family room has an area of 160 square feet. The length of the room is 6 feet greater than its width. Find the dimensions of the room.

Solution

To begin, make a sketch of the room, as shown in Figure 6.4. Label the width of the room as x and the length of the room as $x + 6$ because the length is 6 feet greater than the width.

Verbal Model: | Length $\cdot$ Width $=$ Area |

Labels: Width $= x$ (feet)
          Length $= x + 6$ (feet)
          Area $= 160$ (square feet)

Equation: $x(x + 6) = 160$

$$x^2 + 6x - 160 = 0$$

$$(x + 16)(x - 10) = 0$$

$$x = -16 \text{ or } 10$$

In this application, the negative solution makes no sense, so discard it and use the positive solution. So, the width of the room is 10 feet and the length of the room is 16 feet.

To check this solution, go back to the original statement of the problem. Note that a length of 16 feet is 6 feet greater than a width of 10 feet. Moreover, a rectangular room with dimensions 16 feet by 10 feet has an area of 160 square feet. So, the solution checks.

The Discussing the Concept problem can help students gain valuable insights into quadratic equations.

Discussing the Concept   Misleading Factorization

Suppose a student submits the following steps in solving the equation $x^2 + 3x = 10$:

$x(x + 3) = 10$ Factor.

$x = 10$ and $x + 3 = 10$ Set each factor equal to 10.

$x = 7$

Write an explanation of why the method does not work. Solve the equation correctly and check your answers.

6.5   Exercises

Integrated Review   *Concepts, Skills, and Problem Solving*

Keep mathematically in shape by doing these exercises *before* the problems of this section.

Properties and Definitions

In Exercises 1–4, name the property illustrated.

1. $2ab - 2ab = 0$ **2.** $8t \cdot 1 = 8t$

3. $2x(1 - x) = 2x - 2x^2$

4. $3x + (2x + 5) = (3x + 2x) + 5$

Rewriting Expressions

In Exercises 5–10, perform the required operations and/or simplify.

5. (a) $2(-3) + 9$ (b) $(-5)^2 + 3$

6. (a) $4 - \dfrac{5}{2}$ (b) $\dfrac{|18 - 25|}{6}$

7. $\left(-\frac{7}{12}\right)\left(\frac{3}{28}\right)$ **8.** $\frac{4}{3} \div \frac{5}{6}$

9. $2t(t - 3) + 4t + 1$ **10.** $2u - 5(2u - 3)$

Problem Solving

11. Find the interest on a $1000 bond paying an annual percentage rate of 7.5% for 10 years.

12. A car leaves a town 1 hour after a fully-loaded truck. The speed of the truck is approximately 50 miles per hour. If the car overtakes the truck in 2.5 hours, find the speed of the car.

Developing Skills

In Exercises 1–16, use the Zero-Factor Property to solve the equation.

1. $x(x - 5) = 0$ **2.** $z(z - 3) = 0$

3. $(y - 2)(y - 3) = 0$ **4.** $(s - 4)(s - 10) = 0$

5. $(a + 1)(a - 2) = 0$ **6.** $(t - 3)(t + 8) = 0$

7. $(2t - 5)(3t + 1) = 0$ **8.** $(2 - 3x)(5 - 2x) = 0$

9. $\left(\frac{2}{3}x - 4\right)(x + 2) = 0$ **10.** $\left(\frac{3}{4}u - 2\right)\left(\frac{2}{5}u + \frac{1}{2}\right) = 0$

11. $(0.2y - 12)(0.7y + 10) = 0$

12. $(1.5s + 12)(0.75s - 18) = 0$

13. $3x(x + 8)(4x - 5) = 0$

14. $x(x - 3)(x + 25) = 0$

15. $(y - 1)(2y + 3)(y + 12) = 0$

16. $x(5x + 3)(x - 8) = 0$

In Exercises 17–66, solve the equation. See Examples 1–6.

17. $x^2 - 16 = 0$ **18.** $x^2 - 144 = 0$

19. $100 - v^2 = 0$ **20.** $4 - x^2 = 0$

21. $3y^2 - 27 = 0$ **22.** $25z^2 - 100 = 0$

23. $(t - 3)^2 - 25 = 0$ **24.** $1 - (x + 1)^2 = 0$

25. $81 - (u + 4)^2 = 0$ **26.** $(s + 5)^2 - 49 = 0$

27. $2x^2 + 4x = 0$ **28.** $6x^2 + 3x = 0$

29. $4x^2 - x = 0$ **30.** $x - 3x^2 = 0$

31. $y(y - 4) + 3(y - 4) = 0$

32. $u(u + 2) - 3(u + 2) = 0$

33. $x(x - 8) + 2(x - 8) = 0$

34. $x(x + 2) - 3(x + 2) = 0$

35. $m^2 - 2m + 1 = 0$ **36.** $a^2 + 6a + 9 = 0$

37. $x^2 + 14x + 49 = 0$ **38.** $x^2 - 10x + 25 = 0$

39. $4t^2 - 12t + 9 = 0$ **40.** $16x^2 + 56x + 49 = 0$

41. $x^2 - 2x - 8 = 0$ **42.** $x^2 - 8x - 9 = 0$

43. $3 + 5x - 2x^2 = 0$ **44.** $33 + 5y - 2y^2 = 0$

45. $6x^2 + 4x - 10 = 0$ **46.** $12x^2 + 7x + 1 = 0$

47. $z(z + 2) = 15$ **48.** $x(x - 1) = 6$

49. $x(x - 5) = 14$ **50.** $x(x + 4) = -4$

51. $y(2y + 1) = 3$ **52.** $x(5x - 14) = 3$

53. $(x - 3)(x - 6) = 4$ **54.** $(x + 1)(x - 2) = 4$

55. $(x + 1)(x + 4) = 4$ **56.** $(x - 9)(x + 2) = 12$

57. $x^3 + 5x^2 + 6x = 0$ **58.** $x^3 - 3x^2 - 10x = 0$

59. $2t^3 + 5t^2 - 12t = 0$ **60.** $3u^3 - 5u^2 - 2u = 0$

61. $x^2(x - 2) - 9(x - 2) = 0$

62. $y^2(y + 3) - (y + 3) = 0$

63. $x^3 - x^2 - 16x + 16 = 0$

64. $a^3 + 2a^2 - 4a - 8 = 0$

65. $u^4 + 2u^3 - u^2 - 2u = 0$

66. $x^4 - 4x^3 - 9x^2 + 36x = 0$

Graphical Estimation In Exercises 67–74, use the graph to estimate the *x*-intercepts. Set the polynomial equal to zero and solve. What do you notice?

67. $y = x^2 + 2x - 3$ **68.** $y = 2 + x - x^2$

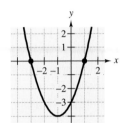   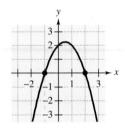

69. $y = 12 + x - x^2$ **70.** $y = 2x^2 + x - 3$

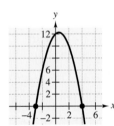   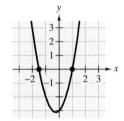

71. $y = x^3 - 6x^2 + 9x$ **72.** $y = 2x^3 + 3x^2 - 5x$

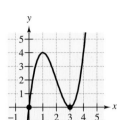   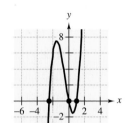

73. $y = 5x - 3x^2 - 2x^3$ **74.** $y = x^4 + 2x^3 - 8x^2$

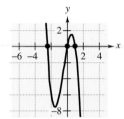   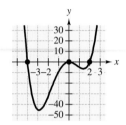

Graphical Estimation In Exercises 75–82, use a graphing utility to graph the function. Use the graph to estimate the *x*-intercepts. Check your estimates by substituting into the function.

75. $y = x^2 - 4$ **76.** $y = x^2 - 4x$

77. $y = 2x^2 - 5x - 12$ **78.** $y = 4x^2 + 3x - 10$

79. $y = x^3 - 4x^2$

80. $y = \frac{1}{4}(x^3 - 2x^2 - x + 2)$

81. $y = x^2(x + 2) - 9(x + 2)$

82. $y = \frac{1}{4}(x^3 + 4x^2 - x - 4)$

Solving Problems

83. Find two consecutive positive integers whose product is 72.

84. Find two consecutive positive integers whose product is 240.

85. Find two consecutive positive even integers whose product is 440.

86. Find two consecutive positive odd integers whose product is 323.

87. *Geometry* The length of a rectangular picture frame is 3 inches greater than its width. The area of the picture frame is 108 square inches. Find the dimensions of the picture frame.

88. *Geometry* The width of a rectangular garden is 4 feet less than its length. The area of the garden is 320 square feet. Find the dimensions of the garden.

89. *Geometry* The length of a rectangle is 2 times its width. The area of the rectangle is 450 square inches. Find the dimensions of the rectangle.

90. *Geometry* The length of a rectangle is $1\frac{1}{2}$ times its width. The area of the rectangle is 600 square inches. Find the dimensions of the rectangle.

91. *Constructing a Box*   An open box is to be made from a square piece of material by cutting 2-inch squares from the corners and turning up the sides (see figure).

(a) Show that the volume is given by $V = 2x^2$.

(b) Complete the table.

x	2	4	6	8
V				

(c) Find the dimensions of the original piece of material if $V = 200$ cubic inches.

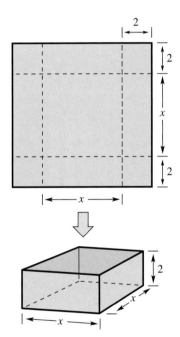

92. *Dimensions of a Box*   An open box with a square base is to be constructed from 108 square inches of material. The height of the box is 3 inches. Find the dimensions of the base of the box. (*Hint:* The surface area is given by $S = x^2 + 4xh$.)

93. *Height of an Object*   An object is dropped from a weather balloon 1600 feet above the ground (see figure). Find the time t for the object to reach the ground. The height (above ground) of the object is

$$\text{Height} = -16t^2 + 1600$$

where the height is measured in feet and the time t is measured in seconds.

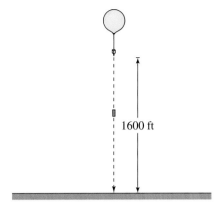

Figure for 93

94. *Height of an Object*   An object is dropped from a cliff 400 feet above the ground. Find the time t for the object to reach the ground. The height (above ground) of the object is

$$\text{Height} = -16t^2 + 400$$

where the height is measured in feet and the time t is measured in seconds.

95. *Profit*   The profit from selling x units of a product is

$$P = -0.4x^2 + 8x - 10.$$

(a) Use a graphing utility to graph the expression for profit.

(b) Use the graph to estimate any values of x that yield a profit of $P = \$20$.

(c) Use factorization to find any values of x that yield a profit of $P = \$20$.

96. *Revenue*   The revenue from selling x units of a product is

$$R = 25x - 0.2x^2.$$

(a) Use a graphing utility to graph the expression for revenue.

(b) Use the graph to estimate the smaller of the two values of x that yield a revenue of $R = \$680$.

(c) Use factorization to find the smaller of the two values of x that yield a revenue of $R = \$680$.

97. *Height of a Diver* A diver jumps from a diving board that is 32 feet above the water (see figure). The height of the diver is modeled by

$$\text{Height} = -16t^2 + 16t + 32$$

where the height is measured in feet and the time t is measured in seconds. How many seconds will it take for the diver to reach the water?

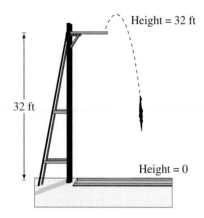

Height = 32 ft

32 ft

Height = 0

98. *Sum of Natural Numbers*

(a) Find the following sums.

$$1 + 2 + 3 + 4 + 5 = \boxed{}$$

$$1 + 2 + 3 + 4 + 5 + 6 + 7 + 8 = \boxed{}$$

$$1 + 2 + 3 + 4 + 5 + 6 + 7 + 8 + 9 + 10 = \boxed{}$$

(b) Use the following formula for the sum of the first n natural numbers to verify your answers to part (a).

$$1 + 2 + 3 + \cdots + n = \frac{1}{2}n(n + 1)$$

(c) Use the formula in part (b) to find n if the sum of the first n natural numbers is 210.

99. *Modeling Data* The bar graph gives the number of passengers y in millions flying Southwest Airline for the years 1987 through 1996. A model for the data is

$$y = (4.65 + 0.41t)^2, \quad -3 \le t \le 6$$

where t is time in years, with $t = 0$ corresponding to 1990. (Source: *Reader's Digest,* June 1997)

(a) Use a graphing utility to plot the data and graph the model.

(b) Use the graph in part (a) to approximate the solution of the equation

$$100 = (4.65 + 0.41t)^2.$$

Interpret the result in the context of the problem.

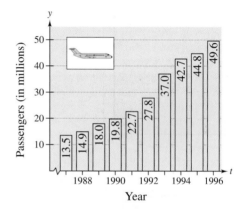

Passengers (in millions)

Year

100. *Exploration* If a and b are nonzero real numbers, show that the equation $ax^2 + bx = 0$ must have two different solutions.

101. *Exploration* If a is a nonzero real number, find two solutions of the equation $ax^2 - ax = 0$.

Explaining Concepts

102. Answer parts (c)–(e) of Motivating the Chapter on page 321.

103. Use the Zero-Factor Property to complete the statement. If $ab = 0$, then $\boxed{}$.

104. In your own words, describe a strategy for solving a quadratic equation by factoring.

105. Explain the difference between a linear equation and a quadratic equation.

106. Is it possible for a quadratic equation to have one solution? Explain.

107. What is the maximum number of solutions of an nth-degree polynomial equation?

108. *True or False?* The only equation with solutions $x = 2$ and $x = -5$ is $(x - 2)(x + 5) = 0$.

109. *True or False?* If $(5x - 1)(x + 3) = 21$, then $5x - 1 = 21$ or $x + 3 = 21$. Explain.

Key Terms

factoring, *p. 322*

greatest common factor, *p. 322*

greatest common monomial factor, *p. 323*

factoring out, *p. 323*

prime polynomials, *p. 332*

factoring completely, *p. 334*

quadratic equation, *p. 357*

Key Concepts

6.1 Factoring polynomials with common factors

Use the Distributive Property to remove the greatest common factor from each term of a polynomial.

6.1 Factoring polynomials by grouping

For polynomials with four terms, group the first two terms together and the last two terms together. Factor these two groupings and then look for a common binomial factor.

6.2 Factoring trinomials of the form $x^2 + bx + c$

To factor $x^2 + bx + c$, you need to find two numbers m and n whose product is c and whose sum is b.

$$x^2 + bx + c = (x + m)(x + n)$$

1. If c is positive, then m and n have like signs that match the sign of b.
2. If c is negative, then m and n have unlike signs.
3. If $|b|$ is small relative to $|c|$, first try those factors of c that are closest to each other in absolute value.

6.3 Factoring trinomials of the form $ax^2 + bx + c$ $(a > 0)$

1. First, factor out any common monomial factor.
2. You don't have to test any binomial factors that have a common monomial factor.
3. If the middle-term test (Outer + Inner) yields the opposite of b, switch the signs of the factors of c.

6.4 Factoring a difference of two squares

Let a and b be real numbers, variables, or algebraic expressions. To factor a difference of two squares, use the pattern shown on page 347.

6.4 Factoring perfect square trinomials

Let a and b be real numbers, variables, or algebraic expressions. To factor a perfect square trinomial, use the pattern shown on page 350.

6.4 Sum and difference of two cubes

Let a and b be real numbers, variables, or algebraic expressions. To factor the sum or difference of two cubes, use the patterns shown on page 351.

6.4 Guidelines for factoring polynomials

1. Factor out any common factors.
2. Factor according to one of the special polynomial forms: difference of two squares, sum or difference of two cubes, or perfect square trinomials.
3. Factor trinomials, $ax^2 + bx + c$, with $a = 1$ or $a \neq 1$.
4. Factor by grouping—for polynomials with four terms.
5. Check to see whether the factors themselves can be factored.
6. Check the results by multiplying the factors.

6.5 Zero-Factor Property

Let a and b be real numbers, variables, or algebraic expressions. If a and b are factors such that

$$ab = 0$$

then $a = 0$ or $b = 0$. This property also applies to three or more factors.

6.5 Solving a quadratic equation

To solve a quadratic equation, write the equation in general form. Factor the quadratic into linear factors and apply the Zero-Factor Property.

REVIEW EXERCISES

Reviewing Skills

6.1 In Exercises 1–4, find the greatest common factor of the expressions.

1. $20, 60, 150$

2. $3x^4, 21x^2$

3. $18ab^2, 27a^2b$

4. $14z^2, 1, 21z$

In Exercises 5–20, factor the polynomial.

5. $3x - 6$

6. $7 + 21x$

7. $3t - t^2$

8. $u^2 - 6u$

9. $5x^2 + 10x^3$

10. $7y - 21y^4$

11. $8a - 12a^3$

12. $6u - 9u^2 + 15u^3$

13. $x(x + 1) - 3(x + 1)$

14. $2u(u - 2) + 5(u - 2)$

15. $y^3 + 3y^2 + 2y + 6$

16. $z^3 - 5z^2 + z - 5$

17. $x^3 + 2x^2 + x + 2$

18. $x^3 - 5x^2 + 5x - 25$

19. $x^2 - 4x + 3x - 12$

20. $2x^2 + 6x - 5x - 15$

6.2 In Exercises 21–30, factor the trinomial.

21. $x^2 - 3x - 28$

22. $x^2 - 3x - 40$

23. $u^2 + 5u - 36$

24. $y^2 + 15y + 56$

25. $x^2 + 9xy - 10y^2$

26. $u^2 + uv - 5v^2$

27. $y^2 - 6xy - 27x^2$

28. $v^2 + 18uv + 32u^2$

29. $4x^2 - 24x + 32$

30. $x^3 + 9x^2 + 18x$

In Exercises 31–34, find all values of b such that the trinomial is factorable.

31. $x^2 + bx + 9$

32. $y^2 + by + 25$

33. $z^2 + bz + 11$

34. $x^2 + bx + 14$

6.3 In Exercises 35–44, factor the trinomial.

35. $5 - 2x - 3x^2$

36. $8x^2 - 18x + 9$

37. $50 - 5x - x^2$

38. $7 + 5x - 2x^2$

39. $6x^2 + 7x + 2$

40. $16x^2 + 13x - 3$

41. $6u^3 + 3u^2 - 30u$

42. $8x^3 - 8x^2 + 30x$

43. $2x^2 - 3x + 1$

44. $3x^2 + 8x + 4$

In Exercises 45–48, find all values of b such that the trinomial is factorable.

45. $x^2 + bx - 24$

46. $2x^2 + bx - 16$

47. $3x^2 + bx - 20$

48. $3x^2 + bx + 1$

In Exercises 49 and 50, find two values of c such that the trinomial is factorable.

49. $2x^2 - 4x + c$

50. $5x^2 + 6x + c$

6.4 In Exercises 51 and 52, insert the missing factors.

51. $x^3 - x = x(\quad)(\quad)$

52. $u^4 - v^4 = (u^2 + v^2)(\quad)(\quad)$

In Exercises 53–72, factor the polynomial completely.

53. $a^2 - 100$

54. $36 - b^2$

55. $25 - 4y^2$

56. $16b^2 - 1$

57. $(u + 1)^2 - 4$

58. $(y - 2)^2 - 9$

59. $x^2 - 8x + 16$

60. $y^2 + 24y + 144$

61. $x^2 + 6x + 9$

62. $v^2 - 10v + 25$

63. $9s^2 + 12s + 4$

64. $u^2 - 2uv + v^2$

65. $s^3t - st^3$

66. $y^3z + 4y^2z^2 + 4yz^3$

67. $a^3 + 1$

68. $z^3 + 8$

69. $27 - 8t^3$

70. $z^3 - 125$

71. $-16a^3 - 16a^2 - 4a$

72. $5t - 125t^3$

6.5 In Exercises 73–86, solve the polynomial equation.

73. $x^2 - 81 = 0$

74. $121 - y^2 = 0$

75. $x^2 - 12x + 36 = 0$

76. $2t^2 - 3t - 2 = 0$

77. $4s^2 + s - 3 = 0$

78. $y^3 - y^2 - 6y = 0$

79. $x(2x - 3) = 0$

80. $3x(5x + 1) = 0$

81. $(z - 2)^2 - 4 = 0$

82. $(x + 1)^2 - 16 = 0$

83. $x(7 - x) = 12$

84. $x(x + 5) = 24$

85. $u^3 + 5u^2 - u = 5$

86. $a^3 - 3a^2 - a = -3$

Solving Problems

87. *Geometry* The cake box shown in the figure has a height of x and a width of $x + 1$. The volume of the box is $3x^3 + 4x^2 + x$. Find the length of the box.

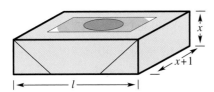

Geometry In Exercises 88 and 89, write an expression for the area of the shaded region and factor the expression.

88.

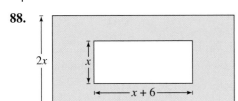

89.

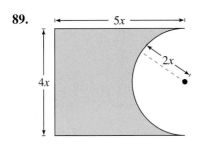

90. *Geometry* A rectangular sheet of metal has dimensions 2 feet by 3 feet. An open box is to be made from the metal by cutting equal squares from the corners and turning up the sides. The volume of the box is

$$V = 4x^3 - 10x^2 + 6x, \quad 0 < x < 1.$$

(a) Sketch the rectangular sheet and the open box. Label the height of the box as x.

(b) Factor the expression for the volume. Show how these factors relate to the dimensions of the box.

(c) Use a graphing utility to graph the volume over the specified interval. Use the graph to approximate the size of the squares to be cut from the corners so that the volume of the box is greatest.

91. *Revenue* The revenue from selling x units of a product is $R = 12x - 0.3x^2$.

(a) Use a graphing utility to graph the revenue function.

(b) Use the graph to estimate the value of x that yields a revenue of $R = \$120$.

(c) Use factorization to find the value of x that yields a revenue of $R = \$120$.

92. *Height of an Object* A rock is thrown vertically upward from a height of 48 feet (see figure) with an initial velocity of 32 feet per second. The height of the rock is given by

$$\text{Height} = -16t^2 + 32t + 48$$

where the height is measured in feet and the time t is measured in seconds. Find the time for the rock to reach the water.

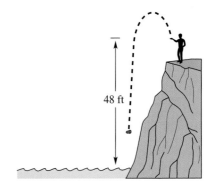

93. *Geometry* The height of a rectangular window is $1\frac{1}{2}$ times its width. The area of the window is 2400 square inches. Find the dimensions of the window.

94. *Geometry* A box with a square base has a surface area of 400 square inches. The height of the box is 5 inches. Find the dimensions of the box. (*Hint:* The surface area is given by $S = 2x^2 + 4xh$.)

95. *Consecutive Integers* The product of two consecutive positive even integers is 168. Find the two integers.

96. *Think About It* In studying for an algebra exam, you and a friend construct trinomials for each other to factor. Explain how you would construct the trinomials and give three examples.

Chapter Test

Take this test as you would take a test in class. After you are done, check your work against the answers given in the back of the book.

In Exercises 1–10, completely factor the polynomial.

1. $7x^2 - 14x^3$

2. $z(z + 7) - 3(z + 7)$

3. $t^2 - 4t - 5$

4. $6x^2 - 11x + 4$

5. $6y^3 + 45y^2 + 75y$

6. $4 - 25v^2$

7. $4x^2 - 20x + 25$

8. $16 - (z + 9)^2$

9. $x^3 + 2x^2 - 9x - 18$

10. $16 - z^4$

11. Find the missing factor: $\dfrac{2}{5}x - \dfrac{3}{5} = \dfrac{1}{5}(\quad\quad)$.

12. Find all values of b such that $x^2 + bx + 5$ can be factored.

13. Find a number c such that $x^2 + 12x + c$ is a perfect square trinomial.

14. Explain why $(x + 1)(3x - 6)$ is not a complete factorization of $3x^2 - 3x - 6$.

In Exercises 15–18, solve the equation.

15. $(x + 4)(2x - 3) = 0$

16. $7x^2 - 14x = 0$

17. $3x^2 + 7x - 6 = 0$

18. $y(2y - 1) = 6$

19. The width of a rectangle is 5 inches less than the length (see figure). The area of the rectangle is 84 square inches. Find the dimensions of the rectangle.

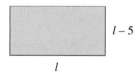

$l - 5$

l

20. An object is dropped from a height of 64 feet. Its height at any time t is modeled by

$$\text{Height} = -16t^2 + 64$$

where the height is measured in feet and the time t is measured in seconds. How long will it take the object to hit the ground? How long will it take the object to fall to a height of 28 feet?

21. The product of two consecutive positive even integers is 624. Find the two integers.

Cumulative Test: Chapters 4–6

Take this test as you would take a test in class. After you are done, check your work against the answers given in the back of the book.

1. Describe how to identify the quadrants in which the points $(-2, y)$ must be located. (y is a real number.)

2. Determine whether the ordered pairs are solution points of the equation $9x - 4y + 36 = 0$.

   (a) $(-1, -1)$ (b) $(8, 27)$ (c) $(-4, 0)$ (d) $(3, -2)$

In Exercises 3 and 4, sketch the graph of the equation and determine any intercepts of the graph.

3. $y = 2 - |x|$

4. $y = \frac{1}{2}x - 2$

5. The slope of a line is $-\frac{1}{4}$ and a point on the line is $(2, 1)$. Find the coordinates of a second point on the line. Explain why there are many correct answers.

6. Find an equation of the line through $\left(0, -\frac{3}{2}\right)$ with slope $m = \frac{5}{6}$.

In Exercises 7 and 8, sketch the lines and determine whether they are parallel, perpendicular, or neither.

7. $y = \frac{2}{3}x - 3$, $y = -\frac{3}{2}x + 1$

8. $y = 2 - 0.4x$, $y = -\frac{2}{5}x$

9. Subtract: $(x^3 - 3x^2) - (x^3 + 2x^2 - 5)$

10. Multiply: $(6z)(-7z)(z^2)$

11. Multiply: $(3x + 5)(x - 4)$

12. Multiply: $(5x - 3)(5x + 3)$

13. Expand: $(5x + 6)^2$

14. Divide: $(6x^2 + 72x) \div 6x$

15. Divide: $\dfrac{x^2 - 3x - 2}{x - 4}$

16. Evaluate: $(3^2 \cdot 4^{-1})^2$

17. Factor: $2u^2 - 6u$

18. Factor and simplify: $(x - 2)^2 - 16$

19. Factor completely: $x^3 + 8x^2 + 16x$

20. Factor completely: $x^3 + 2x^2 - 4x - 8$

21. Solve: $u(u - 12) = 0$

22. Solve: $5x^2 - 12x - 9 = 0$

23. Rewrite the expression $\left(\dfrac{x}{2}\right)^{-2}$ using positive exponents.

24. Evaluate the function $g(t) = 2t^2 - |t|$ at the given values of t.

   (a) $g(-2)$ (b) $g(2)$ (c) $g(0)$ (d) $g\left(-\frac{1}{2}\right)$

25. A sales representative is reimbursed $125 per day for lodging and meals, plus $0.35 per mile driven. Write a linear equation giving the daily cost C to the company in terms of x, the number of miles driven. Explain the reasoning you used to write the model. Find the cost for a day when the representative drives 70 miles.

7 Systems of Linear Equations

Jerry Driendl

The average annual wages and earnings for a person working in the Information Technologies (IT) industry in 1996 was $48,488. (Source: U.S. Department of Commerce)

Motivating the Chapter

 ## Pay Analysis

You have two job offers for sales positions in the technology industry. The first job pays $600 per week plus a sales commission of 4% of your sales. The second job pays $400 per week plus a sales commission of 5% of your sales.

See Section 7.1, Exercise 65

a. Write a linear equation that represents the weekly salary of the first job as a function of sales. Write a second linear equation that represents the weekly salary of the second job as a function of sales.

b. Graph both equations in part (a) on the same coordinate plane. Estimate the point at which the lines intersect. What does this point of intersection represent in the real-life context of this problem?

See Section 7.2, Exercise 65

c. Write the linear equations from part (a) as a system of linear equations. Using the method of substitution, which variable would you solve for first? Explain why you chose that variable.

d. For what amount of sales is the weekly salary the same for both jobs?

See Section 7.3, Exercise 69

e. To solve the system of equations in part (c), you could multiply both equations by 100 to produce a system with integer coefficients. What are the advantages and disadvantages of this when using the method of elimination?

f. Solve the system using the method of elimination. For what level of sales will the second job pay more? Explain.

7.1   Solving Systems of Equations by Graphing

Objectives

1 Determine if an ordered pair is a solution to a system of equations.

2 Use the coordinate plane to solve a system of equations graphically.

1 Determine if an ordered pair is a solution to a system of equations.

Systems of Linear Equations

Up to this point in the text, most problems have involved just one equation in either one or two variables. However, many problems in science, business, health services, and government involve two or more equations in two or more variables. For example, consider the following problem.

> A total of $12,000 is invested in two funds paying 9% and 11% simple interest. The combined annual interest for the two funds is $1180. How much of the $12,000 is invested at each rate?

Letting x and y denote the amounts (in dollars) in the two funds, you can translate this problem into the following pair of linear equations in two variables.

$$x + \quad y = 12{,}000$$

$$0.09x + 0.11y = \quad 1{,}180$$

Taken together, these two equations form a **system of linear equations**. A **solution** of such a system is an ordered pair (a, b) that satisfies *both* equations.

Example 1   Checking a Solution

Show that $(2, -1)$ is a solution of the following system.

$$3x + 2y = \quad 4 \qquad \text{Equation 1}$$

$$-x + 3y = -5 \qquad \text{Equation 2}$$

Solution

To check that a point is a solution, substitute the coordinates of the point into each equation. In the first equation, the substitution produces

$$3(2) + 2(-1) \stackrel{?}{=} 4 \qquad \text{Substitute 2 for } x \text{ and } -1 \text{ for } y.$$

$$6 - 2 = 4 \qquad \text{Solution checks in 1st equation. } \checkmark$$

and in the second equation, the substitution produces

$$-(2) + 3(-1) \stackrel{?}{=} -5 \qquad \text{Substitute 2 for } x \text{ and } -1 \text{ for } y.$$

$$-2 - 3 = -5. \qquad \text{Solution checks in 2nd equation. } \checkmark$$

Because the solution $(2, -1)$ checks in *both* equations, you can conclude that it is a solution of the given system of linear equations. The solution can also be checked graphically by observing that it is the point of intersection of the graphs of the two equations, as shown in Figure 7.1.

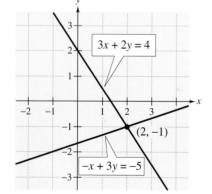

Figure 7.1

2 Use the coordinate plane to solve a system of equations graphically.

Solving a System of Equations by Graphing

In this chapter you will study three methods for solving a system of two linear equations in two variables. The first method is *solution by graphing*. With this method, you first sketch the lines representing the two equations. Then you try to determine whether the two lines intersect in a point, as illustrated in Example 2.

Example 2   Solving a System of Linear Equations

Solve the following system by graphing each equation and locating the point of intersection.

$$x + \ \ y = -2 \qquad \text{Equation 1}$$
$$2x - 3y = -9 \qquad \text{Equation 2}$$

Remind students that they could sketch the graphs of these lines by considering slopes and y-intercepts instead of making tables of values. The line $y = -x - 2$ has slope $m = -1$ and y-intercept $(0, -2)$. The line $y = \frac{2}{3}x + 3$ has slope $m = \frac{2}{3}$ and y-intercept $(0, 3)$.

Solution

One way to begin is to write each equation in slope-intercept form.

Equation 1	*Equation 2*
$x + y = -2$	$2x - 3y = -9$
$y = -x - 2$	$-3y = -2x - 9$
	$y = \dfrac{2}{3}x + 3$

Then employ a numerical approach by creating two tables of values.

Table of Values for Equation 1

x	-4	-3	-2	-1	0	1	2
$y = -x - 2$	2	1	0	-1	-2	-3	-4

Table of Values for Equation 2

x	-4	-3	-2	-1	0	1	2
$y = \frac{2}{3}x + 3$	$\frac{1}{3}$	1	$\frac{5}{3}$	$\frac{7}{3}$	3	$\frac{11}{3}$	$\frac{13}{3}$

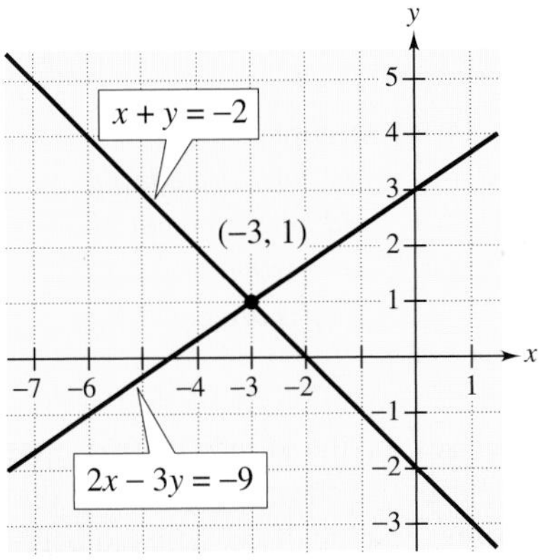

It may happen, as it did in these two tables, that you discover a common solution point, the point $(-3, 1)$. Another way to solve the system is to sketch the graphs of both equations, as shown in Figure 7.2. From the graph, it appears that the lines intersect at the point $(-3, 1)$. To verify this, substitute the coordinates of the point into each of the two given equations.

Substitute into 1st Equation	*Substitute into 2nd Equation*
$x + y = -2$	$2x - 3y = -9$
$-3 + 1 \overset{?}{=} -2$	$2(-3) - 3(1) \overset{?}{=} -9$
$-2 = -2 \ \checkmark$	$-9 = -9 \ \checkmark$

Because both equations are satisfied, the point $(-3, 1)$ is the solution of the system.

Figure 7.2

A good question to ask at this point is, Does every system of two linear equations in two variables have a single solution point? This is the same as asking, Do every two lines in a plane *intersect* in a single point? When you think about it, you can see that the answer to the second question is no. In fact, for two lines in a plane, there are three possible relationships.

▶ Number of Points of Intersection of Two Lines

1. The two lines can intersect in a single point. The corresponding system of linear equations has a single solution and is called **consistent.**

2. The two lines can coincide and have infinitely many points of intersection. The corresponding consistent system of linear equations has infinitely many solutions and is called **dependent.**

3. The two lines can be parallel and have no point of intersection. The corresponding system of linear equations has no solution and is called **inconsistent.**

These three possibilities are shown in Figure 7.3. Note that the word *consistent* is used to mean that the system of linear equations has at least one solution, whereas the word *inconsistent* is used to mean that the system of linear equations has no solution. Here are some examples.

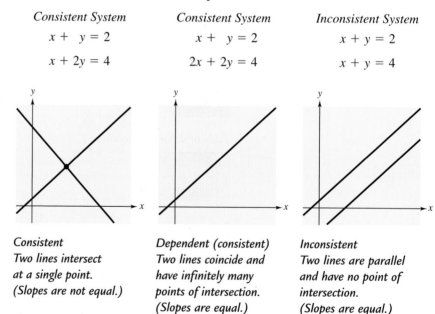

Consistent System	*Consistent System*	*Inconsistent System*
$x + y = 2$	$x + y = 2$	$x + y = 2$
$x + 2y = 4$	$2x + 2y = 4$	$x + y = 4$

Consistent
Two lines intersect at a single point.
(Slopes are not equal.)

Dependent (consistent)
Two lines coincide and have infinitely many points of intersection.
(Slopes are equal.)

Inconsistent
Two lines are parallel and have no point of intersection.
(Slopes are equal.)

Figure 7.3

You can see from Figure 7.3 that a comparison of the slopes of two lines gives useful information about the number of solutions of the corresponding system of equations. So, to solve a system of equations graphically, it helps to begin by writing the equations in slope-intercept form,

$$y = mx + b.$$

Example 3   A System with No Solution

Solve the following system of linear equations.

$$x - y = 2 \qquad \text{Equation 1}$$
$$-3x + 3y = 6 \qquad \text{Equation 2}$$

Solution

Begin by writing each equation in slope-intercept form.

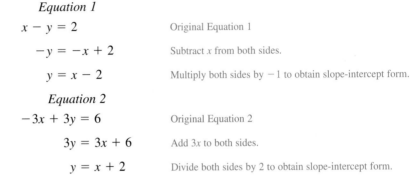

Equation 1

$x - y = 2$	Original Equation 1
$-y = -x + 2$	Subtract x from both sides.
$y = x - 2$	Multiply both sides by -1 to obtain slope-intercept form.

Equation 2

$-3x + 3y = 6$	Original Equation 2
$3y = 3x + 6$	Add $3x$ to both sides.
$y = x + 2$	Divide both sides by 2 to obtain slope-intercept form.

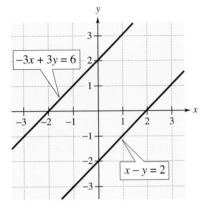

Figure 7.4

From these slope-intercept forms, you can see that the lines representing the two equations are parallel (each has a slope of 1), as shown in Figure 7.4. So, the given system of linear equations has no solution and is an inconsistent system. Try constructing tables of values for the two equations. The tables should help convince you that there is no solution.

Example 4   A System with Infinitely Many Solutions

Solve the following system of linear equations.

$$x - y = 2 \qquad \text{Equation 1}$$
$$-3x + 3y = -6 \qquad \text{Equation 2}$$

Solution

Begin by writing each equation in slope-intercept form.

$y = x - 2$	Slope-intercept form of Equation 1
$y = x - 2$	Slope-intercept form of Equation 2

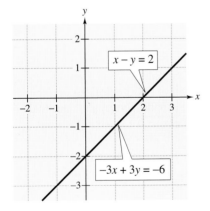

Figure 7.5

From these forms, you can see that the lines representing the two equations are the same (see Figure 7.5). So, the given system of linear equations is dependent and has infinitely many solutions. You can describe the solution set by saying that each point on the line $y = x - 2$ is a solution of the system of linear equations.

Note in Examples 3 and 4 that if the two lines representing a system of linear equations have the same slope, the system must have either no solution or infinitely many solutions. On the other hand, if the two lines have different slopes, they must intersect in a single point and the corresponding system has a single solution.

Example 5 A System with a Single Solution

Solve the following system of linear equations.

$$2x + y = 4 \qquad \text{Equation 1}$$

$$4x + 3y = 9 \qquad \text{Equation 2}$$

Solution

Begin by writing each equation in slope-intercept form.

Equation 1	*Equation 2*
$2x + y = 4$	$4x + 3y = 9$
$y = -2x + 4$	$3y = -4x + 9$
	$y = -\frac{4}{3}x + 3$

The slope-intercept forms of the two equations are as follows.

$$y = -2x + 4 \qquad \text{Slope-intercept form of Equation 1}$$

$$y = -\tfrac{4}{3}x + 3 \qquad \text{Slope-intercept form of Equation 2}$$

Because the lines do not have the same slope, you know that they intersect. To find the point of intersection, sketch both lines on the same rectangular coordinate system, as shown in Figure 7.6. From this sketch, it appears that the solution occurs near the point $\left(\frac{3}{2}, 1\right)$. To check this solution, substitute the coordinates of the point into each of the two given equations.

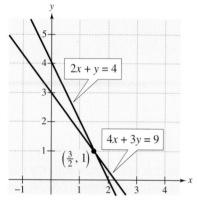

Figure 7.6

$$
\begin{array}{cc}
\textit{Substitute into 1st Equation} & \textit{Substitute into 2nd Equation} \\
2x + y = 4 & 4x + 3y = 9 \\
2\left(\tfrac{3}{2}\right) + 1 \stackrel{?}{=} 4 & 4\left(\tfrac{3}{2}\right) + 3(1) \stackrel{?}{=} 9 \\
3 + 1 = 4 \ \checkmark & 6 + 3 = 9 \ \checkmark
\end{array}
$$

Because *both* equations are satisfied, the point $\left(\frac{3}{2}, 1\right)$ is the solution of the system.

Technology: Tip

The zoom and trace features of a graphing utility can be used to approximate the solution point of a system of linear equations. A more accurate result can be obtained using the *intersect* feature of a graphing utility. Consult the user's guide of your graphing utility for the steps in using this feature. Then, use the intersect feature to find the solution point in Example 5.

There are two things you should note in Example 5. First, your success in applying the graphing method of solving a system of linear equations depends on sketching accurate graphs. Second, once you have made a graph and "guessed" at the point of intersection, it is critical that you check to see whether the point you have chosen is actually the solution.

As you take other courses in algebra, you will study systems of equations that are *not* linear. When you do that, you will learn that the discussion of the number of solutions on page 376 applies only to systems of *linear* equations. A nonlinear system such as

$$y = 2x + 3 \qquad \text{Equation 1}$$

$$y = x^2 \qquad \text{Equation 2}$$

does not have to have zero, one, or infinitely many solutions. Try sketching a graph of this system. How many solutions does it have? Try estimating the solutions from the graphs and then check your estimates in each equation.

| Example 6 | Geometry: Area and Perimeter | |

A rectangular dog pen has an area of 144 square feet and a perimeter of 52 feet. What are the dimensions of the dog pen?

a. Write a system of equations for this problem.

b. Solve the system graphically.

Solution

a. Let x be the width and let y be the length of the dog pen. The equation that represents the area is

$$\text{Area} = \text{width} \cdot \text{length}$$

$$144 = x \cdot y.$$

The equation that represents the perimeter is

$$\text{Perimeter} = 2(\text{width}) + 2(\text{length})$$

$$52 = 2x + 2y$$

$$26 = x + y.$$

So, the system of equations for this problem is

$$x \cdot y = 144$$

$$x + y = 26.$$

b. Solve the first equation for y and graph it using the point-plotting method.

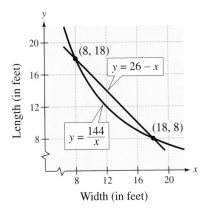

Figure 7.7

x	6	8	9	12	16	18	20
$y = 144/x$	24	18	16	12	9	8	7.2

Solve the second equation for y and graph its equation. Figure 7.7 shows the graphs of $y = 144/x$ and $y = 26 - x$. From the graph you can see that the solutions are $(8, 18)$ and $(18, 8)$. So, the dimension of the dog pen is 8 feet by 18 feet. Check the solution in the original problem.

$$\text{Area} = x \cdot y = 8 \cdot 18 = 144 \text{ square feet} \checkmark$$

$$\text{Perimeter} = 2x + 2y = 2(8) + 2(18) = 16 + 36 = 52 \text{ feet} \checkmark$$

| Discussing the Concept | Creating Systems of Equations from Their Graphs |

Make up a system of linear equations with integer solutions, and graph the system. On your graph, label the point of intersection but not the equations of the lines. Exchange your graph with another class member, and try to find a system of equations for the graph. Compare the system you find with the one made up by the person who made the graph. Discuss whether the two linear systems must be equivalent.

7.1   Exercises

Integrated Review   *Concepts, Skills, and Problem Solving*

Keep mathematically in shape by doing these exercises *before* the problems of this section.

Properties and Definitions

In Exercises 1–4, use $ax^2 + bx + c = (x + m)(x + n)$.

1. $mn =$

2. If $c > 0$, then what must be true about the signs of m and n?

3. If $c < 0$, then what must be true about the signs of m and n?

4. If m and n have like signs, then $m + n =$ _____.

Solving Equations

In Exercises 5–10, solve the equation and check your answer.

5. $x - 6 = 5x$ **6.** $2 - 3x = 14 + x$

7. $y - 3(4y - 2) = 1$ **8.** $y + 6(3 - 2y) = 4$

9. $\dfrac{x}{2} - \dfrac{x}{5} = 15$ **10.** $\dfrac{x - 4}{10} = 6$

Models

In Exercises 11 and 12, translate the phrase into an algebraic expression.

11. The time to travel 250 miles if the average speed is r miles per hour.

12. The perimeter of a rectangle of length L and width $L/2$

Developing Skills

In Exercises 1–6, determine which ordered pair is a solution to the system of equations. See Example 1.

	System	Ordered Pairs	
1.	$x + 3y = 11$ $-x + 3y = 7$	(a) $(2, 3)$	(b) $(5, 4)$
2.	$3x - y = -2$ $x - 3y = 2$	(a) $(0, 2)$	(b) $(-1, -1)$
3.	$2x - 3y = -8$ $x + y = 1$	(a) $(5, -3)$	(b) $(-1, 2)$
4.	$5x - 3y = -12$ $x - 4y = 1$	(a) $(-3, -1)$	(b) $(3, 1)$
5.	$5x - 6y = -2$ $7x + y = -31$	(a) $(-4, -3)$	(b) $(-3, -4)$
6.	$-x - y = 6$ $-5x - 2y = 3$	(a) $(7, -13)$	(b) $(3, -9)$

In Exercises 7–14, use the graph to determine the solution (if any) of the system of linear equations. Check your solution.

7. $2x + y = 4$
   $x - y = 2$

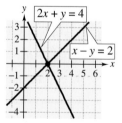

8. $x + 3y = 2$
   $-x + 2y = 3$

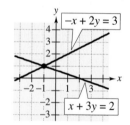

9. $x - y = 0$
   $3x - 2y = -1$

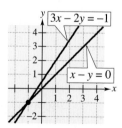

10. $2x - y = 2$
   $4x + 3y = 24$

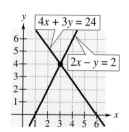

11. $x - 2y = -4$
      $-0.5x + y = 2$

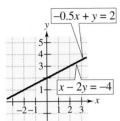

12. $x - 3y = 3$
      $2x - y = 6$

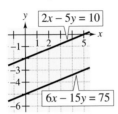

13. $2x - 3y = 6$
      $4x + 3y = 12$

14. $2x - 5y = 10$
      $6x - 15y = 75$

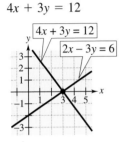

29. $4x - 3y = 3$
      $4x - 3y = 0$

30. $2x + 5y = 5$
      $-2x - 5y = -5$

31. $x - 8y = -40$
      $-5x + 8y = 8$

32. $9x + 8y = 48$
      $-5x + 8y = -8$

33. $x + 2y = 3$
      $x - 3y = 13$

34. $-x + 10y = 30$
      $x + 10y = 10$

35. $x + 7y = -5$
      $3x - 2y = 8$

36. $x + 2y = 4$
      $2x - 2y = -1$

37. $-3x + 10y = 15$
      $3x - 10y = 15$

38. $4x - 9y = 12$
      $-4x + 9y = 12$

39. $4x + 5y = 20$
      $\frac{4}{5}x + y = 4$

40. $3x + 7y = 15$
      $x + \frac{7}{3}y = 5$

41. $8x - 6y = -12$
      $x - \frac{3}{4}y = -2$

42. $-x + \frac{2}{3}y = 5$
      $9x - 6y = 6$

43. $-3x + 7y = 25$
      $7x + 2y = 70$

44. $-4x + 3y = 10$
      $7x + y = 20$

In Exercises 15–44, solve the system of linear equations by graphing. See Examples 1–5.

15. $y = -x + 3$
      $y = x + 1$

16. $y = 2x - 1$
      $y = x + 1$

17. $y = 2x - 4$
      $y = -\frac{1}{2}x + 1$

18. $y = \frac{1}{2}x + 2$
      $y = -x + 8$

19. $x - y = 2$
      $x + y = 2$

20. $x - y = 0$
      $x + y = 4$

21. $3x - 4y = 5$
      $x = 3$

22. $7x + 2y = 18$
      $y = 2$

23. $2x + 3y = 10$
      $y = 3$

24. $x = 4$
      $2x - y = 5$

25. $-x + 2y = 4$
      $x - 2y = 4$

26. $3x - y = 1$
      $-3x + y = 1$

27. $4x - 5y = 0$
      $6x - 5y = 10$

28. $3x + 2y = -6$
      $3x - 2y = 6$

In Exercises 45–48, use a graphing utility to solve the system. Check your solution.

45. $y = 2x - 1$
      $y = -3x + 9$

46. $y = \frac{3}{4}x + 2$
      $y = x + 1$

47. $y = x - 1$
      $y = -2x + 8$

48. $y = 2x + 3$
      $y = -x - 3$

In Exercises 49–56, write the equations of the lines in slope-intercept form. What can you conclude about the number of solutions of the system?

49. $2x - 3y = -12$
      $-8x + 12y = -12$

50. $-5x + 8y = 8$
      $7x - 4y = 14$

51. $-x + 4y = 7$
      $3x - 12y = -21$

52. $3x + 8y = 28$
      $-4x + 9y = 1$

53. $-2x + 3y = 4$
      $2x + 3y = 8$

54. $2x + 5y = 15$
      $2x - 5y = 5$

55. $-6x + 8y = 9$
      $3x - 4y = -6$

56. $-6x + 8y = 9$
      $3x - 4y = -4.5$

Solving Problems

57. *Geometry*   A rectangular play yard has an area of 150 square feet and a perimeter of 50 feet. What are the dimensions of the play yard?

58. *Geometry*   A rectangular garden has an area of 108 square feet and a perimeter of 42 feet. What are the dimensions of the garden?

59. *Writing and Solving a Model*   The sum of two numbers is 20 and the difference of the two numbers is 2. Write a system of equations that models this problem and solve the system graphically.

60. *Writing and Solving a Model*   The sum of two numbers is 35 and the difference of the two numbers is 11. Write a system of equations that models this problem and solve the system graphically.

61. *Break-Even Point*   A small company produces a product that sells for $23 per unit. The cost for producing each unit is $16.75 and the company has fixed costs of $400.

(a) Use a verbal model to show that the cost C for producing x units is $C = 16.75x + 400$ and the revenue R for selling x units is $R = 23x$.

(b) Use a graphing utility to graph the cost and revenue functions. Approximate the point of intersection of the graphs and interpret the result.

62. *Supply and Demand*   The Law of Supply and Demand states that as the price of a product increases, the demand for the product decreases and the supply increases. The demand and supply equations for a product are $x = 90 - p$ and $x = 24 + \frac{1}{2}p$, respectively. Market equilibrium is the point of intersection of the two equations. Use a graphing utility to graph the equations and determine the price that yields market equilibrium.

Think About It   In Exercises 63 and 64, the graphs of the two equations appear parallel. Are the two lines actually parallel? Does the system have a solution? If so, find the solution.

63. $x - 200y = -200$
$x - 199y = 198$

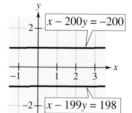

64. $25x - 24y = 0$
$13x - 12y = 24$

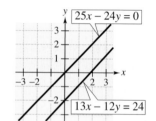

Explaining Concepts

65. Answer parts (a) and (b) of Motivating the Chapter on page 373.

66. Give a geometric description of the three cases for a linear system of equations in two variables.

67. In your own words, explain what is meant by a dependent system of linear equations.

68. In your own words, explain what is meant by an inconsistent system of linear equations.

69. *True or False?*   It is possible for a consistent system of linear equations to have exactly two solutions.

70. *Creating a System*   Write a system of linear equations with integer coefficients that has the unique solution (3, 1). (There are many correct answers.)

71. *Creating an Example*   Write an example of a system of linear equations that has no solution.

72. *Creating an Example*   Write an example of a system of linear equations that has infinitely many solutions.

7.2   Solving Systems of Equations by Substitution

Objectives

1 Use the method of substitution to solve a system of equations algebraically.

2 Use the method of substitution to solve a system with no solution or infinitely many solutions.

3 Use the method of substitution to solve an application problem.

1 Use the method of substitution to solve a system of equations algebraically.

The Method of Substitution

Solving systems of equations by graphing is useful but less accurate than algebraic methods. In this section, you will study an algebraic method called the **method of substitution.** The goal of the method of substitution is to *reduce a system of two linear equations in two variables to a single equation in one variable.* Examples 1 and 2 illustrate the basic steps of the method.

Example 1   The Method of Substitution

Solve the following system of linear equations.

$$-x + y = 1 \qquad \text{Equation 1}$$

$$2x + y = -2 \qquad \text{Equation 2}$$

Solution

Begin by solving for y in the first equation.

$$-x + y = 1 \qquad \text{Original Equation 1}$$

$$y = x + 1 \qquad \text{Revised Equation 1}$$

Next, substitute this expression for y into Equation 2.

$$2x + y = -2 \qquad \text{Equation 2}$$

$$2x + (x + 1) = -2 \qquad \text{Substitute } x + 1 \text{ for } y.$$

$$3x + 1 = -2 \qquad \text{Combine like terms.}$$

$$3x = -3 \qquad \text{Subtract 1 from both sides.}$$

$$x = -1 \qquad \text{Divide both sides by 3.}$$

At this point, you know that the x-coordinate of the solution is -1. To find the y-coordinate, *back-substitute* the x-value into the revised Equation 1.

$$y = x + 1 \qquad \text{Revised Equation 1}$$

$$y = -1 + 1 \qquad \text{Substitute } -1 \text{ for } x.$$

$$y = 0 \qquad \text{Simplify.}$$

The solution is $(-1, 0)$. Check this solution by substituting $x = -1$ and $y = 0$ into both of the original equations.

You might point out that the solution obtained by substitution is the same solution that would be found by graphing. The two lines would intersect at $(-1, 0)$.

Study Tip

The term **back-substitute** implies that you work backwards. After solving for one of the variables, substitute that value back into one of the equations in the original (or revised) system to find the value of the other variable.

Caution students to avoid the common error of forgetting to find values for *both* variables.

Example 2 The Method of Substitution

Solve the following system of linear equations.

$$5x + 7y = 1 \qquad \text{Equation 1}$$

$$x + 4y = -5 \qquad \text{Equation 2}$$

Solution

For this system, it is convenient to begin by solving for x in the second equation.

$$x + 4y = -5 \qquad \text{Original Equation 2}$$

$$x = -4y - 5 \qquad \text{Revised Equation 2}$$

Substituting this expression for x into the first equation produces the following.

$$5(-4y - 5) + 7y = 1 \qquad \text{Substitute } -4y - 5 \text{ for } x \text{ in Equation 1.}$$

$$-20y - 25 + 7y = 1 \qquad \text{Distributive Property}$$

$$-13y - 25 = 1 \qquad \text{Combine like terms.}$$

$$-13y = 26 \qquad \text{Add 25 to both sides.}$$

$$y = -2 \qquad \text{Divide both sides by } -13.$$

Finally, back-substitute this y-value into the revised second equation.

$$x = -4(-2) - 5 \qquad \text{Substitute } -2 \text{ for } y \text{ in revised Equation 2.}$$

$$x = 3 \qquad \text{Simplify.}$$

The solution is $(3, -2)$. Check this by substituting $x = 3$ and $y = -2$ into both of the original equations, as follows.

Substitute into 1st Equation   *Substitute into 2nd Equation*

$$5x + 7y = 1 \qquad\qquad x + 4y = -5$$

$$5(3) + 7(-2) \overset{?}{=} 1 \qquad\qquad (3) + 4(-2) \overset{?}{=} -5$$

$$15 - 14 = 1 \checkmark \qquad\qquad 3 - 8 = -5 \checkmark$$

The method of substitution demonstrated in Examples 1 and 2 has the following four steps.

Study Tip

When you use the method of substitution, it does not matter which variable you choose to solve for first. You should choose the variable that is easier to work with. For instance, in the system

$$3x - 2y = 1 \qquad \text{Equation 1}$$

$$x + 4y = 3 \qquad \text{Equation 2}$$

it is easier first to solve for x in the second equation. On the other hand, in the system

$$2x + y = 5 \qquad \text{Equation 1}$$

$$3x - 2y = 11 \qquad \text{Equation 2}$$

it is easier first to solve for y in the first equation.

▶ **The Method of Substitution**

1. Solve one of the equations for one variable in terms of the other.

2. Substitute the expression obtained in Step 1 into the other equation and solve the resulting one-variable equation.

3. Back-substitute the solution in Step 2 into the expression found in Step 1 to find the other variable.

4. Check your answer to see that it satisfies both of the original equations.

If neither variable has a coefficient of 1 in a system of linear equations, you can still use the method of substitution. However, you may have to work with some fractions in the solution steps.

Example 3   The Method of Substitution

Solve the following system of linear equations.

$$5x + 3y = 18 \qquad \text{Equation 1}$$

$$2x - 7y = -1 \qquad \text{Equation 2}$$

Solution

Step 1   Because neither variable has a coefficient of 1, you can choose to solve for either variable. For instance, you can begin by solving for x in Equation 1.

$$5x + 3y = 18 \qquad \text{Original Equation 1}$$

$$x = -\frac{3}{5}y + \frac{18}{5} \qquad \text{Revised Equation 1}$$

Step 2   Substitute for x in Equation 2 and solve for y.

$$2x - 7y = -1 \qquad \text{Equation 2}$$

$$2\left(-\frac{3}{5}y + \frac{18}{5}\right) - 7y = -1 \qquad \text{Substitute } -\frac{3}{5}y + \frac{18}{5} \text{ for } x.$$

$$-\frac{6}{5}y + \frac{36}{5} - 7y = -1 \qquad \text{Distributive Property}$$

$$-6y + 36 - 35y = -5 \qquad \text{Multiply both sides by 5.}$$

$$36 - 41y = -5 \qquad \text{Combine like terms.}$$

$$-41y = -41 \qquad \text{Subtract 36 from both sides.}$$

$$y = 1 \qquad \text{Divide both sides by } -41.$$

Step 3   Back-substitute for y in the revised first equation.

$$x = -\frac{3}{5}y + \frac{18}{5} \qquad \text{Revised Equation 1}$$

$$x = -\frac{3}{5}(1) + \frac{18}{5} \qquad \text{Substitute 1 for } y.$$

$$x = 3 \qquad \text{Simplify.}$$

Step 4   The solution is $(3, 1)$. Check this in the original system.

In Example 3, notice that you can begin the solution by solving for x or y in either the first or second equation. For instance, suppose you started by solving for y in Equation 1.

$$5x + 3y = 18 \qquad \text{Original Equation 1}$$

$$y = -\tfrac{5}{3}x + 6 \qquad \text{Revised Equation 1}$$

How would you complete this solution? Do you obtain the same solution?

2 Use the method of substitution to solve a system with no solution or infinitely many solutions.

The No-Solution and Many-Solution Cases

The next two examples show how the method of substitution identifies systems of equations that have no solution or infinitely many solutions.

Example 4   The Method of Substitution: No-Solution Case

Solve the following system of linear equations.

$$x - 3y = 2 \qquad \text{Equation 1}$$
$$-2x + 6y = 2 \qquad \text{Equation 2}$$

Solution

Begin by solving for x in Equation 1 to obtain $x = 3y + 2$. Then, substitute for x in Equation 2.

$$-2x + 6y = 2 \qquad \text{Equation 2}$$
$$-2(3y + 2) + 6y = 2 \qquad \text{Substitute } 3y + 2 \text{ for } x.$$
$$-6y - 4 + 6y = 2 \qquad \text{Distributive Property}$$
$$-4 = 2 \qquad \text{Simplify.}$$

Because the substitution results in the false statement $-4 = 2$, the system is inconsistent and has no solution. The graphs in Figure 7.8 confirm this result.

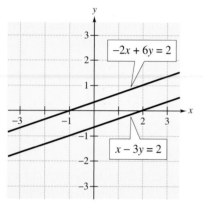

Figure 7.8

Example 5   The Method of Substitution: Many-Solution Case

Solve the following system of linear equations.

$$9x + 3y = 15 \qquad \text{Equation 1}$$
$$3x + y = 5 \qquad \text{Equation 2}$$

Solution

Begin by solving for y in Equation 2 to obtain $y = -3x + 5$. Then substitute for y in Equation 1.

$$9x + 3y = 15 \qquad \text{Equation 1}$$
$$9x + 3(-3x + 5) = 15 \qquad \text{Substitute } -3x + 5 \text{ for } y.$$
$$9x - 9x + 15 = 15 \qquad \text{Distributive Property}$$
$$15 = 15 \qquad \text{Simplify.}$$

Study Tip

By writing both equations in Example 5 in slope-intercept form, you will get identical equations. This means that the lines coincide and the system has infinitely many solutions.

The equation $15 = 15$ is true for any value of x. This implies that any solution of Equation 2 is also a solution of Equation 1. In other words, the given system of linear equations is *dependent* and has infinitely many solutions. The solutions consist of all ordered pairs (x, y) such that $3x + y = 5$. Some sample solutions are $(-1, 8)$, $(0, 5)$, and $(1, 2)$.

3 Use the method of substitution to solve an application problem.

Application

Example 6 uses the method of substitution to solve the interest rate problem introduced on page 374.

| Example 6 | An Application of a System of Linear Equations | |

Solve the following system of equations.

$$x + \quad y = 12{,}000 \qquad \text{Equation 1}$$
$$0.09x + 0.11y = \quad 1{,}180 \qquad \text{Equation 2}$$

Solution

To begin, it is convenient to multiply both sides of the second equation by 100. This eliminates the need to work with decimals.

$$0.09x + 0.11y = \quad 1{,}180 \qquad \text{Equation 2}$$
$$9x + \quad 11y = 118{,}000 \qquad \text{Multiply both sides by 100.}$$

Then solve for x in Equation 1.

$$x + y = 12{,}000 \qquad \text{Equation 1}$$
$$x = 12{,}000 - y \qquad \text{Subtract } y \text{ from both sides.}$$

Next, substitute this expression for x into the revised Equation 2 and solve for y.

$$9x + 11y = 118{,}000 \qquad \text{Revised Equation 2}$$
$$9(12{,}000 - y) + 11y = 118{,}000 \qquad \text{Substitute } 12{,}000 - y \text{ for } x.$$
$$108{,}000 - 9y + 11y = 118{,}000 \qquad \text{Distributive Property}$$
$$2y = 10{,}000 \qquad \text{Simplify.}$$
$$y = 5000 \qquad \text{Divide both sides by 2.}$$

Back-substitute the value $y = 5000$ to solve for x.

$$x = 12{,}000 - 5000 = 7000$$

So, the solution is (7000, 5000). Check this in the statement of the problem given on page 374.

Technology: Tip

The general solution of the linear system

$$ax + by = c$$
$$dx + ey = f$$

is $x = (ce - bf)/(ae - db)$ and $y = (af - cd)/(ae - db)$. If $ae - db = 0$, the system does not have a unique solution. Graphing utility programs for solving such a system can be found at our website *www.hmco.com*. Try using this program to solve the system in Example 6.

| Discussing the Concept | Another Form for a System of Equations |

Your instructor says, "An equation (not in standard form) such as $2x - 3 = 5x - 9$ can be considered a system of equations." Discuss this idea in your class. Create the system, and find the solution point. How many solution points does the "system" $x^2 - 1 = 2x - 1$ have? Illustrate your result with a graphing utility.

7.2 Exercises

Integrated Review   **Concepts, Skills, and Problem Solving**

Keep mathematically in shape by doing these exercises *before* the problems of this section.

Properties and Definitions

1. A linear equation of the form $2x + 8 = 7$ has how many solutions?

2. What is the usual first step when solving an equation such as

$$\frac{x}{6} + \frac{3}{2} = \frac{7}{4}?$$

Factoring and Solving Equations

In Exercises 3–6, factor the expression.

3. $x(3 - x) - 2(3 - x)$ 4. $4t^2 - 9$

5. $4y^2 - 20y + 25$ 6. $6u^2 - 5u - 21$

In Exercises 7–10, solve the equation.

7. $14 - 2x = x + 2$

8. $\dfrac{9 + x}{3} = 15$

9. $z^2 - 4z - 12 = 0$

10. $t^3 + t^2 - 4t - 4 = 0$

Graphs and Models

11. The length of each edge of a cube is x inches. Write the surface area A of the cube as a function of x. Use a graphing utility to graph the model.

12. The speed of an airplane is 475 miles per hour. Write the distance d the plane travels as a function of the flight time t. Graph the model.

Developing Skills

In Exercises 1–8, use substitution to solve the system. Use the graph to check the solution.

1. $x - y = 0$
   $x + y = 2$

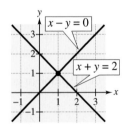

2. $x + y = 1$
   $2x - y = 2$

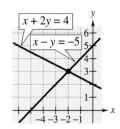

3. $2x + y = 4$
   $-x + y = 1$

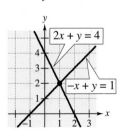

4. $x - y = -5$
   $x + 2y = 4$

5. $-x + y = 1$
   $x - y = 1$

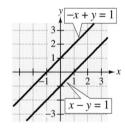

6. $4x + 3y = 8$
   $-4x + y = 8$

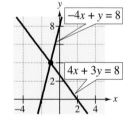

7. $2x - y = 2$
   $4x + 3y = 9$

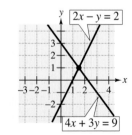

8. $x + 2y = 6$
   $x + 2y = 2$

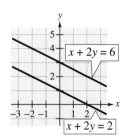

In Exercises 9–42, use substitution to solve the system. See Examples 1–5.

9. $y = 2x - 1$
$y = -x + 5$

10. $y = -2x + 9$
$y = 3x - 1$

11. $x = 4y - 5$
$x = 3y$

12. $x = -5y - 2$
$x = 2y - 23$

13. $2x = 8$
$x + y = 1$

14. $3x - y = 0$
$3y = 6$

15. $x - y = 2$
$x - y = 1$

16. $x + y = 8$
$x + y = -1$

17. $x - y = 0$
$2x + y = 0$

18. $x - y = 0$
$5x - 3y = 10$

19. $x - 2y = -10$
$3x - y = 0$

20. $x - 2y = 0$
$3x - y = 0$

21. $2x - y = -2$
$4x + y = 5$

22. $x + 6y = 7$
$-x + 4y = -2$

23. $x + 2y = 1$
$5x - 4y = -23$

24. $-3x + 6y = 4$
$2x + y = 4$

25. $5x + 3y = 11$
$x - 5y = 5$

26. $-3x + y = 4$
$-9x + 5y = 10$

27. $4x - y = 2$
$2x - \frac{1}{2}y = 1$

28. $3x - y = 6$
$4x - \frac{2}{3}y = -4$

29. $\frac{1}{5}x + \frac{1}{2}y = 8$
$2x + y = 20$

30. $\frac{1}{2}x + \frac{3}{4}y = 10$
$4x - y = 4$

31. $-5x + 4y = 14$
$5x - 4y = 4$

32. $3x - 2y = 3$
$-6x + 4y = -6$

33. $2x + y = 8$
$5x + 2.5y = 10$

34. $0.5x + 0.5y = 4$
$x + y = -1$

35. $-6x + 1.5y = 6$
$8x - 2y = -8$

36. $0.3x - 0.3y = 0$
$x - y = 4$

37. $\frac{x}{3} - \frac{y}{4} = 2$
$\frac{x}{2} + \frac{y}{6} = 3$

38. $-\frac{x}{5} + \frac{y}{2} = -3$
$\frac{x}{4} - \frac{y}{4} = 0$

39. $\frac{x}{4} + \frac{y}{2} = 1$
$\frac{x}{2} - \frac{y}{3} = 1$

40. $-\frac{x}{6} + \frac{y}{12} = 1$
$\frac{x}{2} + \frac{y}{8} = 1$

41. $2(x - 5) = y + 2$
$3x = 4(y + 2)$

42. $3(x - 2) + 5 = 4(y + 3) - 2$
$2x + 7 = 2y + 8$

In Exercises 43–48, use substitution to solve the system. Use a graphing utility to check the solution graphically.

43. $y = -2x + 10$
$y = x + 4$

44. $y = \frac{5}{4}x + 3$
$y = \frac{1}{2}x + 6$

45. $3x + 2y = 12$
$x - y = 3$

46. $2x - y = 1$
$x - y = -2$

47. $5x + 3y = 15$
$2x - 3y = 6$

48. $4x - 5y = 0$
$2x - 5y = -10$

In Exercises 49–52, find a system of linear equations that has the given solution. (There are many correct answers.)

49. $(2, 1)$

50. $(4, -3)$

51. $\left(\frac{7}{2}, -3\right)$

52. $\left(-\frac{1}{2}, 1\right)$

Solving Problems

53. *Problem Solving*   The sum of two numbers is 40 and the difference of the two numbers is 10. Find the numbers.

54. *Problem Solving*   The sum of two numbers is 50 and the difference of the two numbers is 20. Find the numbers.

55. *Problem Solving*   The sum of two numbers is 105 and the difference of the two numbers is 5. Find the numbers.

56. *Interest Problem*   A total of $15,000 is invested in two funds paying 5% and 8% simple interest. The combined annual interest for the two funds is $900. How much of the $15,000 is invested at each rate?

57. *Interest Problem*   A total of $10,000 is invested in two funds paying 7% and 10% simple interest. The combined annual interest for the two funds is $775. How much of the $10,000 is invested at each rate?

58. *Problem Solving*   Six people ate dinner for $63.90. The price for adults was $16.95 and the price for children was $7.50. Determine the number of adults.

59. *Problem Solving*   You are selling football tickets. Student tickets cost $2 and general admission tickets cost $3. You sell 1957 tickets and collect $5035. How many of each type of ticket were sold?

60. *Comparing Costs* One car model costs $16,000 and costs an average of $0.26 per mile to maintain. Another car model costs $18,000 and costs an average of $0.22 per mile to maintain. If one of each model is driven the same number of miles, after how many miles would the total costs of the two models be the same?

61. *Analyzing Data* United States exports (in billions of dollars) for the years 1992 through 1996 are given in the table. (Source: U.S. Bureau of the Census)

Year	1992	1993	1994	1995	1996
Exports	448.2	465.1	512.7	584.7	624.8

(a) Plot the points (x, y) on a rectangular coordinate system where x represents the year, with $x = 0$ corresponding to 1990, and y represents exports.

(b) The slope and y-intercept of the line $y = mx + b$ that best fits the data are given by the solution of the following system.

$$5b + 20m = 2,635.5$$
$$20b + 90m = 11,014.8$$

Use the method of substitution to solve the system and find the equation of the required line. Graph the line on the coordinate system used in part (a).

(c) Interpret the meaning of the slope of the line in the context of this problem.

62. *Analyzing Data* United States imports (in billions of dollars) for the years 1992 through 1996 are given in the table. (Source: U.S. Bureau of the Census)

Year	1992	1993	1994	1995	1996
Imports	532.7	580.7	663.8	743.4	791.4

(a) Plot the points (x, y) on a rectangular coordinate system where x represents the year, with $x = 0$ corresponding to 1990, and y represents imports.

(b) The slope and y-intercept of the line $y = mx + b$ that best fits the data are given by the solution of the following system.

$$5b + 20m = 3,312$$
$$20b + 90m = 13,928.1$$

Use the method of substitution to solve the system and find the equation of the required line. Graph the line on the coordinate system used in part (a).

(c) Find the difference between the linear models found in part (b) of Exercises 61 and 62. Discuss some of the implications of the model for the difference.

63. *Geometry* Find an equation of the line with slope 2 passing through the intersection of the lines $x - 2y = 3$ and $3x + y = 16$.

64. *Geometry* Find an equation of the line with slope -3 passing through the intersection of the lines $4x + 6y = 26$ and $5x - 2y = -15$.

Explaining Concepts

65. Answer parts (c) and (d) of Motivating the Chapter on page 373.

66. In your own words, explain the basic steps in solving a system of linear equations by substitution.

67. When solving a system of linear equations by substitution, how do you recognize that it has no solution?

68. When solving a system of linear equations by substitution, how do you recognize that it has infinitely many solutions?

69. Describe any advantages of the method of substitution over the graphical method of solving a system of linear equations.

70. Explain what is meant by a consistent system of linear equations.

71. Explain how you can check the solution of a system of linear equations algebraically and graphically.

Think About It In Exercises 72–75, find the value of a or b such that the system is inconsistent.

72. $x + by = 1$
$x + 2y = 2$

73. $ax + 3y = 6$
$5x - 5y = 2$

74. $-6x + y = 4$
$2x + by = 3$

75. $6x - 3y = 4$
$ax - y = -2$

Mid-Chapter Quiz

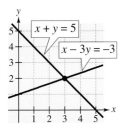

Figure for 2

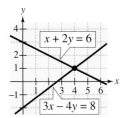

Figure for 3

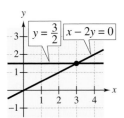

Figure for 4

Take this quiz as you would take a quiz in class. After you are done, check your work against the answers given in the back of the book.

1. Is $(4, -2)$ a solution of $3x + 4y = 4$ *and* $5x - 3y = 14$? Explain your reasoning.

In Exercises 2–4, use the given graphs to solve the system.

2. $\begin{aligned} x + y &= 5 \\ x - 3y &= -3 \end{aligned}$

3. $\begin{aligned} x + 2y &= 6 \\ 3x - 4y &= 8 \end{aligned}$

4. $\begin{aligned} y &= \frac{3}{2} \\ x - 2y &= 0 \end{aligned}$

In Exercises 5–8, solve the system graphically. Check your solution.

5. $\begin{aligned} x &= 6 \\ x + y &= 8 \end{aligned}$

6. $\begin{aligned} y &= \frac{3}{2}x - 1 \\ y &= -x + 4 \end{aligned}$

7. $\begin{aligned} 4x + y &= 0 \\ -x + y &= 5 \end{aligned}$

8. $\begin{aligned} x + y &= -2 \\ x - y &= 4 \end{aligned}$

In Exercises 9–12, use substitution to solve the system.

9. $\begin{aligned} x - y &= 4 \\ y &= 2 \end{aligned}$

10. $\begin{aligned} y &= -\frac{2}{3}x + 5 \\ y &= 2x - 3 \end{aligned}$

11. $\begin{aligned} 2x - y &= -7 \\ 4x + 3y &= 16 \end{aligned}$

12. $\begin{aligned} -x + 3y &= 10 \\ 9x - 4y &= 5 \end{aligned}$

In Exercises 13–16, find a system of linear equations that has the ordered pair as its only solution. (There are many correct answers.)

13. $(0, 0)$

14. $(6, -8)$

15. $\left(2, \frac{5}{2}\right)$

16. $(0.8, 3.4)$

In Exercises 17 and 18, find the value of k such that the system is inconsistent.

17. $\begin{aligned} 5x + ky &= 3 \\ 10x - 4y &= 1 \end{aligned}$

18. $\begin{aligned} 8x - 5y &= 16 \\ kx - 0.5y &= 3 \end{aligned}$

19. The sum of two numbers is 50 and their difference is 22. Write a system of equations that models this problem, and solve the system.

20. A student spent a total of $32 for a book and a calendar. The price of the book was $2 more than four times the price of the calendar. Write a system of equations that models this problem, and solve the system.

Objectives

1 Solve a system of linear equations algebraically using the method of elimination.

2 Choose a method for solving a system of equations.

---

1 Solve a system of linear equations algebraically using the method of elimination.

The Method of Elimination

In this section, you will study another way to solve a system of linear equations algebraically—the **method of elimination.** The key step is to obtain opposite coefficients for one of the variables so that *adding* the two equations eliminates this variable. For instance, by adding the equations

$$3x + 5y = 7 \qquad \text{Equation 1}$$
$$\underline{-3x - 2y = -1} \qquad \text{Equation 2}$$
$$3y = 6 \qquad \text{Add equations.}$$

you eliminate the variable x and obtain a single equation in one variable, y.

Example 1   The Method of Elimination

Solve the following system of equations.

$$4x + 3y = 1 \qquad \text{Equation 1}$$
$$2x - 3y = 5 \qquad \text{Equation 2}$$

Solution

Begin by noting that the coefficients for y are opposites. So, by adding the two equations, you can eliminate y.

$$4x + 3y = 1 \qquad \text{Equation 1}$$
$$\underline{2x - 3y = 5} \qquad \text{Equation 2}$$
$$6x = 6 \qquad \text{Add equations.}$$

So, $x = 1$. By back-substituting this value into the first equation, you can solve for y, as follows.

$$4(1) + 3y = 1 \qquad \text{Substitute 1 for } x \text{ in Equation 1.}$$
$$3y = -3 \qquad \text{Subtract 4 from both sides.}$$
$$y = -1 \qquad \text{Divide both sides by 3.}$$

The solution is $(1, -1)$. Check this in both of the original equations, as follows.

Substitute into 1st Equation   *Substitute into 2nd Equation*

$$4(1) + 3(-1) \overset{?}{=} 1 \qquad\qquad 2(1) - 3(-1) \overset{?}{=} 5$$
$$4 - 3 = 1 \checkmark \qquad\qquad\qquad 2 + 3 = 5 \checkmark$$

Study Tip

Try solving the system in Example 1 by substitution. Which method do you think is easier? Many people find that the method of elimination is more efficient.

To obtain opposite coefficients for one of the variables, you often need to multiply one or both of the equations by a suitable constant. This is demonstrated in Examples 2 and 3.

Corbis-Bettmann

Carl Friedrich Gauss

Gauss is often ranked with Archimedes and Newton as one of the greatest mathematicians in history. Gauss's doctoral thesis proved the Fundamental Theorem of Algebra. His contributions to mathematics can be found in differential geometry, algebra, complex functions, and potential theory. The process used in the method of elimination was developed by Gauss and is called "Gaussian elimination." Gaussian elimination can be used to solve systems of three or more variables.

Example 2   The Method of Elimination

Solve the following system of linear equations.

$$2x - 3y = -7 \qquad \text{Equation 1}$$

$$3x + y = -5 \qquad \text{Equation 2}$$

Solution

For this system, you can obtain opposite coefficients of y by multiplying the second equation by 3.

$$2x - 3y = -7 \qquad\Longrightarrow\qquad 2x - 3y = -7 \qquad \text{Equation 1}$$

$$3x + y = -5 \qquad\Longrightarrow\qquad \underline{9x + 3y = -15} \qquad \text{Multiply Equation 2 by 3.}$$

$$11x = -22 \qquad \text{Add equations.}$$

So, $x = -2$. By back-substituting this value of x into the second equation, you can solve for y.

$$3x + y = -5 \qquad \text{Equation 2}$$

$$3(-2) + y = -5 \qquad \text{Substitute } -2 \text{ for } x.$$

$$-6 + y = -5 \qquad \text{Simplify.}$$

$$y = 1 \qquad \text{Add 6 to both sides.}$$

The solution is $(-2, 1)$. Check this in the original equations, as follows.

Substitute into 1st Equation	*Substitute into 2nd Equation*
$2x - 3y = -7$	$3x + y = -5$
$2(-2) - 3(1) \stackrel{?}{=} -7$	$3(-2) + (1) \stackrel{?}{=} -5$
$-4 - 3 = -7 \checkmark$	$-6 + 1 = -5 \checkmark$

This method is called "elimination" because the first step in the process is to "eliminate" one of the variables. The method of elimination is summarized as follows.

▶ **The Method of Elimination**

1. Obtain opposite coefficients for x (or y) by multiplying all terms of one or both equations by suitably chosen constants.

2. Add the equations to "eliminate" one variable and solve the resulting equation.

3. Back-substitute the value obtained in Step 2 into either of the original equations and solve for the other variable.

4. Check your solution in both of the original equations.

Example 3 The Method of Elimination

Solve the following system of linear equations.

$$5x + 3y = 6 \qquad \text{Equation 1}$$

$$2x - 4y = 5 \qquad \text{Equation 2}$$

Solution

You can obtain opposite coefficients of y by multiplying the first equation by 4 and the second equation by 3.

$5x + 3y = 6$	⟹	$20x + 12y = 24$	Multiply Equation 1 by 4.
$2x - 4y = 5$	⟹	$6x - 12y = 15$	Multiply Equation 2 by 3.
		$26x \qquad = 39$	Add equations.

From this equation, you can see that $x = \frac{3}{2}$. By back-substituting this value of x into the second equation, you can solve for y, as follows.

$$2x - 4y = 5 \qquad \text{Equation 2}$$

$$2\left(\frac{3}{2}\right) - 4y = 5 \qquad \text{Substitute } \tfrac{3}{2} \text{ for } x.$$

$$3 - 4y = 5 \qquad \text{Simplify.}$$

$$-4y = 2 \qquad \text{Subtract 3 from both sides.}$$

$$y = -\frac{1}{2} \qquad \text{Divide both sides by } -4.$$

The solution is $\left(\frac{3}{2}, -\frac{1}{2}\right)$. You can check this as follows.

Substitute into 1st Equation   *Substitute into 2nd Equation*

$$5x + 3y = 6 \qquad\qquad\qquad 2x - 4y = 5$$

$$5\left(\frac{3}{2}\right) + 3\left(-\frac{1}{2}\right) \overset{?}{=} 6 \qquad\qquad 2\left(\frac{3}{2}\right) - 4\left(-\frac{1}{2}\right) \overset{?}{=} 5$$

$$\frac{15}{2} - \frac{3}{2} = 6 ✓ \qquad\qquad\qquad 3 + 2 = 5 ✓$$

The graph of this system is shown in Figure 7.9. From the graph it appears that the solution $\left(\frac{3}{2}, -\frac{1}{2}\right)$ is reasonable.

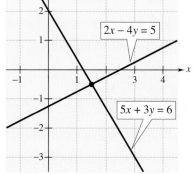

$2x - 4y = 5$

$5x + 3y = 6$

Figure 7.9

In Example 3, the y-variable was eliminated first. You could just as easily solve the system by eliminating the x-variable first, as follows.

$5x + 3y = 6$	⟹	$10x + 6y = 12$	Multiply Equation 1 by 2.
$2x - 4y = 5$	⟹	$-10x + 20y = -25$	Multiply Equation 2 by -5.
		$26y = -13$	Add equations.

From this equation, $y = -\frac{1}{2}$. By back-substituting this value of y into the second equation, you can solve for x to obtain $x = \frac{3}{2}$.

In the next example, note how to use the method of elimination to determine that a system of linear equations has no solution. As with substitution, notice that the key is recognizing the occurrence of a *false statement*.

Example 4   The Method of Elimination: No-Solution Case

Solve the following system of linear equations.

$$2x - 6y = 5 \qquad \text{Equation 1}$$

$$3x - 9y = 2 \qquad \text{Equation 2}$$

Solution

To obtain coefficients that differ only in sign, multiply the first equation by 3 and multiply the second equation by -2.

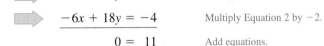

$$2x - 6y = 5 \qquad \Longrightarrow \qquad 6x - 18y = 15 \qquad \text{Multiply Equation 1 by 3.}$$

$$3x - 9y = 2 \qquad \Longrightarrow \qquad \underline{-6x + 18y = -4} \qquad \text{Multiply Equation 2 by } -2.$$

$$0 = 11 \qquad \text{Add equations.}$$

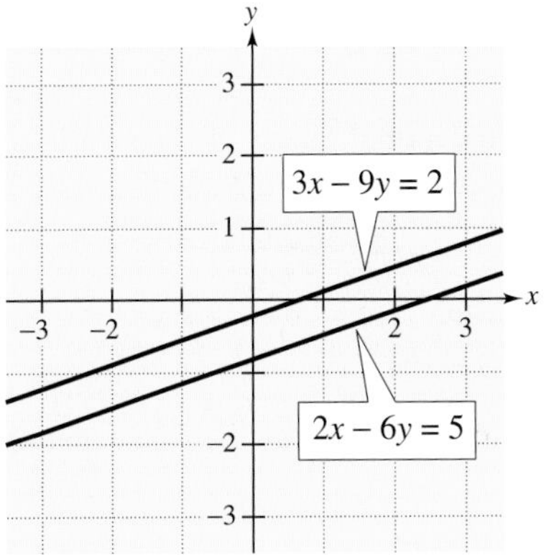

Because $0 = 11$ is a false statement, you can conclude that the system is inconsistent and has no solution. You can check this result graphically by noting that the equations graph as two parallel lines, as shown in Figure 7.10.

Example 5 shows how the method of elimination works with a system that has infinitely many solutions. Notice that you can recognize this case by the occurrence of an equation that is true for all real values of x and y.

Example 5   The Method of Elimination: Many-Solution Case

Solve the following system of linear equations.

$$2x - 6y = -5 \qquad \text{Equation 1}$$

$$-4x + 12y = 10 \qquad \text{Equation 2}$$

Solution

To obtain the coefficients of x that differ only in sign, multiply the first equation by 2.

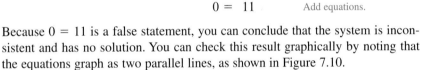

$$2x - 6y = -5 \qquad \Longrightarrow \qquad 4x - 12y = -10 \qquad \text{Multiply Equation 1 by 2.}$$

$$-4x + 12y = 10 \qquad \Longrightarrow \qquad \underline{-4x + 12y = 10} \qquad \text{Equation 2}$$

$$0 = 0 \qquad \text{Add equations.}$$

Because the two equations turned out to be equivalent, you can conclude that the system is dependent and has infinitely many solutions. The solution set consists of all ordered pairs (x, y) such that $2x - 6y = -5$.

Figure 7.10

Study Tip

By writing both equations in Example 5 in slope-intercept form, you will obtain identical equations. This shows that the system has infinitely many solutions.

The next example shows how the method of elimination works with a system of linear equations having decimal coefficients.

> **Example 6** Solving a System Having Decimal Coefficients

Solve the following system of linear equations.

$$0.02x - 0.05y = -0.38 \qquad \text{Equation 1}$$

$$0.03x + 0.04y = 1.04 \qquad \text{Equation 2}$$

Solution

Because the coefficients in this system have two decimal places, begin by multiplying each equation by 100. This produces a system in which the coefficients are all integers.

$$2x - 5y = -38 \qquad \text{Revised Equation 1}$$

$$3x + 4y = 104 \qquad \text{Revised Equation 2}$$

Now, to obtain coefficients of x that differ only in sign, multiply the first equation by 3 and multiply the second equation by -2.

$$2x - 5y = -38 \quad \Longrightarrow \quad 6x - 15y = -114 \qquad \text{Multiply Equation 1 by 3.}$$

$$\underline{3x + 4y = 104} \quad \Longrightarrow \quad \underline{-6x - 8y = -208} \qquad \text{Multiply Equation 2 by } -2.$$

$$-23y = -322 \qquad \text{Add equations.}$$

So, the y-coordinate of the solution is

$$y = \frac{-322}{-23} = 14.$$

Back-substituting this value into revised Equation 2 produces the following.

$$3x + 4y = 104 \qquad \text{Revised Equation 2}$$

$$3x + 4(14) = 104 \qquad \text{Substitute 14 for } y.$$

$$3x + 56 = 104 \qquad \text{Simplify.}$$

$$3x = 48 \qquad \text{Subtract 56 from both sides.}$$

$$x = 16 \qquad \text{Divide both sides by 3.}$$

The solution is $(16, 14)$. You can check this solution as follows.

Substitute into 1st Equation	*Substitute into 2nd Equation*
$0.02x - 0.05y = -0.38$	$0.03x + 0.04y = 1.04$
$0.02(16) - 0.05(14) \overset{?}{=} -0.38$	$0.03(16) + 0.04(14) \overset{?}{=} 1.04$
$0.32 - 0.70 = -0.38 \checkmark$	$0.48 + 0.56 = 1.04 \checkmark$

In Example 6, the value of x could have been found by back-substituting into revised Equation 1, as shown on the following page.

Study Tip

When multiplying an equation by a negative number, be sure to distribute the negative sign to each term of the equation. For instance, in Example 6 the second equation is multiplied by -2.

$$2x - 5y = -38 \qquad \text{Revised Equation 1}$$
$$2x - 5(14) = -38 \qquad \text{Substitute 14 for } y.$$
$$2x - 70 = -38 \qquad \text{Simplify.}$$
$$2x = 32 \qquad \text{Add 70 to both sides.}$$
$$x = 16 \qquad \text{Divide both sides by 2.}$$

2 Choose a method for solving a system of equations.

Choosing Methods

To decide which of the three methods (graphing, substitution, or elimination) to use to solve a system of two linear equations, we suggest the following guidelines.

When you go on to more advanced algebra courses, you will find that these methods can be generalized to systems that contain more than two variables.

These guidelines could be the basis for a classroom discussion of the advantages and disadvantages of each of the three methods.

> ### ▶ Guidelines for Solving a System of Linear Equations
>
> To decide whether to use the method of graphing, substitution, or elimination, consider the following.
>
> 1. The graphing method is useful for approximating the solution and for giving an overall picture of how one variable changes with respect to the other.
>
> 2. To find exact solutions, use either substitution or elimination.
>
> 3. For systems of equations in which one variable has a coefficient of 1, substitution may be more efficient than elimination.
>
> 4. In other cases, the elimination method is usually more efficient. This is especially true when the system contains opposite coefficients for one of the variables.

Discussing the Concept	Discovering the Number of Solutions

A student claims that by cross-multiplying coefficients, it is easy to tell if a system of linear equations has one solution, no solution, or many solutions. For instance,

Example 3 *[one]*	Example 4 *[none]*	Example 5 *[many]*
$5x + 3y = 6$	$2x - 6y = 5$	$2x - 6y = -5$
$2x - 4y = 5$	$3x - 9y = 2$	$-4x + 12y = 10$
$-20 \neq 6$	$-18 = -18$	$24 = 24$

Is the claim valid? Can you further distinguish between the no-solution and many-solution cases? Try the method of elimination on the general system $a_1x + b_1y = c_1$ and $a_2x + b_2y = c_2$ to verify the student's claim.

7.3   Exercises

Integrated Review   *Concepts, Skills, and Problem Solving*

Keep mathematically in shape by doing these exercises *before* the problems of this section.

Properties and Definitions

In Exercises 1–4, name the property illustrated.

1. $2ab \cdot \dfrac{1}{2ab} = 1$

2. $8t + 0 = 8t$

3. $2yx = 2xy$

4. $3(2x) = (3 \cdot 2)x$

Algebraic Operations

In Exercises 5–10, plot the points on the rectangular coordinate system. Find the slope of the line passing through the points. If not possible, state why.

5. $(-6, 4), (-3, -4)$

6. $(4, 6), (8, -2)$

7. $\left(\frac{7}{2}, \frac{9}{2}\right), \left(\frac{4}{3}, -3\right)$

8. $\left(-\frac{3}{4}, -\frac{7}{4}\right), \left(-1, \frac{5}{2}\right)$

9. $(-3, 6), (-3, 2)$

10. $(6, 2), (10, 2)$

Problem Solving

11. A quality control engineer for a certain buyer found three defective units in a sample of 100. At that rate, what is the expected number of defective units in a shipment of 5000 units?

12. The cost for a long-distance telephone call is $0.70 for the first minute and $0.42 for each additional minute. The total cost of the call cannot exceed $8. Find the interval of time that is available for the call.

Developing Skills

In Exercises 1–4, use elimination to solve the system. Use the graph to check your solution.

1. $2x + y = 4$
$x - y = 2$

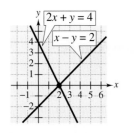

2. $x + 3y = 2$
$-x + 2y = 3$

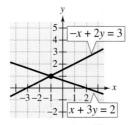

3. $x - y = 0$
$3x - 2y = -1$

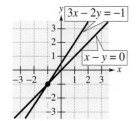

4. $2x - y = 2$
$4x + 3y = 24$

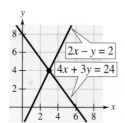

In Exercises 5–32, use elimination to solve the system. Check your solution algebraically. See Examples 1–6.

5. $x - y = 4$
$x + y = 12$

6. $x + y = 7$
$x - y = 3$

7. $-x + 2y = 12$
$x + 6y = 20$

8. $x + 2y = 14$
$x - 2y = 10$

9. $3x - 5y = 1$
$2x + 5y = 9$

10. $-2x + 3y = -4$
$2x - 4y = 6$

11. $3a + 3b = 7$
$3a + 5b = 3$

12. $4a + 5b = 9$
$2a + 5b = 7$

13. $-x + 2y = 12$
$3x - 6y = 10$

14. $-6x + 3y = 18$
$2x - y = 11$

15. $5x + 2y = 7$
$3x - y = 13$

16. $2x - 5y = -1$
$x + y = 3$

17. $2u + v = 120$
$u + 2v = 120$

18. $4x + 3y = 8$
$x - 2y = 13$

19. $3x - 2y = 6$
$-6x + 4y = -12$

20. $10x - 8y = 18$
$5x - 4y = 9$

21. $3x + 2y = 10$
$2x + 5y = 3$

22. $4x + 5y = 7$
$6x - 2y = -18$

23. $5u + 6v = 14$
$3u + 5v = 7$

24. $5x + 3y = 18$
$2x - 7y = -1$

25. $6r + 5s = 3$
$\frac{3}{2}r - \frac{5}{4}s = \frac{3}{4}$

26. $\frac{2}{3}x + \frac{1}{6}y = \frac{2}{3}$
$4x + y = 4$

27. $\frac{1}{2}s - t = \frac{3}{2}$
$4s + 2t = 27$

28. $3u + 4v = 14$
$\frac{1}{6}u - v = -2$

29. $0.4a + 0.7b = 3$
$0.2a + 0.6b = 5$

30. $0.2u - 0.1v = 1$
$-0.8u + 0.4v = 3$

31. $0.02x - 0.05y = -0.19$
$0.03x + 0.04y = 0.52$

32. $0.05x - 0.03y = 0.21$
$0.01x + 0.01y = 0.09$

In Exercises 33–40, use elimination to solve the system. Use a graphing utility to check your solution.

33. $x + 2y = 3$
$-x - y = -1$

34. $-2x + 2y = 7$
$2x + y = 8$

35. $7x + 8y = 6$
$3x - 4y = 10$

36. $10x - 11y = 7$
$2x - y = 5$

37. $5x + 2y = 7$
$3x - 6y = -3$

38. $-4x + 5y = 8$
$2x + 3y = 18$

39. $8x - 4y = 7$
$5x + 2y = 1$

40. $2x - y = -0.1$
$3x + 2y = 1.6$

In Exercises 41–54, use the easiest method (graphing, substitution, or elimination) to solve the system.

41. $x - y = 2$
$y = 3$

42. $y = 7$
$x - 3y = 0$

43. $6x + 21y = 132$
$6x - 4y = 32$

44. $-2x + y = 12$
$2x + 3y = 20$

45. $y = 2x - 1$
$y = x + 1$

46. $2x - y = 4$
$y = x$

47. $-4x + 3y = 11$
$3x - 10y = 15$

48. $-3x + 5y = -11$
$5x - 9y = 19$

49. $x + y = 0$
$8x + 3y = 15$

50. $x - 2y = 0$
$0.2x + 0.8y = 2.4$

51. $-\frac{x}{4} + y = 1$
$\frac{x}{4} + \frac{y}{2} = 1$

52. $\frac{x}{3} - \frac{y}{5} = 1$
$\frac{x}{12} + \frac{y}{40} = 1$

53. $3(x + 5) - 7 = 2(3 - 2y)$
$2x + 1 = 4(y + 2)$

54. $\frac{1}{2}(x - 4) + 9 = y - 10$
$-5(x + 3) = 8 - 2(y - 3)$

Think About It   In Exercises 55–58, find a system of linear equations that has the given solution. (There are many correct answers.)

55. $(-2, 4)$

56. $(-1, -6)$

57. $\left(6, \frac{4}{3}\right)$

58. $(10, -15)$

Solving Problems

59. *Ticket Sales*   Ticket sales for a play were $3799 on the first night and $4905 on the second night. On the first night, 213 student tickets were sold and 632 general admission tickets were sold. On the second night, 275 student tickets were sold and 816 general admission tickets were sold. Find the price of each type of ticket.

60. *Ticket Sales*   Ticket sales for an annual variety show were $540 the first night and $850 the second night. On the first night, 150 student tickets were sold and 80 general admission tickets were sold. On the second night, 200 student tickets were sold and 150 general admission tickets were sold. Find the price of each type of ticket.

61. *Investment*   You invest a total of $10,000 in two investments earning 7.5% and 10% simple interest, respectively. (There is more risk in the 10% fund.) Your goal is to have a total annual interest income of $850. What is the smallest amount you can invest at 10% in order to meet your objective?

62. *Investment*   You invest a total of $12,000 in two investments earning 8% and 11.5% simple interest, respectively. (There is more risk in the 11.5% fund.) Your goal is to have a total annual interest income of $1065. What is the smallest amount that you can invest at 11.5% in order to meet your objective?

63. *Problem Solving*   The sum of two numbers is 82 and the difference of the numbers is 14. Find the numbers.

64. *Problem Solving* The sum of two numbers is 154 and the difference of the numbers is 38. Find the numbers.

65. *Gold Bracelet* A bracelet that is supposed to be 18-karat gold weighs 238 grams. The volume of the bracelet is 15 cubic centimeters. The bracelet is made of gold and copper. Gold weighs 19.3 grams per cubic centimeter and copper weighs 9 grams per cubic centimeter. Is the bracelet really 18-karat gold?

18K = 3/4 gold by weight

66. *Focal Length of a Camera* When parallel rays of light pass through a convex lens, they are bent inward and meet at a *focus* (see figure). The distance from the center of the lens to the focus is called the *focal length*. The equations of the lines containing the two bent rays in the camera are

$$x + 3y = 1$$
$$-x + 3y = -1$$

where x and y are measured in inches. Which equation is the upper ray? What is the focal length?

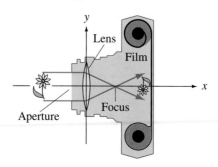

67. *Geometry* Find an equation of the line of slope 3 passing through the intersection of the lines $3x + 4y = 7$ and $5x - 4y = 1$.

68. *Geometry* Find an equation of the line of slope -2 passing through the intersection of the lines $2x + 5y = 11$ and $4x - y = 11$.

Explaining Concepts

69. Answer parts (e) and (f) of Motivating the Chapter on page 373.

70. In your own words, describe the basic steps for solving a system of linear equations by the method of elimination.

71. When solving a system by elimination, how do you recognize that it has no solution?

72. When solving a system by elimination, how do you recognize that it has infinitely many solutions?

73. Give an example of a system that is better solved by elimination than by substitution.

74. Give an example of a system that is better solved by substitution than by elimination.

75. Give an example of "clearing" a system of decimals.

76. Both $(-2, 3)$ and $(8, 1)$ are solutions to a system of linear equations. How many solutions does the system have? Explain.

77. Answer the questions for the following system of linear equations.

$$x + y = 8$$
$$2x + 2y = k$$

(a) Find the value(s) of k for which the system has an infinite number of solutions.

(b) Find one value of k for which the system has no solution.

(c) Can the system have a single solution for some value of k? Why or why not?

7.4	Applications of Systems of Linear Equations

Objectives

1 Construct a system of linear equations from an application problem.

2 Solve a real-life application using a system of linear equations.

---

1 Construct a system of linear equations from an application problem.

Constructing Systems of Linear Equations

At this point, you may be wondering how you can tell which applications can be solved using systems of linear equations. The answer comes from the following considerations.

1. Does the problem involve more than one unknown quantity?

2. Are there two or more equations or conditions to be satisfied?

If one or both of these conditions occur, then the appropriate mathematical model for the problem may be a system of linear equations.

Example 1	Constructing a System of Linear Equations

A total of $12,000 is invested in two funds paying 9% and 11% simple interest. The combined annual interest for the two funds is $1180. How much of the $12,000 is invested at each rate?

Solution

Notice that this problem has two unknowns: the amount (in dollars) invested at 9% and the amount (in dollars) invested at 11%.

Remind students of the importance of verbal models and labels.

Verbal Model:

$$\boxed{\text{Amount in 9\% fund}} + \boxed{\text{Amount in 11\% fund}} = \boxed{\text{Total amount}}$$

$$\boxed{\text{Interest from 9\% fund}} + \boxed{\text{Interest from 11\% fund}} = \boxed{\text{Total interest}}$$

Labels:

Amount in 9% fund $= x$	(dollars)
Amount in 11% fund $= y$	(dollars)
Total amount $= 12,000$	(dollars)
Interest from 9% fund $= 0.09x$	(dollars)
Interest from 11% fund $= 0.11y$	(dollars)
Total interest $= 1180$	(dollars)

System:

$$x + y = 12,000 \quad \text{Equation 1}$$

$$0.09x + 0.11y = 1,180 \quad \text{Equation 2}$$

This system was solved in Example 6 on page 387. There you found that $x = 7000$ and $y = 5000$, which means that $7000 was invested at 9% simple interest and $5000 was invested at 11% simple interest.

2 Solve a real-life application using a system of linear equations.

Applications of Systems of Linear Equations

Many of the problems solved in Chapters 3 and 4 using one variable can now be solved using a system of linear equations in two variables.

Example 2   A Coin Mixture Problem

A cash register contains $20.90 in dimes and quarters. If there are 119 coins in all, how many of each type of coin are in the cash register?

Solution

Note that this problem involves two unknowns: the number of dimes and the number of quarters.

Verbal Model:

$$\boxed{\text{Number of dimes}} + \boxed{\text{Number of quarters}} = \boxed{\text{Number of coins}}$$

$$\boxed{\text{Value of dimes}} + \boxed{\text{Value of quarters}} = \boxed{\text{Value of coins}}$$

Labels:

Number of dimes $= x$	(dimes)
Number of quarters $= y$	(quarters)
Number of coins $= 119$	(coins)
Value of dimes $= 0.10x$	(dollars)
Value of quarters $= 0.25y$	(dollars)
Value of coins $= 20.90$	(dollars)

System:

$$x + y = 119 \qquad \text{Equation 1}$$
$$0.10x + 0.25y = 20.90 \qquad \text{Equation 2}$$

To solve this equation, use the method of elimination. Begin by multiplying the second equation by 100 to eliminate the decimal points. Then, to obtain opposite coefficients, multiply the first equation by -10.

$$x + y = 119 \quad \Longrightarrow \quad -10x - 10y = -1190$$
$$\underline{0.10x + 0.25y = 20.90} \quad \Longrightarrow \quad \underline{10x + 25y = 2090}$$
$$15y = 900$$

So, $y = 60$. To solve for x, back-substitute this value into Equation 1.

$$x + y = 119 \qquad \text{Equation 1}$$
$$x + 60 = 119 \qquad \text{Substitute 60 for } y.$$
$$x = 59 \qquad \text{Subtract 60 from both sides.}$$

So, the cash register has 59 dimes and 60 quarters. Check this in the original statement of the problem, as follows.

The cash register contains $20.90 in dimes and quarters.

$$0.10(59) + 0.25(60) = 5.90 + 15.00 = \$20.90 \qquad \text{Solution checks. } \checkmark$$

There are 119 coins in all.

$$59 + 60 = 119 \qquad \text{Solution checks. } \checkmark$$

| Example 3 | Geometry: Dimensions of a Rectangle |

A rectangle is twice as long as it is wide and its perimeter is 132 inches. Find the dimensions of the rectangle using a system of linear equations.

Solution

The two unknowns in this problem are the length and width of the rectangle, as shown in Figure 7.11.

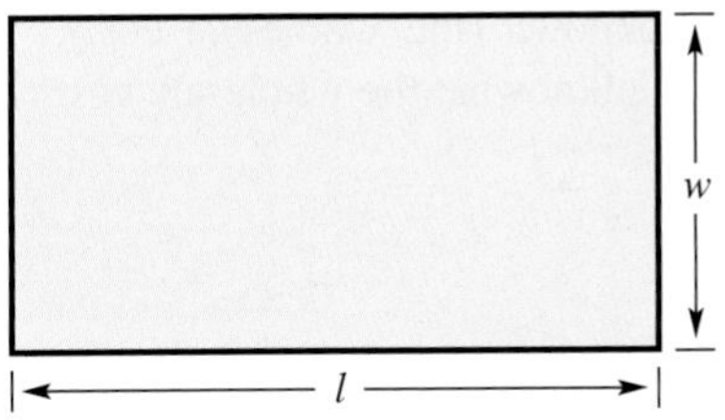

Figure 7.11

Verbal Model:

$$\left(2 \cdot \begin{array}{c} \text{Width of} \\ \text{rectangle} \end{array} \right) + \left(2 \cdot \begin{array}{c} \text{Length of} \\ \text{rectangle} \end{array} \right) = \begin{array}{c} \text{Perimeter} \\ \text{of rectangle} \end{array}$$

$$\begin{array}{c} \text{Length of} \\ \text{rectangle} \end{array} = 2 \cdot \begin{array}{c} \text{Width of} \\ \text{rectangle} \end{array}$$

Labels:

Width of rectangle $= w$	(inches)
Length of rectangle $= l$	(inches)
Perimeter of rectangle $= 132$	(inches)

System:

$2w + 2l = 132$ Equation 1

$l = 2w$ Equation 2

To solve this system, use the method of substitution.

$2w + 2l = 132$ Equation 1

$2w + 2(2w) = 132$ Substitute $2w$ for l.

$6w = 132$ Combine like terms.

So, $w = 22$ inches. To solve for l, back-substitute into Equation 2.

$l = 2(22)$ Substitute 22 for w in Equation 2.

$l = 44$ Simplify.

This implies that the rectangle has a width of 22 inches and a length of 44 inches. Check this in the original statement of the problem, as follows.

The rectangle is twice as long as it is wide.

Length $= 2(\text{width}) = 2(22) = 44$ inches   Solution checks. ✓

The rectangle's perimeter is 132 inches.

$2(\text{width}) + 2(\text{length}) = 2(22) + 2(44) = 132$ inches   Solution checks. ✓

When solving real-life problems, remember that there are several effective problem-solving strategies that you can use. For instance, in Example 3, you could use *Guess, Check, and Revise* to find the dimensions, as shown in the following table.

Width	15	16	17	18	19	20	21	22
Length	30	32	34	36	38	40	42	44
Perimeter	90	96	102	108	114	120	126	132 ✓

You might want to review the three techniques for solving systems of linear equations and discuss which method to use in various situations.

Example 4   Selling Price and Wholesale Cost

The selling price of a pair of ski boots is $99.20. The markup rate is 55% of the wholesale cost. What is the wholesale cost?

Solution

You could solve this problem using only one unknown (the wholesale cost). However, for the sake of illustration, let's use two unknowns: the wholesale cost and the markup (in dollars).

Verbal Model:

$$\boxed{\text{Wholesale cost}} + \boxed{\text{Markup}} = \boxed{\text{Selling price}}$$

$$\boxed{\text{Markup}} = \boxed{\text{Markup rate}} \cdot \boxed{\text{Wholesale cost}}$$

Labels:

Wholesale cost $= C$ (dollars)
Markup $= M$ (dollars)
Selling price $= 99.20$ (dollars)
Markup rate $= 0.55$ (percent in decimal form)

System:

$$C + M = 99.20 \qquad \text{Equation 1}$$
$$M = 0.55C \qquad \text{Equation 2}$$

To solve this system of linear equations, use the method of substitution.

$$C + M = 99.20 \qquad \text{Equation 1}$$
$$C + 0.55C = 99.20 \qquad \text{Substitute } 0.55C \text{ for } M.$$
$$1.55C = 99.20 \qquad \text{Combine like terms.}$$
$$C = 64 \qquad \text{Divide both sides by 1.55.}$$

The wholesale cost of the pair of boots is $64.00. (You weren't asked to find the markup, so it is unnecessary to back-substitute to find the value of M.)

The problem in Example 4 could also have been modeled with a single equation in one variable. Using the verbal model

$$\boxed{\text{Wholesale cost}} + \boxed{\text{Markup}} = \boxed{\text{Selling price}}$$

with C representing the wholesale cost, $0.55C$ representing the markup, and 99.20 representing the selling price, you obtain the equation and solution.

$$C + 0.55C = 99.20 \qquad \text{Original equation}$$
$$(1 + 0.55)C = 99.20 \qquad \text{Distributive Property}$$
$$1.55C = 99.20 \qquad \text{Simplify.}$$
$$C = 64 \qquad \text{Divide both sides by 1.55.}$$

Which of these two solution techniques do you prefer: the one using a system of equations or the one using a single equation?

Example 5   A Mixture Problem

A company with two stores buys six large delivery vans and five small ones. The first store receives four of the large vans and two of the small vans for a total cost of $160,000. The second store receives two of the large vans and three of the small vans for a total cost of $128,000. What does each type of van cost?

Solution

The two unknowns in this problem are the costs of the two types of vans.

Verbal
Model:

$$\left(4 \cdot \begin{array}{c} \text{Cost of} \\ \text{large van} \end{array}\right) + \left(2 \cdot \begin{array}{c} \text{Cost of} \\ \text{small van} \end{array}\right) = \begin{array}{c} \text{Total cost} \\ \text{for 1st store} \end{array}$$

$$\left(2 \cdot \begin{array}{c} \text{Cost of} \\ \text{large van} \end{array}\right) + \left(3 \cdot \begin{array}{c} \text{Cost of} \\ \text{small van} \end{array}\right) = \begin{array}{c} \text{Total cost} \\ \text{for 2nd store} \end{array}$$

Labels: Cost of large van $= x$ (dollars)
             Cost of small van $= y$ (dollars)
             Total cost for 1st store $= 160{,}000$ (dollars)
             Total cost for 2nd store $= 128{,}000$ (dollars)

System: $4x + 2y = 160{,}000$ Equation 1

             $2x + 3y = 128{,}000$ Equation 2

To solve this system of linear equations, use the method of elimination. To obtain coefficients that differ only in sign, multiply the second equation by -2.

$$\begin{array}{ll} 4x + 2y = 160{,}000 \\ 2x + 3y = 128{,}000 \end{array} \implies \begin{array}{r} 4x + 2y = 160{,}000 \\ -4x - 6y = -256{,}000 \\ \hline -4y = -96{,}000 \end{array}$$

So, the cost of each small van is $y = \$24{,}000$. Back-substitution of this value into Equation 1 yields the cost of each large van.

$4x + 2y = 160{,}000$ Equation 1

$4x + 2(24{,}000) = 160{,}000$ Substitute 24,000 for y.

$4x = 112{,}000$ Subtract 48,000 from both sides.

$x = 28{,}000$ Divide both sides by 4.

The cost of each large van is $x = \$28{,}000$. Check this solution in the original statement of the problem, as follows.

The first store receives four large vans and two small vans for $160,000.

$4(28{,}000) + 2(24{,}000) = 112{,}000 + 48{,}000 = \$160{,}000$ Solution checks. ✓

The second store receives two large vans and three small vans for $128,000.

$2(28{,}000) + 3(24{,}000) = 56{,}000 + 72{,}000 = \$128{,}000$ Solution checks. ✓

When assigning labels to a verbal model, remember to check that the units of measure make sense in the problem. For instance, each of the terms in the equations in Example 5 is measured in dollars. If, in the same equation, the terms had different units, you would know that an error had occurred.

| Example 6 | An Application Involving Two Speeds | |

You are taking a motorboat trip on a river—18 miles upstream and 18 miles back downstream. You run the motor at the same speed going up and down the river, but because of the current of the river, the trip upstream takes longer than the trip downstream. You don't know the speed of the river's current, but you know that the trip upstream takes $1\frac{1}{2}$ hours and the trip downstream takes only 1 hour. From this information, determine the speed of the current.

Solution

One unknown in this problem is the speed of the current. The other unknown is the speed of the boat in still water. To set up a model, use the fact that the effective speed of the boat (relative to the land) going upstream is

$$\frac{18}{1.5} = 12 \text{ miles per hour} \qquad \text{Rate} = \text{distance} \div \text{time}$$

and the speed going downstream is

$$\frac{18}{1} = 18 \text{ miles per hour} \qquad \text{Rate} = \text{distance} \div \text{time}$$

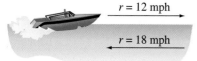

$r = 12$ mph

$r = 18$ mph

Figure 7.12

as shown in Figure 7.12. In the following verbal model, note that the current fights against you going upstream but helps you going downstream.

Verbal Model:

| Boat speed (still water) | − | Speed of current | = | Upstream speed |

| Boat speed (still water) | + | Speed of current | = | Downstream speed |

Labels:
Boat speed in still water $= x$ (miles per hour)
Current speed $= y$ (miles per hour)
Upstream speed $= 12$ (miles per hour)
Downstream speed $= 18$ (miles per hour)

System:
$x - y = 12$ Equation 1
$x + y = 18$ Equation 2

To solve this system of linear equations, use the method of elimination.

$$\begin{aligned} x - y &= 12 \qquad &\text{Equation 1}\\ \underline{x + y} &= \underline{18} \qquad &\text{Equation 2}\\ 2x &= 30 \qquad &\text{Add equations.} \end{aligned}$$

So, the speed of the boat in still water is $x = 15$ miles per hour. To find the speed of the current, back-substitute this value into Equation 2.

$$\begin{aligned} x + y &= 18 \qquad &\text{Equation 2}\\ 15 + y &= 18 \qquad &\text{Substitute 15 for } x.\\ y &= 3 \qquad &\text{Subtract 15 from both sides.} \end{aligned}$$

So, the speed of the current is 3 miles per hour. Check this solution in the original statement of the problem.

In 1997, there were 144,000 chemists employed in the United States. Of these, 25.5% were women. (Source: U.S. Bureau of Labor Statistics)

| Example 7 | A Mixture Problem | |

A chemist has two different solutions. One is 50% alcohol and 50% water, and the other is 75% alcohol and 25% water. How much of each type of solution should be mixed to obtain 8 liters of solution comprised of 60% alcohol and 40% water?

Solution

The two unknowns in this problem are the amounts of each type of solution.

Verbal Model:

$$\boxed{\begin{array}{c}\text{Liters of} \\ \text{50\% solution}\end{array}} + \boxed{\begin{array}{c}\text{Liters of} \\ \text{75\% solution}\end{array}} = \boxed{\begin{array}{c}\text{Liters of} \\ \text{60\% solution}\end{array}}$$

$$\boxed{\begin{array}{c}\text{Alcohol in} \\ \text{50\% solution}\end{array}} + \boxed{\begin{array}{c}\text{Alcohol in} \\ \text{75\% solution}\end{array}} = \boxed{\begin{array}{c}\text{Alcohol in} \\ \text{60\% solution}\end{array}}$$

Labels:

Liters of 50% solution = x	(liters)
Liters of 75% solution = y	(liters)
Liters of 60% solution = 8	(liters)
Alcohol in 50% solution = $0.50x$	(liters)
Alcohol in 75% solution = $0.75y$	(liters)
Alcohol in 60% solution = $0.60(8) = 4.8$	(liters)

System:

$$x + y = 8 \qquad \text{Equation 1}$$
$$0.50x + 0.75y = 4.8 \qquad \text{Equation 2}$$

To solve this system of linear equations, use the method of elimination by multiplying the first equation by -50 and the second equation by 100.

$$x + y = 8 \quad \Longrightarrow \quad -50x - 50y = -400$$
$$0.50x + 0.75y = 4.8 \quad \Longrightarrow \quad \underline{50x + 75y = \quad 480}$$
$$25y = \quad 80$$

From this equation you know that $y = 3.2$. By back-substituting this value of y into the first equation, you find

$$x + 3.2 = 8 \qquad \text{Substitute 3.2 for } y \text{ in Equation 1.}$$
$$x = 4.8. \qquad \text{Subtract 3.2 from both sides.}$$

So, the chemist should use 4.8 liters of the 50% solution and 3.2 liters of the 75% solution. Check this answer in the original statement of the problem.

Similar mixture problems were introduced in Section 3.5, where they were modeled with *one* equation. You might ask students to discuss which method they prefer.

| Discussing the Concept | Creating Word Problems |

Individually, write a word problem that is modeled by the following linear system:

$$a + s = 40$$
$$4.50a + 2.00s = 100.$$

Exchange problems with another class member, and resolve any discrepancies that are discovered.

7.4 Exercises

Integrated Review   *Concepts, Skills, and Problem Solving*

Keep mathematically in shape by doing these exercises *before* the problems of this section.

Properties and Definitions

1. Describe the procedure for finding the x- and y-intercepts of the graph of $f(x) = 4 - (x - 1)^2$.

2. Explain why the domain of the function $f(x) = \sqrt{x - 2}$ is $2 \le x < \infty$.

Algebraic Operations

In Exercises 3–10, perform the operation and simplify.

3. $(3x^2 - 2x) - (x^2 + 10)$

4. $7x - [(3x + 2) + 8x]$

5. $2t(t^2 - 2t + 3)$ 6. $(u + 2)(u^2 + u - 7)$

7. $(5z - 3)(5z + 3)$ 8. $(2y - 11)^2$

9. $\dfrac{10x^2 - 12x}{2x}$ 10. $\dfrac{x^2 + 3x + 6}{x + 1}$

Graphs and Models

11. A business purchases a new machine for $32,000. It is estimated that in 4 years its depreciated value will be $8000. Assume the depreciation of the machine can be approximated by a straight line.

    (a) Write a linear function giving the value y of the machine in terms of time t.

    (b) Use a graphing utility to graph the function in part (a).

    (c) Use the trace feature and the right and left cursor keys to approximate the value of the machine after 3 years.

12. A sales representative is reimbursed $130 per day for lodging and meals plus $0.32 per mile driven. Write a linear equation giving the daily cost C to the company in terms of x, the number of miles driven.

Solving Problems

Modeling   In Exercises 1 and 2, construct and solve a system of linear equations. See Example 1.

1. The total cost of 15 gallons of regular gasoline and 10 gallons of premium gasoline is $35.50. Premium costs $0.20 more per gallon than regular. What is the cost per gallon of each type of gasoline?

    (a) Write a verbal model for this problem.

    (b) Assign labels to the verbal model.

    (c) Use the labels to write a linear system.

    (d) Solve the system and answer the question.

2. A total of $12,000 is invested in two bonds that pay 10.5% and 12% simple interest, respectively. The annual interest is $1380. How much is invested in each bond?

    (a) Write a verbal model for this problem.

    (b) Assign labels to the verbal model.

    (c) Use the labels to write a linear system.

    (d) Solve the system and answer the question.

Number Problems   In Exercises 3–8, find two numbers that satisfy the requirements.

3. The sum of the numbers is 67, and their difference is 17.

4. The sum of the numbers is 75, and their difference is 15.

5. The sum of the numbers is 132, and the larger number is 6 more than twice the smaller number.

6. The sum of the numbers is 46, and the larger number is 2 less than twice the smaller number.

7. The sum of the larger number and twice the smaller number is 100, and their difference is 10.

8. The sum of three times the smaller number and four times the larger number is 225. Nine times the smaller plus two times the larger gives the same sum.

Coin Problems   In Exercises 9–14, determine the number of each type of coin. See Example 2.

	Number	Types of coins	Value
9.	21	Dimes and quarters	$4.05
10.	21	Dimes and quarters	$2.70
11.	35	Nickels and quarters	$5.75
12.	35	Nickels and quarters	$7.75
13.	44	Nickels and dimes	$3.00
14.	28	Nickels and dimes	$2.40

Dimensions of a Rectangle   In Exercises 15–20, find the dimensions of the rectangle that meet the specified conditions. See Example 3.

	Perimeter	Relationship Between Length and Width
15.	40 feet	The length is 4 feet greater than the width.
16.	220 inches	The width is 10 inches less than the length.
17.	16 yards	The width is one-third of the length.
18.	48 meters	The length is twice the width.
19.	35.2 meters	The length is 120% of the width.
20.	35 feet	The width is 75% of the length.

In Exercises 21–26, use a system of two equations to solve the problem. See Example 4.

21. *Wholesale Cost*   The selling price of a watch is $108.75. The markup rate is 45% of the wholesale cost. Find the wholesale cost.

22. *Wholesale Cost*   The selling price of a cordless phone is $119.91. The markup rate is 40% of the wholesale cost. Find the wholesale cost.

23. *Wholesale Cost*   The selling price of an air conditioner is $359. The markup rate is 30% of the wholesale cost. Find the wholesale cost.

24. *List Price*   The sale price of a microwave oven is $275.00. The discount is 20% of the list price. Find the list price.

25. *List Price*   The sale price of a watch is $35.98. The discount is 30% of the list price. Find the list price.

26. *List Price*   The sale price of a stereo system is $716. The discount is 20% of the list price. Find the list price.

In Exercises 27–50, use a system of two equations to solve the problem. See Examples 5–7.

27. *Ticket Sales*   Five hundred tickets were sold for a fundraising dinner. The receipts totaled $3312.50. Adult tickets were $7.50 each and children's tickets were $4.00 each. How many tickets of each type were sold?

28. *Ticket Sales*   A fundraising dinner was held on two consecutive nights. On the first night, 425 adult tickets and 316 children's tickets were sold, for a total of $2915.00. On the second night, 542 adult tickets and 345 children's tickets were sold, for a total of $3572.50. Find the price of each type of ticket.

29. *Mixture Problem*   A bakery with two stores buys three large delivery trucks and six small delivery trucks. One store receives one large delivery truck and four small delivery trucks for a total cost of $118,000. The second store receives two large delivery trucks and two small delivery trucks for a total cost of $107,000. What is the cost of each type of delivery truck?

30. *Mixture Problem*   A furniture company with two stores buys three large delivery trucks and four small delivery trucks. One store receives one large delivery truck and three small delivery trucks for a total cost of $157,000. The second store receives two large delivery trucks and one small delivery truck for a total cost of $139,000. What is the cost of each type of delivery truck?

31. *Gasoline Mixture*   The total cost of 8 gallons of regular gasoline and 12 gallons of premium gasoline is $27.84. Premium gasoline costs $0.17 more per gallon than regular gasoline. Find the price per gallon for each grade of gasoline.

32. *Gasoline Mixture*   The total cost of 6 gallons of regular gasoline and 11 gallons of premium gasoline is $24.03. Premium gasoline costs $0.50 more per gallon than regular gasoline. Find the price per gallon for each type of gasoline.

33. *Food Costs*   You and a friend go to a Mexican restaurant. You order two tacos and three enchiladas, and your friend orders three tacos and five enchiladas. Your bill is $7.80 plus tax, and your friend's bill is $12.70 plus tax. How much is each taco and each enchilada?

34. *Food Costs* You and a friend go to a fast-food restaurant. You order three deluxe hamburgers and two small fries and pay $5.35. Your friend orders two deluxe hamburgers and two small fries and pays $4.16. How much does a deluxe burger cost?

35. *Current Speed* You travel 10 miles upstream and 10 miles downstream on a motorboat trip. You run the motor at the same speed going up and down the river, but because of the speed of the current the trip upstream takes $\frac{1}{2}$ hour and the trip downstream takes $\frac{1}{3}$ hour. Determine the speed of the current.

36. *Boat Speed* You travel 16 miles upstream and 16 miles downstream on a motorboat trip. You run the motor at the same speed going up and down the river, but because of the speed of the current the trip upstream takes 2 hours and the trip downstream takes $1\frac{1}{3}$ hours. Determine the speed of the boat.

37. *Airplane Speed* An airplane flying into a headwind travels 2100 miles in $3\frac{1}{2}$ hours. On the return flight, the same distance is traveled in 3 hours. Find the speed of the plane in still air and the speed of the wind, assuming that both remain constant throughout the round trip.

38. *Airplane Speed* An airplane flying into a headwind travels 1800 miles in 3 hours and 36 minutes. On the return flight, the same distance is traveled in 3 hours. Find the speed of the plane in still air and the speed of the wind, assuming that both remain constant throughout the round trip.

39. *Average Speed* A van travels for 2 hours at an average speed of 40 miles per hour. How much longer must the van travel at an average speed of 55 miles per hour so that the average speed for the entire trip will be 45 miles per hour?

40. *Average Speed* A van travels for 3 hours at an average speed of 40 miles per hour. How much longer must the van travel at an average speed of 55 miles per hour so that the average speed for the entire trip will be 50 miles per hour?

41. *Relay Race* The total time for a two-member team in a 5160-meter relay race is 16 minutes. The first runner on the team averages 300 meters per minute and the second runner averages 360 meters per minute. For how many minutes did the first runner keep the baton before passing it to the second runner?

42. *Driving Distances* In a trip of 450 kilometers, two people drive. One person drives two times as far as the other. Find the distance that each person drives.

43. *Mixture Problem* How many liters of a 35% alcohol solution must be mixed with a 60% solution to obtain 10 liters of a 50% solution?

44. *Mixture Problem* Ten gallons of 30% acid solution is obtained by mixing a 20% solution with a 50% solution. How many gallons of each solution must be used to obtain the desired mixture?

45. *Nut Mixture* Ten pounds of mixed nuts sells for $5.86 per pound. The mixture is obtained from two kinds of nuts: one costs $4.25 per pound and the other costs $6.55 per pound. How many pounds of each variety of nut are used in the mixture?

46. *Nut Mixture* A grocer mixes two kinds of nuts priced at $3.25 and $5.85 per pound to obtain 15 pounds of mixed nuts that sell for $4.29 per pound. How many pounds of each variety should the grocer use?

47. *Feed Mixture* How many tons of hay at $110 per ton and $60 per ton must be purchased to have 100 tons of hay with an average value of $75 per ton?

48. *Feed Mixture* How many pounds of bird feed at $1.68 per pound and $0.83 per pound must be purchased to have 100 pounds of bird feed at a value of $1.34 per pound?

49. *Investment* You invest a total of $24,000 in two bonds that pay 6% and 9.5% simple interest, respectively. (There is more risk in the 9.5% bond.) Your goal is to have a total annual interest income of $2000. What is the smallest amount you can invest at 9.5% in order to meet your objective?

50. *Investment* You invest a total of $12,000 in two bonds that pay 8% and 10% simple interest, respectively. (There is more risk in the 10% bond.) Your goal is to have a total annual interest income of $1000. To meet your objective, what is the smallest amount you can invest at 10%?

Break-Even Point In Exercises 51 and 52, use a graphing utility to graph the cost and revenue functions in the same viewing rectangle. Find the sales x necessary to break even ($R = C$) and the corresponding revenue R obtained by selling x units. (Round x to the nearest whole unit.)

Cost	*Revenue*
51. $C = 7650x + 125,000$	$R = 8950x$
52. $C = 0.25x + 25,000$	$R = 0.45x$

In Exercises 53–56, find m and b such that $y = mx + b$ is the equation of the line through the points. (*Hint:* Generate a linear system in m and b by substituting the coordinates of the specified points into $y = mx + b$.)

53. $(2, -1), (6, 1)$

54. $(1, 3), (4, 9)$

55. $(-3, 6), (5, 2)$

56. $(0, 2), (4, -8)$

57. *Best-Fitting Line*   The line $y = mx + b$ that best fits the three noncollinear points $(0, 0), (1, 2)$, and $(2, 2)$ is given by the following system.

$$3b + 3m = 4$$
$$3b + 5m = 6$$

(a) Solve the system and find the equation of the best-fitting line.

(b) Plot the three points and sketch the graph of the best-fitting line.

58. *Best-Fitting Line*   The line $y = mx + b$ that best fits the three noncollinear points $(0, 2), (1, 1)$, and $(3, 0)$ is given by the following system.

$$3b + 4m = 3$$
$$4b + 10m = 1$$

(a) Solve the system and find the equation of the best-fitting line.

(b) Plot the three points and sketch the graph of the best-fitting line.

59. *Heating Oil Consumption*   A homeowner monitored the average daily temperature x and the amount y (in gallons) of heating oil used to heat the house. After three consecutive days, the ordered pairs generated were $(0, 2), (10, 1.2)$, and $(6, 1.4)$.

(a) Plot the points.

(b) The line $y = mx + b$ that best fits the data is given by the following system.

$$3b + 16m = 4.6$$
$$4b + 34m = 5.1$$

Solve the system and find the equation of the best-fitting line. Graph the line on the coordinate system in part (a).

(c) Interpret the meaning of the slope of the line in the context of the problem.

60. *Data Analysis*   The costs (in cents) per mile of operating an automobile in the United States for the years 1992 through 1996 are given in the following table. (Source: American Automobile Manufacturers Association, Inc.)

Year	1992	1993	1994	1995	1996
Cost	45.77	45.14	46.65	48.91	51.43

(a) Plot the data on a rectangular coordinate system. Let x represent the year with $x = 0$ corresponding to 1990, and let y represent the cost per mile.

(b) The line $y = mx + b$ that best fits the data is given by the following system.

$$5b + 20m = 237.90$$
$$20b + 90m = 966.69$$

Solve the system and find the equation of the best-fitting line. Graph the line on the coordinate system in part (a).

(c) Interpret the meaning of the slope of the line in the context of this problem.

Explaining Concepts

61. How can you determine whether a real-life problem can be modeled with a system of linear equations?

62. What is meant by a verbal model of a real-life problem?

63. Compare the one-variable method with the two-variable method for modeling real-life problems.

64. Summarize the methods for solving systems of linear equations.

Key Terms

system of linear equations, *p. 374*

solution of a system of linear equations, *p. 374*

consistent system, *p. 376*

dependent system, *p. 376*

inconsistent system, *p. 376*

method of substitution, *p. 383*

back-substitute, *p. 383*

method of elimination, *p. 392*

Key Concepts

7.1 Number of points of intersection of two lines

1. The two lines can intersect in a single point. The corresponding system of linear equations has a single solution and is called consistent.

2. The two lines can coincide and have infinitely many points of intersection. The corresponding consistent system of linear equations has infinitely many solutions and is called dependent.

3. The two lines can be parallel and have no point of intersection. The corresponding system of linear equations has no solution and is called inconsistent.

7.2 The method of substitution

1. Solve one of the equations for one variable in terms of the other.

2. Substitute the expression obtained in Step 1 into the other equation and solve the resulting one-variable equation.

3. Back-substitute the solution in Step 2 into the expression found in Step 1 to find the other variable.

4. Check your answer to see that it satisfies both of the original equations.

7.3 The method of elimination

1. Obtain opposite coefficients for x (or y) by multiplying all terms of one or both equations by suitably chosen constants.

2. Add the equations to "eliminate" one variable and solve the resulting equation.

3. Back-substitute the value obtained in Step 2 into either of the original equations and solve for the other variable.

4. Check your solution in both of the original equations.

7.3 Guidelines for solving a system of linear equations

To decide whether to use the method of graphing, substitution, or elimination, consider the following.

1. The graphing method is useful for approximating the solution and for giving an overall picture of how one variable changes with respect to the other.

2. To find exact solutions, use either substitution or elimination.

3. For systems of equations in which one variable has a coefficient of 1, substitution may be more efficient than elimination.

4. In other cases, the elimination method is usually more efficient. This is usually when the system contains opposite coefficients for one of the variables.

REVIEW EXERCISES

Reviewing Skills

7.1 In Exercises 1–4, determine which ordered pair (if any) is a solution to the system of equations.

System	Ordered Pairs

1. $3x - 5y = 11$ (a) $(2, -1)$ (b) $(3, -2)$
   $-x + 2y = -4$

2. $10x + 8y = -2$ (a) $(4, -4)$ (b) $(3, -4)$
   $2x - 5y = 26$

3. $0.2x + 0.4y = 5$ (a) $(0.5, -0.7)$ (b) $(15, 5)$
   $x + 3y = 30$

4. $-\frac{1}{2}x - \frac{2}{3}y = \frac{1}{2}$ (a) $(-5, 6)$ (b) $(7, -3)$
   $x + y = 1$

In Exercises 5–8, match the system with its graph. [The graphs are labeled (a), (b), (c), and (d).]

(a)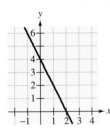

(b)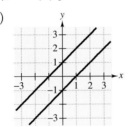

(c)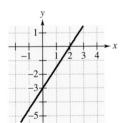

(d)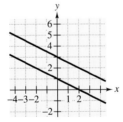

5. $x + 2y = 6$
   $x + 2y = 2$

6. $-x + y = 1$
   $x - y = 1$

7. $2x + y = 4$
   $-4x - 2y = -8$

8. $3x - 2y = 6$
   $-6x + 4y = -12$

In Exercises 9–14, use the coordinate plane to solve the system graphically.

9. $y = x - 4$
   $y = 2x - 9$

10. $y = -\frac{5}{3}x + 6$
   $y = x - 10$

11. $x + y = 2$
   $x - y = 0$

12. $x - y = 9$
   $-x + y = 1$

13. $2x + 3 = 3y$
   $y = \frac{2}{3}x$

14. $x + y = -1$
   $3x + 2y = 0$

7.2 In Exercises 15–22, solve the system algebraically by substitution.

15. $y = 2x$
   $y = x + 4$

16. $x = y + 3$
   $x = y + 1$

17. $x = 3y - 2$
   $x = 6 - y$

18. $y = -4x + 1$
   $y = x - 4$

19. $x - 2y = 6$
   $3x + 2y = 10$

20. $5x + y = 20$
   $7x - 5y = -4$

21. $2x - y = 2$
   $6x + 8y = 39$

22. $3x + 4y = 1$
   $x - 7y = -3$

7.3 In Exercises 23–30, solve the system algebraically by elimination.

23. $3x - y = 5$
   $2x + y = 5$

24. $2x + 4y = 2$
   $-2x - 7y = 4$

25. $5x + 4y = 2$
   $-x + y = -22$

26. $3x - 2y = 9$
   $x + y = 3$

27. $8x - 6y = 4$
   $-4x + 3y = -2$

28. $2x - 5y = 2$
   $3x - 7y = 1$

29. $0.2x + 0.1y = 0.03$
   $0.3x - 0.1y = -0.13$

30. $0.2x - 0.1y = 0.07$
   $0.4x - 0.5y = -0.01$

In Exercises 31–50, use the most convenient method to solve the system.

31. $6x - 5y = 0$
   $y = 6$

32. $-x + 2y = 2$
   $x = 4$

33. $-x + 4y = 4$
   $x + y = 6$

34. $-x + y = 4$
   $x + y = 4$

35. $x - y = 0$
   $x - 6y = 5$

36. $x + 2y = 2$
   $x - 4y = 20$

37. $5x + 8y = 8$
   $x - 8y = 16$

38. $-7x + 9y = 9$
   $2x + 9y = -18$

39. $2x + 5y = 20$
   $4x + 5y = 10$

40. $-3x + 4y = 24$
   $-5x + 4y = 8$

41. $6x - 3y = 27$
   $-2x + y = -9$

42. $-5x + 2y = -4$
   $x - 6y = 4$

43. $\frac{1}{5}x + \frac{3}{2}y = 2$
   $2x + 13y = 20$

44. $-\frac{1}{4}x + \frac{2}{3}y = 1$
   $3x - 8y = 1$

45. $x + y = 0$
   $2x + y = 0$

46. $2x + 6y = 16$
   $2x + 3y = 7$

47. $\frac{1}{3}x + \frac{4}{7}y = 3$
   $2x + 3y = 15$

48. $\frac{1}{2}x - \frac{1}{3}y = 0$
   $3x + 2y = 0$

49. $1.2s + 4.2t = -1.7$
   $3.0s - 1.8t = 1.9$

50. $0.2u + 0.3v = 0.14$
   $0.4u + 0.5v = 0.20$

In Exercises 51–54, find a system of linear equations that has the given solution. (There are many correct answers.)

51. $(5, 10)$

52. $(-3, 8)$

53. $\left(3, \frac{8}{3}\right)$

54. $\left(-\frac{2}{3}, 5\right)$

In Exercises 55–58, find a linear system for the graphical model. If only one line is shown, find two different equations for the line.

55.

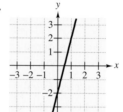

56.

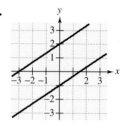

57.

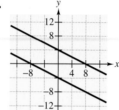

58.

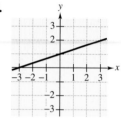

Solving Problems

59. *Geometry*   A rectangular sign (see figure) has a perimeter of 120 inches. The height of the sign is two-thirds of its width. Find the dimensions of the sign.

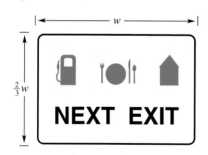

60. *Problem Solving*   A cash register has 15 coins consisting of dimes and quarters. The total value of the coins is $2.85. Find the number of each type of coin.

61. *Price per Gallon*   You buy 2 gallons of gasoline for your lawn mower and 5 gallons of diesel fuel for your garden tractor. The total bill is $8.59. Diesel fuel costs $0.08 more per gallon than gasoline. Find the price per gallon of each type of fuel.

62. *Video Rental*   You go to the video store to rent five movies for the weekend. Videos rent for $2 and $3. You spend $13. How many $2 videos did you rent?

Break-Even Point   In Exercises 63 and 64, use a graphing utility to graph the cost and revenue functions in the same viewing rectangle. Find the sales x necessary to break even ($R = C$) and the corresponding revenue R obtained by selling x units. (Round x to the nearest whole unit.)

	Cost	*Revenue*
63.	$C = 650x + 12,500$	$R = 800x$
64.	$C = 3.30x + 1200$	$R = 4.75x$

65. *Wholesale Cost*   The selling price of a VCR is $434. The markup rate is 40% of the wholesale cost. Find the wholesale cost.

66. *Average Speed*   A car travels for 4 hours at an average speed of 50 miles per hour. How much longer must the car travel at an average speed of 65 miles per hour so that the average speed for the entire trip will be 55 miles per hour?

Chapter Test

Take this test as you would take a test in class. After you are done, check your work against the answers given in the back of the book.

1. Which is the solution of the system $x - 6y = -19$ and $4x - 5y = 0$: $(3, -2)$ or $(5, 4)$? Explain your reasoning.

In Exercises 2-4, determine the number of solutions of the system.

2. $3x + 4y = 16$
   $3x - 4y = 8$

3. $x - 2y = -4$
   $x - 2y = 2$

4. $x + 2y = 4$
   $x + 2y = -2$

In Exercises 5-8, solve the system of equations graphically.

5. $x - 2y = -2$
   $x + y = 4$

6. $2x + y = 4$
   $x - 2y = -3$

7. $x - 3y = -2$
   $2x + y = 10$

8. $2x = 3$
   $2x + 3y = 9$

In Exercises 9-12, solve the system of equations by substitution.

9. $x + 5y = 10$
   $4x - 5y = 15$

10. $x + 3y = 15$
    $-2x + 5y = 14$

11. $0.5x + 0.3y = 3$
    $7x - y = 16$

12. $y = 14 - 5x$
    $x = y - 2$

In Exercises 13-16, solve the system of equations by elimination.

13. $x + y = 8$
    $2x - y = -2$

14. $7x + 6y = 36$
    $5x - 4y = 5$

15. $3x - y = 6$
    $-x + 5y = -6$

16. $4x + 2y = 5$
    $2x + 6y = 7$

17. Find the value of a such that the following system is inconsistent: $ax - 8y = 9$ and $3x + 4y = 0$. Describe the method you used to find a.

18. Find a system of linear equations that has the solution $(-3, 4)$. (There are many correct solutions.)

19. A rectangle has a perimeter of 40 meters. The length of the rectangle is three times its width. Find the dimensions of the rectangle.

20. Twenty liters of 20% acid solution is obtained by mixing a 30% solution and a 5% solution. How many liters of each solution are needed to obtain the specified mixture?

21. The sum of two numbers is 22. The larger number is 6 less than three times the smaller number. Find the two numbers.

8 Rational Expressions and Equations

Richard Shock/Tony Stone Images

The number of women enrolled in college in 1996 was 8.4 million, as compared to only 6.8 million men. (Source: U.S. Bureau of the Census)

Motivating the Chapter

 Predicting College Enrollment

A college recently changed from an all women's college to a coeducational institution. The admissions office projects that enrollment of female students *F* for the next 5 years can be approximated by the model

$$F(t) = \frac{18{,}000 + 2t}{16 - t}$$

where *t* represents the time in years and $t = 0$ is the year before the school became coeducational. The projected enrollment of male students *M* for the next 5 years can be approximated by the model

$$M(t) = \frac{500t}{8 - t}$$

where *t* represents the time in years and $t = 0$ is the year before the school became coeducational.

See Section 8.3, Exercise 99

a. What was the enrollment of the school the year before it became coeducational?

b. Approximate the number of male students for the third year that the school is coeducational. Then, approximate the number of female students for the third year that the school is coeducational. Round your answers to the nearest whole number. What is the projected total enrollment for the third year?

c. Write an expression for the total number of students in any given year *t*. Simplify the result.

d. Use the expression from part (c) to find the projected total enrollment for the third year. Round your answer to the nearest whole number. Does this agree with your answer in part (b)? Explain.

See Section 8.4, Exercise 91

e. Use the table feature of a graphing utility to determine if the male enrollment will reach or surpass the female enrollment at any time over the 5-year projection period.

f. Write an equation in standard quadratic form ($at^2 + bt + c = 0$) that will predict when the male and female enrollments will be equal. Use a graphing utility to graph the equation. From the graph, estimate when the male and female enrollments will be equal.

8.1   Simplifying Rational Expressions

Objectives

1 Find the domain of a rational expression.

2 Simplify a rational expression using the Cancellation Rule for fractions.

1 Find the domain of a rational expression.

Rational Expressions and Their Domains

In this chapter, you will learn how to use the rules for fractions to simplify, add, subtract, multiply, and divide rational expressions. A **rational expression** is a fraction whose numerator and denominator are polynomials. Some examples are

$$\frac{x-2}{5}, \quad \frac{x^3 - 4x}{x - 4}, \quad \text{and} \quad \frac{3x}{x^2 - 1}.$$

Point out that the numerator of an algebraic fraction can be zero. We do not exclude $x = 5$ from the domain of $\frac{x-5}{9}$, and we do not exclude $x = 0$ from the domain of $\frac{x}{x^2 - 16}$.

The **domain** of a rational expression is the set of all real numbers for which it is defined. For instance, the domain of the first expression is the set of all real numbers. Because division by zero is not defined, the domain of the second expression is all real numbers *except* $x = 4$. Similarly, the domain of the third expression is all real numbers *except* $x = \pm 1$. To find the values to *exclude* from the domain, set the denominator equal to zero and find the solutions to that equation.

Example 1   Finding the Domain of a Rational Expression

Find the domain of each rational expression by identifying any excluded values.

a. $\dfrac{7}{x+3}$ **b.** $\dfrac{x-5}{9}$ **c.** $\dfrac{x}{x^2 - 16}$ **d.** $\dfrac{x^2 + 1}{x^2 + 4x - 5}$

Solution

a. The denominator is zero when $x + 3 = 0$ or $x = -3$. So, the domain is all real values of x such that $x \neq -3$.

b. Because the denominator is not zero for any value of x, the domain is the set of *all* real numbers.

c. For this rational expression, the denominator is zero when $x^2 - 16 = 0$.

$$x^2 - 16 = 0 \qquad \text{Original equation}$$
$$(x + 4)(x - 4) = 0 \qquad \text{Factor.}$$

So, the domain is all real values of x such that $x \neq -4$ and $x \neq 4$.

d. For this rational expression, the denominator is zero when $x^2 + 4x - 5 = 0$.

$$x^2 + 4x - 5 = 0 \qquad \text{Original equation}$$
$$(x + 5)(x - 1) = 0 \qquad \text{Factor.}$$

So, the domain is all real values of x such that $x \neq -5$ and $x \neq 1$.

Technology: Discovery

Use a graphing utility to graph the equation

$$y = \frac{7}{x + 3}.$$

Then use the trace feature to determine what happens at $x = -3$, where the denominator is zero. Use the table feature and describe what happens at $x = -3$. Try graphing equations that correspond to parts (b), (c), and (d) of Example 1. What conclusions can you draw about the behavior of the graph at certain values of x?

In applications involving rational expressions, it is often necessary to restrict the domain further. In such cases where the variable represents a quantity such as the number of people, the number of hours worked, or the speed of a vehicle, the domain of the variable is the set of positive numbers. To indicate such a restriction, you should write the domain to the right of the fraction. For instance, if x represents the number of hours worked, the domain of the expression

$$\frac{x^2 + 10}{x + 2}, \quad x > 0$$

is restricted to the set of *positive* real numbers.

| Example 2 | An Application Involving a Restricted Domain | |

A publisher asks a printing company to print copies of a book. The printing company charges $5000 as a start-up fee, plus $4 per book. If x copies of the book are printed, the total cost (in dollars) of the printing is modeled by

$$\text{Total cost} = 5000 + 4x. \qquad \text{Total cost of } x \text{ books}$$

The average cost per book depends on the number of books printed. If 100 books are printed, the average cost is

$$\text{Average cost} = \frac{\text{total cost}}{\text{number of books}}$$

$$= \frac{5000 + 4(100)}{100}$$

$$= \$54 \text{ per book.} \qquad \text{Average cost of 100 books}$$

On the other hand, if 10,000 books are printed, the average cost is

$$\frac{5000 + 4(10,000)}{10,000} = \$4.50 \text{ per book.} \qquad \text{Average cost of 10,000 books}$$

In general, if x copies of the book are printed, the average cost per book is

$$\frac{5000 + 4x}{x}. \qquad \text{Average cost of } x \text{ books}$$

What is the domain of this rational expression?

Solution

If you were simply considering the rational expression

$$\frac{5000 + 4x}{x}$$

as a mathematical quantity, you would say that the domain is all real values of x such that $x \neq 0$. However, because this fraction is a mathematical model representing a real-life situation, you must decide which values of x make sense in real life. For this model, the variable x represents the number of books printed. Because the number of books printed must be a positive integer, we conclude that the domain is the set of positive integers. That is,

$$\text{Domain} = \{1, 2, 3, 4, \ldots\}.$$

In 1996, more than 2 billion books were sold in the United States. Of these, 38% were hardbacks and 62% were paperbacks. (Source: Book Industry Study Group, Inc.)

2 Simplify a rational expression using the Cancellation Rule for fractions.

Simplifying Rational Expressions

The rules for operating with rational expressions are like those for numerical fractions (see Section 1.3). As with numerical fractions, a rational expression is in **simplified form** or **reduced form** if its numerator and denominator have no common factors (other than 1). To write a fraction in simplified form, use this rule.

> ▶ **Cancellation Rule for Fractions**
>
> Let a, b, and c represent real numbers, variables, or algebraic expressions such that $b \neq 0$ and $c \neq 0$. Then the following Cancellation Rule is valid.
>
> $$\frac{ac}{bc} = \frac{a\cancel{c}}{b\cancel{c}} = \frac{a}{b}$$

Study Tip

Using the Cancellation Rule to simplify a rational expression requires two steps.

1. Completely factor the numerator and denominator.
2. Apply the Cancellation Rule to cancel any *factors* that are common to both the numerator and denominator.

Your success in simplifying rational expressions actually lies in your ability to factor completely the polynomials in both the numerator and denominator.

Be sure you see that this rule allows you to cancel only *factors*, not *terms*. For instance, consider the following.

$$\frac{\cancel{3} \cdot x}{\cancel{3}(x + 4)}$$ Yes, you *can* cancel common factor 3.

$$\frac{3 + x}{3 + (x + 4)}$$ No, you *cannot* cancel common term 3.

$$\frac{\cancel{x}(x^2 + 4)}{\cancel{x}}$$ Yes, you *can* cancel common factor x.

Example 3 Simplifying a Rational Expression by Factoring

a. $\dfrac{42}{120} = \dfrac{2 \cdot 3 \cdot 7}{2 \cdot 2 \cdot 2 \cdot 3 \cdot 5}$ Factor completely.

$\quad = \dfrac{{}^1\cancel{2} \cdot {}^1\cancel{3} \cdot 7}{2 \cdot 2 \cdot \cancel{2}_1 \cdot \cancel{3}_1 \cdot 5}$ Cancel common factors.

$\quad = \dfrac{7}{20}$ Simplified form

b. $\dfrac{2x^2 - 4x}{(x - 2)^2} = \dfrac{2x(x - 2)}{(x - 2)(x - 2)}$ Factor completely.

$\quad = \dfrac{2x\cancel{(x - 2)}^1}{(x - 2)\cancel{(x - 2)}_1}$ Cancel common factors.

$\quad = \dfrac{2x}{x - 2}$ Simplified form

c. $\dfrac{15(x^2 - 2x)}{3x^2} = \dfrac{3 \cdot 5 \cdot x(x - 2)}{3 \cdot x \cdot x}$ Factor completely.

$\quad = \dfrac{{}^1\cancel{3} \cdot 5 \cdot \cancel{x}^1(x - 2)}{\cancel{3}_1 \cdot \cancel{x}_1 \cdot x}$ Cancel common factors.

$\quad = \dfrac{5x - 10}{x}$ Simplified form

Emphasize the distinction between terms and factors. Canceling terms is one of the most common algebraic errors.

When simplifying a rational expression, we suggest that you list *by the simplified expression* all values of x that must be specifically excluded from the domain in order to make the domains of the simplified and original expressions agree.

Study Tip

In Example 4, be sure you see that simplifying a rational expression can change its domain. For instance, in part (a) the domain of the original expression is all real values of x such that $x \neq 0$. So, to equate the original expression with the simplified expression, you must restrict the domain of the simplified expression to exclude 0. Similarly, 2 must be excluded in part (b).

| **Example 4** | Adjusting the Domain After Simplifying |

Simplify the rational expressions.

a. $\dfrac{4x^3 - 8x^2}{4x^2}$ **b.** $\dfrac{x^2 + 4x - 12}{3x - 6}$

Solution

a. $\dfrac{4x^3 - 8x^2}{4x^2} = \dfrac{4x^2(x - 2)}{4x^2}$ Factor numerator.

$= \dfrac{{}^1\cancel{4x^2}(x - 2)}{\cancel{4x^2}_1}$ Cancel common factor $4x^2$.

$= x - 2, \quad x \neq 0$ Simplified form

b. $\dfrac{x^2 + 4x - 12}{3x - 6} = \dfrac{(x + 6)(x - 2)}{3(x - 2)}$ Factor numerator and denominator.

$= \dfrac{(x + 6)\cancel{(x - 2)}^1}{3\cancel{(x - 2)}_1}$ Cancel common factor $(x - 2)$.

$= \dfrac{x + 6}{3}, \quad x \neq 2$ Simplified form

Be sure to factor *completely* the numerator and denominator of a rational expression before concluding that there is no common factor. This may involve a change in signs. Remember that the Distributive Property allows you to write $(b - a)$ as $-1(a - b)$. Watch for this in the next example.

Technology: Tip

You can graphically check that you have simplified an expression correctly by graphing both the original and the simplified expressions on the same screen. For instance, try graphing

$$y_1 = \frac{9 - x^2}{2x - 6} \text{ and}$$

$$y_2 = -\frac{x + 3}{2}$$

on the same screen to check the result of Example 5.

| **Example 5** | Simplifying a Rational Expression by a Sign Change |

$\dfrac{9 - x^2}{2x - 6} = \dfrac{(3 + x)(3 - x)}{2(x - 3)}$ Factor completely.

$= \dfrac{(3 + x)(-1)(x - 3)}{2(x - 3)}$ $(3 - x) = (-1)(x - 3)$

$= \dfrac{(3 + x)(-1)\cancel{(x - 3)}^1}{2\cancel{(x - 3)}_1}$ Cancel common factor $(x - 3)$.

$= -\dfrac{x + 3}{2}, \quad x \neq 3$ Simplified form

In the simplified form, we like to list the minus sign in front of the fraction. This, however, is a personal preference. All of the following are equivalent.

$$-\frac{x + 3}{2} = \frac{-(x + 3)}{2} = \frac{-x - 3}{2} = \frac{x + 3}{-2}$$

In the next example, the Cancellation Rule is used to simplify a rational expression that involves more than one variable.

Example 6   A Rational Expression Involving Two Variables

Simplify the rational expression

$$\frac{x^2 - 2xy + y^2}{5x - 5y}.$$

Then describe the domain of the expression.

Solution

$$\frac{x^2 - 2xy + y^2}{5x - 5y} = \frac{(x - y)(x - y)}{5(x - y)} \qquad \text{Factor numerator and denominator.}$$

$$= \frac{(x - y)(x - y)^1}{5(x - y)_1} \qquad \text{Cancel common factor } (x - y).$$

$$= \frac{x - y}{5}, \quad x \neq y \qquad \text{Simplified form}$$

The domain of the expression is all ordered pairs (x, y) of real numbers *except* those for which $x = y$.

As you study the examples and work the exercises in this and the following two sections, keep in mind that you are *rewriting expressions in simpler forms*. You are not solving equations. Equal signs are used in the steps only to indicate that the new form of the expression (fraction) is equivalent to the original form.

Discussing the Concept	Error Analysis

Suppose two of your algebra students hand in the following work.

Student A

$$\frac{\overset{1}{\cancel{x}} - 25}{\overset{}{\cancel{x}} - 5} = -4$$

Student B

$$\frac{3(x + 2)}{3x + 2} = \frac{x + 2}{x + 2} = 1$$

Find all errors or misconceptions in each student's work. In a written, detailed explanation, show the students how to work each problem correctly. Compare your explanations with others in your class, and discuss ways to show the students numerically that an error was made in their work.

8.1   Exercises

Integrated Review   *Concepts, Skills, and Problem Solving*

Keep mathematically in shape by doing these exercises *before* the problems of this section.

Properties and Definitions

1. Define the slope of the line through the points (x_1, y_1) and (x_2, y_2).

2. Make a statement about the slope m of a line for each of the following conditions.

  (a) The line rises from left to right.

  (b) The line falls from left to right.

  (c) The line is horizontal.

  (d) The line is vertical.

3. Are the graphs of $y = -2x + 3$ and $6x + 3y - 3 = 0$ parallel or perpendicular? Explain.

4. Are the graphs of $y = -\frac{1}{2}x + 3$ and $2x - y + 1 = 0$ parallel or perpendicular? Explain.

Algebraic Operations

In Exercises 5–8, find the slope of the line passing through the two points.

5. $(0, 4), (10, 0)$ **6.** $(0, 0), (5, -3)$

7. $(-1, 3), (4, 8)$ **8.** $(2, 6), (5, 1)$

In Exercises 9–12, solve the equation and check your answer.

9. $14 - 2x = x + 2$

10. $7 - 3(1 - 2p) = 2p + 4$

11. $\dfrac{x}{3} + 5 = 8$

12. $\dfrac{x}{3} + \dfrac{x}{2} = \dfrac{1}{3}$

Problem Solving

13. The annual insurance premium for a policy-holder is normally \$645. However, after having an automobile accident, the policy-holder is charged an additional 25%. What is the new annual premium?

14. An employee is paid \$9.50 per hour for the first 40 hours and \$14 for each hour of overtime. During the first week on the job, the employee's gross pay is \$478. How many hours of overtime did the employee work?

Developing Skills

In Exercises 1–4, determine whether the expression is a rational expression. If not, explain why.

1. $\dfrac{x^2 + 1}{5x - 2}$ **2.** $\dfrac{x}{x^{-2} + 2}$

3. $\dfrac{x^{1/2} - 2x}{x + 1}$ **4.** $\dfrac{6}{x - 2}$

In Exercises 5–20, find the domain of the expression. See Example 1.

5. $\dfrac{5}{x - 4}$ **6.** $\dfrac{10}{x - 6}$

7. $\dfrac{x}{x + 2}$ **8.** $\dfrac{2z}{z + 8}$

9. $\dfrac{x^2 - 4}{3}$ **10.** $\dfrac{y^2 - 1}{5}$

11. $\dfrac{3}{x^2 + 4}$ **12.** $\dfrac{5}{x^2 + 4}$

13. $\dfrac{4t}{t^2 - 25}$ **14.** $\dfrac{z + 2}{z^2 - 4}$

15. $\dfrac{-5(y + 2)}{y^2 - 3y - 28}$ **16.** $\dfrac{-3(x - 2)}{x^2 + 6x + 8}$

17. $\dfrac{x^2}{x^2 - x - 2}$ **18.** $\dfrac{x^2}{x^2 + 3x - 10}$

19. $\dfrac{z - 3}{3z^2 - z - 2}$ **20.** $\dfrac{y + 5}{4y^2 + y - 3}$

In Exercises 21–24, evaluate the expression for the specified values. (If not possible, state the reason.)

Expression   *Values*

21. $\dfrac{x}{x-3}$ (a) $x = 0$ (b) $x = 3$

                                 (c) $x = 10$ (d) $x = -3$

22. $\dfrac{3y}{y+6}$ (a) $y = 0$ (b) $y = -3$

                                 (c) $y = -10$ (d) $y = -6$

23. $\dfrac{x+1}{x^2-4}$ (a) $x = 2$ (b) $x = 1$

                                 (c) $x = -5$ (d) $x = -2$

24. $\dfrac{2x-3}{x^2+2x-3}$ (a) $x = 0$ (b) $x = 1$

                                 (c) $x = -\frac{3}{2}$ (d) $x = -3$

Think About It   In Exercises 25–28, write two equivalent versions of the expression by changing signs of the numerator, the denominator, or the fraction.

25. $\dfrac{x}{12}$ **26.** $-\dfrac{4}{y}$

27. $-\dfrac{t+2}{t^2-1}$ **28.** $\dfrac{x-6}{x+1}$

In Exercises 29–40, find the missing factor.

29. $\dfrac{5}{2x} = \dfrac{5\ \ }{6x^2}$ **30.** $\dfrac{3x}{2} = \dfrac{3x\ \ }{4x^2}$

31. $\dfrac{3}{4} = \dfrac{3\ \ }{4(x+1)}$ **32.** $\dfrac{11}{16} = \dfrac{11\ \ }{32(x-4)^2}$

33. $\dfrac{-7}{3x} = \dfrac{7\ \ }{3x^3}$

34. $\dfrac{5x}{8} = \dfrac{25x^2}{8\ \ }$

35. $\dfrac{x}{2} = \dfrac{x(x+2)}{2\ \ }$

36. $\dfrac{-2x}{x+2} = \dfrac{2(x^2+2x)}{(x+2)\ \ }$

37. $\dfrac{x+1}{x} = \dfrac{(x+1)\ \ }{x(x-2)}$

38. $\dfrac{3y-4}{y+1} = \dfrac{(3y-4)\ \ }{y^2-1}$

39. $\dfrac{3x}{x-3} = \dfrac{3x\ \ }{x^2-x-6}$

40. $\dfrac{1-z}{z^2} = \dfrac{(1-z)\ \ }{z^3+z^2}$

In Exercises 41–80, simplify the expression. See Examples 3–5.

41. $\dfrac{4x}{12}$ **42.** $\dfrac{18y}{36}$

43. $\dfrac{2y^2}{y}$ **44.** $\dfrac{5z^3}{z}$

45. $\dfrac{15x^2}{10x}$ **46.** $\dfrac{18y^2}{60y^5}$

47. $\dfrac{75x(x-1)^2}{15x(x-1)}$ **48.** $\dfrac{5b(b-3)}{b(b-3)^2}$

49. $\dfrac{x^2(x+1)}{x(x+1)}$ **50.** $\dfrac{b(b-2)}{b^2(b-2)}$

51. $\dfrac{x-5}{2x-10}$ **52.** $\dfrac{5-x}{2x-10}$

53. $\dfrac{3y+3}{xy+x}$ **54.** $\dfrac{x^2y+x}{xy+1}$

55. $\dfrac{9-3t}{t-3}$ **56.** $\dfrac{y-3}{9-3y}$

57. $\dfrac{x^2-25}{5-x}$ **58.** $\dfrac{x^2-25}{x-5}$

59. $\dfrac{y^2-16}{3y+12}$ **60.** $\dfrac{x^2-25z^2}{x-5z}$

61. $\dfrac{x^2-2x+1}{1-x^2}$ **62.** $\dfrac{u^2-3u-4}{16-u^2}$

63. $\dfrac{a+2}{a^2+4a+4}$ **64.** $\dfrac{u^2-6u+9}{u-3}$

65. $\dfrac{x^2-5x}{x^2-10x+25}$ **66.** $\dfrac{z^2+12z+36}{5z+30}$

67. $\dfrac{y^2-4}{y^2+3y-10}$ **68.** $\dfrac{x^2-7x}{x^2-8x+7}$

69. $\dfrac{x^2-4x+3}{x^2-5x+6}$ **70.** $\dfrac{y^2-7y+12}{y^2+3y-18}$

71. $\dfrac{x^2+8x-20}{x^2+11x+10}$ **72.** $\dfrac{z^2-3z-18}{z^2+2z-48}$

73. $\dfrac{x^3+5x^2+6x}{x^2-4}$ **74.** $\dfrac{t^3-t}{t^3+5t^2-6t}$

75. $\dfrac{x^3-2x^2+x-2}{x-2}$ **76.** $\dfrac{x^2-9}{x^3+x^2-9x-9}$

77. $\dfrac{x^3+2x^2+x+2}{x^2+1}$ **78.** $\dfrac{z-3}{z^3-3z^2+z-3}$

79. $\dfrac{a^3-8}{a^2-4}$ **80.** $\dfrac{1-y^3}{1+y+y^2}$

Graphical Verification   In Exercises 81–86, simplify the expression. Then use a graphing utility to check your result.

81. $\dfrac{2x^2 + 4x}{2x}$

82. $\dfrac{5x^2 - 6x}{2x}$

83. $\dfrac{3(x - 3)^2}{x - 3}$

84. $\dfrac{2(x - 4)^2}{x - 4}$

85. $\dfrac{x^3 - 2x^2}{x^3 + 2x}$

86. $\dfrac{x^3 - 4x^2}{x^3 + 2x}$

✸ *Creating a Table*   In Exercises 87 and 88, complete the table. Explain why the values of the expressions agree for all values of x except one.

87.

x	2	2.5	3	3.5	4
$\dfrac{x^3 - 3x^2}{x - 3}$					
x^2					

88.

x	0	0.5	1	1.5	2
$\dfrac{x - 1}{x^2 + 2x - 3}$					
$\dfrac{1}{x + 3}$					

In Exercises 89 and 90, translate the statement into a rational expression.

89. The cost per unit when x units are manufactured at a total cost of \$500

90. The time required to drive 240 miles at an average speed of $x + 5$ miles per hour

Solving Problems

91. *Using a Model*   A machine shop has a setup cost of \$3000 for the production of a new product. The cost of labor and materials for producing each unit is \$7.50.

(a) Write a rational expression that gives the average cost per unit when x units are produced.

(b) Find the domain of the expression in part (a).

(c) Find the average cost per unit when $x = 100$ units are produced.

92. *Using a Model*   A machine shop has a setup cost of \$5000 for the production of a new product. The cost of labor and materials for producing each unit is \$12.50.

(a) Write a rational expression that gives the average cost per unit when x units are produced.

(b) Find the domain of the expression in part (a).

(c) Find the average cost per unit when $x = 200$ units are produced.

93. *Using a Model*   As air pressure increases, the temperature at which water boils also increases. (This is the purpose of pressure canners.) A model that

relates air pressure to boiling temperature is

$$B = \frac{156.89x + 7.34x^2}{x + 0.017x^2}, \quad 10 \le x \le 100$$

where B is measured in degrees Fahrenheit and x is measured in pounds per square inch.

(a) Simplify the rational expression.

(b) Use the model to estimate the boiling temperature of water when $x = 14.7$ (approximate air pressure at sea level).

94. *Depreciation*   The value V of an automobile t years after it was purchased is given by

$$V = \frac{50P}{51 + 22t}, \quad 0 \le t \le 5$$

where P is the purchase price.

(a) Use a graphing utility to graph the function V for an automobile for which $P = \$20,000$.

(b) Use the model to estimate the value of an automobile 3 years after it was purchased if the purchase price was \$22,500.

95. *Creating a Table*   A utility company burns coal to produce electricity. The cost (in dollars) of removing p percent of the air pollutants in the stack emission of the utility company is given by the rational expression

$$\frac{80,000p}{1-p}.$$

(a) Determine the domain of the expression. (Assume the percentage p is in decimal form.)

(b) Create a table showing the cost of removing several different percentages of pollutants in the stack emission.

(c) Use the table to describe the relationship between the cost and the percent. According to this model, can you remove 100% of the pollutants? Explain.

96. *Comparing Distances*   You start a trip and drive at an average speed of 50 miles per hour. Two hours later a friend starts a trip on the same road and drives at an average speed of 60 miles per hour.

(a) Find polynomial expressions that represent the distance each of you has driven when your friend has been driving for t hours.

(b) Use the result of part (a) to determine the ratio of the distance your friend has driven to the distance you have driven.

(c) Evaluate the ratio described in part (b) when $t = 5$ and $t = 10$.

Probability   In Exercises 97 and 98, consider an experiment in which a marble is tossed into a box whose base is shown in the figure. The probability that the marble will come to rest in the shaded portion of the box is equal to the ratio of the shaded area to the total area of the figure. Find the probability.

97.

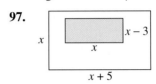

98.

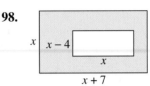

Probability   In Exercises 99 and 100, the probability of hitting the shaded portion of the region with a dart is the ratio of the area of the shaded region to the total area of the figure. Find the probability.

99.

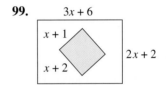

100.

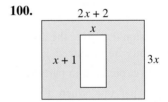

Explaining Concepts

101. Explain what is meant by a rational expression.

102. Define the *domain* of a rational expression.

103. How can you determine whether a rational expression is in simplified form?

104. *True or False?*   To simplify a rational expression, you can cancel common factors of the numerator and denominator.

105. Explain the error.

$$\frac{2x^2 + 3x}{x^2 + 4x} = \frac{2 + 3}{1 + 4} = 1$$

106. Is $(4x)/(2x)$ equivalent to 2? Explain.

107. Construct a rational expression that cannot be simplified.

108. Construct a rational expression that can be simplified.

8.2   Multiplying and Dividing Rational Expressions

Objectives

1 Multiply rational expressions and simplify.

2 Divide rational expressions and simplify.

3 Simplify a complex fraction using rules for dividing fractions.

---

1 Multiply rational expressions and simplify.

Multiplying Rational Expressions

The rule for multiplying rational expressions is the same as the rule for multiplying numerical fractions.

$$\frac{a}{b} \cdot \frac{c}{d} = \frac{ac}{bd}$$

That is, you *multiply numerators, multiply denominators, and simplify.* Here is an example.

$$\frac{x - 2}{x + 1} \cdot \frac{x + 1}{x + 2} = \frac{(x - 2)(x + 1)}{(x + 1)(x + 2)} \qquad \text{Multiply numerators and denominators.}$$

$$= \frac{(x - 2)(x + 1)}{(x + 1)(x + 2)} \qquad \text{Cancel common factor.}$$

$$= \frac{x - 2}{x + 2}, \quad x \neq -1 \qquad \text{Simplified form}$$

To recognize common factors in the product, you should write the numerators and denominators in completely factored form.

Study Tip

In the example at the right, the original expression

$$\frac{x - 2}{x + 1} \cdot \frac{x + 1}{x + 2}$$

has the implied domain of all real numbers except -1 and -2. The domain of the simplified form

$$\frac{x - 2}{x + 2}$$

is all real numbers except -2. To make the simplified form of the expression equivalent to the original expression you must add the domain restriction $x \neq -1$.

$$\frac{x - 2}{x + 1} \cdot \frac{x + 1}{x + 2} = \frac{x - 2}{x + 2},$$

$$x \neq -1$$

Example 1   Multiplying Rational Expressions

a. $\dfrac{5}{12} \cdot \dfrac{6}{15} = \dfrac{5 \cdot 6}{12 \cdot 15}$ Multiply numerators and denominators.

$\qquad = \dfrac{5 \cdot 2 \cdot 3}{2 \cdot 2 \cdot 3 \cdot 3 \cdot 5}$ Cancel common factors.

$\qquad = \dfrac{1}{6}$ Simplified form

b. $\dfrac{3x^2 y}{2xy^2} \cdot \dfrac{-10xy^3}{6x^3} = \dfrac{(3x^2 y)(-10xy^3)}{(2xy^2)(6x^3)}$ Multiply numerators and denominators.

$\qquad = \dfrac{-3(10)x^3 y^4}{2(6)x^4 y^2}$ Simplify.

$\qquad = \dfrac{-3(2)(5)(x^3)(y^2)(y^2)}{2(3)(2)(x^3)(x)(y^2)}$ Cancel common factors.

$\qquad = -\dfrac{5y^2}{2x}, \quad y \neq 0$ Simplified form

Emmy Noether

(1882–1935)

The German mathematician Emmy Noether is now recognized as a prominent figure in 20th century mathematics. After struggling (and succeeding) to gain acceptance as a female mathematician by her peers, she amazed them with her ability to discern and understand the underlying themes of mathematical processes. Her work greatly impacted the development of modern algebra.

Example 2   Multiplying Rational Expressions

Multiply and simplify: $\dfrac{4x}{x^2 - 9} \cdot \dfrac{x - 3}{8x^2 + 12x}$.

Solution

$$\frac{4x}{x^2 - 9} \cdot \frac{x - 3}{8x^2 + 12x}$$

$$= \frac{4x(x - 3)}{(x^2 - 9)(8x^2 + 12x)} \qquad \text{Multiply numerators and denominators.}$$

$$= \frac{4x(x - 3)}{(x + 3)(x - 3)(4x)(2x + 3)} \qquad \text{Factor.}$$

$$= \frac{4x(x - 3)}{(x + 3)(x - 3)(4x)(2x + 3)} \qquad \text{Cancel common factors. Factor of 1 remains in numerator.}$$

$$= \frac{1}{(x + 3)(2x + 3)}, \quad x \neq 0, \ x \neq 3 \qquad \text{Simplified form}$$

The rule for multiplying rational expressions can be extended to cover products involving expressions that are not fractional in form. To do this, rewrite the (nonfractional) expression as a fraction whose denominator is 1.

Example 3   Multiplying Rational Expressions

a. $\dfrac{x + 2}{x + 4} \cdot (3x) = \dfrac{x + 2}{x + 4} \cdot \dfrac{3x}{1}$ Rewrite in fractional form.

$$= \frac{(x + 2)(3x)}{x + 4} \qquad \text{Multiply numerators and denominators.}$$

$$= \frac{3x(x + 2)}{x + 4} \qquad \text{Simplified form}$$

b. $\dfrac{x}{2x^2 - x - 3} \cdot (2x - 3)$

$$= \frac{x}{2x^2 - x - 3} \cdot \frac{2x - 3}{1} \qquad \text{Rewrite in fractional form.}$$

$$= \frac{x(2x - 3)}{2x^2 - x - 3} \qquad \text{Multiply numerators and denominators.}$$

$$= \frac{x(2x - 3)}{(2x - 3)(x + 1)} \qquad \text{Factor.}$$

$$= \frac{x(2x - 3)}{(2x - 3)(x + 1)} \qquad \text{Cancel common factor.}$$

$$= \frac{x}{x + 1}, \quad x \neq \frac{3}{2} \qquad \text{Simplified form}$$

In the next example, note how to cancel factors that differ only in sign.

> **Example 4**   Multiplying Rational Expressions

Study Tip

In Example 4, the factor $(y - x)$ in the denominator is factored as $(-1)(x - y)$. Because the factor $(x - y)$ appears in both the numerator and the denominator, it can be canceled.

Multiply and simplify: $\dfrac{x - y}{6x + 4y} \cdot \dfrac{3x + 2y}{y^2 - x^2}$.

Solution

$$\frac{x - y}{6x + 4y} \cdot \frac{3x + 2y}{y^2 - x^2}$$

$$= \frac{(x - y)(3x + 2y)}{(6x + 4y)(y^2 - x^2)} \qquad \text{Multiply numerators and denominators.}$$

$$= \frac{(x - y)(3x + 2y)}{2(3x + 2y)(y + x)(y - x)} \qquad \text{Factor.}$$

$$= \frac{(x - y)(3x + 2y)}{2(3x + 2y)(y + x)(-1)(x - y)} \qquad (y - x) = (-1)(x - y)$$

$$= \frac{\cancel{(x - y)}\cancel{(3x + 2y)}}{2\cancel{(3x + 2y)}(y + x)(-1)\cancel{(x - y)}} \qquad \text{Cancel common factors.}$$

$$= -\frac{1}{2(y + x)}, \quad x \neq y, \ x \neq -\frac{2}{3}y \qquad \text{Simplified form}$$

In Example 4, the factor -1 could have been written in the numerator instead of the denominator, with the same results.

$$\frac{(x - y)(3x + 2y)}{2(3x + 2y)(y + x)(y - x)} = \frac{(-1)(y - x)(3x + 2y)}{2(3x + 2y)(y + x)(y - x)}$$

The rule for multiplying rational expressions can be extended to cover the product of three or more expressions.

> **Example 5**   Multiplying Three Rational Expressions

Multiply and simplify: $\dfrac{3}{x} \cdot \dfrac{x + 1}{x + 2} \cdot \dfrac{x}{x + 1}$.

Solution

$$\frac{3}{x} \cdot \frac{x + 1}{x + 2} \cdot \frac{x}{x + 1}$$

$$= \frac{3(x + 1)(x)}{x(x + 2)(x + 1)} \qquad \text{Multiply numerators and denominators.}$$

$$= \frac{3\cancel{(x + 1)}\cancel{(x)}}{\cancel{x}(x + 2)\cancel{(x + 1)}} \qquad \text{Cancel common factors.}$$

$$= \frac{3}{x + 2}, \quad x \neq 0, \ x \neq -1 \qquad \text{Simplified form}$$

2 Divide rational expressions and simplify.

Dividing Rational Expressions

To divide two rational expressions, multiply the first fraction by the *reciprocal* of the second.

$$\frac{a}{b} \div \frac{c}{d} = \frac{a}{b} \cdot \frac{d}{c}$$

That is, *invert the divisor and multiply.*

Example 6   Dividing Rational Expressions

a. $\dfrac{8}{5} \div \dfrac{12}{15} = \dfrac{8}{5} \cdot \dfrac{15}{12}$ Invert and multiply.

$= \dfrac{8 \cdot 15}{5 \cdot 12}$ Multiply numerators and denominators.

$= \dfrac{2 \cdot 2 \cdot 2 \cdot 3 \cdot 5}{5 \cdot 3 \cdot 2 \cdot 2}$ Cancel common factors.

$= 2$ Simplified form

b. $\dfrac{x}{x+4} \div \dfrac{x+3}{x+4} = \dfrac{x}{x+4} \cdot \dfrac{x+4}{x+3}$ Invert and multiply.

$= \dfrac{(x)(x+4)}{(x+4)(x+3)}$ Multiply numerators and denominators.

$= \dfrac{(x)(x+4)}{(x+4)(x+3)}$ Cancel common factor.

$= \dfrac{x}{x+3}, \quad x \neq -4$ Simplified form

You might remind students that only common *factors* can be canceled.

Example 7   Dividing Rational Expressions

$\dfrac{x^2 - 2x}{x^2 - 6x + 8} \div \dfrac{2x}{3x - 12}$

$= \dfrac{x^2 - 2x}{x^2 - 6x + 8} \cdot \dfrac{3x - 12}{2x}$ Invert and multiply.

$= \dfrac{(x^2 - 2x)(3x - 12)}{(x^2 - 6x + 8)(2x)}$ Multiply numerators and denominators.

$= \dfrac{(x)(x - 2)(3)(x - 4)}{(x - 2)(x - 4)(2x)}$ Factor.

$= \dfrac{(x)(x - 2)(3)(x - 4)}{(x - 2)(x - 4)(2x)}$ Cancel common factors.

$= \dfrac{3}{2}, \quad x \neq 0, \ x \neq 2, \ x \neq 4$ Simplified form

3 Simplify a complex fraction using rules for dividing fractions.

Complex Fractions

Problems involving the division of two rational expressions are sometimes written as **complex fractions.** A complex fraction is a fraction that has a fraction in its numerator or denominator, or both. The rules for dividing fractions still apply. For instance, consider the following complex fraction.

$$\dfrac{\left(\dfrac{x+2}{3}\right)}{\left(\dfrac{x-2}{x}\right)} \longrightarrow$$

Numerator fraction

Main fraction line

Denominator fraction

Study Tip

If a, b, c, and d represent algebraic expressions, then the domain of the complex fraction

$$\dfrac{\dfrac{a}{b}}{\dfrac{c}{d}}$$

is the set of all real numbers such that $b \neq 0$, $c \neq 0$, and $d \neq 0$.

To perform the division implied by this complex fraction, invert the denominator fraction and multiply, as follows.

$$\dfrac{\left(\dfrac{x+2}{3}\right)}{\left(\dfrac{x-2}{x}\right)} = \dfrac{x+2}{3} \cdot \dfrac{x}{x-2} = \dfrac{x(x+2)}{3(x-2)}, \quad x \neq 0$$

Complex fractions are further discussed in the next section.

Example 8   Simplifying Complex Fractions

Simplify the complex fractions.

a. $\dfrac{\left(\dfrac{5}{14}\right)}{\left(\dfrac{25}{8}\right)}$ b. $\dfrac{\left(\dfrac{4y^3}{(5x)^2}\right)}{\left(\dfrac{(2y)^2}{10x^3}\right)}$

Solution

a. $\dfrac{\left(\dfrac{5}{14}\right)}{\left(\dfrac{25}{8}\right)} = \dfrac{5}{14} \cdot \dfrac{8}{25}$ Invert and multiply.

$$= \dfrac{5 \cdot 2 \cdot 2 \cdot 2}{2 \cdot 7 \cdot 5 \cdot 5}$$ Multiply, factor, and cancel common factors.

$$= \dfrac{4}{35}$$ Simplified form

b. $\dfrac{\left(\dfrac{4y^3}{(5x)^2}\right)}{\left(\dfrac{(2y)^2}{10x^3}\right)} = \dfrac{4y^3}{25x^2} \cdot \dfrac{10x^3}{4y^2}$ Invert and multiply.

$$= \dfrac{4y^2 \cdot y \cdot 2 \cdot 5x^2 \cdot x}{5 \cdot 5x^2 \cdot 4y^2}$$ Multiply and factor.

$$= \dfrac{4y^2 \cdot y \cdot 2 \cdot 5x^2 \cdot x}{5 \cdot 5x^2 \cdot 4y^2}$$ Cancel common factors.

$$= \dfrac{2xy}{5}, \quad x \neq 0, \ y \neq 0$$ Simplified form

Example 9 Simplifying Complex Fractions

Simplify the complex fractions.

a. $\dfrac{\left(\dfrac{x+1}{x+2}\right)}{\left(\dfrac{x+1}{x+5}\right)}$ b. $\dfrac{\left(\dfrac{x^2+4x+3}{x-2}\right)}{2x+6}$

Solution

a. $\dfrac{\left(\dfrac{x+1}{x+2}\right)}{\left(\dfrac{x+1}{x+5}\right)} = \dfrac{x+1}{x+2} \cdot \dfrac{x+5}{x+1}$ Invert and multiply.

$= \dfrac{(x+1)(x+5)}{(x+2)(x+1)}$ Multiply numerators and denominators.

$= \dfrac{\cancel{(x+1)}(x+5)}{(x+2)\cancel{(x+1)}}$ Cancel common factor.

$= \dfrac{x+5}{x+2}, \quad x \neq -1, \; x \neq -5$ Simplified form

b. Begin by writing the denominator in fractional form.

$\dfrac{\left(\dfrac{x^2+4x+3}{x-2}\right)}{2x+6} = \dfrac{\left(\dfrac{x^2+4x+3}{x-2}\right)}{\left(\dfrac{2x+6}{1}\right)}$ Rewrite denominator.

$= \dfrac{x^2+4x+3}{x-2} \cdot \dfrac{1}{2x+6}$ Invert and multiply.

$= \dfrac{(x+1)(x+3)}{(x-2)(2)(x+3)}$ Multiply and factor.

$= \dfrac{(x+1)\cancel{(x+3)}}{(x-2)(2)\cancel{(x+3)}}$ Cancel common factor.

$= \dfrac{x+1}{2(x-2)}, \quad x \neq -3$ Simplified form

Discussing the Concept   **Comparing Rational Expressions**

The following expressions have the same value when $x = 4$.

$$\frac{3x^2 + 4x - 4}{2x^2 + 5x + 2}, \qquad \frac{x+6}{2x+1}, \qquad \frac{3x-2}{2x+1}$$

Are they all equivalent? Is there an equivalent pair? Are there any excluded values? Compare your explanation with others in your class.

8.2   Exercises

Integrated Review   *Concepts, Skills, and Problem Solving*

Keep mathematically in shape by doing these exercises *before* the problems of this section.

Properties and Definitions

1. Explain how to factor the difference of two squares $4x^2 - 9$.

2. Explain how to factor the perfect square trinomial $x^2 - 8x + 16$.

3. Explain how to factor the sum of two cubes $8x^3 + 27$.

4. Factor $3x^2 + 13x - 10$, and explain how you can show that your answer is correct.

Algebraic Operations

In Exercises 5–8, factor the expression completely.

5. $3x^2 + 7x$

6. $16 - (x - 11)^2$

7. $x^2 + 7x - 18$

8. $10x^2 + 13x - 3$

In Exercises 9 and 10, find the missing factor.

9. $\frac{1}{3}x + \frac{5}{9} = \frac{1}{9}\big(\quad\big)$ **10.** $\frac{5}{8}x - \frac{3}{2} = \frac{1}{8}\big(\quad\big)$

Graphs

In Exercises 11 and 12, sketch the graph of the line through the given point with each indicated slope. Make the sketches on the same set of coordinate axes.

	Point		Slopes
11.	$(2, 3)$	(a) 0	(b) 1
		(c) 2	(d) $-\frac{1}{3}$
12.	$(-4, 1)$	(a) 3	(b) -3
		(c) $\frac{1}{2}$	(d) undefined

Developing Skills

In Exercises 1 and 2, evaluate the expression for each value of x. If not possible, state the reason.

	Expression		*Values*	
1.	$\dfrac{x - 5}{3x}$	(a) $x = 5$	(b) $x = 0$	
		(c) $x = -5$	(d) $x = 6$	
2.	$\dfrac{4x}{x - 3}$	(a) $x = 0$	(b) $x = 6$	
		(c) $x = 2$	(d) $x = 3$	

In Exercises 3–12, find the missing factor.

3. $\dfrac{3}{7x} = \dfrac{15}{7x}$

4. $\dfrac{5a}{2} = \dfrac{5a}{16}$

5. $\dfrac{3a}{7} = \dfrac{3a}{7a^2}$

6. $\dfrac{5}{2x} = \dfrac{5x^2}{2x}$

7. $\dfrac{x}{x + 1} = \dfrac{x}{(x + 1)^2}$

8. $\dfrac{x}{x + 3} = \dfrac{x}{(x + 3)^2}$

9. $\dfrac{3t + 6}{t} = \dfrac{(3t + 6)}{5t^2}$

10. $\dfrac{x}{x + 1} = \dfrac{2x^2}{(x + 1)}$

11. $\dfrac{2x}{x + 2} = \dfrac{2x}{4 - x^2}$

12. $\dfrac{x^2}{5 - x} = \dfrac{x^2}{x^2 - 5x}$

In Exercises 13–60, multiply and simplify. See Examples 1–5.

13. $\frac{5}{3} \cdot \frac{1}{4}$

14. $\frac{2}{5} \cdot \frac{3}{7}$

15. $\frac{7}{8} \cdot \frac{2}{21}$

16. $\frac{5}{12} \cdot \frac{15}{16}$

17. $10\big(\frac{3}{5}\big)$

18. $54\big(\frac{5}{6}\big)$

19. $\dfrac{8x^2}{3} \cdot \dfrac{9}{16x}$

20. $\dfrac{6x}{5} \cdot \dfrac{1}{x}$

21. $\dfrac{12x^2}{6x} \cdot \dfrac{12x}{8x^2}$

22. $\dfrac{25x^2}{8x} \cdot \dfrac{8x}{5x}$

23. $\dfrac{10y^3}{6xy} \cdot \dfrac{4x^2y}{5y^2}$

24. $\dfrac{14x^2y^2}{3x^4} \cdot \dfrac{2x^4}{7y^3}$

25. $\dfrac{8rt^2}{5r^3t} \cdot \dfrac{-10r^2t}{2t}$

26. $\dfrac{-7u^3v^2}{6uv^3} \cdot \dfrac{4v^4}{8u^2v}$

27. $\dfrac{y - 1}{5} \cdot \dfrac{5}{y - 1}$

28. $\dfrac{x + 1}{2} \cdot \dfrac{2}{x + 1}$

29. $\dfrac{x + 1}{2} \cdot \dfrac{4x}{x + 1}$

30. $\dfrac{x - 3}{6x} \cdot \dfrac{4}{x - 3}$

31. $\dfrac{1 - r}{3} \cdot \dfrac{3}{r - 1}$

32. $\dfrac{t - 6}{7} \cdot \dfrac{7}{6 - t}$

33. $\dfrac{y + 5}{y - 2} \cdot (2y)$

34. $\dfrac{z - 4}{z - 1} \cdot (-2z)$

35. $\dfrac{x}{6x - 12} \cdot (x - 2)$

36. $\dfrac{3y}{4y + 16} \cdot (y + 4)$

37. $\dfrac{(x - 5)^2}{x + 5} \cdot \dfrac{x + 5}{x - 5}$

38. $\dfrac{y + 2}{y - 2} \cdot \dfrac{(y - 2)^2}{y + 2}$

39. $\dfrac{5}{x - 1} \cdot \dfrac{x - 1}{25(x - 2)}$

40. $\dfrac{8}{r + 3} \cdot \dfrac{r + 3}{16(r - 2)}$

41. $\dfrac{2 - t}{2 + t} \cdot \dfrac{t + 2}{t - 2}$

42. $\dfrac{1 - z}{1 + z} \cdot \dfrac{z + 1}{z - 1}$

43. $\dfrac{(x - 9)(x + 7)}{x + 1} \cdot \dfrac{x}{(9 - x)(x + 1)}$

44. $\dfrac{(x + 5)(x - 3)}{x + 2} \cdot \dfrac{1}{(x + 5)(x + 2)}$

45. $\dfrac{9y - 15z}{7y + 14z} \cdot \dfrac{2y + 4z}{3y - 5z}$

46. $\dfrac{4y - 16x}{5y + 15x} \cdot \dfrac{2y + 6x}{y - 4x}$

47. $\dfrac{r}{r - t} \cdot \dfrac{r^2 - t^2}{r^2}$

48. $\dfrac{y^2 - 16}{2y^3} \cdot \dfrac{4y}{y^2 - 6y + 8}$

49. $(x^2 - 4) \cdot \dfrac{x}{(x - 2)^2}$

50. $(u - 2)^2 \cdot \dfrac{u + 2}{u - 2}$

51. $\dfrac{x - 3}{x^2 - 16} \cdot \dfrac{x + 4}{2x^2 - 6x}$

52. $\dfrac{x + 7}{3x^2 - 15x} \cdot \dfrac{x - 5}{x^2 - 49}$

53. $\dfrac{t^2 - t - 6}{t^2 + 6t + 9} \cdot \dfrac{t + 3}{t^2 - 4}$

54. $\dfrac{x^2 + x - 2}{x^3 + x^2} \cdot \dfrac{x}{x^2 + 3x + 2}$

55. $\dfrac{4}{x} \cdot \dfrac{x + 2}{x + 6} \cdot \dfrac{x}{x + 2}$

56. $\dfrac{x}{7} \cdot \dfrac{x - 7}{x} \cdot \dfrac{x + 1}{x - 7}$

57. $\dfrac{a + 1}{a - 1} \cdot \dfrac{a^2 - 2a + 1}{a} \cdot (3a^2 + 3a)$

58. $\dfrac{z^2 - z - 2}{z} \cdot \dfrac{2z^2 + 3z}{2z + 3} \cdot \dfrac{z}{z - 2}$

59. $\dfrac{2}{z + 3} \cdot \dfrac{z^2 + 6z + 9}{z - 3} \cdot \dfrac{4}{z^2 - 9}$

60. $(x + 5)^2 \cdot \dfrac{x}{x^2 - 25} \cdot \dfrac{x^2 - x - 20}{x^2}$

In Exercises 61–82, divide and simplify. See Examples 6–8.

61. $\dfrac{1}{10} \div \dfrac{1}{5}$

62. $\dfrac{3}{4} \div \dfrac{4}{3}$

63. $\dfrac{17}{6} \div \dfrac{3}{8}$

64. $\dfrac{5}{12} \div \dfrac{15}{2}$

65. $\dfrac{x^3}{6} \div \dfrac{x^2}{3}$

66. $\dfrac{5}{x} \div \dfrac{5}{x}$

67. $\dfrac{7x^2}{10} \div \dfrac{14x^3}{15}$

68. $\dfrac{2x}{3} \div \dfrac{4x^2}{15}$

69. $\dfrac{a}{a + 1} \div \dfrac{6}{(a + 1)^2}$

70. $\dfrac{z + 3}{6} \div \dfrac{z}{2}$

71. $\dfrac{3(x + 4)}{4} \div \dfrac{x + 4}{2}$

72. $\dfrac{10(x - 3)}{7} \div \dfrac{x - 3}{14}$

73. $\dfrac{(2x)^2}{(x + 2)^2} \div \dfrac{2x}{(x + 2)^3}$

74. $\dfrac{3(x + 1)^2}{5x} \div \dfrac{9(x + 1)}{10x^2}$

75. $\dfrac{y^2 - 4}{y^2} \div \dfrac{y - 2}{3y}$

76. $\dfrac{5x - 25}{x^2} \div \dfrac{x^2 - 25}{2x}$

77. $\dfrac{x^2 - 4y^2}{2x} \div \dfrac{x + 2y}{4x}$

78. $\dfrac{x^2 - y^2}{xy} \div \dfrac{(x - y)^2}{xy}$

79. $\dfrac{x^2 - 7x + 12}{x + 4} \div (3 - x)$

80. $\dfrac{x^2 - x - 2}{x + 2} \div (2 - x)$

81. $\dfrac{5x^2 + 30x + 40}{x + 2} \div (15 - x)$

82. $(x + 3) \div \dfrac{3x^2 + 18x + 27}{x^2 + 1}$

In Exercises 83–96, simplify the complex fraction. See Example 9.

83. $\dfrac{\left(\dfrac{3}{10}\right)}{\left(\dfrac{9}{15}\right)}$

84. $\dfrac{\left(\dfrac{7}{16}\right)}{\left(-\dfrac{4}{21}\right)}$

85. $\dfrac{\left(\dfrac{x^3}{4}\right)}{\left(\dfrac{x}{8}\right)}$

86. $\dfrac{\left(\dfrac{y^4}{12}\right)}{\left(\dfrac{y}{16}\right)}$

87. $\dfrac{\left[\dfrac{6x^3}{(5y)^2}\right]}{\left[\dfrac{(3x)^2}{15y^4}\right]}$

88. $\dfrac{\left[\dfrac{(3r)^3}{10t^4}\right]}{\left[\dfrac{9r}{(2t)^2}\right]}$

89. $\dfrac{\left(\dfrac{y}{3-y}\right)}{\left(\dfrac{y^2}{y-3}\right)}$

90. $\dfrac{\left(\dfrac{x}{x-4}\right)}{\left(\dfrac{x}{4-x}\right)}$

91. $\dfrac{\left(\dfrac{2x-10}{x+1}\right)}{\left(\dfrac{x-5}{x+1}\right)}$

92. $\dfrac{\left(\dfrac{a+5}{6a-15}\right)}{\left(\dfrac{a+5}{2a-5}\right)}$

93. $\dfrac{\left(\dfrac{x^2+3x-10}{x+4}\right)}{3x-6}$

94. $\dfrac{\left(\dfrac{x^2-2x-8}{x-1}\right)}{5x-20}$

95. $\dfrac{\left(\dfrac{6x^2-17x+5}{3x^2+3x}\right)}{\left(\dfrac{3x-1}{3x+1}\right)}$

96. $\dfrac{\left(\dfrac{6x^2-13x-5}{5x^2+5x}\right)}{\left(\dfrac{2x-5}{5x+1}\right)}$

In Exercises 97–100, perform the indicated operations and simplify your answer.

97. $\left(\dfrac{x^2}{5}\cdot\dfrac{x+a}{2}\right)\div\dfrac{x}{30}$

98. $\left(\dfrac{4u^2}{3}\cdot\dfrac{5}{u}\right)\div\dfrac{6u^2}{4}$

99. $\left[\left(\dfrac{x+2}{3}\right)^2\cdot\left(\dfrac{x+1}{2}\right)^2\right]\div\dfrac{(x+1)(x+2)}{36}$

100. $\left[\left(\dfrac{4}{x-1}\right)^2\cdot\left(\dfrac{x+1}{3}\right)^3\right]\div\dfrac{(x+1)^2}{27(x-1)}$

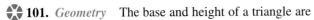

Solving Problems

101. *Geometry*   The base and height of a triangle are

$\dfrac{8}{x^2+5x}$ and $\dfrac{x+5}{2}$

respectively. (Assume $x > 0$.)

(a) Write an expression for the area of the triangle in terms of x. Simplify the expression.

(b) As x increases, determine whether each of the following increases or decreases: (i) base, (ii) height, and (iii) area.

102. *Pump Rate*   A pump in a well can pump water at the rate of 24 gallons per minute. Determine the time required to pump (a) 1 gallon, (b) x gallons, and (c) 120 gallons.

103. *Photocopy Rate*   A photocopier produces copies at a rate of 12 pages per minute. Find the time required to copy (a) 1 page, (b) x pages, and (c) 32 pages.

104. *Analyzing Data*   The number N (in millions) of subscribers and the monthly revenue R (in millions of dollars) for basic cable TV in the United States over the period 1990 through 1996 can be modeled by

$N = 50.4 + 2.1t$ and $R = \dfrac{60(2842 + 149t)}{200 - 9t}$

where $t = 0$ represents 1990. (Source: The Cable TV Financial Databook)

(a) Find a model for the average monthly basic rate per subscriber.

(b) Use the model in part (a) to complete the table.

Year, t	0	2	4	6
Monthly rate				

Explaining Concepts

105. Explain how to multiply two rational expressions.

106. Explain how to divide two rational expressions.

107. Define the reciprocal of an algebraic expression.

108. What is the product of an algebraic expression and its reciprocal? What basic rule of algebra does this demonstrate?

109. Give an example of three rational expressions whose product is 1.

110. *Error Analysis*   Identify the error.

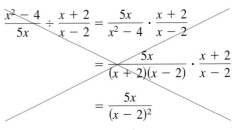

111. *True or False?* $10 \div x = \dfrac{1}{10}\cdot x$

Mid-Chapter Quiz

Take this quiz as you would take a quiz in class. After you are done, check your work against the answers given in the back of the book.

1. In your own words, explain the meaning of *domain*. Find the domain of

(a) $\dfrac{x^2}{x^2 + 4}$ and   (b) $\dfrac{x^2}{x^2 - 4}$.

2. Evaluate $\dfrac{y - 3}{y + 2}$ for (a) $y = 10$, (b) $y = 3$, and (c) $y = -2$.

In Exercises 3–10, simplify the expression.

3. $\dfrac{14z^4}{35z}$

4. $\dfrac{15u(u - 3)^2}{25u^2(u - 3)}$

5. $\dfrac{24(9 - x)}{15(x - 9)}$

6. $\dfrac{y^2 - 4}{8 - 4y}$

7. $\dfrac{b^2 + 3b}{b^3 + 2b^2 - 3b}$

8. $\dfrac{4x^2 - 12x + 9}{2x^2 - x - 3}$

9. $\dfrac{s^3 - 8}{s^3 + 2s^2 + 4s}$

10. $\dfrac{x^3 + 2x^2 - 3x - 6}{x^2 - 3}$

In Exercises 11–18, perform the specified operation and simplify.

11. $\dfrac{3y^3}{5} \cdot \dfrac{25}{9y}$

12. $\dfrac{s - 5}{15} \cdot \dfrac{12s}{25 - s^2}$

13. $(x^3 + 4x^2) \cdot \dfrac{5x}{x^2 + 2x - 8}$

14. $\dfrac{r^2 - 16}{r} \div (r + 4)^2$

15. $\dfrac{x}{25} \div \dfrac{x^2 + 2x}{10} \cdot \dfrac{1}{x + 2}$

16. $\dfrac{10x^2}{3y} \div \left(\dfrac{y}{x} \cdot \dfrac{x^3y}{6}\right)$

17. $\dfrac{2x - 1}{\left(\dfrac{8x^2 - 4x}{x + 3}\right)}$

18. $\dfrac{\left(\dfrac{3x - 12}{x + 1}\right)}{\left(\dfrac{x^2 - 8x + 16}{x^2 + x}\right)}$

19. A small business has a setup cost of $10,000 for the production of a new product. The cost of labor and materials for producing each unit is $25.

(a) Write an expression for the average cost per unit $\overline{C}$, when x number of units are produced.

(b) Complete the table and describe any trends you find.

x	2000	3000	4000	5000
$\overline{C}$				

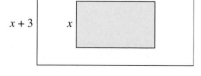

Figure for 20

20. Find the ratio of the area of the shaded region to the total area of the figure.

8.3   Adding and Subtracting Rational Expressions

Objectives

1 Add or subtract rational expressions with like denominators.

2 Find the least common multiple of two polynomials.

3 Add or subtract rational expressions with unlike denominators.

4 Simplify a complex fraction having a sum or difference in the numerator and/or denominator.

---

1 Add or subtract rational expressions with like denominators.

Fractions with Like Denominators

As with numerical fractions, the procedure used to add (or subtract) two rational expressions depends on whether they have *like* or *unlike* denominators.

> ▶ **Combining Fractions with Like Denominators**
>
> Let a, b, and c be numbers, variables, or algebraic expressions.
>
> **1.** $\dfrac{a}{c} + \dfrac{b}{c} = \dfrac{a+b}{c}$, $c \neq 0$ Add fractions with like denominators.
>
> **2.** $\dfrac{a}{c} - \dfrac{b}{c} = \dfrac{a-b}{c}$, $c \neq 0$ Subtract fractions with like denominators.

Example 1   Combining Fractions with Like Denominators

a. $\dfrac{x}{3} + \dfrac{2-x}{3} = \dfrac{x+(2-x)}{3} = \dfrac{2}{3}$

b. $\dfrac{5}{x+4} - \dfrac{2x}{x+4} = \dfrac{5-2x}{x+4}$

c. $\dfrac{x}{x-2} - \dfrac{3x-1}{x-2} = \dfrac{x-(3x-1)}{x-2} = \dfrac{x-3x+1}{x-2} = \dfrac{1-2x}{x-2}$

After adding or subtracting two (or more) fractions, you should check the resulting fraction to see if it can be simplified.

Example 2   Adding Fractions and Simplifying

$$\dfrac{x}{x^2-4} + \dfrac{2}{x^2-4} = \dfrac{x+2}{x^2-4} \qquad \text{Add numerators.}$$

$$= \dfrac{(x+2) \cdot 1}{(x+2)(x-2)} \qquad \text{Factor and cancel common factor.}$$

$$= \dfrac{1}{x-2}, \quad x \neq -2 \qquad \text{Simplified form}$$

---

2 **Find the least common multiple of two polynomials.**

Finding least common multiples is an important skill. Here are some additional examples:

Polynomials

1. $6x^2, 9x$
2. $5a, a + 2$
3. $y - 2, y - 6$
4. $k^2 + 6k, 3k^3$
5. $m - 3, 3 - m$
6. $x^2 - 3x - 10, x^2 - 25$

Least Common Multiples

1. $18x^2$
2. $5a(a + 2)$
3. $(y - 2)(y - 6)$
4. $3k^3(k + 6)$
5. $m - 3$ or $3 - m$
6. $(x - 5)(x + 2)(x + 5)$

Least Common Multiple

To add or subtract fractions with *unlike* denominators, you must first rewrite each fraction using the **least common multiple** of the denominators of the individual fractions. The least common multiple of two (or more) polynomials is the simplest polynomial that is a multiple of each of the original polynomials.

▶ **Guidelines for Finding the Least Common Multiple**

1. Factor each polynomial completely.

2. The least common multiple must contain all the *different* factors of the polynomials and each such factor must be repeated the maximum number of times it occurs in any of the factorizations.

Example 3   Finding Least Common Multiples

Find the least common multiple of each pair of polynomials.

a. $6x, 20x$ **b.** $5x, x^2$ **c.** $x^2 - x, x - 1$

d. $3x^2 + 6x, x^2 + 4x + 4$ **e.** $9 - x^2, x^2 - x - 6$

Solution

a. These polynomials factor as

$$6x = 2 \cdot 3 \cdot x \quad \text{and} \quad 20x = 2 \cdot 2 \cdot 5 \cdot x.$$

The different factors are 2^2, 3, 5, and x. This implies that the least common multiple is $2 \cdot 2 \cdot 3 \cdot 5 \cdot x = 60x$.

b. These polynomials factor as

$$5x = 5 \cdot x \quad \text{and} \quad x^2 = x \cdot x.$$

The different factors are 5 and x^2. This implies that the least common multiple is $5 \cdot x \cdot x = 5x^2$.

c. These polynomials factor as

$$x^2 - x = x(x - 1) \quad \text{and} \quad x - 1.$$

The different factors are x and $x - 1$. This implies that the least common multiple is $x(x - 1)$.

d. These polynomials factor as

$$3x^2 + 6x = 3x(x + 2) \quad \text{and} \quad x^2 + 4x + 4 = (x + 2) \cdot (x + 2).$$

The different factors are 3, x, and $(x + 2)^2$. This implies that the least common multiple is $3x(x + 2) \cdot (x + 2) = 3x(x + 2)^2$.

e. These polynomials factor as

$$9 - x^2 = (-1) \cdot (x - 3) \cdot (x + 3) \quad \text{and} \quad x^2 - x - 6 = (x - 3) \cdot (x + 2).$$

The different factors are -1, $x - 3$, $x + 3$, and $x + 2$. This implies that the least common multiple is $(-1)(x - 3)(x + 3)(x + 2)$.

Study Tip

Remember that the exponent on a number or variable factor indicates the number of repetitions of that factor. For example, in the term $25x^3$, the factorization $5^2 \cdot x^3$ shows that 5 is repeated twice and x is repeated three times.

3 Add or subtract rational expressions with unlike denominators.

Fractions with Unlike Denominators

To add or subtract fractions with *unlike* denominators, you must first rewrite the fractions so that they have *like* denominators. The like denominator that you use is the least common multiple of the original denominators and is called the **least common denominator** (LCD) of the original fractions.

Example 4   Adding Fractions with Unlike Denominators

Add the fractions.

$$\frac{5}{3x} + \frac{7}{4x}$$

Solution

The least common denominator of the fractions is $12x$.

$$\frac{5}{3x} + \frac{7}{4x} = \frac{5(4)}{3x(4)} + \frac{7(3)}{4x(3)} \qquad \text{Rewrite fractions using LCD of } 12x.$$

$$= \frac{20}{12x} + \frac{21}{12x} \qquad \text{Like denominators}$$

$$= \frac{20 + 21}{12x} \qquad \text{Add fractions.}$$

$$= \frac{41}{12x} \qquad \text{Simplified form}$$

Advise students to be especially careful with signs when subtracting more than one term.

Example 5   Subtracting Fractions with Unlike Denominators

Subtract the fractions.

$$\frac{4}{x - 2} - \frac{2}{x + 1}$$

Solution

The least common denominator is $(x - 2)(x + 1)$.

$$\frac{4}{x - 2} - \frac{2}{x + 1}$$

$$= \frac{4(x + 1)}{(x - 2)(x + 1)} - \frac{2(x - 2)}{(x - 2)(x + 1)} \qquad \text{Rewrite fractions using LCD of } (x - 2)(x + 1).$$

$$= \frac{(4x + 4) - (2x - 4)}{(x - 2)(x + 1)} \qquad \text{Subtract numerators.}$$

$$= \frac{4x + 4 - 2x + 4}{(x - 2)(x + 1)} \qquad \text{Distributive Property}$$

$$= \frac{2x + 8}{(x - 2)(x + 1)} \qquad \text{Simplified form}$$

Study Tip

Notice that the subtraction of numerators in Example 5 means that the minus sign has to be distributed over the quantity $(2x - 4)$. That is,

$$-(2x - 4) = -2x + 4.$$

Study Tip

In Example 6, notice that the denominator $3 - x$ is rewritten as $(-1)(x - 3)$ and then the problem is changed from addition to subtraction.

Example 6 Adding Fractions with Unlike Denominators

$$\frac{2x}{x^2 - 9} + \frac{1}{3 - x}$$

$$= \frac{2x}{x^2 - 9} + \frac{1}{(-1)(x - 3)} \qquad 3 - x = -1(x - 3)$$

$$= \frac{2x}{(x + 3)(x - 3)} - \frac{1}{x - 3} \qquad \text{Factor.}$$

$$= \frac{2x}{(x + 3)(x - 3)} - \frac{x + 3}{(x + 3)(x - 3)} \qquad \begin{array}{l}\text{Rewrite fractions} \\ \text{using LCD of} \\ (x + 3)(x - 3).\end{array}$$

$$= \frac{2x - (x + 3)}{(x + 3)(x - 3)} \qquad \text{Subtract numerators.}$$

$$= \frac{2x - x - 3}{(x + 3)(x - 3)} \qquad \text{Distributive Property}$$

$$= \frac{(x - 3) \cdot 1}{(x + 3)(x - 3)} \qquad \begin{array}{l}\text{Cancel common} \\ \text{factor.}\end{array}$$

$$= \frac{1}{x + 3}, \quad x \neq 3 \qquad \text{Simplified form}$$

In the next example, a least common denominator is used to combine three fractions.

Example 7 Combining Fractions with Unlike Denominators

$$\frac{2x - 5}{6x + 9} - \frac{4}{2x^2 + 3x} + \frac{1}{x}$$

$$= \frac{2x - 5}{3(2x + 3)} - \frac{4}{x(2x + 3)} + \frac{1}{x} \qquad \text{Factor denominators.}$$

$$= \frac{(2x - 5)(x)}{3(2x + 3)(x)} - \frac{(4)(3)}{x(2x + 3)(3)} + \frac{3(2x + 3)}{x(3)(2x + 3)} \qquad \begin{array}{l}\text{Rewrite fractions} \\ \text{using LCD of} \\ 3(2x + 3)(x).\end{array}$$

$$= \frac{2x^2 - 5x - 12 + 6x + 9}{3x(2x + 3)} \qquad \text{Combine numerators.}$$

$$= \frac{2x^2 + x - 3}{3x(2x + 3)} \qquad \text{Combine like terms.}$$

$$= \frac{(x - 1)(2x + 3)}{3x(2x + 3)} \qquad \begin{array}{l}\text{Cancel common} \\ \text{factor.}\end{array}$$

$$= \frac{x - 1}{3x}, \quad x \neq -\frac{3}{2} \qquad \text{Simplified form}$$

4 Simplify a complex fraction having a sum or difference in the numerator and/or denominator.

Complex Fractions

Complex fractions can have numerators and/or denominators that are sums or differences of fractions. Here are two examples.

$$\frac{\left(\dfrac{2}{x} - 3\right)}{\left(1 - \dfrac{1}{x}\right)} \quad \text{and} \quad \frac{\left(\dfrac{1}{x+2} - \dfrac{1}{x}\right)}{\left(\dfrac{5}{x} + \dfrac{2}{x^2}\right)}$$

To simplify a complex fraction, combine its numerator and its denominator into single fractions. Then divide by inverting the denominator and multiplying.

Example 8   Simplifying a Complex Fraction

$$\frac{\left(\dfrac{x}{3} + \dfrac{2}{3}\right)}{\left(1 - \dfrac{2}{x}\right)} = \frac{\left(\dfrac{x}{3} + \dfrac{2}{3}\right)}{\left(\dfrac{x}{x} - \dfrac{2}{x}\right)} \qquad \text{Rewrite with least common denominators.}$$

$$= \frac{\left(\dfrac{x+2}{3}\right)}{\left(\dfrac{x-2}{x}\right)} \qquad \text{Add fractions.}$$

$$= \frac{x+2}{3} \cdot \frac{x}{x-2} \qquad \text{Invert and multiply.}$$

$$= \frac{x(x+2)}{3(x-2)}, \quad x \neq 0 \qquad \text{Simplified form}$$

Encourage students to practice both of the methods for simplifying complex fractions that are shown on this page.

Another way of simplifying the complex fraction in Example 8 is to multiply the numerator and denominator by the least common denominator for all fractions in the numerator and denominator.

$$\frac{\left(\dfrac{x}{3} + \dfrac{2}{3}\right)}{\left(1 - \dfrac{2}{x}\right)} = \frac{\left(\dfrac{x}{3} + \dfrac{2}{3}\right)}{\left(1 - \dfrac{2}{x}\right)} \cdot \frac{3x}{3x} \qquad 3x \text{ is the least common denominator.}$$

$$= \frac{\dfrac{x}{3}(3x) + \dfrac{2}{3}(3x)}{(1)(3x) - \dfrac{2}{x}(3x)} \qquad \text{Distributive Property}$$

$$= \frac{x^2 + 2x}{3x - 6}, \quad x \neq 0 \qquad \text{Simplify.}$$

Example 9 Complex Fractions

$$\frac{\left(\dfrac{2}{x+2}\right)}{\left(\dfrac{3}{x+2}+\dfrac{2}{x}\right)} = \frac{\left(\dfrac{2}{x+2}\right)(x)(x+2)}{\left(\dfrac{3}{x+2}+\dfrac{2}{x}\right)(x)(x+2)}$$ $x(x+2)$ is the least common denominator.

$$= \frac{\left(\dfrac{2}{x+2}\right)(x)(x+2)}{\left(\dfrac{3}{x+2}\right)(x)(x+2)+\left(\dfrac{2}{x}\right)(x)(x+2)}$$ Distributive Property

$$= \frac{2x}{3x+2(x+2)}$$ Multiply and simplify.

$$= \frac{2x}{3x+2x+4}$$ Simplify.

$$= -\frac{2x}{5x+4}, \quad x \neq -2, x \neq 0$$ Simplify.

Notice that the numerator and denominator of the complex fraction were multiplied by $(x)(x+2)$, which is the least common denominator of the fractions in the original complex fraction.

Discussing the Concept   Adding Fractions

One way to add *two* fractions is to use the rule

$$\frac{a}{b}+\frac{c}{d}=\frac{ad+bc}{bd}$$

which doesn't require the least common denominator (LCD). To subtract, replace $(+)$ with $(-)$. Here is an example:

$$\frac{x}{2}-\frac{1}{3x}=\frac{x(3x)-1(2)}{2(3x)}$$

$$=\frac{3x^2-2}{6x}.$$

Use this method and the LCD method to do the following problem:

$$\frac{x}{x^2-36}-\frac{1}{2x+12}.$$

Discuss the advantages of each method.

8.3   Exercises

Integrated Review   *Concepts, Skills, and Problem Solving*

Keep mathematically in shape by doing these exercises *before* the problems of this section.

Properties and Definitions

1. Write the equation $3y - 7x = 4$ in the following forms.

   (a) Slope-intercept form

   (b) Point-slope form (more than one correct answer)

   (c) General form

2. Explain how you can visually determine the sign of the slope of a line by observing its graph.

Solving Equations

In Exercises 3–10, solve the equation.

3. $50 - z = 15$

4. $x - 6 = 3x + 10$

5. $\frac{1}{3}x + 5 = 8$

6. $\frac{3}{4}x + \frac{1}{2} = 8$

7. $-3(x + 2) = 0$

8. $\left(\frac{1}{2}x - 3\right)(x + 1) = 0$

9. $4x^2 - 25 = 0$

10. $2x^2 - 7x - 15 = 0$

Creating Expressions

In Exercises 11 and 12, find expressions for the perimeter and area of the region. Simplify the expressions.

11.

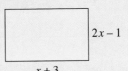

$x + 3$

$2x - 1$

12.

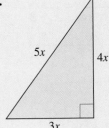

$5x$ $4x$

$3x$

Developing Skills

In Exercises 1–14, combine and simplify. See Examples 1 and 2.

1. $\dfrac{y}{4} + \dfrac{3y}{4}$

2. $\dfrac{2x}{5} - \dfrac{7x}{5}$

3. $\dfrac{9}{x} - \dfrac{4}{x}$

4. $\dfrac{7}{z^2} + \dfrac{10}{z^2}$

5. $\dfrac{5}{3a} + \dfrac{9}{3a}$

6. $\dfrac{16}{5z} - \dfrac{11}{5z}$

7. $\dfrac{x}{3} + \dfrac{1 - x}{3}$

8. $\dfrac{4z}{3} - \dfrac{4z - 3}{3}$

9. $\dfrac{-6t}{9} - \dfrac{12 - 8t}{9}$

10. $\dfrac{-16u}{7} - \dfrac{14 - 16u}{7}$

11. $\dfrac{5 - 2x}{x - 1} + \dfrac{x - 4}{x - 1}$

12. $\dfrac{2x - 1}{x + 3} + \dfrac{1 - x}{x + 3}$

13. $\dfrac{5y + 2}{y - 1} - \dfrac{4y + 1}{y - 1}$

14. $\dfrac{7s - 5}{s + 5} - \dfrac{2s - 10}{s + 5}$

In Exercises 15–28, find the least common multiple. See Example 3.

15. $2x, x^3$

16. $2t^2, 24t$

17. $9y^2, 12y$

18. $x^3, 4x$

19. $16x, 12x(x + 2)$

20. $18y^2, 27y(y - 3)$

21. $x, 3(x + 5)$

22. $x - 7, x^2, x(x + 7)$

23. $x^2 - 4, x(x + 2)$

24. $x^2 - 25x, x^2(x - 5)$

25. $7x^2 - 28x, x^2 - 3x - 4$

26. $t^2 + 3t + 9, t^2 - 9$

27. $x + 2, x^2 - 4, x$

28. $x^2 - 1, x + 1, x$

In Exercises 29–34, rewrite one or both of the fractions so that they have the same denominator.

29. $\dfrac{x + 5}{3x - 6}, \dfrac{10}{x - 2}$

30. $\dfrac{8x}{(x + 2)}, \dfrac{3}{4x + 8}$

31. $\dfrac{2}{(x + 3)^2}, \dfrac{5}{x(x + 3)}$

32. $\dfrac{5t}{(t - 3)^2}, \dfrac{4}{t(t - 3)}$

33. $\dfrac{x - 8}{x^2 - 16}, \dfrac{9x}{x^2 - 8x + 16}$

34. $\dfrac{3y}{y^2 - y - 6}, \dfrac{y + 2}{y^2 - 3y}$

In Exercises 35–72, combine and simplify. See Examples 4–7.

35. $\dfrac{3}{2s} - \dfrac{1}{5s}$

36. $\dfrac{5}{6z} + \dfrac{3}{8z}$

37. $\dfrac{1}{5x} - \dfrac{3}{5}$

38. $\dfrac{2}{3} + \dfrac{1}{2x}$

39. $\dfrac{5}{u} + \dfrac{2}{u^2}$

40. $\dfrac{5}{z} + \dfrac{6}{z^2}$

41. $\dfrac{3}{2b} + \dfrac{5}{2b^2}$

42. $\dfrac{8}{6u^2} - \dfrac{2}{9u}$

43. $\dfrac{4}{x - 3} + \dfrac{4}{3 - x}$

44. $\dfrac{5}{6 - t} - \dfrac{4}{t - 6}$

45. $\dfrac{3}{x - 5} + \dfrac{2}{x + 3}$

46. $\dfrac{6}{x + 4} + \dfrac{3}{x - 1}$

47. $\dfrac{2x}{x - 5} - \dfrac{5}{5 - x}$

48. $\dfrac{3}{x - 2} + \dfrac{5}{2 - x}$

49. $6 - \dfrac{5}{x + 3}$

50. $\dfrac{3}{x - 1} - 5$

51. $7 + \dfrac{2}{2x - 3}$

52. $\dfrac{3}{2x - 5} + 2$

53. $\dfrac{1}{x - 1} - \dfrac{1}{x + 2}$

54. $\dfrac{3}{x - 4} - \dfrac{2}{x + 1}$

55. $\dfrac{3}{2(x - 4)} - \dfrac{1}{2x}$

56. $\dfrac{1}{2x} + \dfrac{1}{2(x - 1)}$

57. $\dfrac{x}{x^2 - 9} + \dfrac{3}{x + 3}$

58. $\dfrac{6}{z + 2} - \dfrac{z - 3}{z^2 - 4}$

59. $\dfrac{5v}{v(v + 4)} + \dfrac{2v}{v^2}$

60. $\dfrac{2t}{t^2} - \dfrac{t}{t(t + 1)}$

61. $\dfrac{x + 2}{x^2 - 5x + 6} - \dfrac{3}{2 - x}$

62. $\dfrac{2}{x + 1} + \dfrac{1 - x}{x^2 - 2x + 3}$

63. $\dfrac{2x}{x^2 - 4} - \dfrac{1}{x^2 - 3x + 2}$

64. $\dfrac{x}{x^2 + x - 2} - \dfrac{1}{x^2 - 4}$

65. $\dfrac{2x + 1}{x^2 - 16} + \dfrac{4x}{4 - x}$

66. $\dfrac{7x}{x - 5} - \dfrac{3x - 4}{25 - x^2}$

67. $\dfrac{3}{x} - \dfrac{1}{x^2} + \dfrac{1}{x + 1}$

68. $\dfrac{6x}{x^2} - \dfrac{3}{x} + \dfrac{7}{x - 3}$

69. $\dfrac{x + 2}{3(x - 2)^2} + \dfrac{4}{3(x - 2)} + \dfrac{1}{2x}$

70. $\dfrac{5}{2(x + 1)} - \dfrac{1}{2x} - \dfrac{3}{2(x + 1)^2}$

71. $\dfrac{3x - 4}{4x + 18} + \dfrac{5 - x}{2x^2 + 9x} - \dfrac{3}{x}$

72. $\dfrac{7 - 4x}{6x + 15} - \dfrac{x - 2}{2x^2 + 5x} + \dfrac{4}{x}$

In Exercises 73–88, simplify the complex fraction. See Examples 8 and 9.

73. $\dfrac{\left(\dfrac{3}{x}\right)}{\left(\dfrac{6}{x^2}\right)}$

74. $\dfrac{\left(\dfrac{2}{3}\right)}{\left(\dfrac{u}{v}\right)}$

75. $\dfrac{\left(1 + \dfrac{3}{y}\right)}{y}$

76. $\dfrac{x}{\left(\dfrac{5}{x} + 2\right)}$

77. $\dfrac{\left(\dfrac{x}{2}\right)}{\left(2 + \dfrac{3}{x}\right)}$

78. $\dfrac{\left(1 - \dfrac{2}{x}\right)}{\left(\dfrac{x}{2}\right)}$

79. $\dfrac{\left(\dfrac{x}{3} - 4\right)}{\left(5 + \dfrac{1}{x}\right)}$

80. $\dfrac{\left(\dfrac{4}{x} + 2\right)}{\left(\dfrac{1}{2x} - 8\right)}$

81. $\dfrac{\left(\dfrac{x}{4} - \dfrac{4}{x}\right)}{(x - 4)}$

82. $\dfrac{x - 5}{\left(\dfrac{x}{5} - \dfrac{5}{x}\right)}$

83. $\dfrac{\left(z - \dfrac{4}{z}\right)}{\left(\dfrac{1}{z} - 4\right)}$

84. $\dfrac{\left(\dfrac{u}{3} - 2\right)}{\left(\dfrac{1}{3} + 2u\right)}$

85. $\dfrac{\left(\dfrac{10}{x + 1}\right)}{\left(\dfrac{1}{2x + 2} + \dfrac{3}{x + 1}\right)}$

86. $\dfrac{\left(\dfrac{2}{x + 5}\right)}{\left(\dfrac{2}{x + 5} + \dfrac{1}{4x + 20}\right)}$

87. $\dfrac{\left(\dfrac{1}{x} - \dfrac{1}{x + 1}\right)}{\left(\dfrac{1}{x + 1}\right)}$

88. $\dfrac{\left(\dfrac{5}{y} - \dfrac{6}{2y + 1}\right)}{\left(\dfrac{5}{2y + 1}\right)}$

Solving Problems

89. *Work Rate*   After two people work together for t hours on a common task, the fractional parts of the job done by each of the workers are $t/8$ and $t/7$. What fractional part of the task has been completed?

90. *Work Rate*   After two people work together for t hours on a common task, the fractional parts of the job done by each of the workers are $t/6$ and $t/9$. What fractional part of the task has been completed?

91. *Average of Two Numbers*   Determine the average of the two real numbers $x/5$ and $x/6$.

92. *Average of Two Numbers*   Determine the average of the two real numbers $2x/3$ and $3x/5$.

93. *Equal Lengths*   Find three real numbers that divide the real number line between $x/9$ and $x/6$ into four parts of equal length (see figure).

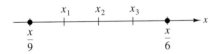

94. *Equal Lengths*   Find two real numbers that divide the real number line between $x/3$ and $5x/4$ into three parts of equal length (see figure).

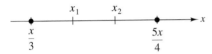

95. *Electrical Resistance*   When two resistors are connected in parallel, the total resistance is modeled by

$$\frac{1}{\dfrac{1}{R_1} + \dfrac{1}{R_2}}.$$

Simplify this complex fraction.

96. *Using Two Models*   From 1980 through 1995, the number of doctors of medicine M (in thousands) and the number of doctors of osteopathy O (in thousands) can be approximated by

$$M = \frac{472{,}860 + 6400t}{1000 - 13t} \quad \text{and} \quad O = 18.73 + 1.16t$$

where $t = 0$ represents 1980.   (Source: American Medical Association)

(a) Write an expression for the total number of doctors. Simplify the result.

(b) Use the result of part (a) to approximate the number of doctors in the United States in 1991.

97. *Rewriting a Fraction*   Consider the following.

$$\frac{x + 5}{x^2 + x - 2} = \frac{x + 5}{(x - 1)(x + 2)} = \frac{A}{x - 1} + \frac{B}{x + 2}$$

The numbers A and B are solutions of the system

$$A + B = 1$$
$$2A - B = 5.$$

Solve the system and verify that the sum of the two resulting fractions is the original fraction.

98. *Rewriting a Fraction*   Consider the following.

$$\frac{x + 35}{x^2 - 25} = \frac{x + 35}{(x + 5)(x - 5)} = \frac{A}{x + 5} + \frac{B}{x - 5}$$

The numbers A and B are solutions of the system

$$A + B = 1$$
$$-5A + 5B = 35.$$

Solve the system and verify that the sum of the two resulting fractions is the original fraction.

Explaining Concepts

99. Answer parts (a)–(d) of Motivating the Chapter on page 417.

100. In your own words, explain how to add or subtract rational expressions with like denominators.

101. In your own words, explain how to add or subtract rational expressions with unlike denominators.

102. Explain how to find the least common multiple of two or more polynomials. Give an example.

103. Can the least common multiple of two polynomials be the same as one of the polynomials? Explain.

104. *Error Analysis*   Identify the error.

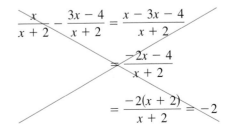

8.4 Rational Equations and Applications

Objectives

1 Solve a rational equation with constant denominators.

2 Solve a rational equation with variable denominators.

3 Solve an application problem using a rational equation with variable denominators.

1 Solve a rational equation with constant denominators.

Equations Containing Constant Denominators

In Section 3.2, you learned how to solve equations containing fractions with *constant* denominators. Examples 1 and 2 review that procedure.

Example 1 An Equation Containing Constant Denominators

Solve $\dfrac{x}{5} = 6 - \dfrac{x}{10}$.

Solution

Begin by multiplying both sides by the least common denominator 10.

$$\frac{x}{5} = 6 - \frac{x}{10} \qquad \text{Original equation}$$

$$10\left(\frac{x}{5}\right) = 10\left(6 - \frac{x}{10}\right) \qquad \text{Multiply both sides by LCD of 10.}$$

$$2x = 60 - x \qquad \text{Distribute and simplify.}$$

$$3x = 60 \qquad \text{Add } x \text{ to both sides.}$$

$$x = 20 \qquad \text{Divide both sides by 3.}$$

The solution is 20. Check this in the original equation.

Example 2 An Equation Containing Constant Denominators

$$\frac{x+6}{9} - \frac{x-2}{5} = \frac{4}{15} \qquad \text{Original equation}$$

$$45\left(\frac{x+6}{9} - \frac{x-2}{5}\right) = 45\left(\frac{4}{15}\right) \qquad \text{Multiply both sides by LCD of 45.}$$

$$5(x+6) - 9(x-2) = 3(4) \qquad \text{Distribute and simplify.}$$

$$5x + 30 - 9x + 18 = 12 \qquad \text{Distributive Property}$$

$$-4x + 48 = 12 \qquad \text{Combine like terms.}$$

$$-4x = -36 \qquad \text{Subtract 48 from both sides.}$$

$$x = 9 \qquad \text{Divide both sides by } -4.$$

The solution is 9. Check this in the original equation.

Study Tip

In Examples 1 and 2, note that the key to solving an equation that involves fractions is to multiply both sides of the equation by the least common denominator of the fractions.

2 Solve a rational equation with variable denominators.

Equations Containing Variable Denominators

As stated in Section 8.1, the domain of a rational expression does not contain the values of a variable that make the denominator zero. This is especially critical in solving equations that contain variable denominators. You will see why in the examples that follow.

| Example 3 | An Equation Containing Variable Denominators |

Solve the equation.

$$\frac{1}{x} - \frac{2}{3} = \frac{3}{x}$$

Students could use a graphing utility to verify that the graph of $y = \frac{1}{x} - \frac{2}{3} - \frac{3}{x}$ has an x-intercept at -3.

Solution

Begin by multiplying both sides by the least common denominator $3x$.

$$\frac{1}{x} - \frac{2}{3} = \frac{3}{x} \qquad \text{Original equation}$$

$$3x\left(\frac{1}{x} - \frac{2}{3}\right) = 3x\left(\frac{3}{x}\right) \qquad \text{Multiply both sides by LCD of } 3x.$$

$$\frac{3x}{x} - \frac{6x}{3} = \frac{9x}{x} \qquad \text{Distributive Property}$$

$$3 - 2x = 9, \quad x \neq 0 \qquad \text{Simplify fractions.}$$

$$-2x = 6 \qquad \text{Subtract 3 from both sides.}$$

$$x = -3 \qquad \text{Divide both sides by } -2.$$

The solution is -3. You can check this in the original equation as follows.

Check

$$\frac{1}{x} - \frac{2}{3} = \frac{3}{x} \qquad \text{Original equation}$$

$$\frac{1}{-3} - \frac{2}{3} \overset{?}{=} \frac{3}{-3} \qquad \text{Substitute } -3 \text{ for } x.$$

$$-\frac{1}{3} - \frac{2}{3} \overset{?}{=} -1 \qquad \text{Simplify.}$$

$$-1 = -1 \qquad \text{Solution checks. } \checkmark$$

In Example 3, notice that the original equation is a *rational equation*—that is, it contains rational expressions. After being multiplied by the least common denominator, the equation is converted into a *linear equation*. As you have seen repeatedly, this is a common strategy in mathematics—*to rewrite complicated problems into simpler forms.*

Notice that during the solution of Example 3, the restriction $x \neq 0$ is placed at the point where the equation becomes linear. The domain of the original equation is all real numbers except $x = 0$. The domain of the equation remains the same throughout the solution even though the form of the equation changes.

Throughout the text we have emphasized the importance of checking solutions. Up to this point the main reason for checking has been to make sure that you didn't make arithmetic errors in the solution process. In the next example you will see that there is another reason for checking solutions in the original equation. That is, even with no mistakes in the solution process, it can happen that a trial solution does not satisfy the original equation. This type of solution is called an **extraneous solution.** An extraneous solution of an equation does not, by definition, satisfy its original equation, and therefore must not be listed as an actual solution. Rational equations can have no real solutions, all real solutions, or some real and some extraneous solutions.

Example 4 An Equation with No Solution

Solve the equation.

$$\frac{2x}{x + 3} = 1 - \frac{6}{x + 3}$$

Solution

Remind students to check for extraneous solutions.

Begin by multiplying both sides by the least common denominator $x + 3$.

$$\frac{2x}{x + 3} = 1 - \frac{6}{x + 3} \qquad \text{Original equation}$$

$$(x + 3)\left(\frac{2x}{x + 3}\right) = (x + 3)\left(1 - \frac{6}{x + 3}\right) \qquad \begin{array}{l}\text{Multiply both sides by}\\ \text{LCD of } x + 3.\end{array}$$

$$\frac{(x + 3)(2x)}{x + 3} = (x + 3) - \frac{(x + 3)6}{x + 3} \qquad \text{Distributive Property}$$

$$2x = (x + 3) - 6, \quad x \neq -3 \qquad \text{Simplify.}$$

$$2x = x - 3 \qquad \text{Combine like terms.}$$

$$x = -3 \qquad \text{Subtract } x \text{ from both sides.}$$

At this point, the solution appears to be -3. However, by performing the following check, you can see that this trial solution is extraneous.

Check

$$\frac{2x}{x + 3} = 1 - \frac{6}{x + 3} \qquad \text{Original equation}$$

$$\frac{2(-3)}{-3 + 3} \stackrel{?}{=} 1 - \frac{6}{-3 + 3} \qquad \text{Substitute } -3 \text{ for } x.$$

$$\frac{-6}{0} \stackrel{?}{=} 1 - \frac{6}{0} \qquad \text{Solution does not check. } ✗$$

Because the check resulted in *division by zero,* you can conclude that -3 is extraneous. So, the given equation has no solution.

Looking back at the original equation, you can see that -3 is excluded from the domain of two of the fractions that occur in the equation. You may find it helpful to list the domain restrictions before beginning the solution process.

Example 5   An Equation with One Solution

Solve $\dfrac{6}{x-1} + \dfrac{2x}{x-2} = 2$.

Solution

$$\frac{6}{x-1} + \frac{2x}{x-2} = 2$$

$$(x-1)(x-2)\left(\frac{6}{x-1} + \frac{2x}{x-2}\right) = 2(x-1)(x-2)$$

$$6(x-2) + 2x(x-1) = 2(x^2 - 3x + 2), \quad x \neq 1, x \neq 2$$

$$6x - 12 + 2x^2 - 2x = 2x^2 - 6x + 4$$

$$10x = 16$$

$$x = \frac{8}{5} \qquad\qquad \text{Solution}$$

Check

$$\frac{6}{\frac{8}{5} - 1} + \frac{2\left(\frac{8}{5}\right)}{\frac{8}{5} - 2} \stackrel{?}{=} 2 \qquad \text{Substitute } \tfrac{8}{5} \text{ for } x \text{ in original equation.}$$

$$\frac{6}{\frac{3}{5}} + \frac{\frac{16}{5}}{-\frac{2}{5}} \stackrel{?}{=} 2 \qquad \text{Simplify.}$$

$$10 + (-8) = 2 \qquad \text{Solution checks. } \checkmark$$

Technology: Discovery

Use a graphing utility to graph the equation

$$y = \frac{2x}{x+2} - \frac{1}{x^2-4} - 1.$$

Then use the root or zero feature of the graphing utility to determine the x-intercepts. How do the x-intercepts compare with the solutions to Example 6? Graph each side of the equation in Example 6 in the same window. Use the intersect feature to find the point(s) of intersection. What can you conclude?

Point out that this problem differs from previous examples in this section because it requires solving a *second-degree* equation.

Study Tip

The symbol $\pm$ in Example 6 is read as "plus or minus." For instance, $x \neq \pm 2$ means that x is not equal to 2 or -2.

Example 6   An Equation with Two Solutions

Solve $\dfrac{2x}{x+2} = \dfrac{1}{x^2-4} + 1$.

Solution

$$\frac{2x}{x+2} = \frac{1}{x^2-4} + 1 \qquad \text{Original equation}$$

$$(x^2-4)\left(\frac{2x}{x+2}\right) = (x^2-4)\left(\frac{1}{x^2-4} + 1\right) \qquad \substack{\text{Multiply both sides} \\ \text{by LCD of } x^2 - 4.}$$

$$(x-2)(2x) = 1 + (x^2 - 4), \quad x \neq \pm 2 \qquad \text{Distribute and simplify.}$$

$$2x^2 - 4x = 1 + x^2 - 4 \qquad \text{Distributive Property}$$

$$x^2 - 4x + 3 = 0 \qquad \text{Standard form}$$

$$(x-3)(x-1) = 0 \qquad \text{Factor.}$$

$$x - 3 = 0 \;\;\Longrightarrow\;\; x = 3 \qquad \text{Set 1st factor equal to 0.}$$

$$x - 1 = 0 \;\;\Longrightarrow\;\; x = 1 \qquad \text{Set 2nd factor equal to 0.}$$

The solutions are 1 and 3. Check these in the original equation.

3 Solve an application problem using a rational equation with variable denominators.

Applications

In Section 3.5, you studied a formula that relates distance, rate, and time.

$$\text{Distance} = (\text{rate})(\text{time})$$

By solving this equation for the rate or the time, you can obtain two other versions of the formula.

$$\text{Rate} = \frac{\text{distance}}{\text{time}} \quad \text{and} \quad \text{Time} = \frac{\text{distance}}{\text{rate}}$$

The second of these is used in Example 7.

Example 7   Average Speeds

You and your friend travel to separate colleges in the same amount of time. You drive 380 miles and your friend drives 400 miles. Your friend's average speed is 3 miles per hour faster than your average speed. What is your average speed and what is your friend's average speed?

Solution

Begin by setting your time equal to your friend's time. Then use the formula above that gives the time in terms of the distance and the rate.

Verbal Model: Your time = Your friend's time

$$\frac{\text{Your distance}}{\text{Your rate}} = \frac{\text{Friend's distance}}{\text{Friend's rate}}$$

Labels:
Your distance = 380   (miles)
Your rate = r (miles per hour)
Friend's distance = 400   (miles)
Friend's rate = $r + 3$ (miles per hour)

Equation:
$$\frac{380}{r} = \frac{400}{r + 3}$$

$$380(r + 3) = 400(r), \quad r \neq 0, r \neq -3$$

$$380r + 1140 = 400r$$

$$1140 = 20r$$

$$57 = r$$

Your average speed is 57 miles per hour and your friend's average speed is $57 + 3 = 60$ miles per hour. Check this solution as follows.

Your friend's average speed is 3 mph faster than yours.

$57 + 3 = 60$ Solution checks. ✓

You drive 380 miles and your friend drives 400 miles in the same time.

$\dfrac{380}{57} = 6\dfrac{2}{3}$ hours and $\dfrac{400}{60} = 6\dfrac{2}{3}$ hours   Solution checks. ✓

| Example 8 | Work Rates | |

With only the cold water valve open, it takes 7 minutes to fill the tub of an automatic washer. With both the hot and cold water valves fully open, it takes only 4 minutes to fill the tub (see Figure 8.1). How long will it take to fill the tub with only the hot water valve open?

After learning to clear an equation of fractions, students may mistakenly attempt to use this technique in an addition or subtraction problem. Ask students to compare an equation with an addition problem that *looks* similar.

$$\frac{4}{x^2 - 4} + \frac{x}{2x - 4} = \frac{1}{2}$$

$$\frac{4}{x^2 - 4} + \frac{x}{2x - 4} + \frac{1}{2}$$

The solution of this equation is $x = -6$; the sum is $\dfrac{x^2 + x + 2}{(x + 2)(x - 2)}$.

Cold: 7 minutes   Hot and cold: 4 minutes

Figure 8.1

Solution

Verbal Model:

| Rate for cold water | + | Rate for hot water | = | Rate for warm water |

Labels:

Warm water time $= 4$	(minutes)
Warm water rate $= \frac{1}{4}$	(tub per minute)
Cold water time $= 7$	(minutes)
Cold water rate $= \frac{1}{7}$	(tub per minute)
Hot water time $= t$	(minutes)
Hot water rate $= 1/t$	(tub per minute)

Equation:

$$\frac{1}{7} + \frac{1}{t} = \frac{1}{4}$$

$$28t\left(\frac{1}{7} + \frac{1}{t}\right) = 28t\left(\frac{1}{4}\right)$$

$$4t + 28 = 7t, \quad t \neq 0$$

$$28 = 3t \quad \Longrightarrow \quad \frac{28}{3} = t$$

It will take $9\frac{1}{3}$ minutes to fill the tub with hot water alone.

Check

$$\frac{1}{7} + \frac{1}{\frac{28}{3}} \stackrel{?}{=} \frac{1}{4} \qquad \text{Substitute } \tfrac{28}{3} \text{ for } t \text{ in original equation.}$$

$$\frac{1}{7} + \frac{3}{28} \stackrel{?}{=} \frac{1}{4} \qquad \text{Simplify complex fraction.}$$

$$\frac{4}{28} + \frac{3}{28} \stackrel{?}{=} \frac{1}{4} \qquad \text{Rewrite } \tfrac{1}{7} \text{ as } \tfrac{4}{28}.$$

$$\frac{7}{28} = \frac{1}{4} \qquad \text{Solution checks. } \checkmark$$

Corbis/Bettmann-UPI

Between 1930 and 1998, only one National League batting champion had a batting average greater than 0.400: Bill Terry of the New York Giants in 1930.

Example 9 Batting Average

In this year's playing season, a baseball player has been up to bat 280 times (excluding walks) and has hit the ball safely 70 times. Thus, the batting average for the player is 70/280 = .250. How many additional *consecutive* times must the player hit the ball safely to obtain a batting average of .300?

Solution

Verbal Model: $\boxed{\text{Batting average}} = \boxed{\text{Total hits}} \div \boxed{\text{Total times at bat}}$

Labels: Current times at bat = 280
Current hits = 70
Additional consecutive hits = x

Equation:
$$.300 = \frac{x + 70}{x + 280}$$

$$.300(x + 280) = x + 70, \quad x \neq -280$$

$$0.3x + 84 = x + 70$$

$$14 = 0.7x$$

$$20 = x$$

The player must hit safely for the next 20 times at bat. After that, the player's batting average will be 90/300 = .300.

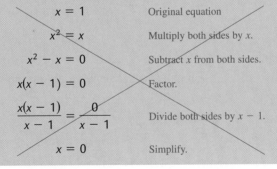

Discussing the Concept   A Mathematical Fallacy

A student submits the following argument to prove that 1 is equal to 0. Discuss what is wrong with the argument.

$x = 1$	Original equation
$x^2 = x$	Multiply both sides by x.
$x^2 - x = 0$	Subtract x from both sides.
$x(x - 1) = 0$	Factor.
$\dfrac{x(x - 1)}{x - 1} = \dfrac{0}{x - 1}$	Divide both sides by $x - 1$.
$x = 0$	Simplify.

8.4   Exercises

Integrated Review   *Concepts, Skills, and Problem Solving*

Keep mathematically in shape by doing these exercises *before* the problems of this section.

Properties and Definitions

1. In the context of solving systems of linear equations, define the terms *consistent*, *inconsistent*, and *dependent*.

2. In your own words, describe the method of substitution for solving a system of linear equations.

Solving Equations and Systems of Equations

In Exercises 3–8, solve the equation.

3. $16x - 3 = 29$

4. $\dfrac{x}{5} + \dfrac{1}{5} = \dfrac{7}{10}$

5. $x(x - 8) = 0$

6. $6x\left(\dfrac{2}{3}x + 1\right) = 0$

7. $x(8 - x) = 16$

8. $x^2 + x - 56 = 0$

In Exercises 9 and 10, solve the system of equations.

9. $3x - 4y = -15$
$\quad\ 2x + 5y = 13$

10. $y = \dfrac{5}{3}x$
$\quad\ \ y = \dfrac{1}{3}x + 4$

Models

11. A business purchases a computer system for $8500. It is estimated that after 4 years the system's depreciated value will be $3000. Assuming straight-line depreciation, write a linear function giving the value V of the system in terms of time t. Estimate the value of the computer system after 1 year.

12. A liberal arts college had an enrollment of 3750 students in 1990. During the next 10 years the enrollment increased by approximately 125 students per year.

    (a) Write a linear function giving the enrollment N in terms of the year t. (Let $t = 0$ correspond to the year 1990.)

    (b) *(Linear Extrapolation)* If this constant rate of growth continues, predict the enrollment in the year 2005.

    (c) *(Linear Interpolation)* Use the function to estimate the enrollment in 1994.

Developing Skills

In Exercises 1–4, determine whether each given value of x is a solution to the equation.

Equation		*Values*	
1. $\dfrac{x}{5} - \dfrac{3}{x} = \dfrac{1}{10}$	(a) $x = 0$	(b) $x = -1$	
	(c) $x = \dfrac{1}{6}$	(d) $x = 6$	
2. $\dfrac{3x}{5} + \dfrac{x^2}{2} = \dfrac{4}{5}$	(a) $x = 0$	(b) $x = -2$	
	(c) $x = \dfrac{4}{5}$	(d) $x = 2$	
3. $\dfrac{5}{2x} - \dfrac{4}{x} = 3$	(a) $x = -\dfrac{1}{2}$	(b) $x = 4$	
	(c) $x = 0$	(d) $x = \dfrac{1}{4}$	
4. $3 + \dfrac{1}{x + 2} = 4$	(a) $x = -1$	(b) $x = -2$	
	(c) $x = 0$	(d) $x = 5$	

Mental Math   In Exercises 5–12, solve the equation mentally and check your solution.

5. $x - 8 = 2$

6. $x + 2 = 15$

7. $8u = 24$

8. $-6v = 18$

9. $\dfrac{1}{4}y = 5$

10. $\dfrac{1}{5}z = -8$

11. $-\dfrac{2}{3}x = 10$

12. $\dfrac{3}{4}t = 9$

In Exercises 13–60, solve the equation. See Examples 1–5.

13. $\dfrac{z}{3} - \dfrac{2z}{8} = 1$

14. $3 + \dfrac{y}{5} = \dfrac{y}{2}$

15. $\dfrac{t}{3} = 25 - \dfrac{t}{6}$

16. $\dfrac{x}{10} + \dfrac{x}{5} = 20$

17. $\dfrac{5x}{7} - \dfrac{2x}{3} = \dfrac{1}{2}$

18. $\dfrac{2}{3} - \dfrac{3x}{6} = -\dfrac{4x}{9}$

19. $\dfrac{a+3}{4} - \dfrac{a-1}{6} = \dfrac{4}{3}$

20. $\dfrac{u-5}{10} + \dfrac{u+8}{15} = \dfrac{7}{10}$

21. $\dfrac{x-4}{3} + \dfrac{2x+1}{4} = \dfrac{5}{6}$

22. $\dfrac{y+6}{5} + \dfrac{3y-2}{20} = \dfrac{3}{4}$

23. $2 - \dfrac{4}{x} = 1$

24. $\dfrac{2}{b} + 1 = 9$

25. $3 - \dfrac{16}{a} = \dfrac{5}{3}$

26. $\dfrac{14}{x} - 4 = 3$

27. $\dfrac{3}{x} + \dfrac{1}{4} = \dfrac{2}{x}$

28. $\dfrac{3}{5} - \dfrac{7}{x} = -\dfrac{4}{x}$

29. $\dfrac{6}{12x} + \dfrac{3}{4} = \dfrac{2}{3x}$

30. $\dfrac{5}{2x} + \dfrac{5}{8} = -\dfrac{5}{8x}$

31. $\dfrac{10}{y+3} + \dfrac{10}{3} = 6$

32. $\dfrac{5}{2} - \dfrac{12}{x-4} = 6$

33. $\dfrac{3}{x} = \dfrac{9}{2(x+2)}$

34. $\dfrac{5}{x+4} = \dfrac{5}{3(x+1)}$

35. $\dfrac{7x}{x+1} = \dfrac{5}{x-3} + 7$

36. $\dfrac{-3x}{x+4} = \dfrac{2}{x+1} - 3$

37. $\dfrac{4}{x+2} - \dfrac{1}{x} = \dfrac{1}{x}$

38. $\dfrac{3}{x+5} + \dfrac{5}{x} = \dfrac{10}{x}$

39. $10 - \dfrac{13}{x} = 4 + \dfrac{5}{x}$

40. $\dfrac{15}{x} - 4 = \dfrac{6}{x} + 3$

41. $\dfrac{3}{x(x-3)} + \dfrac{4}{x} = \dfrac{1}{x-3}$

42. $\dfrac{3}{z+2} = \dfrac{2}{z} + \dfrac{2}{z(z+2)}$

43. $\dfrac{1}{x+3} + \dfrac{4}{x+4} = -\dfrac{x}{(x+3)(x+4)}$

44. $\dfrac{2x}{(x-4)(x-2)} = \dfrac{1}{x-4} + \dfrac{2}{x-2}$

45. $\dfrac{1}{x-3} + \dfrac{1}{x+3} = \dfrac{10}{x^2-9}$

46. $\dfrac{2}{x-4} - \dfrac{3}{x+4} = \dfrac{9x}{x^2-16}$

47. $\dfrac{1}{x-2} + \dfrac{3}{x+3} = \dfrac{4}{x^2+x-6}$

48. $\dfrac{4}{x+5} - \dfrac{2}{x-2} = \dfrac{-6}{x^2+3x-10}$

49. $x + 4 = \dfrac{-4}{x}$

50. $\dfrac{25}{t} = 10 - t$

51. $\dfrac{20-x}{x} = x$

52. $\dfrac{x+30}{x} = x$

53. $2y = \dfrac{y+6}{y+1}$

54. $\dfrac{3x}{x+1} = \dfrac{2}{x-1}$

55. $x + \dfrac{1}{x} = \dfrac{5}{2}$

56. $\dfrac{4}{x} - \dfrac{x}{6} = \dfrac{5}{3}$

57. $\dfrac{x+3}{x^2-9} + \dfrac{4}{x-3} = -2$

58. $-1 - \dfrac{6}{x-4} = \dfrac{x+2}{x^2-16}$

59. $\dfrac{x}{2} = \dfrac{1 + \dfrac{3}{x}}{1 + \dfrac{1}{x}}$

60. $\dfrac{2x}{3} = \dfrac{1 + \dfrac{1}{x}}{1 + \dfrac{2}{x}}$

In Exercises 61–68, (a) use a graphing utility to graph the equation and identify the x-intercepts. (b) Solve the rational equation when $y = 0$. Compare your answer with the result of part (a).

61. $y = \dfrac{5}{x+1} - 1$

62. $y = \dfrac{12}{x} - 6$

63. $y = \dfrac{6}{x} - \dfrac{3x}{2}$

64. $y = \dfrac{7}{x+3} - \dfrac{x}{4}$

65. $y = 2\left(\dfrac{3}{x-4} - 1\right)$

66. $y = \dfrac{5}{x} + 1$

67. $y = x + \dfrac{x-6}{x}$

68. $y = x - \dfrac{5}{x} - 4$

Solving Problems

69. *Number Problem*   Find a number such that the sum of the number and its reciprocal is $\frac{10}{3}$.

70. *Number Problem*   Find a number such that the sum of the number and 3 times its reciprocal is $\frac{28}{5}$.

71. *Number Problem*   Find a number such that the sum of three times the number and 25 times the reciprocal of the number is 20.

72. *Number Problem*   Find consecutive even integers such that the sum of the first and 3 times the reciprocal of the second is $\frac{41}{4}$.

73. *Average Speed*   One car makes a trip of 440 miles. Another car takes the same amount of time to make a trip of 416 miles. The average speed of the second car is 3 miles per hour slower than the average speed of the first car. What is the average speed of each car?

74. *Average Speed*   One car makes a trip of 400 miles. Another car takes the same amount of time to make a trip of 480 miles. The average speed of the second car is 10 miles per hour faster than the average speed of the first car. What is the average speed of each car?

75. *Average Speed*   A car leaves a town 20 minutes after a truck. The speed of the truck is approximately 10 miles per hour slower than that of the car. After traveling 100 miles, the car overtakes the truck. Find the average speed of each vehicle.

76. *Average Speed*   A car leaves a town 30 minutes after a bus. The speed of the bus is 15 miles per hour slower than that of the car. After traveling 150 miles, the car overtakes the bus. Find the average speed of each vehicle.

77. *Wind Speed*   You fly to a meeting in a city 1500 miles away (see figure). After traveling the same amount of time on the return flight, the pilot states that you still have 300 miles to go. If the plane has a speed of 600 miles per hour in still air, how fast is the wind blowing? (Assume that the wind direction is parallel to the flight path and constant all day.)

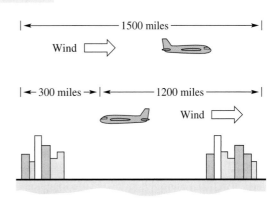

Figure for 77

78. *Wind Speed*   A small plane has a speed of 170 miles per hour in still air. The plane travels a distance of 400 miles with a tail wind in the same time it takes to travel 280 miles into a head wind. In both cases, the wind has the same speed. Find the speed of the wind. Use a diagram and a verbal model to help solve the problem.

In Exercises 79 and 80, the first two columns of the table give the times required by each of two people working *alone* to complete a task. Complete the table by finding the time required for each pair of individuals working *together* to complete the task. (Assume that when they work together, their individual rates do not change.)

79.

Person #1	Person #2	Together
4 days	4 days	
4 hours	6 hours	
4 hours	$2\frac{1}{2}$ hours	

80.

Person #1	Person #2	Together
30 minutes	30 minutes	
$6\frac{1}{2}$ hours	4 hours	
a days	b days	

81. *Work Rate* One person can paint a wall in 4 hours. The same person working with a friend can paint a similar wall in 1 hour. Working alone, how long would it take the second person to accomplish the task?

82. *Work Rate* A pump empties a storage tank in 50 minutes. When a new pump is added to the system, the time to empty the tank using both pumps is 20 minutes. How long would it take to empty the tank using only the new pump?

83. *Work Rate* One landscaper works twice as fast as a second. Find their individual times to complete a task if it takes them 8 hours working together.

84. *Work Rate* The flow rate for one pipe is $1\frac{1}{2}$ times that of a second. Find their individual times to fill a gasoline tank if it takes 6 hours using both pipes.

85. *Batting Average* A softball player has been up to bat 35 times and has hit the ball safely 6 times. How many additional consecutive times must the player hit the ball safely to obtain a batting average of .275?

86. *Batting Average* After 50 times at bat, a baseball player has a batting average of .160. How many additional consecutive hits must the player have to obtain a batting average of .250?

87. *Average Cost* The average cost $\overline{C}$ for producing x units of a product is

$$\overline{C} = \frac{1}{2} + \frac{5000}{x}.$$

Determine the number of units that must be produced to obtain an average cost of $2.50 per unit.

88. *Average Cost* The average cost $\overline{C}$ for producing x units of a product is

$$\overline{C} = \frac{1}{4} + \frac{500}{x}.$$

Determine the number of units that must be produced to obtain an average cost of $0.50 per unit.

89. *Modeling a Population* The game commission introduces 50 deer into newly acquired state game lands. The population N of the herd is given by the model

$$N = \frac{250(5 + 3t)}{25 + t}$$

where t is time in years. Find the time required for the herd to increase to 125 deer.

90. *Air Pollution* A utility company burns oil to generate electricity. The cost C in dollars of removing p percent of the air pollution in the stack emission is given by

$$C = \frac{80,000p}{100 - p}.$$

Determine the percent of the stack emission that can be removed for $240,000. (The percent p is in decimal form.)

Explaining Concepts

91. Answer parts (e) and (f) of Motivating the Chapter on page 417.

92. Explain the difference between the following.

$$\frac{5}{x + 3} + \frac{5}{3} = 3, \qquad \frac{5}{x + 3} + \frac{5}{3} + 3$$

93. Describe the steps used to solve a rational equation.

94. Explain what is meant by an *extraneous* solution. How can you identify an extraneous solution?

95. Describe the steps that can be used to transform an equation into an equivalent equation. (Section 2.4)

96. Which step from your list in Exercise 95 is not followed when an extraneous solution is found for a rational equation? Explain.

97. When can you use cross-multiplication to solve rational equations? Explain. (Section 3.2)

Key Terms

rational expression, *p. 418*
domain, *p. 418*

simplified or reduced form,
    p. 420
Cancellation Rule, *p. 420*

complex fractions, *p. 431*
least common multiple,
    p. 438

least common
    denominator, *p. 439*
extraneous solution,
    p. 448

Key Concepts

8.1 Finding the domain of a rational expression

To find the values to exclude from the domain, do the following.

1. Set the denominator equal to zero.
2. Find the solution to the equation in Step 1.

8.1 Cancellation Rule for fractions

Let a, b, and c represent real numbers, variables, or algebraic expressions such that $b \neq 0$ and $c \neq 0$. Then the following Cancellation Rule is valid.

$$\frac{ac}{bc} = \frac{a\not c}{b\not c} = \frac{a}{b}$$

8.2 Rule for multiplying rational expressions

Let a, b, c, and d represent real numbers, variables, or algebraic expressions. Then, to multiply rational expressions, you multiply numerators, multiply denominators, and simplify.

$$\frac{a}{b} \cdot \frac{c}{d} = \frac{ac}{bd}$$

8.2 Rule for dividing rational expressions

Let a, b, c, and d represent real numbers, variables, or algebraic expressions. Then, to divide rational expressions, you invert the divisor and multiply.

$$\frac{a}{b} \div \frac{c}{d} = \frac{a}{b} \cdot \frac{d}{c}$$

8.3 Combining fractions with like denominators

Let a, b, and c be numbers, variables, or algebraic expressions.

1. $\dfrac{a}{c} + \dfrac{b}{c} = \dfrac{a+b}{c}, \quad c \neq 0$

2. $\dfrac{a}{c} - \dfrac{b}{c} = \dfrac{a-b}{c}, \quad c \neq 0$

8.3 Guidelines for finding the least common multiple

1. Factor each polynomial completely.
2. The least common multiple must contain all the *different* factors of the polynomials and each such factor must be repeated the maximum number of times it occurs in any of the factorizations.

8.3 Combining fractions with unlike denominators

1. Find the least common denominator (LCD) for the rational expressions.
2. Rewrite each rational expression so that it has the LCD in its denominator.
3. Combine these rational expressions with like denominators.

8.4 Solving rational equations

To solve a rational equation, multiply both sides of the equation by the LCD of the fractions, then solve the resulting equation. Check the solutions for any extraneous solutions.

REVIEW EXERCISES

Reviewing Skills

8.1 In Exercises 1–4, find the domain of the rational expression.

1. $\dfrac{8x}{x-5}$

2. $\dfrac{y+1}{y+3}$

3. $\dfrac{t}{t^2-3t+2}$

4. $\dfrac{x-10}{x(x^2-4)}$

In Exercises 5–8, evaluate the expression for the specified values. (If not possible, state the reason.)

Expression	Values

5. $\dfrac{2x}{x+4}$ (a) $x=0$ (b) $x=2$

(c) $x=-3$ (d) $x=-4$

6. $\dfrac{3}{y-10}$ (a) $y=0$ (b) $y=-2$

(c) $y=10$ (d) $y=-5$

7. $\dfrac{x-1}{x^2+4}$ (a) $x=2$ (b) $x=1$

(c) $x=-2$ (d) $x=-5$

8. $\dfrac{3x-2}{x^2-x-6}$ (a) $x=0$ (b) $x=6$

(c) $x=\frac{2}{3}$ (d) $x=-2$

In Exercises 9–26, simplify the expression using the Cancellation Rule for fractions.

9. $\dfrac{6t}{18}$

10. $\dfrac{45x}{15}$

11. $\dfrac{4x^5}{x^2}$

12. $\dfrac{88z^2}{33z}$

13. $\dfrac{7x^2y}{21xy^2}$

14. $\dfrac{2(yz)^2}{6yz^4}$

15. $\dfrac{3b-6}{4b-8}$

16. $\dfrac{2a+5}{10a+25}$

17. $\dfrac{4x-4y}{y-x}$

18. $\dfrac{x-y}{3y-3x}$

19. $\dfrac{x^2-9}{x^2-x-6}$

20. $\dfrac{x^2-4}{x^2+x-6}$

21. $\dfrac{1-x^3}{x^2-1}$

22. $\dfrac{x^2-4}{x^3+8}$

23. $\dfrac{x^2-3xy-18y^2}{x^2+4xy+3y^2}$

24. $\dfrac{x^2+2xy+y^2}{x^2-xy-y^2}$

25. $\dfrac{x(x-4)+7(x-4)}{x^2+7x}$

26. $\dfrac{x^3-5x^2+2x-10}{x^3+2x}$

Creating a Table   In Exercises 27 and 28, complete the table. Explain why the values of the expressions agree for all values of x except one.

27.

x	1	1.5	2	2.5	3
$\dfrac{x-2}{x^2-4}$					
$\dfrac{1}{x+2}$					

28.

x	1	1.5	2	2.5	3
$\dfrac{x-2}{x^2-x-2}$					
$\dfrac{1}{x+1}$					

In Exercises 29–32, find the missing factor.

29. $\dfrac{7}{4x}=\dfrac{7\ \rule{1cm}{0.4pt}}{12x^3}$

30. $\dfrac{5x}{8}=\dfrac{5x\ \rule{1cm}{0.4pt}}{8(x-3)}$

31. $\dfrac{x-3}{x-1}=\dfrac{(x-3)\ \rule{0.8cm}{0.4pt}}{x^2-1}$

32. $\dfrac{x+2}{x-2}=\dfrac{(x+2)\ \rule{0.8cm}{0.4pt}}{x^2-4}$

8.2 In Exercises 33–60, perform the indicated operation and simplify.

33. $\dfrac{36}{12}\cdot\dfrac{4}{18}$

34. $\dfrac{15}{16}\cdot\dfrac{4}{25}$

35. $\dfrac{11}{21}\div\dfrac{9}{14}$

36. $\dfrac{5}{4}\div10$

37. $\dfrac{x^2}{6}\cdot\dfrac{2x}{x^3}$

38. $\dfrac{5y^4}{8y}\cdot\dfrac{12}{-15y^2}$

39. $\dfrac{5}{8}\div\dfrac{u}{v}$

40. $\dfrac{x}{9}\div\dfrac{x^2}{3}$

41. $\dfrac{5x^2y}{4}\cdot\dfrac{6x}{10y^3}$

42. $\dfrac{x^2y^3}{6}\cdot\dfrac{3}{(xy)^3}$

43. $10y^2\div\dfrac{y}{5}$

44. $\dfrac{5}{z^2}\div3z^2$

45. $\dfrac{z}{z+1} \cdot \dfrac{z^2-1}{5}$

46. $\dfrac{u}{u-1} \cdot \dfrac{u-u^2}{3u^2}$

47. $\dfrac{2-x}{x+3} \cdot \dfrac{4x+12}{x^2-4}$

48. $\dfrac{8x-10}{7-x} \cdot \dfrac{x^2-49}{4x-5}$

49. $\dfrac{u^2}{u^2-9} \div \dfrac{u}{u+3}$

50. $\dfrac{v+5}{v^2} \div \dfrac{v+5}{v^2}$

51. $\dfrac{x^2-36}{6} \cdot \dfrac{3}{x^2-12x+36}$

52. $\dfrac{x^2-5x+4}{9} \cdot \dfrac{-18x}{x^2-8x+16}$

53. $\dfrac{x^2-8x}{x-1} \div \dfrac{x^2-16x+64}{x^2-1}$

54. $x \cdot \dfrac{x+1}{x^2-x} \cdot \dfrac{5x-5}{x^2+6x+5}$

55. $\dfrac{\left(\dfrac{4}{x}\right)}{\left(\dfrac{1}{x^2}\right)}$

56. $\dfrac{5x}{\left(\dfrac{x}{y}\right)}$

57. $\dfrac{\left(\dfrac{6x-21}{x+3}\right)}{\left(\dfrac{2x-7}{x^2-9}\right)}$

58. $\dfrac{\left(\dfrac{x^2+x}{x^2+x-12}\right)}{\left(\dfrac{4x+4}{x^2-6x+9}\right)}$

59. $\left(\dfrac{x}{y} \cdot \dfrac{x+1}{y+1}\right) \div \dfrac{x}{y^2-y}$

60. $xy \cdot \dfrac{8x}{y+4} \div \dfrac{x}{y^2-y}$

8.3 In Exercises 61–64, find the least common multiple.

61. $20x^2, 24, 30x^3$

62. $4y^2, 6y, 18z$

63. $x-5, 2x^2, x(x+5)$

64. $5(x-1), 2(x^2+x+1)$

In Exercises 65–86, perform the indicated operation and simplify.

65. $\dfrac{5x}{8} - \dfrac{3x}{8}$

66. $\dfrac{4t}{9} + \dfrac{11t}{9}$

67. $\dfrac{4x-5}{x+2} + \dfrac{2x+1}{x+2}$

68. $\dfrac{3y+4}{2y+1} - \dfrac{y+3}{2y+1}$

69. $\dfrac{5t}{16} - \dfrac{5t}{24}$

70. $\dfrac{x}{8} + \dfrac{5x}{6}$

71. $\dfrac{1}{x+2} - \dfrac{1}{x+1}$

72. $\dfrac{4}{x-3} + \dfrac{1}{x+4}$

73. $\dfrac{1}{x+4} - \dfrac{x-1}{x^2+4x+4}$

74. $\dfrac{1}{x-1} + \dfrac{1-x}{x^2+2x+1}$

75. $\dfrac{x-7}{x^2-16} - \dfrac{3}{4-x}$

76. $\dfrac{2x-7}{x^2-36} - \dfrac{1}{6-x}$

77. $x-1 + \dfrac{1}{x+2} + \dfrac{1}{x-1}$

78. $\dfrac{2}{x} - \dfrac{3}{x-1} + \dfrac{4}{x+1}$

79. $2x + \dfrac{3}{2(x-4)} - \dfrac{1}{2(x+2)}$

80. $\dfrac{1}{x-2} + \dfrac{1}{(x-2)^2} + \dfrac{1}{x+2}$

81. $\dfrac{\left(\dfrac{2}{x}+2\right)}{\left(1-\dfrac{1}{x}\right)}$

82. $\dfrac{\left(1+\dfrac{2}{x}\right)}{\left(\dfrac{2}{x}-1\right)}$

83. $\dfrac{\left(\dfrac{1}{x}-\dfrac{1}{y}\right)}{x^2-y^2}$

84. $\dfrac{\left(\dfrac{1}{x}-\dfrac{1}{y}\right)}{y^2-x^2}$

85. $\dfrac{\left(\dfrac{1}{x+1}-\dfrac{1}{4}\right)}{x-3}$

86. $\dfrac{\left(\dfrac{x}{x+1}-\dfrac{4}{5}\right)}{x-4}$

8.4 In Exercises 87–98, solve the equation. Be sure to check for extraneous solutions.

87. $\dfrac{3x}{5} + 2 = \dfrac{4x}{10}$

88. $1 - \dfrac{7y}{6} = \dfrac{-2y}{4}$

89. $\dfrac{t+1}{9} = \dfrac{2}{3} - t$

90. $\dfrac{2t-5}{14} = \dfrac{5}{7} - 2t$

91. $\dfrac{7}{x} - 2 = \dfrac{3}{x} + 6$

92. $\dfrac{2}{x} + \dfrac{5}{3} = 1 + \dfrac{4}{x}$

93. $\dfrac{x}{x+3} - \dfrac{3x}{x^2-9} = 1$

94. $\dfrac{2x}{x-1} + \dfrac{4}{x+4} = 2$

95. $\dfrac{2}{x} - \dfrac{x}{6} = \dfrac{2}{3}$

96. $\dfrac{x}{2} + \dfrac{5}{x} = \dfrac{13}{x}$

97. $\dfrac{t}{t-4} + \dfrac{3}{t-2} = 0$

98. $\dfrac{2x}{x-3} - \dfrac{4}{x-1} = 4$

In Exercises 99–104, (a) use a graphing utility to graph the equation and identify the x-intercepts. (b) Solve the rational equation when $y=0$. Compare your answer with the result of part (a).

99. $y = \dfrac{3}{x+1} - 2$

100. $y = 5 - \dfrac{2x}{x-2}$

101. $y = \dfrac{1}{x+2} + \dfrac{3}{x-4}$

102. $y = \dfrac{x+2}{x-4} + \dfrac{3}{4}$

103. $y = x - 2 - \dfrac{3}{x}$

104. $y = 2x - 3 - \dfrac{2}{x}$

Solving Problems

Probability In Exercises 105 and 106, the probability of hitting the shaded portion of the region with a dart is the ratio of the shaded region to the total area of the figure. Find the probability.

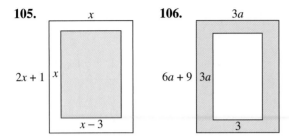

105.

106.

107. *Number Problem* Find a number such that the sum of the number and its reciprocal is $\frac{41}{20}$.

108. *Number Problem* Find a number such that the sum of the number and twice its reciprocal is $\frac{9}{2}$.

109. *Average Speed* You drive 72 miles one way on a service call for your company. The return trip takes 10 minutes less because you drive an average of 6 miles per hour faster. Find the average speed going to the service call and the average speed on the return trip.

110. *Average Speed* You drive 180 miles to pick up supplies for your company. The return trip takes 24 minutes less because you drive an average of 5 miles per hour faster. Find the average speed going to and returning from the supplier.

111. *Work Rate* Your supervisor takes 10 minutes to complete a task that takes you 8 minutes. Determine the time required to complete the task if you work together.

112. *Work Rate* One bricklayer lays $1\frac{1}{4}$ times as many bricks as a second in the same amount of time. Find their individual times to complete a task if it takes them 12 hours working together.

113. *Batting Average* After 40 times at bat, a baseball player has a batting average of .300. How many additional consecutive times must the player hit safely to obtain a batting average of .440?

114. *Batting Average* After 60 times at bat, a baseball player has a batting average of .300. How many additional consecutive times must the player hit safely to obtain a batting average of at least .333?

115. *Data Analysis* The values of exports of domestic agricultural products (in billions of dollars) from the United States for the years 1991 through 1996 are given in the table. (Source: U.S. Department of Agriculture)

Year	1991	1992	1993	1994	1995	1996
Exports	39.2	42.9	42.6	45.7	55.8	60.4

A model for the data is

$$y = \frac{10{,}000}{277 - 18t}$$

where y is the value of the exports and t is time, with $t = 0$ corresponding to 1990.

(a) Use a graphing utility to plot the data and graph the model in the same viewing screen.

(b) Use the model to estimate the value of exports in the year 2000.

116. *Think About It* You drive 100 miles one way on a service call and average x miles per hour. On the return trip you average y miles per hour.

(a) Write expressions for the time in each direction and the total driving time.

(b) Write an expression for the average speed for the round trip. Simplify the complex fraction.

(c) Suppose the average speed for the round trip is 50 miles per hour. Use the result of part (b) to write an equation that models this average speed.

(d) Use the result of part (c) to write y as a function of x. What is the domain of the function? Complete the table.

x	40	45	47	49	50
y					

(e) Do any of the entries in the table surprise you? Explain.

Chapter Test

Take this test as you would take a test in class. After you are done, check your work against the answers given in the back of the book.

1. Find the domain of the rational expression $\dfrac{x}{x - 10}$.

2. Complete the statement: $\dfrac{2x^2}{x + 1} = \dfrac{2x^2(\quad\quad)}{x(x + 1)^2}$.

3. Simplify: $\dfrac{8x^2(x + 1)}{x(x + 1)^2}$

4. Simplify: $\dfrac{x^2 - 64}{x^2 - 3x - 40}$

In Exercises 5–9, perform the indicated operations and simplify.

5. $\dfrac{18x}{5} \cdot \dfrac{15}{3x^3}$

6. $(x + 2)^2 \cdot \dfrac{x - 2}{x^3 + 2x^2}$

7. $\dfrac{3x^2}{4} \div \dfrac{9x^3}{10}$

8. $\dfrac{\left(\dfrac{t}{t - 5}\right)}{\left(\dfrac{t^2}{5 - t}\right)}$

9. $\left[\left(\dfrac{x}{x - 3}\right)^2 \cdot \dfrac{x^2}{x^2 - 3x}\right] \div (x - 3)^5$

10. Find the least common multiple of $6x(x + 3)^2, 9x^3$, and $12(x + 3)$.

In Exercises 11–14, perform the indicated operations and simplify.

11. $\dfrac{8}{3u^2} + \dfrac{3}{u}$

12. $\dfrac{3}{x + 2} - 6$

13. $\dfrac{4}{\left(\dfrac{2}{x} + 8\right)}$

14. $\dfrac{2}{x + 1} - \dfrac{2x}{x^2 + 2x + 1}$

15. Determine whether the given value of x is a solution of $\dfrac{x}{4} + \dfrac{2}{x} = \dfrac{3}{2}$, and explain your reasoning.

   (a) $x = 1$ (b) $x = 2$ (c) $x = -\dfrac{1}{2}$ (d) $x = 4$

In Exercises 16–18, solve the rational equation.

16. $5 + \dfrac{t}{3} = t + 2$

17. $\dfrac{5}{x + 1} - \dfrac{1}{x} = \dfrac{3}{x}$

18. $2\left(x + \dfrac{1}{x}\right) = 5$

19. The capacity of a pump is 80 gallons per minute. Determine the time required to pump (a) 1 gallon, (b) x gallons, and (c) 16 gallons.

20. A car leaves a town 1 hour after a moving van. The speed of the moving van is 12 miles per hour slower than the car. After traveling 240 miles, the car overtakes the moving van. Find the average speed of each vehicle.

9 Radical Expressions and Equations

Leonard Harris/Stock Boston

The Yard at Harvard is surrounded by some of the oldest structures on the campus. Its criss-crossing pathways provide shortcuts to Harvard Hall (built in 1766), Hollis Hall (built in 1763), Stoughton Hall, and Holworthy Hall.

9.1   Roots and Radicals

9.2   Simplifying Radicals

9.3   Operations with Radical Expressions

9.4   Radical Equations and Applications

462

Motivating the Chapter

 Constructing a Walkway

On a college campus, a walkway from point A to point B has a path that contains a right angle, as shown at the right. The original plan was to make a *diagonal* walkway, but several trees block a direct diagonal path from point A to point B. Two options are shown at the right for placement of the new walkway.

See Section 9.3, Exercise 131

a. Can the distance from point A to point C in option 1 be simplified further? If so, write the simplified expression.

b. The distance b_2 in option 2 is one-half the distance from point A to point C in option 1. What is the length of b_2? Use a calculator and round your answer to three decimal places.

c. Find the area of the right triangle in option 1 given $a_1 = 72\sqrt{2}$.

d. Find the area of the right triangle in option 2 given $a_2 = 36\sqrt{2}$.

See Section 9.4, Exercise 93

A coordinate plane is placed over the original plan. Point A is located at $(100, 100)$, point B is located at $(-72, 128)$, and point C is located at $(28, 28)$.

e. Use the Distance Formula to find the distance between points A and B. Round your answer to three decimal places.

f. Use the Distance Formula to find the distance between points C and B. Round your answer to three decimal places.

g. Find the distance you would walk from A to B in option 1 if you use the diagonal walkway. How much further is that than a direct diagonal path from A to B?

h. Find the distance you would walk from A to B in option 2 if you use the diagonal walkway. How much further is that than a direct diagonal path from A to B? How much further is that than the distance in option 1?

Original

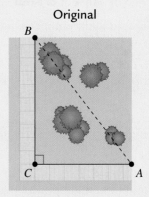

Option 1

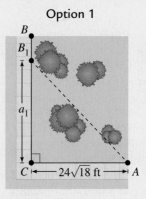

Option 2

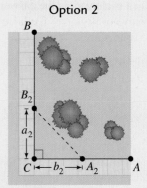

9.1   Roots and Radicals

Objectives

1 Find the *n*th root of a real number.

2 Use the radical symbol to denote the *n*th root of a number.

3 Approximate the value of an expression involving square roots using a calculator.

1 Find the *n*th root of a real number.

Roots

You already know how to find the square of a number (by multiplying the number by itself). For instance, the square of 3 is $3^2 = 9$. In this section, you will study the reverse problem, which is finding a *square root* of a number.

The **square root** of a number is defined as one of its two equal factors. For example, 5 is a square root of 25 because 5 is one of the two equal factors of 25. In a similar way, a **cube root** of a number is one of its three equal factors.

Number	Equal Factors	Root	Type
$9 = 3^2$	$3 \cdot 3$	3	Square root
$25 = (-5)^2$	$(-5)(-5)$	-5	Square root
$-27 = (-3)^3$	$(-3)(-3)(-3)$	-3	Cube root
$16 = 2^4$	$2 \cdot 2 \cdot 2 \cdot 2$	2	Fourth root

Technology: Discovery

A positive number is raised to an even power—for instance, 2^4. When evaluated, is the answer positive or negative? A positive number is raised to an odd power—for instance, 2^5. When evaluated, is the answer positive or negative? Evaluate the following.

a. $(-4)^2$

b. $(-4)^3$

c. $(-2)^4$

d. $(-2)^5$

When a negative number is raised to an even power, is the answer positive or negative? When a negative number is raised to an odd power, is the answer positive or negative?

▶ **Definition of *n*th Root of a Number**

Let a and b be real numbers and let n be an integer such that $n \geq 2$. If

$$a = b^n$$

then b is an ***n*th root of *a*.** If $n = 2$, the root is a **square root,** and if $n = 3$, the root is a **cube root.**

Example 1   Finding Square Roots of Numbers

Find all square roots of the following numbers.

a. 81   **b.** $\frac{4}{9}$ **c.** 0   **d.** -4

Solution

a. The positive number 81 has two square roots, 9 and -9, because $9^2 = (9)(9) = 81$ and $(-9)^2 = (-9)(-9) = 81$.

b. The positive number $\frac{4}{9}$ has two square roots, $\frac{2}{3}$ and $-\frac{2}{3}$, because $\left(\frac{2}{3}\right)^2 = \left(\frac{2}{3}\right)\left(\frac{2}{3}\right) = \frac{4}{9}$ and $\left(-\frac{2}{3}\right)^2 = \left(-\frac{2}{3}\right)\left(-\frac{2}{3}\right) = \frac{4}{9}$.

c. The number 0 has only one square root: 0.

d. The negative number -4 has no square root because there is no real number that can be multiplied by itself to obtain -4.

| Example 2 | Finding nth Roots of Numbers |

a. Find the cube root of 8.   **b.** Find the cube root of -64.

c. Find the fourth roots of 81.   **d.** Find the fourth roots of -16.

Solution

a. The number 8 has one cube root, 2, because $2^3 = (2)(2)(2) = 8$.

b. The number -64 has one cube root, -4, because $(-4)^3 = (-4)(-4)(-4) = -64$.

c. The number 81 has two real fourth roots, 3 and -3, because $3^4 = (3)(3)(3)(3) = 81$ and $(-3)^4 = (-3)(-3)(-3)(-3) = 81$.

d. The number -16 has no real fourth roots because no four real equal factors can be multiplied to produce a negative number.

Study Tip

Notice in Example 2 that there is only one root associated with a cube root. In fact, when finding the nth root of a number, where n is odd, there is only one root.

2 Use the radical symbol to denote the nth root of a number.

Radicals

The symbol $\sqrt{\ }$ is used to denote the nonnegative square root of a number. This symbol is called a **radical symbol.** For instance, to denote the positive square root of 4, you can use a radical symbol and write $\sqrt{4} = 2$.

Some numbers have more than one nth root. For example, both 5 and -5 are square roots of 25 because $25 = 5^2$ and $25 = (-5)^2$. To avoid ambiguity about which root of a number you are talking about, the **principal nth root** of a number is defined as follows.

Study Tip

When used by itself, a radical *always* refers to the principal square root of the radicand. To denote a negative square root, place a negative sign in front of the radical. For instance, the principal square root of 36 is denoted by $\sqrt{36} = 6$, whereas the negative square root of 36 is denoted by $-\sqrt{36} = -6$.

▶ **Principal nth Root of a Number**

Let a be a real number that has at least one (real number) nth root. The **principal nth root of a** is the nth root that has the same sign as a, and it is denoted by the **radical symbol**

$\sqrt[n]{a}.$ Principal nth root

The positive integer n is the **index** of the radical, and the number a is the **radicand.** If $n = 2$, omit the index and write $\sqrt{a}$ rather than $\sqrt[2]{a}$.

| Example 3 | Finding the Principal Square Root of a Number |

a. The number 49 has two square roots, 7 and -7. The principal square root is the positive one.

$\sqrt{49} = 7$ Principal square root

b. The number $\frac{1}{4}$ has two square roots, $\frac{1}{2}$ and $-\frac{1}{2}$. The principal square root is the positive one.

$\sqrt{\frac{1}{4}} = \frac{1}{2}$ Principal square root

> **Example 4**   Finding the Principal nth Root of a Number

a. Find the cube root of 125.

b. Find the cube root of -27.

c. Find the principal fourth root of 16.

Solution

a. The number 125 has one cube root: 5.

$$\sqrt[3]{125} = 5 \qquad\qquad \text{Cube root}$$

b. The number -27 has one cube root: -3.

$$\sqrt[3]{-27} = -3 \qquad\qquad \text{Cube root}$$

c. The number 16 has two fourth roots: 2 and -2. The principal fourth root is the positive one.

$$\sqrt[4]{16} = 2 \qquad\qquad \text{Principal fourth root}$$

A real number is a **perfect square** if its square root is a rational number. Integers

$$4, \quad 9, \quad 16, \quad \text{and} \quad 25 \qquad\qquad \text{Perfect squares}$$

are perfect squares because they have integer square roots. Rational numbers

$$\frac{1}{4}, \quad \frac{1}{9}, \quad \text{and} \quad \frac{9}{25} \qquad\qquad \text{Perfect squares}$$

are also perfect squares. The square roots of numbers that are not perfect squares are *irrational* numbers. For example, the numbers

$$\sqrt{2}, \quad \sqrt{3}, \quad \sqrt{5}, \quad \text{and} \quad \sqrt{6} \qquad \text{Irrational numbers}$$

are all irrational. Remember that a rational number is a real number that can be written as the ratio of two integers. So, when you say that $\sqrt{2}$ is irrational, you are saying that there is no fraction (with integer numerator and denominator) that can be multiplied by itself to obtain the number 2.

> **Example 5**   Classifying Square Roots as Rational or Irrational

Classify the following numbers as rational or irrational.

a. $-\sqrt{100}$ **b.** $\sqrt{11}$

Solution

a. The negative square root of 100 is

$$-\sqrt{100} = -10 \qquad\qquad \text{Rational number}$$

which is a rational number. Remember that every integer is a rational number.

b. The principal square root of 11, which is

$$\sqrt{11} \approx 3.3166\ldots \qquad\qquad \text{Irrational number}$$

is irrational because 11 is not a perfect square.

| Example 6 | Classifying Square Roots as Rational or Irrational |

Classify the following numbers as rational or irrational.

a. $\sqrt{\frac{25}{16}}$ **b.** $\sqrt{0.36}$ **c.** $\sqrt{3.2}$

Solution

a. The principal square root of $\frac{25}{16}$ is

$$\sqrt{\frac{25}{16}} = \frac{5}{4} \qquad \text{Rational number}$$

which is a rational number.

b. Because $(0.6)(0.6) = 0.36$, the principal square root of 0.36 is

$$\sqrt{0.36} = 0.6 \qquad \text{Rational number}$$

which is the rational number $\frac{6}{10}$.

c. The principal square root of 3.2, which is

$$\sqrt{3.2} = 1.7888\ldots \qquad \text{Irrational number}$$

is irrational, because 3.2 is not a perfect square.

3 Approximate the value of an expression involving square roots using a calculator.

Radicals and Calculators

In real-life applications, you often use decimal approximations of square roots. Before calculators were available, this was usually done by looking up the decimal approximation in a table of square roots. Today, however, you can use a calculator to find decimal approximations of square roots. The key that accomplishes this is labeled $\boxed{\sqrt{\ }}$.

| Example 7 | Decimal Approximations of Square Roots |

Use a calculator to approximate the following numbers.

a. Round $\sqrt{3}$ to four decimal places.

b. Round $-\sqrt{12}$ to three decimal places.

Solution

Square Root	Keystrokes	Calculator Display	Rounded Answer	
a. $\sqrt{3}$	3 $\boxed{\sqrt{\ }}$	1.7320508	1.7321	Scientific
$\sqrt{3}$	$\boxed{\sqrt{\ }}$ 3 $\boxed{\text{ENTER}}$	1.7320508	1.7321	Graphing
b. $-\sqrt{12}$	12 $\boxed{\sqrt{\ }}$ $\boxed{+/-}$	-3.4641016	-3.464	Scientific
$-\sqrt{12}$	$\boxed{(-)}$ $\boxed{\sqrt{\ }}$ 12 $\boxed{\text{ENTER}}$	-3.4641016	-3.464	Graphing

When approximating a *negative square root* on a scientific calculator, be sure you press the square root key before pressing the change sign key. For instance, if you used the keystroke sequence 12 $\boxed{+/-}$ $\boxed{\sqrt{\ }}$, the calculator would think you were asking it to find $\sqrt{-12}$, and it would display some sort of error message. Try this with your calculator.

Technology: Discovery

Use a calculator to evaluate the radicals. Which one results in an error message? Explain why.

a. $\sqrt{64}$

b. $-\sqrt{64}$

c. $\sqrt{-64}$

Example 8   Speed of a Car

In an emergency stop on dry pavement, the speed of a car can be approximated by the equation

$$v = \sqrt{24l}$$

where v is the speed of the car in miles per hour and l is the length of the skid mark in feet. What is the estimated speed of the car that produces a skid mark of 110 feet?

Solution

Because $l = 110$, you have

$$v = \sqrt{24(110)} = \sqrt{2640} \approx 51.4. \qquad \text{Use a calculator.}$$

The estimated speed of the car is 51.4 miles per hour. Notice that the multiplication 24(110) is performed before the square root is taken.

Answers to problems in algebra often involve sums, differences, products, and quotients of integers and square roots. Example 9 shows how a calculator can be used to approximate this type of expression. (The keystrokes shown may differ from those used by your calculator. Try approximating the expressions on your calculator to see whether the same keystrokes work.)

Example 9   Approximating Expressions Involving Square Roots

Use a calculator to approximate the following expressions. Round your answers to two decimal places.

a. $2 + 3\sqrt{5}$ **b.** $\dfrac{1 - 2\sqrt{3}}{4}$

Solution

a. The number $2 + 3\sqrt{5}$ can be approximated using the following keystrokes.

Keystrokes	Display	
2 ⊞ 3 ⊠ 5 ✓ ⊟	8.7082039	Scientific
2 ⊞ 3 ⊠ ✓ 5 ENTER	8.7082039	Graphing

Rounded to two decimal places, the answer is $2 + 3\sqrt{5} \approx 8.71$.

b. The number $(1 - 2\sqrt{3})/4$ can be approximated using the following keystrokes.

Keystrokes	Display	
1 ⊟ 2 ⊠ 3 ✓ ⊟ ⊞ 4 ⊟	−.6160254	Scientific
⦅ 1 ⊟ 2 ⊠ ✓ 3 ⦆ ⊞ 4 ENTER	−.6160254	Graphing

Rounded to two decimal places, the answer is

$$\frac{1 - 2\sqrt{3}}{4} \approx -0.62.$$

It's easy to make mistakes with a calculator, and knowing the squares of integers will help you to estimate square root answers as a check of your calculations. For instance, knowing that $10^2 = 100$ and $20^2 = 400$ can serve as a check when finding $\sqrt{330}$. You know it must lie between

$$10 = \sqrt{100} \quad \text{and} \quad 20 = \sqrt{400}$$

and will be closer to 20 than to 10 because 330 is closer to 400 than to 100.

Example 10   Estimating Square Roots

Estimate the following square roots *without* using a calculator.

a. $\sqrt{200}$ **b.** $\sqrt{110}$

Solution

a. The number $\sqrt{200}$ must lie between $\sqrt{196} = 14$ and $\sqrt{225} = 15$. Because 200 is closer to 196 than to 225, you could estimate $\sqrt{200}$ to be about 14.2.

b. The number $\sqrt{110}$ must lie between $\sqrt{100} = 10$ and $\sqrt{121} = 11$. Because 110 is about halfway between 100 and 121, you could estimate $\sqrt{110}$ to be about 10.5.

Example 11   Evaluating a Radical Expression

Evaluate each square root using $x = 2$, $y = 3$, and $z = 5$. Round your answers to two decimal places.

a. $\sqrt{x + y}$ **b.** $\sqrt{x^3 - z}$ **c.** $\sqrt{yz - x^2}$

Solution

a. $\sqrt{x + y} = \sqrt{2 + 3} = \sqrt{5} \approx 2.24$

b. $\sqrt{x^3 - z} = \sqrt{2^3 - 5} = \sqrt{8 - 5} = \sqrt{3} \approx 1.73$

c. $\sqrt{yz - x^2} = \sqrt{3(5) - 2^2} = \sqrt{15 - 4} = \sqrt{11} \approx 3.32$

Discussing the Concept   Interpreting Radicals

The **Pythagorean Theorem** states that the sides of a *right triangle* satisfy the equation $a^2 + b^2 = c^2$, where a and b are the lengths of two sides and c is the length of the hypotenuse. Consider a right triangle that has two sides of length 1 (see figure). From the Pythagorean Theorem, you can conclude that the length of the hypotenuse is

$$c = \sqrt{a^2 + b^2} = \sqrt{1^2 + 1^2} = \sqrt{2}.$$

Is it possible to construct a right triangle with sides of lengths 1, 2, and $\sqrt{3}$? with sides of lengths 1, 2, and $\sqrt{5}$? Explain.

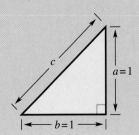

9.1   Exercises

Integrated Review   Concepts, Skills, and Problem Solving

Keep mathematically in shape by doing these exercises *before* the problems of this section.

Properties and Definitions

In Exercises 1–4, complete the property of exponents.

1. $a^m \cdot a^n = $ ▢   **2.** $(ab)^m = $ ▢

3. $(a^m)^n = $ ▢   **4.** $\dfrac{a^m}{a^n} = $ ▢ , if $m > n$

Simplifying Expressions

In Exercises 5–12, simplify the expression.

5. $x^3 \cdot x^2$ **6.** $(-x)^5$

7. $-(2x)^2$ **8.** $t^2 - (3t)^2 \cdot 2$

9. $\dfrac{(x + y)^5}{(x + y)^2}$ **10.** $\dfrac{2x^2}{6}\left(\dfrac{3}{x}\right)^2$

11. $-\left(\dfrac{x}{3}\right)^2\left(-\dfrac{x}{3}\right)^2$ **12.** $\left(-\dfrac{x}{5}\right)^2\left(\dfrac{x}{5}\right)^2$

Graphs

In Exercises 13 and 14, graph the function and identify any intercepts. Use a graphing utility to verify your results.

13. $f(x) = \frac{1}{2}(2x - 5)$

14. $g(x) = 2 - |x - 2|$

Developing Skills

In Exercises 1–4, fill in the blank.

1. $9^2 = 81$ ⟹ A square root of 81 is ▢ .

2. $7^2 = 49$ ⟹ A square root of 49 is ▢ .

3. $(-10)^2 = 100$ ⟹ A square root of 100 is ▢ .

4. $(-13)^2 = 169$ ⟹ A square root of 169 is ▢ .

In Exercises 5–18, find the positive and negative square roots of the real number, if possible. Do not use a calculator. See Example 1.

5. 36   **6.** 144

7. 16   **8.** 25

9. $\frac{9}{49}$ **10.** $\frac{4}{25}$

11. $\frac{81}{16}$ **12.** $\frac{25}{16}$

13. -16 **14.** -25

15. 0.16   **16.** 0.25

17. -0.04 **18.** -0.09

In Exercises 19–28, find the *n*th root. See Example 2.

19. The cube root of 27

20. The cube root of 1

21. The fourth root of 1

22. The fourth root of 625

23. The cube root of -8

24. The cube root of -27

25. The cube root of $\frac{1}{8}$

26. The fourth root of $\frac{1}{81}$

27. The fourth root of -81

28. The fourth root of -625

In Exercises 29–52, find the principal square root, if possible. Do not use a calculator. See Example 3.

29. $\sqrt{100}$ **30.** $\sqrt{64}$

31. $-\sqrt{100}$ **32.** $-\sqrt{64}$

33. $\sqrt{-100}$ **34.** $\sqrt{-64}$

35. $\sqrt{49}$ **36.** $-\sqrt{36}$

37. $\sqrt{169}$ **38.** $\sqrt{225}$

39. $-\sqrt{121}$ **40.** $\sqrt{-121}$

41. $-\sqrt{\frac{1}{9}}$ **42.** $\sqrt{\frac{36}{81}}$

43. $\sqrt{-\frac{1}{25}}$ **44.** $-\sqrt{\frac{1}{25}}$

45. $\sqrt{\frac{49}{64}}$ **46.** $\sqrt{\frac{81}{400}}$

47. $-\sqrt{\frac{81}{121}}$ **48.** $\sqrt{\frac{25}{100}}$

49. $\sqrt{0.16}$ **50.** $\sqrt{0.64}$

51. $\sqrt{0.04}$ **52.** $-\sqrt{0.09}$

In Exercises 53–62, find the principal *n*th root of the number. See Example 4.

53. $\sqrt[3]{8}$

54. $\sqrt[3]{64}$

55. $\sqrt[4]{16}$

56. $-\sqrt[4]{81}$

57. $\sqrt[3]{-125}$

58. $\sqrt[3]{-8}$

59. $-\sqrt[3]{27}$

60. $\sqrt[3]{-27}$

61. $-\sqrt[6]{64}$

62. $\sqrt[5]{-1}$

In Exercises 63–76, classify the number as rational or irrational. See Examples 5 and 6.

63. $\sqrt{15}$

64. $\sqrt{25}$

65. $-\sqrt{49}$

66. $\sqrt{50}$

67. $-\sqrt{24}$

68. $\sqrt{42}$

69. $\sqrt{400}$

70. $\sqrt{300}$

71. $-\sqrt{\frac{36}{25}}$

72. $\sqrt{\frac{4}{9}}$

73. $\sqrt{0.18}$

74. $\sqrt{0.64}$

75. $\sqrt{1.21}$

76. $\sqrt{2.36}$

In Exercises 77–100, use a calculator to approximate the value of the expression, if possible. Round the result to three decimal places. See Examples 7 and 9.

77. $\sqrt{43}$

78. $\sqrt{38}$

79. $\sqrt{-12}$

80. $\sqrt{-8}$

81. $-\sqrt{137}$

82. $\sqrt{150}$

83. $\sqrt{-632}$

84. $\sqrt{326}$

85. $\sqrt{2560}$

86. $-\sqrt{1250}$

87. $-\sqrt{517.8}$

88. $\sqrt{326.2}$

89. $-\sqrt{\frac{15}{24}}$

90. $\sqrt{\frac{10}{14}}$

91. $\sqrt{\frac{95}{6}}$

92. $-\sqrt{\frac{43}{5}}$

93. $16 - \sqrt{92.6}$

94. $27 + \sqrt{32.3}$

95. $2 + 4\sqrt{7}$

96. $5 - 3\sqrt{6}$

97. $\dfrac{9 + \sqrt{45}}{2}$

98. $\dfrac{-3 + \sqrt{1540}}{2}$

99. $\dfrac{-4 - 3\sqrt{2}}{12}$

100. $\dfrac{-3 + 8\sqrt{-24}}{2}$

In Exercises 101–108, estimate the square root without using a calculator. Then check your estimate by using a calculator. See Example 10.

101. $\sqrt{55}$

102. $\sqrt{90}$

103. $\sqrt{70}$

104. $\sqrt{30}$

105. $\sqrt{130}$

106. $\sqrt{125}$

107. $\sqrt{300}$

108. $\sqrt{500}$

In Exercises 109–112, evaluate $\sqrt{b^2 - 4ac}$. Give the exact value if possible. Otherwise, give an approximation to two-decimal-place accuracy. See Example 11.

109. $a = 4,\ b = 5,\ c = 1$

110. $a = -2,\ b = 8,\ c = -8$

111. $a = 3,\ b = -7,\ c = -4$

112. $a = 12,\ b = 21,\ c = 5$

Solving Problems

Geometry   In Exercises 113 and 114, use the formula $h = \dfrac{\sqrt{3}}{2}s$ to find the height *h* of an equilateral triangle whose sides are of length *s*. Approximate the height to two decimal places.

113. $s = 5$ inches

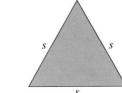

114. $s = 10$ centimeters

Geometry   In Exercises 115 and 116, use the area *A* to find the length of the side.

115. Square: $s = \sqrt{A}$
$A = 27.04$

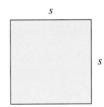

116. Square: $s = \sqrt{A}$
$A = 12.96$

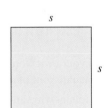

117. *Geometry*   The length of a diagonal of a rectangular solid of length l, width w, and height h is

$$\sqrt{l^2 + w^2 + h^2}.$$

Approximate to two decimal places the length of the diagonal of the solid shown in the figure.

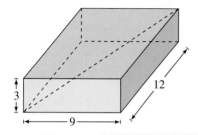

118. *Geometry*   Find the dimensions of a piece of carpet for a classroom with 529 square feet of floor space, assuming that the floor is square.

119. *Geometry*   A square room has 729 square feet of floor space. An area carpet covers all of the floor space except for a 1-foot border all around the room (see figure). How many square feet are in the carpet? How many square yards are in the carpet?

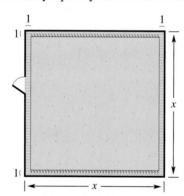

120. *Velocity of a Stream*   A stream of water moving at the rate of v feet per second can carry particles of size $0.03\sqrt{v}$ inches. Find the particle size that can be carried by a stream flowing at the rate of $\frac{3}{4}$ foot per second.

121. *Think About It*

(a) Find all possible last digits of integers that are perfect squares. (For instance, the last digit of 64 is 4.)

(b) Using the results of part (a), is it possible that 5,788,942,862 is a perfect square?

122. *Table and Graph*

(a) Complete the table. Round your answers to two decimal places.

x	0	1	2	4	6	8
$\sqrt{x}$						

x	10	12	14	16	18	20
$\sqrt{x}$						

(b) Sketch a graph of the equation $y = \sqrt{x}$ by using the table generated in part (a). (Remember that negative values of x cannot be used because the square root of a negative number is not a real number.)

(c) Use the Vertical Line Test to determine if y is a function of x.

123. Use a calculator to evaluate the expressions.

(a) $\left(\sqrt{8.2}\right)^2$ (b) $\left(\sqrt{142}\right)^2$

(c) $\left(\sqrt{22}\right)^2$ (d) $\left(\sqrt{850}\right)^2$

124. *Think About It*   Use the results of Exercise 123 to determine $\left(\sqrt{a}\right)^2$ where a is a nonnegative real number.

125. If $f(x) = \sqrt{2 - x}$, find (a) $f(2)$ and (b) $f(-23)$.

Explaining Concepts

126. In your own words, define what it means for b to be a square root of a.

127. Explain why all positive real numbers have two square roots.

128. Explain what is meant by the radicand of a radical.

129. In your own words, explain what is meant by the term *perfect square*.

130. Determine the values of x for which $\sqrt{x^2} \neq x$. Explain.

131. Is it true that $\sqrt{2} = 1.414$? Explain.

9.2   Simplifying Radicals

Objectives

1 Simplify a radical expression involving constants.

2 Simplify a radical expression involving variables.

3 Simplify a radical expression by rationalizing the denominator.

---

1 Simplify a radical expression involving constants.

Simplifying Radicals with Constant Factors

You already know that simplifying algebraic expressions is one of the primary tasks in algebra. In this and the following section, you will learn how to simplify **radical expressions.**

The first step in rewriting a radical in simpler form is to evaluate any perfect nth factors. To do this, you need the property of radicals demonstrated by the following two equations.

$$\sqrt{4 \cdot 25} = \sqrt{100} = 10 \quad \text{and} \quad \sqrt{4} \cdot \sqrt{25} = 2 \cdot 5 = 10$$

Note that in these two equations you obtain the same result whether you first multiply 4 and 25 and then take the square root, or first take the square roots of the factors 4 and 25 and then multiply. So,

$$\sqrt{4 \cdot 25} = \sqrt{4} \cdot \sqrt{25}.$$

This property of radicals is generalized as follows.

> ▶ **Multiplication Property of Radicals**
>
> Let a and b be real numbers, variables, or algebraic expressions. If the nth roots of a and b are real, the following property is true.
>
> $$\sqrt[n]{a}\,\sqrt[n]{b} = \sqrt[n]{ab} \qquad \text{Multiplication Property of Radicals}$$

Students may factor $\sqrt{18} = \sqrt{6} \cdot \sqrt{3}$. Point out that this is a true statement, but because neither factor is a perfect square, this factoring does not help to simplify the radical.

Example 1   Simplifying Radicals

a. $\sqrt{18} = \sqrt{9 \cdot 2}$ 9 is perfect square factor.

$\phantom{\sqrt{18}} = \sqrt{9} \cdot \sqrt{2}$ Multiplication Property of Radicals

$\phantom{\sqrt{18}} = 3\sqrt{2}$ Simplest form

b. $\sqrt[3]{54} = \sqrt[3]{27 \cdot 2}$ 27 is perfect cube factor.

$\phantom{\sqrt[3]{54}} = \sqrt[3]{27} \cdot \sqrt[3]{2}$ Multiplication Property of Radicals

$\phantom{\sqrt[3]{54}} = 3\sqrt[3]{2}$ Simplest form

c. $\sqrt[4]{80} = \sqrt[4]{16 \cdot 5}$ 16 is 2 raised to the fourth power.

$\phantom{\sqrt[4]{80}} = \sqrt[4]{16} \cdot \sqrt[4]{5}$ Multiplication Property of Radicals

$\phantom{\sqrt[4]{80}} = 2\sqrt[4]{5}$ Simplest form

Some radicands have more than one perfect nth factor. In such cases, choose the *largest perfect nth factor* because this will minimize the number of steps needed to write the radical in simplest form. Compare the following two versions of the same problem.

First Solution

$$\sqrt{72} = \sqrt{36 \cdot 2} \qquad \text{36 is largest perfect square factor of 72.}$$

$$= \sqrt{36} \cdot \sqrt{2} \qquad \text{Multiplication Property of Radicals}$$

$$= 6\sqrt{2} \qquad \text{Simplest form}$$

Second Solution

$$\sqrt{72} = \sqrt{9 \cdot 8} \qquad \text{9 is a perfect square factor of 72.}$$

$$= \sqrt{9} \cdot \sqrt{8} \qquad \text{Multiplication Property of Radicals}$$

$$= 3\sqrt{8} \qquad \text{Simplify.}$$

$$= 3\sqrt{4 \cdot 2} \qquad \text{4 is perfect square factor of 8.}$$

$$= 3\sqrt{4} \cdot \sqrt{2} \qquad \text{Multiplication Property of Radicals}$$

$$= 3 \cdot 2 \cdot \sqrt{2} \qquad \text{Simplify.}$$

$$= 6\sqrt{2} \qquad \text{Simplest form}$$

By finding the largest perfect square factor of 72, you can save several steps.

Example 2   **Simplifying Radicals**

Simplify the following radicals.

a. $\sqrt{96}$ **b.** $\sqrt{108}$ **c.** $\sqrt{288}$

d. $\sqrt[3]{-192}$ **e.** $\sqrt[3]{5000}$ **f.** $\sqrt[4]{512}$

Solution

a. The largest perfect square factor of 96 is 16.

$$\sqrt{96} = \sqrt{16 \cdot 6} = \sqrt{16} \cdot \sqrt{6} = 4\sqrt{6}$$

b. The largest perfect square factor of 108 is 36.

$$\sqrt{108} = \sqrt{36 \cdot 3} = \sqrt{36} \cdot \sqrt{3} = 6\sqrt{3}$$

c. The largest perfect square factor of 288 is 144.

$$\sqrt{288} = \sqrt{144 \cdot 2} = \sqrt{144} \cdot \sqrt{2} = 12\sqrt{2}$$

d. The largest perfect cube factor of -192 is -64.

$$\sqrt[3]{-192} = \sqrt[3]{-64 \cdot 3} = \sqrt[3]{-64} \cdot \sqrt[3]{3} = -4\sqrt[3]{3}$$

e. The largest perfect cube factor of 5000 is 1000.

$$\sqrt[3]{5000} = \sqrt[3]{1000 \cdot 5} = \sqrt[3]{1000} \cdot \sqrt[3]{5} = 10\sqrt[3]{5}$$

f. The largest perfect fourth powered factor of 512 is 256.

$$\sqrt[4]{512} = \sqrt[4]{256 \cdot 2} = \sqrt[4]{256} \cdot \sqrt[4]{2} = 4\sqrt[4]{2}$$

2 Simplify a radical expression involving variables.

Simplifying Radicals with Variable Factors

Simplifying radicals that involve *variable* radicands is trickier than simplifying radicals involving only constant radicands. The reason for this can be seen by considering the radical $\sqrt{x^2}$. At first glance, it would appear that this radical simplifies as x. However, doing so overlooks the possibility that x might be negative. For instance, consider the following.

$$\text{If } x = 2, \text{ then } \sqrt{x^2} = \sqrt{2^2} = \sqrt{4} = 2 = x.$$

$$\text{If } x = -2, \text{ then } \sqrt{x^2} = \sqrt{(-2)^2} = \sqrt{4} = 2 = |x|.$$

In both of these cases, you can conclude that

$$\sqrt{x^2} = |x|$$

but without knowing whether x is positive, zero, or negative, you *cannot* conclude that $\sqrt{x^2} = x$.

▶ **The Square Root of x^2**

If x is a real number, then

$$\sqrt{x^2} = |x|.$$

For the special case in which you know that x is a *nonnegative* real number, you can write $\sqrt{x^2} = x$.

Example 3   Simplifying Square Roots Involving Even Powers

Simplify the following radicals.

a. $\sqrt{25x^2}$ **b.** $\sqrt{18a^2}$ **c.** $\sqrt{x^4}$ **d.** $\sqrt{9x^6}$

Solution

a. $\sqrt{25x^2} = \sqrt{25} \cdot \sqrt{x^2}$ Multiplication Property of Radicals

$\qquad\qquad = 5|x|$ $\sqrt{x^2} = |x|$

b. $\sqrt{18a^2} = \sqrt{9 \cdot 2 \cdot a^2}$ Factor radicand.

$\qquad\qquad = \sqrt{9} \cdot \sqrt{2} \cdot \sqrt{a^2}$ Multiplication Property of Radicals

$\qquad\qquad = 3\sqrt{2}|a|$ $\sqrt{x^2} = |x|$

c. This problem is different. Note that the absolute value signs are not necessary in the final simplified version because you know that x^2 cannot be negative.

$$\sqrt{x^4} = \sqrt{(x^2)^2} = |x^2| = x^2$$

d. $\sqrt{9x^6} = \sqrt{9 \cdot (x^3)^2}$ Factor radicand.

$\qquad\qquad = \sqrt{9} \cdot \sqrt{(x^3)^2}$ Multiplication Property of Radicals

$\qquad\qquad = 3|x^3|$ $\sqrt{(x^3)^2} = |x^3|$

Study Tip

In Example 3(d), the value of the expression $\sqrt{9x^6}$ is positive for any value of x. When the expression is simplified, you must use absolute value signs so that the expression $3|x^3|$ is also positive for any value of x.

Study the following simplifications of square roots of powers of x. Try to see why absolute values are necessary in some cases and not necessary in others.

$\sqrt{x^2} = |x|$ In $\sqrt{x^2}$, x can be positive or negative.

$\sqrt{x^3} = x\sqrt{x}$ In $\sqrt{x^3}$, x cannot be negative.

$\sqrt{x^4} = x^2$ In $\sqrt{x^4}$, x can be positive or negative.

$\sqrt{x^5} = x^2\sqrt{x}$ In $\sqrt{x^5}$, x cannot be negative.

$\sqrt{x^6} = |x^3|$ In $\sqrt{x^6}$, x can be positive or negative.

The reason you don't need to use absolute values in simplifying $\sqrt{x^3} = x\sqrt{x}$ is that the original radical would be undefined if x were negative. So, if someone asks you to simplify the radical $\sqrt{x^3}$, you can assume that x must be nonnegative (which means that the absolute value signs are not necessary).

Example 4   Simplifying Square Roots Involving Odd Powers

a. $\sqrt{16x^3} = \sqrt{16 \cdot x^2 x}$ Factor radicand.

$\phantom{\sqrt{16x^3}} = \sqrt{16} \cdot \sqrt{x^2} \cdot \sqrt{x}$ Multiplication Property of Radicals

$\phantom{\sqrt{16x^3}} = 4x\sqrt{x}$ Simplified form

b. $\sqrt{9a^5} = \sqrt{9 \cdot a^4 a}$ Factor radicand.

$\phantom{\sqrt{9a^5}} = \sqrt{9} \cdot \sqrt{a^4} \cdot \sqrt{a}$ Multiplication Property of Radicals

$\phantom{\sqrt{9a^5}} = 3a^2\sqrt{a}$ Simplified form

Example 5   Simplifying Radicals Involving nth Roots

a. $\sqrt[3]{54a^3} = \sqrt[3]{27 \cdot 2 \cdot a^3}$ Factor radicand.

$\phantom{\sqrt[3]{54a^3}} = \sqrt[3]{27} \cdot \sqrt[3]{2} \cdot \sqrt[3]{a^3}$ Multiplication Property of Radicals

$\phantom{\sqrt[3]{54a^3}} = 3a\sqrt[3]{2}$ Simplify.

b. $\sqrt[5]{x^6} = \sqrt[5]{x^5 \cdot x}$ Factor radicand.

$\phantom{\sqrt[5]{x^6}} = \sqrt[5]{x^5} \cdot \sqrt[5]{x}$ Multiplication Property of Radicals

$\phantom{\sqrt[5]{x^6}} = x\sqrt[5]{x}$ Simplify.

c. $\sqrt[4]{16b^9} = \sqrt[4]{16 \cdot b^8 \cdot b}$ Factor radicand.

$\phantom{\sqrt[4]{16b^9}} = \sqrt[4]{16} \cdot \sqrt[4]{b^8} \cdot \sqrt[4]{b}$ Multiplication Property of Radicals

$\phantom{\sqrt[4]{16b^9}} = \sqrt[4]{2^4} \cdot \sqrt[4]{(b^2)^4} \cdot \sqrt[4]{b}$ $b^8 = (b^2)^4$

$\phantom{\sqrt[4]{16b^9}} = 2b^2\sqrt[4]{b}$ Simplify.

d. $\sqrt[4]{32x^7} = \sqrt[4]{16 \cdot 2 \cdot x^4 \cdot x^3}$ Factor radicand.

$\phantom{\sqrt[4]{32x^7}} = \sqrt[4]{2^4} \cdot \sqrt[4]{2} \cdot \sqrt[4]{x^4} \cdot \sqrt[4]{x^3}$ Multiplication Property of Radicals

$\phantom{\sqrt[4]{32x^7}} = 2 \cdot x \cdot \sqrt[4]{2} \cdot \sqrt[4]{x^3}$ Simplify.

$\phantom{\sqrt[4]{32x^7}} = 2x\sqrt[4]{2x^3}$ Multiplication Property of Radicals

3 Simplify a radical expression by rationalizing the denominator.

Rationalizing Denominators

To simplify a square root having a fractional radicand, you can use the following Division Property of Radicals.

▶ Division Property of Radicals

Let a and b be real numbers, variables, or algebraic expressions. If the nth roots of a and b are real, the following property is true.

$$\frac{\sqrt[n]{u}}{\sqrt[n]{v}} = \sqrt[n]{\frac{u}{v}}, \qquad v \neq 0 \qquad\qquad \text{Division Property of Radicals}$$

Note how this property is used to simplify radicals in Example 6.

| **Example 6** | Simplifying Radicals Involving Fractions |

a. $\sqrt{\dfrac{21}{4}} = \dfrac{\sqrt{21}}{\sqrt{4}}$ Division Property of Radicals

$\phantom{a.\sqrt{\dfrac{21}{4}}} = \dfrac{\sqrt{21}}{2}$ Simplify.

Show students that they can use their calculators to verify that

$\sqrt{\dfrac{45}{25}} = \dfrac{3\sqrt{5}}{5}.$

b. $\sqrt{\dfrac{45}{25}} = \dfrac{\sqrt{9 \cdot 5}}{\sqrt{25}}$ Division Property of Radicals

$\phantom{b.\sqrt{\dfrac{45}{25}}} = \dfrac{3\sqrt{5}}{5}$ Simplify.

c. $\sqrt{\dfrac{48x^4}{3}} = \sqrt{16x^4}$ Simplify fraction.

$\phantom{c.\sqrt{\dfrac{48x^4}{3}}} = 4x^2$ Simplify.

d. $\sqrt{\dfrac{3x^2}{12y^4}} = \sqrt{\dfrac{x^2}{4y^4}}$ Simplify fraction.

$\phantom{d.\sqrt{\dfrac{3x^2}{12y^4}}} = \dfrac{\sqrt{x^2}}{\sqrt{4y^4}}$ Division Property of Radicals

$\phantom{d.\sqrt{\dfrac{3x^2}{12y^4}}} = \dfrac{|x|}{2y^2}$ Simplify.

In Example 6, note that the denominators are free of radicals. This simplifying process is called **rationalizing the denominator.** In Example 6 the rationalizing was easy because (after canceling) the denominators were perfect squares. For more general fractions, rationalizing the denominator can require a little more work. The goal is to find a *rationalizing* factor that creates (in the denominator) a perfect square radicand for square roots, a perfect cube radicand for cube roots, and so on.

Study Tip

Remember that when rationalizing the denominator of a fraction, you must multiply both the numerator and denominator by the rationalizing factor, as shown in Examples 7, 8, and 9.

You might show students that there can be more than one approach to finding the simplified forms of these radical expressions. Here are some "less efficient" ways of simplifying Example 7(c).

$$\sqrt{\frac{7}{20}} = \frac{\sqrt{7}}{\sqrt{20}} = \frac{\sqrt{7}}{\sqrt{4}\sqrt{5}}$$
$$= \frac{\sqrt{7}}{2\sqrt{5}} \cdot \frac{\sqrt{5}}{\sqrt{5}} = \frac{\sqrt{35}}{10}$$
$$\sqrt{\frac{7}{20}} = \frac{\sqrt{7}}{\sqrt{20}} \cdot \frac{\sqrt{20}}{\sqrt{20}} = \frac{\sqrt{140}}{20}$$
$$= \frac{\sqrt{4}\sqrt{35}}{20} = \frac{2\sqrt{35}}{20} = \frac{\sqrt{35}}{10}$$

Compare two examples such as $\frac{\sqrt{10}}{\sqrt{5}}$ and $\frac{10}{\sqrt{5}}$.

$$\frac{\sqrt{10}}{\sqrt{5}} = \sqrt{\frac{10}{5}} = \sqrt{2}$$
$$\frac{10}{\sqrt{5}} = \frac{10}{\sqrt{5}} \cdot \frac{\sqrt{5}}{\sqrt{5}} = \frac{10\sqrt{5}}{5} = 2\sqrt{5}$$

Example 7 Rationalizing Denominators

a. $\sqrt{\dfrac{13}{3}} = \dfrac{\sqrt{13}}{\sqrt{3}} \cdot \dfrac{\sqrt{3}}{\sqrt{3}} = \dfrac{\sqrt{39}}{3}$

b. $\sqrt{\dfrac{1}{6}} = \dfrac{\sqrt{1}}{\sqrt{6}} \cdot \dfrac{\sqrt{6}}{\sqrt{6}} = \dfrac{\sqrt{6}}{6}$

c. $\sqrt{\dfrac{7}{20}} = \dfrac{\sqrt{7}}{\sqrt{20}} \cdot \dfrac{\sqrt{5}}{\sqrt{5}} = \dfrac{\sqrt{35}}{\sqrt{100}} = \dfrac{\sqrt{35}}{10}$

d. $\dfrac{12}{\sqrt{18}} = \dfrac{12}{\sqrt{18}} \cdot \dfrac{\sqrt{2}}{\sqrt{2}}$ — Create perfect square in denominator.

$= \dfrac{12\sqrt{2}}{\sqrt{36}}$ — Multiplication Property of Radicals

$= \dfrac{12\sqrt{2}}{6}$ — Simplify.

$= 2\sqrt{2}$ — Divide out common factor.

The three criteria for a radical expression to be in simplest form are summarized as follows.

> ▶ **Simplifying Radical Expressions**
>
> A radical expression is said to be in simplest form if all three of the following are true.
>
> 1. All possible nth powered factors have been removed from each radical.
> 2. No radical contains a fraction.
> 3. No denominator of a fraction contains a radical.

The next two examples show how to rationalize denominators that contain variable factors.

Example 8 Rationalizing Denominators

a. $\sqrt{\dfrac{3}{a}} = \dfrac{\sqrt{3}}{\sqrt{a}} \cdot \dfrac{\sqrt{a}}{\sqrt{a}} = \dfrac{\sqrt{3a}}{\sqrt{a^2}} = \dfrac{\sqrt{3a}}{a}$

b. $\sqrt{\dfrac{1}{4x^3}} = \dfrac{\sqrt{1}}{\sqrt{4x^3}} \cdot \dfrac{\sqrt{x}}{\sqrt{x}} = \dfrac{\sqrt{x}}{\sqrt{4x^4}} = \dfrac{\sqrt{x}}{2x^2}$

c. $\sqrt{\dfrac{10x}{8y^5}} = \sqrt{\dfrac{5x}{4y^5}} = \dfrac{\sqrt{5x}}{\sqrt{4y^5}} \cdot \dfrac{\sqrt{y}}{\sqrt{y}} = \dfrac{\sqrt{5xy}}{\sqrt{4y^6}} = \dfrac{\sqrt{5xy}}{2y^3}$

In the next example, in order to rationalize the denominator, you need to find the rationalizing factor that will create a perfect cube radicand in the denominator.

Example 9   Rationalizing Denominators with Cube Roots

a. $\dfrac{5}{\sqrt[3]{9}} = \dfrac{5}{\sqrt[3]{9}} \cdot \dfrac{\sqrt[3]{3}}{\sqrt[3]{3}}$ The factor $\sqrt[3]{3}$ creates a perfect cube denominator.

$ \quad = \dfrac{5\sqrt[3]{3}}{\sqrt[3]{27}}$ Multiply.

$ \quad = \dfrac{5\sqrt[3]{3}}{3}$ Simplify.

b. $\sqrt[3]{\dfrac{5}{x}} = \dfrac{\sqrt[3]{5}}{\sqrt[3]{x}}$ Division Property of Radicals

$ \quad = \dfrac{\sqrt[3]{5}}{\sqrt[3]{x}} \cdot \dfrac{\sqrt[3]{x^2}}{\sqrt[3]{x^2}}$ The factor $\sqrt[3]{x^2}$ creates a perfect cube denominator.

$ \quad = \dfrac{\sqrt[3]{5} \cdot \sqrt[3]{x^2}}{\sqrt[3]{x^3}}$ Multiply.

$ \quad = \dfrac{\sqrt[3]{5x^2}}{x}$ Simplify.

c. $\sqrt[3]{\dfrac{1}{8x^4}} = \dfrac{\sqrt[3]{1}}{\sqrt[3]{8x^4}}$ Division Property of Radicals

$ \quad = \dfrac{\sqrt[3]{1}}{\sqrt[3]{8x^4}} \cdot \dfrac{\sqrt[3]{x^2}}{\sqrt[3]{x^2}}$ The factor $\sqrt[3]{x^2}$ creates a perfect cube denominator.

$ \quad = \dfrac{\sqrt[3]{x^2}}{\sqrt[3]{8x^6}}$ Multiply.

$ \quad = \dfrac{\sqrt[3]{x^2}}{2x^2}$ Simplify $\left[x^6 = (x^2)^3 \right]$.

Discussing the Concept   **Interpreting Radicals**

Individually, determine which of the following statements is true for any real number x.

a. $\sqrt{x^2} = x$ **b.** $\sqrt{x^2} = |x|$ **c.** $\sqrt[3]{x^3} = |x|$ **d.** $\sqrt[3]{x^3} = x$

Give an example to show any false statements. Exchange your conclusions and examples with another class member and resolve any differences. Together, verify your conclusions by using a graphing utility to graph

$$y_1 = \sqrt{x^2}, \quad y_2 = x, \quad y_3 = |x|, \quad \text{and} \quad y_4 = \sqrt[3]{x^3}.$$

9.2   Exercises

Integrated Review   Concepts, Skills, and Problem Solving

Keep mathematically in shape by doing these exercises *before* the problems of this section.

Properties and Definitions

1. Explain how to determine the half-plane satisfying $x - y < 2$.

2. Describe the difference between the graphs of $2x - 3y \leq 6$ and $2x - 3y < 6$.

Graphing Inequalities

In Exercises 3–8, graph the inequality.

3. $3x - 2y > 6$ **4.** $y \leq 2 - \frac{1}{2}x$

5. $y \leq 3$ **6.** $x > 5$

7. $5x + 10y < 30$ **8.** $4x + y - 3 \geq 2$

Solving Equations

In Exercises 9–12, solve the equation.

9. $0.60x = 24$ **10.** $\dfrac{5}{8} = \dfrac{x}{4}$

11. $(2x + 3)(x - 9) = 0$ **12.** $t^2 - 5t = 0$

Problem Solving

13. A car travels for t hours at an average speed of 65 miles per hour. Write the distance d as a function of time t. Graph the function and determine the time required to travel 160 miles.

14. How many liters of a 65% alcohol solution must be mixed with a 40% solution to obtain 100 liters of a 50% solution?

Developing Skills

In Exercises 1–10, write as a single radical.

1. $\sqrt{2} \cdot \sqrt{7}$ **2.** $\sqrt{5} \cdot \sqrt{19}$

3. $\sqrt{11} \cdot \sqrt{10}$ **4.** $\sqrt{35} \cdot \sqrt{3}$

5. $\sqrt{5} \cdot \sqrt{6}$ **6.** $\sqrt{7} \cdot \sqrt{10}$

7. $\sqrt{2} \cdot \sqrt{x}$ **8.** $\sqrt{3} \cdot \sqrt{y}$

9. $\sqrt{2x} \cdot \sqrt{3y}$ **10.** $\sqrt{5a} \cdot \sqrt{3b}$

In Exercises 11–14, write the expression as a product of two radicals and simplify.

11. $\sqrt{4 \cdot 15}$ **12.** $\sqrt{16 \cdot 3}$

13. $\sqrt{64 \cdot 11}$ **14.** $\sqrt{100 \cdot 3}$

In Exercises 15–34, simplify the radical. See Examples 1 and 2.

15. $\sqrt{8}$ **16.** $\sqrt{12}$

17. $\sqrt{27}$ **18.** $\sqrt{50}$

19. $\sqrt{32}$ **20.** $\sqrt{20}$

21. $\sqrt{180}$ **22.** $\sqrt{128}$

23. $\sqrt{300}$ **24.** $\sqrt{432}$

25. $\sqrt{500}$ **26.** $\sqrt{800}$

27. $\sqrt[3]{24}$ **28.** $\sqrt[3]{16}$

29. $\sqrt[3]{81}$ **30.** $\sqrt[3]{40}$

31. $\sqrt[4]{48}$ **32.** $\sqrt[4]{32}$

33. $\sqrt[4]{162}$ **34.** $\sqrt[4]{512}$

In Exercises 35–58, simplify the radical. Use absolute value signs if appropriate. See Examples 3–5.

35. $\sqrt{4x^2}$ **36.** $\sqrt{9x^4}$

37. $\sqrt{64x^3}$ **38.** $\sqrt{49z^5}$

39. $\sqrt{x^6}$ **40.** $\sqrt{y^8}$

41. $\sqrt{u^7}$ **42.** $\sqrt{v^5}$

43. $\sqrt{28a^4}$ **44.** $\sqrt{45b^8}$

45. $\sqrt{x^2y^3}$ **46.** $\sqrt{a^5b^4}$

47. $\sqrt{u^4v^8}$ **48.** $\sqrt{x^2y^6}$

49. $\sqrt{200x^2y^9}$ **50.** $\sqrt{128u^4v^7}$

51. $\sqrt[3]{27a^4}$ **52.** $\sqrt[3]{8x^5}$

53. $\sqrt[3]{2y^4}$ **54.** $\sqrt[3]{6r^5}$

55. $\sqrt[4]{t^6}$ **56.** $\sqrt[4]{x^5}$

57. $\sqrt[4]{16y^5}$ **58.** $\sqrt[4]{80t^7}$

In Exercises 59–74, write as a single radical. Simplify the result.

59. $\dfrac{\sqrt{6}}{\sqrt{3}}$

60. $\dfrac{\sqrt{21}}{\sqrt{7}}$

61. $\dfrac{\sqrt{54}}{\sqrt{6}}$

62. $\dfrac{\sqrt{48}}{\sqrt{8}}$

63. $\dfrac{\sqrt{39}}{\sqrt{13}}$

64. $\dfrac{\sqrt{84}}{\sqrt{12}}$

65. $\dfrac{\sqrt{24}}{\sqrt{2}}$

66. $\dfrac{\sqrt{60}}{\sqrt{3}}$

67. $\dfrac{\sqrt{156}}{\sqrt{3}}$

68. $\dfrac{\sqrt{160}}{\sqrt{5}}$

69. $\dfrac{\sqrt{15x}}{\sqrt{5x}}$

70. $\dfrac{\sqrt{10u}}{\sqrt{2u}}$

71. $\dfrac{\sqrt{18a^3}}{\sqrt{a}}$

72. $\dfrac{\sqrt{16y^4}}{\sqrt{y^2}}$

73. $\dfrac{\sqrt{54b^4}}{\sqrt{2b^2}}$

74. $\dfrac{\sqrt{45x^7}}{\sqrt{5x}}$

In Exercises 75–90, simplify the expression. See Example 6.

75. $\dfrac{\sqrt{35}}{\sqrt{16}}$

76. $\dfrac{\sqrt{11}}{\sqrt{25}}$

77. $\dfrac{\sqrt{48}}{\sqrt{64}}$

78. $\dfrac{\sqrt{72}}{\sqrt{9}}$

79. $\sqrt{\dfrac{32}{4}}$

80. $\sqrt{\dfrac{24}{36}}$

81. $\sqrt{\dfrac{12x^2}{25}}$

82. $\dfrac{\sqrt{5u^2}}{\sqrt{4u^4}}$

83. $\sqrt{\dfrac{3x^2}{27}}$

84. $\sqrt{\dfrac{5x^4}{20}}$

85. $\sqrt{\dfrac{56y^3}{14}}$

86. $\sqrt{\dfrac{50x^5}{2}}$

87. $\sqrt{\dfrac{x^6}{16y^2}}$

88. $\sqrt{\dfrac{u^4}{36v^4}}$

89. $\sqrt{\dfrac{9u^5}{48u^7}}$

90. $\sqrt{\dfrac{6x}{27x^5}}$

In Exercises 91–114, rationalize the denominator and simplify. (Assume that the variables are positive.) See Examples 7 and 8.

91. $\sqrt{\dfrac{1}{3}}$

92. $\sqrt{\dfrac{1}{5}}$

93. $\dfrac{1}{\sqrt{7}}$

94. $\dfrac{1}{\sqrt{10}}$

95. $\dfrac{5}{\sqrt{10}}$

96. $\dfrac{7}{\sqrt{14}}$

97. $\dfrac{\sqrt{2}}{\sqrt{3}}$

98. $\dfrac{\sqrt{3}}{\sqrt{8}}$

99. $\sqrt{\dfrac{11}{8}}$

100. $\sqrt{\dfrac{7}{18}}$

101. $\dfrac{\sqrt{6}}{\sqrt{12}}$

102. $\dfrac{\sqrt{10}}{\sqrt{32}}$

103. $\sqrt{\dfrac{100}{11}}$

104. $\sqrt{\dfrac{169}{2}}$

105. $\dfrac{1}{\sqrt{y}}$

106. $\dfrac{1}{\sqrt{z}}$

107. $\sqrt{\dfrac{5}{x}}$

108. $\sqrt{\dfrac{3}{a}}$

109. $\sqrt{\dfrac{3}{16x^5}}$

110. $\sqrt{\dfrac{6}{25u^3}}$

111. $\dfrac{\sqrt{2t}}{\sqrt{8r}}$

112. $\dfrac{\sqrt{2x}}{\sqrt{50y}}$

113. $\dfrac{\sqrt{12x^3}}{\sqrt{3y}}$

114. $\dfrac{\sqrt{20x^2}}{\sqrt{5y^2}}$

In Exercises 115–122, rationalize the denominator and simplify. Assume all variables are positive. See Example 9.

115. $\dfrac{4}{\sqrt[3]{9}}$

116. $\dfrac{9}{\sqrt[3]{4}}$

117. $\dfrac{7}{\sqrt[3]{3}}$

118. $\dfrac{5}{\sqrt[3]{2}}$

119. $\sqrt[3]{\dfrac{1}{x^2}}$

120. $\sqrt[3]{\dfrac{3}{x}}$

121. $\sqrt[3]{\dfrac{1}{8y^2}}$

122. $\sqrt[3]{\dfrac{1}{27a}}$

Graphical Reasoning   In Exercises 123–126, use a graphing utility to graph the equations on the same screen. What inference can you make from the graphs?

123. $y_1 = \sqrt{2} \cdot \sqrt{x}$
$y_2 = \sqrt{2x}$

124. $y_1 = \dfrac{\sqrt{x}}{\sqrt{4}}$
$y_2 = \tfrac{1}{2}\sqrt{x}$

125. $y_1 = \dfrac{\sqrt{x}}{\sqrt{8}}$
$y_2 = \tfrac{1}{4}\sqrt{2x}$

126. $y_1 = \dfrac{\sqrt{3x}}{\sqrt{27}}$
$y_2 = \tfrac{1}{3}\sqrt{x}$

In Exercises 127–130, place the correct inequality symbol between the real numbers. Do not use a calculator.

127. $4\sqrt{2}$ ___ 5

128. $\sqrt{300}$ ___ 12

129. $5\sqrt{6}$ ___ $6\sqrt{5}$

130. 4 ___ $\sqrt{5} + \sqrt{10}$

Solving Problems

Geometry In Exercises 131–134, find the area of the figure. Round the result to two decimal places.

131.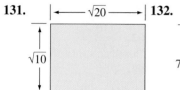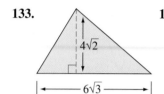

132.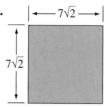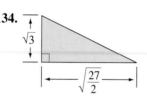

133.

134.

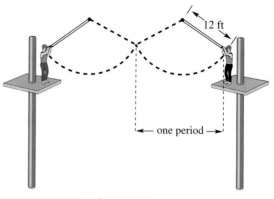

Figure for 135

136. Find the period of the pendulum clock in the figure.

Period of a Pendulum In Exercises 135 and 136, use the formula

$$t = 2\pi\sqrt{\frac{L}{32}}$$

which gives the period t (in seconds) of a simple pendulum whose length is L (in feet).

135. How long will it take the performer in the figure to swing through one period of the 12-foot trapeze?

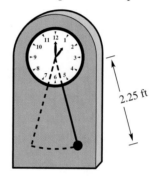

Explaining Concepts

137. State the Multiplication Property of Radicals.

138. State the Division Property of Radicals.

139. In your own words, describe the three conditions that must be true for a radical expression to be in simplest form.

140. Explain how the Multiplication Property of Radicals can be used to simplify $\sqrt{28}$.

141. Explain how to simplify $1/\sqrt{3}$.

142. *True or False?* $\sqrt{3x^2} \overset{?}{=} x\sqrt{3}$

143. *True or False?* $\dfrac{\sqrt{50}}{\sqrt{2}} \overset{?}{=} 25$

144. *True or False?* $\sqrt{x^2 + 16} \overset{?}{=} x + 4$

Mid-Chapter Quiz

Take this quiz as you would take a quiz in class. After you are done, check your work against the answers given in the back of the book.

In Exercises 1–3, determine if the number is rational or irrational.

1. $\sqrt{5}$ **2.** $\sqrt{\frac{3}{4}}$ **3.** $\sqrt{900}$

In Exercises 4–8, evaluate the expression, if possible.

4. $\sqrt{121}$ **5.** $-\sqrt{0.25}$ **6.** $\sqrt[3]{-8}$

7. $\sqrt[4]{-16}$ **8.** $\sqrt{-\frac{1}{16}}$

In Exercises 9 and 10, use a calculator to approximate the expression. Round the result to three decimal places.

9. $\sqrt{15.8}$ **10.** $\dfrac{-5 + 3\sqrt{20}}{10}$

In Exercises 11 and 12, write as a single radical.

11. $\sqrt{15} \cdot \sqrt{7}$ **12.** $\dfrac{\sqrt{42}}{\sqrt{6}}$

In Exercises 13–20, simplify the expression. Use absolute value signs if appropriate.

13. $\sqrt{45}$ **14.** $\dfrac{\sqrt{600}}{\sqrt{12}}$ **15.** $\sqrt{72x^2}$ **16.** $\sqrt[3]{-54}$

17. $\sqrt[3]{64x^3}$ **18.** $\sqrt[4]{x^9}$ **19.** $\sqrt{\dfrac{90b^4}{2b^2}}$ **20.** $\sqrt{18u^5v^2}$

In Exercises 21–26, rationalize the denominator and simplify. (Assume that the variables are positive.)

21. $\sqrt{\dfrac{3}{2}}$ **22.** $\dfrac{2}{\sqrt{12}}$ **23.** $\sqrt[3]{\dfrac{1}{9}}$

24. $\dfrac{4a}{\sqrt{2a}}$ **25.** $\sqrt{\dfrac{5a^3}{4a}}$ **26.** $\dfrac{\sqrt[3]{x}}{\sqrt[3]{27x^4}}$

27. The length of a diagonal of a rectangular solid of length l, width w, and height h is

$$\sqrt{l^2 + w^2 + h^2}.$$

Approximate to two decimal places the length of the diagonal of the solid shown in the figure.

28. A square room has 361 square feet of floor space. An area carpet covers all of the floor space except for a 2-foot border all around the room (see figure). How many square feet are in the carpet? How many square yards are in the carpet?

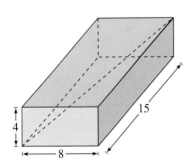

Figure for 27

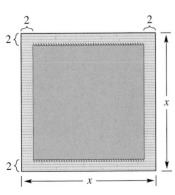

Figure for 28

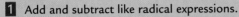

9.3   Operations with Radical Expressions

Objectives

1 Add and subtract like radical expressions.

2 Multiply radical expressions using the Distributive Property, the FOIL Method, or a special product pattern.

3 Determine the conjugate of an expression and find the product of the expression and its conjugate.

4 Simplify the quotient of a radical expression by rationalizing the denominator.

---

1 Add and subtract like radical expressions.

Bhaskara
(1114–1185)

More than 3000 years ago, Hindu mathematicians in India were aware of irrational numbers. Approximately 900 years ago, Bhaskara, a Hindu mathematician, developed a formula for adding two irrational numbers.

$$\sqrt{a} + \sqrt{b} = \sqrt{(a+b) + 2\sqrt{ab}}$$

For example,

$$\sqrt{5} + \sqrt{20} =$$

$$\sqrt{(5+20) + 2\sqrt{5 \cdot 20}}$$

$$= \sqrt{45} = 3\sqrt{5}.$$

Study Tip

It is important to realize that the expression $\sqrt{a} + \sqrt{b}$ is not equal to $\sqrt{a+b}$. For instance, in Example 1(b), you may have been tempted to add $\sqrt{6} + \sqrt{3}$ and get $\sqrt{9}$ or 3. But remember, you cannot add unlike radicals. So, $\sqrt{6} + \sqrt{3}$ cannot be simplified further.

Adding and Subtracting Radical Expressions

Two radical expressions are called **like radicals** if they have the same index and radicand. For instance, the expressions $3\sqrt{2}$ and $5\sqrt{2}$ are like radicals, whereas the expressions $2\sqrt{3}$ and $2\sqrt{5}$ are not. You can combine like radicals by the Distributive Property. For instance, you can simplify the radical expression $2\sqrt{5} + 7\sqrt{5}$ as follows.

$$2\sqrt{5} + 7\sqrt{5} = (2+7)\sqrt{5} \qquad \text{Distributive Property}$$

$$= 9\sqrt{5} \qquad \text{Simplify.}$$

Note the similarity between this and the procedure used to combine like polynomial terms such as $2x + 7x = (2+7)x = 9x$.

Example 1   Combining Radical Expressions

Simplify the following expressions by combining like terms.

a. $\sqrt{7} + 5\sqrt{7} - 2\sqrt{7}$ **b.** $6\sqrt{6} - \sqrt{3} - 5\sqrt{6} + 2\sqrt{3}$

c. $3\sqrt[4]{5} + 7\sqrt[4]{5}$ **d.** $\sqrt[5]{2} + 6\sqrt[5]{2} - 2\sqrt[5]{2}$

Solution

a. $\sqrt{7} + 5\sqrt{7} - 2\sqrt{7} = (1 + 5 - 2)\sqrt{7}$ Distributive Property

$$= 4\sqrt{7} \qquad \text{Simplify.}$$

b. $6\sqrt{6} - \sqrt{3} - 5\sqrt{6} + 2\sqrt{3}$

$$= 6\sqrt{6} - 5\sqrt{6} - \sqrt{3} + 2\sqrt{3} \qquad \text{Group like terms.}$$

$$= (6 - 5)\sqrt{6} + (-1 + 2)\sqrt{3} \qquad \text{Distributive Property}$$

$$= \sqrt{6} + \sqrt{3} \qquad \text{Simplify.}$$

c. $3\sqrt[4]{5} + 7\sqrt[4]{5} = (3 + 7)\sqrt[4]{5}$ Distributive Property

$$= 10\sqrt[4]{5} \qquad \text{Simplify.}$$

d. $\sqrt[5]{2} + 6\sqrt[5]{2} - 2\sqrt[5]{2} = (1 + 6 - 2)\sqrt[5]{2}$ Distributive Property

$$= 5\sqrt[5]{2} \qquad \text{Simplify.}$$

| Example 2 | Combining Radicals with Variable Radicands

Simplify the following expressions.

a. $3 + 3\sqrt{x} - \sqrt{x} + 2$ **b.** $2\sqrt[3]{2} + 2\sqrt[3]{y^2} - 4\sqrt[3]{2} + 5\sqrt[3]{y^2}$

Solution

a. $3 + 3\sqrt{x} - \sqrt{x} + 2$

$\qquad = (3 + 2) + \left(3\sqrt{x} - \sqrt{x}\right)$ Group like terms.

$\qquad = (3 + 2) + (3 - 1)\sqrt{x}$ Distributive Property

$\qquad = 5 + 2\sqrt{x}$ Simplify.

b. $2\sqrt[3]{2} + 2\sqrt[3]{y^2} - 4\sqrt[3]{2} + 5\sqrt[3]{y^2}$

$\qquad = \left(2\sqrt[3]{2} - 4\sqrt[3]{2}\right) + \left(2\sqrt[3]{y^2} + 5\sqrt[3]{y^2}\right)$ Group like terms.

$\qquad = (2 - 4)\sqrt[3]{2} + (2 + 5)\sqrt[3]{y^2}$ Distributive Property

$\qquad = -2\sqrt[3]{2} + 7\sqrt[3]{y^2}$ Simplify.

Sometimes you may have to simplify individual radicals before combining like radicals. This is demonstrated in Example 3.

Study Tip

Remember that the square root of a negative number is not a real number. Because of this, you can assume that when someone writes $\sqrt{x^3}$, they are implying that the domain of the expression is the set of nonnegative real numbers. This assumption allows you to write $\sqrt{x^3} = x\sqrt{x}$.

| Example 3 | Simplifying Radical Expressions

a. $2\sqrt{72} - 2\sqrt{32} = 2\sqrt{36 \cdot 2} - 2\sqrt{16 \cdot 2}$ Factor radicands.

$\qquad = 12\sqrt{2} - 8\sqrt{2}$ Simplify radicals.

$\qquad = 4\sqrt{2}$ Combine like radicals.

b. $3\sqrt{x} + \sqrt{4x} = 3\sqrt{x} + \sqrt{4 \cdot x}$ Factor radicand.

$\qquad = 3\sqrt{x} + 2\sqrt{x}$ Simplify radical.

$\qquad = 5\sqrt{x}$ Combine like radicals.

c. $\sqrt{45x} + 2\sqrt{20x} = \sqrt{9 \cdot 5x} + 2\sqrt{4 \cdot 5x}$ Factor radicands.

$\qquad = 3\sqrt{5x} + 4\sqrt{5x}$ Simplify radicals.

$\qquad = 7\sqrt{5x}$ Combine like radicals.

d. $5\sqrt{2x^3} - x\sqrt{8x} = 5\sqrt{2 \cdot x^2 \cdot x} - x\sqrt{4 \cdot 2 \cdot x}$ Factor radicands.

$\qquad = 5x\sqrt{2x} - 2x\sqrt{2x}$ Simplify radicals.

$\qquad = (5x - 2x)\sqrt{2x}$ Distributive Property

$\qquad = 3x\sqrt{2x}$ Combine like radicals.

e. $\sqrt{50y^5} + \sqrt{32y^5} = \sqrt{25y^4 \cdot 2y} + \sqrt{16y^4 \cdot 2y}$ Factor radicands.

$\qquad = 5y^2\sqrt{2y} + 4y^2\sqrt{2y}$ Simplify radicals.

$\qquad = 9y^2\sqrt{2y}$ Combine like radicals.

2 Multiply radical expressions using the Distributive Property, the FOIL Method, or a special product pattern.

Multiplying Radical Expressions

You can multiply radicals by using the Distributive Property, the FOIL Method, or a special product pattern. These procedures also use the Multiplication Property of Radicals.

Example 4 Multiplying Radicals

a. $\sqrt{2}\left(1 + \sqrt{3}\right) = \sqrt{2} + \sqrt{2}\sqrt{3}$ Distributive Property

$= \sqrt{2} + \sqrt{6}$ Multiplication Property of Radicals

b. $\sqrt{5}\left(\sqrt{15} - \sqrt{5}\right) = \sqrt{5}\sqrt{15} - \sqrt{5}\sqrt{5}$ Distributive Property

$= \sqrt{75} - \sqrt{25}$ Multiplication Property of Radicals

$= \sqrt{25 \cdot 3} - 5$ Factor radicand.

$= 5\sqrt{3} - 5$ Simplify.

c. $\sqrt[3]{25}\left(\sqrt[3]{5} + 4\right) = \sqrt[3]{25}\,\sqrt[3]{5} + \sqrt[3]{25} \cdot 4$ Distributive Property

$= \sqrt[3]{125} + 4\sqrt[3]{25}$ Multiplication Property of Radicals

$= 5 + 4\sqrt[3]{25}$ Simplify.

d. $\sqrt[3]{4}\left(3 - \sqrt[3]{2}\right) = \sqrt[3]{4} \cdot 3 - \sqrt[3]{4}\,\sqrt[3]{2}$ Distributive Property

$= 3\sqrt[3]{4} - \sqrt[3]{8}$ Multiplication Property of Radicals

$= 3\sqrt[3]{4} - 2$ Simplify.

Example 5 Multiplying Radicals

Point out the analogies with the multiplication of polynomials.

a. $\left(\sqrt{7} - 1\right)\left(\sqrt{7} + 3\right) = \overset{F}{\overbrace{\sqrt{7 \cdot 7}}} + \overset{O}{\overbrace{3\sqrt{7}}} - \overset{I}{\overbrace{\sqrt{7}}} - \overset{L}{3}$ FOIL Method

$= 7 + (3 - 1)\sqrt{7} - 3$ Combine like radicals.

$= 4 + 2\sqrt{7}$ Combine like terms.

b. $\left(2 - \sqrt{6}\right)\left(2 + \sqrt{6}\right) = 2^2 - \left(\sqrt{6}\right)^2$ Special product pattern

$= 4 - 6$ Simplify.

$= -2$ Simplify.

c. $\left(\sqrt[3]{4} + 5\right)\left(\sqrt[3]{2} + 6\right) = \overset{F}{\overbrace{\sqrt[3]{4 \cdot 2}}} + \overset{O}{\overbrace{6\sqrt[3]{4}}} + \overset{I}{\overbrace{5\sqrt[3]{2}}} + \overset{L}{30}$ FOIL Method

$= 2 + 6\sqrt[3]{4} + 5\sqrt[3]{2} + 30$ Simplify radical.

$= (2 + 30) + 6\sqrt[3]{4} + 5\sqrt[3]{2}$ Group like terms.

$= 32 + 6\sqrt[3]{4} + 5\sqrt[3]{2}$ Combine like terms.

3 Determine the conjugate of an expression and find the product of the expression and its conjugate.

Conjugates

Recall from Section 5.2 the special product pattern, *the product of the sum and the difference of two terms.*

$$(a + b)(a - b) = a^2 - ab + ab - b^2 \qquad \text{Sum and difference of two terms}$$

$$= a^2 - b^2 \qquad \text{Difference of two squares}$$

The resulting product is the difference of two squares. For example,

$$(x + 3)(x - 3) = x^2 - 3x + 3x - (3)^2 \qquad \text{Sum and difference of two terms}$$

$$= x^2 - 9. \qquad \text{Product has no middle term.}$$

In Example 5(b), the expressions $2 - \sqrt{6}$ and $2 + \sqrt{6}$ fit the special product pattern and the result was the rational number -2. The expressions $2 - \sqrt{6}$ and $2 + \sqrt{6}$ are called **conjugates** of each other, and their product is a rational number.

Example 6   Multiplying Conjugates

Determine the conjugate of the expression. Then find the product of the expression and its conjugate.

a. $3 - \sqrt{6}$ **b.** $\sqrt{3} + \sqrt{7}$ **c.** $\sqrt{x} + 3$ **d.** $\sqrt{t} - \sqrt{8}$

Solution

a. The conjugate of $3 - \sqrt{6}$ is $3 + \sqrt{6}$. The product of $3 - \sqrt{6}$ and $3 + \sqrt{6}$ is

$$\left(3 - \sqrt{6}\right)\left(3 + \sqrt{6}\right) = (3)^2 - \left(\sqrt{6}\right)^2 \qquad \text{Difference of two squares}$$

$$= 9 - 6 \qquad \text{Simplify.}$$

$$= 3. \qquad \text{The product is a rational number.}$$

b. The conjugate of $\sqrt{3} + \sqrt{7}$ is $\sqrt{3} - \sqrt{7}$. The product of $\sqrt{3} + \sqrt{7}$ and $\sqrt{3} - \sqrt{7}$ is

$$\left(\sqrt{3} + \sqrt{7}\right)\left(\sqrt{3} - \sqrt{7}\right) = \left(\sqrt{3}\right)^2 - \left(\sqrt{7}\right)^2 \qquad \text{Difference of two squares}$$

$$= 3 - 7 \qquad \text{Simplify.}$$

$$= -4. \qquad \text{The product is a rational number.}$$

c. The conjugate of $\sqrt{x} + 3$ is $\sqrt{x} - 3$. The product of $\sqrt{x} + 3$ and $\sqrt{x} - 3$ is

$$\left(\sqrt{x} + 3\right)\left(\sqrt{x} - 3\right) = \left(\sqrt{x}\right)^2 - (3)^2 \qquad \text{Difference of two squares}$$

$$= x - 9. \qquad \text{Simplify.}$$

d. The conjugate of $\sqrt{t} - \sqrt{8}$ is $\sqrt{t} + \sqrt{8}$. The product of $\sqrt{t} - \sqrt{8}$ and $\sqrt{t} + \sqrt{8}$ is

$$\left(\sqrt{t} - \sqrt{8}\right)\left(\sqrt{t} + \sqrt{8}\right) = \left(\sqrt{t}\right)^2 - \left(\sqrt{8}\right)^2 \qquad \text{Difference of two squares}$$

$$= t - 8. \qquad \text{Simplify.}$$

4 Simplify the quotient of a radical expression by rationalizing the denominator.

Dividing Radical Expressions

To simplify a *quotient* involving radicals, you can rationalize the denominator by multiplying by its conjugate. Note how this is done in Examples 7, 8, and 9.

Example 7 Simplifying Quotients Involving Radicals

Simplify the quotient $\dfrac{2}{3 - \sqrt{5}}$.

Solution

$$\frac{2}{3 - \sqrt{5}} = \frac{2}{3 - \sqrt{5}} \cdot \frac{3 + \sqrt{5}}{3 + \sqrt{5}} \qquad \text{Multiply by conjugate.}$$

$$= \frac{2(3 + \sqrt{5})}{(3)^2 - (\sqrt{5})^2} \qquad \text{Special product}$$

$$= \frac{2(3 + \sqrt{5})}{4} \qquad \text{Simplify.}$$

$$= \frac{3 + \sqrt{5}}{2} \qquad \text{Cancel common factors.}$$

Example 8 Simplifying Quotients Involving Radicals

Simplify the quotients.

a. $\dfrac{5\sqrt{2}}{\sqrt{3} + \sqrt{2}}$ **b.** $\dfrac{2 - \sqrt{3}}{\sqrt{6} + \sqrt{2}}$

Solution

Remind students that they can verify these results on their calculators.

a. $\dfrac{5\sqrt{2}}{\sqrt{3} + \sqrt{2}} = \dfrac{5\sqrt{2}}{\sqrt{3} + \sqrt{2}} \cdot \dfrac{\sqrt{3} - \sqrt{2}}{\sqrt{3} - \sqrt{2}}$ $\qquad$ Multiply by conjugate.

$\qquad\qquad = \dfrac{5\sqrt{6} - 5\sqrt{4}}{(\sqrt{3})^2 - (\sqrt{2})^2}$ $\qquad$ Multiply fractions.

$\qquad\qquad = \dfrac{5\sqrt{6} - 10}{3 - 2}$ $\qquad$ Simplify.

$\qquad\qquad = 5\sqrt{6} - 10$ $\qquad$ Simplify.

b. $\dfrac{2 - \sqrt{3}}{\sqrt{6} + \sqrt{2}} = \dfrac{2 - \sqrt{3}}{\sqrt{6} + \sqrt{2}} \cdot \dfrac{\sqrt{6} - \sqrt{2}}{\sqrt{6} - \sqrt{2}}$ $\qquad$ Multiply by conjugate.

$\qquad\qquad = \dfrac{2\sqrt{6} - 2\sqrt{2} - \sqrt{18} + \sqrt{6}}{(\sqrt{6})^2 - (\sqrt{2})^2}$ $\qquad$ Multiply fractions.

$\qquad\qquad = \dfrac{3\sqrt{6} - 2\sqrt{2} - 3\sqrt{2}}{6 - 2}$ $\qquad$ Combine like radicals.

$\qquad\qquad = \dfrac{3\sqrt{6} - 5\sqrt{2}}{4}$ $\qquad$ Simplify.

Example 9   Dividing Radical Expressions

Divide 6 by $\sqrt{x} - 2$.

Solution

To divide this radical expression, multiply the numerator and the denominator by the conjugate of the denominator.

$$\frac{6}{\sqrt{x} - 2} = \frac{6}{\sqrt{x} - 2} \cdot \frac{\sqrt{x} + 2}{\sqrt{x} + 2}$$ Multiply by conjugate.

$$= \frac{6\left(\sqrt{x} + 2\right)}{\left(\sqrt{x}\right)^2 - (2)^2}$$ Multiply fractions.

$$= \frac{6\sqrt{x} + 12}{x - 4}$$ Simplify.

Example 10   Simplifying a Mixed Radical Expression

Write $3 - \dfrac{2}{\sqrt{5}}$ as a single fraction in simplest form.

Solution

First, write the expression as a single fraction.

$$3 - \frac{2}{\sqrt{5}} = \frac{3}{1} \cdot \frac{\sqrt{5}}{\sqrt{5}} - \frac{2}{\sqrt{5}}$$ Multiply by LCD.

$$= \frac{3\sqrt{5} - 2}{\sqrt{5}}$$ Subtract fractions.

Next, rationalize the denominator.

$$\frac{3\sqrt{5} - 2}{\sqrt{5}} \cdot \frac{\sqrt{5}}{\sqrt{5}} = \frac{3\sqrt{25} - 2\sqrt{5}}{\sqrt{25}}$$ Rationalize denominator and multiply fractions.

$$= \frac{15 - 2\sqrt{5}}{5}$$ Simplify.

Discussing the Concept   Closure Property

Some subsets of real numbers are **closed** with respect to certain operations. For instance, the set of rational numbers is closed with respect to multiplication because the product of any two rational numbers must be another rational number. Show that the set of irrational numbers is *not* closed with respect to multiplication by finding two irrational numbers whose product is rational. Can you find other examples of subsets of real numbers that are closed (or not closed) with respect to multiplication?

9.3   Exercises

Integrated Review   *Concepts, Skills, and Problem Solving*

Keep mathematically in shape by doing these exercises *before* the problems of this section.

Properties and Definitions

1. Is it possible for the system

$$3x + 5y = 2$$
$$x - y = 6$$

to have exactly two solutions? Explain.

2. Explain why the following system has no solution.

$$4x - 2y = 5$$
$$-2x + y = 1$$

Solving Equations and Systems of Equations

In Exercises 3–6, solve the equation.

3. $4[2x - 3(x + 2)] = 5(x - 6)$

4. $2 - 5(x - 1) = 2[x + 10(x - 1)]$

5. $\dfrac{x}{6} + \dfrac{x}{3} = 1$

6. $\dfrac{x + 1}{2} + \dfrac{x}{4} = 1$

In Exercises 7–10, solve the system.

7. $x - 3y = 2$
$x + y = 6$

8. $5x + y = 20$
$2x - y = 1$

9. $-x + 7y = -1$
$2x - 10y = 6$

10. $9x - 7y = 39$
$4x + 3y = -1$

Problem Solving

11. One combine harvests a field of wheat in r hours and a second combine requires $\frac{5}{4}r$ hours. Find the individual times to harvest the field if it takes 5 hours using both machines.

12. A plane has a speed of 300 miles per hour in still air. Find the speed of the wind if the plane traveled a distance of 700 miles with a tail wind in the same time it took to travel 500 miles into a head wind.

Developing Skills

In Exercises 1–48, simplify the expression. See Examples 1–3.

1. $3\sqrt{5} - \sqrt{5}$

2. $5\sqrt{6} - 10\sqrt{6}$

3. $10\sqrt{11} + 8\sqrt{11}$

4. $\sqrt{15} + 7\sqrt{15}$

5. $\frac{2}{5}\sqrt{3} - \frac{6}{5}\sqrt{3}$

6. $\frac{2}{3}\sqrt{6} + \frac{4}{3}\sqrt{6}$

7. $\sqrt{3} - 5\sqrt{7} - 12\sqrt{3}$

8. $9\sqrt{17} + 7\sqrt{2} - 11\sqrt{17} + \sqrt{2}$

9. $2\sqrt{2} - 3\sqrt{5} + 8\sqrt{2}$ **10.** $\sqrt{6} + 5\sqrt{3} - 7\sqrt{3}$

11. $4\sqrt[3]{5} + 2\sqrt[3]{5}$ **12.** $7\sqrt[5]{4} + 3\sqrt[5]{4}$

13. $9\sqrt[4]{8} - 4\sqrt[4]{8}$ **14.** $6\sqrt[3]{3} - 5\sqrt[3]{3}$

15. $9\sqrt[3]{7} + 3\sqrt[3]{7} - 4\sqrt[3]{7}$ **16.** $8\sqrt[4]{6} - 3\sqrt[4]{6} + 5\sqrt[4]{6}$

17. $4\sqrt[3]{5} + 8\sqrt[3]{5} + \sqrt[3]{5}$ **18.** $5\sqrt[5]{2} + 3\sqrt[5]{2} - \sqrt[5]{2}$

19. $5\sqrt{x} - 3\sqrt{x}$ **20.** $2\sqrt{y} + 6\sqrt{y}$

21. $4\sqrt{u} - 3 + \sqrt{u} + 8$ **22.** $12\sqrt{v} + 6 - 5\sqrt{v} - 9$

23. $3 + \sqrt[3]{x} + 5 + 4\sqrt[3]{x}$ **24.** $7\sqrt[4]{a} + 6 + 3\sqrt[4]{a} + 2$

25. $9 + 3\sqrt[5]{y} - \sqrt[5]{y} - 6$

26. $8\sqrt[3]{x^2} + 3 - 3\sqrt[3]{x^2} + 2$

27. $8\sqrt[5]{a^3} - 3\sqrt[5]{a^3} + 5 + 6\sqrt[5]{a^3}$

28. $4\sqrt[3]{b^2} - 8 + 4\sqrt[3]{b^2} - \sqrt[3]{b^2}$

29. $12\sqrt{8} - 3\sqrt{8}$ **30.** $4\sqrt{32} + 2\sqrt{32}$

31. $2\sqrt{50} + 12\sqrt{8}$ **32.** $4\sqrt{27} - \sqrt{75}$

33. $8\sqrt{75} + \sqrt{50} + \sqrt{2}$ **34.** $3\sqrt{18} - \sqrt{12} - \sqrt{8}$

35. $\sqrt{9x} + \sqrt{36x}$ **36.** $\sqrt{64t} - \sqrt{16t}$

37. $\sqrt{16b} + \sqrt{b}$ **38.** $\sqrt{x} - \sqrt{25x}$

39. $\sqrt{45z} - \sqrt{125z}$ **40.** $\sqrt{18u} + 3\sqrt{8u}$

41. $3\sqrt{3y} - \sqrt{27y} + \sqrt{y}$ **42.** $\sqrt{49v} + 2\sqrt{7v} + \sqrt{v}$

43. $\sqrt{32x^3} - 2\sqrt{8x^3}$ **44.** $3\sqrt{45u^5} + 5\sqrt{48u^5}$

45. $\sqrt{x^3y} + 4\sqrt{xy}$ **46.** $3t\sqrt{st^3} - s\sqrt{s^3t}$

47. $\sqrt{\dfrac{a}{4}} - \sqrt{\dfrac{a}{9}}$ **48.** $\sqrt{\dfrac{v}{36}} - \sqrt{\dfrac{v}{9}}$

In Exercises 49–90, multiply and simplify. See Examples 4 and 5.

49. $\sqrt{2} \cdot \sqrt{8}$ **50.** $\sqrt{3} \cdot \sqrt{12}$

51. $\sqrt{3} \cdot \sqrt{27}$ **52.** $\sqrt{5} \cdot \sqrt{15}$

53. $\sqrt{10} \cdot \sqrt{6}$ **54.** $\sqrt{7} \cdot \sqrt{21}$

55. $\sqrt[3]{4} \cdot \sqrt[3]{2}$ **56.** $\sqrt[3]{9} \cdot \sqrt[3]{3}$

57. $\sqrt[4]{2} \cdot \sqrt[4]{8}$ **58.** $\sqrt[4]{9} \cdot \sqrt[4]{9}$

59. $\sqrt{7}(1 - \sqrt{2})$ **60.** $\sqrt{3}(\sqrt{5} - 3)$

61. $\sqrt{6}(\sqrt{12} + 8)$ **62.** $\sqrt{2}(\sqrt{14} + 3)$

63. $\sqrt[3]{2}(\sqrt[3]{4} + 5)$ **64.** $\sqrt[3]{4}(\sqrt[3]{2} - 3)$

65. $\sqrt[4]{2}(6 + \sqrt[4]{8})$ **66.** $\sqrt[4]{4}(9 - \sqrt[4]{4})$

67. $(\sqrt{2} - 1)(\sqrt{2} + 3)$

68. $(\sqrt{5} + \sqrt{2})(\sqrt{5} - \sqrt{3})$

69. $(\sqrt{2} + 1)(\sqrt{3} - 5)$

70. $(\sqrt{6} + 5)(\sqrt{6} + 3)$

71. $(1 + \sqrt{11})(1 - \sqrt{11})$

72. $(\sqrt{7} + 3)(\sqrt{7} - 3)$

73. $(\sqrt{10} + \sqrt{5})(\sqrt{10} - \sqrt{5})$

74. $(\sqrt{2} + \sqrt{3})(\sqrt{2} - \sqrt{3})$

75. $(\sqrt[3]{4} + 5)(\sqrt[3]{3} + 2)$

76. $(\sqrt[4]{6} - 3)(\sqrt[4]{2} + 7)$

77. $(\sqrt[3]{2} - 1)^2$

78. $(\sqrt[4]{6} + 3)^2$

79. $(\sqrt{13} + 2)^2$

80. $(\sqrt{7} + 3)^2$

81. $(3 - \sqrt{8})^2$

82. $(4 - \sqrt{12})^2$

83. $\sqrt{x}(\sqrt{x} + 5)$

84. $\sqrt{x}(3 - \sqrt{x})$

85. $(\sqrt{x} + 1)(\sqrt{x} - 3)$

86. $(\sqrt{u} - 3)(\sqrt{u} - 4)$

87. $(3 + \sqrt{x})^2$

88. $(5 - \sqrt{v})^2$

89. $(2\sqrt{x} - 3)(2\sqrt{x} + 3)$

90. $(4 - 3\sqrt{t})(4 + 3\sqrt{t})$

In Exercises 91–98, determine the conjugate. Then find the product of the expression and its conjugate. See Example 6.

91. $4 + \sqrt{3}$ **92.** $\sqrt{7} - 3$

93. $\sqrt{15} - \sqrt{7}$ **94.** $\sqrt{10} + \sqrt{2}$

95. $\sqrt{x} - 4$ **96.** $\sqrt{t} + 5$

97. $\sqrt{u} - \sqrt{2}$ **98.** $\sqrt{a} + \sqrt{3}$

In Exercises 99–112, rationalize the denominator and simplify. See Examples 7–9.

99. $\dfrac{5}{\sqrt{14} - 2}$ **100.** $\dfrac{5}{\sqrt{10} - 5}$

101. $\dfrac{4}{\sqrt{7} - \sqrt{3}}$ **102.** $\dfrac{3}{\sqrt{5} + \sqrt{6}}$

103. $\dfrac{3\sqrt{6}}{\sqrt{5} + \sqrt{6}}$ **104.** $\dfrac{2\sqrt{3}}{\sqrt{3} - \sqrt{7}}$

105. $\dfrac{\sqrt{5} + 1}{\sqrt{7} + 1}$ **106.** $\dfrac{2 - \sqrt{7}}{1 + \sqrt{7}}$

107. $\dfrac{2}{5 - \sqrt{y}}$ **108.** $\dfrac{6}{\sqrt{x} - 1}$

109. $\dfrac{-\sqrt{x}}{\sqrt{x} - \sqrt{2}}$ **110.** $\dfrac{6\sqrt{x}}{2\sqrt{x} - \sqrt{5}}$

111. $\dfrac{\sqrt{x} - 5}{\sqrt{x} - 1}$ **112.** $\dfrac{\sqrt{t} + 1}{\sqrt{t} - 1}$

In Exercises 113–116, rewrite the expression as a single fraction and simplify. See Example 10.

113. $3 - \dfrac{1}{\sqrt{3}}$ **114.** $\dfrac{1}{\sqrt{5}} - 5$

115. $\sqrt{50} - \dfrac{6}{\sqrt{2}}$ **116.** $\dfrac{7}{\sqrt{3}} + \sqrt{12}$

Graphical Interpretation   In Exercises 117–120, use a graphing utility to graph the two equations on the same screen. Use the graphs to verify the simplification.

117. $y_1 = \sqrt{8x} + \sqrt{2x}$ **118.** $y_1 = \sqrt{3} \cdot \sqrt{12x}$

      $y_2 = 3\sqrt{2x}$ $y_2 = 6\sqrt{x}$

119. $y_1 = \dfrac{2}{\sqrt{x+1}}$ **120.** $y_1 = \dfrac{x}{\sqrt{2} - 1}$

      $y_2 = \dfrac{2\sqrt{x+1}}{x+1}$ $y_2 = (\sqrt{2} + 1)x$

In Exercises 121–124, insert the correct symbol ($<$, $>$, or $=$) between the two real numbers.

121. $\sqrt{5} + \sqrt{3}$ $\sqrt{5 + 3}$

122. $\sqrt{5} - \sqrt{3}$ $\sqrt{5 - 3}$

123. 5 $\sqrt{3^2 + 2^2}$

124. 5 $\sqrt{3^2 + 4^2}$

Solving Problems

Geometry In Exercises 125–128, write expressions for the perimeter and area of the rectangle. Then simplify the expressions.

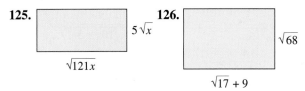

125. $5\sqrt{x}$

$\sqrt{121x}$

126. $\sqrt{68}$

$\sqrt{17} + 9$

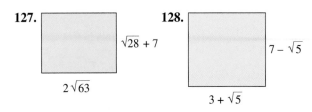

127. $\sqrt{28} + 7$

$2\sqrt{63}$

128. $7 - \sqrt{5}$

$3 + \sqrt{5}$

129. *The Golden Section* The ratio of the width of the Temple of Hephaestus to its height (see figure) is

$$\frac{w}{h} \approx \frac{2}{\sqrt{5} - 1}.$$

This number is called the **golden section.** Early Greeks believed that the most esthetically pleasing rectangles were those whose sides were in this ratio. Rationalize the denominator for this number. Approximate your answer, rounded to two decimal places.

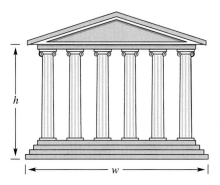

h

w

Figure for 129

130. *Wind Chill* The National Weather Service uses the following formula for determining "wind chill"

$$T_{wc} = 0.0817\left(3.71\sqrt{v} + 5.81 - 0.25v\right)(T - 91.4) + 91.4$$

where T is the air temperature in degrees Fahrenheit, T_{wc} is the wind chill, and v is the wind speed in miles per hour. Use the formula to determine the wind chill for each combination of air temperature and wind speed in the table.

$v\backslash T$	0°	5°	10°	15°	20°	25°
10 mi/hr						
20 mi/hr						
30 mi/hr						
40 mi/hr						

Explaining Concepts

131. Answer parts (a)–(d) of Motivating the Chapter on page 463.

132. In your own words, explain what it means for two square root radicals to be like radicals.

133. Give an example of two like radical expressions. Give an example of two unlike radical expressions.

134. Explain how the Distributive Property can be used to add or subtract like radicals. Give examples.

135. Can $\sqrt{2} + \sqrt{18}$ be simplified? Explain.

136. Explain the relationship between $3 - \sqrt{2}$ and $3 + \sqrt{2}$.

137. Is the number $3/(1 + \sqrt{5})$ in simplest form? If not, explain the steps for writing it in simplest form.

138. Square the real number $3/\sqrt{2}$. Is this equivalent to rationalizing the denominator? Explain.

139. Enter any positive real number in your calculator and repeatedly take the square root. What real number does the display appear to be approaching?

9.4   Radical Equations and Applications

Objectives

1 Use the Squaring Property of Equality to solve a radical equation.

2 Solve an application problem using a radical equation.

---

1 Use the Squaring Property of Equality to solve a radical equation.

Solving Radical Equations

In this section, you will study techniques for solving equations involving radicals *and* applications involving radicals. This chapter gives, in miniature, a picture of what algebra is. In other words, the algebra of radicals consists of the following five types of problems.

Definitions of roots and radicals, and techniques for evaluating radicals	Section 9.1
Simplifying radicals and radical expressions	Section 9.2
Operations with radicals	Section 9.3
Solving equations involving radicals	Section 9.4
Applications involving radicals	Section 9.4

Think back—didn't the algebra of *linear equations* have the same five types of problems? Or how about the algebra of *polynomials* or the algebra of *rational expressions*?

A **radical equation** is an equation that contains one or more radicals with variable radicands. Here are some examples.

$$\sqrt{x} = 5, \quad \sqrt{3x - 2} = 7, \quad \text{and} \quad \sqrt{x + 3} = \sqrt{7 - x}$$

Solving radical equations is somewhat like solving equations that contain fractions—first try to get rid of the radicals and obtain a polynomial equation. Then, solve the polynomial equation using the standard procedures. For square root radicals, the following property plays a key role.

> ▶ **Squaring Property of Equality**
>
> Let a and b be real numbers, variables, or algebraic expressions. If $a = b$, then it follows that
>
> $$a^2 = b^2.$$
>
> This operation is called **squaring both sides of an equation.**

To see how squaring both sides of an equation removes a radical, let's look at the equation $\sqrt{x} = 5$.

$\sqrt{x} = 5$	Original equation
$\left(\sqrt{x}\right)^2 = 5^2$	Square both sides.
$x = 25$	Simplify.

To apply the Squaring Property of Equality to solve a radical equation, first try to isolate the radical on one side of the equation.

| **Example 1** | Solving a Radical Equation with One Radical |

Solve the radical equation.

$$\sqrt{2x + 1} - 2 = 3$$

Solution

$\sqrt{2x + 1} - 2 = 3$	Original equation
$\sqrt{2x + 1} = 5$	Isolate the radical.
$\left(\sqrt{2x + 1}\right)^2 = (5)^2$	Square both sides.
$2x + 1 = 25$	Simplify.
$2x = 24$	Subtract 1 from both sides.
$x = 12$	Divide both sides by 2.

Check

$\sqrt{2x + 1} - 2 = 3$	Original equation
$\sqrt{2(12) + 1} - 2 \overset{?}{=} 3$	Substitute 12 for x.
$\sqrt{25} - 2 \overset{?}{=} 3$	Simplify.
$5 - 2 = 3$	Solution checks. ✔

So, the solution is 12.

———

Some radical equations have no solution, as shown in the next example.

| **Example 2** | A Radical with No Solution |

Solve the radical equation.

$$\sqrt{3x} = -9$$

Solution

$\sqrt{3x} = -9$	Original equation
$\left(\sqrt{3x}\right)^2 = (-9)^2$	Square both sides.
$3x = 81$	Simplify.
$x = 27$	Divide both sides by 3.

Check

$\sqrt{3x} = -9$	Original equation
$\sqrt{3(27)} \overset{?}{=} -9$	Substitute 27 for x.
$9 \neq -9$	Solution does not check. ✗

So, the equation has no solution.

———

Example 3   A Radical Equation with Two Radicals

$$\sqrt{5x + 3} = \sqrt{x + 11}$$ Original equation

$$\left(\sqrt{5x + 3}\right)^2 = \left(\sqrt{x + 11}\right)^2$$ Square both sides.

$$5x + 3 = x + 11$$ Simplify.

$$4x = 8$$ Subtract 3 and x from both sides.

$$x = 2$$ Divide both sides by 4.

Check

$$\sqrt{5x + 3} = \sqrt{x + 11}$$ Original equation

$$\sqrt{5(2) + 3} \overset{?}{=} \sqrt{2 + 11}$$ Substitute 2 for x.

$$\sqrt{13} = \sqrt{13}$$ Solution checks. ✓

Example 4   Radical Equations with Two Radicals

Study Tip

In Examples 4(a) and 4(b) it is necessary to isolate the radicals on each side of the equal sign. If both sides of the equation were squared before isolating the radicals, the resulting equation would still contain a radical, which would require isolating the radical and squaring both sides a second time.

a. $\sqrt{6x - 4} - 2\sqrt{4 - x} = 0$ Original equation

$$\sqrt{6x - 4} = 2\sqrt{4 - x}$$ Isolate radicals.

$$6x - 4 = 2^2(4 - x)$$ Square both sides.

$$6x - 4 = 16 - 4x$$ Distributive Property

$$10x = 20$$ Add 4 and $4x$ to both sides.

$$x = 2$$ Divide both sides by 10.

Check

$$\sqrt{6x - 4} - 2\sqrt{4 - x} = 0$$ Original equation

$$\sqrt{6(2) - 4} - 2\sqrt{4 - 2} \overset{?}{=} 0$$ Substitute 2 for x.

$$\sqrt{8} - 2\sqrt{2} \overset{?}{=} 0$$ Simplify.

$$2\sqrt{2} - 2\sqrt{2} = 0$$ Solution checks. ✓

b. $\sqrt{3x} + \sqrt{2x - 5} = 0$ Original equation

$$\sqrt{3x} = -\sqrt{2x - 5}$$ Isolate radicals.

$$\left(\sqrt{3x}\right)^2 = \left(-\sqrt{2x - 5}\right)^2$$ Square both sides.

$$3x = 2x - 5$$ Simplify.

$$x = -5$$ Subtract $2x$ from both sides.

Emphasize the necessity of checking any solution obtained by squaring both sides of an equation.

Check

$$\sqrt{3x} + \sqrt{2x - 5} = 0$$ Original equation

$$\sqrt{3(-5)} + \sqrt{2(-5) - 5} \overset{?}{=} 0$$ Substitute -5 for x.

$$\sqrt{-15} + \sqrt{-15} \neq 0$$ Solution does not check. ✗

The equation has no solution, because -5 results in negative radicands.

Remind students that $(a + b)^2 = a^2 + 2ab + b^2$. Squaring a binomial incorrectly is a common cause of errors in equations involving radicals.

The next two examples show how squaring both sides of an equation can yield a *nonlinear* equation.

Example 5 Solving a Radical Equation

$1 - 2x = \sqrt{x}$	Original equation
$(1 - 2x)^2 = \left(\sqrt{x}\right)^2$	Square both sides.
$1 - 4x + 4x^2 = x$	Binomial square pattern
$4x^2 - 5x + 1 = 0$	Standard form
$(4x - 1)(x - 1) = 0$	Factor.
$4x - 1 = 0 \implies x = \frac{1}{4}$	Set 1st factor equal to 0.
$x - 1 = 0 \implies x = 1$	Set 2nd factor equal to 0.

After checking the solutions as follows, you can determine that only $x = \frac{1}{4}$ is a valid solution. The value $x = 1$ is extraneous.

Substitute $\frac{1}{4}$ into Equation

$$1 - 2x = \sqrt{x}$$
$$1 - 2\left(\tfrac{1}{4}\right) \overset{?}{=} \sqrt{\tfrac{1}{4}}$$
$$1 - 2\left(\tfrac{1}{4}\right) \overset{?}{=} \tfrac{1}{2}$$
$$\tfrac{1}{2} = \tfrac{1}{2} \checkmark$$

Substitute 1 into Equation

$$1 - 2x = \sqrt{x}$$
$$1 - 2(1) \overset{?}{=} \sqrt{1}$$
$$1 - 2(1) \overset{?}{=} 1$$
$$-1 \neq 1 \times$$

Example 6 Solving a Radical Equation

$\sqrt{6x + 1} = x - 1$	Original equation
$\left(\sqrt{6x + 1}\right)^2 = (x - 1)^2$	Square both sides.
$6x + 1 = x^2 - 2x + 1$	Simplify.
$0 = x^2 - 8x$	Standard form
$0 = x(x - 8)$	Factor.
$x = 0 \implies x = 0$	Set 1st factor equal to 0.
$x - 8 = 0 \implies x = 8$	Set 2nd factor equal to 0.

After checking the solutions as follows, you can determine that only $x = 8$ is a valid solution. The value $x = 0$ is extraneous.

Substitute 0 into Equation

$$\sqrt{6x + 1} = x - 1$$
$$\sqrt{6(0) + 1} \overset{?}{=} 0 - 1$$
$$\sqrt{1} \overset{?}{=} -1$$
$$1 \neq -1 \times$$

Substitute 8 into Equation

$$\sqrt{6x + 1} = x - 1$$
$$\sqrt{6(8) + 1} \overset{?}{=} 8 - 1$$
$$\sqrt{49} \overset{?}{=} 7$$
$$7 = 7 \checkmark$$

Technology: Tip

You can use a graphing approach to determine the number of solutions of a radical equation.

Using the equation in Example 5, set each side of the equation equal to y.

$$y_1 = 1 - 2x$$
$$y_2 = \sqrt{x}$$

Graph the equations with your graphing utility. The number of intersections of the two graphs is the number of solutions of the equation. The x-value of the intersection is the solution.

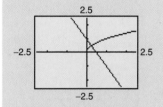

From the graph you can see that there is one solution, $x = \frac{1}{4}$. Determine the number of solutions of $\sqrt{2x} + 4 = 0$.

2 Solve an application problem using a radical equation.

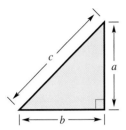

Figure 9.1

Applications of Radicals

A common use of radicals is in applications involving right triangles. Recall that a right triangle is one that contains a right (or 90°) angle, as shown in Figure 9.1. The relationship among the three sides of a right triangle is described by the **Pythagorean Theorem,** which says that if a and b are the lengths of the legs (the two sides that form the right angle) and c is the length of the hypotenuse (the side across from the right angle), then

$$c^2 = a^2 + b^2 \qquad \text{Pythagorean Theorem}$$

$$c = \sqrt{a^2 + b^2}. \qquad \text{Take square root of both sides.}$$

Example 7   Dimensions of a Softball Diamond

A softball diamond has the shape of a square with 60-foot sides, as shown in Figure 9.2. The catcher is 4 feet behind home plate. How far does the catcher have to throw to second base?

Solution

In Figure 9.2, let x be the hypotenuse of a right triangle with 60-foot sides. So, by the Pythagorean Theorem, you have the following equation.

$$x = \sqrt{60^2 + 60^2} \qquad \text{Pythagorean Theorem}$$

$$x = \sqrt{7200} \qquad \text{Simplify.}$$

$$x \approx 84.9 \text{ feet} \qquad \text{Use a calculator.}$$

The distance from home plate to second base is approximately 84.9 feet. Because the catcher is 4 feet behind home plate, the catcher must make a throw of

$$x + 4 \approx 84.9 + 4 = 88.9 \text{ feet.}$$

Check this solution in the original statement of the problem.

In 1996, there were 263,000 softball teams in the United States. Of these, 184,000 were adult teams and 79,000 were youth teams. (Source: Amateur Softball Association)

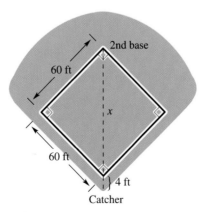

Figure 9.2

The Pythagorean Theorem can be used to establish the following Distance Formula for finding the distance between two points in the coordinate plane.

▶ **The Distance Formula**

The distance d between the two points (x_1, y_1) and (x_2, y_2) in a coordinate plane is

$$d = \sqrt{(x_2 - x_1)^2 + (y_2 - y_1)^2}.$$

Example 8 The Distance Formula

Find the distance between the points $(-1, -5)$ and $(2, -2)$.

Solution

Let $(x_1, y_1) = (-1, -5)$ and $(x_2, y_2) = (2, -2)$, as shown in Figure 9.3.

$$
\begin{aligned}
d &= \sqrt{[2 - (-1)]^2 + [-2 - (-5)]^2} && \text{Distance Formula}\\
&= \sqrt{3^2 + 3^2} && \text{Simplify.}\\
&= \sqrt{18} && \text{Simplify.}\\
&\approx 4.24 && \text{Use a calculator.}
\end{aligned}
$$

So, the distance between the two points is 4.24 units.

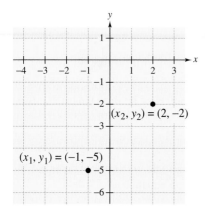

Figure 9.3

Notice in Example 8 that you could have chosen (x_1, y_1) to be the point $(2, -2)$ and (x_2, y_2) to be the point $(-1, -5)$. The results would have been the same.

$$
\begin{aligned}
d &= \sqrt{(-1 - 2)^2 + [-5 - (-2)]^2} && \text{Distance Formula}\\
&= \sqrt{(-3)^2 + (-3)^2} && \text{Simplify.}\\
&= \sqrt{18} && \text{Simplify.}\\
&\approx 4.24 && \text{Use a calculator.}
\end{aligned}
$$

Discussing the Concept **Verifying Extraneous Solutions**

Solving the equation

$$x + 1 - \sqrt{3x + 7} = 0$$

algebraically gives the solutions $x = -2$ and $x = 3$. Use a graphing utility to determine whether either of these solutions is extraneous. Explain to another class member how you drew your conclusions from the graph. Together, decide how the no-solution case would appear graphically. Verify your conclusion with an equation that contains a radical and has no real solution.

9.4 Exercises

Integrated Review   Concepts, Skills, and Problem Solving

Keep mathematically in shape by doing these exercises *before* the problems of this section.

Properties and Definitions

1. Explain how to determine the domain of the function

$$f(x) = \frac{10}{x + 2}.$$

2. Explain the excluded value $(x \neq -2)$ in the following.

$$\frac{x^2 - x - 6}{x^2 - 4} = \frac{x - 3}{x - 2}, \quad x \neq -2$$

Simplifying Expressions

In Exercises 3–8, perform the operation and/or simplify.

3. $\dfrac{15x^2}{10x}$

4. $\dfrac{8x^2 + 4x}{2x + 1}$

5. $\dfrac{5}{x + 1} \cdot \dfrac{x + 1}{25}$

6. $\dfrac{r}{r - 1} \div \dfrac{r^2}{r^2 - 1}$

7. $6 - \dfrac{5}{x + 3}$

8. $\dfrac{\left(\dfrac{x}{2} - 1\right)}{(x - 2)}$

Graphs

In Exercises 9 and 10, graph the function and identify any intercepts. Use a graphing utility to verify your results.

9. $h(u) = 3 - \frac{2}{3}u$

10. $g(t) = 2t - 5$

Developing Skills

In Exercises 1–4, is *x* a solution of the equation?

Equation	*Values of x*
1. $\sqrt{x} - 6 = 0$	(a) $x = -1$ (b) $x = -36$
	(c) $x = 36$ (d) $x = 6$
2. $\sqrt{2x} - 3 = 0$	(a) $x = \frac{9}{2}$ (b) $x = -\frac{9}{2}$
	(c) $x = 0$ (d) $x = \frac{3}{2}$
3. $x = \sqrt{2x + 3}$	(a) $x = -1$ (b) $x = 2$
	(c) $x = 8$ (d) $x = 3$
4. $\sqrt{3x + 4} = 2\sqrt{x}$	(a) $x = -2$ (b) $x = 2$
	(c) $x = 4$ (d) $x = 0$

In Exercises 5–56, solve the equation. See Examples 1–6.

5. $\sqrt{x} = 7$

6. $\sqrt{t} = 5$

7. $\sqrt{x} = 10$

8. $\sqrt{x} = 3$

9. $\sqrt{y} - 5 = 0$

10. $\sqrt{t} - 12 = 0$

11. $\sqrt{u} + 3 = 0$

12. $\sqrt{y} + 10 = 0$

13. $8 - \sqrt{t} = 3$

14. $12 - \sqrt{s} = 25$

15. $\sqrt{a + 3} = 20$

16. $\sqrt{b + 8} = 4$

17. $\sqrt{10x} = 100$

18. $\sqrt{8x} = 4$

19. $\sqrt{3x} - 4 = -7$

20. $\sqrt{2x} + 5 = 1$

21. $\sqrt{3x - 2} = 4$

22. $\sqrt{5x - 1} = 8$

23. $\sqrt{3y + 5} = 2$

24. $\sqrt{5z - 2} = 6$

25. $\sqrt{x - 2} + 1 = 7$

26. $\sqrt{4 - x} - 5 = 1$

27. $\sqrt{4x + 3} - 6 = -5$

28. $\sqrt{2x - 5} - 9 = -4$

29. $\sqrt{1 - 4x} - 3 = 2$

30. $\sqrt{3 - 2x} + 1 = 8$

31. $5\sqrt{x + 1} = 6$

32. $2\sqrt{x + 3} = 5$

33. $\sqrt{3x + 4} = \sqrt{5x - 2}$

34. $\sqrt{6 - 7x} = \sqrt{4x + 17}$

35. $\sqrt{x + 4} = \sqrt{2x + 1}$

36. $\sqrt{3x + 2} = \sqrt{x + 20}$

37. $\sqrt{5x - 1} = 3\sqrt{x}$

38. $\sqrt{2x + 3} = 2\sqrt{x}$

39. $\sqrt{3x - 4} = 2\sqrt{x}$

40. $\sqrt{u - 4} = \sqrt{2u}$

41. $\sqrt{3t + 11} = 5\sqrt{t}$

42. $\sqrt{5 - 4u} = 4\sqrt{u}$

43. $2\sqrt{y + 1} = \sqrt{3y + 6}$

44. $2\sqrt{x + 4} = 3\sqrt{x - 1}$

45. $\sqrt{x^2 + 5} = x + 1$

46. $\sqrt{x^2 - 2} = x - 1$

47. $\sqrt{x} = 2 - x$ **48.** $6 - x = \sqrt{x}$

49. $x - 5 = 4\sqrt{x}$ **50.** $5\sqrt{x} = x + 4$

51. $x = \sqrt{20 - x}$ **52.** $x = \sqrt{6 - x}$

53. $x = \sqrt{18 - 3x}$ **54.** $x = \sqrt{77 - 4x}$

55. $\sqrt{6x + 7} = x + 2$ **56.** $\sqrt{4x + 17} = x + 3$

In Exercises 57–60, use a graphing utility to graph the function and estimate its x-intercepts. Set $y = 0$ and solve the resulting radical equation. Compare the result with the x-intercepts of the graph.

57. $y = \sqrt{x - 1} - 2$ **58.** $y = 6 - \sqrt{3x}$

59. $y = x - \sqrt{4x + 5}$ **60.** $y = 2\sqrt{x} - x + 3$

In Exercises 61–66, use the Pythagorean Theorem to solve for x. Round the result to two decimal places.

61.

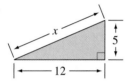

62.

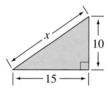

63.

64.

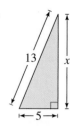

65.

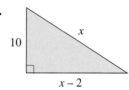

66.

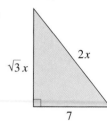

In Exercises 67–74, find the distance between the two points. Round your result to two decimal places. See Example 8.

67. $(1, 2), (5, 5)$ **68.** $(2, 5), (7, 1)$

69. $(4, 5), (7, 2)$ **70.** $(1, -2), (-4, 8)$

71. $(3, -2), (4, 6)$ **72.** $(1, 5), (2, -6)$

73. $(-4, 0), (2, 3)$ **74.** $(-1, 2), (7, -2)$

Solving Problems

Estimation   In Exercises 75 and 76, the time t in seconds for a free-falling object to fall d feet is

$$t = \sqrt{\frac{d}{16}}.$$

75. A construction worker drops a nail from a building and observes it strike a water puddle after approximately 3 seconds. Estimate the height from which the nail was dropped.

76. A construction worker drops a nail from a building and observes it strike a water puddle after approximately 5 seconds. Estimate the height from which the nail was dropped.

Velocity   In Exercises 77 and 78, use the equation for the velocity of a free-falling object

$$v = \sqrt{2gh}$$

where v is measured in feet per second, $g = 32$ feet per second squared, and h is height in feet.

77. An object strikes the ground with a velocity of 75 feet per second. Estimate the height from which it was dropped.

78. An object strikes the ground with a velocity of 100 feet per second. Estimate the height from which it was dropped.

Pendulum Length   In Exercises 79 and 80, the time t in seconds for a pendulum of length L in feet to move through one complete cycle (its period) is

$$t = 2\pi\sqrt{\frac{L}{32}}.$$

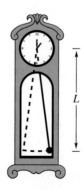

79. How long is the pendulum of a grandfather clock with a period of 2 seconds?

80. How long is the pendulum of a mantel clock with a period of 0.8 second?

81. *Geometry*   A ladder is 15 feet long, and the bottom of the ladder is 3 feet from the wall of a house (see figure). How far does the ladder reach up the side of the house?

15 ft

3 ft

82. *Geometry*   A 39-foot guy wire on a sailboat is attached to the top of the mast and to the deck 15 feet from the base of the mast (see figure). How tall is the mast?

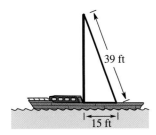

39 ft

15 ft

83. *Geometry*   A volleyball court is 30 feet wide and 60 feet long. Find the length of a diagonal of the court.

84. *Geometry*   A house has dimensions 30 feet by 40 feet. The gas hot water heater and furnace are diagonally across the basement from where the natural gas line enters the house. Find the length of the gas line across the basement.

85. *Geometry*   A 12-foot plank is used to brace a basement wall during construction of a home. The plank is nailed to the wall 4 feet above the floor (see figure). Find the slope of the plank.

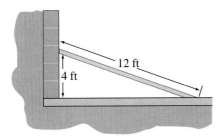

12 ft

4 ft

86. *Geometry*   A baseball diamond is a square that is 90 feet on a side. Determine the distance between first base and third base.

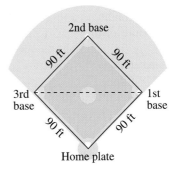

2nd base

90 ft   90 ft

3rd base ←- - - - - - - -→ 1st base

90 ft   90 ft

Home plate

87. *Geometry*   For a television set with a 25-inch screen, it is actually the diagonal of the screen that is 25 inches. Find the dimensions of the square screen.

88. *Geometry*   For a television set with a 32-inch screen, it is actually the diagonal of the screen that is 32 inches. Find the dimensions of the square screen.

89. *Using a Model*   The demand equation for a certain product is

$$p = 40 - \sqrt{x - 1}$$

where x is the number of units demanded per day and p is the price per unit. Find the demand if the price is set at \$34.70.

90. *Using a Model*   An airline offers daily flights between Chicago and Denver. The total monthly cost of these flights is modeled by

$$C = \sqrt{0.2x + 1}$$

where C is measured in millions of dollars and x is measured in thousands of passengers. The total cost of the flights for a certain month is 2.5 million dollars. Estimate the number of passengers for that month.

91. *Analyzing Data* The atmospheric pressure decreases with increasing altitude. At sea level, the average air pressure is 1.033227 kilograms per square centimeter, which is called 1 atmosphere. Variations in weather conditions cause changes in the atmospheric pressure of up to ±5%. The table gives the pressure p (in atmospheres) at given altitudes h (in kilometers).

h	0	5	10	15	20	25
p	1	0.55	0.25	0.12	0.06	0.02

A model for these data is $p = 1 - 0.206\sqrt{h}$.

(a) Use a graphing utility to plot the data and graph the model on the same viewing screen.

(b) Approximate the altitude if the atmospheric pressure is 0.4 atmosphere.

 92. *Exploration* Pythagorean triples are sets of positive integers a, b, and c that satisfy the Pythagorean Theorem $a^2 + b^2 = c^2$.

Consider the positive integers u and v where $u > v$, one is even and the other is odd, and their only common factor is 1. Select some values of u and v that satisfy these criteria, and then generate the numbers

$a = u^2 - v^2$

$b = 2uv$

$c = u^2 + v^2$.

In each case, verify that a, b, and c are a Pythagorean triple.

Explaining Concepts

93. Answer parts (e)–(h) of Motivating the Chapter on page 463.

94. In your own words, describe a radical equation.

95. Describe a strategy for solving a radical equation.

96. Is $x = 25$ a solution of $\sqrt{x} = -5$? Explain.

97. Give two reasons why it is important to check solutions of a radical equation.

98. State the Pythagorean Theorem.

99. Can a right triangle be isosceles (have two sides of the same length)? Explain.

Key Terms

Key Concepts

9.1 Definition of *n*th root of a number

Let a and b be real numbers and let n be an integer such that $n \geq 2$. If

$$a = b^n$$

then b is an *n*th root of a. If $n = 2$, the root is a square root, and if $n = 3$, the root is a cube root.

9.1 Principal *n*th root of a number

Let a be a real number that has at least one (real number) *n*th root. The principal *n*th root of a is the *n*th root that has the same sign as a, and it is denoted by the radical symbol

$$\sqrt[n]{a}.$$

The positive integer n is the index of the radical, and the number a is the radicand. If $n = 2$, omit the index and write $\sqrt{a}$ rather than $\sqrt[2]{a}$.

9.2 Multiplication Property of Radicals

Let a and b be real numbers, variables, or algebraic expressions. If the *n*th roots of a and b are real, the following property is true.

$$\sqrt[n]{a}\,\sqrt[n]{b} = \sqrt[n]{ab}$$

9.2 The square root of x^2

If x is a real number, then

$$\sqrt{x^2} = |x|.$$

For the special case in which you know that x is a non-negative real number, you can write $\sqrt{x^2} = x$.

9.2 Division Property of Radicals

Let a and b be real numbers, variables, or algebraic expressions. If the *n*th roots of a and b are real, the following property is true.

$$\frac{\sqrt[n]{u}}{\sqrt[n]{v}} = \sqrt[n]{\frac{u}{v}}, \quad v \neq 0$$

9.2 Simplifying a radical expression

A radical expression is said to be in simplest form if all three of the following are true.

1. All *n*th powered factors have been removed from each radical.
2. No radical contains a fraction.
3. No denominator of a fraction contains a radical.

9.4 Squaring Property of Equality

Let a and b be real numbers, variables, or algebraic expressions. If $a = b$, then it follows that

$$a^2 = b^2.$$

This operation is called squaring both sides of an equation.

9.4 The Distance Formula

The distance d between the two points (x_1, y_1) and (x_2, y_2) in a coordinate plane is

$$d = \sqrt{(x_2 - x_1)^2 + (y_2 - y_1)^2}.$$

REVIEW EXERCISES

Reviewing Skills

9.1 In Exercises 1–12, find the nth root of the number, if possible. (Do not use a calculator.)

1. $\sqrt{121}$

2. $\sqrt{-25}$

3. $-\sqrt{36}$

4. $\sqrt{49}$

5. $\sqrt{1.44}$

6. $\sqrt{0.09}$

7. $\sqrt{-\frac{1}{16}}$

8. $-\sqrt{\frac{64}{9}}$

9. $\sqrt[3]{-27}$

10. $\sqrt[4]{16}$

11. $\sqrt[3]{\frac{8}{125}}$

12. $\sqrt[4]{\frac{1}{81}}$

In Exercises 13–20, use a calculator to approximate the value of the expression. Round the result to two decimal places.

13. $\sqrt{53}$

14. $\sqrt{5335}$

15. $\sqrt{\frac{7}{8}}$

16. $-\sqrt{\frac{45}{8}}$

17. $3 + 2\sqrt{6}$

18. $-4 - 3\sqrt{10}$

19. $\dfrac{5 - 3\sqrt{3}}{2}$

20. $\dfrac{7 - 4\sqrt{2}}{4}$

9.2 In Exercises 21–44, simplify the radical expression. Assume that the variables are positive.

21. $\sqrt{48}$

22. $\sqrt{72}$

23. $\sqrt{160}$

24. $\sqrt{45}$

25. $\sqrt{\frac{23}{9}}$

26. $\sqrt{\frac{26}{16}}$

27. $\sqrt{\frac{20}{9}}$

28. $\sqrt{\frac{27}{16}}$

29. $\sqrt[3]{24}$

30. $\sqrt[4]{48}$

31. $\sqrt[4]{96}$

32. $\sqrt[3]{54}$

33. $\sqrt{36x^4}$

34. $\sqrt{81z^2}$

35. $\sqrt{4y^3}$

36. $\sqrt{100u^5}$

37. $\sqrt{32a^3b}$

38. $\sqrt{75u^4v^2}$

39. $\sqrt{0.04x^2y}$

40. $\sqrt{1.44x^2y^3}$

41. $\sqrt[3]{8x^6}$

42. $\sqrt[4]{16y^5}$

43. $\sqrt[3]{64a^5}$

44. $\sqrt[4]{a^8b^{10}}$

In Exercises 45–60, rationalize the denominator and simplify. (Assume that the variables are positive.)

45. $\sqrt{\frac{3}{5}}$

46. $\sqrt{\frac{7}{10}}$

47. $\dfrac{6}{\sqrt{3}}$

48. $\dfrac{15}{\sqrt{5}}$

49. $\sqrt{\frac{5}{12}}$

50. $\sqrt{\frac{13}{32}}$

51. $\dfrac{3}{\sqrt[3]{2}}$

52. $\dfrac{5}{\sqrt[3]{4}}$

53. $\dfrac{1}{\sqrt[3]{3}}$

54. $\dfrac{2}{\sqrt[3]{9}}$

55. $\dfrac{3}{\sqrt{x}}$

56. $\dfrac{7}{\sqrt{t}}$

57. $\sqrt{\dfrac{11a}{b}}$

58. $\sqrt{\dfrac{4y}{z}}$

59. $\dfrac{\sqrt{6x^2}}{\sqrt{27y^3}}$

60. $\dfrac{\sqrt{10a^2}}{\sqrt{8b^2}}$

9.3 In Exercises 61–98, perform the operations and simplify. (Assume that the variables are positive.)

61. $\sqrt[3]{\dfrac{4}{x^2}}$

62. $\sqrt[3]{\dfrac{7}{y^5}}$

63. $7\sqrt{2} + 5\sqrt{2}$

64. $15\sqrt{15} - 7\sqrt{15}$

65. $3\sqrt{5} - 7\sqrt{3} + 11\sqrt{3}$

66. $5\sqrt{11} + 6\sqrt{2} - 8\sqrt{11}$

67. $3\sqrt{20} - 10\sqrt{20}$

68. $25\sqrt{98} + 2\sqrt{98}$

69. $4\sqrt{48} + 2\sqrt{3} - 5\sqrt{12}$

70. $12\sqrt{50} - 3\sqrt{8} + \sqrt{32}$

71. $\sqrt[4]{4} + 5\sqrt[4]{4}$

72. $2\sqrt[3]{7} - 6\sqrt[3]{7} + 9\sqrt[3]{7}$

73. $\sqrt[5]{x} + 8\sqrt[5]{x}$

74. $5\sqrt[4]{x^2} - 3\sqrt[4]{y^3} + 4\sqrt[4]{x^2}$

75. $\sqrt{36y} - \sqrt{16y}$

76. $\sqrt{25x} + \sqrt{49x}$

77. $\sqrt{18x^3} - 3x\sqrt{2x}$

78. $\sqrt{28y^5} + 4y^2\sqrt{7y^3}$

79. $\sqrt{3}\left(\sqrt{6} - 1\right)$

80. $\sqrt{7}\left(10 - \sqrt{7}\right)$

81. $\sqrt[4]{6}\left(\sqrt[4]{2} - 1\right)$

82. $\sqrt[3]{5}\left(\sqrt[3]{4} + 2\right)$

83. $\left(\sqrt{3} - \sqrt{5}\right)\left(\sqrt{3} + \sqrt{5}\right)$

84. $\left(\sqrt{7} - 2\right)\left(\sqrt{7} + 2\right)$

85. $\left(\sqrt{5} - 2\right)^2$

86. $\left(\sqrt{3} + 1\right)^2$

87. $\left(\sqrt{8} + 2\right)\left(3\sqrt{2} - 1\right)$

88. $\left(2\sqrt{3} + 10\right)\left(\sqrt{2} - 3\right)$

89. $\left(\sqrt[5]{2} + 3\right)\left(\sqrt[5]{3} + 5\right)$

90. $\left(\sqrt[4]{3} - 1\right)\left(\sqrt[4]{3} - 1\right)$

91. $\sqrt{x}\left(\sqrt{x} + 10\right)$

92. $\sqrt{z}\left(15 - \sqrt{z}\right)$

93. $\dfrac{3}{\sqrt{12} - 3}$

94. $\dfrac{9}{\sqrt{7} - 4}$

95. $\dfrac{\sqrt{6}}{\sqrt{2} + \sqrt{3}}$

96. $\dfrac{5\sqrt{2}}{\sqrt{3} + \sqrt{2}}$

97. $\left(\sqrt{x} - 3\right) \div \left(\sqrt{x} + 3\right)$

98. $\left(3\sqrt{s} + 2\right) \div \left(\sqrt{s} + 1\right)$

9.4 In Exercises 99–110, use the Squaring Property of Equality to solve the equation. (Some of the equations have no solution.)

99. $\sqrt{y} = 13$

100. $\sqrt{z} = 25$

101. $\sqrt{x} + 2 = 0$

102. $\sqrt{x} - 10 = 0$

103. $\sqrt{2t + 3} = 5$

104. $\sqrt{2a - 7} = 15$

105. $\sqrt{4x - 3} = \sqrt{x + 6}$

106. $\sqrt{5x + 3} = \sqrt{x + 15}$

107. $x = 2\sqrt{3 - x}$

108. $\sqrt{2x - 1} = x$

109. $\sqrt{x - 4} = x - 6$

110. $\sqrt{2x + 7} = x + 4$

In Exercises 111 and 112, use a graphing utility to graph the function and estimate its x-intercepts. Set $y = 0$ and solve the resulting radical equation. Compare the result with the x-intercepts of the graph.

111. $y = \sqrt{x + 3} - 4\sqrt{x}$

112. $y = x + 2 - \sqrt{x + 8}$

In Exercises 113–120, find the distance between the two points. Round your result to two decimal places.

113. $(1, 4), (-2, 0)$

114. $(3, 8), (-3, 5)$

115. $(-5, -2), (-1, 9)$

116. $(6, 0), (1, -5)$

117. $(-4, -3), (2, -4)$

118. $(8, 10), (-1, -1)$

119. $(7, 3), (2, -8)$

120. $(-6, 5), (9, -2)$

Solving Problems

Geometry In Exercises 121 and 122, use the area A to find the length of the side or radius.

121. Square: $s = \sqrt{A}$

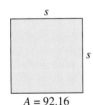

$A = 92.16$

122. Circle: $r = \sqrt{\dfrac{A}{\pi}}$

$A = 28.27$

Velocity In Exercises 123 and 124, use the equation for the velocity of a free-falling object

$v = \sqrt{2gh}$

where v is measured in feet per second, $g = 32$ feet per second squared, and h is height in feet.

123. An object is dropped from a height of 30 feet. Find the velocity of the object when it strikes the ground.

124. An object is dropped from a height of 100 feet. Find the velocity of the object when it strikes the ground.

125. *Pendulum Length* The time t in seconds for a pendulum of length L in feet to go through one complete cycle (its period) is

$$t = 2\pi\sqrt{\dfrac{L}{32}}.$$

How long is the pendulum of a grandfather clock with a period of 1.75 seconds?

126. *Height* The time t in seconds for a free-falling object to fall d feet is

$$t = \sqrt{\dfrac{d}{16}}.$$

A child drops a rock from a bridge and observes it strike the water after approximately 1.5 seconds (see figure). Estimate the height of the bridge.

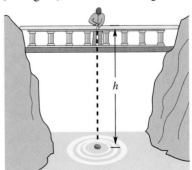

Geometry In Exercises 127 and 128, use the Pythagorean Theorem to solve for *x*. Round your answer to two decimal places.

127.

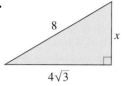

128.

Geometry In Exercises 129 and 130, verify that the triangle is a right triangle. (*Hint:* Use the Distance Formula to find the length of each side of the triangle.)

129.

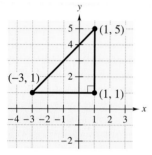

130.

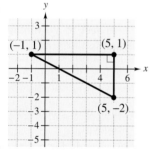

131. *Wire Length* A guy wire on a radio tower is attached to the top of the tower and to an anchor 60 feet from the base of the tower (see figure). The tower is 100 feet high. How long is the wire?

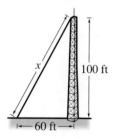

132. *Geometry* A baseball diamond is a square that is 90 feet on a side (see figure). The right fielder catches a fly ball on the first-base line approximately 70 feet beyond first base. He then throws a runner out at third base. Determine the distance *d* between the right fielder and third base.

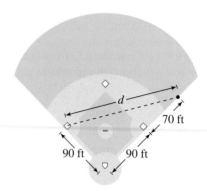

133. *Geometry* Determine the length and width of a rectangle that has a perimeter of 70 inches and a diagonal length of 25 inches.

134. *Geometry* A circle of diameter 8 inches is circumscribed around a square. A square is then circumscribed around the circle (see figure). What is the ratio of the area of the smaller square to the area of the larger square? Does the ratio change if the diameter of the circle is changed?

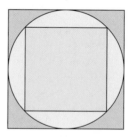

Error Analysis In Exercises 135 and 136, describe the error and then make the necessary correction.

135. $\sqrt{3^2 + 4^2} = 3 + 4$

136. $\sqrt{10x} = 10\sqrt{x}$

Chapter Test

Take this test as you would take a test in class. After you are done, check your work against the answers given in the back of the book.

1. If possible, evaluate each of the following without a calculator. If it is not possible, explain why.

   (a) $\sqrt{144}$ (b) $\sqrt{-36}$ (c) $\sqrt[4]{81}$ (d) $\sqrt[3]{-64}$

In Exercises 2–8, simplify the radical expression.

2. $\sqrt{48}$

3. $\sqrt[3]{54}$ 4. $\sqrt{32x^2y^3}$

5. $\dfrac{\sqrt{128}}{\sqrt{2}}$ 6. $\sqrt{\dfrac{3x^3}{y^4}}$

7. $\dfrac{5}{\sqrt{15}}$ 8. $\dfrac{2}{\sqrt[3]{4}}$

In Exercises 9–15, perform the indicated operation.

9. $10\sqrt{27} - 7\sqrt{12}$ 10. $7\sqrt[3]{5} - 6\sqrt[3]{4} + \sqrt[3]{5}$

11. $4\sqrt{2x} - 6\sqrt{32x} + \sqrt{2x^2}$ 12. $\sqrt{2}\left(\sqrt{8} - 5\right)$

13. $\sqrt[3]{5}\left(\sqrt[3]{2} + 3\right)$ 14. $\left(\sqrt{6} - 3\right)\left(\sqrt{6} + 5\right)$

15. $\left(1 - 2\sqrt{x}\right)\left(-2\sqrt{x}\right)$

16. In your own words, explain what *conjugate* means. Determine the conjugate of the real number $\sqrt{3} - 5$. Then find the product of the number and its conjugate.

17. Rationalize the denominator: $\dfrac{10}{\sqrt{6} + 1}$.

In Exercises 18–21, solve the equation.

18. $\sqrt{y} = 4$

19. $2\sqrt{x + 3} = 5$

20. $\sqrt{3x + 7} = \sqrt{7x - 5}$

21. $2\sqrt{2x} = x + 2$

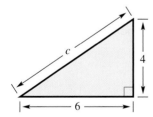

Figure for 22

22. Solve for c in the figure.

23. Find the distance between the points $(-3, 8)$ and $(5, 2)$ in the coordinate plane.

24. The demand equation for a certain product is $p = 100 - \sqrt{x - 25}$, where x is the number of units demanded per day and p is the price per unit. Find the demand when the price is $90.

Cumulative Test: Chapters 7–9

In Exercises 1–6, solve the system of equations by the specified method.

1. Graphical method:

$$x + 5y = 0$$
$$7x + 5y = 30$$

2. Graphical method:

$$2x + y = 5$$
$$3x - 2y = 4$$

3. Substitution:

$$x - y = 0$$
$$5x - 3y = 10$$

4. Substitution:

$$-\tfrac{1}{2}x + \tfrac{3}{4}y = 3$$
$$\tfrac{3}{4}x - y = 13$$

5. Elimination:

$$3x + 2y = 14$$
$$x - 2y = 10$$

6. Elimination:

$$2x + y = 4$$
$$4x - 3y = 3$$

7. Use a graphing utility to graph the lines in the system. Use the graphs to find the solution of the system.

$$2x - 5y = 0$$
$$x - y = 3$$

8. Give examples of (a) a system of linear equations that has no solution and (b) a system that has an infinite number of solutions.

9. Find the domain of the rational expression $\dfrac{x - 5}{x + 2}$.

10. Complete the statement: $\dfrac{7}{3x} = \dfrac{7\,\rule{1.5em}{0.8em}}{12x^2}$.

In Exercises 11 and 12, simplify each expression.

11. $\dfrac{5x - 25}{x^2 - 25}$

12. $\dfrac{x^2 - 3x - 10}{x^2 - 4}$

In Exercises 13–17, perform the indicated operations and simplify.

13. $\dfrac{c}{c - 1} \cdot \dfrac{c^2 + 9c - 10}{c^3}$

14. $\dfrac{6}{(c - 1)^2} \div \dfrac{8}{c^3 - c^2}$

15. $\dfrac{3}{x - 2} + \dfrac{x}{4 - x^2}$

16. $\dfrac{5}{x - 1} - \dfrac{2}{x}$

17. $\left(a - \dfrac{1}{a}\right) \div \left(\dfrac{1}{2} + \dfrac{1}{a}\right)$

In Exercises 18–21, solve the equation.

18. $\dfrac{5}{x} + \dfrac{3}{x} = 24$

19. $\dfrac{x}{5} - \dfrac{x}{2} = 3$

20. $\dfrac{1}{x} + \dfrac{2}{x - 5} = 0$

21. $\dfrac{2x - 1}{2x + 1} = \dfrac{4}{5}$

In Exercises 22–25, evaluate the expression, if possible.

22. $\sqrt{-\frac{4}{9}}$

23. $-\sqrt{\frac{4}{9}}$

24. $5\sqrt{144}$

25. $\sqrt[3]{-125}$

In Exercises 26–28, simplify the expression.

26. $\sqrt{24}$

27. $\sqrt{50x^3}$

28. $3\sqrt[3]{32u^4 v^6}$

In Exercises 29–32, perform the operations and simplify.

29. $5\sqrt{x} - 3\sqrt{x}$

30. $\sqrt{7}\left(\sqrt{7} + 2\right)$

31. $\left(4 - \sqrt{8}\right)^2$

32. $\dfrac{8y}{\sqrt{5} - 1}$

In Exercises 33–36, solve the equation.

33. $\sqrt{z} = 8$

34. $\sqrt{a - 4} = 5$

35. $\sqrt{2x + 7} = 3\sqrt{x}$

36. $x\left(\sqrt{x} - 2\right) = 0$

37. The total cost of 10 gallons of regular gasoline and 12 gallons of premium gasoline is $31.88. Premium costs $0.20 more per gallon than regular. Find the price per gallon of each grade of gasoline.

38. On the second half of a 200-mile trip, you average 10 more miles per hour than on the first half. What is your average speed on the second half of the trip if the total time for the trip is $4\frac{1}{2}$ hours?

39. A new employee takes twice as long as an experienced employee to complete a task. Together they can complete the task in 3 hours. Determine the time it takes each of them to do the task individually.

In Exercises 40 and 41, find the exact distance between the two points. Find the distance rounded to two decimal places.

40.

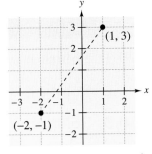

41.

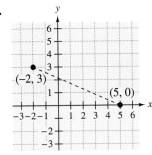

Figure for 42

42. Solve for x in the figure. Round your answer to two decimal places.

10 Quadratic Equations and Functions

Raymond Barnes/Tony Stone Images

The observation deck of the Space Needle in Seattle is located 518 feet above the ground. An object dropped from that height would hit the ground in approximately 5.7 seconds.

Motivating the Chapter

 Vertical Motion

The mathematical model for the height h in feet of an object moving in a vertical path is given by the quadratic function

$$\text{Height} = h(t) = -16t^2 + bt + c, \quad t \geq 0$$

where t is the time in seconds. This function is also called the *position function*. The coefficient b represents the velocity in feet per second at which the object is initially propelled upward ($b > 0$) or downward ($b < 0$), and the constant c represents the initial height (when $t = 0$) of the object.

See Section 10.1, Exercise 109

a. Write the quadratic function for an object that is dropped from a height of 40 feet.

b. An object has a position function of $h(t) = -16t^2 + 48t$. What is the initial velocity of the object? What is its initial height? How long will it take for the object to hit the ground?

c. An object has a position function of $h(t) = -16t^2 + 80$. What is the initial velocity of the object? What is its initial height? How long will it take for the object to hit the ground?

d. Suppose the object in part (b) had an initial height of 64 feet. How long would it take for the object to hit the ground? How long would it take for the object to hit the ground if its initial velocity were -48 feet per second?

See Section 10.3, Exercise 73

e. For an object whose position function is $h(t) = -16t^2 + 48t + 64$, find the time(s) at which the height of the object is 80 feet.

f. Use the given conditions in the table at the right to identify which method—extracting square roots, factoring, or the Quadratic Formula—is most practical for solving for t in the position function $h(t) = -16t^2 + bt + c$.

Condition	Method
$b = 0$	?
$b \neq 0, c = 0$	?
$b \neq 0, c \neq 0$	?

See Section 10.4, Exercise 98

g. An object has a position function of $h(t) = -16t^2 + 48t + 64$. Use the table feature of a graphing utility to estimate the object's maximum height. Verify this height by using the formula for locating the vertex of a parabola.

10.1   Solution by Extracting Square Roots

Objectives

1 Solve a quadratic equation by factoring.

2 Solve a quadratic equation by extracting square roots.

1 Solve a quadratic equation by factoring.

Solving Quadratic Equations by Factoring

Recall that a quadratic equation in x is an equation that can be written in the general form

$$ax^2 + bx + c = 0$$

Remind students that they can verify solutions by using graphing utilities to check the x-intercepts of the graph of $y = ax^2 + bx + c$.

where a, b, and c are real numbers with $a \neq 0$. In Section 6.5, you learned how to solve a quadratic equation by factoring. Example 1 reviews this procedure.

Example 1   Solving Quadratic Equations by Factoring

Solve the quadratic equations.

Discuss these two equations as a comparison of two common monomial factors, one a variable and one a constant:

$x^2 - 5x = 0$

$x(x - 5) = 0$

$x = 0$

$x - 5 = 0 \rightarrow x = 5$

and

$2x^2 - 14x + 24 = 0$

$2(x^2 - 7x + 12) = 0$

$2(x - 3)(x - 4) = 0$

$2 \neq 0$

$x - 3 = 0 \rightarrow x = 3$

$x - 4 = 0 \rightarrow x = 4$.

The common monomial factor x in the first example gives us a solution, $x = 0$. The common monomial factor 2 (a constant) in the second example does not provide a solution.

a. $x^2 + 5x = 14$ **b.** $2x^2 = 32$

Solution

a.
$$x^2 + 5x = 14 \qquad \text{Original equation}$$
$$x^2 + 5x - 14 = 0 \qquad \text{General form}$$
$$(x + 7)(x - 2) = 0 \qquad \text{Factor.}$$
$$x + 7 = 0 \implies x = -7 \qquad \text{Set 1st factor equal to 0.}$$
$$x - 2 = 0 \implies x = 2 \qquad \text{Set 2nd factor equal to 0.}$$

The solutions are -7 and 2. Check these solutions in the original equation.

b.
$$2x^2 = 32 \qquad \text{Original equation}$$
$$2x^2 - 32 = 0 \qquad \text{General form}$$
$$2(x^2 - 16) = 0 \qquad \text{Common monomial factor}$$
$$2(x + 4)(x - 4) = 0 \qquad \text{Factor as difference of squares.}$$
$$x + 4 = 0 \implies x = -4 \qquad \text{Set 1st factor equal to 0.}$$
$$x - 4 = 0 \implies x = 4 \qquad \text{Set 2nd factor equal to 0.}$$

The solutions are -4 and 4. Check these solutions in the original equation.

In Example 1(b) it is not necessary to set the *constant* factor 2 equal to zero. Because of this, when an equation has a constant factor, you can divide both sides by the factor. This is valid because dividing both sides of an equation by a constant factor produces an equivalent equation.

2 Solve a quadratic equation by extracting square roots.

Extracting Square Roots

In Example 1(b), suppose you had written the equation $2x^2 = 32$ in the form $x^2 = 16$ by first dividing both sides by 2. In this form, you could have concluded that the solutions are simply the two square roots of 16—namely, $x = 4$ and $x = -4$. This is a nice shortcut for solving quadratic equations of the form $u^2 = d$ where $d > 0$ and u is an algebraic expression.

▶ Extracting Square Roots

Let u be a real number, a variable, or an algebraic expression. The equation $u^2 = d$, where $d > 0$, has exactly two solutions:

$$u = \sqrt{d} \quad \text{and} \quad u = -\sqrt{d}.$$

These solutions can also be written as $u = \pm\sqrt{d}$. This form of the solution is read as "u is equal to plus or minus the square root of d." Solving an equation of the form $u^2 = d$ without going through the steps of factoring is called **extracting square roots.**

Study Tip

Not all quadratic equations have real number solutions. For instance, there is no real number that is the solution of the equation

$$x^2 + 4 = 0$$

because this would imply that there is a real number x such that $x^2 = -4$. Keep this possibility in mind as you do the exercises for this section.

Checking these solutions is easier than it may first appear. You might want to discuss this with students.

Example 2 Extracting Square Roots

Solve $4x^2 = 12$ by extracting square roots.

Solution

$$4x^2 = 12 \qquad \text{Original equation}$$
$$x^2 = 3 \qquad \text{Divide both sides by 4.}$$
$$x = \pm\sqrt{3} \qquad \text{Extract square roots.}$$

The solutions are $\sqrt{3}$ and $-\sqrt{3}$. You can check these solutions as follows.

Check

Substitute $\sqrt{3}$ into Equation
$$4x^2 = 12$$
$$4(\sqrt{3})^2 \overset{?}{=} 12$$
$$4(3) = 12 \checkmark$$

Substitute $-\sqrt{3}$ into Equation
$$4x^2 = 12$$
$$4(-\sqrt{3})^2 \overset{?}{=} 12$$
$$4(3) = 12 \checkmark$$

Example 3 Extracting Square Roots

Solve $(x - 3)^2 = 7$ by extracting square roots.

Solution

$$(x - 3)^2 = 7 \qquad \text{Original equation}$$
$$x - 3 = \pm\sqrt{7} \qquad \text{Extract square roots.}$$
$$x = 3 \pm \sqrt{7} \qquad \text{Add 3 to both sides.}$$

The solutions are $3 + \sqrt{7}$ and $3 - \sqrt{7}$. Check these in the original equation.

Caution students about the common error of forgetting the $\pm$ sign.

| Example 4 | Extracting Square Roots |

Solve the following quadratic equation by extracting square roots.

$$9(3x + 5)^2 - 16 = 0$$

Solution

$9(3x + 5)^2 - 16 = 0$	Original equation
$9(3x + 5)^2 = 16$	Add 16 to both sides.
$(3x + 5)^2 = \frac{16}{9}$	Divide both sides by 9.
$3x + 5 = \pm\frac{4}{3}$	Extract square roots.
$3x = -5 \pm \frac{4}{3}$	Subtract 5 from both sides.
$x = -\frac{5}{3} \pm \frac{4}{9}$	Divide both sides by 3.

The solutions are $x = -\frac{5}{3} + \frac{4}{9} = -\frac{11}{9}$ and $x = -\frac{5}{3} - \frac{4}{9} = -\frac{19}{9}$.

| Example 5 | Calculating a Compound Interest Rate | |

Five hundred dollars is deposited in an account. At the end of 2 years, the balance in the account is $561.80. If the interest earned on the account is compounded annually, what is the interest rate?

Solution

The mathematical model used to find the interest earned on an account is

$$A = P(1 + r)^t$$

where A is the balance in the account, P is the amount deposited, r is the annual interest rate (in decimal form), and t is the number of years.

$A = P(1 + r)^t$	Model for compound interest
$561.80 = 500(1 + r)^2$	Substitute 561.80 for A, 500 for P, and 2 for t.
$1.1236 = (1 + r)^2$	Divide both sides by 500.
$\sqrt{1.1236} = 1 + r$	Extract positive square root.
$\sqrt{1.1236} - 1 = r$	Subtract 1 from both sides.
$0.06 = r$	Interest rate in decimal form

So, the interest rate is 6%.

Study Tip

In Example 5, only the positive square root is used in the solution. The negative square root would have resulted in a negative value for r. In the context of this real-life application, the value of r must be positive, so only the positive square root is needed for the solution.

| Discussing the Concept | Solving Equations |

Write a short paragraph explaining how to solve an equation of the form $ax^2 + c = 0$ by extracting square roots. Exchange paragraphs with a class member, and use the described procedure to solve the equation $2x^2 + 6 = 0$. Do you have any revisions to suggest to make the procedure valid?

10.1   Exercises

Integrated Review   *Concepts, Skills, and Problem Solving*

Keep mathematically in shape by doing these exercises *before* the problems of this section.

Properties and Definitions

1. Identify the leading coefficient in $11x - 2x^4 + 5x^2$. Explain.

2. State the degree of the product $(x^3 - 1)(x^2 + 1)$. Explain.

3. Sketch a graph for which y is not a function of x. Explain.

4. Sketch a graph for which y is a function of x. Explain.

In Exercises 5–10, completely factor the expression.

5. $4b^3 - 12b^2$

6. $t^3 + 4t^2 - 4t - 16$

7. $12y^2 - 75$

8. $4x^2 - 28x + 49$

9. $2u^2 + 12u - 54$

10. $6x^2 - 11x - 35$

Problem Solving

11. The selling price of a jacket is $234. The mark-up rate is 30% of the wholesale cost. Find the wholesale cost.

12. How many liters of a 20% alcohol solution must be mixed with a 50% solution to obtain 12 liters of a 40% solution?

Developing Skills

In Exercises 1–24, solve by factoring. See Example 1.

1. $y^2 - 3y = 0$

2. $t^2 + 5t = 0$

3. $4x^2 - 8x = 0$

4. $25y^2 - 100y = 0$

5. $a^2 - 25 = 0$

6. $16 - v^2 = 0$

7. $9m^2 = 64$

8. $16y^2 = 81$

9. $u(u - 10) - 6(u - 10) = 0$

10. $2y(y + 3) - 5(y + 3) = 0$

11. $3z(z + 20) + 12(z + 20) = 0$

12. $16x(x - 3) - 4(x - 3) = 0$

13. $x^2 - 5x + 6 = 0$

14. $x^2 - 7x + 12 = 0$

15. $x^2 + 4x + 4 = 0$

16. $x^2 - 10x + 25 = 0$

17. $16x^2 - 40x + 25 = 0$

18. $9x^2 - 12x + 4 = 0$

19. $5x^2 - 16x - 16 = 0$

20. $3x^2 - 14x - 24 = 0$

21. $6x^2 = -13x + 28$

22. $2x^2 = 5x - 2$

23. $(x - 3)(x + 1) = 5$

24. $(6 + x)(1 - x) = 10$

In Exercises 25–82, solve by extracting square roots. (Some equations have no real solutions.) See Examples 2–4.

25. $x^2 = 9$

26. $h^2 = 25$

27. $x^2 = 49$

28. $z^2 = 121$

29. $3x^2 = 363$

30. $2b^2 = 98$

31. $6x^2 = 30$

32. $5x^2 = 35$

33. $7x^2 = 42$

34. $3x^2 = 33$

35. $9x^2 = 49$

36. $16z^2 = 121$

37. $16y^2 = 25$

38. $36v^2 = 4$

39. $u^2 - 100 = 0$

40. $v^2 - 25 = 0$

41. $9u^2 - 100 = 0$

42. $16v^2 - 25 = 0$

43. $x^2 + 1 = 0$

44. $a^2 + 9 = 0$

45. $2s^2 - 5 = 27$

46. $81x^2 - 5 = 20$

47. $\frac{1}{2}x^2 - 1 = 3$

48. $\frac{1}{5}x^2 + 4 = 5$

49. $\frac{1}{3}t^2 - 14 = 2$

50. $\frac{1}{4}z^2 - 4 = 4$

51. $\frac{1}{4}x^2 + 6 = 2$

52. $\frac{1}{3}y^2 - 5 = -6$

53. $(x + 4)^2 = 3$

54. $(x - 2)^2 = 11$

55. $(y - 7)^2 = 6$

56. $(t + 1)^2 = 10$

57. $(x + 4)^2 = 144$

58. $(y - 7)^2 = 121$

59. $(x - 1)^2 = 5$

60. $(x - 10)^2 = 20$

61. $(y + 2)^2 = 12$

62. $(a - 5)^2 = 8$

63. $(x - 3)^2 = 18$

64. $(x + 6)^2 = 24$

65. $(3x - 4)^2 = 7$

66. $(2x - 1)^2 = 3$

67. $(5x + 2)^2 = 5$

68. $(4x + 5)^2 = 10$

69. $(2x + 5)^2 = 8$

70. $(3x - 7)^2 = 32$

71. $(3x - 4)^2 = 27$

72. $(5x - 2)^2 = 20$

73. $(2x + 1)^2 = -4$

74. $(3x + 2)^2 = -7$

75. $4(x + 3)^2 = 25$

76. $9(x - 1)^2 = 16$

77. $16(x - 5)^2 = 49$

78. $25(y + 3)^2 = 81$

79. $9(3x - 1)^2 = 4$

80. $4(2x + 3)^2 = 25$

81. $8(4x + 3)^2 = 14$

82. $12(3x - 7)^2 = 15$

In Exercises 83–86, factor the left side of the equation and solve the resulting equation.

83. $x^2 - 4x + 4 = 9$

84. $x^2 + 6x + 9 = 4$

85. $4x^2 + 4x + 1 = 25$

86. $4x^2 - 12x + 9 = 16$

In Exercises 87–92, use a graphing utility to graph the function. Use the graph to estimate the x-intercepts of the graph. Set $y = 0$ and solve the resulting equation. Compare the result with the x-intercepts of the graph.

87. $y = x^2 - 9$

88. $y = 1 - x^2$

89. $y = 4 - (x - 1)^2$

90. $y = (x + 3)^2 - 9$

91. $y = (x + 2)^2 - 1$

92. $y = 25 - (x - 3)^2$

Solving Problems

Geometry   In Exercises 93–96, solve for x.

93. Area = 16 square centimeters

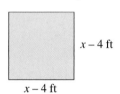

x cm

$x + 6$ cm

94. Area = 64 square feet

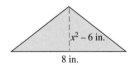

$x - 4$ ft

$x - 4$ ft

95. Area = 12 square inches

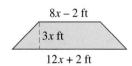

$x^2 - 6$ in.

8 in.

96. Area = 120 square feet

8x – 2 ft

3x ft

12x + 2 ft

97. *Geometry*   An oil spill from an offshore drilling platform covers a circular region of approximately 10 square miles. Approximate the diameter of the region. (Use $\pi \approx 3.14$.)

98. *Geometry*   The circular base of a chemical storage bin has an area of 706 square inches. Approximate the diameter of the circular base. (Use $\pi \approx 3.14$.)

99. *Compound Interest*   After 2 years, a \$1000 investment, compounded annually at interest rate r, will yield an amount of $1000(1 + r)^2$. If this amount is \$1166.40, find the rate r.

100. *Compound Interest*   After 2 years, a \$1500 investment, compounded annually at interest rate r, will yield an amount of $1500(1 + r)^2$. If this amount is \$1701.34, find the rate r.

101. *Compound Interest*   Four hundred dollars is deposited in an account. At the end of 2 years, the balance in the account is \$462.25. If the interest earned on the account is compounded annually, what is the interest rate?

102. *Compound Interest*   Seven hundred dollars is deposited in an account. At the end of 2 years, the balance in the account is \$801.43. If the interest earned on the account is compounded annually, what is the interest rate?

103. *Revenue*   The revenue R (in dollars) when x units of a product are sold is modeled by

$$R = x\left(5 - \frac{1}{10}x\right), \quad 0 < x < 25.$$

Determine the number of units that must be sold to produce a revenue of \$60.

104. *Revenue*   The revenue R (in dollars) when x units of a product are sold is given by

$$R = x\left(100 - \frac{1}{2}x\right), \quad 0 < x < 100.$$

Determine the number of units that must be sold to produce a revenue of \$4200.

105. *Falling Time*   The height h (in feet) of an object dropped from a tower 64 feet high (see figure) is modeled by

$$h = 64 - 16t^2$$

where t measures the time in seconds. How long does it take for the object to reach the ground?

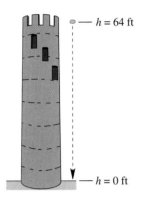

$\circ - h = 64$ ft

$- h = 0$ ft

106. *Falling Time*   The height h (in feet) of an object dropped from a bridge 100 feet high is modeled by

$$h = 100 - 16t^2$$

where t measures the time in seconds. How long does it take for the object to reach the ground?

107. *Analyzing the Fall of an Object*   An object is dropped from a height of 300 feet. Its height (in feet) after t seconds of falling is modeled by

$$h = 300 - 16t^2.$$

(a) Complete the table. Round the times to two decimal places.

Height, h	Time, t
300	0
250	
200	
150	
100	
50	
0	

(b) Consecutive heights in the table differ by a constant amount of 50 feet. Do the corresponding times differ by a constant amount? Explain.

108. *The Hammer and the Feather*   In 1971, astronaut David Scott demonstrated that a feather and a hammer fall at the same rate on the moon because the moon has no atmosphere (and hence no air resistance). The height h (in feet) of a falling object on the moon is modeled by

$$h = -\frac{27}{10}t^2 + s$$

where t is time in seconds and s is the height from which the object is dropped. If a hammer and a feather are dropped 5 feet from the surface of the moon, how long will it take for each to hit the surface?

Explaining Concepts

109. Answer parts (a)–(d) of Motivating the Chapter on page 511.

110. The general form of a quadratic equation in x is $ax^2 + bx + c = 0$, where a, b, and c are real numbers with $a \neq 0$. Explain why b and c can equal 0, but a cannot.

111. Explain the Zero-Factor Property. How can it be used to solve a quadratic equation?

112. *True or False?*   The only solution of the equation $x^2 = 16$ is $x = 4$. Explain.

113. Using your own words, explain how to solve a quadratic equation by extracting square roots.

114. State whether factoring or extracting square roots is usually the easier method of solving the quadratic equation $ax^2 + bx + c = 0$ when (a) $b = 0$ and (b) $c = 0$. Explain.

115. Without attempting to solve the equations, state which of the following equations do not have real solutions. Explain.

(a) $(x - 2)^2 = 0$ (b) $(x - 2)^2 = 36$

(c) $(x - 2)^2 + 36 = 0$ (d) $(x - 2)^2 - 5 = 0$

10.2 Solution by Completing the Square

Objectives

1 Construct a perfect square trinomial.

2 Solve a quadratic equation by completing the square.

1 Construct a perfect square trinomial.

Constructing Perfect Square Trinomials

Consider the quadratic equation

$$(x - 3)^2 = 7.$$ Completed square form

You know from Example 3 of the preceding section that this equation has two solutions: $3 + \sqrt{7}$ and $3 - \sqrt{7}$. Now suppose the equation were given in its general form

$$(x - 3)^2 = 7$$ Completed square form

$$x^2 - 6x + 9 = 7$$ Multiply binomials.

$$x^2 - 6x + 2 = 0.$$ General form

How could you solve this form of the quadratic equation? You could try factoring, but you would find that the left side of the equation is not factorable using integer coefficients. What is needed is a procedure for reversing the steps shown above.

In this section, you will study a technique for rewriting an equation in completed square form. This process is called **completing the square.**

To complete the square, you must realize that all perfect square trinomials with leading coefficients of 1 have a similar form.

Perfect Square Trinomial = Square of Binomial

$$x^2 + bx + \left(\frac{b}{2}\right)^2 = \left(x + \frac{b}{2}\right)^2$$

(half of b)²

Note that the constant term of the perfect square trinomial is the square of half of the coefficient of the x-term. So, to complete the square for an expression of the form $x^2 + bx$, you must add $(b/2)^2$ to the expression.

▶ Completing the Square

To **complete the square** for the expression

$$x^2 + bx$$

add $(b/2)^2$, which is the square of half the coefficient of x.
Consequently,

$$x^2 + bx + \left(\frac{b}{2}\right)^2 = \left(x + \frac{b}{2}\right)^2.$$

| Example 1 | Constructing a Perfect Square Trinomial |

What term should be added to the expression

$$x^2 - 4x$$

so that it becomes a perfect square trinomial? Write the new expression as the square of a binomial.

Solution

For this expression, the coefficient of the x-term is -4. Taking half of this and squaring the result shows that $\left(-\frac{4}{2}\right)^2$ or 4 should be added to the expression to make it a perfect square trinomial.

$$x^2 - 4x + \left(-\frac{4}{2}\right)^2 = x^2 - 4x + 4 \qquad \text{Perfect square trinomial}$$

$$= (x - 2)^2 \qquad \text{Square of binomial}$$

In Example 1, don't make the mistake of concluding that $x^2 - 4x$ is equal to $(x - 2)^2$. The point of the example is that $x^2 - 4x$ is not a perfect square trinomial. If, however, you add 4 to the expression, then the *new* expression is a perfect square trinomial.

| Example 2 | Constructing Perfect Square Trinomials |

Here are some additional examples. What term should be added to each expression so that it becomes a perfect square trinomial?

$y^2 - 16y$:
$y^2 - 16y + 64 = (y - 8)^2$

$b^2 + 11b$:
$b^2 + 11b + \frac{121}{4} = \left(b + \frac{11}{2}\right)^2$

$k^2 - \frac{8}{9}k$:
$k^2 - \frac{8}{9}k + \frac{16}{81} = \left(k - \frac{4}{9}\right)^2$

$w^2 + \frac{1}{6}w$:
$w^2 + \frac{1}{6}w + \frac{1}{144} = \left(w + \frac{1}{12}\right)^2$

What terms should be added to the expressions so that each becomes a perfect square trinomial? Write each new expression as the square of a binomial.

a. $x^2 + 12x$

b. $x^2 - 7x$

Solution

a. For this expression, the coefficient of the x-term is 12. Taking half of this and squaring the result shows that $\left(\frac{12}{2}\right)^2$ or 36 should be added to the expression to make it a perfect square trinomial.

$$x^2 + 12x + \left(\frac{12}{2}\right)^2 = x^2 + 12x + 36 \qquad \text{Perfect square trinomial}$$

$$= (x + 6)^2 \qquad \text{Square of binomial}$$

b. For this expression, the coefficient of the x-term is -7. Taking half of this and squaring the result shows that $\left(-\frac{7}{2}\right)^2$ or $\frac{49}{4}$ should be added to the expression to make it a perfect square trinomial.

$$x^2 - 7x + \left(-\frac{7}{2}\right)^2 = x^2 - 7x + \frac{49}{4} \qquad \text{Perfect square trinomial}$$

$$= \left(x - \frac{7}{2}\right)^2 \qquad \text{Square of binomial}$$

2 Solve a quadratic equation by completing the square.

Completing the Square

Completing the square can be used to solve a quadratic equation. When using this procedure, remember to *preserve the equality* by adding the same constant to *both* sides of the equation.

Study Tip

In Example 3, completing the square is used for the sake of illustration. This particular equation would be easier to solve by factoring. Try reworking the problem by factoring to see that you obtain the same two solutions.

Example 3 Completing the Square: Leading Coefficient Is 1

Solve $x^2 + 10x = 0$ by completing the square.

Solution

$$x^2 + 10x = 0 \qquad \text{Original equation}$$

$$x^2 + 10x + 5^2 = 25 \qquad \text{Add } 5^2 = 25 \text{ to both sides.}$$

(half of 10)^2

$$(x + 5)^2 = 25 \qquad \text{Square of binomial}$$

$$x + 5 = \pm\sqrt{25} \qquad \text{Extract square roots.}$$

$$x = -5 \pm 5 \qquad \text{Subtract 5 from both sides.}$$

$$x = 0 \text{ or } -10 \qquad \text{Solutions}$$

The solutions are 0 and -10. You can check these solutions as follows.

Check

Substitute 0 into Equation	*Substitute -10 into Equation*
$x^2 + 10x = 0$	$x^2 + 10x = 0$
$0^2 + 10(0) \stackrel{?}{=} 0$	$(-10)^2 + 10(-10) \stackrel{?}{=} 0$
$0 = 0$ ✓	$100 - 100 = 0$ ✓

Example 4 Completing the Square: Leading Coefficient Is 1

Solve $x^2 - 4x + 1 = 0$ by completing the square.

Solution

$$x^2 - 4x + 1 = 0 \qquad \text{Original equation}$$

$$x^2 - 4x = -1 \qquad \text{Subtract 1 from both sides.}$$

$$x^2 - 4x + (-2)^2 = -1 + 4 \qquad \text{Add } (-2)^2 = 4 \text{ to both sides.}$$

(half of -4)^2

$$(x - 2)^2 = 3 \qquad \text{Square of binomial}$$

$$x - 2 = \pm\sqrt{3} \qquad \text{Extract square roots.}$$

$$x = 2 \pm \sqrt{3} \qquad \text{Add 2 to both sides.}$$

Remind students that the statement $x = 2 \pm \sqrt{3}$ indicates two distinct solutions.

The solutions are $2 + \sqrt{3}$ and $2 - \sqrt{3}$. Use your graphing utility to check these solutions in the original equation.

If the leading coefficient of a quadratic expression is not 1, you must divide both sides of the equation by this coefficient *before* completing the square.

> **Example 5**   Completing the Square: Leading Coefficient Is Not 1

Solve $2x^2 + 5x = 3$ by completing the square.

Solution

You might point out that the procedure for completing the square is also used in subsequent algebra courses for purposes other than solving quadratic equations.

$$2x^2 + 5x = 3 \qquad \text{Original equation}$$

$$x^2 + \frac{5}{2}x = \frac{3}{2} \qquad \text{Divide both sides by 2.}$$

$$x^2 + \frac{5}{2}x + \left(\frac{5}{4}\right)^2 = \frac{3}{2} + \frac{25}{16} \qquad \text{Add } \left(\frac{5}{4}\right)^2 = \frac{25}{16} \text{ to both sides.}$$

$$\underbrace{}_{\left(\text{half of } \frac{5}{2}\right)^2}$$

$$\left(x + \frac{5}{4}\right)^2 = \frac{49}{16} \qquad \text{Square of binomial}$$

$$x + \frac{5}{4} = \pm\frac{7}{4} \qquad \text{Extract square roots.}$$

$$x = -\frac{5}{4} \pm \frac{7}{4} \qquad \text{Subtract } \frac{5}{4} \text{ from both sides.}$$

The solutions are

$$x = -\frac{5}{4} + \frac{7}{4} = \frac{2}{4} = \frac{1}{2} \quad \text{and} \quad x = -\frac{5}{4} - \frac{7}{4} = -\frac{12}{4} = -3.$$

You can check these solutions in the original equation as follows.

Check

Substitute $\frac{1}{2}$ into Equation	Substitute -3 into Equation
$2x^2 + 5x = 3$	$2x^2 + 5x = 3$
$2\left(\frac{1}{2}\right)^2 + 5\left(\frac{1}{2}\right) \overset{?}{=} 3$	$2(-3)^2 + 5(-3) \overset{?}{=} 3$
$2\left(\frac{1}{4}\right) + \frac{5}{2} \overset{?}{=} 3$	$2(9) - 15 \overset{?}{=} 3$
$\frac{1}{2} + \frac{5}{2} = 3$ ✓	$18 - 15 = 3$ ✓

If you solve a quadratic equation by completing the square and obtain solutions that do not involve radicals, you could have solved the equation by factoring. For instance, in Example 5, the equation could have been factored as follows:

$$2x^2 + 5x - 3 = 0 \qquad \text{Original equation}$$

$$(2x - 1)(x + 3) = 0 \qquad \text{Factor.}$$

$$2x - 1 = 0 \quad \Longrightarrow \quad x = \tfrac{1}{2} \qquad \text{Set 1st factor equal to 0.}$$

$$x + 3 = 0 \quad \Longrightarrow \quad x = -3 \qquad \text{Set 2nd factor equal to 0.}$$

Example 6	Completing the Square: Leading Coefficient Is Not 1

Solve the quadratic equation by completing the square. Use a calculator to approximate the solutions to two decimal places.

$$3x^2 - 2x - 4 = 0$$

Solution

$$3x^2 - 2x - 4 = 0 \qquad \text{Original equation}$$

$$3x^2 - 2x = 4 \qquad \text{Add 4 to both sides.}$$

$$x^2 - \frac{2}{3}x = \frac{4}{3} \qquad \text{Divide both sides by 3.}$$

$$x^2 - \frac{2}{3}x + \left(-\frac{1}{3}\right)^2 = \frac{4}{3} + \frac{1}{9} \qquad \text{Add } \left(-\frac{1}{3}\right)^2 = \frac{1}{9} \text{ to both sides.}$$

$$\left(\text{half of } -\frac{2}{3}\right)^2$$

$$\left(x - \frac{1}{3}\right)^2 = \frac{13}{9} \qquad \text{Square of binomial}$$

$$x - \frac{1}{3} = \pm\frac{\sqrt{13}}{3} \qquad \text{Extract square roots.}$$

$$x = \frac{1}{3} \pm \frac{\sqrt{13}}{3} \qquad \text{Add } \frac{1}{3} \text{ to both sides.}$$

The solutions are

$$x = \frac{1}{3} + \frac{\sqrt{13}}{3} \approx 1.54 \quad \text{and} \quad x = \frac{1}{3} - \frac{\sqrt{13}}{3} \approx -0.87.$$

Use your graphing utility to check these solutions in the original equation.

⩘ Technology: Tip

When you are solving an equation, remember that you can use a graphing utility to approximate the solutions. For instance, in Example 6, you can approximate the solutions by sketching the graph of $y = 3x^2 - 2x - 4$ as shown below. Notice that the graph has two x-intercepts at $x \approx 1.54$ and $x \approx -0.87$. If you have access to a graphing utility, graph this function and use the root or zero feature to check that the x-intercepts occur at these two x-values.

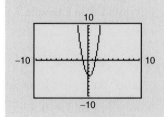

The method of completing the square can be used to solve *any* quadratic equation. Moreover, this method will identify those quadratic equations that have no real solutions, as demonstrated in the next example.

Example 7   A Quadratic Equation with No Real Solution

Show that

$$x^2 - 4x + 7 = 0$$

has no real solution by completing the square.

Solution

Begin by writing the equation in completed square form, as follows.

$x^2 - 4x + 7 = 0$	Original equation
$x^2 - 4x = -7$	Subtract 7 from both sides.
$x^2 - 4x + 4 = -7 + 4$	Add $(-2)^2 = 4$ to both sides.
$(x - 2)^2 = -3$	Square of binomial

Because the square of a real number cannot be negative, you can conclude that this equation has no real solution.

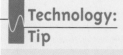 **Technology: Tip**   Use a graphing utility to graph the quadratic equation

$$y = x^2 - 4x + 7.$$

How can you tell from the graph that the quadratic equation has no real solution? What do you think the graph of a quadratic equation having one (repeated) solution looks like? How about a quadratic equation having two solutions?

Discussing the Concept   Completing the Square

The figure on the left represents the expression $x^2 + 2x$. The figure on the right represents the expression $(x + 1)^2$. Find the area of the part that was added to the left figure to "complete the square." Draw two such figures for the expression $x^2 + 5x$. What was added to complete the square? Compare your results with those of others in your class.

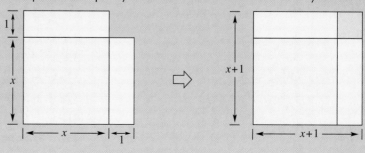

10.2 Exercises

Integrated Review Concepts, Skills, and Problem Solving

Keep mathematically in shape by doing these exercises *before* the problems of this section.

Properties and Definitions

In Exercises 1–4, consider the equation of the line $4x - 3y - 12 = 0$.

1. Is the point $(6, 4)$ on the line? Explain.
2. Find two points on the line and use the two points to find the slope of the line. Does it matter which two points you use? Explain.
3. Write the equation of the line in point-slope form.
4. Write the equation of the line in slope-intercept form.

Linear Equations

In Exercises 5–8, determine an equation of the line passing through the two points.

5. $(-3, 2), (5, 0)$
6. $(-10, -5), (4, 10)$
7. $(-4, -4), (-4, 6)$
8. $\left(\frac{2}{3}, \frac{1}{2}\right), \left(\frac{5}{6}, \frac{3}{4}\right)$

In Exercises 9 and 10, solve the system.

9. $3x - 5y = 8$
   $x + 2y = 10$

10. $6x + 2y = -22$
    $5x - 3y = -37$

Problem Solving

11. A sales representative is reimbursed $125 per day for lodging and meals plus $0.32 per mile driven. Write a linear function giving the daily cost C to the company in terms of x, the number of miles driven.

12. A tennis court is 36 feet wide and 78 feet long. Find the length of the diagonal of the court.

Developing Skills

In Exercises 1–4, find the product.

1. $(x + 2)^2$
2. $(t + 3)^2$
3. $(y - 10)^2$
4. $(u - 6)^2$

In Exercises 5–20, what term should be added to the expression to make it a perfect square trinomial? See Examples 1 and 2.

5. $x^2 + 10x$
6. $x^2 + 14x$
7. $y^2 - 24y$
8. $y^2 - 8y$
9. $x^2 + 16x$
10. $t^2 - 18t$
11. $t^2 + 3t$
12. $u^2 + 9u$
13. $y^2 - 7y$
14. $x^2 - 11x$
15. $x^2 - x$
16. $y^2 + 5y$
17. $x^2 + \frac{1}{2}x$
18. $y^2 - \frac{1}{3}y$
19. $t^2 - \frac{3}{4}t$
20. $u^2 + \frac{4}{5}u$

In Exercises 21–60, solve by completing the square. (Some equations have no real solutions.) See Examples 3–5.

21. $x^2 - 8x = 0$
22. $x^2 + 12x = 0$
23. $y^2 + 20y = 0$
24. $u^2 - 16u = 0$
25. $x^2 - 2x - 1 = 0$
26. $x^2 - 6x + 7 = 0$
27. $u^2 - 4u - 1 = 0$
28. $a^2 - 10a + 15 = 0$
29. $x^2 - 2x + 3 = 0$
30. $x^2 - 6x + 14 = 0$
31. $x^2 - 8x - 2 = 0$
32. $x^2 + 6x - 3 = 0$
33. $y^2 + 14y + 17 = 0$
34. $y^2 + 2y - 26 = 0$
35. $x^2 + 2x - 35 = 0$
36. $x^2 - 6x - 27 = 0$
37. $x^2 - x - 3 = 0$
38. $x^2 + 3x + 1 = 0$
39. $t^2 + 5t + 2 = 0$
40. $u^2 - 9u - 5 = 0$
41. $y^2 - 7y + 12 = 0$
42. $t^2 + 5t + 6 = 0$
43. $v^2 + 3v - 10 = 0$
44. $z^2 - 7z + 5 = 0$

45. $u^2 + 9u + 21 = 0$ **46.** $x^2 - 11x + 31 = 0$

47. $3x^2 - 6x + 9 = 0$ **48.** $2x^2 - 4x + 6 = 0$

49. $2x^2 + 6x - 5 = 0$ **50.** $3x^2 - 12x + 7 = 0$

51. $3x^2 + 4x + 5 = 0$ **52.** $2z^2 - z + 1 = 0$

53. $2y^2 + 3y - 1 = 0$ **54.** $4z^2 - 3z - 2 = 0$

55. $6x^2 - 10x - 9 = 0$ **56.** $10x^2 - 8x + 15 = 0$

57. $\frac{1}{3}x^2 + \frac{1}{3}x - 4 = 0$ **58.** $\frac{1}{5}x^2 + \frac{3}{5}x - 2 = 0$

59. $\frac{1}{2}x^2 + x - 1 = 0$ **60.** $\frac{2}{3}x^2 - 4x + 1 = 0$

In Exercises 61–68, solve the quadratic equation (a) by completing the square and (b) by factoring.

61. $x^2 - 4x = 0$ **62.** $x^2 - 2x = 0$

63. $t^2 + 6t + 5 = 0$ **64.** $x^2 + 2x - 15 = 0$

65. $x^2 + 5x + 6 = 0$ **66.** $x^2 - 7x - 8 = 0$

67. $2x^2 - 5x + 2 = 0$ **68.** $4x^2 - 4x - 3 = 0$

In Exercises 69–76, solve by completing the square. Use a calculator to approximate the solution. Round the result to two decimal places. See Example 6.

69. $x^2 + x - 3 = 0$ **70.** $c^2 - 3c + 1 = 0$

71. $x^2 - 6x + 7 = 0$ **72.** $y^2 + 4y - 1 = 0$

73. $4z^2 - 4z - 3 = 0$ **74.** $2x^2 + 6x + 1 = 0$

75. $3y^2 - y - 1 = 0$ **76.** $2x^2 + 2x - 7 = 0$

In Exercises 77–86, solve the equation.

77. $\dfrac{x}{2} + \dfrac{1}{x} = 2$ **78.** $\dfrac{x}{3} + \dfrac{2}{x} = 4$

79. $\dfrac{3}{x - 2} = 2x$ **80.** $\dfrac{4}{x} + \dfrac{2}{x - 2} = 1$

81. $\sqrt{2x + 3} = x - 2$ **82.** $\sqrt{4x + 5} = x - 6$

83. $2\sqrt{x - 1} = x - 4$ **84.** $3\sqrt{x + 1} = x - 3$

85. $\sqrt{x^2 + 3} - 2\sqrt{x} = 0$ **86.** $3\sqrt{x} = \sqrt{x^2 - 10}$

In Exercises 87–90, use a graphing utility to graph the function. Graphically estimate the x-intercepts. Set $y = 0$ and solve the resulting equation. Compare the results with the x-intercepts of the graph.

87. $y = x^2 - 4x + 2$ **88.** $y = x^2 + 2x - 2$

89. $y = \sqrt{2x + 1} - x$ **90.** $y = \sqrt{x} - x + 3$

Solving Problems

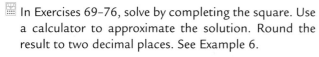

Geometry   In Exercises 91–94, solve for x.

91. Area = 12 square centimeters

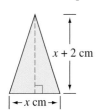

$x + 2$ cm

$\leftarrow x$ cm $\rightarrow$

92. Area = 31 square feet

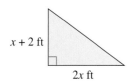

$x + 2$ ft

$2x$ ft

93. Area = 16 square millimeters

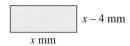

$x - 4$ mm

x mm

94. Area = 160 square feet

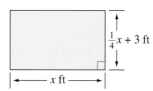

$\frac{1}{4}x + 3$ ft

x ft

95. *Problem Solving*   Find two consecutive positive integers such that the sum of their squares is 85.

96. *Problem Solving*   Find two consecutive positive integers such that the sum of their squares is 41.

97. *Revenue*   The revenue R (in dollars) for selling x units of a product is modeled by

$$R = x\left(25 - \frac{1}{2}x\right), \quad 0 < x < 25.$$

How many units are sold if the revenue is $304.50?

98. *Revenue*   The revenue (in dollars) for selling x units of a product is modeled by

$$R = x\left(50 - \frac{1}{4}x\right), \quad 0 < x < 100.$$

Find the number of units sold if the revenue is $2059.

99. *Geometry* The sum of the base and height of a triangle is 100 centimeters. The area of the triangle is 1200 square centimeters.

    (a) Draw a figure that gives a visual representation of the problem.

    (b) If the height of the triangle is h, write the base in terms of h.

    (c) Write an expression for the area of the triangle in terms of h. Use the result to find the dimensions of the triangle.

100. *Geometry* The sum of the base and height of a triangle is 120 centimeters. The area of the triangle is 1792 square centimeters.

    (a) Draw a figure that gives a visual representation of the problem.

    (b) If the height of the triangle is h, write the base in terms of h.

    (c) Write an expression for the area of the triangle in terms of h. Use the result to find the dimensions of the triangle.

101. *Exploration*

    (a) Perform the multiplication on the left side of the equation

$$\left[x - \left(1 + \sqrt{2}\right)\right]\left[x - \left(1 - \sqrt{2}\right)\right] = 0.$$

    (b) Solve the equation in part (a) by factoring.

    (c) Solve the equation in part (a) by completing the square.

    (d) Write a quadratic equation that has solutions $2 + \sqrt{5}$ and $2 - \sqrt{5}$.

Explaining Concepts

102. What is a perfect square trinomial? Give an example.

103. Describe how to complete the square for a quadratic equation when the leading coefficient is 1.

104. Describe how to complete the square for a quadratic equation when the leading coefficient *is not* 1.

105. Would you solve $x^2 - 2x - 3 = 0$ by factoring or by completing the square? Explain.

106. Would you solve $x^2 - 2x - 2 = 0$ by factoring or by completing the square? Explain.

107. Is it possible for a quadratic equation to have no real number solution? If so, give an example.

108. *True or False?* There exist quadratic equations with real solutions that cannot be solved by completing the square. Explain.

109. *Error Analysis* Find the error.

$$9x^2 - 4x - 2 = 0$$
$$9x^2 - 4x = 2$$
$$9x^2 - 4x + 4 = 2 + 4$$
$$(3x - 2)^2 = 6$$
$$3x - 2 = \pm\sqrt{6}$$
$$x = \frac{2 \pm \sqrt{6}}{3}$$

10.3   Solution by the Quadratic Formula

Objectives

1 Use the completing the square technique to develop the Quadratic Formula.

2 Solve a quadratic equation using the Quadratic Formula.

---

1 Use the completing the square technique to develop the Quadratic Formula.

You might first present this formula, illustrate its use, and then, when students are somewhat familiar with the formula, discuss its derivation.

The Quadratic Formula

Another technique for solving a quadratic equation involves the **Quadratic Formula.** This formula is obtained by completing the square for a general quadratic equation.

$$ax^2 + bx + c = 0 \qquad \text{General form, } a \neq 0$$

$$ax^2 + bx = -c \qquad \text{Subtract } c \text{ from both sides.}$$

$$x^2 + \frac{b}{a}x = -\frac{c}{a} \qquad \text{Divide both sides by } a.$$

$$x^2 + \frac{b}{a}x + \left(\frac{b}{2a}\right)^2 = -\frac{c}{a} + \left(\frac{b}{2a}\right)^2 \qquad \text{Complete the square.}$$

$$\left(x + \frac{b}{2a}\right)^2 = \frac{b^2 - 4ac}{4a^2} \qquad \text{Simplify.}$$

$$x + \frac{b}{2a} = \pm\sqrt{\frac{b^2 - 4ac}{4a^2}} \qquad \text{Extract square roots.}$$

$$x = -\frac{b}{2a} \pm \frac{\sqrt{b^2 - 4ac}}{2|a|} \qquad \text{Subtract } \frac{b}{2a} \text{ from both sides.}$$

$$x = \frac{-b \pm \sqrt{b^2 - 4ac}}{2a} \qquad \text{Simplify.}$$

Study Tip

The Quadratic Formula is one of the most important formulas in algebra and you should memorize it. We have found that it helps to try to memorize a verbal statement of the rule. For instance, you might try to remember the following verbal statement of the Quadratic Formula: "Negative b, plus or minus the square root of b squared minus $4ac$, all divided by $2a$."

> ▶ **The Quadratic Formula**
>
> The solutions of $ax^2 + bx + c = 0$, $a \neq 0$, are given by the **Quadratic Formula**
>
> $$x = \frac{-b \pm \sqrt{b^2 - 4ac}}{2a}.$$
>
> The expression inside the radical, $b^2 - 4ac$, is called the **discriminant.**
>
> **1.** If $b^2 - 4ac > 0$, the equation has two real solutions.
> **2.** If $b^2 - 4ac = 0$, the equation has one (repeated) real solution.
> **3.** If $b^2 - 4ac < 0$, the equation has no real solution.

Example 1   Determining the Number of Solutions

For the equation $x^2 + 5x - 14 = 0$ with $a = 1$, $b = 5$, and $c = -14$, the discriminant is $b^2 - 4ac = 5^2 - 4(1)(-14) = 25 + 56 = 81$. Because $81 > 0$, there are two real solutions to the quadratic equation.

Solving Equations by the Quadratic Formula

When using the Quadratic Formula, remember that before the formula can be applied, you must first write the quadratic equation in general form, as shown in Example 2.

| Example 2 | The Quadratic Formula: Two Distinct Solutions |

Use the Quadratic Formula to solve

$$x^2 + 5x = 14.$$

Solution

To begin, write the equation in general form, $ax^2 + bx + c = 0$.

$$x^2 + 5x = 14 \qquad \text{Original equation}$$
$$x^2 + 5x - 14 = 0 \qquad \text{General form}$$

From Example 1, you know that this equation has two solutions. Use the values $a = 1$, $b = 5$, and $c = -14$ from the general form to substitute into the Quadratic Formula and obtain the solution.

$$x = \frac{-b \pm \sqrt{b^2 - 4ac}}{2a} \qquad \text{Quadratic Formula}$$

$$x = \frac{-5 \pm \sqrt{5^2 - 4(1)(-14)}}{2(1)} \qquad \text{Substitute 1 for } a, \text{ 5 for } b, \text{ and } -14 \text{ for } c.$$

$$x = \frac{-5 \pm \sqrt{25 + 56}}{2} \qquad \text{Simplify.}$$

$$x = \frac{-5 \pm \sqrt{81}}{2} \qquad \text{Simplify.}$$

$$x = \frac{-5 \pm 9}{2} \qquad \text{Simplify.}$$

The solutions are

$$x = \frac{-5 + 9}{2} = \frac{4}{2} = 2 \quad \text{and} \quad x = \frac{-5 - 9}{2} = -\frac{14}{2} = -7.$$

You can check these solutions in the original equation as follows.

Substitute 2 into Equation	*Substitute −7 into Equation*
$x^2 + 5x = 14$	$x^2 + 5x = 14$
$(2)^2 + 5(2) \overset{?}{=} 14$	$(-7)^2 + 5(-7) \overset{?}{=} 14$
$4 + 10 = 14$ ✓	$49 - 35 = 14$ ✓

The equation in Example 2 could have been solved by factoring. Try doing so, and compare your results with those obtained in Example 2.

Example 3   The Quadratic Formula: Two Distinct Solutions

$$-x^2 - 2x = -4 \qquad \text{Original equation}$$

$$-x^2 - 2x + 4 = 0 \qquad \begin{array}{l}\text{General form with}\\ a = -1, b = -2, c = 4\end{array}$$

$$x = \frac{-b \pm \sqrt{b^2 - 4ac}}{2a} \qquad \text{Quadratic Formula}$$

$$x = \frac{-(-2) \pm \sqrt{(-2)^2 - 4(-1)(4)}}{2(-1)} \qquad \begin{array}{l}\text{Substitute } -1 \text{ for } a, -2\\ \text{for } b, \text{ and } 4 \text{ for } c.\end{array}$$

$$x = \frac{2 \pm \sqrt{4 + 16}}{-2} \qquad \text{Simplify.}$$

$$x = \frac{2 \pm \sqrt{20}}{-2} \qquad \text{Simplify.}$$

$$x = \frac{2 \pm 2\sqrt{5}}{-2} \qquad \text{Simplify radical.}$$

$$x = \frac{(-2)(-1 \pm \sqrt{5})}{(-2)} \qquad \text{Cancel common factor.}$$

$$x = -1 \pm \sqrt{5} \qquad \text{Simplify.}$$

Check

$$-x^2 - 2x = -4 \qquad \text{Original equation}$$

$$-\left(-1 + \sqrt{5}\right)^2 - 2\left(-1 + \sqrt{5}\right) \overset{?}{=} -4 \qquad \text{Substitute } -1 + \sqrt{5} \text{ for } x.$$

$$-\left(1 - 2\sqrt{5} + 5\right) + 2 - 2\sqrt{5} \overset{?}{=} -4 \qquad \text{Multiply.}$$

$$(-1 - 5 + 2) + \left(2\sqrt{5} - 2\sqrt{5}\right) \overset{?}{=} -4 \qquad \text{Group like terms.}$$

$$-4 = -4 \qquad \text{Solution checks. } \checkmark$$

Checking of the solution $x = -1 - \sqrt{5}$ is left for you to do.

Example 4   The Quadratic Formula: One Repeated Solution

$$8x^2 - 24x + 18 = 0 \qquad \text{Original equation}$$

$$4x^2 - 12x + 9 = 0 \qquad \begin{array}{l}\text{General form with}\\ a = 4, b = -12, c = 9\end{array}$$

$$x = \frac{-b \pm \sqrt{b^2 - 4ac}}{2a} \qquad \text{Quadratic Formula}$$

$$x = \frac{-(-12) \pm \sqrt{(-12)^2 - 4(4)(9)}}{2(4)} \qquad \begin{array}{l}\text{Substitute } 4 \text{ for } a,\\ -12 \text{ for } b, \text{ and } 9 \text{ for } c.\end{array}$$

$$x = \frac{12 \pm \sqrt{144 - 144}}{8} \qquad \text{Simplify.}$$

$$x = \frac{12 \pm \sqrt{0}}{8} = \frac{3}{2} \qquad \text{Simplify.}$$

This equation has only one solution, $\frac{3}{2}$. Check this solution in the original equation.

In the next example, note how the Quadratic Formula can be used to determine that a quadratic equation has no real solution.

| Example 5 | The Quadratic Formula: No Real Solution |

Use the Quadratic Formula to solve

$$2x^2 - 4x + 5 = 0.$$

Students can use graphing utilities to verify that the graph of $y = 2x^2 - 4x + 5$ has *no* x-intercept.

Solution

$$2x^2 - 4x + 5 = 0 \qquad \text{General form with } a = 2, b = -4, c = 5$$

$$x = \frac{-b \pm \sqrt{b^2 - 4ac}}{2a} \qquad \text{Quadratic Formula}$$

$$x = \frac{-(-4) \pm \sqrt{(-4)^2 - 4(2)(5)}}{2(2)} \qquad \text{Substitute 2 for } a, -4 \text{ for } b, \text{ and 5 for } c.$$

$$x = \frac{4 \pm \sqrt{16 - 40}}{4} \qquad \text{Simplify.}$$

$$x = \frac{4 \pm \sqrt{-24}}{4} \qquad \text{Simplify.}$$

Because $\sqrt{-24}$ is not a real number, you can conclude that the original equation has no real solution. Notice that -24 is the discriminant, $b^2 - 4ac$, which could have been calculated first to show that the given equation has no real solution.

You have now studied four ways to solve quadratic equations.

1. Extracting square roots
2. Factoring
3. Completing the square
4. The Quadratic Formula

The following guidelines may help you decide which method best applies to an equation. Note that *completing the square* is not recommended as a practical technique—it is used more as a theoretical technique.

> ▶ **Guidelines for Solving Quadratic Equations**
>
> 1. First check to see whether you can solve the equation by extracting square roots.
> 2. If you can't extract square roots, write the equation in general form and try factoring.
> 3. If you can't factor the quadratic equation in general form, apply the Quadratic Formula.

Example 6   Mountain Biker's Speed

A mountain biker spends a total of 5 hours going up a 25-mile mountain trail and coming back down. The biker's speed up the trail is 4 miles per hour slower than the speed down the trail. What is the biker's speed coming down the trail?

Solution

Form a verbal model for the total time. Remember that *Distance* = *rate* × *time* so,

$$Time = distance \div rate.$$

Let x represent the rate coming down the trail and let $x - 4$ represent the rate going up the trail.

Verbal Model: Total time = Time up + Time down

Labels: Total time = 5   (hours)

Time up $= \dfrac{25}{x - 4}$ (hours)

Time down $= \dfrac{25}{x}$ (hours)

Equation: $5 = \dfrac{25}{x - 4} + \dfrac{25}{x}$

$5x^2 - 20x = 25x + 25x - 100$ Multiply both sides by $x(x - 4)$.

$5x^2 - 70x + 100 = 0$ Quadratic equation

$x^2 - 14x + 20 = 0$ Divide both sides by 5.

$x = \dfrac{-(-14) \pm \sqrt{(-14)^2 - 4(1)(20)}}{2(1)}$ Substitute $a = 1$, $b = -14$, and $c = 20$ into Quadratic Formula.

$x = \dfrac{14 \pm \sqrt{116}}{2}$ Simplify.

$x = \dfrac{14 \pm 2\sqrt{29}}{2}$ Simplify radical.

$x = 7 \pm \sqrt{29}$ Solution to quadratic equation

The biker's speed coming down the trail is $7 + \sqrt{29} \approx 12.4$ miles per hour. The solution $7 - \sqrt{29} \approx 1.6$ is excluded because the uphill rate $x - 4$ would be negative.

Technology: Tip

Graphing utility programs for solving a quadratic equation in general form can be found at our website *www.hmco.com*. Try using this program to solve the equation in Example 6.

Discussing the Concept   Graphic Interpretations of Solutions

Write descriptions of the graph of $y = ax^2 + bx + c$ for the three possible cases of $ax^2 + bx + c = 0$ having two, one (repeated), and no solutions. Create a quadratic equation for each case and graph each equation on a graphing utility to check the validity of your descriptions.

10.3   Exercises

Integrated Review   *Concepts, Skills, and Problem Solving*

Keep mathematically in shape by doing these exercises *before* the problems of this section.

Properties and Definitions

1. Explain how to simplify the fraction $\dfrac{x^2 - 4}{x + 2}$.

2. Explain how to divide $\dfrac{4x^2}{3y}$ by $\dfrac{15y^2}{6x}$.

3. Describe the steps for finding the sum $\dfrac{3}{x} + \dfrac{5}{1 - x}$.

Rational Expressions and Equations

In Exercises 4–7, perform the operation and simplify.

4. $\dfrac{5}{x - 1} \cdot \dfrac{x - 1}{25(x - 2)}$

5. $\dfrac{x + 2}{5(x - 3)} \div \dfrac{x - 2}{5(x - 3)}$

6. $\dfrac{6}{x - 3} + \dfrac{x}{x - 3}$

7. $\dfrac{3}{x - 1} - 5$

In Exercises 8 and 9, solve the equation.

8. $\dfrac{5x - 4}{5x + 4} = \dfrac{2}{3}$

9. $\dfrac{15}{x} - 4 = \dfrac{6}{x} + 3$

Problem Solving

10. Determine the number of gallons of a 25% solution that must be mixed with a 50% solution to obtain 10 gallons of a 40% solution.

11. To get an A in a course, a student must have an average of at least 90 on four tests of 100 points each. A certain student scores 83, 92, and 88 on the first three tests. What must the student score on the fourth test to earn a 90% average for the course?

Developing Skills

In Exercises 1–4, write the quadratic equation in general form.

1. $x^2 = 3 - 2x$

2. $2x^2 + 3x = 5$

3. $x(4 - x) = 10$

4. $x(8x + 3) = 2$

In Exercises 5–12, use the discriminant to determine the number of real solutions of the equation. See Example 1.

5. $2x^2 - 3x - 1 = 0$

6. $4x^2 + 4x + 1 = 0$

7. $x^2 + 4x + 5 = 0$

8. $x^2 - 2x + 5 = 0$

9. $x^2 + 6x + 1 = 0$

10. $x^2 + 6x - 10 = 0$

11. $9x^2 - 12x + 4 = 0$

12. $2x^2 + 5x + 3 = 0$

In Exercises 13–42, use the Quadratic Formula to solve the equation. (Some equations have no real solutions.) See Examples 2–5.

13. $y^2 - 9y + 10 = 0$

14. $x^2 + 5x - 14 = 0$

15. $x^2 - 5x + 2 = 0$

16. $t^2 + t - 3 = 0$

17. $t^2 + 5t + 6 = 0$

18. $y^2 + y + 1 = 0$

19. $x^2 - 6x + 7 = 0$

20. $x^2 - 10x + 22 = 0$

21. $t^2 + t + 3 = 0$

22. $u^2 + 5u + 2 = 0$

23. $x^2 = 3x + 1$

24. $x^2 = 12x - 20$

25. $2x^2 + 7x + 3 = 0$

26. $3x^2 + 11x + 10 = 0$

27. $8x^2 - 10x + 3 = 0$

28. $4x^2 - 13x + 3 = 0$

29. $3z^2 + 4z + 4 = 0$

30. $9z^2 + 10z + 4 = 0$

31. $5x^2 + 2x - 2 = 0$

32. $2x^2 - 7x - 9 = 0$

33. $4x^2 - 4x - 1 = 0$

34. $3x^2 + 4x - 1 = 0$

35. $\frac{1}{2}x^2 + 2x - 3 = 0$

36. $\frac{3}{2}z^2 + 1 = 2z$

37. $0.5x^2 - 0.8x + 0.3 = 0$

38. $0.3x^2 + 0.7x - 0.4 = 0$

39. $0.2y^2 + y + 6 = 0$

40. $0.1x^2 - x - 1 = 0$

41. $0.36s^2 - 0.12s + 0.01 = 0$

42. $0.06t^2 + 0.05t - 0.10 = 0$

In Exercises 43–56, solve the quadratic equation by the most convenient method.

43. $x^2 = 18$

44. $t^2 = 27$

45. $y^2 + 8y = 0$

46. $7u^2 - 49u = 0$

47. $2y(y - 12) + 3(y - 12) = 0$

48. $x(x + 2) - 5(x + 2) = 0$

49. $(x - 3)^2 - 75 = 0$ **50.** $(y - 8)^2 - 20 = 0$

51. $x^2 - 6x + 3 = 0$ **52.** $x^2 + 14x + 49 = 0$

53. $-2x^2 + 6x + 1 = 0$ **54.** $6x^2 + 20x + 5 = 0$

55. $10x^2 + x - 3 = 0$ **56.** $4a^2 - 12a + 9 = 0$

In Exercises 57–60, solve the quadratic equation using the Quadratic Formula. Use a calculator to approximate your solution to three decimal places.

57. $3x^2 - 14x + 4 = 0$ **58.** $7x^2 + x - 35 = 0$

59. $-0.03x^2 + 2x - 0.5 = 0$

60. $1.7x^2 - 4.2x + 2.1 = 0$

In Exercises 61–64, solve the equation.

61. $\dfrac{x + 3}{2} - \dfrac{4}{x} = 2$

62. $\dfrac{2}{r + 1} + \dfrac{2}{r} = 1$

63. $\sqrt{4x + 3} = x - 1$

64. $\sqrt{3x - 2} = x - 2$

Solving Problems

65. *Biker's Speed* A mountain biker spends a total of 4 hours going up a 20-mile mountain trail and coming back down. The biker's speed up the trail is 5 miles per hour slower than the speed down the trail. What is the biker's speed coming down the trail?

66. *Hiker's Speed* A hiker spends a total of 4 hours going up a 6-mile trail and coming back down. The hiker's speed up the trail is 1 mile per hour slower than the speed down the trail. What is the hiker's speed coming down the trail?

67. *Falling Time* A ball is thrown upward with an initial velocity of 20 feet per second from a bridge that is 100 feet above the water. The height h (in feet) of the ball t seconds after it is thrown is modeled by

$$h = -16t^2 + 20t + 100.$$

(a) Find the two times when the ball is 100 feet above the water level.

(b) Find the time when the ball strikes the water.

68. *Falling Time* A ball is thrown upward with an initial velocity of 18 feet per second from a bridge that is 20 feet above the water. The height h (in feet) of the ball t seconds after it is thrown is modeled by

$$h = -16t^2 + 18t + 20.$$

(a) Find the two times when the ball is 20 feet above the water level.

(b) Find the time when the ball strikes the water.

69. *Problem Solving* Find two consecutive positive even integers whose product is 224.

70. *Problem Solving* Find two consecutive positive even integers whose product is 528.

71. *Geometry* The area of the rectangle is 58.14 square inches. Use the Quadratic Formula to find its dimensions.

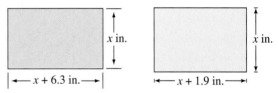

Figure for 71   Figure for 72

72. *Geometry* The area of the rectangle is 26.66 square inches. Use the Quadratic Formula to find its dimensions.

Explaining Concepts

73. Answer parts (e) and (f) of Motivating the Chapter on page 511.

74. State the Quadratic Formula *in words*.

75. In your own words, describe how the discriminant can be used to determine the number of real solutions of a quadratic equation.

76. Can the Quadratic Formula be used to solve the equation $(x - 2)(x - 3) = 0$? If it can, would it be the simplest method?

77. State the four methods used to solve quadratic equations.

78. Construct a quadratic equation with irrational solutions.

79. Use the Quadratic Formula to show that the sum of the solutions of a quadratic equation is $-b/a$ and the product of the solutions is c/a.

Mid-Chapter Quiz

Take this quiz as you would take a quiz in class. After you are done, check your work against the answers given in the back of the book.

In Exercises 1–14, solve the equation. If indicated, use the specified method.

1. $(x - 5)(4x + 15) = 0$

2. $x^2 = 400$

3. Factoring:
$$2x^2 - 50x = 0$$

4. Factoring:
$$9x^2 - 24x + 16 = 0$$

5. Factoring:
$$2x^2 + 9x - 35 = 0$$

6. Factoring:
$$x(x - 4) + 3(x - 4) = 0$$

7. Extracting square roots:
$$x^2 - 2500 = 0$$

8. Extracting square roots:
$$(z - 4)^2 - 81 = 0$$

9. Completing the square:
$$y^2 + 6y - 11 = 0$$

10. Completing the square:
$$4u^2 + 12u - 1 = 0$$

11. Quadratic Formula:
$$x^2 + 3x + 1 = 0$$

12. Quadratic Formula:
$$3x^2 - 4x - 10 = 0$$

13. $x - \dfrac{24}{x} = 5$

14. $\sqrt{x + 4} = x - 2$

In Exercises 15–18, use the discriminant to determine the number of real solutions of the equation.

15. $x^2 + x + \dfrac{9}{4} = 0$

16. $y^2 - 7y - 1 = 0$

17. $3x^2 - 4x - 4 = 0$

18. $9x^2 + 6x + 1 = 0$

19. Fifteen hundred dollars is deposited in an account. After 2 years, the balance in the account is $1669.54. If the interest earned on the account is compounded annually, what is the interest rate?

20. On September 9, 1979, Kitty O'Neill dove 180 feet from a helicopter into a 30- by 60-foot air cushion for a TV film stunt. Her height h (in feet) after t seconds into the fall is modeled by

$$h = 180 - 16t^2.$$

How long was O'Neill in the air? (Source: Guinness Book of World Records)

21. Find the dimensions of the rectangle in the figure if its area is 153.92 square inches.

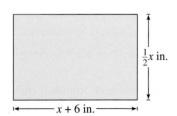

$\frac{1}{2}x$ in.

$x + 6$ in.

Figure for 21

10.4   Graphing Quadratic Functions

Objectives

1 Determine whether a parabola opens up or down using the Leading Coefficient Test.

2 Sketch the graph of a quadratic function using the point-plotting method and the vertex of a parabola.

---

1 Determine whether a parabola opens up or down using the Leading Coefficient Test.

Quadratic Functions

In this section, you will study the graphs of quadratic functions. A **quadratic function** of x is a function that can be written in the form

$$y = ax^2 + bx + c, \quad a \neq 0. \qquad f(x) \text{ can be used in place of } y.$$

The graph of a quadratic function is called a **parabola.** Parabolas are cup-shaped like the reflective part of a flashlight or like the flight path of a baseball. If the coefficient of x^2 (the leading coefficient) is positive, the parabola opens up, as shown in Figure 10.1. The lowest point on a parabola that opens up is the **vertex** of the parabola. If the leading coefficient is negative, the parabola opens down, and its vertex is the highest point on the parabola.

Recall that the graph of a function of x must pass the *Vertical Line Test,* which states that no vertical line can intersect the graph of a function of x more than once. In Figure 10.1, note that both types of parabolas pass the Vertical Line Test.

Technology: Discovery

You can use a graphing utility to discover a rule for determining the appearance of a parabola. Graph the equations below.

$$y_1 = x^2 + 4x + 3$$

$$y_2 = 5 - 2x^2$$

$$y_3 = -7 + 3x^2$$

$$y_4 = -x^2 + 6x$$

In your own words, write a rule for determining whether the graph of a parabola opens up or down by just looking at the equation. Does $y = 9 - 4x - 2x^2$ open up or down?

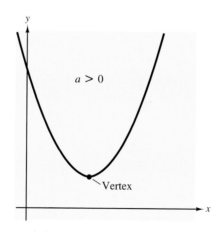

Parabola opens up.

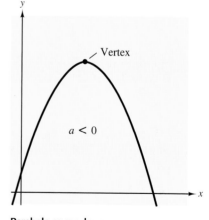

Parabola opens down.

Figure 10.1

▶ The Leading Coefficient Test for Parabolas

The graph of the quadratic function $y = ax^2 + bx + c$ is a **parabola.**

1. If $a > 0$, the parabola opens up.

2. If $a < 0$, the parabola opens down.

Example 1 shows how to use the Leading Coefficient Test to determine whether the graph of a quadratic equation opens up or down.

Example 1   Using the Leading Coefficient Test

Determine whether the parabolas open up or down.

a. $y = -x^2 + 2x + 3$ **b.** $y = 4x^2 - 1$

c. $y = 2 - 5x - 3x^2$ **d.** $y = 4 - 2x(3 - x)$

Solution

a. In general form, you can see that the leading coefficient is negative.

$$y = ax^2 + bx + c \qquad \text{General form}$$

$$y = -x^2 + 2x + 3 \quad \Longrightarrow \quad a = -1 \qquad \text{Leading coefficient is negative.}$$

The graph of the function opens down, as shown in Figure 10.2(a).

b. In general form, you can see that the leading coefficient is positive.

$$y = ax^2 + bx + c \qquad \text{General form}$$

$$y = 4x^2 - 1 \quad \Longrightarrow \quad a = 4 \qquad \text{Leading coefficient is positive.}$$

The graph of the function opens up, as shown in Figure 10.2(b).

c. In general form, you can see that the leading coefficient is negative.

$$y = ax^2 + bx + c \qquad \text{General form}$$

$$y = -3x^2 - 5x + 2 \quad \Longrightarrow \quad a = -3 \qquad \text{Leading coefficient is negative.}$$

The graph of the function opens down, as shown in Figure 10.2(c).

d. In general form, you can see that the leading coefficient is positive.

$$y = ax^2 + bx + c \qquad \text{General form}$$

$$y = 4 - 6x + 2x^2 \qquad \text{Distributive Property}$$

$$y = 2x^2 - 6x + 4 \quad \Longrightarrow \quad a = 2 \qquad \text{Leading coefficient is positive.}$$

The graph of the function opens up, as shown in Figure 2.10(d).

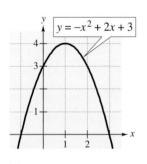

(a)
Figure 10.2

(b)

(c)

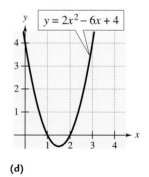

(d)

Verify the graphs shown in Example 1 using a graphing utility.

2 Sketch the graph of a quadratic function using the point-plotting method and the vertex of a parabola.

Sketching the Graph of a Quadratic Function

There are three basic approaches to sketching the graph of a quadratic function.

1. *Numerical Approach* You can create a table of values and use a point-plotting approach.
2. *Graphing Utility* You can use a graphing utility to graph the function.
3. *Analytic Approach* You can analyze the characteristics of the graph and use the results to draw the graph.

You will probably find that a combination of these approaches is most efficient.

Review the techniques for determining intercepts in Section 4.2.

Example 2   Using the Point-Plotting Method

Find the intercepts of the graph of $y = x^2 - 4$. Then sketch the graph of the function and label its intercepts.

Solution

To find the x-intercepts, set y equal to zero and solve the resulting equation for x.

$$x^2 - 4 = 0 \qquad \text{Let } y = 0 \text{ and solve for } x.$$

$$(x + 2)(x - 2) = 0 \qquad \text{Factor.}$$

$$x + 2 = 0 \implies x = -2 \qquad \text{Set 1st factor equal to 0.}$$

$$x - 2 = 0 \implies x = 2 \qquad \text{Set 2nd factor equal to 0.}$$

From these two solutions, you can see that the graph has two x-intercepts: $(-2, 0)$ and $(2, 0)$.

To find the y-intercept, let x equal zero in the original equation, and solve for y. Doing this produces

$$y = (0)^2 - 4 \qquad \text{Substitute 0 for } x.$$

$$= -4. \qquad \text{Simplify.}$$

So, the y-intercept is $(0, -4)$. To sketch the graph of the function, create a table of values. (Note that the three intercepts are included in the table.)

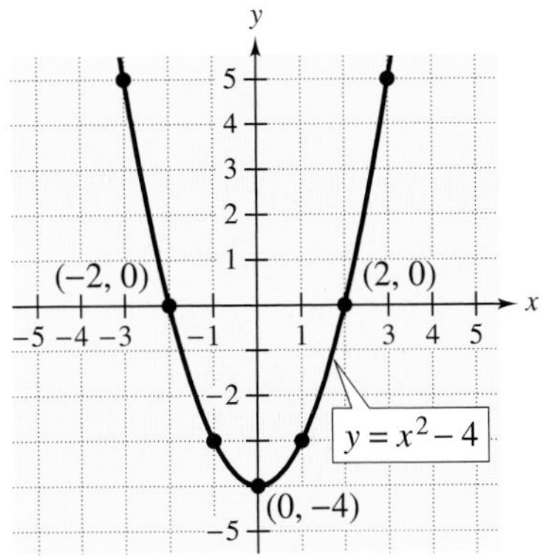

x	-3	-2	-1	0	1	2	3
$y = x^2 - 4$	5	0	-3	-4	-3	0	5
Solution	$(-3, 5)$	$(-2, 0)$	$(-1, -3)$	$(0, -4)$	$(1, -3)$	$(2, 0)$	$(3, 5)$

Plot the points and connect them with a smooth curve, as shown in Figure 10.3. Note that the parabola opens up because the leading coefficient is positive.

Figure 10.3

When creating a table of values, we suggest that you include any intercepts you have found. We also suggest that you include points to the left and right of the intercepts.

> ▶ **Vertex of a Parabola**
>
> The vertex of a parabola given by $y = ax^2 + bx + c$ occurs at the point whose x-coordinate is
>
> $$x = -\frac{b}{2a}.$$
>
> To find the y-coordinate of the vertex, substitute the x-coordinate in the equation $y = ax^2 + bx + c$.

Example 3 **Finding the Vertex of a Parabola**

Find the vertex of each parabola.

a. $y = x^2 + 2x - 1$ **b.** $y = -x^2 + 3x$

Solution

a. For this function, $a = 1$ and $b = 2$. So, the x-coordinate of the vertex is

$$x = -\frac{b}{2a} = -\frac{2}{2(1)} = -1. \qquad \text{Substitute 1 for } a \text{ and 2 for } b.$$

The y-coordinate of the vertex is

$$y = (-1)^2 + 2(-1) - 1 = -2. \qquad \text{Substitute } -1 \text{ for } x.$$

So, the vertex occurs at $(-1, -2)$, as shown in Figure 10.4(a).

b. For this function, $a = -1$ and $b = 3$. So, the x-coordinate of the vertex is

$$x = -\frac{b}{2a} = -\frac{3}{2(-1)} = \frac{3}{2}. \qquad \text{Substitute } -1 \text{ for } a \text{ and 3 for } b.$$

The y-coordinate of the vertex is

$$y = -\left(\tfrac{3}{2}\right)^2 + 3\left(\tfrac{3}{2}\right) = \tfrac{9}{4}. \qquad \text{Substitute } \tfrac{3}{2} \text{ for } x.$$

So, the vertex occurs at $\left(\tfrac{3}{2}, \tfrac{9}{4}\right)$, as shown in Figure 10.4(b).

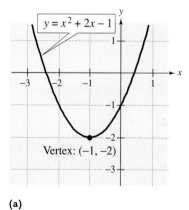

(a)

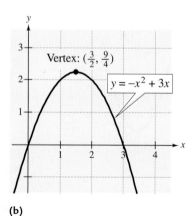

(b)

Figure 10.4

> ▶ **Guidelines for Sketching a Parabola**
>
> **1.** Use the Leading Coefficient Test to determine whether the parabola opens up or down.
>
> **2.** Find and plot the x-intercepts (if any) and the y-intercept.
>
> **3.** Find and plot the vertex.
>
> **4.** Create a table of values that includes a few additional points.
>
> **5.** Complete the graph with a smooth, cup-shaped curve.

The graph of every quadratic function has exactly one y-intercept. The number of x-intercepts, however, can vary. In Examples 4, 5, and 6, notice that parabolas can have two x-intercepts, one x-intercept, or no x-intercept.

Example 4   Sketching a Parabola: Two x-Intercepts

Sketch the graph of $y = -2x^2 - x + 6$.

Solution

From the Leading Coefficient Test, the parabola opens down. The y-intercept is $(0, 6)$ and the x-intercepts are $\left(\frac{3}{2}, 0\right)$ and $(-2, 0)$. The vertex is $\left(-\frac{1}{4}, \frac{49}{8}\right)$.

When finding these x-intercepts, you could multiply both sides of the equation by -1.

$$0(-1) = (-2x^2 - x + 6)(-1)$$
$$0 = 2x^2 + x - 6$$
$$0 = (2x - 3)(x + 2)$$
$$2x - 3 = 0 \rightarrow x = \frac{3}{2}$$
$$x + 2 = 0 \rightarrow x = -2$$

The x-intercepts are $\left(\frac{3}{2}, 0\right)$ and $(-2, 0)$.

x		-3	-1	1	2
$y = -2x^2 - x + 6$		-9	5	3	-4
Solution		$(-3, -9)$	$(-1, 5)$	$(1, 3)$	$(2, -4)$

Plot the intercepts, the vertex, and the additional points shown in the table of values. Then connect the points with a smooth curve, as shown in Figure 10.5.

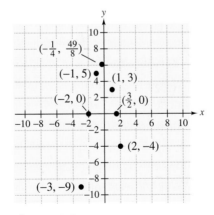
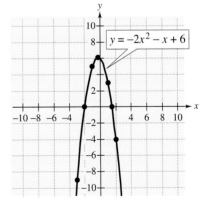

Figure 10.5

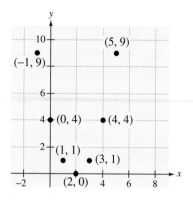

Example 5 Sketching a Parabola: One *x*-Intercept

Sketch the graph of $y = x^2 - 4x + 4$.

Solution

From the Leading Coefficient Test, the parabola opens up. The *y*-intercept is $(0, 4)$ and the *x*-intercept is $(2, 0)$. The vertex is $(2, 0)$. Plot the intercepts, the vertex, and some additional points. Connect the points, as shown in Figure 10.6.

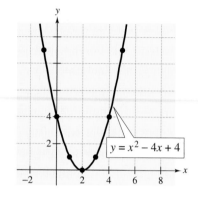

Figure 10.6

Example 6 Sketching a Parabola: No *x*-Intercept

Sketch the graph of $y = x^2 - 6x + 10$.

Solution

From the Leading Coefficient Test, the parabola opens up. The *y*-intercept is $(0, 10)$ and there is no *x*-intercept. The vertex is $(3, 1)$. Plot the vertex and some additional points. Then connect the points, as shown in Figure 10.7.

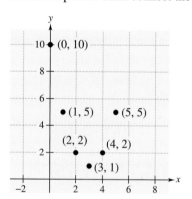

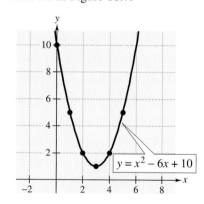

Figure 10.7

In Example 6, notice the relationship between the graph of the function $y = x^2 - 6x + 10$ and the equation $x^2 - 6x + 10 = 0$. The discriminant of the quadratic is $(-6)^2 - 4(1)(10) = 36 - 40 = -4$. Because the discriminant is less than 0, the graph has no *x*-intercept and the equation has no real solution.

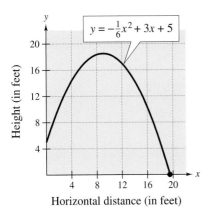

$$y = -\frac{1}{6}x^2 + 3x + 5$$

Height (in feet)

Horizontal distance (in feet)

Figure 10.8

| Example 7 | Analyzing the Path of a Ball |

The height y (in feet) of a ball thrown on a parabolic path is modeled by

$$y = f(x) = -\frac{1}{6}x^2 + 3x + 5$$

where x is the horizontal distance (in feet) from where the ball is thrown. (See Figure 10.8.)

a. From what height is the ball thrown?

b. What is the maximum height reached by the ball?

c. How far does the ball travel horizontally through the air?

Solution

a. The height from which the ball is thrown occurs when $x = 0$. So,

$$y = f(0) = -\frac{1}{6}(0)^2 + 3(0) + 5 = 5 \text{ feet.} \qquad \text{Substitute 0 for } x.$$

b. The maximum height occurs at the vertex of the parabolic path. The x-value of this vertex is

$$x = -\frac{b}{2a} = -\frac{3}{2\left(-\frac{1}{6}\right)} = 9. \qquad \text{Substitute } -\frac{1}{6} \text{ for } a \text{ and 3 for } b.$$

At this x-value the height is

$$y = -\frac{1}{6}(9)^2 + 3(9) + 5 = 18.5 \text{ feet.} \qquad \text{Substitute 9 for } x.$$

c. The distance that the ball travels horizontally through the air corresponds to the x-intercept of the parabolic path. This intercept can be found using the Quadratic Formula.

$$x = \frac{-3 \pm \sqrt{3^2 - 4\left(-\frac{1}{6}\right)(5)}}{2\left(-\frac{1}{6}\right)} \qquad \text{Substitute } -\frac{1}{6} \text{ for } a, \text{ 3 for } b, \text{ and } 5 \text{ for } c \text{ in the Quadratic Formula.}$$

$$= \frac{-3 \pm \sqrt{\frac{37}{3}}}{-\frac{1}{3}} \qquad \text{Simplify.}$$

$$= 9 \pm \sqrt{111} \qquad \text{Simplify.}$$

Because you want the positive distance, the ball travels

$$x = 9 + \sqrt{111} \approx 9 + 10.5 = 19.5 \text{ feet}$$

horizontally through the air.

| Discussing the Concept | **Finding the Equation of a Parabola** |

The parabola given by $y = (x - 6)(x - 2)$ has x-intercepts at $(2, 0)$ and $(6, 0)$. The vertex of this parabola is $(4, -4)$. Find equations of parabolas that have the same x-intercepts but that have vertices at the points $(4, 4)$, $(4, 8)$, and $(4, -8)$. Use a graphing utility to verify your answers.

10.4   Exercises

Integrated Review   *Concepts, Skills, and Problem Solving*

Keep mathematically in shape by doing these exercises *before* the problems of this section.

Properties and Definitions

In Exercises 1 and 2, rewrite the expression, where *a* and *b* are nonnegative real numbers, using the specified property.

1. Multiplication Property: $\sqrt{ab} =$

2. Division Property: $\sqrt{\dfrac{a}{b}} =$

3. Is $\sqrt{80}$ in simplest form? Explain.

4. Is $10\sqrt{5}$ in simplest form? Explain.

Simplifying Expressions

In Exercises 5–10, perform the operation and simplify the expression.

5. $8\sqrt{15} - 6\sqrt{15}$

6. $\sqrt{10}(1 - \sqrt{2})$

7. $(\sqrt{3} + 2)(\sqrt{3} - 2)$

8. $\dfrac{4}{5 - \sqrt{2}}$

9. $\sqrt{\dfrac{6}{5}}$

10. $\dfrac{2 + \sqrt{8}}{\frac{1}{2}}$

Problem Solving

11. A 20-foot board leans against the side of a house. The bottom is 5 feet from the house. How far does the board reach up the side of the house?

12. A quality control engineer for a manufacturer found one defective unit in a sample of 125. At that rate, what is the expected number of defective units in a shipment of 150,000?

Developing Skills

In Exercises 1–6, match the equation with its graph. [The graphs are labeled (a), (b), (c), (d), (e), and (f).]

(a)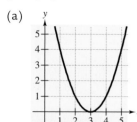

(b)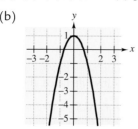

(c)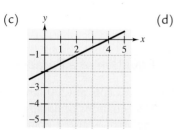

(d)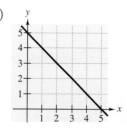

(e)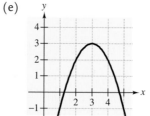

(f)

1. $y = 5 - x$

2. $y = \frac{1}{2}x - 2$

3. $y = x^2 + 1$

4. $y = -2x^2 + 1$

5. $y = x^2 - 6x + 9$

6. $y = -(x^2 - 6x + 6)$

In Exercises 7–14, determine whether the parabola opens up or down. See Example 1.

7. $y = 6x^2 + 2$

8. $y = -3x^2 + x - 3$

9. $y = 4 + 10x - x^2$

10. $y = 1 + 8x - 8x^2$

11. $y = 3 + x(3 - x)$

12. $y = 6 - 2x(2 - x)$

13. $y = -(x + 1)^2 - 1$

14. $y = (x - 3)^2 - 2$

In Exercises 15–28, find the intercepts of the graph. See Example 2.

15. $y = 16 - x^2$

16. $y = x^2 - 36$

17. $y = x^2 - 2x$

18. $y = x^2 - 4x$

19. $y = x^2 - x - 6$

20. $y = x^2 + 3x + 4$

21. $y = x^2 - 2x + 3$

22. $y = x^2 - 2x + 1$

23. $y = 3x^2 + 4x - 4$

24. $y = 2x^2 - 7x + 3$

25. $y = 3x^2 + 5x + 4$

26. $y = 4x^2 - 6x + 7$

27. $y = \frac{1}{2}x^2 - 2x + 1$

28. $y = \frac{1}{3}x^2 + 2x - 1$

In Exercises 29–40, find the vertex of the parabola. See Example 3.

29. $y = -x^2 + 2$

30. $y = 3x^2 - 3$

31. $y = x^2 - 4x + 7$

32. $y = 1 - 2x - x^2$

33. $y = 6 + 10x - x^2$

34. $y = x^2 - 12x + 9$

35. $y = x^2 + 5x - 3$

36. $y = x^2 + 3x + 4$

37. $y = 2x^2 - 8x - 2$

38. $y = 5 + 12x - 2x^2$

39. $y = 8 - 9x - 3x^2$

40. $y = 3x^2 + 4x - 1$

In Exercises 41–66, sketch the graph. Label the vertex and the intercepts. See Examples 4–6.

41. $y = x^2 - 1$

42. $y = x^2 - 9$

43. $y = -x^2 + 1$

44. $y = -x^2 + 9$

45. $y = x^2 - 4x$

46. $y = x^2 - 6x$

47. $y = -x^2 + 4x$

48. $y = -x^2 + 6x$

49. $y = x^2 - 4x + 4$

50. $y = -(x^2 + 4x + 4)$

51. $y = x^2 + 6x + 8$

52. $y = x^2 - 6x + 8$

53. $y = -(x^2 + 2x - 3)$

54. $y = -(x^2 + 4x + 2)$

55. $y = -(x^2 + 4x + 8)$

56. $y = x^2 - 6x + 12$

57. $y = x^2 - 4x + 1$

58. $y = x^2 + 6x + 11$

59. $y = \frac{1}{2}x^2 - 4x + 6$

60. $y = \frac{1}{2}x^2 - x - 1$

61. $y = 2x^2 + 8x + 9$

62. $y = 3x^2 - 6x + 4$

63. $y = 8 + 4x - 3x^2$

64. $y = 2x^2 + 2x - 3$

65. $y = \frac{2}{3}x^2 - x - 3$

66. $y = \frac{3}{2}x^2 + 2x - 2$

In Exercises 67–74, use a graphing utility to graph the function. Approximate the vertex from the graph.

67. $y = -x^2 + 6x$

68. $y = x^2 - x$

69. $y = x^2 + 4x + 3$

70. $y = x^2 - 4x + 3$

71. $y = -4x^2 + 4x + 1$

72. $y = -2(x^2 - x - 2)$

73. $y = \frac{1}{2}x^2 + x - 4$

74. $y = -\frac{1}{2}x^2 + 4x - 2$

In Exercises 75–78, sketch the parabola and the horizontal line. Find any points of intersection.

75. $y = -x^2 + 3$
   $y = 2$

76. $y = x^2 - 6x + 6$
   $y = 1$

77. $y = \frac{1}{2}x^2 - 4x + 10$
   $y = 3$

78. $y = -2x^2 + 12x - 14$
   $y = 5$

79. *Exploration*   Use a graphing utility to graph the functions on the same screen. Describe the relationship between the graph of $y = x^2$ and each of the other graphs.

(a) $y = x^2$

(b) $y = \frac{1}{8}x^2$

(c) $y = -2x^2$

(d) $y = -\frac{1}{6}x^2$

80. *Exploration*   Use a graphing utility to graph the functions on the same screen. Describe the relationship between the graph of $y = x^2$ and each of the other graphs.

(a) $y = x^2$

(b) $y = x^2 + 3$

(c) $y = x^2 - 3$

(d) $y = x^2 - 8$

81. *Exploration*   Use a graphing utility to graph the functions on the same screen. Describe the relationship between the graph of $y = x^2$ and each of the other graphs.

(a) $y = x^2$

(b) $y = (x - 2)^2$

(c) $y = (x - 6)^2$

(d) $y = (x + 4)^2$

82. *Exploration*   Use a graphing utility to graph the functions on the same screen. Describe the relationship between the graph of $y = x^2$ and each of the other graphs.

(a) $y = x^2$

(b) $y = 9 - x^2$

(c) $y = -4 + (x + 1)^2$

(d) $y = 1 - (x - 2)^2$

Exploration   In Exercises 83–86, find two quadratic functions whose graphs—one opening upward and the other downward—have the given x-intercepts. (The answers are not unique.)

83. $(-2, 0), (2, 0)$

84. $(-4, 0), (4, 0)$

85. $(-3, 0), (1, 0)$

86. $(2, 0), (5, 0)$

Exploration   In Exercises 87 and 88, graph the equation. Then describe how the vertex can be determined from the completed square form of the equation.

87. $y = (x - 2)^2 - 2$

88. $y = -(x - 3)^2 + 1$

In Exercises 89 and 90, complete the square for the right side of the equation and write it in the form of Exercises 87 and 88. What is the vertex of the parabola?

89. $y = x^2 - 10x + 26$ **90.** $y = x^2 + 8x + 14$

Solving Problems

91. *Tossing a Ball*   The height y (in feet) of a ball thrown by a child is modeled by

$$y = -\frac{1}{10}x^2 + 2x + 4$$

where x is the horizontal distance (in feet) from where the ball is thrown (see figure).

(a) From what height is the ball thrown?

(b) What is the maximum height?

(c) How far from the child is the ball when it strikes the ground?

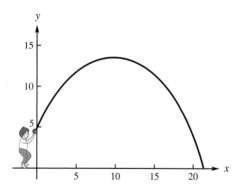

92. *Tossing a Ball*   The height y (in feet) of a ball thrown by a child is modeled by

$$y = -\frac{1}{20}x^2 + 2x + 4$$

where x is the horizontal distance (in feet) from where the ball is thrown.

(a) From what height is the ball thrown?

(b) What is the maximum height?

(c) How far from the child is the ball when it strikes the ground?

93. *Golden Gate Bridge*   The suspension cables on the Golden Gate Bridge can be modeled by

$$y = \frac{1}{9000}x^2 + 5$$

where x and y are measured in feet. The roadbed of the bridge lies on the x-axis, and the y-axis is midway between the towers.

(a) What are the coordinates of the lowest points on the cables?

(b) The span between the two towers is 4200 feet. How high above the roadbed are the cables connected to the towers?

94. *Modeling a Punt*   A football player kicks a 41-yard punt. The path of the ball is modeled by

$$y = -0.035x^2 + 1.4x + 1$$

where x and y are measured in yards.

(a) What is the maximum height of the ball?

(b) The player kicks the ball toward midfield from the 18-yard line. Over which yard line is the ball at its maximum height?

95. *Geometry*   The perimeter of a rectangle is 36 meters.

(a) If the length of the rectangle is x, find its width in terms of x.

(b) Use the result of part (a) to write the area of the rectangle as a function of x.

(c) Use a graphing utility to graph the area function in part (b).

(d) Use the graph in part (c) to approximate the dimensions of the rectangle of maximum area.

96. *Conjecture*   Use the results of Exercise 95 to make a conjecture about the dimensions of a rectangle of fixed perimeter that has a maximum area.

97. *Data Analysis*   For 1989 through 1996, the numbers of cellular phone subscribers S (in millions) in the United States are shown in the table.   (Source: Cellular Telecommunications Industry Association)

Year	1989	1990	1991	1992
S	3.5	5.3	7.6	11.0

Year	1993	1994	1995	1996
S	16.0	24.1	33.8	44.0

These data can be modeled by

$$S = 0.842t^2 + 1.509t + 4.704$$

where $t = 0$ corresponds to 1990.

(a) Use a graphing utility to plot the data and graph the model.

(b) Use the graph to approximate the year in which there were 75 million subscribers.

(c) Find the required year in part (b) algebraically.

Explaining Concepts

98. Answer part (g) of Motivating the Chapter on page 511.

99. Describe the general shape of the graph of a quadratic function.

100. Explain what is meant by the intercepts of a graph of a function. Explain the method for finding any x- or y-intercepts of a graph.

101. In your own words, describe the use of the Leading Coefficient Test for a quadratic function.

102. Explain the relationship between the number of x-intercepts of the graph of $y = ax^2 + bx + c$ and the discriminant of $ax^2 + bx + c = 0$.

103. What is the relationship between the x-coordinate of the vertex of a parabola and the x-intercepts? Check your conjecture for the graphs in Exercises 83–86.

104. Is it possible for the graph of a quadratic function to have two y-intercepts? Explain.

10.5 **Applications of Quadratic Equations**

Objectives

1 Solve an application problem that can be modeled by a quadratic equation.

1 Solve an application problem that can be modeled by a quadratic equation.

Applications of Quadratic Equations

In this section, you will study real-life problems that can be modeled by quadratic equations. For such problems, the verbal model may be the *product* of two variable quantities, or the model may be a previously known formula that describes the situation. Watch for these variations in the following examples.

Example 1 Geometry

A picture is 3 inches longer than it is wide and has an area of 108 square inches, as shown in Figure 10.9. What are the dimensions of the picture?

Solution

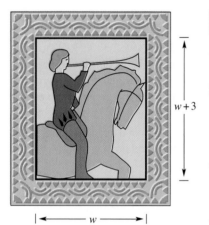

Figure 10.9

Verbal Model:	$\boxed{\text{Area of picture}} = \boxed{\text{Picture width}} \cdot \boxed{\text{Picture length}}$

Labels: Picture width $= w$ (inches)
Picture length $= w + 3$ (inches)
Area $= 108$ (square inches)

Equation:
$$108 = w(w + 3)$$
$$0 = w^2 + 3w - 108$$
$$0 = (w + 12)(w - 9)$$
$$w + 12 = 0 \quad\Longrightarrow\quad w = -12$$
$$w - 9 = 0 \quad\Longrightarrow\quad w = 9$$

Of the two possible solutions, choose the positive value of w and conclude that the width of the picture is

Picture width $= w = 9$ inches.

Because the picture is 3 inches longer than it is wide, you can conclude that the length of the picture is

Picture length $= w + 3 = 9 + 3 = 12$ inches.

Check these dimensions in the original statement of the problem, as follows.

The picture is 3 inches longer than it is wide.

$12 - 9 = 3$ Solution checks. ✓

The area of the picture is 108 square inches.

$12 \times 9 = 108$ Solution checks. ✓

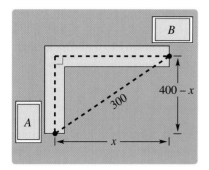

Figure 10.10

Example 2   Using the Pythagorean Theorem

An L-shaped sidewalk from Building A to Building B on a college campus is 400 meters long, as shown in Figure 10.10. By cutting diagonally across the grass, students shorten the walking distance to 300 meters. What are the lengths of the two parts of the existing sidewalk?

Solution

From Figure 10.10, you can see that the L-shaped sidewalk and the diagonal form a right triangle. So, to find the lengths of the two parts of the existing sidewalk, you can use the Pythagorean Theorem.

Common
Formula: $a^2 + b^2 = c^2$ Pythagorean Theorem

Labels: a = length of one part = x (meters)
            b = length of other part = $400 - x$ (meters)
            c = length of diagonal = 300 (meters)

Equation: $x^2 + (400 - x)^2 = (300)^2$

$$2x^2 - 800x + 160{,}000 = 90{,}000$$

$$2x^2 - 800x + 70{,}000 = 0$$

$$x^2 - 400x + 35{,}000 = 0$$

Using the Quadratic Formula, the solutions of this equation are

$$x = \frac{-(-400) \pm \sqrt{(-400)^2 - 4(1)(35{,}000)}}{2(1)}$$ Substitute 1 for a, -400 for b, and 35,000 for c.

$$= \frac{400 \pm \sqrt{160{,}000 - 140{,}000}}{2(1)}$$

$$= \frac{400 \pm \sqrt{20{,}000}}{2}$$

$$= \frac{400 \pm 100\sqrt{2}}{2}$$

$$= 200 \pm 50\sqrt{2}.$$

Both solutions are positive, so it doesn't matter which you choose. If you let

$$x = 200 + 50\sqrt{2}$$

$$\approx 270.7 \text{ meters}$$

the length of the other part is

$$400 - x \approx 400 - 270.7$$

$$\approx 129.3 \text{ meters.}$$

Try choosing the other value of x to see that the same two lengths result.

⌁ Technology:
Tip

Use a graphing utility to graph the quadratic equation $y_1 = x^2 - 400x + 35{,}000$ shown in Example 2 using the range below.

```
Xmin = 0
Xmax = 300
Xscl = 25
Ymin = -6000
Ymax = 1000
Yscl = 50
```

Use the root or zero feature to find the x-intercepts of the graph. How do they compare with the solutions of the equation shown in the example?

Be aware that in real-life applications involving measurements, units of production, or time, you can exclude any negative solution. In Example 2, both solutions are positive and yield the same two dimensions.

In Examples 1 and 2, the verbal model or common formula leads directly to a quadratic equation. In many real-life applications, however, the verbal model produces a rational equation, which in turn leads indirectly to a quadratic equation. Notice how this occurs in Examples 3 and 4.

Example 3 Work Problem

An office contains two copy machines. Machine B is known to take 12 minutes longer than machine A to copy the company's monthly report. When the two machines are used together, it takes 8 minutes to reproduce the report. How long would it take each machine alone to reproduce the report?

Solution

The technology for modern photocopying was invented in 1938, but not perfected until 1959. Originally called xerography, it has revolutionized the modern office.

Bob Daemmrich/Stock Boston

Verbal Model:
$$\boxed{\text{Rate for A}} + \boxed{\text{Rate for B}} = \boxed{\text{Rate for both}}$$

Labels:
Time for both machines = 8 (minutes)
Rate for both machines = $\frac{1}{8}$ (job per minute)
Time for machine A = t (minutes)
Rate for machine A = $1/t$ (job per minute)
Time for machine B = $t + 12$ (minutes)
Rate for machine B = $1/(t + 12)$ (job per minute)

Equation:
$$\frac{1}{t} + \frac{1}{t + 12} = \frac{1}{8}$$

$$\left(\frac{1}{t} + \frac{1}{t + 12}\right)(8t)(t + 12) = \frac{1}{8}(8t)(t + 12)$$

$$8(t + 12) + 8t = t(t + 12)$$

$$16t + 96 = t^2 + 12t$$

$$0 = t^2 - 4t - 96$$

$$0 = (t - 12)(t + 8)$$

$$t - 12 = 0 \implies t = 12$$

$$t + 8 = 0 \implies t = -8$$

By choosing the positive value for t, you can conclude that the times for the two machines are

Time for machine A = t = 12 minutes
Time for machine B = $t + 12$ = 24 minutes.

Check

$$\frac{1}{12} + \frac{1}{12 + 12} \stackrel{?}{=} \frac{1}{8} \qquad \text{Substitute 12 for } t \text{ in original equation.}$$

$$\frac{2}{24} + \frac{1}{24} \stackrel{?}{=} \frac{1}{8} \qquad \text{Rewrite using LCD of 24.}$$

$$\frac{3}{24} = \frac{1}{8} \qquad \text{Solution checks. } \checkmark$$

Example 4   Reduced Rates

A ski club chartered a bus for a ski trip at a cost of $480. In an attempt to lower the bus fare per skier, the club invited nonmembers to go along. When five nonmembers agreed to go on the trip, the fare per skier decreased by $4.80. How many club members are going on the trip?

Solution

Verbal Model: Cost per skier · Number of skiers = 480

Labels:

Number of ski club members = x	(people)
Number of skiers = $x + 5$	(people)
Original cost = $480/x$	(dollars per person)
New cost = $(480/x) - 4.80$	(dollars per person)

Equation:

$$\left(\frac{480}{x} - 4.80\right)(x + 5) = 480$$

$$\left(\frac{480 - 4.8x}{x}\right)(x + 5) = 480$$

$$(480 - 4.8x)(x + 5) = 480x, \quad x \neq 0$$

$$480x + 2400 - 4.8x^2 - 24x = 480x$$

$$-4.8x^2 - 24x + 2400 = 0$$

$$x^2 + 5x - 500 = 0$$

$$(x + 25)(x - 20) = 0$$

$$x + 25 = 0 \implies x = -25$$

$$x - 20 = 0 \implies x = 20$$

Both sides of this equation were divided by -4.8. If -4.8 had not been a factor of each term, we might have multiplied both sides by -10 to clear the equation of decimals and then solved the resulting equation.

Choosing the positive value of x, you can conclude that 20 ski club members are going on the trip. Check this solution in the original statement of the problem, as follows.

Original cost for 20 ski club members

$$480/20 = \$24$$

New cost with 5 nonmembers

$$480/25 = \$19.20$$

Decrease in fare with 5 nonmembers

$$24 - 19.20 = \$4.80 \qquad \text{Solution checks.} ✓$$

This Discussing the Concept exercise could be the basis for a "concluding" classroom discussion. You might refer to the related information on page 85 and in Section 2.3.

Discussing the Concept   What is Algebra?

Now that you are completing this course, suppose someone asks you, "What is algebra?" Write a short paper describing how you would answer this question.

10.5 Exercises

Integrated Review — Concepts, Skills, and Problem Solving

Keep mathematically in shape by doing these exercises *before* the problems of this section.

Properties and Definitions

1. Define the slope of the line through the points (x_1, y_1) and (x_2, y_2).

2. Give the following forms of an equation of a line.

    (a) General form   (b) Slope-intercept form

    (c) Vertical line   (d) Point-slope form

Simplifying Expressions

In Exercises 3–6, find the product and simplify.

3. $-2x^2(5x^3)$ **4.** $(x + 4)(2x - 5)$

5. $(x + 7)^2$ **6.** $(x + 1)(x^2 - x + 1)$

In Exercises 7–10, factor the expression completely.

7. $9x^2 - 4y^2$ **8.** $10x^4 + 3x^3 - 4x^2$

9. $15x^2 - 11x - 14$ **10.** $4x^2 - 28x + 49$

Graphs

In Exercises 11 and 12, graph the function.

11. $f(t) = \frac{3}{2}t - \frac{1}{2}$

12. $g(x) = -\frac{1}{2}x^2 + 2x - 1$

Solving Problems

Problem Solving   In Exercises 1–8, find two positive integers satisfying the given requirement.

1. The product of two consecutive integers is 132.

2. The product of two consecutive integers is 420.

3. The product of two consecutive odd integers is 323.

4. The product of two consecutive odd integers is 143.

5. The product of two consecutive even integers is 288.

6. The product of two consecutive even integers is 168.

7. The sum of the squares of two consecutive integers is 113.

8. The sum of the squares of two consecutive integers is 421.

Falling Time   In Exercises 9–14, the height h (in feet) of a falling object at any time t (in seconds) is modeled by

$$h = h_0 - 16t^2$$

where h_0 is the initial height. Use the model to find the time it takes for an object to fall to the ground given h_0.

9. $h_0 = 1600$ **10.** $h_0 = 400$

11. $h_0 = 1152$ **12.** $h_0 = 1728$

13. $h_0 = 550$ (height of the Washington Monument)

14. $h_0 = 1350$ (height of the World Trade Center)

Geometry   In Exercises 15–24, use the perimeter or area to find the length and width of the rectangle. Then find the area or perimeter, as indicated.

	Width	Length	Perimeter	Area
15.	$0.6l$	l	64 in.	
16.	w	$1.5w$	75 m	
17.	w	$2w$		50 ft^2
18.	w	$1.2w$		1440 cm^2
19.	$\frac{1}{4}l$	l		100 in.^{2}
20.	$\frac{2}{3}l$	l		24 in.^{2}
21.	w	$w + 4$	56 km	
22.	$l - 5$	l	18 ft	
23.	$l - 10$	l		75 m^2
24.	w	$w + 6$		160 ft^2

In Exercises 25–28, write a quadratic equation to solve the problem. See Example 1.

25. *Geometry*   A picture is 6 inches longer than it is wide and has an area of 187 square inches. What are the dimensions of the picture?

26. *Geometry*   A picture whose width is 7 inches less than its length has an area of 144 square inches. What are the dimensions of the picture?

27. *Geometry*   A rectangular region in a lumberyard is to be fenced for storage. The region will be fenced on three sides with 175 feet of fence, and the fourth side will be bounded by a building (see figure). The area of the fenced region is 3750 square feet. Find the dimensions of the region.

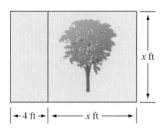

28. *Geometry*   To add more space to your yard, you purchase an additional 4 feet along the side of the property (see figure). The area of the lot is now 9600 square feet. What are the dimensions of the new lot?

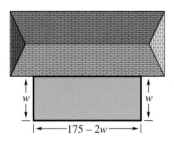

29. *Geometry*   A radio station advertises that its broadcasts are heard over a circular region covering approximately 10,000 square miles. Approximate the distance between the station and the listeners farthest from the station.

30. *Geometry*   A bag of lawn fertilizer covers 10,000 square feet. Determine the diameter of the circular region that can be fertilized with one bag.

31. *Geometry*   The height of a triangle is one-third its base and the area of the triangle is 24 square inches. Find the dimensions of the triangle.

32. *Geometry*   The height of a triangle is three times its base and the area of the triangle is 864 square inches. Find the dimensions of the triangle.

In Exercises 33–38, use the Pythagorean Theorem to solve the problem. See Example 2.

33. *Pulling a Boat*   A windlass is used to pull a boat to the dock (see figure). The rope is attached to the boat at a point 15 feet below the level of the windlass. Find the distance from the boat to the dock when the length of the rope is 75 feet.

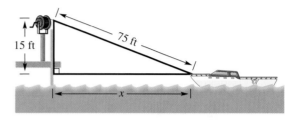

34. *Length of a Ladder*   A 20-foot ladder is leaning against a building (see figure). The ladder must reach a point 19 feet above the ground. Determine the distance from the base of the ladder to the building.

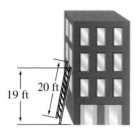

35. *Geometry*   A corner lot has sidewalks on two adjacent sides for a total of 90 feet. The diagonal path across the lot is 64 feet. What are the lengths of the two sides of the sidewalk?

36. *Geometry*   You are delivering pizza to offices *B* and *C* (see figure) and you are required to keep a log of all mileages between stops. You forget to look at the odometer at office *B*, but after getting to office *C* you record the total distance traveled from the pizza shop as 14 miles. The return distance on the beltway from *C* to *A* is 10 miles. The route forms a right triangle. Find the distance from *A* to *B*.

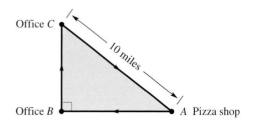

37. *Geometry* The perimeter of a rectangle is 68 inches and the length of the diagonal is 26 inches. Find the dimensions of the rectangle.

38. *Geometry* The perimeter of a rectangle is 84 centimeters and the length of the diagonal is 30 centimeters. Find the dimensions of the rectangle.

39. *Geometry* The floor plan of a building is shown in the figure. Find x if the building has 2400 square feet of floor space.

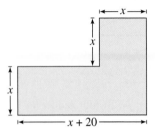

40. *Geometry* The floor plan of a building is shown in the figure. Find x if the building has 26,250 square feet of floor space.

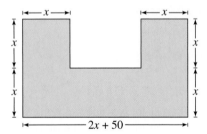

In Exercises 41–44, begin by writing a rational equation to solve the problem. See Example 3.

41. *Work Rate* Working together, two people can complete a task in 4 hours. Working alone, one person takes 6 hours longer than the other. How long would it take each person to complete the task alone?

42. *Work Rate* Working together, two people can complete a task in $3\frac{1}{2}$ hours. Working alone, one person takes 2 hours longer than the other. How long would it take each person to complete the task alone?

43. *Work Rate* A farmer has two combines. Combine B is known to take 2 hours longer than combine A to harvest a field. Using both machines, it takes 4 hours to harvest the field. How long would it take to harvest the field using each machine individually?

44. *Work Rate* An office contains two printers. Printer B is known to take 5 minutes longer than printer A to produce the company's monthly financial report. With the two printers working together, it takes 3 minutes to produce the report. How long would it take each machine individually to produce the report?

In Exercises 45–48, begin by writing a rational equation to solve the problem. See Example 4.

45. *Ticket Prices* A service organization paid $100 for a block of tickets to a ball game. The block contained five more tickets than the organization needed for its members. By inviting five more people to attend (and share in the cost), the organization lowered the price per ticket by $1. How many people are going to the game?

46. *Ticket Prices* A service organization paid $150 for a block of tickets to a ball game. The block contained four more tickets than the organization needed for its members. By inviting four more people to attend (and share in the cost), the organization lowered the price per ticket by $1.25. How many people are going to the game?

47. *Bus Fares* A science club chartered a bus for $360 to attend a science fair. In order to lower the bus fare per member, the club invited nonmembers to go along. When 10 nonmembers agreed to go on the trip, the fare per person decreased by $3. How many people are going on the excursion?

48. *Bus Fares* A literary club chartered a bus for $600 to attend a Shakespearean festival. In order to lower the bus fare per member, the club invited nonmembers to go along. When 10 nonmembers agreed to go on the trip, the fare per person decreased by $3. How many people are going to the festival?

49. *Average Speeds* A truck traveled the first 200 miles of a trip at one speed and the last 225 miles at an average speed of 5 miles per hour less. If the entire trip took 10 hours, what were the two average speeds?

50. *Average Speeds* A truck traveled the first 150 miles of a trip at one speed and the last 200 miles at an average speed of 10 miles per hour less. If the entire trip took 8 hours, what were the two average speeds?

Compound Interest   In Exercises 51–54, find the interest rate *r*. The amount *A* in an account earning *r* percent compounded annually for 2 years is given by $A = P(1 + r)^2$, where *P* is the original investment.

51. $P = \$1000$
$A = \$1123.60$

52. $P = \$2500$
$A = \$2862.25$

53. $P = \$200$
$A = \$235.44$

54. $P = \$10,000$
$A = \$11,990$

55. *Geometry*   Consider the rectangle in the figure, with the requirement that its perimeter *P* and area *A* are equal.

(a) Since $P = A$, it follows that

$$2l + 2w = lw.$$

Solve this equation for *w*.

(b) Use the result of part (a) to write the perimeter and area as functions of *l*.

(c) Find the dimensions of the rectangle if $A = 18$.

(d) Find the area and perimeter of the rectangle if $w = 4$.

(e) Determine the domain of the area and perimeter functions if $w \leq l$.

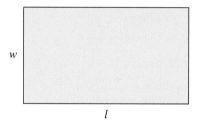

56. *Data Analysis*   The table gives the death rates *y* by suicide per 100,000 population for selected ages *x* in the United States.   (Source: U.S. National Center for Health Statistics)

Age, *x*	7	12	17	22
Rate, *y*	4	318	1948	3008

Age, *x*	27	32	37	42
Rate, *y*	3026	3328	3397	2978

These data can be modeled by

$$y = -5.10x^2 + 345.89x - 2495.$$

(a) Use a graphing utility to plot the data and graph the model.

(b) Use the graph in part (a) to approximate the age when the rate is maximum.

(c) If a goal were to decrease this death rate by 25% in 10 years, give a model for the rate in 10 years.

57. *Data Analysis*   Experimental data are obtained in a lab for the breaking strength *y* (in tons) of a steel cable of diameter *x* (in inches). The data are given in the table.

x	0.50	0.75	1.0	1.25	1.50	1.75
y	9.9	21.8	38.3	59.2	84.4	114.0

A model for these data is

$$y = 35.23x^2 + 4.07x - 1.$$

(a) Use a graphing utility to plot the data and graph the model.

(b) Use the graph in part (a) to estimate the diameter of a cable that would support 75 tons.

(c) Use the model and the Quadratic Formula to estimate the diameter of a cable that would support 30 tons.

Explaining Concepts

58. In your own words, describe what is meant by the term *equivalent equations*. Give an example.

59. Describe the steps that can be used to transform an equation into an equivalent equation.

60. The phrase *increased by* indicates what operation?

61. The word *per* indicates what operation?

62. State the guidelines for solving word problems.

63. State the Pythagorean Theorem and draw a diagram that illustrates this theorem.

Key Terms

extracting square roots, *p. 513*

completing the square, *p. 518*

Quadratic Formula, *p. 527*

discriminant, *p. 527*

quadratic function, *p. 535*

parabola, *p. 535*

vertex, *p. 535*

Key Concepts

10.1 Extracting square roots

Let u be a real number, a variable, or an algebraic expression. The equation $u^2 = d$, where $d > 0$, has exactly two solutions:

$$u = \sqrt{d} \text{ and } u = -\sqrt{d}.$$

These solutions can also be written as $u = \pm\sqrt{d}$. This form of the solution is read as "u is equal to plus or minus the square root of d." Solving an equation of the form $u^2 = d$ without going through the steps of factoring is called extracting square roots.

10.2 Completing the square

To complete the square for the expression

$$x^2 + bx$$

add $(b/2)^2$, which is the square of half the coefficient of x. Consequently,

$$x^2 + bx + \left(\frac{b}{2}\right)^2 = \left(x + \frac{b}{2}\right)^2.$$

10.3 The Quadratic Formula

The solutions of $ax^2 + bx + c = 0$, $a \neq 0$, are given by the Quadratic Formula

$$x = \frac{-b \pm \sqrt{b^2 - 4ac}}{2a}.$$

The expression inside the radical, $b^2 - 4ac$, is called the discriminant.

1. If $b^2 - 4ac > 0$, the equation has two real solutions.
2. If $b^2 - 4ac = 0$, the equation has one (repeated) real solution.
3. If $b^2 - 4ac < 0$, the equation has no real solution.

10.3 Guidelines for solving quadratic equations

1. First check to see whether you can solve the equation by extracting square roots.
2. If you can't extract square roots, write the equation in general form and try factoring.
3. If you can't factor the quadratic equation in general form, apply the Quadratic Formula.

10.4 The Leading Coefficient Test for parabolas

The graph of the quadratic function $y = ax^2 + bx + c$ is a parabola.

1. If $a > 0$, the parabola opens up.
2. If $a < 0$, the parabola opens down.

10.4 Vertex of a parabola

The vertex of a parabola given by $y = ax^2 + bx + c$ occurs at the point whose x-coordinate is

$$x = -\frac{b}{2a}.$$

To find the y-coordinate of the vertex, substitute the x-coordinate in the equation $y = ax^2 + bx + c$.

10.4 Guidelines for sketching a parabola

1. Use the Leading Coefficient Test to determine whether the parabola opens up or down.
2. Find and plot the x-intercepts (if any) and the y-intercept.
3. Find and plot the vertex.
4. Create a table of values that includes a few additional points.
5. Complete the graph with a smooth, cup-shaped curve.

REVIEW EXERCISES

Reviewing Skills

10.1 In Exercises 1–6, solve the quadratic equation by factoring.

1. $x^2 + 10x = 0$

2. $u^2 - 12u = 0$

3. $x^2 - 5x + 6 = 0$

4. $3y^2 + 7y - 6 = 0$

5. $4y^2 - 25 = 0$

6. $8z^2 - 32 = 0$

In Exercises 7–22, solve the quadratic equation by extracting square roots. (Some equations may have no real solutions.)

7. $x^2 = 49$

8. $a^2 = 81$

9. $x^2 - 48 = 0$

10. $x^2 - 72 = 0$

11. $y^2 + 8 = 0$

12. $y^2 - 8 = 0$

13. $(x - 5)^2 = 3$

14. $(x + 2)^2 = 5$

15. $(x - 2)^2 - 6 = 0$

16. $(x + 1)^2 + 3 = 0$

17. $2(x + 4)^2 - 16 = 0$

18. $3(y - 1)^2 - 36 = 0$

19. $9(x - 7)^2 - 25 = 0$

20. $4(x + 3)^2 - 9 = 0$

21. $8(x - 4)^2 + 32 = 0$

22. $7(y - 6)^2 + 63 = 0$

10.2 In Exercises 23–30, solve the quadratic equation by completing the square. (Some equations may have no real solutions.)

23. $x^2 - 6x - 1 = 0$

24. $x^2 + 10x + 12 = 0$

25. $x^2 - x - 1 = 0$

26. $t^2 + 3t + 1 = 0$

27. $2y^2 + 10y + 5 = 0$

28. $3x^2 - 2x + 1 = 0$

29. $4x^2 - 2x + 1 = 0$

30. $2y^2 + y + 3 = 0$

10.3 In Exercises 31–46, solve the quadratic equation using the Quadratic Formula. (Some equations may have no real solutions.)

31. $y^2 + y - 42 = 0$

32. $x^2 - x - 20 = 0$

33. $c^2 - 6c + 6 = 0$

34. $c^2 - 6c + 5 = 0$

35. $-x^2 + 3x + 70 = 0$

36. $y^2 + y + 1 = 0$

37. $2y^2 + y - 42 = 0$

38. $2x^2 - x - 20 = 0$

39. $3x^2 - 5x + 3 = 0$

40. $4x^2 + 4x + 1 = 0$

41. $v^2 = 250$

42. $x^2 - 45x = 0$

43. $0.3t^2 - 2t + 1 = 0$

44. $-u^2 + 3.1u + 5 = 0$

45. $0.6x^2 - 0.14x + 1 = 0$

46. $0.5y^2 + 0.75y - 2 = 0$

In Exercises 47–50, solve the equation.

47. $\dfrac{1}{x} + \dfrac{1}{x + 1} = \dfrac{1}{2}$

48. $\dfrac{3}{t - 1} - \dfrac{2}{t^2 + t - 2} = 4$

49. $\sqrt{2x + 5} = x - 3$

50. $x = \sqrt{4x + 5}$

10.4 In Exercises 51–56, determine whether the parabola opens up or down.

51. $y = 3x^2 + 4x - 8$

52. $y = -4x^2 + 2x + 10$

53. $y = -7x^2 - 5x - 6$

54. $y = x^2 - 9x + 3$

55. $y = 3 - (x + 4)^2$

56. $y = 7 + (2x - 1)^2$

In Exercises 57–68, sketch the graph of the equation. Identify the vertex and any intercepts.

57. $y = x^2 - 2x + 1$

58. $y = -(x^2 - 2x + 1)$

59. $y = -x^2 + 4x - 3$

60. $y = x^2 - 6x + 9$

61. $y = -x^2 + 3x$

62. $y = x^2 - 10x$

63. $y = \frac{1}{4}(4x^2 - 4x + 3)$

64. $y = \frac{1}{3}(x^2 - 4x + 6)$

65. $y = 2x^2 + 4x + 5$

66. $y = -2x^2 + 8x - 5$

67. $y = -(3x^2 - 4x - 2)$

68. $y = 3x^2 + 2x + 3$

In Exercises 69–72, use a graphing utility to graph the function. Approximate the vertex from the graph.

69. $y = 3 - x^2$

70. $y = 3 - \frac{1}{3}x^2$

71. $y = x^2 - 6x + 5$

72. $y = 20 - 11x - 3x^2$

Solving Problems

73. *Problem Solving* Find two consecutive positive integers whose product is 240.

74. *Problem Solving* Find two consecutive positive integers such that the sum of their squares is 365.

75. *Compound Interest* After 2 years, a $2000 investment, compounded annually at interest rate r, will yield an amount $2000(1 + r)^2$. If this amount is $2332.80, find the rate r.

76. *Compound Interest* After 2 years, an $800 investment, compounded annually at interest rate r, will yield an amount $800(1 + r)^2$. If this amount is $882.00, find the rate r.

77. *Falling Time* The height h (in feet) of an object above the ground is given by $h = 48 - 16t^2$, where t is time in seconds. How long does it take for the object to hit the ground? Describe the motion of this object. Was it dropped, thrown upward, or thrown downward? Explain.

78. *Falling Time* The height h (in feet) of an object above the ground is given by $h = -16t^2 + 48t + 160$, where t is time in seconds. How long does it take for the object to hit the ground? Describe the motion of the object. Was it dropped, thrown upward, or thrown downward? Explain.

In Exercises 79–82, solve for x.

79. Area $= 32$ square centimeters

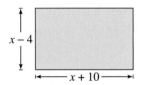

80. Area $= 20$ square feet

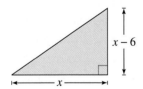

81. Area $= 1800$ square meters

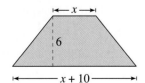

82. Area $= 1300$ square feet

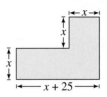

83. *Geometry* The height of a triangle is one and one-half times its base, and its area is 60 square inches. Find the dimensions of the triangle.

84. *Geometry* The height of a triangle is three times its base, and its area is 24 square inches. Find the dimensions of the triangle.

85. *Ticket Sales* A Little League baseball team paid $72 for a block of tickets to a ball game. The block contained three more tickets than the team needed. By inviting three more people to attend (and share in the cost), the team lowered the price per ticket by $1.20. How many people are going to the game?

86. *Ticket Sales* A Little League baseball team paid $120 for a block of tickets to a ball game. The block contained four more tickets than the team needed. By inviting four more people to attend (and share in the cost), the team lowered the price per ticket by $1. How many people are going to the game?

87. *Average Speeds* A train traveled the first 165 miles of a trip at one speed and the last 300 miles at an average speed that was 5 miles per hour greater. The entire trip took 8 hours. What were the two average speeds?

88. *Average Speeds* A bus traveled the first 220 miles of a trip at one speed and the last 130 miles at an average speed that was 10 miles per hour greater. The entire trip took 6 hours. What were the two average speeds?

89. *Work Rate* Working together, two people can complete a task in 10 hours. Working alone, one person takes 4 hours longer than the other to complete the task. Working alone, how long would it take each person to complete the task?

90. *Work Rate* Working together, two people can complete a task in 15 hours. Working alone, one person takes 2 hours longer than the other to complete the task. Working alone, how long would it take each person to complete the task?

91. *Geometry*   The perimeter of a rectangle is 34 feet and the length of the diagonal is 13 feet. Find the dimensions of the rectangle.

92. *Geometry*   The perimeter of a rectangle is 122 centimeters and the length of the diagonal is 43.6 centimeters. Find the dimensions of the rectangle.

93. *Tossing a Ball*   The height y (in feet) of a ball thrown by a child is modeled by

$$y = -\frac{1}{10}x^2 + 3x + 3$$

where x is the horizontal distance (in feet) from where the ball is thrown.

(a) From what height is the ball thrown?

(b) What is the maximum height?

(c) How far from the child is the ball when it strikes the ground?

94. *Tossing a Ball*   The height y (in feet) of a ball thrown by a child is modeled by

$$y = -\frac{1}{4}x^2 + x + 3$$

where x is the horizontal distance (in feet) from where the ball is thrown.

(a) From what height is the ball thrown?

(b) What is the maximum height?

(c) How far from the child is the ball when it strikes the ground?

95. *Geometry*   The perimeter of a rectangle of length l and width w is 40 feet (see figure).

w

l

(a) Show that $w = 20 - l$.

(b) Show that the area A is given by

$$A = lw = l(20 - l).$$

(c) Complete the table.

l	2	4	6	8	10	12	14	16	18
A									

(d) Sketch the graph of the function $A = l(20 - l)$.

(e) Of all rectangles with perimeters of 40 feet, which has the maximum area? How can you tell?

96. *Exploration*   In this chapter, you have seen that if a quadratic equation

$$ax^2 + bx + c = 0$$

can be factored into the form

$$(x - r_1)(x - r_2) = 0,$$

then the solutions to the equation are $x = r_1$ and $x = r_2$. This process can be reversed by starting with the solutions, forming the factors, and finally expanding to find a quadratic equation with the given solutions. Find a quadratic equation with the specified solutions.

(a) $x = 3, x = 5$ (b) $x = \frac{1}{2}, x = 3$

(c) $x = -4, x = -1$ (d) $x = -10, x = -2$

97. *Data Analysis*   From 1990 through 1996, the net orders for U.S. civil jet transport aircraft y can be modeled by

$$y = 62.75t^2 - 379.89t + 653.50$$

where t is the year, with $t = 0$ corresponding to 1990. (Source: Aerospace Industries Association of America)

(a) Use a graphing utility to graph the model.

(b) During which years between 1990 and 1996 were orders decreasing? During which years were they increasing?

(c) How are the questions in part (b) related to the vertex of the graph?

Chapter Test

Take this test as you would take a test in class. After you are done, check your work against the answers given in the back of the book.

In Exercises 1–10, solve the equation. If indicated, use the specified method.

1. Extracting square roots:

   $x^2 - 144 = 0$

2. Extracting square roots:

   $(x + 2)^2 - 16 = 0$

3. Factoring:

   $x(x + 3) - 10(x + 3) = 0$

4. Factoring:

   $2x^2 + x - 15 = 0$

5. Completing the square:

   $t^2 - 6t + 7 = 0$

6. Completing the square:

   $3z^2 + 9z + 5 = 0$

7. Quadratic Formula:

   $x^2 - x - 3 = 0$

8. Quadratic Formula:

   $2u^2 + 4u + 1 = 0$

9. $\dfrac{1}{x + 1} - \dfrac{1}{x - 2} = 1$

10. $\sqrt{2x} = x - 1$

In Exercises 11–13, determine whether the parabola opens up or down. Then find the coordinates of the vertex.

11. $y = -2x^2 + 4$ 12. $y = 5 - 2x - x^2$ 13. $y = (x - 2)^2 + 3$

14. Explain how to find the x-intercepts of a quadratic equation and demonstrate with the graph of $y = x^2 - 8x + 12$.

15. Sketch the graph of $y = x^2 - 4x$.

16. Find two consecutive positive integers whose product is 342.

17. The height of a triangle is three times the length of its base. The area of the triangle is 54 square inches. Sketch a diagram and label the height as h and the base as $3h$. Find the dimensions of the triangle.

18. The rectangle in the figure has an area of 96 square inches. Use a quadratic equation to find its dimensions. Show your work.

19. Together, two people can mow a lawn in 6 hours. When working alone, it takes one person 5 hours longer than the other. Find the time required for each person to mow the lawn alone.

20. After 2 years, a $600 investment, compounded annually at interest rate r, will yield an amount $600(1 + r)^2$. If this amount is $655.22, find the rate r.

21. A train traveled the first 360 miles of a trip at one speed and the last 360 miles at an average speed that was 12 miles per hour greater. The entire trip took 11 hours. What were the two average speeds?

x in.

$x + 10$ in.

Figure for 18

Appendix A

Introduction to Graphing Utilities

Introduction ■ Using a Graphing Utility ■ Using Special Features of a Graphing Utility

Introduction

In Section 4.2 you studied the point-plotting method for sketching the graph of an equation. One of the disadvantages of the point-plotting method is that to get a good idea about the shape of a graph you need to plot *many* points. By plotting only a few points, you can badly misrepresent the graph.

For instance, consider the equation $y = x^3$. To graph this equation, suppose you calculated only the following three points.

x	-1	0	1
$y = x^3$	-1	0	1

By plotting these three points, as shown in Figure A.1(a), you might assume that the graph of the equation is a straight line. This, however, is not correct. By plotting several more points, as shown in Figure A.1(b), you can see that the actual graph is not straight at all.

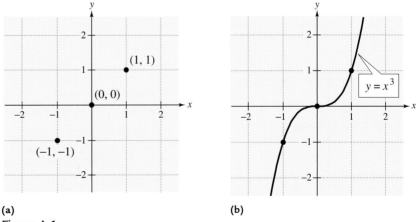

(a)   (b)

Figure A.1

So, the point-plotting method leaves you with a dilemma. On the one hand, the method can be very inaccurate if only a few points are plotted. But, on the other hand, it is very time-consuming to plot a dozen (or more) points. Technology can help you solve this dilemma. Plotting several points (or even hundreds of points) on a rectangular coordinate system is something that a computer or graphing calculator can do easily.

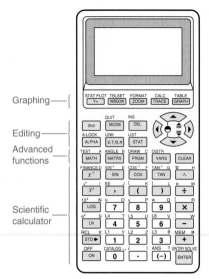

Graphing

Editing

Advanced
functions

Scientific
calculator

Figure A.2 *Keypad of a TI-83 Graphics Calculator*

Using a Graphing Utility

There are many different graphing utilities: some are graphing packages for computers and some are hand-held graphing calculators. In this section we describe the steps used to graph an equation with a *TI-83* graphing utility. (See Figure A.2.) We will often give keystroke sequences for illustration; however, these may not agree precisely with the steps required by *your* calculator.*

▶ **Graphing an Equation with a *TI-83* Graphing Calculator**

Before performing the following steps, set your calculator so that all of the standard defaults are active. For instance, all of the options at the left of the MODE screen should be highlighted.

1. Set the viewing window for the graph. (See Example 3.) To set the standard viewing window, press ZOOM 6.

2. Rewrite the equation so that y is isolated on the left side of the equation.

3. Press the Y= key. Then enter the right side of the equation on the first line of the display. (The first line is labeled $Y_1 = .$)

4. Press the GRAPH key.

Example 1   Graphing a Linear Equation

Sketch the graph of $2y + x = 4$.

Solution

To begin, solve the given equation for y in terms of x.

$$2y + x = 4 \qquad \text{Original equation}$$

$$2y = -x + 4 \qquad \text{Subtract } x \text{ from both sides.}$$

$$y = -\frac{1}{2}x + 2 \qquad \text{Divide both sides by 2.}$$

Press the Y= key, and enter the following keystrokes.

(−) X,T,θ,n ÷ 2 + 2

The top row of the display should now be as follows.

$$Y_1 = \text{-X/2} + 2$$

Press the GRAPH key, and the screen should look like that shown in Figure A.3.

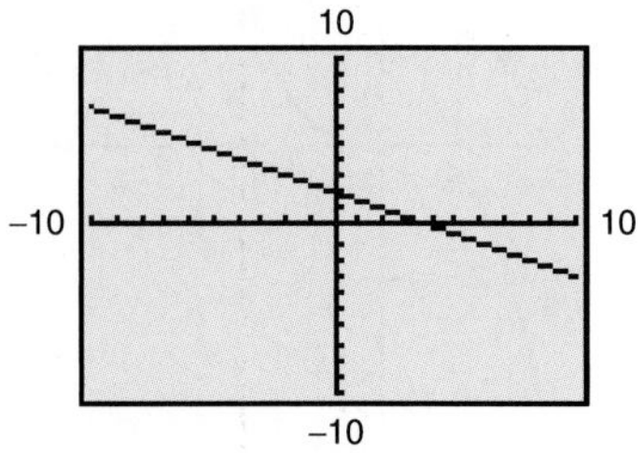

Figure A.3

---

*The graphing calculator keystrokes given in this section correspond to the *TI-83* graphing utility by Texas Instruments. For other graphing utilities, the keystrokes may differ. Consult your user's guide.

In Figure A.3, notice that the calculator screen does not label the tick marks on the *x*-axis or the *y*-axis. To see what the tick marks represent, you can press WINDOW . If you set your calculator to the standard graphing defaults before working Example 1, the screen should show the following values.

Xmin = -10	The minimum *x*-value is −10.
Xmax = 10	The maximum *x*-value is 10.
Xscl = 1	The *x*-scale is 1 unit per tick mark.
Ymin = -10	The minimum *y*-value is −10.
Ymax = 10	The maximum *y*-value is 10.
Yscl = 1	The *y*-scale is 1 unit per tick mark.
Xres = 1	Sets the pixel resolution

These settings are summarized visually in Figure A.4.

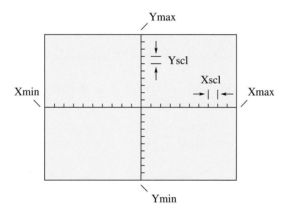

Figure A.4

Example 2   Graphing an Equation Involving Absolute Value

Sketch the graph of $y = |x - 3|$.

Solution

This equation is already written so that *y* is isolated on the left side of the equation. Press the Y= key, and enter the following keystrokes.

ABS (X,T,θ,n − 3)

The top row of the display should now be as follows.

$$Y_1 = \text{abs}(X - 3)$$

Press the GRAPH key, and the screen should look like that shown in Figure A.5.

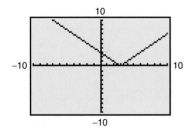

Figure A.5

Using the Special Features of a Graphing Utility

To use your graphing utility to its best advantage, you must learn to set the viewing window, as illustrated in the next example.

Example 3   Setting the Viewing Window

Sketch the graph of $y = x^2 + 12$.

Solution

Press $\boxed{Y=}$ and enter $x^2 + 12$ on the first line.

$$\boxed{X,T,\theta,n} \ \boxed{x^2} \ \boxed{+} \ 12$$

Press the $\boxed{GRAPH}$ key. If your calculator is set to the standard viewing window, nothing will appear on the screen. The reason for this is that the lowest point on the graph of $y = x^2 + 12$ occurs at the point $(0, 12)$. Using the standard viewing window, you obtain a screen whose largest y-value is 10. In other words, none of the graph is visible on a screen whose y-values vary between -10 and 10, as shown in Figure A.6(a). To change these settings, press $\boxed{WINDOW}$ and enter the following values.

Xmin = -10	The minimum x-value is -10.
Xmax = 10	The maximum x-value is 10.
Xscl = 1	The x-scale is 1 unit per tick mark.
Ymin = -10	The minimum y-value is -10.
Ymax = 30	The maximum y-value is 30.
Yscl = 5	The y-scale is 5 units per tick mark.
Xres = 1	Sets the pixel resolution

Press $\boxed{GRAPH}$ and you will obtain the graph shown in Figure A.6(b). On this graph, note that each tick mark on the y-axis represents 5 units because you changed the y-scale to 5. Also note that the highest point on the y-axis is now 30 because you changed the maximum value of y to 30.

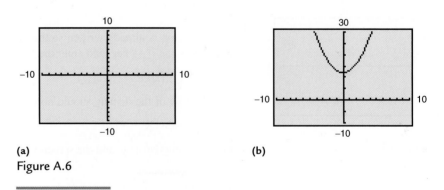

(a)   (b)

Figure A.6

If you changed the y-maximum and y-scale on your utility as indicated in Example 3, you should return to the standard settings before working Example 4. To do this, press $\boxed{ZOOM}$ 6.

Example 4   Using a Square Setting

Sketch the graph of $y = x$. The graph of this equation is a straight line that makes a 45° angle with the x-axis and with the y-axis. From the graph on your utility, does the angle appear to be 45°?

Solution

Press [Y=] and enter x on the first line.

$Y_1 = X$

Press the [GRAPH] key and you will obtain the graph shown in Figure A.7(a). Notice that the angle the line makes with the x-axis doesn't appear to be 45°. The reason for this is that the screen is wider than it is tall. This makes the tick marks on the x-axis farther apart than the tick marks on the y-axis. To obtain the same distance between tick marks on both axes, you can change the graphing settings from "standard" to "square." To do this, press the following keys.

[ZOOM] 5   Square setting

The screen should look like that shown in Figure A.7(b). Note in this figure that the square setting has changed the viewing window so that the x-values vary between -15 and 15.

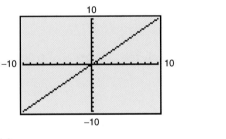
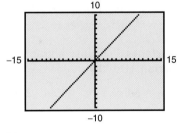

(a)   (b)

Figure A.7

There are many possible square settings on a graphing utility. To create a square setting, you need the following ratio to be $\frac{2}{3}$.

$$\frac{Ymax - Ymin}{Xmax - Xmin}$$

For instance, the setting in Example 4 is square because $(Ymax - Ymin) = 20$ and $(Xmax - Xmin) = 30$.

Example 5   Sketching More than One Graph on the Same Screen

Sketch the graphs of the following equations on the same screen.

$$y = -x + 4, \quad y = -x, \quad \text{and} \quad y = -x - 4$$

Solution

To begin, press [Y=] and enter all three equations on the first three lines. The display should now be as follows.

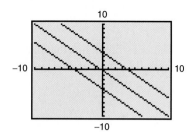

Figure A.8

$Y_1 = \text{-}X + 4$ (−) [X,T,θ,n] [+] 4

$Y_2 = \text{-}X$ (−) [X,T,θ,n]

$Y_3 = \text{-}X - 4$ (−) [X,T,θ,n] [−] 4

Press the [GRAPH] key and you will obtain the graph shown in Figure A.8. Note that the graph of each equation is a straight line, and that the lines are parallel to each other.

Another special feature of a graphing utility is the trace feature. This feature is used to find solution points of an equation. For example, you can approximate the x- and y-intercepts of $y = 3x + 6$ by first graphing the equation, then pressing the [TRACE] key, and finally pressing the [◄] [►] keys. To get a better approximation of a solution point, you can use the following keystrokes repeatedly.

[ZOOM] 2 [ENTER]

Check to see that you get an x-intercept of $(-2, 0)$ and a y-intercept of $(0, 6)$. Use the trace feature to find the x- and y-intercepts of $y = \frac{1}{2}x - 4$.

Appendix A   Exercises

In Exercises 1–12, use a graphing utility to graph the equation. (Use the standard setting.)

1. $y = -3x$ **2.** $y = x - 4$

3. $y = \frac{3}{4}x - 6$ **4.** $y = -3x + 2$

5. $y = \frac{1}{2}x^2$ **6.** $y = -\frac{2}{3}x^2$

7. $y = x^2 - 4x + 2$ **8.** $y = -0.5x^2 - 2x + 2$

9. $y = |x - 3|$ **10.** $y = |x + 4|$

11. $y = |x^2 - 4|$ **12.** $y = |x - 2| - 5$

In Exercises 13–16, use a graphing utility to graph the equation using the given window settings.

13. $y = 27x + 100$ **14.** $y = 50{,}000 - 6000x$

| Xmin = 0 |
| Xmax = 5 |
| Xscl = .5 |
| Ymin = 75 |
| Ymax = 250 |
| Yscl = 25 |
| Xres = 1 |

| Xmin = 0 |
| Xmax = 7 |
| Xscl = .5 |
| Ymin = 0 |
| Ymax = 50000 |
| Yscl = 5000 |
| Xres = 1 |

15. $y = 0.001x^2 + 0.5x$ **16.** $y = 100 - 0.5|x|$

| Xmin = -500 |
| Xmax = 200 |
| Xscl = 50 |
| Ymin = -100 |
| Ymax = 100 |
| Yscl = 20 |
| Xres = 1 |

| Xmin = -300 |
| Xmax = 300 |
| Xscl = 60 |
| Ymin = -100 |
| Ymax = 100 |
| Yscl = 20 |
| Xres = 1 |

In Exercises 17–20, find a viewing window that shows the important characteristics of the graph.

17. $y = 15 + |x - 12|$ **18.** $y = 15 + (x - 12)^2$

19. $y = -15 + |x + 12|$ **20.** $y = -15 + (x + 12)^2$

In Exercises 21–24, graph both equations on the same screen. Are the graphs identical? If so, what rule of algebra is being illustrated?

21. $y_1 = 2x + (x + 1)$ **22.** $y_1 = \frac{1}{2}(3 - 2x)$

$y_2 = (2x + x) + 1$ $y_2 = \frac{3}{2} - x$

23. $y_1 = 2(\frac{1}{2})$ **24.** $y_1 = x(0.5x)$

$y_2 = 1$ $y_2 = (0.5x)x$

In Exercises 25–32, use the trace feature of a graphing utility to approximate the x- and y-intercepts of the graph.

25. $y = 9 - x^2$

26. $y = 3x^2 - 2x - 5$

27. $y = 6 - |x + 2|$

28. $y = |x - 2|^2 - 3$

29. $y = 2x - 5$

30. $y = 4 - |x|$

31. $y = x^2 + 1.5x - 1$

32. $y = x^3 - 4x$

Geometry   In Exercises 33–36, graph the equations on the same display. Using a "square setting," determine the geometrical shape bounded by the graphs.

33. $y = -4, \quad y = -|x|$

34. $y = |x|, \quad y = 5$

35. $y = |x| - 8, \quad y = -|x| + 8$

36. $y = -\frac{1}{2}x + 7, \quad y = \frac{8}{3}(x + 5), \quad y = \frac{2}{7}(3x - 4)$

Modeling Data   In Exercises 37 and 38, use the following models, which give the number of pieces of first-class mail and the number of periodicals handled by the U.S. Postal Service.

First Class

$y = 0.07x^2 + 1.06x + 88.97, \quad 0 \le x \le 7$

Periodicals

$y = 0.02x^2 - 0.23x + 10.70, \quad 0 \le x \le 7$

In these models, y is the number of pieces handled (in billions) and x is the year, with $x = 0$ corresponding to 1990.   (Source: U.S. Postal Service)

37. Use the following setting to graph both models on the same display of a graphing utility.

Xmin = 0
Xmax = 7
Xscl = 1
Ymin = -5
Ymax = 115
Yscl = 10
Xres = 1

38. (a) Were the numbers of pieces of first-class mail and periodicals increasing or decreasing over time?

  (b) Is the distance between the graphs increasing or decreasing over time? What does this mean to the U.S. Postal Service?

Appendix B

Further Concepts in Geometry

B.1 Exploring Congruence and Similarity

Identifying Congruent Figures ■ Identifying Similar Figures ■
Reading and Using Definitions ■ Congruent Triangles ■ Classifying Triangles

Identifying Congruent Figures

Two figures are *congruent* if they have the same shape and the same size. Each of the triangles in Figure B.1 is congruent to each of the other triangles. The triangles in Figure B.2 are not congruent to each other.

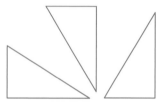

Congruent
Figure B.1

Not Congruent
Figure B.2

Notice that two figures can be congruent without having the same orientation. If two figures are congruent, then either one can be moved (and turned or flipped if necessary) so that it coincides with the other figure.

Example 1   Dividing Regions into Congruent Parts

Divide the region into two congruent parts.

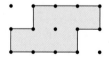

Solution

There are many solutions to this problem. Some of the solutions are shown in Figure B.3. Can you think of others?

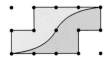

Figure B.3

Identifying Similar Figures

Two figures are *similar* if they have the same shape. (They may or may not have the same size.) Each of the quadrilaterals in Figure B.4 is similar to the others. The quadrilaterals in Figure B.5 are not similar to each other.

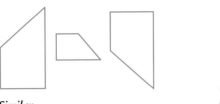
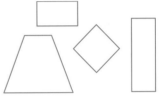

Similar
Figure B.4

Not Similar
Figure B.5

Example 2   Determining Similarity

Two of the figures are similar. Which two are they?

a.    **b.** 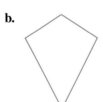   **c.**

Solution

The first figure has five sides and the other two figures have four sides. Because similar figures must have the same shape, the first figure is not similar to either of the others. Because you are told that two figures are similar, it follows that the second and third figures are similar.

Example 3   Determining Similarity

You wrote an essay on Euclid, the Greek mathematician who is famous for writing a geometry book titled *Elements of Geometry*. You are making a copy of the essay using a photocopier that is set at 75% reduction. Is each image on the copied pages similar to its original?

Solution

Every image on a copied page *is* similar to its original. The copied pages are smaller, but that doesn't matter because similar figures do not have to be the same size.

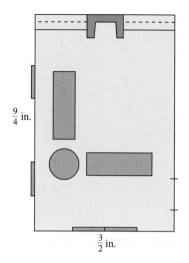

$\frac{9}{4}$ in.

$\frac{3}{2}$ in.

Figure B.6

| Example 4 | Drawing an Object to Scale | |

You are drawing a floor plan of a building. You choose a scale of $\frac{1}{8}$ inch to 1 foot. That is, $\frac{1}{8}$ inch of the floor plan represents 1 foot of the actual building. What dimensions should you draw for a room that is 12 feet wide and 18 feet long?

Solution

Because each foot is represented as $\frac{1}{8}$ inch, the width of the room should be

$$12\left(\tfrac{1}{8}\right) = \tfrac{12}{8} = \tfrac{3}{2} = 1\tfrac{1}{2}$$

and the length of the room should be

$$18\left(\tfrac{1}{8}\right) = \tfrac{18}{8} = \tfrac{9}{4} = 2\tfrac{1}{4}.$$

The scale dimensions of the room are $1\frac{1}{2}$ inches by $2\frac{1}{4}$ inches. See Figure B.6.

Reading and Using Definitions

A definition uses *known* words to describe a *new* word. If no words were known, then no new words could be defined. Hence, some words such as **point, line,** and **plane** must be commonly understood without being defined. Some statements such as "a point lies on a line" and "point C lies between points A and B" are also not defined. See Figure B.7.

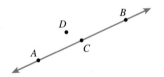

C is between A and B. D is not between A and B.

Figure B.7

▶ **Segments and Rays**

Consider the line $\overleftrightarrow{AB}$ that contains the points A and B. (In geometry, the word *line* means a *straight line*.)

The **line segment** (or simply **segment**) $\overline{AB}$ consists of the *endpoints* A and B and all points on the line $\overleftrightarrow{AB}$ that lie between A and B.

The **ray** $\overrightarrow{AB}$ consists of the *initial point* A and all points on the line $\overleftrightarrow{AB}$ that lie on the same side of A as B lies. If C is between A and B, then $\overrightarrow{CA}$ and $\overrightarrow{CB}$ are **opposite** rays.

Points, segments, or rays that lie on the same line are **collinear.**

Lines are drawn with two arrowheads, line segments are drawn with no arrowhead, and rays are drawn with a single arrowhead. See Figure B.8.

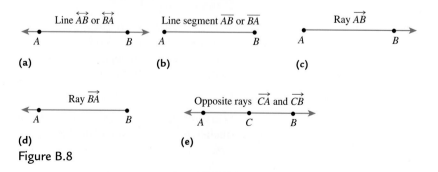

(a) Line $\overleftrightarrow{AB}$ or $\overleftrightarrow{BA}$

(b) Line segment $\overline{AB}$ or $\overline{BA}$

(c) Ray $\overrightarrow{AB}$

(d) Ray $\overrightarrow{BA}$

(e) Opposite rays $\overrightarrow{CA}$ and $\overrightarrow{CB}$

Figure B.8

It follows that $\overline{AB}$ and $\overline{BA}$ denote the same segment, but $\overrightarrow{AB}$ and $\overrightarrow{BA}$ do not denote the same ray. No length is given to lines or rays because each is infinitely long. The *length* of the line segment $\overline{AB}$ is denoted by AB.

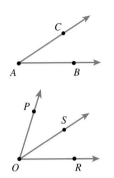

▶ **Angles**

An **angle** consists of two different rays that have the same initial point. The rays are the *sides* of the angle. The angle that consists of the rays $\overrightarrow{AB}$ and $\overrightarrow{AC}$ is denoted by $\angle BAC$, $\angle CAB$, or $\angle A$. The point A is the **vertex** of the angle. See Figure B.9.

The measure of $\angle A$ is denoted by $m\angle A$. Angles are classified as **acute, right, obtuse,** and **straight.**

Acute	$0° < m\angle A < 90°$
Right	$m\angle A = 90°$
Obtuse	$90° < m\angle A < 180°$
Straight	$m\angle A = 180°$

The top angle can be denoted by $\angle A$ or by $\angle BAC$. In the lower figure, the angle $\angle ROS$ should not be denoted by $\angle O$ because the figure contains three angles whose vertex is O.
Figure B.9

In geometry, *unless specifically stated otherwise*, angles are assumed to have a measure that is greater than 0° and less than or equal to 180°.

Every nonstraight angle has an **interior** and an **exterior.** A point D is in the interior of $\angle A$ if it is between points that lie on each side of the angle. Two angles (such as $\angle ROS$ and $\angle SOP$ shown in Figure B.9) are **adjacent** if they share a common vertex and side, but have no common interior points. In Figure B.10, $\angle 1$ and $\angle 3$ share a vertex, but not a common side, so $\angle 1$ and $\angle 3$ are not adjacent.

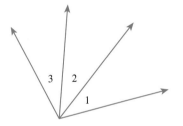

$\angle 1$ and $\angle 2$ are adjacent.
$\angle 1$ and $\angle 3$ are not adjacent.
Figure B.10

▶ **Segment and Angle Congruence**

Two segments are **congruent,** $\overline{AB} \cong \overline{CD}$, if they have the same length. Two angles are **congruent,** $\angle P \cong \angle Q$, if they have the same measure.

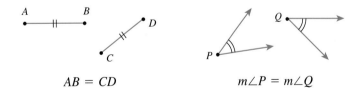

$AB = CD$ \qquad\qquad $m\angle P = m\angle Q$

Definitions can always be interpreted "forward" and "backward." For instance, the definition of congruent segments means (1) if two segments have the same measure, then they are congruent, and (2) if two segments are congruent, then they have the same measure. You learned that two figures are congruent if they have the same shape and size.

Congruent Triangles

If △*ABC* is **congruent** to △*PQR*, then there is a correspondence between their angles and sides such that corresponding angles are congruent and corresponding sides are congruent. The notation △*ABC* ≅ △*PQR* indicates the congruence *and* the correspondence, as shown in Figure B.11. If two triangles are congruent, then you know that they share many properties.

$$\triangle ABC \cong \triangle PQR$$

Corresponding angles are

∠*A* ≅ ∠*P*
∠*B* ≅ ∠*Q*
∠*C* ≅ ∠*R*

Corresponding sides are

$\overline{AB} \cong \overline{PQ}$
$\overline{BC} \cong \overline{QR}$
$\overline{CA} \cong \overline{RP}$

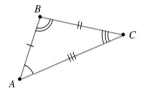
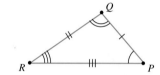

Figure B.11

Example 5   Naming Congruent Parts

You and a friend have identical drafting triangles, as shown in Figure B.12. Name all congruent parts.

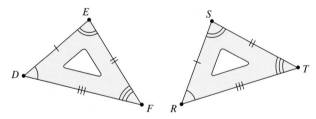

Figure B.12

Solution

Given that △*DEF* ≅ △*RST*, the congruent angles and sides are as follows.

Angles: ∠*D* ≅ ∠*R*,   ∠*E* ≅ ∠*S*,   ∠*F* ≅ ∠*T*
Sides: $\overline{DE} \cong \overline{RS}$, $\overline{EF} \cong \overline{ST}$, $\overline{FD} \cong \overline{TR}$

Classifying Triangles

A triangle can be classified by relationships among its sides or among its angles, as shown in the following definitions.

▶ Classification by Sides

    1. An **equilateral triangle** has three congruent sides.

    2. An **isosceles triangle** has at least two congruent sides.

    3. A **scalene triangle** has no sides congruent.

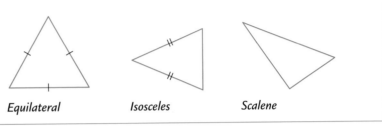

      Equilateral   *Isosceles*   *Scalene*

▶ Classification by Angles

    1. An **acute triangle** has three acute angles. If these angles are all congruent, then the triangle is also **equiangular.**

    2. A **right triangle** has exactly one right angle.

    3. An **obtuse triangle** has exactly one obtuse angle.

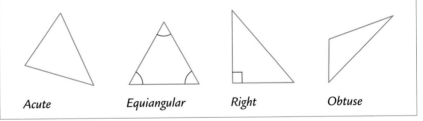

    Acute   *Equiangular*   *Right*   *Obtuse*

    In $\triangle ABC$, each of the points A, B, and C is a **vertex** of the triangle. (The plural of vertex is *vertices*.) The side $\overline{BC}$ is the side *opposite* $\angle A$. Two sides that share a common vertex are *adjacent sides* (see Figure B.13).

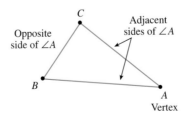

Figure B.13

The sides of right triangles and isosceles triangles are given special names. In a right triangle, the sides adjacent to the right angle are the **legs** of the triangle. The side opposite the right angle is the **hypotenuse** of the triangle (see Figure B.14).

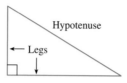

Figure B.14

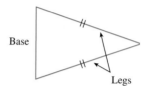

Figure B.15

An isosceles triangle can have three congruent sides. If it has only two, then the two congruent sides are the **legs** of the triangle. The third side is the **base** of the triangle (see Figure B.15).

B.1   Exercises

In Exercises 1–3, copy the region on a piece of dot paper. Then divide the region into two congruent parts. How many different ways can you do this?

1.

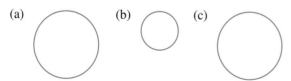

2.   **3.**

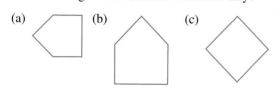

4. Two of the figures are congruent. Which are they?

(a)   (b)   (c)

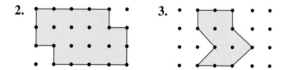

5. Two of the figures are similar. Which are they?

(a)   (b)   (c)

In Exercises 6 and 7, copy the region on a piece of paper. Then divide the region into four congruent parts.

6.   **7.**

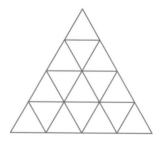

In Exercises 8–11, use the triangular grid below. In the grid, each small triangle has sides of 1 unit.

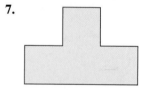

8. How many congruent triangles with 1-unit sides are in the grid?

9. How many congruent triangles with 2-unit sides are in the grid?

10. How many congruent triangles with 3-unit sides are in the grid?

11. Does the grid contain triangles that are not similar to each other?

12. *True or False?*   If two figures are congruent, then they are similar.

13. *True or False?*   If two figures are similar, then they are congruent.

14. *True or False?*   A triangle can be similar to a square.

15. *True or False?*   Any two squares are similar.

In Exercises 16–19, match the description with its correct notation.

(a) $\overline{PQ}$ (b) PQ (c) $\overleftrightarrow{PQ}$ (d) $\overrightarrow{PQ}$

16. The line through P and Q

17. The ray from P through Q

18. The segment between P and Q

19. The length of the segment between P and Q

20. The point R is between points S and T. Which of the following are true?

   (a) R, S, and T are collinear.

   (b) $\overrightarrow{SR}$ is the same as $\overrightarrow{ST}$.

   (c) $\overline{ST}$ is the same as $\overline{TS}$.

   (d) $\overrightarrow{ST}$ is the same as $\overrightarrow{TS}$.

In Exercises 21–23, use the figure below.

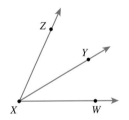

21. The figure shows three angles whose vertex is X. Write two names for each angle. Which two angles are adjacent?

22. Is Y in the interior or exterior of $\angle WXZ$?

23. Which is the best estimate for $m\angle WXY$?

   (a) $15°$ (b) $30°$ (c) $45°$

In Exercises 24–29, match the triangle with its name.

(a) Equilateral   (b) Scalene   (c) Obtuse

(d) Equiangular   (e) Isosceles   (f) Right

24. Side lengths: 2 cm, 3 cm, 4 cm

25. Angle measures: $60°, 60°, 60°$

26. Side lengths: 3 cm, 2 cm, 3 cm

27. Angle measures: $30°, 60°, 90°$

28. Side lengths: 4 cm, 4 cm, 4 cm

29. Angle measures: $20°, 145°, 15°$

In Exercises 30–32, use the figure, in which $\triangle LMP \cong \triangle ONQ$.

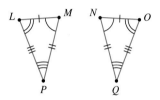

30. Name three pairs of congruent angles.

31. Name three pairs of congruent sides.

32. If $\triangle LMP$ is isosceles, explain why $\triangle ONQ$ must be isosceles.

In Exercises 33–36, use the definition of congruence to complete the statement.

33. If $\triangle ABC \cong \triangle TUV$, then $m\angle C = \underline{\quad}$.

34. If $\triangle PQR \cong \triangle XYZ$, then $\angle P \cong \underline{\quad}$.

35. If $\triangle LMN \cong \triangle TUV$, then $\overline{LN} \cong \underline{\quad}$.

36. If $\triangle DEF \cong \triangle NOP$, then $DE = \underline{\quad}$.

37. Copy and complete the table. Write *Yes* if it is possible to sketch a triangle with both characteristics. Write *No* if it is not possible. Illustrate your results with sketches. (The first is done for you.)

	Scalene	Isosceles	Equilateral
Acute	Yes	?	?
Obtuse	?	?	?
Right	?	?	?

Acute and Scalene

In Exercises 38–41, △*ABC* is isosceles with $\overline{AC} \cong \overline{BC}$. Solve for *x*. Then decide whether the triangle is equilateral. (The figures are not necessarily drawn to scale.)

38.

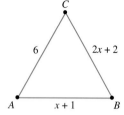

39.

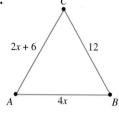

40.

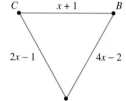

41.

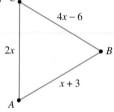

42. *Landscape Design*   You are designing a patio. Your plans use a scale of $\frac{1}{8}$ inch to 1 foot. The patio is 24 feet by 36 feet. What are its dimensions on the plans?

43. *Architecture*   The Pentagon, near Washington D.C., covers a region that is about 1200 feet by 1200 feet. About how large would a $\frac{1}{8}$-inch to 1-foot scale drawing of the Pentagon be? Would such a scale be reasonable?

Coordinate Geometry   In Exercises 44 and 45, use the following figure.

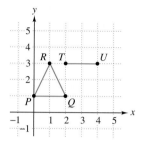

44. Find a location of *S* such that △*PQR* ≅ △*PQS*.

45. Find two locations of *V* such that △*PQR* ≅ △*TUV*.

46. *Logical Reasoning*   Arrange 16 toothpicks as shown below. What is the least number of toothpicks you must remove to create four congruent triangles? (Each toothpick must be the side of at least one triangle.) Sketch your result.

47. *Logical Reasoning*   Show how you could arrange six toothpicks to form four congruent triangles. Each triangle has one toothpick for each side, and you cannot bend, break, or overlap the toothpicks. (*Hint:* The figure can be three-dimensional.)

B.2   Angles

Identifying Special Pairs of Angles ▪ Angles Formed by a Transversal ▪ Angles of a Triangle

Identifying Special Pairs of Angles

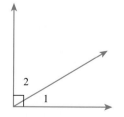

∠1 *and* ∠2 *are complementary angles.*
Figure B.16

You have been introduced to several definitions concerning angles. For instance, you know that two angles are *adjacent* if they share a common vertex and side but have no common interior points. Here are some other definitions for pairs of angles. See Figure B.16.

▶ **Definitions for Pairs of Angles**

Two angles are **vertical angles** if their sides form two pairs of opposite rays.

Two adjacent angles are a **linear pair** if their noncommon sides are opposite rays.

Two angles are **complementary** if the sum of their measures is 90°. Each angle is the *complement* of the other.

Two angles are **supplementary** if the sum of their measures is 180°. Each angle is the *supplement* of the other.

Figure B.17

Example 1   Identifying Special Pairs of Angles

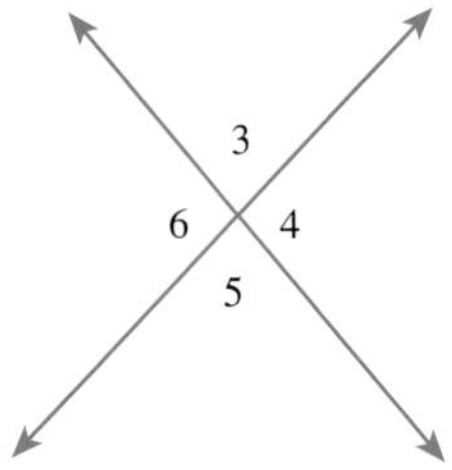

Use the terms defined above to describe relationships between the labeled angles in Figure B.17.

Solution

a. $\angle 3$ and $\angle 5$ are vertical angles. So are $\angle 4$ and $\angle 6$.

b. There are four sets of linear pairs:

$\angle 3$ and $\angle 4$, $\angle 4$ and $\angle 5$, $\angle 5$ and $\angle 6$, and $\angle 3$ and $\angle 6$.

The angles in each of these pairs are also supplementary angles.

In Example 1(b), note that the linear pairs are also supplementary. This result is stated in the following postulate.

▶ **Linear Pair Postulate**

If two angles form a linear pair, then they are supplementary—i.e., the sum of their measures is 180°.

The relationship between vertical angles is stated in the following theorem.

▶ **Vertical Angles Theorem**

If two angles are vertical angles, then they are congruent.

Angles Formed by a Transversal

A **transversal** is a line that intersects two or more coplanar lines at different points. The angles that are formed when the transversal intersects the lines have the following names.

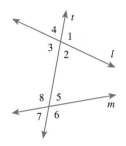

Figure B.18

▶ Angles Formed by a Transversal

In Figure B.18, the transversal t intersects the lines l and m.

Two angles are **corresponding angles** if they occupy corresponding positions, such as $\angle 1$ and $\angle 5$.

Two angles are **alternate interior angles** if they lie between l and m on opposite sides of t, such as $\angle 2$ and $\angle 8$.

Two angles are **alternate exterior angles** if they lie outside l and m on opposite sides of t, such as $\angle 1$ and $\angle 7$.

Two angles are **consecutive interior angles** if they lie between l and m on the same side of t, such as $\angle 2$ and $\angle 5$.

Example 2   Naming Pairs of Angles

In Figure B.19, how is $\angle 9$ related to the other angles?

Solution

You can consider that $\angle 9$ is formed by the transversal l as it intersects m and n, or you can consider $\angle 9$ to be formed by the transversal m as it intersects l and n. Considering one or the other of these, you have the following.

a. $\angle 9$ and $\angle 10$ are a linear pair. So are $\angle 9$ and $\angle 12$.

b. $\angle 9$ and $\angle 11$ are vertical angles.

c. $\angle 9$ and $\angle 7$ are alternate exterior angles. So are $\angle 9$ and $\angle 3$.

d. $\angle 9$ and $\angle 5$ are corresponding angles. So are $\angle 9$ and $\angle 1$.

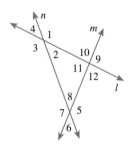

Figure B.19

To help build understanding regarding angles formed by a transversal, consider relationships between two lines. **Parallel lines** are coplanar lines that do not intersect. (Recall from Section 4.4 that two nonvertical lines are parallel if and only if they have the same slope.) **Intersecting lines** are coplanar and have exactly one point in common. If intersecting lines meet at right angles, they are perpendicular; otherwise, they are **oblique.** See Figure B.20.

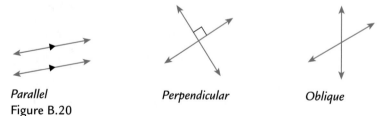

Parallel   *Perpendicular*   *Oblique*
Figure B.20

Many of the angles formed by a transversal that intersects *parallel* lines are congruent. The following postulate and theorems list useful results.

▶ Corresponding Angles Postulate

If two parallel lines are cut by a transversal, then the pairs of corresponding angles are congruent.

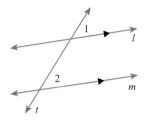

l ∥ *m*, ∠1 ≅ ∠2
Figure B.21

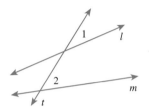

l ∦ *m*, ∠1 ≇ ∠2
Figure B.22

Note that the hypothesis of this postulate states that the lines must be parallel, as shown in Figure B.21. If the lines are not parallel, then the corresponding angles are not congruent, as shown in Figure B.22.

> ▶ **Angle Theorems**
>
> **Alternate Interior Angles Theorem** If two parallel lines are cut by a transversal, then the pairs of alternate interior angles are congruent.
>
> **Consecutive Interior Angles Theorem** If two parallel lines are cut by a transversal, then the pairs of consecutive interior angles are supplementary.
>
> **Alternate Exterior Angles Theorem** If two parallel lines are cut by a transversal, then the pairs of alternate exterior angles are congruent.
>
> **Perpendicular Transversal Theorem** If a transversal is perpendicular to one of two parallel lines, then it is perpendicular to the second.

Example 3   Using Properties of Parallel Lines

In Figure B.23, lines *r* and *s* are parallel lines cut by a transversal, *l*. Find the measure of each labeled angle.

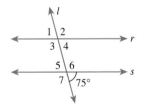

Figure B.23

Solution

∠1 and the given angle are alternate exterior angles and are congruent. So $m\angle 1 = 75°$. ∠5 and the given angle are vertical angles. Because vertical angles are congruent, they have the same measure. So, $m\angle 5 = 75°$. Similarly, ∠1 ≅ ∠4 and $m\angle 1 = m\angle 4 = 75°$. There are several sets of linear pairs, including

∠1 and ∠2; ∠3 and ∠4; ∠5 and ∠6; ∠5 and ∠7.

The angles in each of these pairs are also supplementary angles; the sum of the measures of each pair of angles is 180°. Because one angle of each pair measures 75°, the supplements each measure 105°. So ∠2, ∠3, ∠6, and ∠7 each measure 105°.

Angles of a Triangle

The word "triangle" means "three angles." When the sides of a triangle are extended, however, other angles are formed. The original three angles of the triangle are the **interior angles.** The angles that are adjacent to the interior angles are the **exterior angles** of the triangle. Each vertex has a pair of exterior angles, as shown in Figure B.24 on the following page.

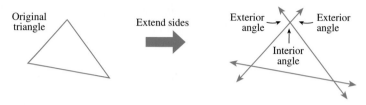

Figure B.24

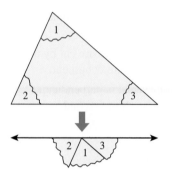

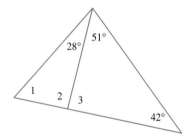

Figure B.25

You could cut a triangle out of a piece of paper. Tear off the three angles and place them adjacent to each other, as shown in Figure B.25. What do you observe? (You could perform this investigation by measuring with a protractor or using a computer drawing program.) You should arrive at the conclusion given in the following theorem.

> ▶ **Triangle Sum Theorem**
>
> The sum of the measures of the interior angles of a triangle is 180°.

Example 4 Using the Triangle Sum Theorem

In the triangle in Figure B.26, find $m\angle 1$, $m\angle 2$, and $m\angle 3$.

Solution

To find the measure of $\angle 3$, use the Triangle Sum Theorem, as follows.

$$m\angle 3 = 180° - (51° + 42°) = 87°$$

Knowing the measure of $\angle 3$, you can use the Linear Pair Postulate to write $m\angle 2 = 180° - 87° = 93°$. Using the Triangle Sum Theorem, you have

$$m\angle 1 = 180° - (28° + 93°) = 59°.$$

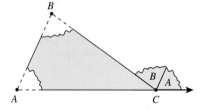

Figure B.26

The next theorem is one that you might have anticipated from the investigation earlier. As shown in Figure B.27, if you had torn only two of the angles from the paper triangle, you could put them together to cover exactly one of the exterior angles.

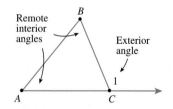

Figure B.27

> ▶ **Exterior Angle Theorem**
>
> The measure of an exterior angle of a triangle is equal to the sum of the measures of the two remote (nonadjacent) interior angles. (See Figure B.28.)

Figure B.28

B.2   Exercises

In Exercises 1–6, sketch a pair of angles that fits the description. Label the angles as $\angle 1$ and $\angle 2$.

1. A linear pair of angles

2. Supplementary angles for which $\angle 1$ is acute

3. Acute vertical angles

4. Adjacent congruent complementary angles

5. Obtuse vertical angles

6. Adjacent congruent supplementary angles

In Exercises 7–12, use the figure to determine relationships between the given angles.

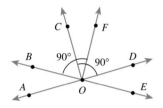

7. $\angle AOC$ and $\angle COD$

8. $\angle AOB$ and $\angle BOC$

9. $\angle BOC$ and $\angle COE$

10. $\angle AOB$ and $\angle EOD$

11. $\angle BOC$ and $\angle COF$

12. $\angle AOB$ and $\angle AOE$

In Exercises 13–18, use the following information to decide whether the statement is true or false. (*Hint*: Make a sketch.)

Vertical angles: $\angle 1$ and $\angle 2$;
Linear pairs: $\angle 1$ and $\angle 3$, $\angle 1$ and $\angle 4$.

13. If $m\angle 3 = 30°$, then $m\angle 4 = 150°$.

14. If $m\angle 1 = 150°$, then $m\angle 4 = 30°$.

15. $\angle 2$ and $\angle 3$ are congruent.

16. $m\angle 3 + m\angle 1 = m\angle 4 + m\angle 2$

17. $\angle 3 \cong \angle 4$

18. $m\angle 3 = 180° - m\angle 2$

In Exercises 19–24, find the value of x.

19.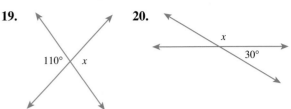

20.

21.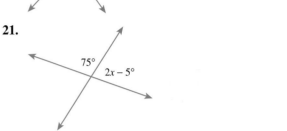

22.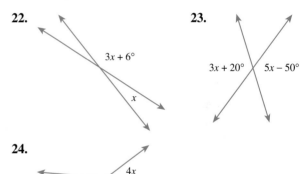

23.

24.

25. In the figure, P, S, and T are collinear. If $m\angle P = 40°$ and $m\angle QST = 110°$, what is $m\angle Q$? (*Hint*: $m\angle P + m\angle Q + m\angle PSQ = 180°$)

(a) 40°   (b) 55°   (c) 70°   (d) 110°   (e) 140°

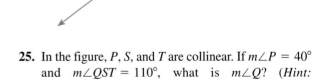
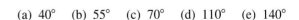
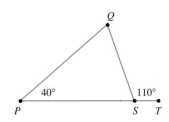

In Exercises 26–29, use the figure below.

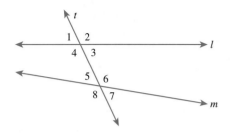

26. Name two corresponding angles.

27. Name two alternate interior angles.

28. Name two alternate exterior angles.

29. Name two consecutive interior angles.

In Exercises 30–33, $l_1 \parallel l_2$. Find the measures of $\angle 1$ and $\angle 2$. Explain your reasoning.

30.

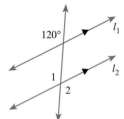

31.

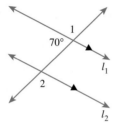

32.

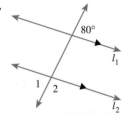

33.

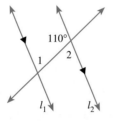

In Exercises 34–36, $m \parallel n$ and $k \parallel l$. Determine the values of a and b.

34.

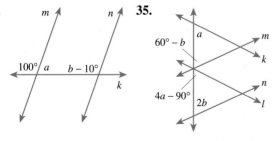

35.

36.

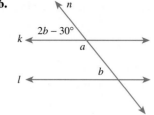

In Exercises 37–39, use the following figure.

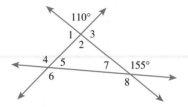

37. Name the interior angles of the triangle.

38. Name the exterior angles of the triangle.

39. Two angle measures are given in the figure. Find the measure of the eight labeled angles.

In Exercises 40–43, use the following figure, in which $\triangle ABC \cong \triangle DEF$.

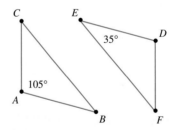

40. What is the measure of $\angle D$?

41. What is the measure of $\angle B$?

42. What is the measure of $\angle C$?

43. What is the measure of $\angle F$?

44. *True or False?*   A right triangle can have an obtuse angle.

45. *True or False?*   A triangle that has two 60° angles must be equiangular.

46. *True or False?*   If a right triangle has two congruent angles, then it must have two 45° angles.

In Exercises 47 and 48, find the measure of each labeled angle.

47.

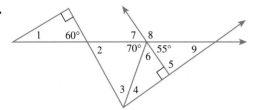

48.

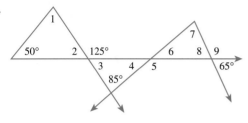

In Exercises 49 and 50, draw and label a right triangle, $\triangle ABC$, for which the right angle is $\angle C$. What is $m\angle B$?

49. $m\angle A = 13°$ **50.** $m\angle A = 47°$

In Exercises 51 and 52, draw two noncongruent, isosceles triangles that have an exterior angle with the given measure.

51. $130°$ **52.** $145°$

In Exercises 53–56, find the measures of the interior angles.

53.

$x + 30°$ x

$x + 60°$

54.

x

$x + 25°$ $x - 25°$

55.

$6x + 11°$

$3x + 2°$

$5x - 1°$

56.

$2x$

$3x - 10°$

$110° - x$

Appendix C

Further Concepts in Statistics

Stem-and-Leaf Plots ■ Histograms and Frequency Distributions ■
Line Graphs ■ Choosing an Appropriate Graph ■ Scatter Plots ■
Fitting a Line to Data ■ Measures of Central Tendency

Stem-and-Leaf Plots

Statistics is the branch of mathematics that studies techniques for collecting, organizing, and interpreting data. In this section, you will study several ways to organize and interpret data.

One type of plot that can be used to organize sets of numbers by hand is a **stem-and-leaf plot.** A set of test scores and the corresponding stem-and-leaf plot are shown below.

Test Scores	*Stems*	*Leaves*
93, 70, 76, 58, 86, 93, 82, 78, 83, 86,	5	8
64, 78, 76, 66, 83, 83, 96, 74, 69, 76,	6	4 4 6 9
64, 74, 79, 76, 88, 76, 81, 82, 74, 70	7	0 0 4 4 4 6 6 6 6 8 8 9
	8	1 2 2 3 3 3 6 6 8
	9	3 3 6

Note that the *leaves* represent the units digits of the numbers and the *stems* represent the tens digits. Stem-and-leaf plots can also be used to compare two sets of data, as shown in the following example.

Example 1   Comparing Two Sets of Data

Use a stem-and-leaf plot to compare the test scores given above with the following test scores. Which set of test scores is better?

> 90, 81, 70, 62, 64, 73, 81, 92, 73, 81, 92, 93, 83, 75, 76,
> 83, 94, 96, 86, 77, 77, 86, 96, 86, 77, 86, 87, 87, 79, 88

Solution

Begin by ordering the second set of scores.

> 62, 64, 70, 73, 73, 75, 76, 77, 77, 77, 79, 81, 81, 81, 83,
> 83, 86, 86, 86, 86, 87, 87, 88, 90, 92, 92, 93, 94, 96, 96

Now that the data have been ordered, you can construct a *double* stem-and-leaf plot by letting the leaves to the right of the stems represent the units digits for the first group of test scores and letting the leaves to the left of the stems represent the units digits for the second group of test scores.

Leaves (2nd Group)	Stems	Leaves (1st Group)
	5	8
4 2	6	4 4 6 9
9 7 7 7 6 5 3 3 0	7	0 0 4 4 4 6 6 6 6 6 8 8 9
8 7 7 6 6 6 6 3 3 1 1 1	8	1 2 2 3 3 3 6 6 8
6 6 4 3 2 2 0	9	3 3 6

By comparing the two sets of leaves, you can see that the second group of test scores is better than the first group.

Example 2   Using a Stem-and-Leaf Plot

The table below shows the percent of the population of each state and the District of Columbia that was at least 65 years old in 1997. Use a stem-and-leaf plot to organize the data.   (Source: U.S. Bureau of the Census)

AK	5.3	AL	13.0	AR	14.3	AZ	13.2	CA	11.1
CO	10.1	CT	14.4	DC	13.9	DE	12.9	FL	18.5
GA	9.9	HI	13.2	IA	15.0	ID	11.3	IL	12.5
IN	12.5	KS	13.5	KY	12.5	LA	11.4	MA	14.1
MD	11.5	ME	13.9	MI	12.4	MN	12.3	MO	13.7
MS	12.2	MT	13.2	NC	12.5	ND	14.4	NE	13.7
NH	12.1	NJ	13.7	NM	11.2	NV	11.5	NY	13.4
OH	13.4	OK	13.4	OR	13.3	PA	15.8	RI	15.8
SC	12.1	SD	14.3	TN	12.5	TX	10.1	UT	8.7
VA	11.2	VT	12.3	WA	11.5	WI	13.2	WV	15.1
WY	11.3								

Solution

Begin by ordering the numbers, as shown below.

5.3, 8.7, 9.9, 10.1, 10.1, 11.1, 11.2, 11.2, 11.3, 11.3, 11.4,
11.5, 11.5, 11.5, 12.1, 12.1, 12.2, 12.3, 12.3, 12.4, 12.5,
12.5, 12.5, 12.5, 12.5, 12.9, 13.0, 13.2, 13.2, 13.2, 13.2,
13.3, 13.4, 13.4, 13.4, 13.5, 13.7, 13.7, 13.7, 13.9, 13.9,
14.1, 14.3, 14.3, 14.4, 14.4, 15.0, 15.1, 15.8, 15.8, 18.5

Next construct the stem-and-leaf plot using the leaves to represent the digits to the right of the decimal points.

Stems	*Leaves*	
5.	3	Alaska has the lowest percent.
6.		
7.		
8.	7	
9.	9	
10.	1 1	
11.	1 2 2 3 3 4 5 5 5	
12.	1 1 2 3 3 4 5 5 5 5 5 9	
13.	0 2 2 2 2 3 4 4 4 5 7 7 7 9 9	
14.	1 3 3 4 4	
15.	0 1 8 8	
16.		
17.		
18.	5	Florida has the highest percent.

Histograms and Frequency Distributions

With data such as those given in Example 2, it is useful to group the numbers into intervals and plot the frequency of the data in each interval. For instance, the **frequency distribution** and **histogram** shown in Figure C.1 represent the data given in Example 2.

Frequency Distribution

Interval	*Tally*
$[5, 7)$	I
$[7, 9)$	I
$[9, 11)$	III
$[11, 13)$	⊔⊓⊤ ⊔⊓⊤ ⊔⊓⊤ ⊔⊓⊤ I
$[13, 15)$	⊔⊓⊤ ⊔⊓⊤ ⊔⊓⊤ ⊔⊓⊤
$[15, 17)$	IIII
$[17, 19)$	I

Histogram

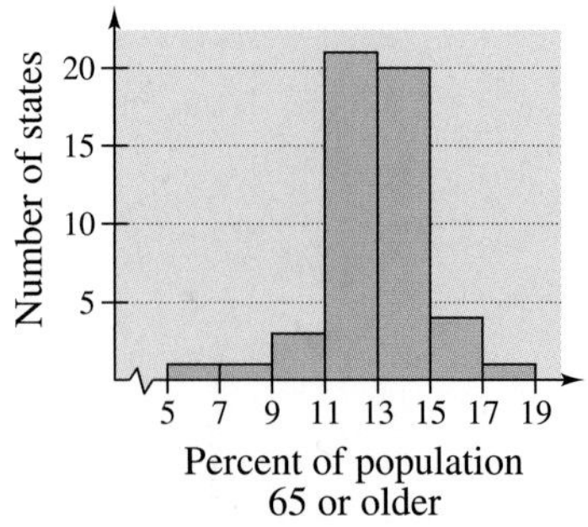

Figure C.1

A histogram has a portion of a real number line as its horizontal axis. A **bar graph** is similar to a histogram, except that the rectangles (bars) can be either horizontal or vertical and the labels of the bars are not necessarily numbers.

Another difference between a bar graph and a histogram is that the bars in a bar graph are usually separated by spaces, whereas the bars in a histogram are not separated by spaces.

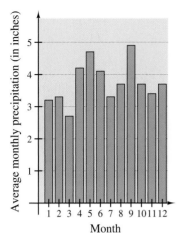

Figure C.2

Example 3 Constructing a Bar Graph

The data below show the average monthly precipitation (in inches) in Houston, Texas. Construct a bar graph for these data. What can you conclude? (Source: PC USA)

January	3.2	February	3.3	March	2.7
April	4.2	May	4.7	June	4.1
July	3.3	August	3.7	September	4.9
October	3.7	November	3.4	December	3.7

Solution

To create a bar graph, begin by drawing a vertical axis to represent the precipitation and a horizontal axis to represent the months. The bar graph is shown in Figure C.2. From the graph, you can see that Houston receives a fairly consistent amount of rain throughout the year—the driest month tends to be March and the wettest month tends to be September.

Line Graphs

A **line graph** is similar to a standard coordinate graph. Line graphs are usually used to show trends over periods of time.

Example 4 Constructing a Line Graph

The following data show the number of immigrants (in thousands) to the United States for the years 1970 through 1996. Construct a line graph of the data. What can you conclude? (Source: U.S. Immigration and Naturalization Service)

Year	Number	Year	Number	Year	Number
1970	373	1971	370	1972	385
1973	400	1974	395	1975	386
1976	399	1977	462	1978	601
1979	460	1980	531	1981	597
1982	594	1983	560	1984	544
1985	570	1986	602	1987	602
1988	643	1989	1091	1990	1536
1991	1827	1992	974	1993	904
1994	804	1995	720	1996	916

Solution

Begin by drawing a vertical axis to represent the number of immigrants in thousands. Then label the horizontal axis with years and plot the points shown in the table. Finally, connect the points with line segments, as shown on the next page in Figure C.3. From the line graph, you can see that the number of immigrants steadily increased until 1989, when there was a sharp increase followed by a sudden decrease in 1992.

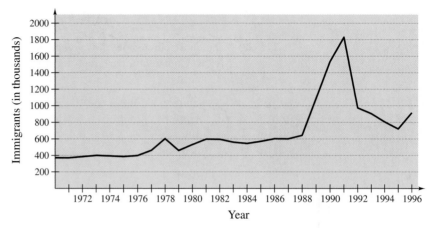

Figure C.3

Choosing an Appropriate Graph

Line graphs and bar graph are commonly used for displaying data. When you are using a graph to organize and present data, you must first decide which type of graph to use.

Example 5 Organizing Data with a Graph

Listed below are the daily average numbers of miles walked by people while working at their jobs. Organize the data graphically. (Source: American Podiatry Association)

Occupation	Miles Walked per Day
Mail Carrier	4.4
Medical Doctor	3.5
Nurse	3.9
Police Officer	6.8
Television Reporter	4.2

Solution

You can use a bar graph because the data fall into distinct categories, and it would be useful to compare totals. The bar graph shown in Figure C.4 is horizontal. This makes it easier to label each bar. Also notice that the occupations are listed in order of the number of miles walked.

Study Tip

Here are some guidelines to use when you must decide which type of graph to use.

1. Use a bar graph when the data fall into distinct categories and you want to compare totals.
2. Use a line graph when you want to show the relationship between consecutive amounts or data over time.

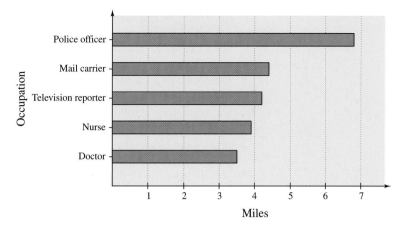

Figure C.4

Scatter Plots

Many real-life situations involve finding relationships between two variables, such as the year and the number of people in the labor force. In a typical situation, data are collected and written as a set of ordered pairs. The graph of such a set is called a **scatter plot.**

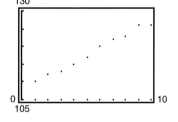

Figure C.5

From the scatter plot in Figure C.5 that relates the year t with the number of people in the labor force P, it appears that the points describe a relationship that is nearly linear. (The relationship is not *exactly* linear because the labor force did not increase by precisely the same amount each year.) A mathematical equation that approximates the relationship between t and P is called a *mathematical model*. When developing a mathematical model, you strive for two (often conflicting) goals—accuracy and simplicity.

Consider a collection of ordered pairs of the form (x, y). If y tends to increase as x increases, the collection is said to have a **positive correlation.** If y tends to decrease as x increases, the collection is said to have a **negative correlation.** Figure C.6 shows three examples: one with a positive correlation, one with a negative correlation, and one with no (discernible) correlation.

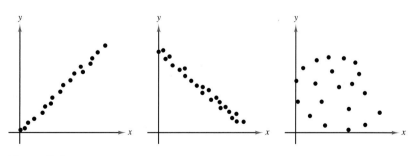

Figure C.6

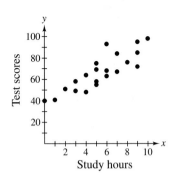

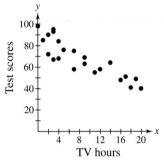

Figure C.7

Example 6   Interpreting Scatter Plots

On a Friday, 22 students in a class were asked to keep track of the numbers of hours they spent studying for a test on Monday and the numbers of hours they spent watching television. The numbers are shown below. Construct a scatter plot for each set of data. Then determine whether the points are positively correlated, are negatively correlated, or have no discernible correlation. What can you conclude? (The first coordinate is the number of hours and the second coordinate is the score obtained on Monday's test.)

Study Hours: (0, 40), (1, 41), (2, 51), (3, 58), (3, 49), (4, 48), (4, 64), (5, 55), (5, 69), (5, 58), (5, 75), (6, 68), (6, 63), (6, 93), (7, 84), (7, 67), (8, 90), (8, 76), (9, 95), (9, 72), (9, 85), (10, 98)

TV Hours: (0, 98), (1, 85), (2, 72), (2, 90), (3, 67), (3, 93), (3, 95), (4, 68), (4, 84), (5, 76), (7, 75), (7, 58), (9, 63), (9, 69), (11, 55), (12, 58), (14, 64), (16, 48), (17, 51), (18, 41), (19, 49), (20, 40)

Solution

Scatter plots for the two sets of data are shown in Figure C.7. The scatter plot relating study hours and test scores has a positive correlation. This means that the more a student studied, the higher his or her score tended to be. The scatter plot relating television hours and test scores has a negative correlation. This means that the more time a student spent watching television, the lower his or her score tended to be.

Fitting a Line to Data

Finding a linear model that represents the relationship described by a scatter plot is called **fitting a line to data.** You can do this graphically by simply sketching the line that appears to fit the points, finding two points on the line, and then finding the equation of the line that passes through the two points.

Example 7   Fitting a Line to Data

Find a linear model that relates the year and the number of people *P* (in millions) who were part of the United States labor force from 1987 through 1997. In the table below, *t* represents the year, with $t = 0$ corresponding to 1987.   (Source: U.S. Bureau of Labor Statistics)

t	0	1	2	3	4	5	6	7	8	9	10
P	120	122	124	126	126	128	129	131	132	134	136

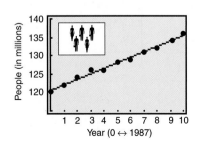

Figure C.8

Solution

After plotting the data from the table, draw the line that you think best represents the data, as shown in Figure C.8. Two points that lie on this line are (0, 120) and (9, 134). Using the point-slope form, you can find the equation of the line to be $P = 14t/9 + 120$.

Once you have found a model, you can measure how well the model fits the data by comparing the actual values with the values given by the model, as shown in the following table for the data and model in Example 7.

t	0	1	2	3	4	5	6	7	8	9	10
Actual P	120	122	124	126	126	128	129	131	132	134	136
Model P	120	121.6	123.1	124.7	126.2	127.8	129.3	130.9	132.4	134	135.6

The sum of the squares of the differences between the actual values and the model's values is the **sum of the squared differences.** The model that has the least sum is called the **least squares regression line** for the data. For the model in Example 7, the sum of the squared differences is 3.16. The least squares regression line for the data is

$$P = 1.5t + 120.5. \qquad \text{\small Best-fitting linear model}$$

The sum of the squared differences is 2.5.

Many graphing utilities have "built-in" least squares regression programs. If your graphing utility has such a program, enter the data in the table and use it to find the least squares regression line.

Measures of Central Tendency

In many real-life situations, it is helpful to describe data by a single number that is most representative of the entire collection of numbers. Such a number is called a **measure of central tendency.** The most commonly used measures are as follows.

1. The **mean,** or **average,** of n numbers is the sum of the numbers divided by n.
2. The **median** of n numbers is the middle number when the numbers are written in order. If n is even, the median is the average of the two middle numbers.
3. The **mode** of n numbers is the number that occurs most frequently. If two numbers tie for most frequent occurrence, the collection has two modes and is called **bimodal.**

Example 8   Comparing Measures of Central Tendency

You are interviewing for a job. The interviewer tells you that the average income of the company's 25 employees is $60,849. The actual annual incomes of the 25 employees are shown below. What are the mean, median, and mode of the incomes? Was the person telling you the truth?

$17,305	$478,320	$45,678	$18,980	$17,408
$25,676	$28,906	$12,500	$24,540	$33,450
$12,500	$33,855	$37,450	$20,432	$28,956
$34,983	$36,540	$250,921	$36,853	$16,430
$32,654	$98,213	$48,980	$94,024	$35,671

Solution

The mean of the incomes is

$$\text{Mean} = \frac{17{,}305 + 478{,}320 + 45{,}678 + 18{,}980 + \cdots + 35{,}671}{25}$$

$$= \frac{1{,}521{,}225}{25} = \$60{,}849.$$

To find the median, order the incomes as follows.

$12,500	$12,500	$16,430	$17,305	$17,408
$18,980	$20,432	$24,540	$25,676	$28,906
$28,956	$32,654	$33,450	$33,855	$34,983
$35,671	$36,540	$36,853	$37,450	$45,678
$48,980	$94,024	$98,213	$250,921	$478,320

From this list, you can see that the median (the middle number) is $33,450. From the same list, you can see that $12,500 is the only income that occurs more than once. Thus, the mode is $12,500. Technically, the person was telling the truth because the average is (generally) defined to be the mean. However, of the three measures of central tendency

Mean: $60,849   *Median:* $33,450   *Mode:* $12,500

it seems clear that the median is most representative. The mean is inflated by the two highest salaries.

Which of the three measures of central tendency is the most representative? The answer is that it depends on the distribution of the data *and* the way in which you plan to use the data.

For instance, in Example 8, the mean salary of $60,849 does not seem very representative to a potential employee. To a city income tax collector who wants to estimate 1% of the total income of the 25 employees, however, the mean is precisely the right measure.

Example 9   Choosing a Measure of Central Tendency

Which measure of central tendency is the most representative of the data given in each of the following frequency distributions?

a. *Number*	*Tally*	b. *Number*	*Tally*	c. *Number*	*Tally*
1	7	1	9	1	6
2	20	2	8	2	1
3	15	3	7	3	2
4	11	4	6	4	3
5	8	5	5	5	5
6	3	6	6	6	5
7	2	7	7	7	4
8	0	8	8	8	3
9	15	9	9	9	0

Solution

a. For these data, the mean is 4.23, the median is 3, and the mode is 2. Of these, the mode is probably the most representative.

b. For these data, the mean and median are each 5 and the modes are 1 and 9 (the distribution is bimodal). Of these, the mean or median is the most representative.

c. For these data, the mean is 4.59, the median is 5, and the mode is 1. Of these, the mean or median is the most representative.

Appendix C   Exercises

1. Construct a stem-and-leaf plot for the following exam scores for a class of 30 students. The scores are for a 100-point exam.

77, 100, 77, 70, 83, 89, 87, 85, 81, 84, 81, 78, 89, 78, 88, 85, 90, 92, 75, 81, 85, 100, 98, 81, 78, 75, 85, 89, 82, 75

2. *Insurance Coverage*   The following table shows the total number of persons (in thousands) without health insurance coverage in the 50 states and the District of Columbia in 1996. Use a stem-and-leaf plot to organize the data.   (Source: U.S. Bureau of the Census)

AK	89	AL	550	AR	566	AZ	1159	CA	6514
CO	644	CT	368	DC	80	DE	98	FL	2722
GA	1319	HI	101	IA	335	ID	196	IL	1337
IN	600	KS	292	KY	601	LA	890	MA	766
MD	581	ME	146	MI	857	MN	480	MO	700
MS	518	MT	124	NC	1160	ND	62	NE	190
NH	109	NJ	1317	NM	412	NV	255	NY	3132
OH	1292	OK	570	OR	496	PA	1133	RI	93
SC	634	SD	67	TN	841	TX	4680	UT	240
VA	811	VT	65	WA	761	WI	438	WV	261
WY	66								

In Exercises 3 and 4, use the following set of data, which lists students' scores on a 100-point exam.

93, 84, 100, 92, 66, 89, 78, 52, 71, 85, 83, 95, 98, 99, 93, 81, 80, 79, 67, 59, 90, 55, 77, 62, 90, 78, 66, 63, 93, 87, 74, 96, 72, 100, 70, 73

3. Use a stem-and-leaf plot to organize the data.

4. Draw a histogram to represent the data.

5. Complete the following frequency distribution table and draw a histogram to represent the data.

44, 33, 17, 23, 16, 18, 44, 47, 18, 20, 25, 27, 18, 29, 29, 28, 27, 18, 36, 22, 32, 38, 33, 41, 49, 48, 45, 38, 49, 15

Interval	Tally
[15, 22)	
[22, 29)	
[29, 36)	
[36, 43)	
[43, 50)	

6. *Snowfall*   The data below show the seasonal snowfall (in inches) in Lincoln, Nebraska for the years 1968 through 1997 (the amounts are listed in order by year). How would you organize these data? Explain your reasoning.   (Source: University of Nebraska-Lincoln)

39.8, 26.2, 49.0, 21.6, 29.2, 33.6, 42.1, 21.1, 21.8, 31.0, 34.4, 23.3, 13.0, 32.3, 38.0, 47.5, 21.5, 18.9, 15.7, 13.0, 19.1, 18.7, 25.8, 23.8, 32.1, 21.3, 21.8, 30.7, 29.0, 44.6

7. *Travel to the United States*   The data below give the places of origin and the numbers of travelers (in millions) to the United States in 1995. Construct a bar graph for these data.   (Source: U.S. Department of Commerce)

Canada	14.7
Europe	8.8
Mexico	8.0
Far East	6.6
Other	5.2

8. *Fruit Crops*   The data below show the cash receipts (in millions of dollars) from fruit crops of farmers in 1996. Construct a bar graph for these data. (Source: U.S. Department of Agriculture)

Apples	1846	Peaches	380
Cherries	264	Pears	292
Grapes	2334	Plums and Prunes	295
Lemons	228	Strawberries	770
Oranges	1798		

Handling Garbage   In Exercises 9–14, use the line graph given below.   (Source: Franklin Associates)

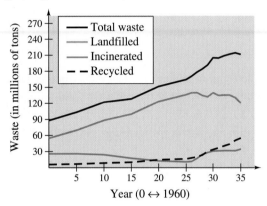

Year (0 ↔ 1960)

9. Estimate the total waste in 1985 and 1995.

10. Estimate the amount of incinerated garbage in 1990.

11. Which quantities increased every year?

12. During which time period did the amount of incinerated garbage decrease?

13. What is the relationship among the four quantities in the line graph?

14. Why do you think landfill garbage is decreasing?

15. *College Attendance*   The following table shows the enrollment in a liberal arts college. Construct a line graph for the data.

Year	1993	1994	1995	1996
Enrollment	1675	1704	1710	1768

Year	1997	1998	1999	2000
Enrollment	1833	1918	1967	1972

16. *Oil Imports*   The table shows the crude oil imports into the United States in millions of barrels for the years 1988 through 1997. Construct a line graph for the data and state what information it reveals. (Source: U.S. Energy Information Administration)

Year	1988	1989	1990	1991	1992
Oil imports	1864	2133	2151	2110	2220

Year	1993	1994	1995	1996	1997
Oil imports	2477	2578	2643	2748	2918

Table for 16

17. *Stock Market*   The list below shows stock prices for selected companies in April of 1999. Draw a graph that best represents the data. Explain why you chose that type of graph.   (Source: Value Line)

Company	Stock Price
Sears, Roebuck	$46
Wal-Mart Stores	$98
JC Penney	$40
K Mart Corp.	$16
The Gap, Inc.	$68

18. *Net Profit*   The table shows the net profits (in millions of dollars) of Callaway Golf Co. for the years 1992 through 1997. Draw a graph that best represents the net profit and explain why you chose that type of graph.   (Source: Value Line)

Year	1992	1993	1994	1995	1996	1997
Net profit	19.3	41.2	78.0	97.7	122.3	139.9

19. *Camcorders*   The factory sales (in millions of dollars) of camcorders for the years 1990 through 1996 are given in the table. Organize the data graphically. Explain your reasoning. (Source: Electronic Industries Association)

Year	1990	1991	1992	1993	1994	1995	1996
Number	2260	2013	1841	1958	1985	2135	2084

20. *Owning Cats*   The average numbers (out of 100) of cat owners who state various reasons for owning a cat are listed below. Organize the data graphically. Explain your reasoning.   (Source: Gallup Poll)

Reason for Owning a Cat	Number
Have a pet to play with	93
Companionship	84
Help children learn responsibility	78
Have a pet to communicate with	62
Security	51

Interpreting a Scatter Plot   In Exercises 21–24, use the scatter plot shown. The scatter plot compares the number of hits x made by 30 softball players during the first half of the season with the number of runs batted in y.

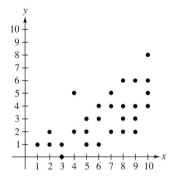

21. Do x and y have a positive correlation, a negative correlation, or no correlation?

22. Why does the scatter plot show only 28 points?

23. From the scatter plot, does it appear that players with more hits tend to have more runs batted in?

24. Can a player have more runs batted in than hits? Explain.

In Exercises 25–28, decide whether a scatter plot relating the two quantities would tend to have a positive, a negative, or no correlation. Explain.

25. The age and value of a car

26. A student's study time and test scores

27. The height and age of a pine tree

28. A student's height and test scores

In Exercises 29–32, use the data in the table, which shows the relationship between the altitude A (in thousands of feet) and the air pressure P (in pounds per square foot).

A	0	5	10	15	20	25
P	14.7	12.3	10.2	8.4	6.8	5.4

A	30	35	40	45	50
P	4.5	3.5	2.8	2.1	1.8

29. Sketch a scatter plot of the data.

30. How are A and P related?

31. Estimate the air pressure at 42,500 feet.

32. Estimate the altitude at which the air pressure is 5.0 pounds per square foot.

Crop Yield   In Exercises 33–36, use the data in the table, where x is the number of units of fertilizer applied to sample plots and y is the yield (in bushels) of a crop.

x	0	1	2	3	4	5	6	7	8
y	58	60	59	61	63	66	65	67	70

33. Sketch a scatter plot of the data.

34. Determine whether the points are positively correlated, are negatively correlated, or have no discernible correlation.

35. Sketch a linear model that you think best represents the data. Find an equation of the line you sketched. Use the line to predict the yield if 10 units of fertilizer are used.

36. Can the model found in Exercise 35 be used to predict yields for arbitrarily large values of x? Explain.

Speed of Sound   In Exercises 37–40, use the data in the table, where h is altitude in thousands of feet and v is the speed of sound in feet per second.

h	0	5	10	15	20	25	30	35
v	1116	1097	1077	1057	1036	1015	995	973

37. Sketch a scatter plot of the data.

38. Determine whether the points are positively correlated, are negatively correlated, or have no discernible correlation.

39. Sketch a linear model that you think best represents the data. Find an equation of the line you sketched. Use the line to predict the speed of sound at an altitude of 27,000 feet.

40. The speed of sound at an altitude of 70,000 feet is approximately 971 feet per second. What does this suggest about the validity of using the model in Exercise 39 to extrapolate beyond the data given in the table?

In Exercises 41–44, use a graphing utility to find the least squares regression line for the data. Sketch a scatter plot and the regression line.

41. (0, 23), (1, 20), (2, 19), (3, 17), (4, 15), (5, 11), (6, 10)

42. (4, 52.8), (5, 54.7), (6, 55.7), (7, 57.8), (8, 60.2), (9, 63.1), (10, 66.5)

43. (−10, 5.1), (−5, 9.8), (0, 17.5), (2, 25.4), (4, 32.8), (6, 38.7), (8, 44.2), (10, 50.5)

44. $(-10, 213.5)$, $(-5, 174.9)$, $(0, 141.7)$, $(5, 119.7)$, $(8, 102.4)$, $(10, 87.6)$

45. *School Enrollment*   The table gives the preprimary school enrollments y (in millions) for the years 1990 through 1995, where $t = 0$ corresponds to 1990. (Source: U.S. Bureau of the Census)

t	0	1	2	3	4	5
y	11.21	11.37	11.54	11.95	12.33	12.52

(a) Use a graphing utility to find the least squares regression line. Use the equation to estimate enrollment in 1996.

(b) Make a scatter plot of the data and sketch the graph of the regression line.

(c) Use a graphing utility to determine the correlation coefficient.

46. *Advertising*   The management of a department store ran an experiment to determine if a relationship existed between sales S (in thousands of dollars) and the amount spent on advertising x (in thousands of dollars). The following data were collected.

x	1	2	3	4	5	6	7	8
S	405	423	455	466	492	510	525	559

(a) Use a graphing utility to find the least squares regression line. Use the equation to estimate sales if $4500 is spent on advertising.

(b) Make a scatter plot of the data and sketch the graph of the regression line.

(c) Use a graphing utility to determine the correlation coefficient.

In Exercises 47–52, find the mean, median, and mode of the set of measurements.

47. 5, 12, 7, 14, 8, 9, 7   **48.** 30, 37, 32, 39, 33, 34, 32

49. 5, 12, 7, 24, 8, 9, 7   **50.** 20, 37, 32, 39, 33, 34, 32

51. *Electric Bills*   A person had the following monthly bills for electricity. What are the mean and median of the collection of bills?

Jan.	$67.92	Feb.	$59.84	Mar.	$52.00
Apr.	$52.50	May	$57.99	June	$65.35
July	$81.76	Aug.	$74.98	Sept.	$87.82
Oct.	$83.18	Nov.	$65.35	Dec.	$57.00

52. *Car Rental*   A car rental company kept the following record of the numbers of miles driven by a car that was rented. What are the mean, median, and mode of these data?

Monday	410	Tuesday	260
Wednesday	320	Thursday	320
Friday	460	Saturday	150

53. *Six-Child Families*   A study was done on families having six children. The table gives the number of families in the study with the indicated number of girls. Determine the mean, median, and mode of this set of data.

Number of girls	0	1	2	3	4	5	6
Frequency	1	24	45	54	50	19	7

54. *Baseball*   A baseball fan examined the records of a favorite baseball player's performance during his last 50 games. The number of games in which the player had 0, 1, 2, 3, and 4 hits are recorded in the table.

Number of hits	0	1	2	3	4
Frequency	14	26	7	2	1

(a) Determine the average number of hits per game.

(b) Determine the player's batting average if he had 200 at bats during the 50-game series.

55. *Think About It*   Construct a collection of numbers that has the following properties. If this is not possible, explain why it is not.

Mean $= 6$, median $= 4$, mode $= 4$

56. *Think About It*   Construct a collection of numbers that has the following properties. If this is not possible, explain why it is not.

Mean $= 6$, median $= 6$, mode $= 4$

57. *Test Scores*   A professor records the following scores for a 100-point exam.

99, 64, 80, 77, 59, 72, 87, 79, 92, 88, 90, 42, 20, 89, 42, 100, 98, 84, 78, 91

Which measure of central tendency best describes these test scores?

58. *Shoe Sales*   A salesperson sold eight pairs of a certain style of men's shoes. The sizes of the eight pairs were as follows: $10\frac{1}{2}$, 8, 12, $10\frac{1}{2}$, 10, $9\frac{1}{2}$, 11, and $10\frac{1}{2}$. Which measure (or measures) of central tendency best describes the typical shoe size for these data?

Answers to Integrated Reviews, Odd-Numbered Exercises, Quizzes, and Tests

Chapter 1

Section 1.1 (page 9)

1. (a) $2, \frac{9}{3}$ (b) $-3, 2, \frac{9}{3}$ (c) $-3, 2, -\frac{3}{2}, \frac{9}{3}, 4.5$

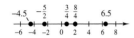

3. (a) $\frac{8}{4}$ (b) $\frac{8}{4}$ (c) $-\frac{5}{2}, 6.5, -4.5, \frac{8}{4}, \frac{3}{4}$ **5.** $2 < 5$

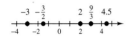

7. $-4 < -1$ **9.** $-2 < \frac{3}{2}$ **11.** $-\frac{9}{2} < -3$

13. $3 > -4$ **15.** $4 > -\frac{7}{2}$

17. $0 > -\frac{7}{16}$ **19.** $-4.6 < 1.5$

21. $\frac{7}{16} < \frac{5}{8}$ **23.** $-2\pi > -10$

25. 2 **27.** 4

29. -5

Distance: 5

31. 3.8 **33.** $\frac{5}{2}$

Distance: 3.8   Distance: $\frac{5}{2}$

35. $\frac{5}{2}, \frac{5}{2}$

37. $\frac{4}{3}, \frac{4}{3}$ **39.** 7 **41.** 3.4 **43.** $\frac{7}{2}$ **45.** -4.09

47. -23.6 **49.** 3.2 **51.** $|-15| = |15|$

53. $|-4| > |3|$ **55.** $|32| < |-50|$ **57.** $\left|\frac{3}{16}\right| < \left|\frac{3}{2}\right|$

59. $-|-48.5| < |-48.5|$ **61.** $|-\pi| > -|-2\pi|$

63.  **65.**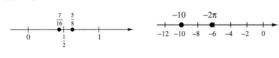

67. $-4.5, 20.5$ **69.** $-5.5, 1.5$

71. (a) $A = \{1°, -4°, -15°, 0°, 5°, 8°, 2°, 3°\}$

(b) $B = \{-3°, -5°, -12°, -20°, -6°, -\frac{4}{3}°, 0°, 2°,$
$-1°, -2°, -9°, -10°, -8°\}$

(c) $C = \{0°, 2°\}$

(d) $-15°, -4\frac{1}{2}°, -4°, 0°, 1°, 2°, 2.5°, 3°, 5°, 7.2°, 8°$

(e) $2°, 0°, -1°, -\frac{4}{3}°, -2°, -3°, -5°, -6°, -8°, -9°,$
$-10°, -12°, -20°$

(f) December 11

73. Two. They are -3 and 3.

75. 3. -10 is 3 units from -7 and 3 is 10 units from -7.

77. $\frac{3}{8} = 0.375$, so 0.35 is the smaller number.

79. True **81.** True

83. False. $\frac{1}{2}$ is not an integer.

Section 1.2 (page 24)

1. 9 **3.** -2

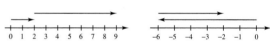

5. -1 **7.** 0 **9.** -1 **11.** -19 **13.** -30

15. -16 **17.** 8 **19.** 4 **21.** 30 **23.** -36

25. -16 **27.** 2225 **29.** 4558 **31.** 898 **33.** 3

35. 0 **37.** 35 **39.** 10 **41.** -103 **43.** -6

45. -610 **47.** 0 **49.** 8 **51.** 8 **53.** -14

55. -50 **57.** 500 **59.** -15 **61.** $2 + 2 + 2 = 6$

63. $(-3) + (-3) + (-3) + (-3) + (-3) = -15$

65. 21 **67.** -32 **69.** 72 **71.** -930 **73.** 90

75. -30 **77.** 90 **79.** 12 **81.** 338

83. -4725 **85.** $-62,352$ **87.** 3 **89.** -6

91. Division by zero is undefined. **93.** 27 **95.** -6

97. 0 **99.** 4 **101.** 32 **103.** -32 **105.** 110

107. 4540 **109.** 86 **111.** 1045 **113.** $-532,000$

115. Composite **117.** Prime **119.** Prime

121. Composite **123.** Prime **125.** $2 \cdot 2 \cdot 3$

127. $2 \cdot 3 \cdot 5 \cdot 7$ **129.** $2 \cdot 2 \cdot 2 \cdot 2 \cdot 2 \cdot 2 \cdot 3$

131. $3 \cdot 5 \cdot 5 \cdot 7$ **133.** $3 \cdot 5 \cdot 13 \cdot 13$

135. $12°F$ **137.** $\$1,012,000$ **139.** (a) $\$180$ million
(b) $\$30$ million

141. $-24°$ **143.** \$6000 **145.** 57,600 square feet

147. 65 miles per hour **149.** 594 cubic inches

151. (a) $3 + 2 = 5$

 (b) Adding two integers with like signs

 (c) On the last two plays, the team gained 3 yards and 2 yards for a total of 5 yards.

153. 2; it is divisible only by 1 and itself. Any other even number is divisible by 1, itself, and 2.

155. $\sqrt{1997} < 45$

157. To add two negative integers, add their absolute values and attach the negative sign.

159. Negative

161. The sum of three terms each equal to -5

163. $(2m)n = 2(mn)$. The product of two odd integers is odd.

165. n is a multiple of 4. $\frac{12}{2} = 6$

167. Perfect (< 25): 6
Abundant (< 25): 12, 18, 20, 24
First perfect greater than 25 is 28.

Mid-Chapter Quiz *(page 28)*

1. $-2.5 > -4$ **2.** $\frac{3}{16} < \frac{3}{8}$

3. $-3.1 < 2.7$ **4.** $2\pi > 6$

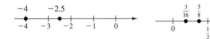

5. -0.75 **6.** 25.2

7. $\left|\frac{7}{2}\right| = |-3.5|$ **8.** $\left|\frac{3}{4}\right| > -|0.75|$

9. $\frac{3}{2}, -\frac{5}{2}$ **10.** $\frac{3}{4}, -\frac{9}{4}$

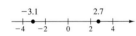 

11. -27 **12.** -3 **13.** 100 **14.** -60 **15.** 15

16. -4 **17.** \$450,450 **18.** 128 cubic feet **19.** 15 feet

20. False. The sum of two positive integers is positive.

Section 1.3 *(page 40)*

1. 5 **3.** 4 **5.** 6 **7.** 60 **9.** 1 **11.** $\frac{1}{4}$

13. $\frac{2}{3}$ **15.** $\frac{5}{16}$ **17.** $\frac{2}{25}$ **19.** $\frac{3}{5}$ **21.** $\frac{3}{5}$ **23.** $\frac{3}{5}$

25. $\frac{14}{11}$ **27.** $\frac{3}{8}$ **29.** -1 **31.** $-\frac{1}{2}$ **33.** $\frac{4}{3}$

35. $\frac{6}{16}$ **37.** $\frac{10}{25}$ **39.** $\frac{5}{6}$ **41.** $-\frac{1}{12}$ **43.** $\frac{9}{16}$

45. $-\frac{7}{24}$ **47.** $\frac{4}{3}$ **49.** $-\frac{41}{24}$ **51.** $-\frac{1}{12}$ **53.** $\frac{17}{48}$

55. $-\frac{17}{12}$ **57.** $\frac{5}{6}$ **59.** $\frac{23}{5}$ **61.** $\frac{37}{10}$ **63.** $\frac{26}{3}$

65. $-\frac{115}{11}$ **67.** $\frac{55}{6}$ **69.** $-\frac{17}{16}$ **71.** $-\frac{53}{12}$ **73.** $-\frac{121}{12}$

75. $\frac{3}{10}$ **77.** $\frac{3}{8}$ **79.** $-\frac{3}{8}$ **81.** $\frac{21}{20}$ **83.** $\frac{27}{40}$

85. $-\frac{3}{16}$ **87.** $\frac{12}{5}$ **89.** 1 **91.** $\frac{121}{12}$ **93.** $\frac{56}{3}$

95. $\frac{1}{7}$ **97.** $\frac{7}{4}$ **99.** $\frac{1}{2}$ **101.** $-\frac{8}{27}$

103. Division by zero is undefined. **105.** -90 **107.** $\frac{5}{6}$

109. $-\frac{16}{3}$ **111.** $\frac{5}{2}$ **113.** $\frac{10}{7}$ **115.** 0.75

117. 0.5625 **119.** $0.\overline{6}$ **121.** $0.58\overline{3}$ **123.** $0.\overline{45}$

125. 2.27 **127.** -1.90 **129.** -57.02 **131.** 0.04

133. 39.08 **135.** ≈ 1 **137.** $\$1\frac{5}{8}$

139. $\frac{1013}{40} = 25.325$ tons **141.** $\frac{5}{8}$ **143.** \$11.85

145. 48 breadsticks **147.** \$677.49

149. (a) \$30,600 **151.** (a) Answers will vary.

 (b) \$30,600 (b) 4.7 hours

153. (g) December 4 (h) December 4 and 5

 (i) December 4 and 5 (j) $-\frac{2}{35} \approx -0.06°$

 (k) $-\frac{113}{21} \approx -5.38°$ (l) g, h, i

155. No. Rewrite both fractions with like denominators. Then add their numerators and write the sum over the common denominator.

157. (a) $\frac{1}{3}$ (b) $\frac{1}{6}$ (c)

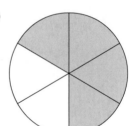

159. There are 12 one-fourths in 3.

161. False **163.** True **165.** True **167.** $\frac{3}{6} + \frac{4}{5} = \frac{13}{10}$

Section 1.4 *(page 51)*

1. 2^5 **3.** $\left(-\frac{1}{4}\right)^3$ **5.** $(-3)(-3)(-3)(-3)(-3)(-3)$

7. $(9.8)(9.8)(9.8)$ **9.** $\left(-\frac{1}{2}\right)\left(-\frac{1}{2}\right)\left(-\frac{1}{2}\right)\left(-\frac{1}{2}\right)\left(-\frac{1}{2}\right)$

11. Negative **13.** Negative **15.** 9 **17.** 64

19. -125 **21.** $\frac{1}{64}$ **23.** -1.728 **25.** 8 **27.** -9

29. 27 **31.** $-\frac{11}{2}$ **33.** 9 **35.** 17 **37.** -64

39. $\frac{7}{3}$ **41.** $\frac{8}{3}$ **43.** $\frac{5}{4}$ **45.** -1 **47.** $\frac{5}{6}$ **49.** 4

51. Division by zero is undefined. **53.** 13 **55.** 210

57. 5840 **59.** 0.0084 **61.** 7.32 **63.** 0

65. 1.19 **67.** 836.94 **69.** $24^2 = (4 \cdot 6)^2 = 4^2 \cdot 6^2$

71. $-3^2 = -(3)(3) = -9$

73. Commutative Property of Multiplication

75. Commutative Property of Addition

77. Additive Identity Property

79. Additive Inverse Property

81. Associative Property of Addition

83. Associative Property of Multiplication

85. Multiplicative Inverse Property

87. Distributive Property   **89.** Distributive Property

91. Associative Property of Addition

93. $(u + v)5$ or $5(v + u)$ **95.** $x + 3$ **97.** $6x + 12$

99. $100 + 25y$ **101.** $(3x + 2y) + 5$ **103.** $6(xy)$

105. (a) -50 (b) $\frac{1}{50}$ **107.** (a) 1 (b) -1

109. (a) $-2x$ (b) $\frac{1}{2x}$ **111.** (a) $-ab$ (b) $\frac{1}{ab}$

113. 48   **115.** 22   **117.** $5(x + 3) = 5x + 15$

119. Division by zero is undefined.

121. $4(2 + x) = 4(x + 2)$ Commutative Property of Addition

   $= 4x + 8$ Distributive Property

123. $7x + 9 + 2x$

   $= 7x + 2x + 9$ Commutative Property of Addition

   $= (7x + 2x) + 9$ Associative Property of Addition

   $= (7 + 2)x + 9$ Distributive Property

   $= 9x + 9$ Addition of Real Numbers

   $= 9(x + 1)$ Distributive Property

125. 36 square units   **127.** $0.07, \$31,500$

129. $\$11,070$ **131.** (a) $x(1 + 0.06) = 1.06x$ (b) $\$27.51$

133. $a + b + 2c + 12$ **135.** No

137. (a) Base (b) Exponent

139. No. $2 \cdot 5^2 = 2 \cdot 25 = 50$, $10^2 = 100$

141. $12 + (48 \div 6) - 5$

143. Commutative Property of Addition:
   $a + b = b + a, \ 3 + x = x + 3$
   Commutative Property of Multiplication:
   $ab = ba, \ 3x = x(3)$

145. (a) Additive Identity Property: $a + 0 = a$. The addition of any quantity and 0 yields the same quantity.
   $7 + 0 = 7$

   (b) Additive Inverse Property: $a + (-a) = 0$. Adding any quantity and its opposite yields the additive identity 0.
   $7 + (-7) = 0$

Review Exercises *(page 56)*

1. $-\frac{1}{10} < 4$ **3.** $-3 > -7$

5. $-152, 152$ **7.** $\frac{7}{3}, \frac{7}{3}$ **9.** 8.5 **11.** -8.5

13. $|-84| = |84|$ **15.** $\left|\frac{3}{10}\right| > -\left|\frac{4}{5}\right|$ **17.** 100

19. 11 **21.** 240 **23.** -268 **25.** -38 **27.** 45

29. 1500 **31.** -558 **33.** -18

35. Division by zero is undefined.   **37.** 1162

39. -102 **41.** -469 **43.** $-15,869$ **45.** 789

47. Prime   **49.** Composite   **51.** $2 \cdot 3 \cdot 3 \cdot 3 \cdot 7$

53. $2 \cdot 2 \cdot 13 \cdot 31$ **55.** 18 **57.** 21 **59.** $\frac{2}{3} = \frac{10}{15}$

61. $\frac{6}{10} = \frac{15}{25}$ **63.** $\frac{2}{5}$ **65.** $\frac{3}{4}$ **67.** $\frac{1}{9}$ **69.** $\frac{103}{96}$

71. $\frac{5}{4}$ **73.** $\frac{17}{8}$ **75.** $-\frac{1}{12}$ **77.** 1 **79.** $\frac{2}{3}$

81. $\frac{6}{7}$ **83.** Division by zero is undefined.   **85.** 21

87. 796.11 **89.** 1841.74 **91.** 343 **93.** -343

95. $2^2 < 2^4$ **97.** $\frac{3}{4} > \left(\frac{3}{4}\right)^2$ **99.** $\frac{81}{625}$ **101.** 160

103. 54 **105.** $\frac{37}{8}$ **107.** 140 **109.** -3 **111.** 7

113. 0 **115.** Additive Inverse Property

117. Commutative Property of Multiplication

119. Multiplicative Identity Property

121. Distributive Property   **123.** 0.6

125. False. If the absolute value of the negative integer is less than the positive integer, the sum will be positive.

127. 32,000 miles   **129.** (a) $\$5030, \$3090, \$4510, \$5700$

   (b) $\$14,850, \$3480$

   (c) $\$18,330$

131. $\$36$ **133.** $\$3.52$ **135.** (a) $\$6750$ (b) $\$9250$

Chapter Test *(page 59)*

1. (a) $8, \frac{12}{4}$ (b) $-10, 8, \frac{12}{4}$ (c) $-10, 8, \frac{3}{4}, \frac{12}{4}, 6.5$

2. $-\frac{3}{5} > -|-2|$ **3.** -4 **4.** 10 **5.** 10 **6.** 47

7. -160 **8.** 8 **9.** 3 **10.** 1 **11.** $\frac{17}{24}$

12. $-\frac{45}{2}$ **13.** $\frac{7}{12}$ **14.** -27 **15.** $-\frac{4}{9}$ **16.** 33

17. Distributive Property

18. Multiplicative Inverse Property

19. Associative Property of Addition

20. Commutative Property of Multiplication

21. $\frac{5}{12}$ **22.** $-3^4 = -1(3^4)$

23. Exponentiation, multiplication, subtraction

24.

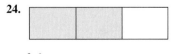

$\frac{2}{3}, \frac{6}{9}$

Chapter 2

Section 2.1   *(page 68)*

Integrated Review   *(page 68)*

1. Commutative Property of Multiplication
2. Additive Inverse Property
3. Distributive Property
4. Associative Property of Addition
5. 3   6. 8   7. $\frac{9}{2}$ 8. $\frac{2}{7}$ 9. $-\frac{7}{11}$ 10. $\frac{10}{3}$
11. $6000   12. 15 feet

---

1. $60t$ **3.** $2.19m$ **5.** Variable: x
                                    Constant: 3

7. Variables: x, z **9.** $4x, 3$ **11.** $3x^2, 5$

13. $\frac{5}{3}, -3y^3$ **15.** $2x, -3y, 1$ **17.** $3(x + 5), 10$

19. $\frac{x}{4}, \frac{5}{x}$ **21.** $\frac{3}{x + 2}, -3x, 4$ **23.** -6 **25.** $-\frac{1}{3}$

27. $-\frac{3}{2}$ **29.** 2π **31.** 4.7 **33.** $y \cdot y \cdot y \cdot y \cdot y$

35. $2 \cdot 2 \cdot x \cdot x \cdot x \cdot x$ **37.** $4 \cdot y \cdot y \cdot z \cdot z \cdot z$

39. $a^2 \cdot a^2 \cdot a^2 = a \cdot a \cdot a \cdot a \cdot a \cdot a$

41. $4 \cdot x \cdot x \cdot x \cdot x \cdot x \cdot x \cdot x$ **43.** $a \cdot a \cdot a \cdot b \cdot b \cdot b$

45. $(x + y)(x + y)$ **47.** $\left(\frac{a}{3s}\right)\left(\frac{a}{3s}\right)\left(\frac{a}{3s}\right)\left(\frac{a}{3s}\right)$

49. $3 \cdot 3 \cdot 3 \cdot (r + s)(r + s)(r + s)(r + s)$ **51.** $2u^4$

53. $(2u)^4$ **55.** a^3b^2 **57.** $3^3(x - y)^2$ **59.** $\left(\frac{x^2}{2}\right)^3$

61. (a) 0   **63.** (a) 3   **65.** (a) 6   **67.** (a) 3
    (b) 7   (b) 13   (b) 0   (b) -20

69. (a) 17   **71.** (a) 0
    (b) 4   (b) Division by zero is undefined.

73. (a) 10
    (b) Division by zero is undefined.

75. (a) $\frac{15}{2}$ **77.** (a) 175
    (b) 10   (b) 140

79. (a)

x	-1	0	1	2	3	4
$3x - 2$	-5	-2	1	4	7	10

(b) 3
(c) $\frac{2}{3}$

---

81. n^2, 64 square units   **83.** $a(a + b)$, 45 square units

85. (a) Square: 2 diagonals
    (b) Pentagon: 5 diagonals
    (c) Hexagon: 9 diagonals

87. (a) 4, 5, 5.5, 5.75, 5.875, 5.938, 5.9698
        Approaches 6.
    (b) 9, 7.5, 6.75, 6.375, 6.188, 6.094, 6.047
        Approaches 6.

89. (a) $(15 \cdot 12)c = 180c$
        Plastic/aluminum chairs: $351
        Wood/padded seat chairs: $531

    (b) Canopy 1: $215
        Canopy 2: $265
        Canopy 3: $415
        Canopy 4: $565
        Canopy 5: $715

91. No. The term includes the sign and is $-3x$.

93. No. When $y = 3$, the expression is undefined.

Section 2.2   *(page 80)*

Integrated Review   *(page 80)*

1. $a^m \cdot a^n = a^{m+n}$ 2. Distributive Property
3. 12   4. 120   5. -11 6. -5760
7. 35   8. -350 9. $\frac{1}{80}$ 10. $\frac{45}{16}$
11. 2,362,000   12. 52 miles per hour

---

1. u^6 **3.** $3x^7$ **5.** $5x^7$ **7.** $-15z^5$ **9.** $2xy^2z^2$

11. $-6ab^7$ **13.** t^8 **15.** $5u^5v^5$ **17.** $-8s^3$

19. $a^{10}b^{11}$ **21.** $16u^6v^{11}$ **23.** $(x - 3)^8$

25. $(x - 2y)^6$ **27.** $x^5 \cdot x^3 = x^{5+3} = x^8 \neq x^{15}$

29. $-3x^3 \neq -27x^3 = (-3x)^3$

31. Commutative Property of Addition

33. Associative Property of Multiplication

35. Multiplicative Identity Property

37. Commutative Property of Multiplication

39. Additive Inverse Property

41. Multiplicative Inverse Property

43. Additive Inverse Property, Additive Identity Property

45. $(x + 10) - (x + 10) = 0$

    Additive Inverse Property

47. $v(2) = 2v$

Commutative Property of Multiplication

49. $5(t - 2) = 5t + 5(-2)$

Distributive Property

51. $5x \cdot \dfrac{1}{5x} = 1$

Multiplicative Inverse Property

53. $12 + (8 - x) = (12 + 8) - x$

Associative Property of Addition

55. $-10x + 5y$ **57.** $3x + 6$ **59.** $4x + 4xy + 4y^2$

61. $3x^2 + 3x$ **63.** $-12y^2 + 16y$ **65.** $-u + v$

67. $3x^2 - 4xy$ **69.** $ab;\ ac;\ a(b + c) = ab + ac$

71. $2a;\ 2(b - a);\ 2a + 2(b - a) = 2b$

73. $6x^2, -3xy, y^2;\ 6, -3, 1$ **75.** $16t^3, 3t^3;\ 4, -5$

77. $6x^2y, -4x^2y;\ 2xy$

79. Variable factors are not alike. $x^2y \neq xy^2$ **81.** $-2y$

83. $-2x + 5$ **85.** $11x + 4$ **87.** $3r + 7$

89. $x^2 - xy + 4$ **91.** $17z + 11$

93. $z^3 + 3z^2 + 3z + 1$ **95.** $-x^2y + 4xy + 12xy^2$

97. $2\left(\dfrac{1}{x}\right) + 8$ **99.** $11\left(\dfrac{1}{t}\right) - 2t$

101. False. $3(x - 4) = 3x - 12$ **103.** True   **105.** 416

107. 39.9   **109.** $12x$ **111.** $4x$ **113.** $6x^2$

115. $-10z^3$ **117.** $9a$ **119.** $-6x^5$ **121.** $-24x^4y^4$

123. $2x$ **125.** $13s - 2$ **127.** $-2m + 15$

129. $44 + 2x$ **131.** $8x + 26$ **133.** $2x - 17$

135. $10x - 7x^2$ **137.** $3x^2 + 5x$ **139.** $4t^2 - 11t$

141. $26t - 2t^2$ **143.** $\dfrac{x}{3}$ **145.** $\dfrac{7z}{5}$ **147.** $-\dfrac{11x}{12}$

149. x **151.** \$21,589.25   **153.** Area of the square: x^2
Volume of the cube: x^3

155. $4x + 12$ **157.** 9375 square feet

159. $(6x)^4 = (6x)(6x)(6x)(6x)$

$6x^4 = 6x \cdot x \cdot x \cdot x$

161. (a), (c), and (d)

163. To combine like terms, add the respective coefficients and attach the common variable factor(s). $3x^2 - 5x^2 = -2x^2$

165. Remove the innermost symbols first and combine like terms. A symbol of grouping preceded by a *minus* sign can be removed by changing the sign of each term within the symbols.

167. It does not change if the parentheses are removed because multiplication is a higher-order operation than subtraction. Removing the brackets does change the expression because the division would be performed prior to the subtraction.

Mid-Chapter Quiz *(page 84)*

1. (a) 0   **2.** (a) 2

  (b) 10   (b) 0

  (c) 0   (c) Division by zero is undefined.

3. (a) -5 **4.** (a) $(3y)^4$ **5.** x^7 **6.** v^{10}

  (b) $\dfrac{5}{16}$ (b) $2^3(x - 3)^2$

7. $9y^5$ **8.** $8(x - 4)^6$ **9.** $\dfrac{10z^3}{21y^4}$ **10.** $\left(\dfrac{x}{y}\right)^7$

11. Associative Property of Multiplication

12. Distributive Property

13. Multiplicative Inverse Property

14. Commutative Property of Addition   **15.** $6x - 2$

16. $-8y + 12$ **17.** $y^2 + 4xy + y$ **18.** $3\left(\dfrac{1}{u}\right) + 3u$

19. $8a - 7b$ **20.** $-8x - 66$ **21.** $\frac{1}{10}\pi r^4 h$

22. 45,700

Section 2.3 *(page 95)*

Integrated Review *(page 95)*

1. Negative   **2.** 15, 3

3. False. $-4^2 = -1 \cdot 4 \cdot 4 = -16$

4. True. $(-4)^2 = (-4)(-4) = 16$ **5.** 78

6. 120   **7.** $\frac{3}{4}$ **8.** $\frac{14}{3}$ **9.** $\frac{23}{9}$ **10.** $-\frac{111}{10}$

11. 5 weeks, \$16.50   **12.** 40 meters

---

1. (d)   **3.** (e)   **5.** (b)   **7.** $x + 5$ **9.** $x - 25$

11. $x - 6$ **13.** $2x$ **15.** $\dfrac{x}{3}$ **17.** $\dfrac{x}{50}$ **19.** $\dfrac{3}{10}x$

21. $3x + 5$ **23.** $8 + 5x$ **25.** $10(x + 4)$

27. $|x + 4|$ **29.** $x^2 + 1$ **31.** A number decreased by 10

33. The product of 3 and a number, increased by 2

35. Seven times a number increased by 4

37. Three times the difference of 2 and a number

39. The sum of a number and 1, divided by 2

41. The square of a number, increased by 5

43. $(x + 3)x = x^2 + 3x$ **45.** $(25 + x) + x = 25 + 2x$

47. $(x - 9)(3) = 3x - 27$ **49.** $\dfrac{8(x + 24)}{2} = 4x + 96$

51. $0.10d$ **53.** $0.06L$ **55.** $\dfrac{100}{r}$ **57.** $15m + 2n$

59. $t = 10.2$ years   **61.** $t = 11.9$ years

63.

n	0	1	2	3	4	5
$2n - 1$	-1	1	3	5	7	9
Differences		2	2	2	2	2

65. 3   **67.** $a = 5, b = 4$ **69.** $3x(6x - 1) = 18x^2 - 3x$

71. $\frac{1}{2}(12)(5x^2 + 2) = 30x^2 + 12$

73.

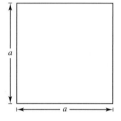 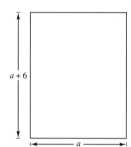

Perimeter of the square: $4a$ centimeters
Area of the square: a^2 square centimeters
Perimeter of the rectangle: $4a + 12$ centimeters
Area of the rectangle: $a(a + 6)$ square centimeters

75. s^2 square inches   **77.** $5w$ **79.** (a) $m + n$

(b) 3, 5, 8, 13, 21

81. Subtraction   **83.** (a), (b), (e)   **85.** $\left(\dfrac{5}{n}\right)3, \dfrac{5}{3n}$

Section 2.4   *(page 105)*

Integrated Review   *(page 105)*

1. Negative

2. Positive. The product of an even number of negative factors is positive.

3. $10 + 6$ **4.** Multiplicative Inverse Property

5. t^7 **6.** $-3y^5$ **7.** u^6 **8.** $2a^5b^5$

9. $12a^3b$ **10.** $2(x + 3)^5$

11. Perimeter: $6x$ **12.** Perimeter: $9x - 2$

Area: $\dfrac{9x^2}{4}$ Area: $5x^2 - 4x$

---

1. (a) Solution   **3.** (a) Not a solution
     (b) Not a solution   (b) Solution

5. (a) Not a solution   **7.** (a) Solution
     (b) Solution   (b) Not a solution

9. (a) Solution   **11.** (a) Solution
     (b) Not a solution   (b) Solution

13. (a) Not a solution   **15.** (a) Not a solution
     (b) Not a solution   (b) Not a solution

17. (a) Not a solution   **19.** (a) Solution
     (b) Not a solution   (b) Not a solution

21. (a) Solution   **23.** (a) Not a solution
     (b) Not a solution   (b) Solution

25. (a) Solution
     (b) Not a solution

27.

$5x + 12 = 22$	Given equation
$5x + 12 - 12 = 22 - 12$	Subtract 12 from both sides.
$5x = 10$	Combine like terms.
$\dfrac{5x}{5} = \dfrac{10}{5}$	Divide both sides by 5.
$x = 2$	Solution

29.

$\dfrac{2}{3}x = 12$	Given equation
$\dfrac{3}{2}\left(\dfrac{2}{3}x\right) = \dfrac{3}{2}(12)$	Multiply both sides by $\frac{3}{2}$.
$x = 18$	Solution

31.

$2(x - 1) = x + 3$	Given equation
$2x - 2 = x + 3$	Distributive Property
$-x + 2x - 2 = -x + x + 3$	Subtract x from both sides.
$x - 2 = 3$	Combine like terms.
$x - 2 + 2 = 3 + 2$	Add 2 to both sides.
$x = 5$	Solution

33.

$x = -2(x + 3)$	Given equation
$x = -2x - 6$	Distributive Property
$2x + x = 2x - 2x - 6$	Add $2x$ to both sides.
$3x = 0 - 6$	Additive Inverse Property
$3x = -6$	Combine like terms.
$\dfrac{3x}{3} = \dfrac{-6}{3}$	Divide both sides by 3.
$x = -2$	Solution

35. 2   **37.** 10   **39.** The sum of a number and 8 is 25.

41. Ten times a number decreased by 3 is 8 times the number.

43. The sum of a number and 1 divided by 3 is 8.

45. $x + 6 = 94$ **47.** $3650 + x = 4532$

49. $x + 12 = 45$ **51.** $4(x + 6) = 100$

53. $2x - 14 = \dfrac{x}{3}$ **55.** $0.32m = 135.36$

57. $2l + 2\left(\frac{1}{3}l\right) = 96$ **59.** $3r + 25 = 160$

61. $135 = 2.5x$ **63.** $p + 45 = 375$

65. $750{,}000 - 3D = 75{,}000$ **67.** $1.75n = 2000$

69. 15 dollars   **71.** 15 dollars   **73.** 6000 feet

75. An equation whose solution set is not the entire set of real numbers is called a conditional equation. The solution set of an identity is all real numbers.

77. Simplifying an expression means removing all symbols of grouping and combining like terms. Solving an equation means finding all values of the variable for which the equation is true.

     Simplify: $3(x - 2) - 4(x + 1) = 3x - 6 - 4x - 4$
$$= -x - 10$$

     Solve: $3(x - 2) = 6$
$$3x - 6 = 6$$
$$3x = 12 \rightarrow x = 4$$

79. (a) Simplify each side by removing symbols of grouping, combining like terms, and reducing fractions on one or both sides.

     (b) Add (or subtract) the same quantity to (from) both sides of the equation.

     (c) Multiply (or divide) both sides of the equation by the same nonzero real number.

     (d) Interchange the two sides of the equation.

Review Exercises   *(page 110)*

1. 4; $-\frac{1}{2}x^3, -\frac{1}{2}$ **3.** $y^2, 1$; $-10yz, -10$; $\frac{2}{3}z^2, \frac{2}{3}$

5. $(5z)^3$ **7.** $a^2(b - c)^2$ **9.** (a) 5   (b) 5

11. (a) 4   (b) -2 **13.** x^7 **15.** x^6 **17.** $-2t^6$

19. $-5x^3y^4$ **21.** $-64y^7$

23. Multiplicative Inverse Property

25. Commutative Property of Multiplication

27. Associative Property of Addition

29. $4x + 12y$ **31.** $-10u + 15v$ **33.** $8x^2 + 5xy$

35. $a - 3b$ **37.** $-2a$ **39.** $11p - 3q$ **41.** $\frac{15}{4}s - 5t$

43. $x^2 + 2xy + 4$ **45.** $3x - 3y + 3xy$

47. $3\left(1 + \dfrac{r}{n}\right)^2$ **49.** $5u - 10$ **51.** $5s - r$

53. $10z - 1$ **55.** $2z - 2$ **57.** $8x - 32$

59. $-2x + 4y$ **61.** $\frac{2}{3}x + 5$ **63.** $2x - 10$

65. $50 + 7x$ **67.** $\dfrac{x + 10}{8}$ **69.** $x^2 + 64$

71. A number plus 3

73. A number decreased by 2, divided by 3

75. (a) Not a solution   **77.** (a) Not a solution
     (b) Solution   (b) Solution

79. (a) Solution   **81.** (a) Not a solution
     (b) Not a solution   (b) Solution

83. (a) Solution   **85.** $P\left(\frac{9}{10}\right)^5$ **87.** $0.28I$ **89.** $9x^2$
     (b) Solution

91. $10s$ **93.** $625n$

95. (a)

n	0	1	2	3	4	5
$n^2 + 3n + 2$	2	6	12	20	30	42
Differences		4	6	8	10	12
Differences			2	2	2	2

     (b) Third row: entries increase by 2
        Fourth row: constant 2

97. $x + \dfrac{1}{x} = \dfrac{37}{6}$ **99.** $6x - \dfrac{1}{2}(6x) = \dfrac{1}{2}(6x) = 24$

Chapter Test   *(page 113)*

1. $2x^2, 2$; $-7xy, -7$; $3y^3, 3$ **2.** $x^3(x + y)^2$

3. Associative Property of Multiplication

4. Commutative Property of Addition

5. Additive Inverse Property

6. Multiplicative Identity Property

7. $3x + 24$ **8.** $-3y + 2y^2$ **9.** c^8 **10.** $-10u^4v$

11. $-a - 7b$ **12.** $8u - 8v$ **13.** $4z - 4$

14. $18 - 2t$ **15.** (a) 25   (b) -31

16. Division by zero is undefined.   **17.** $\frac{1}{5}n + 2$

18. (a) Perimeter: $2w + 2(2w - 4)$; Area: $w(2w - 4)$

     (b) Perimeter: $6w - 8$; Area: $2w^2 - 4w$

     (c) Perimeter: unit of length; Area: square units

     (d) Perimeter: 64 feet; Area: 240 square feet

19. $3n + 2m$ **20.** (a) Not a solution   (b) Solution

Chapter 3

Section 3.1 *(page 124)*

> ### Integrated Review *(page 124)*
>
> **1.** (a) $(ab)^n = a^n b^n$ (b) $(a^m)^n = a^{mn}$
>
> **2.** Associative Property of Addition **3.** u^8
>
> **4.** $9a^6$ **5.** $-3(x-5)^5$ **6.** $-40r^3 s^4$
>
> **7.** $\dfrac{2m^3}{5n^4}$ **8.** $\dfrac{(x+3)^2}{2(x+8)}$ **9.** $-9x + 11y$
>
> **10.** $8v - 4$ **11.** $\frac{1}{12}$ mile **12.** $30\frac{23}{30}$ tons

1. 8 **3.** 13 **5.** 4 **7.** 3

9. Original equation
Subtract 15 from both sides.
Combine like terms.
Divide both sides by 5.
Simplify.

11. Original equation **13.** 6 **15.** $-\frac{7}{3}$
Subtract 5 from both sides.
Combine like terms.
Divide both sides by -2.
Simplify.

17. 3 **19.** 2 **21.** 4 **23.** $\frac{2}{3}$ **25.** 2 **27.** $\frac{1}{3}$

29. -2 **31.** No solution **33.** 1 **35.** $\frac{5}{2}$ **37.** $-\frac{1}{4}$

39. Identity **41.** $\frac{2}{5}$ **43.** 0 **45.** $\frac{2}{3}$ **47.** 30

49. $\frac{5}{3}$ **51.** $\frac{5}{6}$ **53.** Identity **55.** 2 **57.** 36 feet

59. 3 feet, 3 feet, 6 feet **61.** $2\frac{1}{4}$ hours **63.** 150

65. 7 hours 20 minutes **67.** 30 **69.** 35, 37

71. (a)

t	1	1.5	2
Width	300	240	200
Length	300	360	400
Area	90,000	86,400	80,000

t	3	4	5
Width	150	120	100
Length	450	480	500
Area	67,500	57,600	50,000

(b) The area decreases.

73. The red box weighs 6 ounces. If you removed three blue boxes from each side, the scale would still balance. The Addition (or Subtraction) Property of Equality

75. Subtract 5 from each side of the equation. Addition Property of Equality

77. The answer is probably incorrect, because it implies an average speed of approximately 83.5 miles per hour. It is unlikely that a moving van would have an average speed that great.

79. True

Section 3.2 *(page 134)*

> ### Integrated Review *(page 134)*
>
> **1.** (a) $\dfrac{1}{5} + \dfrac{7}{5} = \dfrac{1+7}{5} = \dfrac{8}{5}$
>
> (b) $\dfrac{1}{5} + \dfrac{7}{3} = \dfrac{3}{15} + \dfrac{35}{15} = \dfrac{38}{15}$
>
> **2.** Answers vary. Examples are given.
>
> $3x^2 + 2\sqrt{x}$
>
> $\dfrac{4}{x^2 + 1}$
>
> **3.** $4x^6$ **4.** $8y^5$ **5.** $5z^7$ **6.** $(a+3)^7$
>
> **7.** $3x - 4$ **8.** $-x^2 + 1$ **9.** $-y^4 + 2y^2$
>
> **10.** $10t - 4t^2$ **11.** 7.5 gallons **12.** (a) \$24,300
>
> (b) \$4301

1. -3 **3.** 10 **5.** 5 **7.** 2 **9.** -10 **11.** 2

13. -5 **15.** Identity **17.** -4 **19.** No solution

21. $\frac{8}{5}$ **23.** 1 **25.** $\frac{1}{2}$ **27.** $\frac{2}{9}$ **29.** 1 **31.** 3

33. 3 **35.** $-\frac{3}{2}$ **37.** $\frac{5}{2}$ **39.** $-\frac{2}{5}$ **41.** $-\frac{10}{3}$

43. No solution **45.** $\frac{1}{6}$ **47.** 50 **49.** $\frac{32}{5}$ **51.** 10

53. 0 **55.** $\frac{16}{3}$ **57.** $\frac{4}{3}$ **59.** $\frac{4}{11}$ **61.** 6 **63.** 5.00

65. 7.71 **67.** 123.00 **69.** 3.51 **71.** 8.99

73. 4.8 hours

75. (a) 97

(b) No. A 100 on the final will yield only 86.25% for the course.

77. 25 quarts **79.** $1\frac{1}{3}$ quarts **81.** $x = 4$ feet

83. (a) Each of the n bricks is 8 inches long. Each of the $(n-1)$ mortar joints is $\frac{1}{2}$ inch wide. The total length is 93 inches.

(b) 11

85. Use the Distributive Property to remove symbols of grouping. Remove the innermost symbols first and combine like terms. Symbols of grouping preceded by a *minus* sign can be removed by changing the sign of each term within the symbols.

$$2x - [3 + (x - 1)] = 2x - [3 + x - 1]$$
$$= 2x - [2 + x]$$
$$= 2x - 2 - x = x - 2$$

87. Divide both sides by 3.

89. It clears the equation of fractions.

Section 3.3 *(page 145)*

Integrated Review *(page 145)*

1. $-28 < 63$

2. 0 **3.** 0

4. -38 **5.** -530 **6.** 29 **7.** $8x - 20$

8. $-xz^2 + 2y^2z$ **9.** (a) 7 (b) 16

10. (a) Division by zero is undefined. (b) 2

11. $14.67 **12.** $5r$

Percent	Parts out of 100	Decimal	Fraction
1. 40%	40	0.40	$\frac{2}{5}$
3. 7.5%	7.5	0.075	$\frac{3}{40}$
5. 63%	63	0.63	$\frac{63}{100}$
7. 15.5%	15.5	0.155	$\frac{31}{200}$
9. 60%	60	0.60	$\frac{3}{5}$
11. 150%	150	1.50	$\frac{3}{2}$

13. 62% **15.** 20% **17.** 7.5% **19.** 250%

21. 0.125 **23.** 1.25 **25.** 2.50 **27.** 0.0075

29. 80% **31.** 125% **33.** $83\frac{1}{3}$% **35.** 35%

37. $37\frac{1}{2}$% **39.** $41\frac{2}{3}$% **41.** 45 **43.** 77.52

45. 0.42 **47.** 176 **49.** 2100 **51.** 2200

53. 132 **55.** 360 **57.** 72% **59.** 12.5%

61. 2.75% **63.** 500%

	Cost	Selling Price	Markup	Markup Rate
65.	$26.97	$49.95	$22.98	85.2%
67.	$40.98	$74.38	$33.40	81.5%
69.	$69.29	$125.98	$56.69	81.8%
71.	$13,250.00	$15,900.00	$2650.00	20%
73.	$107.97	$199.96	$91.99	85.2%

	List Price	Sale Price	Discount	Discount Rate
75.	$39.95	$29.95	$10.00	25%
77.	$23.69	$18.95	$4.74	20%
79.	$189.99	$159.99	$30.00	15.8%
81.	$119.96	$59.98	$59.98	50%
83.	$995.00	$695.00	$300.00	30.2%

85. $544 **87.** $3435 **89.** $71\frac{2}{3}$% **91.** 7.2%

93. $312.50 **95.** $24,409 **97.** 10,210

99. 500 **101.**

< 15	131.8 million
15–24	56.5 million
25–44	181.9 million
45–64	159.6 million
65–74	90.6 million
> 75	77.4 million

103. (a) 1,345,098

(b) 97,854

(c) The number of men in biology increased at a faster rate.

105. (a) $3(19.50) + x = 99$, $40.50

(b) $24 + x = 80$, $56.00, Second package

(c) $40.50 = p(99)$, 40.9%

(d) $56 = p(80)$, 70%

(e) $x = 99 + 0.05(99)$, $103.95

(f) $19.50 + 60(3.2)x = 92.46$, $0.38

107. A rate is a fixed ratio.

109. Decimal to percent: Multiply by 100.
$0.37 = 37$%

111. Yes. Multiply by 100 and affix the percent sign.

Section 3.4 *(page 156)*

Integrated Review *(page 156)*

1. $\dfrac{15}{12} = \dfrac{5 \cdot 3}{4 \cdot 3} = \dfrac{5}{4}$ **2.** $\dfrac{3}{5} \div \dfrac{x}{2} = \dfrac{3}{5} \cdot \dfrac{2}{x} = \dfrac{6}{5x}$

3. $(3x)y = 3(xy)$ **4.** Additive Identity Property

5. 13 **6.** -122 **7.** 9,300,000 **8.** -4

9. $\dfrac{77}{5}$ **10.** 8 **11.** $2(n - 10)$ **12.** $\frac{1}{4}b(b + 6)$

1. $\frac{4}{1}$ **3.** $\frac{1}{2}$ **5.** $\frac{2}{3}$ **7.** $\frac{9}{1}$ **9.** $\frac{3}{2}$ **11.** $\frac{2}{3}$ **13.** $\frac{1}{4}$

15. $\frac{7}{15}$ **17.** $\frac{2}{1}$ **19.** $\frac{3}{8}$ **21.** $\frac{3}{50}$ **23.** $\frac{3}{4}$ **25.** $\frac{3}{10}$

27. $0.0395 **29.** $0.0645 **31.** $27\frac{3}{4}$-ounce can

33. 16-ounce package   **35.** 2-liter bottle   **37.** 12

39. 50   **41.** $\frac{10}{3}$ **43.** 16   **45.** $\frac{3}{16}$

47. $\frac{1}{2}$ **49.** 27   **51.** $\frac{14}{5}$ **53.** $\frac{2}{1}$

55. $\frac{12}{1}$ **57.** $\frac{20}{1}$ **59.** $\frac{3}{2}$ **61.** $\frac{100}{49}$

63. 16 gallons   **65.** 250 blocks   **67.** $1142

69. 22,691   **71.** $46\frac{2}{3}$ minutes   **73.** 20 pints

75. 245 miles   **77.** $\frac{5}{2}$ **79.** $6\frac{2}{3}$ feet   **81.** 80%

83. $5216   **85.** $0.52   **87.** $57.00

89. No. It is necessary to know one of the following: the total number of students in the class, the number of men in the class, or the number of women in the class.

91. A proportion is a statement that equates two ratios.

Mid-Chapter Quiz   *(page 160)*

1. 40   **2.** 8   **3.** $\frac{19}{2}$ **4.** 0   **5.** $-\frac{1}{3}$ **6.** $\frac{40}{13}$

7. 36   **8.** 11   **9.** 5   **10.** -2 **11.** 2.06

12. 51.23   **13.** 15.5   **14.** 42   **15.** 200%

16. 455   **17.** 12 meters $\times$ 18 meters   **18.** 10 hours

19. 6 square meters, 12 square meters, 24 square meters

20. 93   **21.** $495.37   **22.** 44.1%   **23.** $\frac{225}{64}$

Section 3.5   *(page 169)*

Integrated Review   *(page 169)*

1. $2n$ is an even integer and $2n + 1$ is an odd integer.

2. $2x - 3 = 10$

$2x - 3 + 3 = 10 + 3$

$2x = 13$

3. $-28y^3$ **4.** $81x^8$ **5.** $\dfrac{20u^3}{3}$ **6.** $2y$

7. $13x - 5x^2$ **8.** $-5t + 32$ **9.** $10v - 40$

10. $60 - 10x$ **11.** 6%   **12.** 20% off

---

1. $\dfrac{2A}{b}$ **3.** $\dfrac{E}{I}$ **5.** $\dfrac{V}{wh}$ **7.** $\dfrac{A - P}{Pt}$ **9.** $\dfrac{S}{1 + R}$

11. $\dfrac{2A - ah}{h}$ **13.** $\dfrac{3V + \pi h^3}{3\pi h^2}$ **15.** $\dfrac{2(h - v_0 t)}{t^2}$

17. 100π meters^3 **19.** 165 miles   **21.** 5.6 hours

23. 2112 feet per second   **25.** 784 square feet

27. 8 meters   **29.** 30 inches

31. Radius: 3.98 inches   **33.** 24 square inches
Area: 49.74 square inches

35. 96 cubic inches   **37.** $540   **39.** $15,975

41. 11%   **43.** $1200   **45.** $4000

47. 0.176 hour $\approx$ 10.6 minutes   **49.** 28 miles

51. 1154 miles per hour   **53.** $\frac{1}{3}$ hour

55. (a) Answers will vary.   **57.** Solution 1: 25 gallons
(b) 48 miles per hour   Solution 2: 75 gallons

59. Solution 1: 5 quarts   **61.** 20-cent stamps: 40
Solution 2: 5 quarts   33-cent stamps: 60

63. 8 nickels   **65.** 30 pounds at $2.49 per pound
12 dimes   70 pounds at $3.89 per pound

67. $\frac{8}{7}$ gallon

69.

Corn x	Soybeans $100 - x$	Price per ton of the mixture
0	100	$200
20	80	$185
40	60	$170
60	40	$155
80	20	$140
100	0	$125

(a) Decreases

(b) Decreases

(c) Average of the two prices

71. $1\frac{1}{5}$ hours   **73.** Answers will vary.   **75.** 15

77. Candidate A: 250 votes
Candidate B: 250 votes
Candidate C: 500 votes

79. Perimeter: units—inches, feet, meters
Area: units squared—square inches, square meters
Volume: units cubed—cubic inches, cubic centimeters

81. The circumference would double; the area would quadruple.

Circumference: $C = 2\pi r$. If r is doubled, you have $C = 2\pi(2r) = 2(2\pi r)$.

Area: $A = \pi r^2$. If r is doubled, you have $A = \pi(2r)^2 = 4\pi r^2$.

83. $\frac{1}{5}$

Section 3.6   *(page 183)*

Integrated Review   *(page 183)*

1. Distributive Property
2. $(x + 2) - 4 = x + (2 - 4)$
3. $|a| = -a$ if $a < 0$ 4. $a \cdot b < 0$
5. $-\frac{1}{2} > -7$ 6. $-\frac{1}{3} < -\frac{1}{6}$ 7. $-\pi < -3$
8. $-6 > -\frac{13}{2}$ 9. Perimeter: $2x^2 + 7x - 3$
              Area: $\frac{5}{2}x^3 - \frac{3}{2}x^2$
10. Perimeter: $2y^2$
          Area: $y^3 - 2y^2 + y$
11. \$332,050   12. 53 miles per hour

---

1. x is greater than or equal to 3.

3. x is less than or equal to 10.

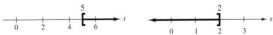

5. y is greater than $-\frac{3}{2}$ *and* less than or equal to 5.

7. (a) Yes	**9.** (a) No	**11.** (a) Yes	**13.** (a) Yes
(b) No	(b) No	(b) No	(b) No
(c) Yes	(c) Yes	(c) No	(c) Yes
(d) No	(d) Yes	(d) Yes	(d) No

15. b   **16.** f   **17.** c   **18.** a   **19.** d   **20.** e

21. $t \geq 5$ **23.** $x \leq 2$

25. $x < 3$ **27.** $x > -4$

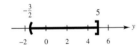

29. $x \leq 18$ **31.** $x > 6$

33. $x > \frac{1}{2}$ **35.** $x > \frac{11}{3}$

37. $y > 1$ **39.** $z \leq -1$

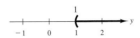

41. $y > \frac{1}{3}$ **43.** $x > -2$

45. $x \geq -\frac{10}{3}$ **47.** $-1 < x < 3$

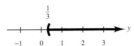

49. $-\frac{1}{2} < x < \frac{7}{2}$ **51.** $-16 < x < 8$

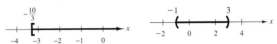

53. $-\frac{3}{4} < x < -\frac{1}{4}$ **55.** $-4 < x \leq 3$

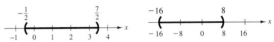

57. $x < -1$ or $x > 4$ **59.** $A = \{x | x < -5\}$
                                   $B = \{x | x > 3\}$

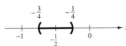

                                   $A \cup B$

61. $A = \{x | x < 6\}$ **63.** $A = \{x | x \geq -3\}$
      $B = \{x | x > 0\}$ $B = \{x | x \leq 7\}$
      $A \cap B$ $A \cap B$

65. $A = \{x | x < 7\}$
      $B = \{x | x > 8\}$
      $A \cup B$

67. $x \geq 0$ **69.** $y > -6$ **71.** $x \geq 4$ **73.** $y \leq 25$

75. $0 < x \leq 6$ **77.** Mars is farther from the sun than
                           Mercury.

79. $0 \leq t \leq 12.4$ minutes   **81.** $m \leq 19,555$ miles

83. $a + b > c$ **85.** $180 \leq x \leq 260$ miles

87. $0 \leq 0.35x + 19.50 \leq 75.00$

     $0 \leq x \leq 158.57$ minutes

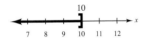

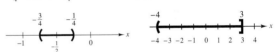

89. Yes. Addition and Subtraction Properties of Inequalities

91. Infinite number. $x - 3 > 0 \rightarrow x > 3$

93. The process is similar except that the direction of the inequality must be reversed if both sides of the inequality are multiplied or divided by a negative number.

95. $<$ **97.** False.   **99.** True

$$-\tfrac{1}{2}x + 6 > 0$$
$$-\tfrac{1}{2}x > -6$$
$$x < 12$$

Section 3.7   *(page 190)*

Integrated Review   *(page 190)*

1. $2n$ is an even integer and $2n - 1$ is an odd integer.

2. No. $-3x^2 \neq (-3x)^2 = 9x^2$

3. $\dfrac{27}{12} = \dfrac{3 \cdot 9}{3 \cdot 4} = \dfrac{9}{4}$ **4.** $\dfrac{2}{3} \div \dfrac{5}{3} = \dfrac{2}{3} \cdot \dfrac{3}{5} = \dfrac{2}{5}$

5. $3 > -2$ **6.** $-3 < -2$ **7.** $-\tfrac{1}{2} > -3$

8. $-\tfrac{1}{3} > -\tfrac{2}{3}$ **9.** $\tfrac{1}{2} > \tfrac{5}{16}$ **10.** $4 < \tfrac{45}{11}$

11. $\$76{,}300 - \$75{,}926 = 374 < 500$

12. $\$39{,}632 - \$37{,}800 = 1832 > 500$

---

1. Yes   **3.** No

5. $u - 3 = 7$ **7.** $\tfrac{1}{2}x + 7 = \tfrac{3}{2}$

$\quad\; u - 3 = -7$ $\quad\;\; \tfrac{1}{2}x + 7 = -\tfrac{3}{2}$

9. ± 7 **11.** ± 15 **13.** No solution   **15.** ± 6

17. 8, 16   **19.** $-14, 8$ **21.** 13, 19   **23.** No solution

25. $-9, 12$ **27.** $-\tfrac{7}{3}, 1$ **29.** $1, \tfrac{13}{5}$ **31.** 3, 12

33. $-8, 24$ **35.** $|x + 3| = 8$ **37.** $|x - 4| = 2$

39. (a) Yes   **41.** (a) No   **43.** (a) No   **45.** (a) Yes

(b) No   (b) Yes   (b) No   (b) No

(c) No   (c) Yes   (c) No   (c) Yes

(d) Yes   (d) No   (d) Yes   (d) No

47. $-1 < z + 2 < 1$ **49.** $5 - h \geq 2$

$\qquad\qquad\qquad\qquad\quad\;\; 5 - h \leq -2$

51.
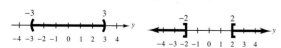

53.

55. $-3 < y < 3$ **57.** $y \leq -2$ or $y \geq 2$

---

59. $t < -5$ or $t > 5$ **61.** $0 \leq y \leq 4$

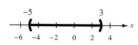

63. $-5 < x < 3$ **65.** $-6 < x < 6$

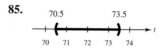

67. $y < 3$ or $y > 7$ **69.** $m \leq -5$ or $m \geq 1$

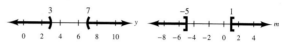

71. c   **73.** a   **75.** $|x - 1| < 2$ **77.** $|x + 5| \geq 10$

79. $|x| < 2$ **81.** $|x| > 5$ **83.** $|x - 4| > 2$

85.

87. (a) $|s - x| \leq 0.005$

(b) $3.495 \leq x \leq 3.5005$

89. $|a|$ represents the two real numbers that are a units from 0 on the real number line.

91. To solve an absolute value equation, rewrite the equation in equivalent forms that can be solved by previously learned methods. If the form is an absolute value of an expression that equals a constant, form two equations by writing the expression without the absolute value signs equal to plus or minus the constant.

Review Exercises   *(page 194)*

1. 35   **3.** 28   **5.** Original equation

Add 12 to both sides.

Combine like terms.

Divide both sides by 10.

Simplify.

7. 3   **9.** 3   **11.** 5   **13.** 4   **15.** 3   **17.** $\tfrac{4}{3}$

19. 20   **21.** 20   **23.** $\tfrac{5}{3}$ **25.** 7   **27.** $\tfrac{19}{3}$ **29.** 20

31. 7.99   **33.** 224.31

35.

Percent	Parts out of 100	Decimal	Fraction
35%	35	0.35	$\tfrac{7}{20}$

37. 20   **39.** 400   **41.** 60%   **43.** $\tfrac{1}{8}$ **45.** $\tfrac{4}{3}$

47. $\tfrac{7}{2}$ **49.** $-\dfrac{10}{3}$ **51.** 9   **53.** $\dfrac{2A}{r^2}$ **55.** 520 miles

57. 8 hours   **59.** 60 miles per hour   **61.** $1 \leq x < 4$

63. $x < 3$

65. $x \geq 2$ **67.** $x < 3$

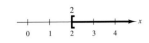   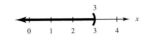

69. $x \geq 2$ **71.** $x > 10$

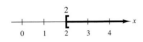   

73. $t > 4$ **75.** $y \leq -1$

   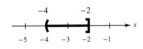

77. $-4 < x \leq -2$ **79.** $-7 < x < -1$

81. $A = \{x | x < -3\}$ **83.** $A = \{x | x < 0\}$
   $B = \{x | x > 7\}$ $B = \{x | x > -6\}$
   $A \cup B$ $A \cap B$

85. $A = \{x | x \geq -8\}$ **87.** $A = \{x | x < 2\}$
   $B = \{x | x \leq -5\}$ $B = \{x | x > 3\}$
   $A \cap B$ $A \cup B$

89. $z \geq 10$ **91.** $8 < y < 12$ **93.** $V < 12$

95. $20, 30$ **97.** $-6, 6$ **99.** -8

101. $-6 \leq v \leq 6$ **103.** $y < 1$ or $y > 7$

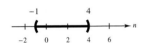   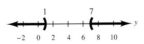

105. $-1 < n < 4$ **107.** 480 miles, 720 miles

109. 80×50 meters   **111.** 3.5%

113. Living with spouse: 9,525,120
   Living with other relatives: 1,587,520
   Living alone or with nonrelatives: 8,731,360

115. $1687   **117.** 214 miles   **119.** 9.4 hours

121. 5.3 kilometers per hour   **123.** 13 dimes, 17 quarters

125. 30×26 feet   **127.** $475   **129.** $285,714.29

131. $\frac{30}{11} \approx 2.7$ hours

Chapter Test   *(page 198)*

1. $\frac{21}{4}$ **2.** 7   **3.** -10 **4.** 10   **5.** 3, 7

6. $-\frac{1}{3}, 3$ **7.** 11.03   **8.** $2\frac{1}{2}$ hours   **9.** $37\frac{1}{2}\%, 0.375$

10. 1200   **11.** 36%   **12.** $\frac{5}{9}$ **13.** $\frac{12}{7}$

14. 110 miles   **15.** 48 miles per hour

16. $\frac{36}{7} \approx 5.1$ hours   **17.** $\frac{S - C}{C}$ **18.** $6250

19. $x \leq 4$ **20.** $x < -6$

21. $-1 < x \leq 2$ **22.** $-1 \leq x < 5$

   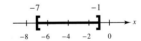

23. $-7 \leq x \leq -1$ **24.** $x < -1$ or $x > 2$

Cumulative Test: Chapters 1–3   *(page 199)*

1. $-\frac{3}{4} < \left| -\frac{7}{8} \right|$ **2.** 1200   **3.** $-\frac{11}{24}$ **4.** $-\frac{25}{12}$ **5.** 8

6. 14   **7.** 28   **8.** 5   **9.** 20   **10.** $3^3(x + y)^2$

11. $-2x^2 + 6x$ **12.** Associative Property of Addition

13. $15x^7$ **14.** $a^8 b^7$ **15.** $7x^2 - 6x - 2$ **16.** 6

17. $\frac{52}{3}$ **18.** 5   **19.** $-5 \leq x < 1$

20. $\dfrac{15{,}000 \text{ miles}}{1 \text{ year}} \cdot \dfrac{1 \text{ gallon}}{28.3 \text{ miles}} \cdot \dfrac{\$1.179}{1 \text{ gallon}} \approx \$624.91$ per year

21. $\frac{3}{4}$ **22.** 246, 248

23. $920   **24.** $57,000

Chapter 4

Section 4.1   *(page 209)*

Integrated Review   *(page 209)*

1. $3x = 7$ is a linear equation since it has the form $ax + b = c$. $x^2 + 3x = 2$ is not of that form, and therefore is not linear.

2. Substitute 3 for x in the equation to verify that it satisfies the equation.

3. -10 **4.** 4   **5.** 14   **6.** 4   **7.** 6

8. $\frac{1}{9}$ **9.** 144   **10.** 200   **11.** $19,250

12. 8 hours 45 minutes

1.

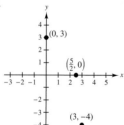

3.

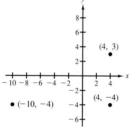

5.

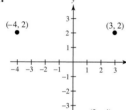

7.

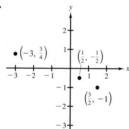

9.

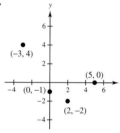

11. A: $(5, 2)$
B: $(-3, 4)$
C: $(2, -5)$
D: $(-2, -2)$

13. A: $(-1, 3)$ **15.** Quadrant II   **17.** Quadrant III
B: $(5, -3)$
C: $(2, 1)$
D: $(-1, -2)$

19. Quadrant III   **21.** Quadrant II or III

23. Quadrant III or IV   **25.** Quadrant II or IV

27. $(0, 3)$ **29.** $(-5, -10)$

31.

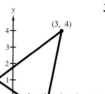

33.

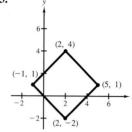

35.

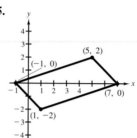

37.

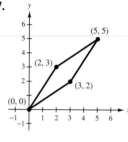

39.

x	-2	0	2	4	6
$y = 3x - 4$	-10	-4	2	8	14

41.

x	-4	-2	4	6	8
$y = -\frac{3}{2}x + 5$	11	8	-1	-4	-7

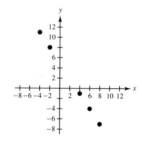

43.

x	-2	-1	0	1	2
$y = 2x - 1$	-5	-3	-1	1	3

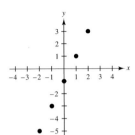

45. $y = 2x - 1$ **47.** $y = -\frac{1}{4}x + 2$ **49.** $y = \frac{4}{5}x - \frac{3}{5}$

51. (a) Solution   **53.** (a) Solution
(b) Not a solution   (b) Solution
(c) Not a solution   (c) Not a solution
(d) Solution   (d) Solution

55. (a) Not a solution   **57.** (a) Solution
(b) Solution   (b) Not a solution
(c) Solution   (c) Not a solution
(d) Not a solution   (d) Not a solution

59.

x	20	40	60	80	100
$y = 0.066x$	1.32	2.64	3.96	5.28	6.60

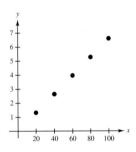

61. $y = 35x + 5000$

x	100	150	200	250	300
$y = 35x + 5000$	8500	10,250	12,000	13,750	15,500

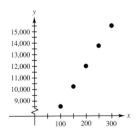

63. (a) 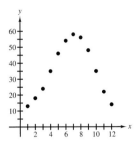 (b) No
(c) June, July, August

65. (a) 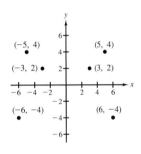 (b) Scores increase with increased study time.

67. 1,800,000   **69.** 170,000, 13%   **71.** $20,750

73. 5%   **75.** 7%

77. (a) and (b)

(c) Reflection in the y-axis

79. Order is significant because each number in the pair has a particular interpretation. The first measures horizontal distance and the second measures vertical distance.

81. The x-coordinate of any point on the y-axis is 0. The y-coordinate of any point on the x-axis is 0.

83. Third quadrant: $(-, -)$
Fourth quadrant: $(+, -)$

85. The y-coordinates increase if the coefficient of x is positive and decrease if the coefficient is negative.

Section 4.2 *(page 219)*

Integrated Review *(page 219)*

1. $x - 2 + c > 5 + c$ **2.** $(x - 2)c > 5c$

3. $x\left(\dfrac{1}{x}\right) = 1$

4. Commutative Property of Addition

5. $-9x + 11y$ **6.** $8z - 4$ **7.** $-y^4 + 2y^2$

8. $10t - 4t^2$ **9.** $3x + 30$ **10.** 0

11. (a) 65 miles

(b) 1 day, since $2(30) > 50.80$

(c) No.
1 day, 208.75 miles
2 days, 115 miles
3 days, 21.25 miles

12. 25×15 inches

1. g **3.** a **5.** h **7.** d

9.

x	-2	-1	0	1	2
y	11	10	9	8	7

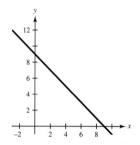

11.

x	-2	-1	0	1	2
y	-10	-6	-2	2	6

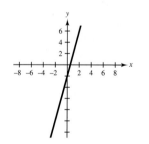

13.

x	-2	0	2	4	6
y	3	2	1	0	-1

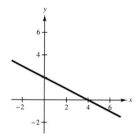

15.

x	-3	-2	-1	0	1
y	2	1	0	1	2

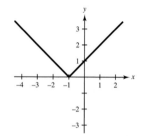

17. $(-2, 0), (0, 4)$ **19.** $(6, 0), (0, 2)$

21. $(-3, 0), (3, 0), (0, -3)$ **23.** $(-4, 0), (4, 0), (0, 16)$

25. $\left(-\frac{1}{3}, 0\right), (0, 2)$ **27.** $(2, 0), (0, -1)$

29. $(1, 0), (0, -1)$ **31.** $(2, 0), (0, 4)$

33. $\left(\frac{9}{2}, 0\right), \left(0, \frac{3}{2}\right)$ **35.** $(4, 0), (0, -6)$

37.

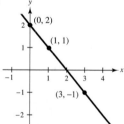

39.

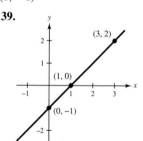

41.

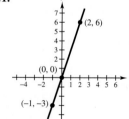

43.

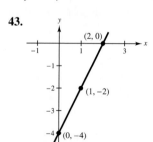

45.

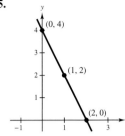

47.

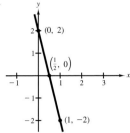

49.

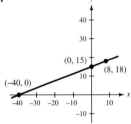

51.

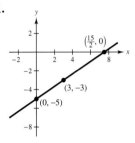

53.

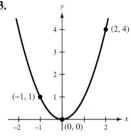

55.

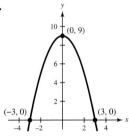

57.

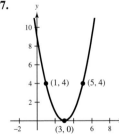

59.

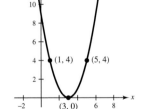

61.

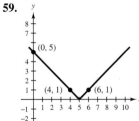

63.

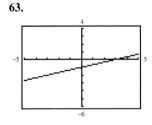

Commutative Property of Addition

65.

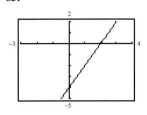

67.

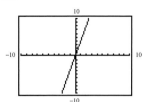

Distributive Property

69.

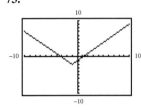

71.

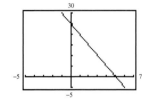

73.

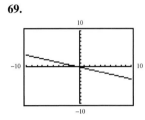

75.

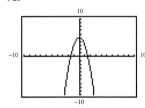

77.

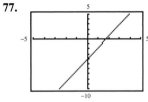

79.

Xmin = -15
Xmax = 15
Xscl = 1
Ymin = -10
Ymax = 10
Yscl = 1

81.

Xmin = -5
Xmax = 20
Xscl = 5
Ymin = -5
Ymax = 20
Yscl = 5

83. $y = 35t$

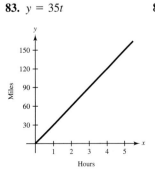

85. (a)

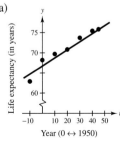

(b) 78.7

87. Left: Declining balances
Right: Straight-line depreciation

89. Straight-line depreciation is easier to compute. The declining balances method yields a more realistic approximation of the faster rate of depreciation early in the useful lifetime of the equipment.

91. The set of all solutions of an equation plotted on a rectangular coordinate system is called its graph.

93. Make up a table of values showing several solution points. Plot these points on a rectangular coordinate system and connect them with a smooth curve or line.

95. To find the x-intercept(s), let $y = 0$ and solve the equation for x. To find the y-intercept(s), let $x = 0$ and solve the equation for y.

97. Answers will vary.

Section 4.3   *(page 229)*

Integrated Review   *(page 229)*

1. $a < c$

Transitive Property

2. $\dfrac{7x}{7} = \dfrac{21}{7}$

$x = 3$

3. $11s - 5t$ **4.** $-x^2 + 1$ **5.** $x - 4$

6. $3x^2y - xy^2 - 5xy$ **7.** -3 **8.** $\frac{4}{7}$ **9.** $\frac{9}{2}$

10. 2 **11.** 9.2% **12.** $833\frac{1}{3}$ miles per hour

---

1. Domain: $\{-4, 1, 2, 4\}$

Range: $\{-3, 2, 3, 5\}$

3. Domain: $\left\{-9, \frac{1}{2}, 2\right\}$

Range: $\{-10, 0, 16\}$

5. Domain: $\{-1, 1, 5, 8\}$

Range: $\{-7, -2, 3, 4\}$

7. Function

9. Not a function   **11.** Function   **13.** Not a function

15. Not a function   **17.** Function   **19.** Function

21. Not a function   **23.** Function   **25.** Function

27. Function   **29.** Not a function   **31.** Function

33. Not a function   **35.** Function

37. (a) 1   **39.** (a) -1 **41.** (a) 5   **43.** (a) 49
   (b) $\frac{5}{2}$ (b) 5   (b) -3 (b) -4
   (c) -2 (c) -7 (c) -15 (c) 1
   (d) $-\frac{1}{3}$ (d) -2 (d) $-\frac{13}{3}$ (d) $-\frac{13}{8}$

45. (a) 8   **47.** (a) 1   **49.** (a) 4   **51.** (a) -1
   (b) 8   (b) 15   (b) 0   (b) 0
   (c) 0   (c) 0   (c) 12   (c) 26
   (d) 2   (d) 0   (d) $\frac{1}{2}$ (d) $-\frac{7}{8}$

53. $R = \{4, 3, 2, 1, 0\}$ **55.** $R = \{100\}$

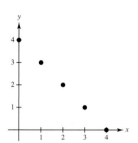   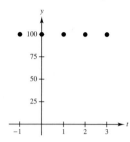

57. $R = \{-8, -1, 0, 1, 8\}$ **59.** $R = \{0, 1, 2\}$

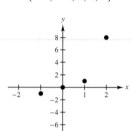   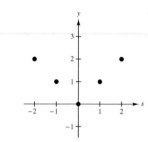

61. (a) $f(10) = 15$, $f(15) = 12.5$ **63.** (a) 100 miles
   (b) Demand decreases.   (b) 200 miles
             (c) 500 miles

65. High school enrollment is a function of the year.

67. 12,900,000   **69.** $P = 4s$

P is a function of s.

71. (a) L is a function of t.
   (b) $9.5 \le L \le 15$

73. A relation is any set of ordered pairs. A function is a relation in which no two ordered pairs have the same first component and different second components.

Example:

Domain	Range
1	4
2	5
3	6

75. The domain is the set of inputs of a function, and the range is the set of outputs of the function.

77. If the graph of an equation has the property that no vertical line intersects the graph at two (or more) points, then the equation represents y as a function of x.

79. Yes. Example: $f(x) = 10$

Mid-Chapter Quiz *(page 233)*

1.

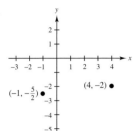

2. Quadrants I and II

3. (a) Solution

(b) Not a solution

(c) Solution

(d) Not a solution

4. 1991: 180 million
1992: 200 million
1993: 270 million
1994: 290 million
1995: 350 million
1996: 410 million
1997: 530 million

5. $(12, 0), (0, -4)$ **6.** $\left(\frac{3}{2}, 0\right), (0, 6)$

7.

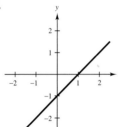

8.

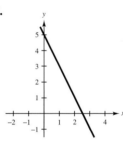

9.

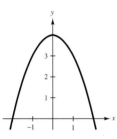

10.

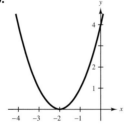

11.

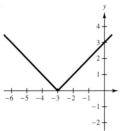

12.

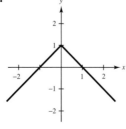

13. Yes. There is one value of y corresponding to each value of x.

14. No. There are two values of y corresponding to $x > 0$.

15. (a) -8 (b) -2 (c) 13 (d) -3

16. (a) 6   (b) 6   (c) 0   (d) 0

17. $R = \{0, 2, 6\}$ **18.** $s > 0$

19.

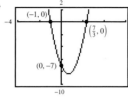

20. $V = 3000 - 500t$

Domain: $0 \le t \le 4$

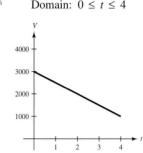

Section 4.4 *(page 242)*

Integrated Review *(page 242)*

1. Equivalent   **2.** $5x = 6 + 2$ **3.** x^9

4. y^2z^5 **5.** u^8v^4 **6.** a^4b^4 **7.** $50x^5$

8. $54y^3z^5$ **9.** $x + 2$ **10.** $x^2 - 4x - 2$

11. 2 feet, 2 feet, 6 feet   **12.** 1.5 hours

1. 1   **3.** 0   **5.** $-\frac{1}{3}$ **7.** Undefined   **9.** $\frac{5}{4}$

11. (a) L_2 (b) L_3 (c) L_4 (d) L_1

13. $m = \frac{5}{4}$
The line rises.

15. $m = -\frac{1}{2}$
The line falls.

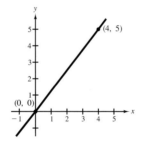

17. $m = -\frac{3}{4}$
The line falls.

19. $m = 2$
The line rises.

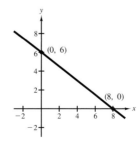

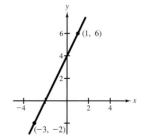

21. m is undefined.
The line is vertical.

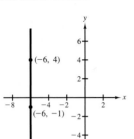

23. $m = 0$
The line is horizontal.

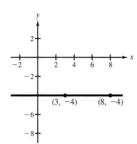

25. $m = -\dfrac{18}{17}$
The line falls.

27. $m = -\dfrac{25}{32}$
The line falls.

29. $m = \dfrac{7}{3}$
The line rises.

31. $m = 0$
The line is horizontal.

33.

x	-2	0	2	4
y	2	-2	-6	-10
Solution points	$(-2, 2)$	$(0, -2)$	$(2, -6)$	$(4, -10)$

$m = -2$

35. $y = 22$ **37.** $y = -\dfrac{43}{2}$

39.

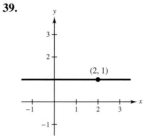

$(0, 1), (1, 1)$

41.

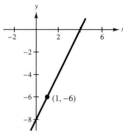

$(2, -4), (3, -2)$

43.

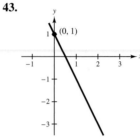

$(1, -1), (2, -3)$

45.

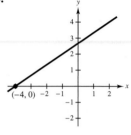

$(-1, 2), (2, 4)$

47.

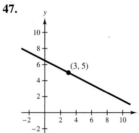

$(5, 4), (7, 3)$

49.

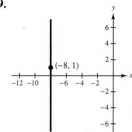

$(-8, 0), (-8, -1)$

51.

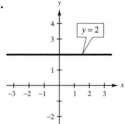

53.

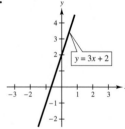

55.

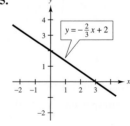

57.

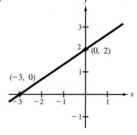

59.

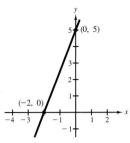

61.

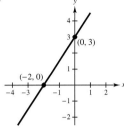

63. $y = -x$

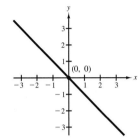

65. $y = -\frac{1}{2}x$

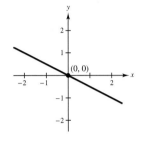

67. $y = 2x - 3$

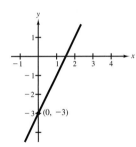

69. $y = \frac{1}{3}x + 2$

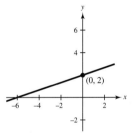

71. $y = -\frac{1}{2}x + 1$

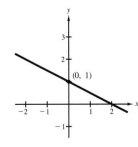

73. $y = \frac{3}{4}x + \frac{1}{2}$

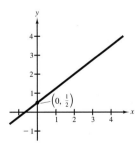

75. $y = -5$

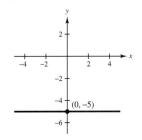

77. Perpendicular   **79.** Parallel

81. Parallel   **83.** Perpendicular

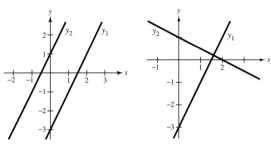

85. $\frac{2}{5}$ **87.** (a)

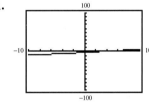

(b) $\frac{3}{200}$

(c) Yes

89. (a) 11.8, 15.2, 11.1, 11.3

(b) 12.35 is the average annual increase in net sales.

91.

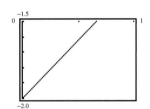

(a) No

(b) No. Use the square feature.

(c) Answers will vary.

93. Yes. The slope is the ratio of the change in y to the change in x.

95. False

97. No. The slopes of nonvertical perpendicular lines have opposite signs. The slopes are the negative reciprocals of each other.

99. The slope

101. If the points lie on the same line, the slopes of the lines between any two pairs of points will be the same.

Section 4.5   *(page 253)*

Integrated Review   *(page 253)*

1. 60. The greatest common factor is the product of the common prime factors.

2. 900. The least common multiple is the product of the highest powers of the prime factors of the numbers.

3. $12 - 8x$ **4.** x^3y^3 **5.** $x + 10$ **6.** 1

7. $y = -3x + 4$ **8.** $y = x + 4$

9. $y = \frac{4}{5}x + \frac{2}{5}$ **10.** $y = -\frac{3}{4}x + \frac{5}{4}$

1. $2x + y = 0$

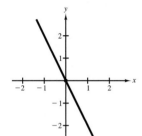

3. $x - 2y = 6$

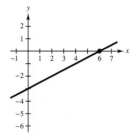

5. $2x - y = -5$

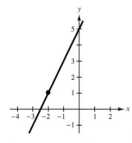

7. $x + 4y = -12$

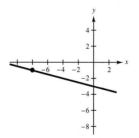

9. $y = -3$

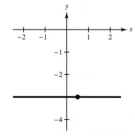

11. $4x - 6y = -9$

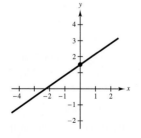

13. $4x + 5y = 28$ **15.** $y = 3x - 4$

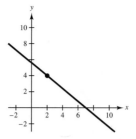

17. $y = -2x$ **19.** $y = -\frac{1}{3}x + 3$ **21.** $y = 4$

23. $y = -\frac{3}{4}x + 7$ **25.** $y = \frac{2}{3}x + \frac{7}{3}$ **27.** $\frac{3}{8}$ **29.** 5

31. $\frac{2}{3}$ **33.** -3 **35.** 2   **37.** $\frac{3}{2}$ **39.** $y = \frac{1}{2}x + 2$

41. $y = -3x - 1$ **43.** $y - 2 = -\frac{1}{2}(x + 1)$

45. $y + 1 = \frac{1}{3}(x + 2)$ or $y - 1 = \frac{1}{3}(x - 4)$

47. $x - y = 0$ **49.** $2x + y = 0$

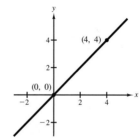

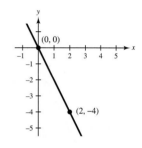

51. $x - 2y + 4 = 0$ **53.** $x - 3y + 12 = 0$

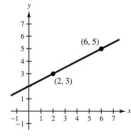

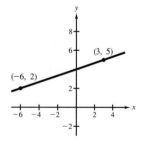

55. $3x + 2y - 13 = 0$ **57.** $4x - y - 11 = 0$

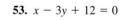

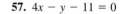

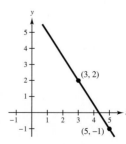

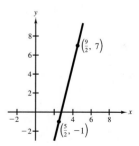

59. $x + y - 3 = 0$ **61.** $3x + 5y - 10 = 0$

63. $2x - y - 6 = 0$ **65.** $3x + 2y - 13 = 0$

67. $3x + 5y - 31 = 0$ **69.** $8x + 6y - 19 = 0$

71. $6x + 5y - 9 = 0$ **73.** (a) $x - y - 1 = 0$

  (b) $x + y - 3 = 0$

75. (a) $3x + 4y + 20 = 0$ **77.** (a) $2x + y - 5 = 0$

  (b) $4x - 3y + 60 = 0$ (b) $x - 2y + 5 = 0$

79. (a) $y = 0$ **81.** (a) $2x - 3y - 11 = 0$

  (b) $x + 1 = 0$ (b) $3x + 2y - 10 = 0$

83. $x = -2$ **85.** $y = \frac{2}{3}$ **87.** $x = 4$

89. $y = -8$

91. **93.**

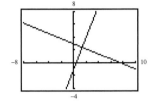 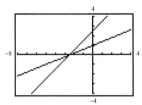

Perpendicular Neither

95.

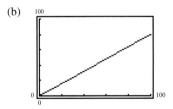

  (a) and (c) are perpendicular.
  (b) and (d) are perpendicular.

97. $C = 225 + 0.28x$ **99.** $W = 2300 + 0.03S$

101. (a) $S = L - 0.2L = 0.8L$

  (b)

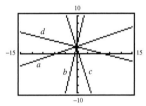

  (c) $39.98

103. (a) $V = 200{,}000 - 30{,}000t$

  (b) $50,000

105. (a) $N = 1200 + 50t$

  (b) 1900

  (c) 1600

107. (a) (f): $m = -10$; Loan decreases by $10 per week.

  (b) (e): $m = 1.50$; Pay increases $1.50 per unit.

  (c) (g): $m = 0.32$; Amount increases $0.32 per mile.

  (d) (h): $m = -100$; Annual depreciation is $100.

109. Yes. When different pairs of points are selected, the change in y and the change in x are the lengths of the sides of similar triangles. Corresponding sides of similar triangles are proportional.

111. m is the slope of the line and b is its y-intercept.

113. Set $y = 0$ and solve the resulting equation.

115. Answers will vary.

Section 4.6 *(page 262)*

Integrated Review *(page 262)*

1. $a + 5 < b + 5$ **2.** $2a < 2b$

3. $-3a > -3b$ **4.** $a < c$

5. $x > -3$ **6.** $x \le 2$

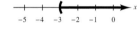

7. $t \le 8$ **8.** $y < 8$

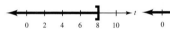

9. $1 < x < 6$ **10.** $-4 < x < 8$

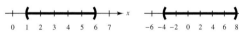

11. $12{,}100.00 **12.** $\frac{12}{7}$ hours

1. (a) Not a solution **3.** (a) Solution

  (b) Solution (b) Solution

  (c) Solution (c) Solution

  (d) Not a solution (d) Not a solution

5. (a) Solution **7.** (a) Solution

  (b) Not a solution (b) Solution

  (c) Solution (c) Solution

  (d) Not a solution (d) Solution

9. Dashed **11.** Solid **13.** b **15.** d

17. c **19.** b

21. $y \geq 3$

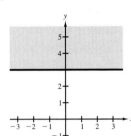

23. $x > \frac{3}{2}$

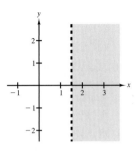

37. $y \geq \frac{2}{3}x + \frac{1}{3}$

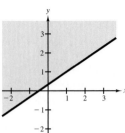

39. $y \geq -2x + 6$

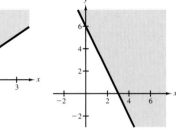

25. $y < \frac{1}{2}x$

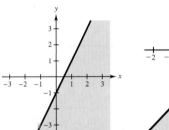

27. $y > x$

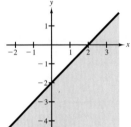

41. $y < \frac{3}{2}x + 3$

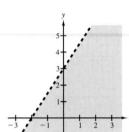

43. $y < -\frac{5}{2}x + \frac{5}{2}$

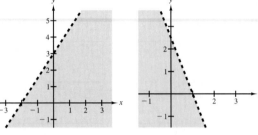

29. $y \leq 2x - 1$

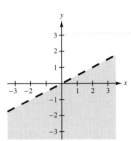

31. $y \leq x - 2$

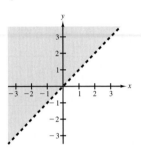

45. $y \leq \frac{1}{3}(x + 5)$

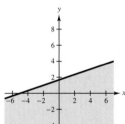

47. $y < \frac{1}{2}x + 1$

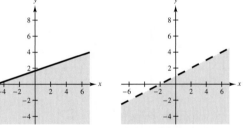

33. $y > x - 2$

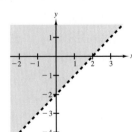

35. $y > -2x + 10$

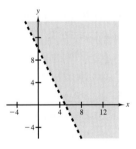

49. $y < -\frac{4}{3}x + 4$

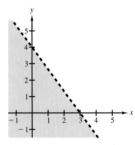

51. $y \geq 2x - 1$

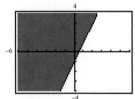

53. $y \leq -2x + 4$

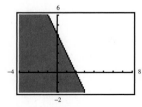

55. $y \geq \frac{1}{2}x + 2$

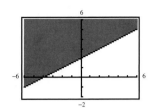

57. $y \leq -\frac{3}{5}x + \frac{3}{2}$

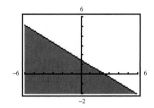

59. $y \geq 2$ **61.** $2x + y \leq 2$ **63.** $2x - y > 0$

65. $7x + 5y \geq 140$
  x: hours at \$7 per hour
  y: hours at \$5 per hour
  (x, y): $(20, 0), (10, 15), (5, 30)$

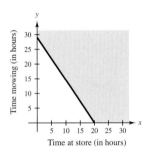

67. $T + \frac{3}{2}C \leq 12$
  T: number of tables
  C: number of chairs
  (T, C): $(5, 4), (2, 6), (0, 8)$

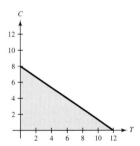

69. $20x + 10y \geq 300$
  x: number of ounces of food X
  y: number of ounces of food Y
  (x, y): $(10, 10), (5, 20), (0, 30)$

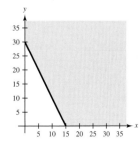

71. $ax + by < c$, $ax + by \leq c$
  $ax + by > c$, $ax + by \geq c$

73. Use dashed lines for the inequalities $<$ and $>$ and solid lines for the inequalities $\leq$ and $\geq$.

75. (a) The solution is an unbounded interval on the x-axis.
  (b) The solution is a half-plane.

77. Yes

Review Exercises *(page 266)*

1.

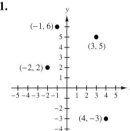

3.

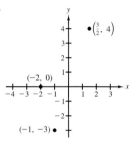

5. Quadrant II **7.** x-axis **9.** Quadrant II

11. Quadrant II or III **13.** $y = -\frac{3}{4}x + 3$

15. $y = \frac{1}{2}x - 4$

17.

x	-1	0	1	2
$y = 2x - 1$	-3	-1	1	3

19. (a) Solution **21.** (a) Solution
  (b) Not a solution   (b) Solution
  (c) Not a solution   (c) Not a solution
  (d) Not a solution   (d) Solution

23.

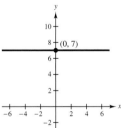

25.

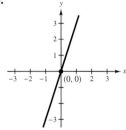

27.

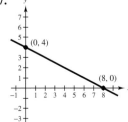

29.

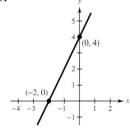

31.

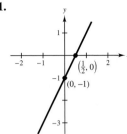

33.

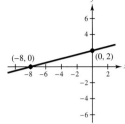

35.

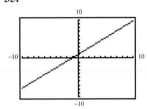

37.

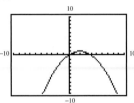

39.

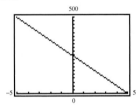

41.

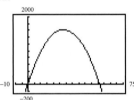

43. Domain: $\{-2, 3, 5, 8\}$

Range: $\{1, 3, 7, 8\}$

45. Domain: $\{-4, -2, 2, 7\}$

Range: $\{-3, -2, 0, 3\}$

47. Not a function   **49.** Function   **51.** Not a function

53. Function   **55.** Function

57. (a) 3   **59.** (a) 0   **61.** (a) -9

(b) 13   (b) 0   (b) -1

(c) 5   (c) -16 (c) -6

(d) 0   (d) $\frac{27}{8}$ (d) -15

63.

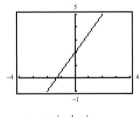

$(0, 2), \left(-\frac{4}{3}, 0\right)$

65.

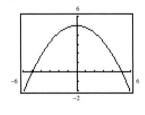

$(5, 0), (-5, 0), (0, 5)$

67.

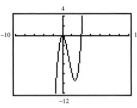

$(0, 0), (4, 0)$

69.

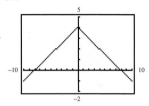

$(-8, 0), (8, 0), (0, 4)$

71. $\frac{1}{2}$ **73.** c   **75.** b   **77.** $\frac{5}{12}$ **79.** $\frac{2}{7}$

81. Undefined   **83.** $-\frac{4}{3}$ **85.** $\frac{7}{2}$ **87.** -3

89. $y = -\frac{1}{2}x + 2$ **91.** $y = \frac{2}{5}x + 1$

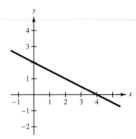

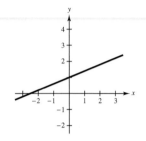

93. Perpendicular   **95.** Parallel   **97.** $(1, 3), (2, 1)$

99. $(6, 6), (10, 9)$ **101.** $(1, 4), (5, 4)$

103. $2x - y - 9 = 0$ **105.** $4x + y - 6 = 0$

107. $4x - 5y + 10 = 0$ **109.** $8x + 3y - 1 = 0$

111. $x - 3 = 0$ **113.** $m = 5$ **115.** $m = \frac{4}{3}$

117. $x + 2y + 4 = 0$ **119.** $y - 8 = 0$

121. $x - y + 3 = 0$ **123.** $25x - 20y + 6 = 0$

125. (a) $2x + 3y + 3 = 0$

(b) $3x - 2y + 24 = 0$

127. (a) $8x + 6y - 27 = 0$

(b) $24x - 32y + 119 = 0$

129.

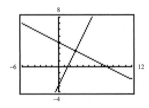

Perpendicular

131.

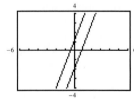

Parallel

133. (a) Not a solution

(b) Not a solution

(c) Solution

(d) Solution

135. $x \geq 2$ **137.** $y < -2x + 1$

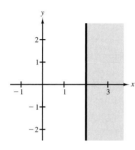 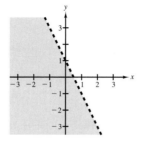

139. $y \geq \frac{1}{4}x + \frac{1}{2}$

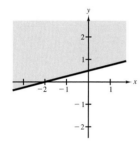

141. $y < 2$ **143.** $y \leq x + 1$

145. (a)

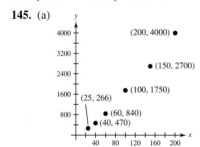

(b) Approximately linear

(c) 2225 lumens, graph

147. $C = 2.25 + 0.75x$

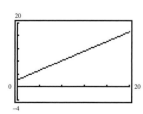

149. $A = x(12 - x), \ 0 < x < 12$

151. (a)

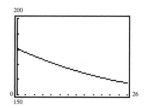

(b) About 157.8 pounds

(c) About 4.3 weeks

155. (a) $C = 5.35x + 16,000$

(b) $P = 2.85x - 16,000$

153. $-\frac{25}{88}$

Chapter Test *(page 271)*

1.

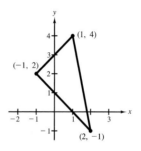

2. (a) Not a solution

(b) Solution

(c) Solution

(d) Not a solution

3. 0   **4.** $(-4, 0), (0, 3)$

5. No. There are two values of y corresponding to $x = 0$.

6. Yes. For each value of x there corresponds one and only one value of y.

7. (a) 0   (b) 0   (c) -16 (d) $-\frac{3}{8}$

8. $\frac{3}{14}$ **9.** $(-2, 2), (-1, 0)$ **10.** $-\frac{5}{3}$

11.

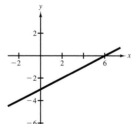

12.

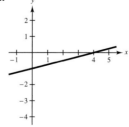

13. 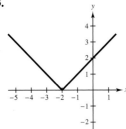   **14.**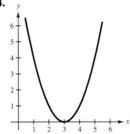

15. $3x + 8y - 48 = 0$ **16.** (a) Solution
                                    (b) Solution
                                    (c) Solution
                                    (d) Solution

17. 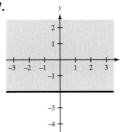   **18.**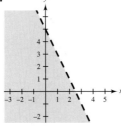

19. 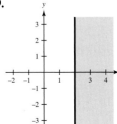   **20.**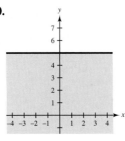

21. Sales are increasing at a rate of 230 units per year.

Chapter 5

Section 5.1   *(page 280)*

Integrated Review   *(page 280)*

1. An algebraic expression is a collection of letters (called variables) and real numbers (called constants) combined by using addition, subtraction, multiplication, or division.

2. The terms of an algebraic expression are those parts separated by addition or subtraction.

3. $10x - 10$ **4.** $12 - 8z$ **5.** $-2 + 3x$

6. $-50x + 75$ **7.** $5x - 2y$ **8.** $\frac{1}{6}x + 8$

9. $7x - 16$ **10.** $-12x - 6$

11. 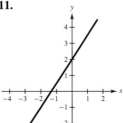   **12.**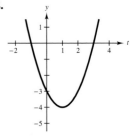

1. Polynomial

3. Not a polynomial because the exponent in the first term is not an integer.

5. Not a polynomial because the exponent is negative.

7. Not a polynomial because the exponent in the first term is negative.

9. Polynomial: $5 - 32x$
Standard form: $-32x + 5$
Degree: 1
Leading coefficient: -32

11. Polynomial: $x^3 - 4x^2 + 9$
Standard form: $x^3 - 4x^2 + 9$
Degree: 3
Leading coefficient: 1

13. Polynomial: $8x + 2x^5 - x^2 - 1$
Standard form: $2x^5 - x^2 + 8x - 1$
Degree: 5
Leading coefficient: 2

15. Polynomial: 10
Standard form: 10
Degree: 0
Leading coefficient: 10

17. Polynomial: $v_0 t - 16t^2$
Standard form: $-16t^2 + v_0 t$
Degree: 2
Leading coefficient: -16

19. Trinomial   **21.** Binomial   **23.** Monomial

25. $5x^3 - 10$ **27.** $3y^2$ **29.** $x^6 - 4x^3 - 2$

31. $14x + 6$ **33.** $4z^2 - z - 2$ **35.** $2b^3 - b^2$

37. $13 - 8t^2$ **39.** $4b^2 - 3$ **41.** $\frac{3}{2}y^2 + \frac{5}{4}$

43. $1.6t^3 - 3.4t^2 - 7.3$ **45.** $5x + 13$ **47.** $-x - 28$

49. $2x^3 + 2x^2 + 8$ **51.** $3x^4 - 2x^3 - 3x^2 - 5x$

53. $3x^2 + 2$ **55.** $y^4 + 4$ **57.** $4x^2 + 2x + 2$

59. $5y^3 + 12$ **61.** $4x^2 + 8$ **63.** $9x - 11$

65. $x^2 - 2x + 2$ **67.** $-3x^3 + 1$ **69.** $-u^2 + 5$

71. $-3x^5 - 3x^4 + 2x^3 - 6x + 6$ **73.** $x - 1$

75. $-x^2 - 2x + 3$ **77.** $-2x^4 - 5x^3 - 4x^2 + 6x - 10$

79. $-2x^3$ **81.** $4t^3 - 3t^2 + 15$ **83.** $5x^3 - 6x^2$

85. $3x^3 + 4x + 10$ **87.** $-2x - 20$

89. $3x^3 - 2x + 2$ **91.** $2x^4 + 9x + 2$

93. $8x^3 + 29x^2 + 11$ **95.** $12z + 8$ **97.** $4t^2 + 20$

99. $6v^2 + 90v + 30$ **101.** $10z + 4$ **103.** $2x^2 - 2x$

105. $21x^2 - 8x$ **107.** $6x$

109. (a) $T = -0.03t^2 + 1.55t + 106.28$

(b)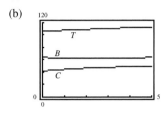

(c) Increasing

111. (a) Length: $2x^2$; Width: $3x + 5$

(b) $4x^2 + 6x + 10$

(c) Girth: $8x + 10$
Length and girth: $2x^2 + 8x + 10$
Yes.

113. (a) Sometimes true. $x^3 - 2x^2 + x + 1$ is a polynomial that is not a trinomial.

(b) True

115. Add (or subtract) their respective coefficients and attach the common variable factor.

117. To subtract one polynomial from another, add the opposite. You can do this by changing the sign of each of the terms of the polynomial that is being subtracted and then adding the resulting like terms.

Section 5.2   *(page 292)*

Integrated Review   *(page 292)*

1. The point represented by $(3, -2)$ is located 3 units to the right of the y-axis and 2 units below the x-axis.

2. $(3, 4), (-3, 4), (-3, -4), (3, -4)$ **3.** $\frac{9}{4}x - \frac{5}{2}$

4. $2x - 2$ **5.** $7x - 8$ **6.** $-2y + 14$

7. $-4z + 12$ **8.** $-5u - 5$ **9.** \$29,090.91

10. 1 hour, 5 miles

11.   **12.**

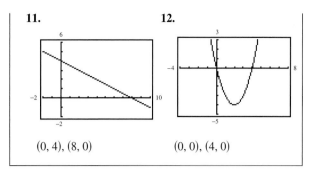

$(0, 4), (8, 0)$ $(0, 0), (4, 0)$

1. $-2x^2$ **3.** $4t^3$ **5.** $\frac{5}{2}x^2$ **7.** $6b^3$ **9.** $3y - y^2$

11. $-x^3 + 4x$ **13.** $6t^2 - 15t$

15. $-12x - 12x^3 + 24x^4$ **17.** $3x^3 - 6x^2 + 3x$

19. $2x^3 - 4x^2 + 16x$ **21.** $4t^4 - 12t^3$

23. $4x^4 - 3x^3 + x^2$ **25.** $-12x^5 + 18x^4 - 6x^3$

27. $30x^3 + 12x^2$ **29.** $12x^5 - 6x^4$ **31.** $x^2 + 7x + 12$

33. $6x^2 - 7x - 5$ **35.** $2x^2 - 5xy + 2y^2$

37. $2x^2 + 6x + 4$ **39.** $-8x^2 + 18x + 18$

41. $3x^2 - 5xy + 2y^2$ **43.** $3x^3 + 6x^2 - 4x - 8$

45. $2x^5 + 12x^3 + 4x^2 + 24$ **47.** $15s + 4$

49. $7x^3 + 32x^2 - 2x - 8$ **51.** $x^2 + 12x + 20$

53. $2x^2 - x - 10$ **55.** $x^3 + 3x^2 + x - 1$

57. $x^4 - 5x^3 - 2x^2 + 11x - 5$ **59.** $x^3 - 8$

61. $x^4 - 6x^3 + 5x^2 - 18x + 6$

63. $3x^4 - 12x^3 - 5x^2 - 4x - 2$ **65.** $x^2 + x - 6$

67. $x^3 + 27$ **69.** $x^4 - x^2 + 4x - 4$

71. $x^5 + 5x^4 - 3x^3 + 8x^2 + 11x - 12$

73. $x^3 - 6x^2 + 12x - 8$ **75.** $x^4 - 4x^3 + 6x^2 - 4x + 1$

77. $x^3 - 12x - 16$ **79.** $4u^3 + 4u^2 - 5u - 3$

81. $x^2 - 9$ **83.** $x^2 - 16$ **85.** $4u^2 - 9$

87. $16t^2 - 36$ **89.** $4x^2 - 9y^2$ **91.** $16u^2 - 9v^2$

93. $4x^4 - 25$ **95.** $x^2 + 12x + 36$ **97.** $t^2 - 6t + 9$

99. $9x^2 + 12x + 4$ **101.** $64 - 48z + 9z^2$

103. $4x^2 - 20xy + 25y^2$ **105.** $36t^2 + 60st + 25s^2$

107. $x^2 + y^2 + 2xy + 2x + 2y + 1$

109. $u^2 + v^2 - 2uv + 6u - 6v + 9$ **111.** $8x$

113. Yes   **115.** $x^3 + 6x^2 + 12x + 8$

117. (a) $x^2 - 1$ **119.** (a) $6w$

(b) $x^3 - 1$ (b) $2w^2$

(c) $x^4 - 1$

(d) $x^5 - 1$

121. $x^2 + 7x + 12 = (x + 4)(x + 3)$

123. $2x^2 + 4x = 2x(x + 2)$ **125.** $x^2 + bx + ax + ab$

127. $2x[2(x + 1)] = 4x^2 + 4x$

129. $z(z + 4) = (z + 5)(z + 4) - 5(z + 4)$

131. (a)
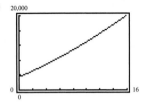

(b) $40.27t^3 + 5674.61t^2 + 182,524.82t + 800,052.01$

(c) $3,233,031 million

133. $500r^2 + 1000r + 500$

135. (d) $16x^3 + 26x^2 + 10x$ square inches

(e) $(3x + 5)^2 = 9x^2 + 30x + 25$ square inches

(f) $9x^3 + 30x^2 + 25x$ cubic inches

137. $a^m \cdot a^n = a^{m+n}$

$(ab)^m = a^m \cdot b^m$

$(a^m)^n = a^{mn}$

139. First, Outer, Inner, Last

141. mn. Each term of the first factor must be multiplied by each term of the second factor.

143. False. $(x + 2)^2 = x^2 + 4x + 4$

Mid-Chapter Quiz   *(page 296)*

1. Because the exponent of the third term is negative.

2. Degree: 4   **3.** $3x^5 - 3x + 1$
Leading coefficient: -3

4. False.
$(x - 1)(x + 5) = x^2 + 4x - 5$

5. $y^2 + 6y + 3$ **6.** $-v^3 + v^2 + 6v - 5$

7. $3s - 11$ **8.** $3x^2 + 5x - 4$ **9.** $10r^3$

10. $-2m^4$ **11.** $2y^2 + 7y - 15$

12. $2x^3 + 5x^2 - 14x - 8$ **13.** $16 - 24x + 9x^2$

14. $4u^2 - 9$ **15.** $5x^4 + 3x^3 - 2x + 2$

16. $2x^3 - 4x^2 + 3x + 1$ **17.** $6x^3 - x^2 - 33x - 5$

18. $5x^5 - 21x^4 + 18x^3 + 3x^2 - 9x$

19. $10x + 36$ **20.** $x^2 + 4x$

Section 5.3   *(page 302)*

Integrated Review   *(page 302)*

1. The graph of a function is the set of all solution points of the function.

2. Construct a table of solution points, plot these solution points on a rectangular coordinate system, and use the pattern to connect the points with a smooth curve or line.

3. $(0, 0)$, $(9, 3)$ (The answer is not unique.)

4. To find the x-intercept(s), solve the equation $f(x) = 0$ for x. To find the y-intercept, find $f(0)$.

5. x^5 **6.** $y^2 z^{11}$ **7.** $\dfrac{x^6}{y^3}$ **8.** $\dfrac{2a^3 b^3}{3c}$

9.
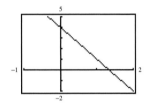

10.
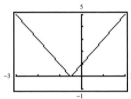

$(0, 4)$, $\left(\frac{4}{3}, 0\right)$ $\left(-\frac{1}{2}, 0\right)$, $(0, 1)$

11.
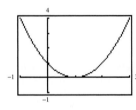

12.
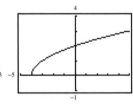

$(1, 0)$, $(0, 1)$ $(-4, 0)$, $(0, 2)$

1. $\dfrac{1}{3^3}$ **3.** $\dfrac{1}{y^5}$ **5.** $\dfrac{8}{x^7}$ **7.** $\dfrac{7}{x^4 y}$ **9.** $\dfrac{z^4}{2}$

11. $\dfrac{2xy^2}{3}$ **13.** 4^{-1} **15.** x^{-2} **17.** $10t^{-5}$

19. $5x^{-n}$ **21.** $2x^2 y^{-4}$ **23.** $\dfrac{1}{3^2} = \dfrac{1}{9}$

25. $\dfrac{1}{(-4)^3} = -\dfrac{1}{64}$ **27.** $4^2 = 16$ **29.** $2(3^4) = 162$

31. $\dfrac{3^2}{2^4} = \dfrac{9}{16}$ **33.** $\dfrac{3^4}{4^2} = \dfrac{81}{16}$ **35.** $\left(\dfrac{3}{2}\right)^2 = \dfrac{9}{4}$

37. 0.0048 **39.** 41.7265 **41.** 4 **43.** x^2

45. $\dfrac{1}{u^3}$ **47.** $\dfrac{x}{y}$ **49.** x^5 **51.** $\dfrac{1}{y^6}$ **53.** $\dfrac{1}{x^2}$

55. $\dfrac{1}{y^6}$ **57.** $\dfrac{1}{s^2}$ **59.** 1 **61.** $\dfrac{1}{b^5}$ **63.** $\dfrac{1}{9x^4y^2}$

65. $\dfrac{a^6}{64b^9}$ **67.** $-\dfrac{8}{x}$ **69.** $\dfrac{10}{x}$ **71.** $\dfrac{x^2}{9z^4}$ **73.** 1

75. $-\dfrac{81}{16}$ **77.** $\dfrac{1}{32x}$ **79.** 1 **81.** 1

83. 9.3×10^7 **85.** 1.637×10^9 **87.** 4.35×10^{-4}

89. 4.392×10^{-3} **91.** 1.6×10^7 **93.** 1,090,000

95. 0.0867 **97.** 0.00852 **99.** 6.21 **101.** 8003.05

103. 4.984×10^{12} **105.** 3.0981×10^6

107. 3.35544×10^{32} **109.** 1.15743×10^{-22}

111. 5.2345679×10^2 **113.** 9.894×10^{13}

115. 8.45 minutes

117.

Planet	Mercury	Saturn	Neptune	Pluto
Kilometers	5.83×10^7	1.43×10^9	4.50×10^9	5.90×10^9

119. (a)

x	-1	-2	-3	-4	-5
2^x	$\frac{1}{2}$	$\frac{1}{4}$	$\frac{1}{8}$	$\frac{1}{16}$	$\frac{1}{32}$

(b)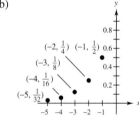

(c) Approaches 0. No.

121. 1.38×10^{-16} **123.** True **125.** False. Let $x = 2$.

127. True **129.** $3.4 \times 10^7 = 34{,}000{,}000$

$$3.4 \times 10^{-6} = 0.0000034$$

131. $(3 \times 10^5)(4 \times 10^6)$

$= (3 \times 10^5)(10^6 \times 4)$ Commutative Property of Multiplication

$= 3(10^5 \times 10^6)(4)$ Associative Property of Multiplication

$= 3(10^{5+6})(4)$ Property of exponents

$= (3 \cdot 4)10^{11}$ Commutative Property of Multiplication

$= 12 \times 10^{11}$ Multiplication

$= 1.2 \times 10^{12}$ Scientific notation

Section 5.4 *(page 312)*

Integrated Review *(page 312)*

1. $\dfrac{24x}{18} = \dfrac{6 \cdot 4x}{6 \cdot 3} = \dfrac{4x}{3}$

2. Quadrant II. Since the x-coordinate is negative, the point lies to the left of the y-axis. Since the y-coordinate is positive, the point lies above the x-axis.

3. $\frac{2}{3}$ **4.** $\frac{1}{8}$ **5.** $\frac{2}{5}$ **6.** $\frac{25}{6}$ **7.** $-10x^5$

8. $4z^2 - 1$ **9.** $x^2 + 14x + 49$

10. $2x^2 + 3x - 20$

11. $(2n + 1)(2n + 3) = 4n^2 + 8n + 3$

12. 51.4 miles per hour

1. x^3 **3.** $\dfrac{1}{x^3}$ **5.** $\dfrac{1}{z^3}$ **7.** $3u$ **9.** $2y^2$ **11.** $\dfrac{4^4}{x^2}$

13. $\dfrac{27}{ab}$ **15.** $-3x$ **17.** $\dfrac{4}{x^3}$ **19.** $4z^2$ **21.** $\dfrac{8b}{3}$

23. $-\dfrac{11y}{2}$ **25.** $\dfrac{3s^3}{2r^2}$ **27.** $\dfrac{1}{2z}$ **29.** $\dfrac{x^2}{2y}$ **31.** $\dfrac{4}{3v^2}$

33. $z + 1$ **35.** $z - 3$ **37.** $3x - \frac{5}{3}$ **39.** $b - 2$

41. $5x - 2$ **43.** $-5z^2 - 2z$ **45.** $4z^2 + \frac{3}{2}z - 1$

47. $m^2 + 3 - \dfrac{4}{m}$ **49.** $1 - \dfrac{3}{x}$

51. $3x - 1 + \dfrac{3}{2x} - \dfrac{1}{2x^2} + \dfrac{2}{x^3}$ **53.** $x - 2$ **55.** $x + 5$

57. $y + 2$ **59.** $6t + 1$ **61.** $x^2 - 2x + 5 + \dfrac{3}{x - 2}$

63. $7 - \dfrac{11}{x + 2}$ **65.** $x^2 + 2x + 4$ **67.** $x - 3 + \dfrac{18}{x + 3}$

69. $3x - 1$ **71.** $x^3 + x^2 + x + 1$

73. $4x - 1 + \dfrac{2}{x + 1}$ **75.** $x^2 + 2x - 3$

77. $3t^2 + t + 1 - \dfrac{4}{t + 2}$ **79.** $2x$ **81.** $5uv$

83. $-2x + 5$

85. Error; You can only cancel common factors of the numerator and denominator.

87. Valid

89. (a) Yes

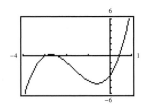

(b) $(x + 3)(x^2 + 2x - 1)$

$\quad = x(x^2) + x(2x) - x(1) + 3(x^2) + 3(2x) - 3(1)$

$\quad = x^3 + 5x^2 + 5x - 3$

(c) $(x^3 + 5x^2 + 5x - 3) \div (x + 3) = x^2 + 2x - 1$

91. (a) $1 + \dfrac{10}{t + 8}$

(b)

t	0	10	20	30	40	50	60
$\dfrac{t + 18}{t + 8}$	2.25	1.56	1.36	1.26	1.21	1.17	1.15

(c) The values approach 1.

93. $x - 3$

95. (a) $x^2 + 2$ **97.** $\dfrac{3x^8}{2x^3} = \left(\dfrac{3}{2}\right)\left(\dfrac{x^8}{x^3}\right) = \dfrac{3}{2}x^{8-3} = \dfrac{3}{2}x^5$

(b) $x - 3$

(c) $x + 3$

(d) 11

99. The remainder is 0 and the divisor is a factor of the dividend.

Review Exercises   *(page 316)*

1. Polynomial: $10x - 4 - 5x^3$
Standard form: $-5x^3 + 10x - 4$
Degree: 3
Leading coefficient: -5

3. Polynomial: $4x^3 - 2x + 5x^4 - 7x^2$
Standard form: $5x^4 + 4x^3 - 7x^2 - 2x$
Degree: 4
Leading coefficient: 5

5. Polynomial: $7x^4 - 1$
Standard form: $7x^4 - 1$
Degree: 4
Leading coefficient: 7

7. Polynomial: -2
Standard form: -2
Degree: 0
Leading coefficient: -2

9. $x^4 + x^2 + 2$ **11.** $3 - 2x$ **13.** $3x - 1$

15. $-2t - 4$ **17.** $3x^3 - 2x + 3$ **19.** $4x^2 - 7$

21. $3x^4 - 3x^3 - 2x^2 + 5x + 4$ **23.** $-x^2 + 2x$

25. $-5x^3 - 5x - 2$ **27.** $7y^2 - y + 6$

29. $2x^4 - 7x^2 + 3$ **31.** $3x^2 + 4x - 14$

33. $2x^2 + 8x$ **35.** $x^2 + 2x - 24$ **37.** $2x^2 + 2x - 12$

39. $12x^2 + 7x - 12$ **41.** $2x^3 + 13x^2 + 19x + 6$

43. $2t^3 - 7t^2 + 9t - 3$ **45.** $u^2 - 6u + 5$

47. $x^2 + 6x + 9$ **49.** $16x^2 - 56x + 49$

51. $\frac{1}{4}x^2 - 4x + 16$ **53.** $u^2 - 36$ **55.** $9t^2 - 1$

57. $4x^2 - 4xy + y^2$ **59.** $4x^2 - 16y^2$ **61.** $\frac{1}{16}$

63. $\frac{1}{36}$ **65.** 9   **67.** 64   **69.** $\frac{125}{27}$ **71.** $-\frac{2}{5}$

73. 9,000,000   **75.** 37,000   **77.** $\dfrac{1}{y^4}$ **79.** $\dfrac{6}{t^2}$

81. $\dfrac{x^6}{7}$ **83.** $\dfrac{2}{xy^3}$ **85.** $\dfrac{1}{t^2}$ **87.** $4y^2$ **89.** $\dfrac{1}{9a^4}$

91. $\dfrac{x^4}{y^6}$ **93.** $\dfrac{1}{t^3}$ **95.** 1   **97.** $\dfrac{25}{y^2}$ **99.** $\dfrac{2}{uv}$

101. $2x - \dfrac{3}{x}$ **103.** $x + 3$ **105.** $x + 2$

107. $8x + 5 + \dfrac{2}{3x - 2}$ **109.** $2x^2 + 4x + 3 + \dfrac{5}{x - 1}$

111. $x^2 - 2$ **113.** $80 - 2x^2$ **115.** $2x^2 + 8x + 8$

117. (a) $4x - 6$ (b) $x^2 - 3x$ **119.** $2x + 3$

121. 0.15 foot   **123.** $x^2 - y^2 = (x + y)(x - y)$

Chapter Test   *(page 319)*

1. Degree: 4   **2.** $z^4 + 2z^2 - 3$
Leading coefficient: -3

3. $2z^2 - 3z + 15$ **4.** $7u^3 - 1$ **5.** $-y^2 + 8y + 3$

6. $-6x^2 + 12x$ **7.** $10b^2 + b - 3$ **8.** $9x^3$

9. $2z^3 + z^2 - z + 10$ **10.** $x^2 - 10x + 25$

11. $4x^2 - 9$ **12.** $3x + 5$ **13.** $x^2 + 2x + 3$

14. $2x^2 + 4x - 3 - \dfrac{2}{2x + 1}$ **15.** $\dfrac{2a}{3}$ **16.** $\dfrac{x^4}{9y^6}$

17. (a) $\frac{1}{64}$ (b) $\frac{3}{8}$ (c) 22,500,000,000

18. $4x^2 - x$ **19.** $2x^2 + 11x - 6$ **20.** 384,000,000

21. 1.013×10^5 **22.** $x - 3$

Chapter 6

Section 6.1 *(page 327)*

Integrated Review *(page 327)*

1. A function is a set of ordered pairs in which no two ordered pairs have the same first component and a different second component.

2. The set of first components is the domain of a function. The set of second components is the range.

3. 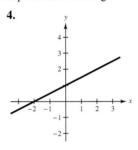   4.

5. (a) 1   6. (a) 0   7. (a) 1   8. (a) 3
   (b) 3   (b) 0   (b) 3   (b) 1
   (c) $-\frac{1}{2}$ (c) 12   (c) 0   (c) 1
   (d) $\frac{1}{4}$ (d) $\frac{65}{4}$ (d) $\sqrt{21}$ (d) 6

9. 3%   10. 3 hours 45 minutes

11. 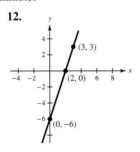   12.

13. 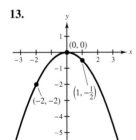   14.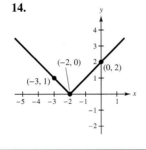

1. 6   3. 2   5. z^2 7. $2x$ 9. u^2v 11. $3yz^2$
13. 1   15. $14a^2b^2$ 17. $3(x + 1)$ 19. $6(z - 1)$

21. $8(t - 2)$ 23. $-5(5x + 2)$ 25. $6(4y^2 - 3)$
27. $x(x + 1)$ 29. $u(25u - 14)$ 31. $2x^3(x + 3)$
33. No common factor   35. $2x(6x - 1)$
37. $-5r(2r^2 + 7)$ 39. $8a^3b^3(2 + 3a)$
41. $10ab(1 + a)$ 43. $4(3x^2 + 4x - 2)$
45. $25(4 + 3z - 2z^2)$ 47. $3x^2(3x^2 + 2x + 6)$
49. $5u(2u + 1)$ 51. $(x - 3)(x + 5)$
53. $(s + 10)(t - 8)$ 55. $(b + 2)(a^2 - b)$
57. $z^2(z + 5)(z + 1)$ 59. $(a + b)(2a - b)$
61. $-5(2x - 1)$ 63. $-3(x - 1000)$
65. $-(x^2 - 2x - 4)$ 67. $-2(x^2 - 6x - 2)$
69. $(x + 10)(x + 1)$ 71. $(a - 4)(a + 1)$
73. $(y - 4)(ky + 2)$ 75. $(t - 3)(t^2 + 2)$
77. $(x + 2)(x^2 + 1)$ 79. $(2z + 1)(3z^2 - 1)$
81. $(x - 1)(x^2 - 3)$ 83. $(4 - x)(x^2 - 2)$
85. $x + 3$ 87. $10y - 1$ 89. $14x + 5y$
91. $y_1 = y_2$ 93. $y_1 = y_2$

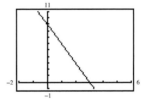   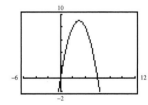

95. $x + 1$ 97. $6x^2$ 99. $9x^2\left(6 - \dfrac{\pi}{2}\right)$

101. $2\pi r(r + h)$ 103. $kx(Q - x)$

105. $x^2 + x - 6 = (x - 2)(x + 3)$

107. Determine the prime factorization of each term. The greatest common factor contains each common prime factor, repeated the minimum number of times it occurs in any one of the factorizations.

109. Noun: Any one of the expressions that, when multiplied together, yield the product

   Verb: To find the expressions that, when multiplied together, yield the given product

111. $x^3 - 3x^2 - 5x + 15 = (x^3 - 3x^2) + (-5x + 15)$
   $$= x^2(x - 3) - 5(x - 3)$$
   $$= (x - 3)(x^2 - 5)$$

Section 6.2   *(page 335)*

> ### Integrated Review   *(page 335)*
>
> **1.** If there are two y-intercepts, then there are two values of y that correspond to $x = 0$.
>
> **2.** 4   **3.** $y^2 + 2y$ **4.** $-a^3 + a^2$
>
> **5.** $x^2 - 7x + 10$ **6.** $v^2 + 3v - 28$
>
> **7.** $4x^2 - 25$ **8.** $x^3 - 4x^2 + 10$ **9.** \$3,975,000
>
> **10.** \$717   **11.** $x \geq 46$ **12.** $140 \leq x \leq 227.5$

1. $x + 1$ **3.** $a - 2$ **5.** $y - 5$ **7.** $z - 2$

9. $(x + 1)(x + 11)$ **11.** $(x + 12)(x + 1)$
  $(x - 1)(x - 11)$ $(x - 12)(x - 1)$
                          $(x + 6)(x + 2)$
                          $(x - 6)(x - 2)$
                          $(x + 4)(x + 3)$
                          $(x - 4)(x - 3)$

13. $(x + 2)(x + 4)$ **15.** $(x - 5)(x - 8)$

17. $(z - 3)(z - 4)$ **19.** Prime   **21.** $(x + 2)(x - 3)$

23. $(x - 3)(x + 5)$ **25.** Prime   **27.** $(u + 2)(u - 24)$

29. $(x + 15)(x + 4)$ **31.** $(x - 8)(x - 9)$

33. $(x + 12)(x - 20)$ **35.** $(x + 2y)(x - y)$

37. $(x + 5y)(x + 3y)$ **39.** $(x - 9z)(x + 2z)$

41. $(a + 5b)(a - 3b)$ **43.** $3(x + 5)(x + 2)$

45. $4(y - 3)(y + 1)$ **47.** Prime   **49.** $9(x^2 + 2x - 2)$

51. $x(x - 10)(x - 3)$ **53.** $x^2(x - 2)(x - 3)$

55. $-3x(y - 3)(y + 6)$ **57.** $x(x + 2y)(x + 3y)$

59. $2xy(x + 3y)(x - y)$ **61.** $\pm 8, \pm 16$ **63.** $\pm 4, \pm 20$

65. $\pm 12, \pm 13, \pm 15, \pm 20, \pm 37$ **67.** $2, -10$ **69.** $5, -7$

71. $8, -10$

73. $y_1 = y_2$

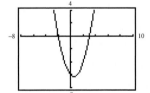

75. $y_1 = y_2$

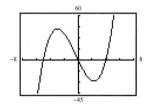

77. $(x + 3)(x + 1)$

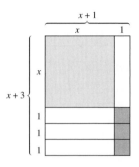

79. $(x + 3)(x + 2)$

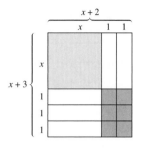

81. (a) $4x(x - 2)(x - 3)$

(b)

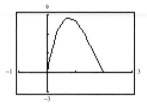

0.785 foot

83. 70 square units

85. Because the constant term is positive in the polynomial, the signs in the binomial factors must be the same.

87. The polynomial is not factorable using factors with integer coefficients.

89. The prime number, because there are not as many possible factorizations to examine.

Section 6.3   *(page 343)*

> ### Integrated Review   *(page 343)*
>
> **1.** Prime   **2.** The sum of the digits is divisible by 3.
>
> **3.** $2^2 \cdot 5^3$ **4.** $3^2 \cdot 5 \cdot 7$ **5.** $2^3 \cdot 3^2 \cdot 11$
>
> **6.** $5^2 \cdot 7 \cdot 13$ **7.** $2x^2 + 9x - 35$
>
> **8.** $9x^2 - 12x + 4$
>
> **9.**
>
>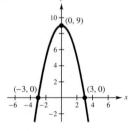
>
> **10.**
>
>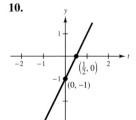

11. (a)

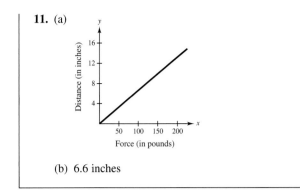

(b) 6.6 inches

1. $5x + 3$ **3.** $5a - 3$ **5.** $2y - 9$ **7.** $4z - 1$

9. $(5x + 3)(x + 1)$ $(5x - 3)(x - 1)$
$(5x + 1)(x + 3)$ $(5x - 1)(x - 3)$

11. $(5x + 12)(x + 1)$ $(5x - 12)(x - 1)$
$(5x + 6)(x + 2)$ $(5x - 6)(x - 2)$
$(5x + 4)(x + 3)$ $(5x - 4)(x - 3)$
$(5x + 1)(x + 12)$ $(5x - 1)(x - 12)$
$(5x + 2)(x + 6)$ $(5x - 2)(x - 6)$
$(5x + 3)(x + 4)$ $(5x - 3)(x - 4)$

13. $(2x + 3)(x + 1)$ **15.** $(4y + 1)(y + 1)$

17. $(2y - 1)(y - 1)$ **19.** $(2x - 3)(x + 1)$ **21.** Prime

23. Prime **25.** Prime **27.** $(x + 4)(4x - 3)$

29. $(3x - 2)(3x - 4)$ **31.** $(3u - 2)(6u + 1)$

33. $(5a - 2)(3a + 4)$ **35.** $(5t + 6)(2t - 3)$

37. $(5m - 3)(3m + 5)$ **39.** $(8z - 5)(2z - 3)$

41. $-(2x - 3)(x + 1)$ **43.** $-(3x - 2)(x + 2)$

45. $-(6x + 5)(x - 2)$ **47.** $-(10x - 1)(6x + 1)$

49. $-(5x - 4)(3x + 4)$ **51.** $3x(2x - 1)$

53. $3y(5y + 6)$ **55.** $(u - 3)(u + 9)$

57. $2(v + 7)(v - 3)$ **59.** $-3(x^2 + x + 20)$

61. $3(z - 1)(3z - 5)$ **63.** $2(2x^2 + 2x + 1)$

65. $-x^2(5x + 4)(3x - 2)$ **67.** $x(3x^2 + 4x + 2)$

69. $6x(x - 4)(x + 8)$ **71.** $9u^2(2u^2 + 2u - 3)$

73. $\pm 11, \pm 13, \pm 17, \pm 31$ **75.** $\pm 1, \pm 4, \pm 11$

77. $\pm 22, \pm 23, \pm 26, \pm 29, \pm 34, \pm 43, \pm 62, \pm 121$

79. $-1, -7$ **81.** $-8, 3$ **83.** $-6, -1$

85. $(3x + 1)(x + 2)$ **87.** $(2x + 3)(x - 1)$

89. $(3x + 4)(2x - 1)$ **91.** $(5x - 2)(3x - 1)$

93. $(3a + 5)(a + 2)$ **95.** $(8x - 3)(2x + 1)$

97. $(3x - 2)(4x - 3)$ **99.** $(u - 2)(6u + 7)$

101. $(2x + 1)(x + 2)$ **103.** $l = 2x + 3$

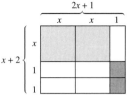

105. $2x + 10$

107. (a) $y_1 = y_2$

(b)

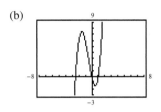

(c) $\left(-\frac{5}{2}, 0\right), (0, 0), (1, 0)$

109. (a) $3x^2 + 16x - 12$

(b) $3x - 2$ and $x + 6$

111. The product of the last terms of the binomials is 15, not -15.

113. Four. $(ax + 1)(x + c), (ax + c)(x + 1),$
$(ax - 1)(x - c), (ax - c)(x - 1)$

115. $2x^3 + 2x^2 + 2x$

Mid-Chapter Quiz *(page 346)*

1. $2x - 3$ **2.** $x - y$ **3.** $y - 6$ **4.** $2x + 1$

5. $10(x^2 + 7)$ **6.** $2a^2b(a - 2b)$ **7.** $(x + 2)(x - 3)$

8. $(t - 3)(t^2 + 1)$ **9.** $(y + 6)(y + 5)$

10. $(u + 6)(u - 5)$ **11.** $x(x - 6)(x + 5)$

12. $2y(x + 8)(x - 4)$ **13.** Prime

14. $(3 + z)(2 - 5z)$ **15.** $(3x - 2)(2x + 1)$

16. $2s^2(5s^2 - 7s + 1)$ **17.** $\pm 7, \pm 8, \pm 13$ **18.** 16, 21

19. $(3x + 1)(x + 6)$ $(3x - 1)(x - 6)$
$(3x + 6)(x + 1)$ $(3x - 6)(x - 1)$
$(3x + 2)(x + 3)$ $(3x - 2)(x - 3)$
$(3x + 3)(x + 2)$ $(3x - 3)(x - 2)$

20. $10(2x + 8)$ **21.** $y_1 = y_2$

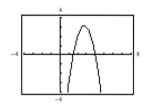

Section 6.4   *(page 353)*

Integrated Review   *(page 353)*

1. Quadrant II   **2.** Quadrant I or II   **3.** $(-4, 0)$
4. $(9, -6)$ **5.** 4   **6.** 1   **7.** -1 **8.** $\frac{16}{9}$
9. $\frac{5}{2}$ **10.** 10   **11.** 6954   **12.** \$12,155

1. $(x + 6)(x - 6)$ **3.** $(u + 8)(u - 8)$
5. $(7 + x)(7 - x)$ **7.** $\left(u + \frac{1}{2}\right)\left(u - \frac{1}{2}\right)$
9. $\left(t + \frac{1}{4}\right)\left(t - \frac{1}{4}\right)$ **11.** $(4y + 3)(4y - 3)$
13. $(10 + 7x)(10 - 7x)$ **15.** $(x + 1)(x - 3)$
17. $-z(10 + z)$ **19.** $2(x + 6)(x - 6)$
21. $2(2 + 5x)(2 - 5x)$ **23.** $(y^2 + 9)(y + 3)(y - 3)$
25. $(1 + x^2)(1 + x)(1 - x)$ **27.** $3(x + 2)(x - 2)(x^2 + 4)$
29. $(3x + 2)(3x - 2)(9x^2 + 4)$ **31.** $(x - 2)^2$
33. $(z + 3)^2$ **35.** $(2t + 1)^2$ **37.** $(5y - 1)^2$
39. $\left(b + \frac{1}{2}\right)^2$ **41.** $\left(2x - \frac{1}{4}\right)^2$ **43.** $(x - 3y)^2$
45. $(2y + 5z)^2$ **47.** $(3a - 2b)^2$ **49.** ± 2 **51.** $\pm\frac{8}{5}$
53. ± 36 **55.** 9   **57.** 4   **59.** $(x - 2)(x^2 + 2x + 4)$
61. $(y + 4)(y^2 - 4y + 16)$ **63.** $(1 + 2t)(1 - 2t + 4t^2)$
65. $(3u + 2)(9u^2 - 6u + 4)$ **67.** $6(x - 6)$
69. $u(u + 3)$ **71.** $5y(y - 5)$ **73.** $5(y + 5)(y - 5)$
75. $y^2(y + 5)(y - 5)$ **77.** $(1 - 2x)^2$ **79.** $(x - 1)^2$
81. $(9x + 1)(x + 1)$ **83.** $2x(2 - x)(1 + x)$
85. $(3t + 4)(3t - 4)$ **87.** $-z(z + 12)$
89. $(t + 10)(t - 12)$ **91.** $u(u^2 + 2u + 3)$ **93.** Prime
95. $2(t - 2)(t^2 + 2t + 4)$ **97.** $2(1 - 2x)(1 + 2x + 4x^2)$
99. $(x^2 + 9)(x + 3)(x - 3)$
101. $(1 + x^2)(1 + x)(1 - x)$ **103.** $(x + 1)(x - 1)(x - 4)$
105. $x(x + 3)(x + 4)(x - 4)$
107. $(2 + y)(2 - y)(y^2 + 2y + 4)(y^2 - 2y + 4)$

109. $y_1 = y_2$

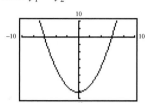

111. $y_1 = y_2$

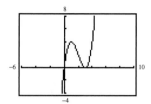

113. 441   **115.** 3599   **117.** $\pi(R - r)(R + r)$
119. $(x + 4)^2 - 2^2 = (x + 6)(x + 2)$
121. $2x^2 + 4x + 2 = (2x + 2)(x + 1)$ **123.** 15×15 feet
125. $a^2 - b^2 = (a + b)(a - b)$ **127.** No. $(x + 2)(x - 2)$
129. False. $a^3 + b^3 = (a + b)(a^2 - ab + b^2)$

Section 6.5   *(page 363)*

Integrated Review   *(page 363)*

1. Additive Inverse Property
2. Multiplicative Identity Property
3. Distributive Property
4. Associative Property of Addition
5. (a) 3   (b) 28   **6.** (a) $\frac{3}{2}$ (b) $\frac{7}{6}$ **7.** $-\frac{1}{16}$
8. $\frac{8}{5}$ **9.** $2t^2 - 2t + 1$ **10.** $-8u + 15$
11. \$750   **12.** 70 miles per hour

1. $0, 5$ **3.** $2, 3$ **5.** $-1, 2$ **7.** $-\frac{1}{3}, \frac{5}{2}$ **9.** $-2, 6$
11. $\frac{100}{7}, 60$ **13.** $-8, 0, \frac{5}{4}$ **15.** $-12, -\frac{3}{2}, 1$
17. $-4, 4$ **19.** $-10, 10$ **21.** $-3, 3$ **23.** $-2, 8$
25. $-13, 5$ **27.** $-2, 0$ **29.** $0, \frac{1}{4}$ **31.** $-3, 4$
33. $-2, 8$ **35.** 1   **37.** -7 **39.** $\frac{3}{2}$ **41.** $-2, 4$
43. $-\frac{1}{2}, 3$ **45.** $-\frac{5}{3}, 1$ **47.** $-5, 3$ **49.** $-2, 7$
51. $-\frac{3}{2}, 1$ **53.** $2, 7$ **55.** $-5, 0$ **57.** $-3, -2, 0$
59. $-4, 0, \frac{3}{2}$ **61.** $-3, 2, 3$ **63.** $-4, 1, 4$
65. $-2, -1, 0, 1$
67. $(-3, 0), (1, 0)$; The number of solutions equals the number of x-intercepts.
69. $(-3, 0), (4, 0)$; The number of solutions equals the number of x-intercepts.
71. $(0, 0), (3, 0)$; The number of solutions equals the number of x-intercepts.
73. $\left(-\frac{5}{2}, 0\right), (0, 0), (1, 0)$; The number of solutions equals the number of x-intercepts.

75.

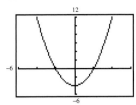

$(-2, 0), (2, 0)$

77.

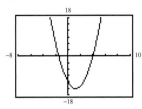

$\left(-\frac{3}{2}, 0\right), (4, 0)$

79.

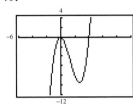

$(0, 0), (4, 0)$

81.

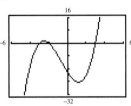

$(-3, 0), (-2, 0), (3, 0)$

83. 8, 9   **85.** 20, 22   **87.** 9 inches $\times$ 12 inches

89. 15 inches $\times$ 30 inches

91. (a) $V = lwh$

$V = (x)(x)(2)$

$V = 2x^2$

(b)

x	2	4	6	8
V	8	32	72	128

(c) 14 inches $\times$ 14 inches

93. $t = 10$ seconds

95. (a)

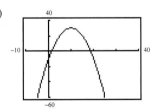

(b) 5, 15   (c) 5, 15

97. 2 seconds

99. (a)

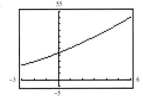

(b) $t = 13$. The model predicts that 100 million passengers will fly Southwest Airline in 2003.

101. 0, 1   **103.** If $ab = 0$, then $a = 0$ or $b = 0$.

105. A linear equation has degree 1 and a quadratic equation has degree 2.

107. n

109. False. This is not an application of the Zero-Factor Property because the number of factors whose product is 21 is unlimited.

Review Exercises   *(page 368)*

1. 10   **3.** $9ab$ **5.** $3(x - 2)$ **7.** $t(3 - t)$

9. $5x^2(1 + 2x)$ **11.** $4a(2 - 3a^2)$

13. $(x + 1)(x - 3)$ **15.** $(y + 3)(y^2 + 2)$

17. $(x^2 + 1)(x + 2)$ **19.** $(x + 3)(x - 4)$

21. $(x - 7)(x + 4)$ **23.** $(u - 4)(u + 9)$

25. $(x - y)(x + 10y)$ **27.** $(y + 3x)(y - 9x)$

29. $4(x - 2)(x - 4)$ **31.** $\pm 6, \pm 10$ **33.** ± 12

35. $(1 - x)(5 + 3x)$ **37.** $(10 + x)(5 - x)$

39. $(3x + 2)(2x + 1)$ **41.** $3u(2u + 5)(u - 2)$

43. $(2x - 1)(x - 1)$ **45.** $\pm 2, \pm 5, \pm 10, \pm 23$

47. $\pm 4, \pm 7, \pm 11, \pm 17, \pm 28, \pm 59$ **49.** $2, -6$

51. $(x + 1)(x - 1)$ **53.** $(a + 10)(a - 10)$

55. $(5 + 2y)(5 - 2y)$ **57.** $(u + 3)(u - 1)$

59. $(x - 4)^2$ **61.** $(x + 3)^2$ **63.** $(3s + 2)^2$

65. $st(s + t)(s - t)$ **67.** $(a + 1)(a^2 - a + 1)$

69. $(3 - 2t)(9 + 6t + 4t^2)$ **71.** $-4a(2a + 1)^2$

73. $-9, 9$ **75.** 6   **77.** $-1, \frac{3}{4}$ **79.** $0, \frac{3}{2}$ **81.** $0, 4$

83. 3, 4   **85.** $-5, -1, 1$ **87.** $3x + 1$

89. $2x^2(10 - \pi)$

91. (a)

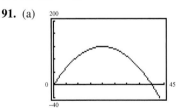

(b) 20   (c) 20

93. 40 inches $\times$ 60 inches   **95.** 12, 14

Chapter Test   *(page 370)*

1. $7x^2(1 - 2x)$ **2.** $(z + 7)(z - 3)$

3. $(t - 5)(t + 1)$ **4.** $(3x - 4)(2x - 1)$

5. $3y(2y + 5)(y + 5)$ **6.** $(2 + 5v)(2 - 5v)$

7. $(2x - 5)^2$ **8.** $(-z - 5)(z + 13)$

9. $(x + 2)(x + 3)(x - 3)$ **10.** $(4 + z^2)(2 + z)(2 - z)$

11. $\frac{1}{5}(2x - 3)$ **12.** ± 6 **13.** 36

14. $3x^2 - 3x - 6 = 3(x + 1)(x - 2)$ **15.** $-4, \frac{3}{2}$

16. $0, 2$ **17.** $-3, \frac{2}{3}$ **18.** $-\frac{3}{2}, 2$

19. 7 inches × 12 inches   **20.** 2 seconds; $\frac{3}{2}$ seconds

21. 24, 26

Cumulative Test: Chapters 4–6   (page 371)

1. Because $x = -2$, the point must lie in Quadrant II or Quadrant III.

2. (a) Not a solution   (b) Solution   (c) Solution   (d) Not a solution

3. 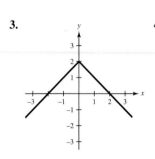   **4.**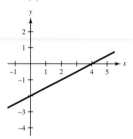

$(-2, 0), (2, 0), (0, 2)$ $(4, 0), (0, -2)$

5. $(-2, 2)$ **6.** $y = \frac{5}{6}x - \frac{3}{2}$ **7.** Perpendicular

8. Parallel   **9.** $-5x^2 + 5$ **10.** $-42z^4$

11. $3x^2 - 7x - 20$ **12.** $25x^2 - 9$

13. $25x^2 + 60x + 36$ **14.** $x + 12$

15. $x + 1 + \dfrac{2}{x - 4}$ **16.** $\dfrac{81}{16}$ **17.** $2u(u - 3)$

18. $(x + 2)(x - 6)$ **19.** $x(x + 4)^2$

20. $(x + 2)^2(x - 2)$ **21.** $0, 12$ **22.** $-\frac{3}{5}, 3$

23. $\dfrac{4}{x^2}$ **24.** (a) 6   (b) 6   (c) 0   (d) 0

25. $C = 125 + 0.35x$

$149.50

Chapter 7

Section 7.1   (page 380)

Integrated Review   (page 380)

1. $mn = c$ **2.** Like signs   **3.** Unlike signs

4. $m + n = b$ **5.** $-\frac{3}{2}$ **6.** -3 **7.** $\frac{5}{11}$

8. $\dfrac{14}{11}$ **9.** 50   **10.** 64   **11.** $\dfrac{250}{r}$ **12.** $3L$

---

1. (a) Solution   (b) Not a solution

3. (a) Not a solution   (b) Solution

5. (a) Solution   (b) Not a solution

7. $(2, 0)$ **9.** $(-1, -1)$ **11.** Infinitely many solutions

13. $(3, 0)$ **15.** $(1, 2)$ **17.** $(2, 0)$ **19.** $(2, 0)$

21. $(3, 1)$ **23.** $\left(\frac{1}{2}, 3\right)$ **25.** No solution   **27.** $(5, 4)$

29. No solution   **31.** $(8, 6)$ **33.** $(7, -2)$

35. $(2, -1)$ **37.** No solution

39. Infinitely many solutions   **41.** No solution

43. $(8, 7)$ **45.** $(2, 3)$ **47.** $(3, 2)$

49. $y = \frac{2}{3}x + 4, \ y = \frac{2}{3}x - 1$ **51.** $y = \frac{1}{4}x + \frac{7}{4}, \ y = \frac{1}{4}x + \frac{7}{4}$
No solution   Infinitely many solutions

53. $y = \frac{2}{3}x + \frac{4}{3}, \ y = -\frac{2}{3}x + \frac{8}{3}$ **55.** $y = \frac{3}{4}x + \frac{9}{8}, \ y = \frac{3}{4}x + \frac{3}{2}$
One solution   No solution

57. 10 feet × 15 feet   **59.** $x + y = 20$
$$x - y = 2$$
$$(11, 9)$$

61. (a) $\text{Cost} = \boxed{\begin{array}{c}\text{Cost per}\\\text{unit}\end{array}} \cdot \boxed{\begin{array}{c}\text{Number}\\\text{of units}\end{array}} + \boxed{\begin{array}{c}\text{Fixed}\\\text{costs}\end{array}}$

$\text{Revenue} = \boxed{\begin{array}{c}\text{Price per}\\\text{unit}\end{array}} \cdot \boxed{\begin{array}{c}\text{Number}\\\text{of units}\end{array}}$

(b)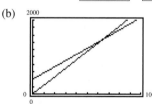

$x = 64$ units
$C = R = 1472$

63. Because the slopes of the two lines are not equal, the lines intersect and the system has one solution: $(79,400, 398)$.

65. (a) $W = 600 + 0.04s$
$$W = 400 + 0.05s$$

(b)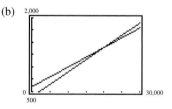

$(20,000, 1400)$

Point where the two job offers yield the same weekly salary

67. A system that has an infinite number of solutions

69. False   **71.** $x + y = 0$
$$x + y = 1$$

Section 7.2   *(page 388)*

Integrated Review   *(page 388)*

1. One

2. Multiply both sides of the equation by the lowest common denominator.

3. $(3 - x)(x - 2)$ **4.** $(2t + 3)(2t - 3)$

5. $(2y - 5)^2$ **6.** $(3u - 7)(2u + 3)$ **7.** 4

8. 36   **9.** $-2, 6$ **10.** $-2, -1, 2$

11. $A = 6x^2$ **12.** $d = 475t$

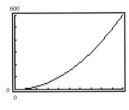

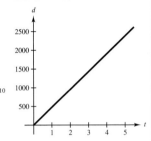

1. $(1, 1)$ **3.** $(1, 2)$ **5.** No solution   **7.** $\left(\frac{3}{2}, 1\right)$

9. $(2, 3)$ **11.** $(15, 5)$ **13.** $(4, -3)$

15. No solution   **17.** $(0, 0)$ **19.** $(2, 6)$ **21.** $\left(\frac{1}{2}, 3\right)$

23. $(-3, 2)$ **25.** $\left(\frac{5}{2}, -\frac{1}{2}\right)$ **27.** Infinitely many solutions

29. $\left(\frac{5}{2}, 15\right)$ **31.** No solution   **33.** No solution

35. Infinitely many solutions   **37.** $(6, 0)$ **39.** $\left(\frac{5}{2}, \frac{3}{4}\right)$

41. $(8, 4)$

43. $(2, 6)$ **45.** $\left(\frac{18}{5}, \frac{3}{5}\right)$

47. $(3, 0)$

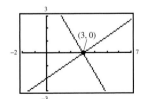

49. $x - 2y = 0$
    $x + y = 3$

51. $2x - y = 10$ **53.** $15, 25$ **55.** $50, 55$
    $4x + 3y = 5$

57. 7%: \$7500; 10%: \$2500

59. Student tickets: 836; General admission: 1121

61. (a)

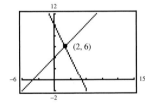

(b) $y_E = 47.3x + 338.0$

(c) Average annual increase in exports

63. $2x - y - 9 = 0$

65. (c) $W - 0.04s = 600$
    $W - 0.05s = 400$

Solve for W because the coefficient is 1.

(d) \$20,000

67. Solve one of the equations for one variable in terms of the other variable. Substitute that expression into the other equation. If a false statement results, the system has no solution.

69. Algebraic methods yield exact solutions.

71. Algebraically: Substitute the solution into each equation of the original system.

Graphically: Graph the two lines and verify that the solution is the point of intersection of the lines.

73. $a = -3$ **75.** $a = 2$

Mid-Chapter Quiz   *(page 391)*

1. Not a solution   **2.** $(3, 2)$ **3.** $(4, 1)$ **4.** $\left(3, \frac{3}{2}\right)$

5. $(6, 2)$ **6.** $(2, 2)$ **7.** $(-1, 4)$ **8.** $(1, -3)$

9. $(6, 2)$ **10.** $(3, 3)$ **11.** $\left(-\frac{1}{2}, 6\right)$ **12.** $\left(\frac{55}{23}, \frac{95}{23}\right)$

13. $x + y = 0$ **14.** $4x + 3y = 0$
    $3x - y = 0$ $x + y = -2$

15. $x + 2y = 7$ **16.** $2x + y = 5$
    $5x - 4y = 0$ $5x + y = 7.4$

17. $k = -2$ **18.** $k = 0.8$

19. $x + y = 50$ **20.** $b + c = 32$
    $x - y = 22$ $b = 4c + 2$
    $(36, 14)$ $(26, 6)$

Section 7.3   *(page 398)*

Integrated Review   *(page 398)*

1. Multiplicative Inverse Property
2. Additive Identity Property
3. Commutative Property of Multiplication
4. Associative Property of Multiplication
5. $-\frac{8}{3}$ 6. -2

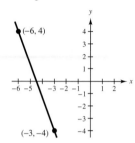 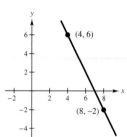

7. $\frac{45}{13}$ 8. -17

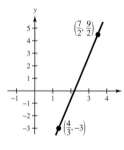 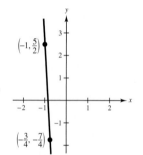

9. Undefined   10. 0

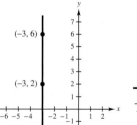 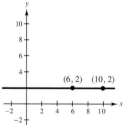

11. 150 units   12. $0 < t \le 17.4$

1. $(2, 0)$ 3. $(-1, -1)$ 5. $(8, 4)$ 7. $(-4, 4)$
9. $(2, 1)$ 11. $\left(\frac{13}{3}, -2\right)$ 13. No solution
15. $(3, -4)$ 17. $(40, 40)$ 19. Infinitely many solutions
21. $(4, -1)$ 23. $(4, -1)$ 25. $\left(\frac{1}{2}, 0\right)$ 27. $\left(6, \frac{3}{2}\right)$
29. $(-17, 14)$ 31. $(8, 7)$

33. $(-1, 2)$

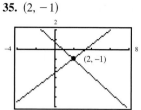

35. $(2, -1)$

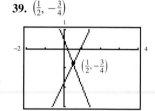

37. $(1, 1)$

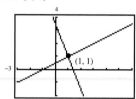

39. $\left(\frac{1}{2}, -\frac{3}{4}\right)$

41. $(5, 3)$ 43. $(8, 4)$ 45. $(2, 3)$ 47. $(-5, -3)$
49. $(3, -3)$ 51. $\left(\frac{4}{3}, \frac{4}{3}\right)$ 53. $\left(1, -\frac{5}{4}\right)$
55. $2x + 3y = 8$ 57. $x + 3y = 10$
$\ -x +\ y = 6$ $\ x - 3y =\ 2$
59. Student ticket: \$3   61. \$4000   63. 34, 48
General admission: \$5
65. Yes   67. $3x - y - 2 = 0$
69. (e) When adding the equations, the addition is easier if the coefficients are integers.

(f) Sales greater than \$20,000

71. When you add the equations to eliminate one variable, both are eliminated, yielding a contradiction. For example, adding the equations in the system $x - y = 3$ and $-x + y = 8$ yields $0 = 11$.

73. $3x - 2y =\ 9$
$\ 7x + 2y = 11$

75. $0.3x - 0.2y = 0.9$

$0.7x + 0.2y = 1.1$

Multiply both sides of each equation by 10 to clear the decimals.

$3x - 2y =\ 9$
$7x + 2y = 11$

77. (a) $k = 16$

(b) $k = 1$

(c) No. Both variables vanish when the second equation is subtracted from 2 times the first equation.

Section 7.4   *(page 408)*

Integrated Review   *(page 408)*

1. To find the x-intercepts, let $f(x) = 0$ and solve the equation for x. To find the y-intercept, let $x = 0$ and solve the equation for y.

2. The radicand $x - 2$ must be nonnegative.

3. $2x^2 - 2x - 10$ **4.** $-4x - 2$

5. $2t^3 - 4t^2 + 6t$ **6.** $u^3 + 3u^2 - 5u - 14$

7. $25z^2 - 9$ **8.** $4y^2 - 44y + 121$ **9.** $5x - 6$

10. $x + 2 + \dfrac{4}{x + 1}$

11. (a) $y = -6000t + 32{,}000$

(b) 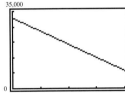   (c) $14{,}000

12. $C = 130 + 0.32x$

1. (a) $15(\text{price of regular}) + 10(\text{price of premium})$
$= \text{total cost}$

$(\text{Price of premium}) = (\text{price of regular}) + 0.20$

(b) $x = $ price per gallon of regular;
$y = $ price per gallon of premium

(c) $15x + 10y = 35.50$

$y = x + 0.20$

(d) Regular: $1.34 per gallon; Premium: $1.54 per gallon

3. $42, 25$ **5.** $90, 42$ **7.** $40, 30$

9. 8 dimes, 13 quarters   **11.** 15 nickels, 20 quarters

13. 28 nickels, 16 dimes   **15.** 8 feet $\times$ 12 feet

17. 2 yards $\times$ 6 yards   **19.** 8 meters $\times$ 9.6 meters

21. $75   **23.** $276.15   **25.** $51.40

27. 375 adults, 125 children

29. Large truck: $32{,}000; Small truck: $21{,}500

31. Regular: $1.29 per gallon; Premium: $1.46 per gallon

33. Taco: $0.90; Enchilada: $2.00

35. 5 miles per hour

37. Plane in still air: 650 miles per hour
Speed of the wind: 50 miles per hour

39. 1 hour   **41.** 10 minutes

43. 35% solution: 4 liters; 60% solution: 6 liters

45. $4.25 nuts: 3 pounds; $6.55 nuts: 7 pounds

47. $110 hay: 30 tons; $60 hay: 70 tons   **49.** $16{,}000

51.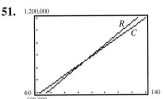

96 units
$R(96) = $859{,}200$

53. $m = \frac{1}{2}, b = -2$ **55.** $m = -\frac{1}{2}, b = \frac{9}{2}$

57. (a) $y = x + \frac{1}{3}$

(b)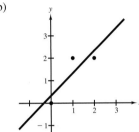

59. (a)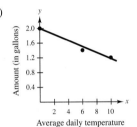

Average daily temperature

(b) $y = -0.08x + 1.97$

(c) The average change in fuel consumption per degree of temperature change

61. (a) Does the problem involve more than one unknown quantity?

(b) Are there two or more equations or conditions to be satisfied?

63. The one-variable method for modeling real-life problems involves the use of one unknown quantity and the writing of one equation.

The two-variable method involves the use of two unknowns and the writing of two equations.

Review Exercises   *(page 413)*

1. (a) Solution   (b) Not a solution

3. (a) Not a solution   (b) Solution

5. d   **7.** a   **9.** $(5, 1)$ **11.** $(1, 1)$

13. No solution   **15.** $(4, 8)$ **17.** $(4, 2)$ **19.** $(4, -1)$

21. $\left(\frac{5}{2}, 3\right)$ **23.** $(2, 1)$ **25.** $(10, -12)$

27. Infinitely many solutions   **29.** $(-0.2, 0.7)$

31. $(5, 6)$ **33.** $(4, 2)$ **35.** $(-1, -1)$ **37.** $\left(4, -\frac{3}{2}\right)$

39. $(-5, 6)$ **41.** Infinitely many solutions

43. $(10, 0)$ **45.** $(0, 0)$ **47.** $(-3, 7)$ **49.** $\left(\frac{1}{3}, -\frac{1}{2}\right)$

51. $x + y = 15$ **53.** $x + 3y = 11$
$\ 2x - y = \ \ 0$ $\ 3x - 3y = \ \ 1$

55. $4x - \ \ y = \ \ 2$ **57.** $x + 2y = \ \ 8$
$\ -x + \frac{1}{4}y = -\frac{1}{2}$ $\ x + 2y = -8$

59. 24 inches by 36 inches

61. Gasoline: \$1.17 per gallon
Diesel fuel: \$1.25 per gallon

63.

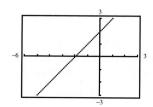

83 units
$R(83) = \$66{,}400$

65. \$310

Chapter Test   *(page 415)*

1. $(5, 4)$ **2.** One solution   **3.** No solution

4. No solution   **5.** $(2, 2)$ **6.** $(1, 2)$ **7.** $(4, 2)$

8. $\left(\frac{3}{2}, 2\right)$ **9.** $(5, 1)$ **10.** $(3, 4)$ **11.** $(3, 5)$

12. $(2, 4)$ **13.** $(2, 6)$ **14.** $\left(3, \frac{5}{2}\right)$ **15.** $\left(\frac{12}{7}, -\frac{6}{7}\right)$

16. $\left(\frac{4}{5}, \frac{9}{10}\right)$ **17.** $a = -6$ **18.** $2x + 5y = \ \ 14$
$\ 3x + 2y = -1$

19. 5 meters × 15 meters   **20.** 12 liters of 30% solution
8 liters of 5% solution

21. 7, 15

Chapter 8

Section 8.1   *(page 423)*

Integrated Review   *(page 423)*

1. $m = \dfrac{y_2 - y_1}{x_2 - x_1}$

2. (a) $m > 0$ (b) $m < 0$

   (c) $m = 0$ (d) m is undefined.

3. They are parallel because the slope of each is $m = -2$.

4. They are perpendicular because the slopes are the negative reciprocals of each other.

5. $-\frac{2}{5}$ **6.** $-\frac{3}{5}$ **7.** 1   **8.** $-\frac{5}{3}$ **9.** 4

10. 0   **11.** 9   **12.** $\frac{2}{5}$ **13.** \$806.25   **14.** 7

1. Rational

3. Not rational because the numerator is not a polynomial

5. All real values of x such that $x \neq 4$

7. All real values of x such that $x \neq -2$

9. All real values of x **11.** All real values of x

13. All real values of t such that $t \neq -5$ and $t \neq 5$

15. All real values of y such that $y \neq -4$ and $y \neq 7$

17. All real values of x such that $x \neq -1$ and $x \neq 2$

19. All real values of z such that $z \neq -\frac{2}{3}$ and $z \neq 1$

21. (a) 0   (b) Division by zero is undefined.
   (c) $\frac{10}{7}$ (d) $\frac{1}{2}$

23. (a) Division by zero is undefined.   (b) $-\frac{2}{3}$
   (c) $-\frac{4}{21}$ (d) Division by zero is undefined.

25. $-\dfrac{x}{12}, \dfrac{-x}{-12}$ **27.** $\dfrac{t + 2}{1 - t^2}, \dfrac{-t - 2}{t^2 - 1}$ **29.** $(3x)$

31. $(x + 1)$ **33.** $(-x^2)$ **35.** $(x + 2)$ **37.** $(x - 2)$

39. $(x + 2)$ **41.** $\dfrac{x}{3}$ **43.** $2y, y \neq 0$

45. $\dfrac{3x}{2}, x \neq 0$ **47.** $5(x - 1), x \neq 0, x \neq 1$

49. $x, x \neq 0, x \neq -1$ **51.** $\dfrac{1}{2}, x \neq 5$ **53.** $\dfrac{3}{x}, y \neq -1$

55. $-3, t \neq 3$ **57.** $-(x + 5), x \neq 5$

59. $\dfrac{y - 4}{3}, y \neq -4$ **61.** $\dfrac{1 - x}{1 + x}, x \neq 1$ **63.** $\dfrac{1}{a + 2}$

65. $\dfrac{x}{x - 5}$ **67.** $\dfrac{y + 2}{y + 5}, y \neq 2$ **69.** $\dfrac{x - 1}{x - 2}, x \neq 3$

71. $\dfrac{x - 2}{x + 1}, x \neq -10$ **73.** $\dfrac{x(x + 3)}{x - 2}, x \neq -2$

75. $x^2 + 1, x \neq 2$ **77.** $x + 2$

79. $\dfrac{a^2 + 2a + 4}{a + 2}, a \neq 2$

81. $x + 2, x \neq 0$

83. $3(x - 3)$, $x \neq 3$

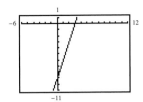

85. $\dfrac{x(x - 2)}{x^2 + 2}$, $x \neq 0$

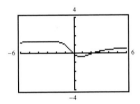

87.

x	2	2.5	3	3.5	4
$\dfrac{x^3 - 3x^2}{x - 3}$	4	6.25	Undef.	12.25	16
x^2	4	6.25	9	12.25	16

89. $\dfrac{500}{x}$

91. (a) $\overline{C} = \dfrac{3000 + 7.50x}{x}$ (b) $\{1, 2, 3, 4, \ldots\}$ (c) \$37.50

93. (a) $B = \dfrac{156.89 + 7.34x}{1 + 0.017x}$, $10 \leq x \leq 100$

  (b) $211.847°$ F

95. (a) $0 \leq p < 1$

  (b)

p	0.2	0.4	0.6	0.8
C	\$20,000	\$53,333	\$120,000	\$320,000

  (c) As p increases, the cost increases. No: the function is not defined for $p = 1$.

97. $\dfrac{x - 3}{x + 5}$ **99.** $\dfrac{1}{6}$

101. A rational expression is a fraction whose numerator and denominator are polynomials.

103. A rational expression is in simplified form if its numerator and denominator have no common factors other than 1.

105. A fraction can be reduced only by canceling common factors of the numerator and denominator.

107. $\dfrac{x}{x^2 + 1}$

Section 8.2   *(page 433)*

Integrated Review   *(page 433)*

1. $a^2 - b^2 = (a + b)(a - b)$
  $4x^2 - 9 = (2x + 3)(2x - 3)$

2. $x^2 - 2ax + a^2 = (x - a)^2$
  $x^2 - 8x + 16 = (x - 4)^2$

3. $x^3 + a^3 = (x + a)(x^2 - ax + a^2)$
  $8x^3 + 27 = (2x + 3)(4x^2 - 6x + 9)$

4. $3x^2 + 13x - 10 = (3x - 2)(x + 5)$
  Show by multiplying $(3x - 2)(x + 5)$.

5. $x(3x + 7)$ **6.** $-(x - 7)(x - 15)$

7. $(x + 9)(x - 2)$ **8.** $(5x - 1)(2x + 3)$

9. $\frac{1}{9}(3x + 5)$ **10.** $\frac{1}{8}(5x - 12)$

11.   **12.**

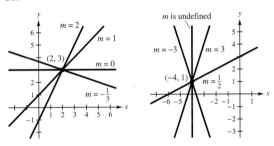

1. (a) 0   (b) Division by zero is undefined.
  (c) $\frac{2}{3}$ (d) $\frac{1}{18}$

3. (5) **5.** (a^2) **7.** $(x + 1)$ **9.** $(5t)$

11. $(2 - x)$ **13.** $\frac{5}{12}$ **15.** $\frac{1}{12}$ **17.** 6

19. $\dfrac{3x}{2}$, $x \neq 0$ **21.** 3, $x \neq 0$ **23.** $\dfrac{4xy}{3}$, $x \neq 0$, $y \neq 0$

25. $-8t$, $t \neq 0$, $r \neq 0$ **27.** 1, $y \neq 1$ **29.** $2x$, $x \neq -1$

31. -1, $r \neq 1$ **33.** $\dfrac{2y(y + 5)}{y - 2}$ **35.** $\dfrac{x}{6}$, $x \neq 2$

37. $x - 5$, $x \neq \pm 5$ **39.** $\dfrac{1}{5(x - 2)}$, $x \neq 1$

41. -1, $t \neq \pm 2$ **43.** $-\dfrac{x(x + 7)}{(x + 1)^2}$, $x \neq 9$

45. $\dfrac{6}{7}$, $y \neq -2z$, $3y \neq 5z$ **47.** $\dfrac{r + t}{r}$, $r \neq t$

49. $\dfrac{x(x + 2)}{x - 2}$ **51.** $\dfrac{1}{2x(x - 4)}$, $x \neq -4$, $x \neq 3$

53. $\dfrac{t-3}{(t+3)(t-2)}$, $t \neq -2$ **55.** $\dfrac{4}{x+6}$, $x \neq 0$, $x \neq -2$

57. $3(a+1)^2(a-1)$, $a \neq 0$, $a \neq 1$

59. $\dfrac{8}{(z-3)^2}$, $z \neq -3$ **61.** $\dfrac{1}{2}$ **63.** $\dfrac{68}{9}$

65. $\dfrac{x}{2}$, $x \neq 0$ **67.** $\dfrac{3}{4x}$ **69.** $\dfrac{a(a+1)}{6}$, $a \neq -1$

71. $\dfrac{3}{2}$, $x \neq -4$ **73.** $2x(x+2)$, $x \neq -2$

75. $\dfrac{3(y+2)}{y}$, $y \neq 2$ **77.** $2(x-2y)$, $x \neq 0$, $x \neq -2y$

79. $\dfrac{4-x}{4+x}$, $x \neq 3$ **81.** $\dfrac{5(x+4)}{15-x}$, $x \neq -2$ **83.** $\dfrac{1}{2}$

85. $2x^2$, $x \neq 0$ **87.** $\dfrac{2xy^2}{5}$, $x \neq 0$, $y \neq 0$ **89.** $-\dfrac{1}{y}$, $y \neq 3$

91. 2, $x \neq -1$, $x \neq 5$ **93.** $\dfrac{x+5}{3(x+4)}$, $x \neq 2$

95. $\dfrac{(2x-5)(3x+1)}{3x(x+1)}$, $x \neq \pm\dfrac{1}{3}$ **97.** $3x(x+a)$, $x \neq 0$

99. $(x+2)(x+1)$, $x \neq -2$, $x \neq -1$

101. (a) $\dfrac{2}{x}$ (b) Base: Decreases
                                Height: Increases
                                Area: Decreases

103. (a) $\dfrac{1}{12}$ minute   (b) $\dfrac{x}{12}$ minutes   (c) $\dfrac{8}{3}$ minutes

105. To multiply two rational expressions, multiply numerators, multiply denominators, and simplify.

107. The reciprocal of $\dfrac{a}{b}$ is $\dfrac{b}{a}$.

109. $\dfrac{x+2}{x} \cdot \dfrac{x^2}{(x+2)^3} \cdot \dfrac{(x+2)^2}{x}$

111. False. $10 \div x = \dfrac{10}{x}$

Mid-Chapter Quiz   (page 436)

1. (a) All real x (b) $x \neq \pm 2$

2. (a) $\dfrac{7}{12}$ (b) 0 (c) Division by zero is undefined.

3. $\dfrac{2z^3}{5}$, $z \neq 0$ **4.** $\dfrac{3(u-3)}{5u}$, $u \neq 3$ **5.** $-\dfrac{8}{5}$, $x \neq 9$

6. $-\dfrac{y+2}{4}$, $y \neq 2$ **7.** $\dfrac{1}{b-1}$, $b \neq 0$, $b \neq -3$

8. $\dfrac{2x-3}{x+1}$, $x \neq \dfrac{3}{2}$ **9.** $\dfrac{s-2}{s}$ **10.** $x+2$, $x \neq \pm\sqrt{3}$

11. $\dfrac{5y^2}{3}$, $y \neq 0$ **12.** $-\dfrac{4s}{5(s+5)}$, $s \neq 5$

13. $\dfrac{5x^3}{x-2}$, $x \neq -4$ **14.** $\dfrac{r-4}{r(r+4)}$

15. $\dfrac{2}{5(x+2)^2}$, $x \neq 0$ **16.** $\dfrac{20}{y^3}$, $x \neq 0$

17. $\dfrac{x+3}{4x}$, $x \neq -3$, $x \neq \dfrac{1}{2}$ **18.** $\dfrac{3x}{x-4}$, $x \neq -1$, $x \neq 0$

19. (a) $\overline{C} = \dfrac{10{,}000 + 25x}{x}$

(b)

x	2000	3000	4000	5000
$\overline{C}$	\$30.00	\$28.33	\$27.50	\$27.00

As the number of units increases, the cost per unit decreases.

20. $\dfrac{x}{x+10}$, $x \neq -3$

Section 8.3   (page 443)

Integrated Review   (page 443)

1. (a) $y = \dfrac{7}{3}x + \dfrac{4}{3}$ (b) $y - 6 = \dfrac{7}{3}(x-2)$
(c) $7x - 3y + 4 = 0$

2. If the line moves upward from left to right, $m > 0$. If the line moves downward from left to right, $m < 0$.

3. 35 **4.** -8 **5.** 9 **6.** 10 **7.** -2

8. $-1, 6$ **9.** $-\dfrac{5}{2}, \dfrac{5}{2}$ **10.** $-\dfrac{3}{2}, 5$

11. Perimeter: $6x + 4$ **12.** Perimeter: $12x$
Area: $2x^2 + 5x - 3$ Area: $6x^2$

1. y **3.** $\dfrac{5}{x}$ **5.** $\dfrac{14}{3a}$ **7.** $\dfrac{1}{3}$ **9.** $\dfrac{2t-12}{9}$

11. -1 **13.** $\dfrac{y+1}{y-1}$ **15.** $2x^3$ **17.** $36y^2$

19. $48x(x+2)$ **21.** $3x(x+5)$ **23.** $x(x^2-4)$

25. $7x(x-4)(x+1)$ **27.** $x(x+2)(x-2)$

29. $\dfrac{x+5}{3x-6}, \dfrac{30}{3x-6}$ **31.** $\dfrac{2x}{x(x+3)^2}, \dfrac{5(x+3)}{x(x+3)^2}$

33. $\dfrac{(x-8)(x-4)}{(x+4)(x-4)^2}, \dfrac{9x(x+4)}{(x+4)(x-4)^2}$ **35.** $\dfrac{13}{10s}$

37. $\dfrac{1-3x}{5x}$ **39.** $\dfrac{5u+2}{u^2}$ **41.** $\dfrac{3b+5}{2b^2}$ **43.** 0, $x \neq 3$

45. $\dfrac{5x-1}{(x+3)(x-5)}$ **47.** $\dfrac{2x+5}{x-5}$ **49.** $\dfrac{6x+13}{x+3}$

51. $\dfrac{14x - 19}{2x - 3}$ **53.** $\dfrac{3}{(x + 2)(x - 1)}$ **55.** $\dfrac{x + 2}{x(x - 4)}$

57. $\dfrac{4x - 9}{(x + 3)(x - 3)}$ **59.** $\dfrac{7v + 8}{v(v + 4)}$ **61.** $\dfrac{4x - 7}{(x - 2)(x - 3)}$

63. $\dfrac{2x + 1}{(x + 2)(x - 1)}, x \neq 2$ **65.** $\dfrac{4x^2 + 14x - 1}{(4 + x)(4 - x)}$

67. $\dfrac{4x^2 + 2x - 1}{x^2(x + 1)}$ **69.** $\dfrac{13x^2 - 24x + 12}{6x(x - 2)^2}$

71. $\dfrac{3x^2 - 18x - 44}{2x(2x + 9)}$ **73.** $\dfrac{x}{2}, x \neq 0$ **75.** $\dfrac{y + 3}{y^2}$

77. $\dfrac{x^2}{4x + 6}, x \neq 0$ **79.** $\dfrac{x(x - 12)}{3(5x + 1)}, x \neq 0$

81. $\dfrac{x + 4}{4x}, x \neq 4$ **83.** $\dfrac{z^2 - 4}{1 - 4z}, z \neq 0$

85. $\dfrac{20}{7}, x \neq -1$ **87.** $\dfrac{1}{x}, x \neq -1$ **89.** $\dfrac{15t}{56}$

91. $\dfrac{11x}{60}$ **93.** $\dfrac{x}{8}, \dfrac{5x}{36}, \dfrac{11x}{72}$ **95.** $\dfrac{R_1 R_2}{R_1 + R_2}$

97. $\dfrac{x + 5}{x^2 + x - 2} = \dfrac{2}{x - 1} - \dfrac{1}{x + 2}$

99. (a) 1125

  (b) $M(3) = 300, F(3) \approx 1385, M(3) + F(3) \approx 1685$

  (c) $F(t) + M(t) = \dfrac{2(251t^2 + 4992t - 72{,}000)}{(8 - t)(t - 16)}$

  (d) 1685. Yes

101. Rewrite each fraction in terms of the lowest common denominator, combine the numerators, and place the result over the lowest common denominator.

103. Yes. For example, for $2(x + 2)$ and $x + 2$, the least common multiple is $2(x + 2)$.

Section 8.4   *(page 453)*

Integrated Review   *(page 453)*

1. Consistent: The system of linear equations has a single solution.
 Inconsistent: The system of linear equations has no solution.
 Dependent: The system of linear equations has infinitely many solutions.

2. (i) Solve one of the equations for one variable in terms of the other.
  (ii) Substitute the expression obtained in Step (i) into the other equation and solve the resulting one-variable equation.

  (iii) Back-substitute the solution in Step (ii) into the equation found in Step (i) to find the other variable.

  (iv) Check your answer to see that it satisfies both of the original equations.

3. 2   **4.** $\frac{5}{2}$ **5.** 0, 8   **6.** $0, -\frac{3}{2}$ **7.** 4

8. $-8, 7$ **9.** $(-1, 3)$ **10.** $(3, 5)$

11. $V = 8500 - 1375t;\ \$7125$

12. (a) $N = 3750 + 125t$ (b) 5625   (c) 4250

1. (a) Not a solution   (b) Not a solution

  (c) Not a solution   (d) Not a solution

3. (a) Solution   (b) Not a solution

  (c) Not a solution   (d) Not a solution

5. 10   **7.** 3   **9.** 20   **11.** -15 **13.** 12   **15.** 50

17. $\frac{21}{2}$ **19.** 5   **21.** $\frac{23}{10}$ **23.** 4   **25.** 12   **27.** -4

29. $\frac{2}{9}$ **31.** $\frac{3}{4}$ **33.** 4   **35.** $\frac{4}{3}$ **37.** 2   **39.** 3

41. No solution   **43.** $-\frac{8}{3}$ **45.** 5   **47.** $\frac{7}{4}$ **49.** -2

51. $-5, 4$ **53.** $-2, \frac{3}{2}$ **55.** $\frac{1}{2}, 2$ **57.** $\frac{1}{2}$ **59.** $-2, 3$

61. (a)   (b) 4

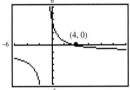

63. (a)   (b) $2, -2$

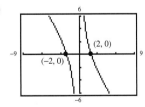

65. (a)   (b) 7

67. (a)   (b) $2, -3$

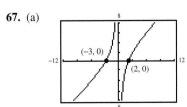

69. $\frac{1}{3}, 3$ **71.** $\frac{5}{3}, 5$

73. First car: 55 miles per hour
    Second car: 52 miles per hour

75. Truck: 50 miles per hour
    Car: 60 miles per hour

77. $66\frac{2}{3}$ miles per hour

79.

Person #1	Person #2	Together
4 days	4 days	2 days
4 hours	6 hours	$2\frac{2}{5}$ hours
4 hours	$2\frac{1}{2}$ hours	$1\frac{7}{13}$ hours

81. $\frac{4}{3}$ hours   **83.** 12 hours, 24 hours   **85.** 5 hits

87. 2500 units   **89.** 3 years

91. (e) It will not.

(f) $249t^2 - 12{,}992t + 72{,}000 = 0$

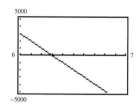

$t \approx 6.3$

93. Multiply both sides of the equation by the lowest common denominator, solve the resulting equation, and check the result. It is important to check the result for any errors or extraneous solutions.

95. (i) Simplify each side by removing symbols of grouping, combining like terms, and reducing fractions on one or both sides.

(ii) Add (or subtract) the same quantity to (from) both sides of the equation.

(iii) Multiply (or divide) both sides of the equation by the same nonzero real number.

(iv) Interchange the two sides of the equation.

97. When the equation involves only two fractions, one on each side of the equation, the equation can be solved by cross-multiplication.

Review Exercises   *(page 458)*

1. All real numbers x such that $x \neq 5$

3. All real numbers t such that $t \neq 1$ and $t \neq 2$

5. (a) 0   (b) $\frac{2}{3}$ (c) -6 (d) Division by zero is undefined.

7. (a) $\frac{1}{8}$ (b) 0   (c) $-\frac{3}{8}$ (d) $-\frac{6}{29}$ **9.** $\frac{t}{3}$

11. $4x^3, x \neq 0$ **13.** $\frac{x}{3y}, x \neq 0$ **15.** $\frac{3}{4}, b \neq 2$

17. $-4, x \neq y$ **19.** $\frac{x+3}{x+2}, x \neq 3$

21. $-\frac{x^2+x+1}{x+1}, x \neq 1$ **23.** $\frac{x-6y}{x+y}, x \neq -3y$

25. $\frac{x-4}{x}, x \neq -7$

27.

x	1	1.5	2	2.5	3
$\dfrac{x-2}{x^2-4}$	$\frac{1}{3}$	$\frac{2}{7}$	Undef.	$\frac{2}{9}$	$\frac{1}{5}$
$\dfrac{1}{x+2}$	$\frac{1}{3}$	$\frac{2}{7}$	$\frac{1}{4}$	$\frac{2}{9}$	$\frac{1}{5}$

29. $(3x^2)$ **31.** $(x+1)$ **33.** $\frac{2}{3}$ **35.** $\frac{22}{27}$

37. $\frac{1}{3}, x \neq 0$ **39.** $\frac{5v}{8u}, v \neq 0$ **41.** $\frac{3x^3}{4y^2}$

43. $50y, y \neq 0$ **45.** $\frac{z(z-1)}{5}, z \neq -1$

47. $-\frac{4}{x+2}, x \neq -3, x \neq 2$ **49.** $\frac{u}{u-3}, u \neq 0, u \neq -3$

51. $\frac{x+6}{2(x-6)}$ **53.** $\frac{x(x+1)}{x-8}, x \neq -1, x \neq 1$

55. $4x, x \neq 0$ **57.** $3(x-3), x \neq \pm 3, x \neq \frac{7}{2}$

59. $\frac{(x+1)(y-1)}{y+1}, x \neq 0, y \neq 0, y \neq 1$

61. $120x^3$ **63.** $2x^2(x^2-25)$ **65.** $\frac{x}{4}$

67. $\frac{6x-4}{x+2}$ **69.** $\frac{5t}{48}$ **71.** $-\frac{1}{(x+1)(x+2)}$

73. $\frac{x+8}{(x+4)(x+2)^2}$ **75.** $\frac{4x+5}{(x+4)(x-4)}$

77. $\frac{x^3-x+3}{(x+2)(x-1)}$ **79.** $\frac{2x^3-4x^2-15x+5}{(x-4)(x+2)}$

81. $\frac{2(x+1)}{x-1}, x \neq 0$ **83.** $-\frac{1}{xy(x+y)}, x \neq y$

85. $\frac{-1}{4(x+1)}, x \neq 3$ **87.** -10 **89.** $\frac{1}{2}$ **91.** $\frac{1}{2}$

93. $\frac{3}{2}$ **95.** $2, -6$ **97.** $3, -4$

99. (a) and (b)

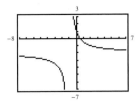

$\left(\frac{1}{2}, 0\right)$

101. (a) and (b)

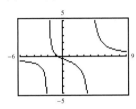

$\left(-\frac{1}{2}, 0\right)$

103. (a) and (b)

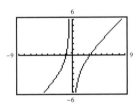

$(-1, 0), (3, 0)$

105. $\dfrac{x-3}{2x+1}$ **107.** $\dfrac{5}{4}, \dfrac{4}{5}$

109. 48 miles per hour, 54 miles per hour

111. $\frac{40}{9}$ minutes   **113.** 10 hits

115. (a)

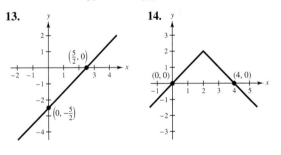

(b) 103 billion dollars

Chapter Test   *(page 461)*

1. All real numbers x such that $x \neq 10$

2. $x^2 + x$ **3.** $\dfrac{8x}{x+1}, x \neq 0$ **4.** $\dfrac{x+8}{x+5}, x \neq 8$

5. $\dfrac{18}{x^2}$ **6.** $\dfrac{(x+2)(x-2)}{x^2}, x \neq -2$ **7.** $\dfrac{5}{6x}$

8. $-\dfrac{1}{t}, t \neq 5$ **9.** $\dfrac{x^3}{(x-3)^8}, x \neq 0$ **10.** $36x^3(x+3)^2$

11. $\dfrac{9u+8}{3u^2}$ **12.** $-\dfrac{6x+9}{x+2}$ **13.** $\dfrac{2x}{1+4x}, x \neq 0$

14. $\dfrac{2}{(x+1)^2}$

15. (a) Not a solution   (b) Solution
    (c) Not a solution   (d) Solution

16. $\frac{9}{2}$ **17.** 4   **18.** $2, \frac{1}{2}$

19. (a) $\dfrac{1}{80}$ minute   (b) $\dfrac{x}{80}$ minute   (c) $\dfrac{1}{5}$ minute

20. Van: 48 miles per hour; car: 60 miles per hour

Chapter 9
Section 9.1   *(page 470)*

Integrated Review   *(page 470)*

1. $a^m \cdot a^n = a^{m+n}$ **2.** $(ab)^m = a^m b^m$

3. $(a^m)^n = a^{mn}$ **4.** $\dfrac{a^m}{a^n} = a^{m-n}$ **5.** x^5

6. $-x^5$ **7.** $-4x^2$ **8.** $-17t^2$ **9.** $(x+y)^3$

10. 3   **11.** $-\dfrac{x^4}{81}$ **12.** $\dfrac{x^4}{625}$

13.

y
2
1
$\left(\frac{5}{2}, 0\right)$
-2 -1   1   3   4   x
-1
-2
$\left(0, -\frac{5}{2}\right)$
-4

14.

y
3
2
1
(0, 0)   (4, 0)   x
-1   1   2   3   4   5
-1
-2
-3

1. 9   **3.** -10 **5.** $6, -6$ **7.** $4, -4$ **9.** $\frac{3}{7}, -\frac{3}{7}$

11. $\frac{9}{4}, -\frac{9}{4}$ **13.** Not possible   **15.** $0.4, -0.4$

17. Not possible   **19.** 3   **21.** 1   **23.** -2

25. $\frac{1}{2}$ **27.** Not possible   **29.** 10   **31.** -10

33. Not possible   **35.** 7   **37.** 13   **39.** -11

41. $-\frac{1}{3}$ **43.** Not possible   **45.** $\frac{7}{8}$ **47.** $-\frac{9}{11}$

49. 0.4   **51.** 0.2   **53.** 2   **55.** 2   **57.** -5

59. -3 **61.** -2 **63.** Irrational   **65.** Rational

67. Irrational   **69.** Rational   **71.** Rational

73. Irrational   **75.** Rational   **77.** 6.557

79. Not possible   **81.** -11.705 **83.** Not possible

85. 50.596   **87.** -22.755 **89.** -0.791 **91.** 3.979

93. 6.377   **95.** 12.583   **97.** 7.854   **99.** -0.687

101. 7.416   **103.** 8.367   **105.** 11.402   **107.** 17.321

109. 3   **111.** $\sqrt{97} \approx 9.85$ **113.** $\dfrac{5\sqrt{3}}{2} \approx 4.33$

115. 5.2   **117.** 15.30

119. 625 square feet; 69.4 square yards

121. (a) 0, 1, 4, 5, 6, 9   (b) No

123. (a) 8.2   (b) 142   (c) 22   (d) 850

125. (a) 0   (b) 5

127. There are two square roots of a because
$\left(-\sqrt{a}\right)^2 = \left(\sqrt{a}\right)^2 = a.$

129. A real number is a perfect square if its square root is a rational number.

131. No. $\sqrt{2}$ is an irrational number. Its decimal representation is a nonterminating, nonrepeating decimal.

Section 9.2   *(page 480)*

Integrated Review   *(page 480)*

1. You determine whether or not the points in a half-plane satisfy the inequality by testing one point in the region.

2. In the first inequality the points on the boundary are solutions to the inequality and in the second they are not.

3. 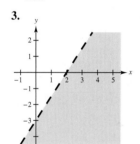   **4.**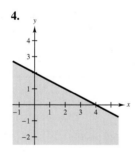

5. 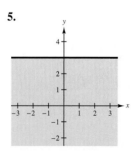   **6.**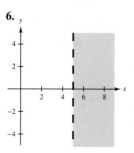

7. 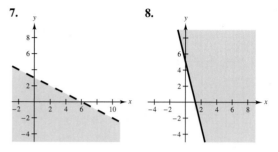   **8.**

9. 40   **10.** $\frac{5}{2}$ **11.** $-\frac{3}{2}, 9$ **12.** 0, 5

13. $d = 65t$ **14.** 40 liters

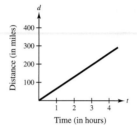

2 hours 28 minutes

1. $\sqrt{14}$ **3.** $\sqrt{110}$ **5.** $\sqrt{30}$ **7.** $\sqrt{2x}$

9. $\sqrt{6xy}$ **11.** $2\sqrt{15}$ **13.** $8\sqrt{11}$ **15.** $2\sqrt{2}$

17. $3\sqrt{3}$ **19.** $4\sqrt{2}$ **21.** $6\sqrt{5}$ **23.** $10\sqrt{3}$

25. $10\sqrt{5}$ **27.** $2\sqrt[3]{3}$ **29.** $3\sqrt[3]{3}$ **31.** $2\sqrt[4]{3}$

33. $3\sqrt[4]{2}$ **35.** $2|x|$ **37.** $8x\sqrt{x}$ **39.** $|x^3|$

41. $u^3\sqrt{u}$ **43.** $2a^2\sqrt{7}$ **45.** $|x|y\sqrt{y}$ **47.** u^2v^4

49. $10|x|y^4\sqrt{2y}$ **51.** $3a\sqrt[3]{a}$ **53.** $y\sqrt[3]{2y}$

55. $|t|\sqrt[4]{t^2}$ **57.** $2y\sqrt[4]{y}$ **59.** $\sqrt{2}$ **61.** 3

63. $\sqrt{3}$ **65.** $2\sqrt{3}$ **67.** $2\sqrt{13}$ **69.** $\sqrt{3}, x \neq 0$

71. $3|a|\sqrt{2}, a \neq 0$ **73.** $3\sqrt{3}|b|, b \neq 0$ **75.** $\dfrac{\sqrt{35}}{4}$

77. $\dfrac{\sqrt{3}}{2}$ **79.** $2\sqrt{2}$ **81.** $\dfrac{2\sqrt{3}|x|}{5}$ **83.** $\dfrac{|x|}{3}$

85. $2y\sqrt{y}$ **87.** $\dfrac{|x^3|}{4|y|}$ **89.** $\dfrac{\sqrt{3}}{4|u|}$ **91.** $\dfrac{\sqrt{3}}{3}$

93. $\dfrac{\sqrt{7}}{7}$ **95.** $\dfrac{\sqrt{10}}{2}$ **97.** $\dfrac{\sqrt{6}}{3}$ **99.** $\dfrac{\sqrt{22}}{4}$

101. $\dfrac{\sqrt{2}}{2}$ **103.** $\dfrac{10\sqrt{11}}{11}$ **105.** $\dfrac{\sqrt{y}}{y}$ **107.** $\dfrac{\sqrt{5x}}{x}$

109. $\dfrac{\sqrt{3x}}{4x^3}$ **111.** $\dfrac{\sqrt{rt}}{2r}$ **113.** $\dfrac{2x\sqrt{xy}}{y}$ **115.** $\dfrac{4\sqrt[3]{3}}{3}$

117. $\dfrac{7\sqrt[3]{9}}{3}$ **119.** $\dfrac{\sqrt[3]{x}}{x}$ **121.** $\dfrac{\sqrt[3]{y}}{2y}$

123.

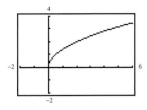

The equations are equivalent.

125.

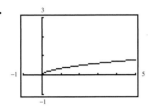

The equations are equivalent.

127. $4\sqrt{2} > 5$ **129.** $5\sqrt{6} < 6\sqrt{5}$

131. $10\sqrt{2} \approx 14.14$ **133.** $12\sqrt{6} \approx 29.39$

135. $\dfrac{\pi\sqrt{6}}{2} \approx 3.85$ seconds

137. If a and b are nonnegative real numbers, then $\sqrt{a \cdot b} = \sqrt{a} \cdot \sqrt{b}$.

139. (i) All possible factors have been removed from the radical.

(ii) No radical contains a fraction.

(iii) No denominator of a fraction contains a radical.

141. $\dfrac{1}{\sqrt{3}} = \dfrac{1}{\sqrt{3}} \cdot \dfrac{\sqrt{3}}{\sqrt{3}} = \dfrac{\sqrt{3}}{3}$

143. False. $\dfrac{\sqrt{50}}{\sqrt{2}} = \sqrt{25} = 5$

Mid-Chapter Quiz   *(page 483)*

1. Irrational   **2.** Irrational   **3.** Rational   **4.** 11

5. -0.5 **6.** -2 **7.** Not possible

8. Not possible   **9.** 3.975   **10.** 0.842   **11.** $\sqrt{105}$

12. $\sqrt{7}$ **13.** $3\sqrt{5}$ **14.** $5\sqrt{2}$ **15.** $6|x|\sqrt{2}$

16. $-3\sqrt[3]{2}$ **17.** $4x$ **18.** $x^2\sqrt[4]{x}$ **19.** $3|b|\sqrt{5}$

20. $3u^2|v|\sqrt{2u}$ **21.** $\dfrac{\sqrt{6}}{2}$ **22.** $\dfrac{\sqrt{3}}{3}$ **23.** $\dfrac{\sqrt[3]{3}}{3}$

24. $2\sqrt{2a}$ **25.** $\dfrac{a\sqrt{5}}{2}$ **26.** $\dfrac{1}{3x}$ **27.** 17.46

28. 225 square feet; 25 square yards

Section 9.3   *(page 490)*

Integrated Review   *(page 490)*

1. No. There is exactly one solution, an infinite number of solutions, or no solution.

2. The graphs of the equations are distinct parallel lines.

3. $\frac{2}{3}$ **4.** 1   **5.** 2   **6.** $\frac{2}{3}$ **7.** $(5, 1)$

8. $(3, 5)$ **9.** $(8, 1)$ **10.** $(2, -3)$

11. 9 hours, 11.25 hours   **12.** 50 miles per hour

1. $2\sqrt{5}$ **3.** $18\sqrt{11}$ **5.** $-\frac{4}{5}\sqrt{3}$

7. $-11\sqrt{3} - 5\sqrt{7}$ **9.** $10\sqrt{2} - 3\sqrt{5}$ **11.** $6\sqrt[3]{5}$

13. $5\sqrt[4]{8}$ **15.** $8\sqrt[3]{7}$ **17.** $13\sqrt[3]{5}$ **19.** $2\sqrt{x}$

21. $5\sqrt{u} + 5$ **23.** $5\sqrt[3]{x} + 8$ **25.** $2\sqrt[5]{y} + 3$

27. $11\sqrt[5]{a^3} + 5$ **29.** $18\sqrt{2}$ **31.** $34\sqrt{2}$

33. $40\sqrt{3} + 6\sqrt{2}$ **35.** $9\sqrt{x}$ **37.** $5\sqrt{b}$

39. $-2\sqrt{5z}$ **41.** $\sqrt{y}$ **43.** 0   **45.** $(4 + x)\sqrt{xy}$

47. $\frac{1}{6}\sqrt{a}$ **49.** 4   **51.** 9   **53.** $2\sqrt{15}$ **55.** 2

57. 2   **59.** $\sqrt{7} - \sqrt{14}$ **61.** $6\sqrt{2} + 8\sqrt{6}$

63. $2 + 5\sqrt[3]{2}$ **65.** $6\sqrt[4]{2} + 2$ **67.** $-1 + 2\sqrt{2}$

69. $\sqrt{3} + \sqrt{6} - 5\sqrt{2} - 5$ **71.** -10 **73.** 5

75. $5\sqrt[3]{3} + 2\sqrt[3]{4} + \sqrt[3]{12} + 10$ **77.** $\sqrt[3]{4} - 2\sqrt[3]{2} + 1$

79. $4\sqrt{13} + 17$ **81.** $17 - 12\sqrt{2}$ **83.** $x + 5\sqrt{x}$

85. $x - 2\sqrt{x} - 3$ **87.** $x + 6\sqrt{x} + 9$ **89.** $4x - 9$

91. $4 - \sqrt{3}, 13$ **93.** $\sqrt{15} + \sqrt{7}, 8$

95. $\sqrt{x} + 4, x - 16$ **97.** $\sqrt{u} + \sqrt{2}, u - 2$

99. $\dfrac{\sqrt{14} + 2}{2}$ **101.** $\sqrt{7} + \sqrt{3}$ **103.** $3(6 - \sqrt{30})$

105. $\dfrac{\sqrt{35} - \sqrt{5} + \sqrt{7} - 1}{6}$ **107.** $\dfrac{2(5 + \sqrt{y})}{25 - y}$

109. $\dfrac{\sqrt{2x} + x}{2 - x}$ **111.** $\dfrac{x - 4\sqrt{x} - 5}{x - 1}$ **113.** $\dfrac{9 - \sqrt{3}}{3}$

115. $2\sqrt{2}$

117.

The equations are equivalent.

119.

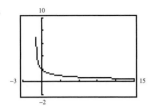

The equations are equivalent.

121. $\sqrt{5} + \sqrt{3} > \sqrt{5+3}$ **123.** $5 > \sqrt{3^2 + 2^2}$

125. Perimeter: $32\sqrt{x}$; Area: $55x$

127. Perimeter: $16\sqrt{7} + 14$; Area: $42\sqrt{7} + 84$

129. $\dfrac{\sqrt{5} + 1}{2} \approx 1.62$

131. (a) Yes. $72\sqrt{2}$ feet   (b) $36\sqrt{2} \approx 50.912$ feet
    (c) 5184 square feet   (d) 1296 square feet

133. Like: $3\sqrt{2}, -5\sqrt{2}$; Unlike: $3\sqrt{2}, -5\sqrt{7}$

135. Yes. $\sqrt{2} + \sqrt{18} = \sqrt{2} + 3\sqrt{2} = 4\sqrt{2}$

137. No. Multiply the numerator and denominator by the conjugate of the denominator.

139. 1

Section 9.4 *(page 499)*

Integrated Review *(page 499)*

1. The domain is the set of all real numbers for which the function is defined. Because $f(-2)$ is not defined, -2 is not in the domain of f.

2. $x = -2$ is in the domain of the reduced fraction, but not in the domain of the original fraction.

3. $\dfrac{3x}{2}, x \neq 0$ **4.** $4x, x \neq -\dfrac{1}{2}$ **5.** $\dfrac{1}{5}, x \neq -1$

6. $\dfrac{r+1}{r}, r \neq 1$ **7.** $\dfrac{6x+13}{x+3}$ **8.** $\dfrac{1}{2}, x \neq 2$

9.

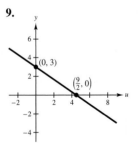

10.

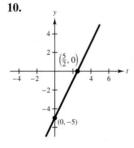

1. (a) Not a solution   (b) Not a solution
    (c) Solution   (d) Not a solution

3. (a) Not a solution   (b) Not a solution
    (c) Not a solution   (d) Solution

5. 49   **7.** 100   **9.** 25   **11.** No solution

13. 25   **15.** 397   **17.** 1000   **19.** No solution

21. 6   **23.** $-\dfrac{1}{3}$ **25.** 38   **27.** $-\dfrac{1}{2}$ **29.** -6

31. $\dfrac{11}{25}$ **33.** 3   **35.** 3   **37.** No solution

39. No solution   **41.** $\dfrac{1}{2}$ **43.** 2   **45.** 2   **47.** 1

49. 25   **51.** 4   **53.** 3   **55.** $-1, 3$

57.

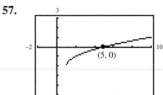

59.

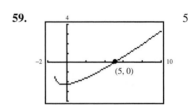

61. 13   **63.** 1   **65.** 26   **67.** 5

69. $3\sqrt{2} \approx 4.24$ **71.** $\sqrt{65} \approx 8.06$ **73.** $3\sqrt{5} \approx 6.71$

75. 144 feet   **77.** 87.89 feet   **79.** 3.24 feet

81. $6\sqrt{6} \approx 14.70$ feet   **83.** $30\sqrt{5} \approx 67.08$ feet

85. $\dfrac{\sqrt{2}}{4}$ **87.** $\dfrac{25\sqrt{2}}{2}$ inches   **89.** 29 units

91. (a)

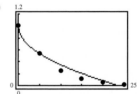

(b) 8.5 kilometers

93. (e) 174.264 feet   (f) 141.421 feet
    (g) 183.598 feet, 9.334 feet
    (h) 213.421 feet, 39.157 feet, 29.823 feet

95. Isolate a radical on one side of the equation and then square both sides of the equation. If there are more radicals, continue the process. When the radicals have been eliminated, solve the resulting equation and check your results.

97. To check for any errors and to identify extraneous solutions

99. Yes. The two legs can be of the same length l and the hypotenuse of length $\sqrt{2}\,l$.

Review Exercises *(page 504)*

1. 11   **3.** -6 **5.** 1.2   **7.** Not possible

9. -3 **11.** $\frac{2}{5}$ **13.** 7.28   **15.** 0.94   **17.** 7.90

19. -0.10 **21.** $4\sqrt{3}$ **23.** $4\sqrt{10}$ **25.** $\frac{\sqrt{23}}{3}$

27. $\frac{2\sqrt{5}}{3}$ **29.** $2\sqrt[3]{3}$ **31.** $2\sqrt[4]{6}$ **33.** $6x^2$

35. $2y\sqrt{y}$ **37.** $4a\sqrt{2ab}$ **39.** $0.2x\sqrt{y}$ **41.** $2x^2$

43. $4a\sqrt[3]{a^2}$ **45.** $\frac{\sqrt{15}}{5}$ **47.** $2\sqrt{3}$ **49.** $\frac{\sqrt{15}}{6}$

51. $\frac{3}{2}\sqrt[3]{4}$ **53.** $\frac{1}{3}\sqrt[3]{9}$ **55.** $\frac{3\sqrt{x}}{x}$ **57.** $\frac{\sqrt{11ab}}{b}$

59. $\frac{x\sqrt{2y}}{3y^2}$ **61.** $\frac{\sqrt[3]{4x}}{x}$ **63.** $12\sqrt{2}$

65. $3\sqrt{5} + 4\sqrt{3}$ **67.** $-14\sqrt{5}$ **69.** $8\sqrt{3}$

71. $6\sqrt[4]{4}$ **73.** $9\sqrt[5]{x}$ **75.** $2\sqrt{y}$ **77.** 0

79. $3\sqrt{2} - \sqrt{3}$ **81.** $\sqrt[4]{12} - \sqrt[4]{6}$ **83.** -2

85. $9 - 4\sqrt{5}$ **87.** $10 + 4\sqrt{2}$

89. $\sqrt[5]{6} + 5\sqrt[5]{2} + 3\sqrt[5]{3} + 15$ **91.** $x + 10\sqrt{x}$

93. $2\sqrt{3} + 3$ **95.** $3\sqrt{2} - 2\sqrt{3}$ **97.** $\frac{x - 6\sqrt{x} + 9}{x - 9}$

99. 169   **101.** No solution   **103.** 11

105. 3   **107.** 2   **109.** 8

111.

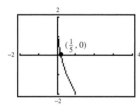

$\frac{1}{5}$

     113. 5

115. $\sqrt{137} \approx 11.70$ **117.** $\sqrt{37} \approx 6.08$

119. $\sqrt{146} \approx 12.08$ **121.** 9.6

123. $8\sqrt{30} \approx 43.8$ feet per second   **125.** 2.48 feet

127. 4   **129.** $4^2 + 4^2 = \left(4\sqrt{2}\right)^2$

131. $20\sqrt{34} \approx 116.6$ feet   **133.** 20 inches $\times$ 15 inches

135. $\sqrt{3^2 + 4^2} = \sqrt{25} = 5$

Chapter Test *(page 507)*

1. (a) 12   (b) Not possible   (c) 3   (d) -4

2. $4\sqrt{3}$ **3.** $3\sqrt[3]{2}$ **4.** $4|x|y\sqrt{2y}$ **5.** 8

6. $\frac{x\sqrt{3x}}{y^2}$ **7.** $\frac{\sqrt{15}}{3}$ **8.** $\sqrt[3]{2}$ **9.** $16\sqrt{3}$

10. $8\sqrt[3]{5} - 6\sqrt[3]{4}$ **11.** $\sqrt{2}|x| - 20\sqrt{2x}$

12. $4 - 5\sqrt{2}$ **13.** $\sqrt[3]{10} + 3\sqrt[3]{5}$ **14.** $2\sqrt{6} - 9$

15. $4x - 2\sqrt{x}$ **16.** $\sqrt{3} + 5, -22$ **17.** $2\left(\sqrt{6} - 1\right)$

18. 16   **19.** $\frac{13}{4}$ **20.** 3   **21.** 2   **22.** $2\sqrt{13}$

23. 10   **24.** 125 units per day

Cumulative Test: Chapters 7–9 *(page 508)*

1. $(5, -1)$ **2.** $(2, 1)$ **3.** $(5, 5)$ **4.** $(204, 140)$

5. $(6, -2)$ **6.** $\left(\frac{3}{2}, 1\right)$

7.

     8. Answers will vary.

$(5, 2)$

9. $(-\infty, -2) \cup (-2, \infty)$ **10.** $\frac{7}{3x} = \frac{7(4x)}{12x^2}$

11. $\frac{5}{x + 5}, x \neq 5$ **12.** $\frac{x - 5}{x - 2}, x \neq -2$

13. $\frac{c + 10}{c^2}, c \neq 1$ **14.** $\frac{3c^2}{4(c - 1)}, c \neq 0$

15. $\frac{2(x + 3)}{(x + 2)(x - 2)}$ **16.** $\frac{3x + 2}{x(x - 1)}$ **17.** $\frac{2a^2 - 2}{a + 2}, a \neq 0$

18. $\frac{1}{3}$ **19.** -10 **20.** $\frac{5}{3}$ **21.** $\frac{9}{2}$ **22.** Not possible

23. $-\frac{2}{3}$ **24.** 60   **25.** -5 **26.** $2\sqrt{6}$

27. $5x\sqrt{2x}$ **28.** $6uv^2\sqrt[3]{4u}$ **29.** $2\sqrt{x}$

30. $7 + 2\sqrt{7}$ **31.** $24 - 16\sqrt{2}$ **32.** $2y\left(\sqrt{5} + 1\right)$

33. 64   **34.** 29   **35.** 1   **36.** 0, 4

37. Regular: \$1.34, Premium: \$1.54   **38.** 50 miles per hour

39. Experienced employee: $4\frac{1}{2}$ hours   **40.** 5
New employee: 9 hours

41. $\sqrt{58} \approx 7.62$ **42.** 8

Chapter 10

Section 10.1 *(page 515)*

Integrated Review *(page 515)*

1. -2. The coefficient of the term of highest degree.

2. 5. The degree of the term that is the product of the terms of highest degree in the factors.

3.

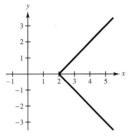

For some x there corresponds more than one value of y. A vertical line can be drawn that intersects the graph at more than one point.

4.

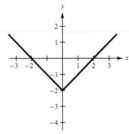

For each value of x there corresponds one and only one value of y. Any vertical line will intersect the graph in at most one point.

5. $4b^2(b - 3)$ **6.** $(t + 4)(t + 2)(t - 2)$

7. $3(2y + 5)(2y - 5)$ **8.** $(2x - 7)^2$

9. $2(u + 9)(u - 3)$ **10.** $(3x + 5)(2x - 7)$

11. $180   **12.** 4 liters

1. $0, 3$ **3.** $0, 2$ **5.** $-5, 5$ **7.** $-\frac{8}{3}, \frac{8}{3}$ **9.** $6, 10$

11. $-20, -4$ **13.** $2, 3$ **15.** -2 **17.** $\frac{5}{4}$

19. $-\frac{4}{5}, 4$ **21.** $-\frac{7}{2}, \frac{4}{3}$ **23.** $-2, 4$ **25.** $-3, 3$

27. $-7, 7$ **29.** $-11, 11$ **31.** $-\sqrt{5}, \sqrt{5}$

33. $-\sqrt{6}, \sqrt{6}$ **35.** $-\frac{7}{3}, \frac{7}{3}$ **37.** $-\frac{5}{4}, \frac{5}{4}$

39. $-10, 10$ **41.** $-\frac{10}{3}, \frac{10}{3}$ **43.** No real solution

45. $-4, 4$ **47.** $-2\sqrt{2}, 2\sqrt{2}$ **49.** $-4\sqrt{3}, 4\sqrt{3}$

51. No real solution   **53.** $-4 - \sqrt{3}, -4 + \sqrt{3}$

55. $7 - \sqrt{6}, 7 + \sqrt{6}$ **57.** $-16, 8$

59. $1 - \sqrt{5}, 1 + \sqrt{5}$ **61.** $-2 - 2\sqrt{3}, -2 + 2\sqrt{3}$

63. $3 - 3\sqrt{2}, 3 + 3\sqrt{2}$ **65.** $\dfrac{4 - \sqrt{7}}{3}, \dfrac{4 + \sqrt{7}}{3}$

67. $\dfrac{-2 - \sqrt{5}}{5}, \dfrac{-2 + \sqrt{5}}{5}$ **69.** $\dfrac{-5 - 2\sqrt{2}}{2}, \dfrac{-5 + 2\sqrt{2}}{2}$

71. $\dfrac{4 - 3\sqrt{3}}{3}, \dfrac{4 + 3\sqrt{3}}{3}$ **73.** No real solution

75. $-\frac{11}{2}, -\frac{1}{2}$ **77.** $\frac{13}{4}, \frac{27}{4}$ **79.** $\frac{1}{9}, \frac{5}{9}$

81. $\dfrac{-6 - \sqrt{7}}{8}, \dfrac{-6 + \sqrt{7}}{8}$ **83.** $-1, 5$ **85.** $-3, 2$

87.

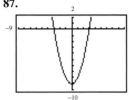

$3, -3$

89.

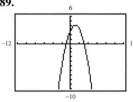

$-1, 3$

91.

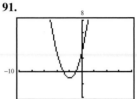

$-1, -3$

93. 2 **95.** 3

97. 3.57 miles   **99.** $0.08 = 8\%$ **101.** $0.075 = 7.5\%$

103. 20 units   **105.** 2 seconds

107. (a)

Height, h	300	250	200	150	100	50	0
Time, t	0	1.77	2.50	3.06	3.54	3.95	4.33

   (b) No; the difference in times decreases, because the velocity of the object is increasing.

109. (a) $h(t) = -16t^2 + 40$

   (b) 48 feet per second, 0 feet, 3 seconds

   (c) 0 feet per second, 80 feet, $\sqrt{5} \approx 2.2$ seconds

   (d) 4 seconds, 1 second

111. Factoring and the Zero-Factor Property allow you to solve a quadratic equation by converting it into two linear equations, which you know how to solve.

113. Write the equation in the form $u^2 = d$, where u is an algebraic expression and d is a positive constant. Take the square roots of both sides to obtain the solutions $u = \pm\sqrt{d}$.

115. Equation (c). $(x - 2)^2 + 36 \geq 36$ for all x.

Section 10.2   (page 524)

Integrated Review   (page 524)

1. Yes. The equation is true when $x = 6$ and $y = 4$.

2. $m = \frac{4}{3}$. Any two points may be used because the rate of change remains the same on the line.

3. There are many correct answers. One example is $y - 4 = \frac{4}{3}(x - 6)$.

4. $y = \frac{4}{3}x - 4$ **5.** $x + 4y - 5 = 0$

6. $15x - 14y + 80 = 0$ **7.** $x + 4 = 0$

8. $3x - 2y - 1 = 0$ **9.** $(6, 2)$ **10.** $(-5, 4)$

11. $C = 125 + 0.32x$ **12.** $6\sqrt{205} \approx 85.9$ feet

---

1. $x^2 + 4x + 4$ **3.** $y^2 - 20y + 100$ **5.** 25

7. 144 **9.** 64 **11.** $\frac{9}{4}$ **13.** $\frac{49}{4}$ **15.** $\frac{1}{4}$

17. $\frac{1}{16}$ **19.** $\frac{9}{64}$ **21.** $0, 8$ **23.** $-20, 0$

25. $1 \pm \sqrt{2}$ **27.** $2 \pm \sqrt{5}$ **29.** No real solution

31. $4 \pm 3\sqrt{2}$ **33.** $-7 \pm 4\sqrt{2}$ **35.** $-7, 5$

37. $\dfrac{1 \pm \sqrt{13}}{2}$ **39.** $\dfrac{-5 \pm \sqrt{17}}{2}$ **41.** $3, 4$

43. $-5, 2$ **45.** No real solution   **47.** No real solution

49. $\dfrac{-3 \pm \sqrt{19}}{2}$ **51.** No real solution

53. $\dfrac{-3 \pm \sqrt{17}}{4}$ **55.** $\dfrac{5 \pm \sqrt{79}}{6}$ **57.** $-4, 3$

59. $-1 \pm \sqrt{3}$ **61.** $0, 4$ **63.** $-5, -1$

65. $-3, -2$ **67.** $\frac{1}{2}, 2$

69. $\dfrac{-1 + \sqrt{13}}{2} \approx 1.30; \dfrac{-1 - \sqrt{13}}{2} \approx -2.30$

71. $3 + \sqrt{2} \approx 4.41; 3 - \sqrt{2} \approx 1.59$ **73.** $-0.50, 1.50$

75. $\dfrac{1 + \sqrt{13}}{6} \approx 0.77; \dfrac{1 - \sqrt{13}}{6} \approx -0.43$ **77.** $2 \pm \sqrt{2}$

79. $\dfrac{2 \pm \sqrt{10}}{2}$ **81.** $3 + 2\sqrt{2}$ **83.** 10 **85.** $1, 3$

87.

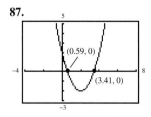

$2 + \sqrt{2} \approx 3.41$
$2 - \sqrt{2} \approx 0.59$

89.

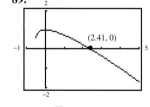

$1 + \sqrt{2} \approx 2.41$

91. 4 **93.** $2 + 2\sqrt{5}$ **95.** $6, 7$ **97.** 21 units

99. (a)

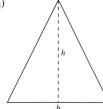

(b) $100 - h$

(c) $A = \frac{1}{2}(100 - h)h$
Height: 40 centimeters
Base: 60 centimeters
or
Height: 60 centimeters
Base: 40 centimeters

101. (a) $x^2 - 2x - 1 = 0$ (b) $1 \pm \sqrt{2}$ (c) $1 \pm \sqrt{2}$
(d) $x^2 - 4x - 1 = 0$

103. Divide the coefficient of the first-degree term by 2, square, and add the result to both sides of the equation. Write the side containing the variable as a perfect square trinomial. Then solve the equation by extracting square roots.

105. Factoring, because it is easily factored.

107. Yes. $x^2 + 1 = 0$ **109.** $9x^2 - 4x + 4 \neq (3x - 2)^2$

Section 10.3   *(page 532)*

Integrated Review   *(page 532)*

1. Factor completely and cancel the common factor $x + 2$.

2. Invert the divisor and multiply.

3. Rewrite the fractions using the lowest common denominator $x(1 - x)$ and add the fractions.

4. $\dfrac{1}{5(x - 2)}$ **5.** $\dfrac{x + 2}{x - 2}$ **6.** $\dfrac{x + 6}{x - 3}$ **7.** $-\dfrac{5x - 8}{x - 1}$

8. 4 **9.** $\frac{9}{7}$ **10.** 4 gallons   **11.** 97

1. $x^2 + 2x - 3 = 0$ **3.** $-x^2 + 4x - 10 = 0$

5. 2 **7.** 0 **9.** 2 **11.** 1 **13.** $\dfrac{9 \pm \sqrt{41}}{2}$

15. $\dfrac{5 \pm \sqrt{17}}{2}$ **17.** $-3, -2$ **19.** $3 \pm \sqrt{2}$

21. No real solution   **23.** $\dfrac{3 \pm \sqrt{13}}{2}$ **25.** $-3, -\dfrac{1}{2}$

27. $\dfrac{1}{2}, \dfrac{3}{4}$ **29.** No real solution   **31.** $\dfrac{-1 \pm \sqrt{11}}{5}$

33. $\dfrac{1 \pm \sqrt{2}}{2}$ **35.** $-2 \pm \sqrt{10}$ **37.** $\dfrac{3}{5}, 1$

39. No real solution   **41.** $\frac{1}{6}$ **43.** $\pm 3\sqrt{2}$

45. $-8, 0$ **47.** $-\frac{3}{2}, 12$ **49.** $3 \pm 5\sqrt{3}$

51. $3 \pm \sqrt{6}$ **53.** $\dfrac{3 \pm \sqrt{11}}{2}$ **55.** $-\dfrac{3}{5}, \dfrac{1}{2}$

57. $\dfrac{7 + \sqrt{37}}{3} \approx 4.361; \dfrac{7 - \sqrt{37}}{3} \approx 0.306$

59. $\dfrac{100 + 5\sqrt{394}}{3} \approx 66.416; \dfrac{100 - 5\sqrt{394}}{3} \approx 0.251$

61. $\dfrac{1 \pm \sqrt{33}}{2}$ **63.** $3 + \sqrt{11}$

65. 13.0 miles per hour

67. (a) 0 seconds; $\frac{5}{4}$ seconds   (b) 3.20 seconds

69. 14, 16   **71.** 11.4 inches $\times$ 5.1 inches

73. (e) 0.38 second, 2.62 seconds

(f) $b = 0$: Extracting square roots
$b \neq 0$, $c = 0$: Factoring
$b \neq 0$, $c \neq 0$: Quadratic Formula

75. If the discriminant is positive, the quadratic equation has two real solutions; if it is zero, the equation has one (repeated) real solution; and if it is negative, the equation has no real solution.

77. The four methods are factoring, extracting square roots, completing the square, and the Quadratic Formula.

79. Proof

Mid-Chapter Quiz   *(page 534)*

1. $-\frac{15}{4}, 5$ **2.** ± 20 **3.** $0, 25$ **4.** $\frac{4}{3}$ **5.** $-7, \frac{5}{2}$

6. $-3, 4$ **7.** ± 50 **8.** $-5, 13$ **9.** $-3 \pm 2\sqrt{5}$

10. $\dfrac{-3 \pm \sqrt{10}}{2}$ **11.** $\dfrac{-3 \pm \sqrt{5}}{2}$ **12.** $\dfrac{2 \pm \sqrt{34}}{3}$

13. $-3, 8$ **14.** 5   **15.** 0   **16.** 2   **17.** 2

18. 1   **19.** 5.5%   **20.** $\dfrac{3\sqrt{5}}{2} \approx 3.35$ seconds

21. 7.4 inches $\times$ 20.8 inches

Section 10.4   *(page 542)*

> ### Integrated Review   *(page 542)*
>
> **1.** $\sqrt{ab} = \sqrt{a}\sqrt{b}$ **2.** $\sqrt{\dfrac{a}{b}} = \dfrac{\sqrt{a}}{\sqrt{b}}$
>
> **3.** No. $\sqrt{80} = 4\sqrt{5}$
>
> **4.** Yes. All possible factors have been removed from the radical.
>
> **5.** $2\sqrt{15}$ **6.** $\sqrt{10} - 2\sqrt{5}$ **7.** -1
>
> **8.** $\dfrac{4(5 + \sqrt{2})}{23}$ **9.** $\dfrac{\sqrt{30}}{5}$ **10.** $4(1 + \sqrt{2})$
>
> **11.** $5\sqrt{15} \approx 19.36$ feet   **12.** 1200

1. d   **3.** f   **5.** a   **7.** Up   **9.** Down

11. Down   **13.** Down   **15.** $(-4, 0), (4, 0), (0, 16)$

17. $(0, 0), (2, 0)$ **19.** $(-2, 0), (3, 0), (0, -6)$

21. $(0, 3)$ **23.** $(-2, 0), \left(\frac{2}{3}, 0\right), (0, -4)$ **25.** $(0, 4)$

27. $\left(2 - \sqrt{2}, 0\right), \left(2 + \sqrt{2}, 0\right), (0, 1)$ **29.** $(0, 2)$

31. $(2, 3)$ **33.** $(5, 31)$ **35.** $\left(-\frac{5}{2}, -\frac{37}{4}\right)$

37. $(2, -10)$ **39.** $\left(-\frac{3}{2}, \frac{59}{4}\right)$

41. 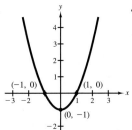   **43.**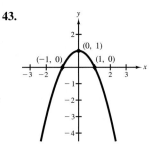

45. 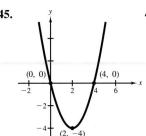   **47.**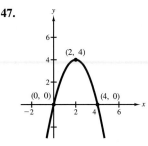

49. 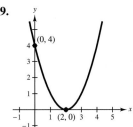   **51.**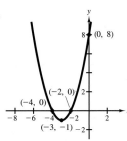

53. 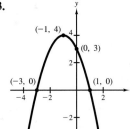   **55.**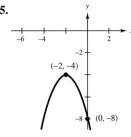

57. 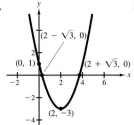   **59.**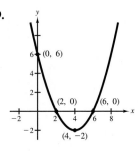

61.

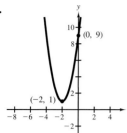

63.

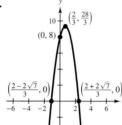

(b) Parabola is wider. For the same x, y is $\frac{1}{8}$ what it was in part (a).

(c) Parabola opens downward. Graph is not as wide; y is -2 times what it was in part (a).

(d) Parabola opens downward. Graph is wider.

81.

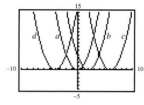

(a) The vertex is at the origin.

(b) The graph is shifted 2 units to the right of (a).

(c) The graph is shifted 6 units to the right of (a).

(d) The graph is shifted 4 units to the left of (a).

65.

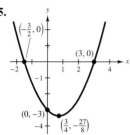

83. $y = x^2 - 4$; $y = 4 - x^2$

85. $y = x^2 + 2x - 3$; $y = -x^2 - 2x + 3$

87.

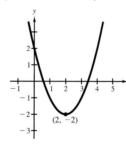

If the equation is in the form $y = (x - b)^2 + c$, the vertex is (b, c). So, the vertex is $(2, -2)$.

67.

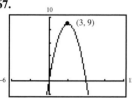

69.

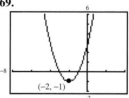

89. $y = (x - 5)^2 + 1$; $(5, 1)$

91. (a) 4 feet   (b) 14 feet   (c) $10 + 2\sqrt{35} \approx 21.8$ feet

93. (a) $(0, 5)$ (b) 495 feet

95. (a) $y = 18 - x$ (b) $A = x(18 - x)$

71.

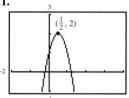

73.

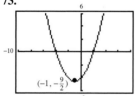

(c)

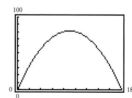

(d) 9 meters $\times$ 9 meters

75.

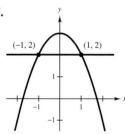

77.

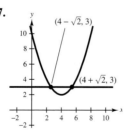

97. (a)

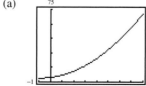

(b) and (c) 1998

79.

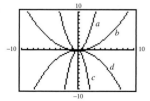

99. Parabola

(a) The parabola opens upward with vertex at the origin.

101. Given the function $y = ax^2 + bx + c$, its graph is a parabola opening upward if $a > 0$ and downward if $a < 0$.

103. The x-coordinate of the vertex is the average of the x-coordinates of the x-intercepts.

Section 10.5 *(page 550)*

Integrated Review *(page 550)*

1. $m = \dfrac{y_2 - y_1}{x_2 - x_1}$

2. (a) $Ax + By + C = 0$ (b) $y = mx + b$
(c) $x = a$ (d) $y - y_1 = m(x - x_1)$

3. $-10x^5$ **4.** $x^2 + 3x - 20$

5. $x^2 + 14x + 49$ **6.** $x^3 + 1$

7. $(3x + 2)(3x - 2)$ **8.** $x^2(2x - 1)(5x + 4)$

9. $(3x + 2)(5x - 7)$ **10.** $(2x - 7)^2$

11. **12.**

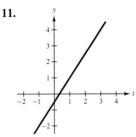 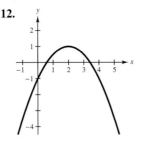

---

1. 11, 12 **3.** 17, 19 **5.** 16, 18 **7.** 7, 8

9. 10 seconds **11.** 8.49 seconds **13.** 5.86 seconds

15. Width: 12 in.; Length: 20 in.; Area: 240 in.^{2}

17. Width: 5 ft; Length: 10 ft; Perimeter: 30 ft

19. Width: 5 in.; Length: 20 in.; Perimeter: 50 in.

21. Width: 12 km; Length: 16 km; Area: 192 km^2

23. Width: 5 m; Length: 15 m; Perimeter: 40 m

25. $x(x + 6) = 187$; Width: 11 in.; Length: 17 in.

27. $w(175 - 2w) = 3750$; 50 ft $\times$ 75 ft or 37.5 ft $\times$ 100 ft

29. 56.4 miles **31.** Base: 12 inches; Height: 4 inches

33. 73.48 feet **35.** 49.80 feet, 40.20 feet

37. 10 inches $\times$ 24 inches **39.** 30 feet

41. 6 hours; 12 hours

43. Combine A: 7.12 hours; Combine B: 9.12 hours

45. 25 people **47.** 40 people

49. 45.3 miles per hour; 40.3 miles per hour

51. 6% **53.** 8.5%

55. (a) $w = \dfrac{2l}{l - 2}$ (b) $A = P = \dfrac{2l^2}{l - 2}$ (c) 6×3
(d) 16 (e) $l \geq 4$

57. (a)

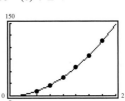

(b) 1.41 inches

(c) $\dfrac{-407 + \sqrt{43,850,849}}{7046} \approx 0.88$ inches

59. (i) Simplify each side by removing symbols of grouping, combining like terms, and reducing fractions on one or both sides.

(ii) Add (or subtract) the same quantity to (from) both sides of the equation.

(iii) Multiply (or divide) both sides of the equation by the same nonzero real number.

(iv) Interchange the two sides of the equation.

61. Division

63. If a and b are the lengths of the legs of a right triangle and c is the length of the hypotenuse, then $a^2 + b^2 = c^2$.

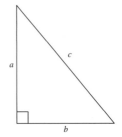

Review Exercises *(page 555)*

1. $-10, 0$ **3.** 2, 3 **5.** $-\frac{5}{2}, \frac{5}{2}$ **7.** ± 7 **9.** $\pm 4\sqrt{3}$

11. No real solution **13.** $5 \pm \sqrt{3}$ **15.** $2 \pm \sqrt{6}$

17. $-4 \pm 2\sqrt{2}$ **19.** $\frac{16}{3}, \frac{26}{3}$ **21.** No real solution

23. $3 \pm \sqrt{10}$ **25.** $\dfrac{1 \pm \sqrt{5}}{2}$ **27.** $\dfrac{-5 \pm \sqrt{15}}{2}$

29. No real solution **31.** $-7, 6$ **33.** $3 \pm \sqrt{3}$

35. $-7, 10$ **37.** $\dfrac{-1 \pm \sqrt{337}}{4}$ **39.** No real solution

41. $\pm 5\sqrt{10}$ **43.** $\dfrac{10 \pm \sqrt{70}}{3}$ **45.** No real solution

47. $\dfrac{3 \pm \sqrt{17}}{2}$ **49.** $4 + 2\sqrt{3}$ **51.** Up **53.** Down

55. Down

57.

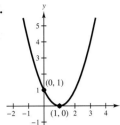

59.

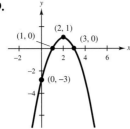

61.

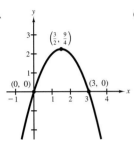

63.

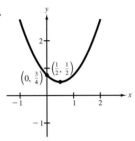

65.

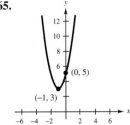

67.

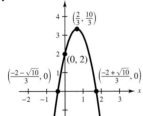

69.

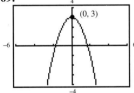

71.

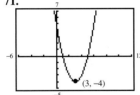

73. 15, 16   **75.** 8%

77. $\sqrt{3} \approx 1.73$ seconds. The object was dropped from a height of 48 feet.

79. 6 centimeters   **81.** 295 meters

83. Base: $4\sqrt{5} \approx 8.94$ inches; Height: $6\sqrt{5} \approx 13.42$ inches

85. 15 people   **87.** 55 miles per hour; 60 miles per hour

89. 18.2 hours; 22.2 hours   **91.** 5 feet × 12 feet

93. (a) 3 feet (b) 25.5 feet (c) 31.0 feet

95. (a) $2l + 2w = 40$ (b) $A = lw$
$\quad\quad l + w = 20$ $w = 20 - l$
$\quad\quad w = 20 - l$ $A = l(20 - l)$

(c)

l	2	4	6	8	10	12	14	16	18
A	36	64	84	96	100	96	84	64	36

(d)

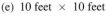

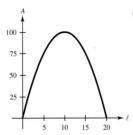

(e) 10 feet × 10 feet

97. (a)

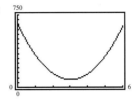

(b) Decreasing: 1900–1993; Increasing: 1993–1996

(c) The vertex is the point where the graph changes from decreasing to increasing.

Chapter Test *(page 558)*

1. $12, -12$ **2.** $2, -6$ **3.** $-3, 10$ **4.** $-3, \frac{5}{2}$

5. $3 \pm \sqrt{2}$ **6.** $\dfrac{-9 \pm \sqrt{21}}{6}$ **7.** $\dfrac{1 \pm \sqrt{13}}{2}$

8. $\dfrac{-2 \pm \sqrt{2}}{2}$ **9.** No real solution   **10.** $2 + \sqrt{3}$

11. Down; Vertex: $(0, 4)$ **12.** Down; Vertex: $(-1, 6)$

13. Up; Vertex: $(2, 3)$ **14.** $(6, 0), (2, 0)$

15.

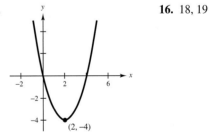

16. 18, 19

17.

Base: 6 inches
Height: 18 inches

18. 6 inches × 16 inches

19. 10 hours, 15 hours   **20.** 4.5%

21. 60 miles per hour; 72 miles per hour

Appendix A   *(page A6)*

1.
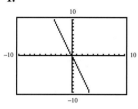

3.
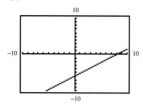

5.
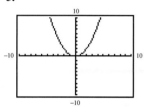

7.
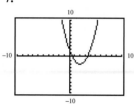

9.
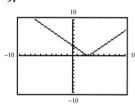

11.
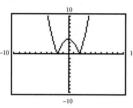

13.
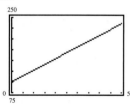

15.
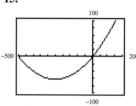

17.
```
Xmin = 4
Xmax = 20
Xscl = 1
Ymin = 14
Ymax = 22
Yscl = 1
```

19.
```
Xmin = -20
Xmax = -4
Xscl = 1
Ymin = -16
Ymax = -8
Yscl = 1
```

21.
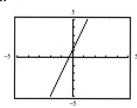

Associative Property of Addition

23.
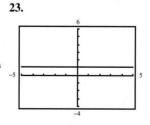

Multiplicative Inverse Property

25. $(-3, 0), (3, 0), (0, 9)$ **27.** $(-8, 0), (4, 0), (0, 4)$

29. $\left(\frac{5}{2}, 0\right), (0, -5)$ **31.** $(-2, 0), \left(\frac{1}{2}, 0\right), (0, -1)$

33. Triangle   **35.** Square

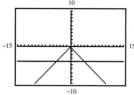

37.
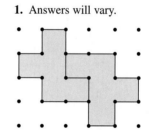

Appendix B

Section B.1   *(page A14)*

1. Answers will vary.   **3.**
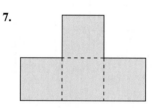

5. a and b   **7.**
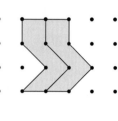
    9. 7

11. No   **13.** False   **15.** True   **17.** d   **19.** b

21. $\angle ZXW$ or $\angle WXZ$, $\angle ZXY$ or $\angle YXZ$,   **23.** b   **25.** d
$\angle YXW$ or $\angle WXY$; $\angle ZXY$ and $\angle YXW$

27. f   **29.** c   **31.** $\overline{LM} \cong \overline{NO}$, $\overline{MP} \cong \overline{NQ}$, $\overline{LP} \cong \overline{OQ}$

33. $m\angle V$ **35.** $\overline{TV}$

37.

	Scalene	Isosceles	Equilateral
Acute	Yes	Yes	Yes
Obtuse	Yes	Yes	No
Right	Yes	Yes	No

39. 3; Yes   **41.** 3; Yes   **43.** 12.5 feet by 12.5 feet; No

45. $(3, 5), (3, 1)$ **47.** Form a tetrahedron.

Section B.2 *(page A21)*

1.
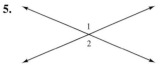

3.
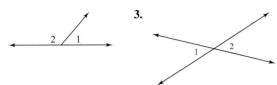

5.

7. Adjacent ≅ suppl. ∠   **9.** Adjacent suppl. ∠

11. Adjacent compl. ∠   **13.** False   **15.** False

17. True   **19.** 110°   **21.** 55°   **23.** 35°   **25.** c

27. ∠3 and ∠5 *or* ∠4 and ∠6

29. ∠4 and ∠5 *or* ∠3 and ∠6

31. $m\angle 1 = 110°$ because it forms a linear pair with the given angle; $m\angle 2 = 110°$ by the Alternate Exterior Angles Theorem

33. $m\angle 1 = 70°$ by the Consecutive Interior Angles Theorem; $m\angle 2 = 70°$ because it forms a linear pair with the given angle, or by the Alternate Interior Angles Theorem

35. $a = 30°, b = 20°$ **37.** ∠2, ∠5, ∠7

39. $m\angle 1 = m\angle 3 = 70°, m\angle 4 = m\angle 6 = 135°,$
$m\angle 2 = 110°, m\angle 5 = 45°, m\angle 7 = 25°, m\angle 8 = 155°$

41. 35°   **43.** 40°

45. True. The third angle must be $180° - 2(60°) = 60°$.

47. $m\angle 1 = 30°, m\angle 2 = 60°, m\angle 3 = 50°, m\angle 4 = 35°,$
$m\angle 5 = 90°, m\angle 6 = 55°, m\angle 7 = 55°, m\angle 8 = 125°,$
$m\angle 9 = 35°$

49.

$m\angle B = 77°$

51.
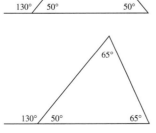

53. 30°, 60°, 90°   **55.** 38°, 59°, 83°

Appendix C *(page A33)*

1.

Stems	Leaves
7	0 5 5 5 7 7 8 8 8
8	1 1 1 1 2 3 4 5 5 5 5 5 7 8 9 9 9
9	0 2 8
10	0 0

3.

Stems	Leaves
5	2 5 9
6	2 3 6 6 7
7	0 1 2 3 4 7 8 8 9
8	0 1 3 4 5 7 9
9	0 0 2 3 3 3 5 6 8 9
10	0 0

5. Frequency Distribution

Interval	Tally
[15, 22)	⊹⊹⊹ |||
[22, 29)	⊹⊹⊹	
[29, 36)	⊹⊹⊹
[36, 43)	||||
[43, 50)	⊹⊹⊹ ||

Histogram

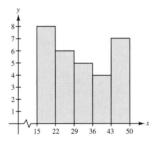

7.
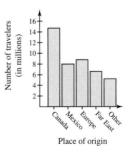

9. 1985: 165 million tons
1995: 210 million tons

11. Recycled waste

13. Total waste equals the sum of the other three quantities.

15.

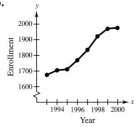

17.

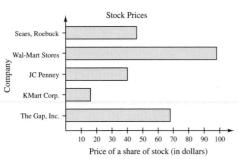

19.

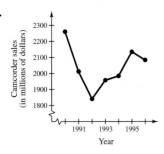

21. Positive correlation   **23.** Yes

25. Negative correlation   **27.** Positive correlation

29.

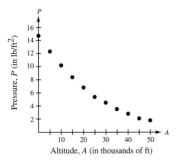

31. 2.45 pounds per square inch

33.

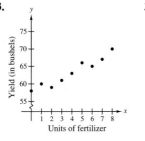

35. $y = 57.49 + 1.43x$; 71.8

37.

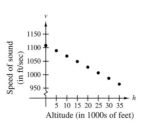

39. $v = 1117.3 - 4.1h$; 1006.6

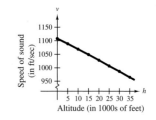

41. $y = -2.179x + 22.964$ **43.** $y = 2.378x + 23.546$

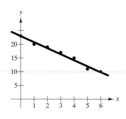
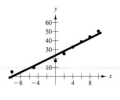

45. (a) $y = 11.1 + 0.28t$; 12.78

(b)   (c) $r \approx 0.987$

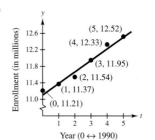

47. Mean: 8.86; median: 8; mode: 7

49. Mean: 10.29; median: 8; mode: 7

51. Mean: \$67.14; median: \$65.35

53. Mean: 3.065; median: 3; mode: 3

55. One possibility: $\{4, 4, 10\}$

57. The median gives the most representative description.

Instructor's Answers

Chapter 1

Section 1.1   *(page 9)*

2. (a) 100   (b) 100, -82, $-\frac{24}{3}$ (c) 100, -82, $-\frac{24}{3}$, -8.2

$$\begin{array}{c}
-82 \quad -8.2 \; -\frac{24}{3} \qquad 100 \\
\hline
-100\,-75\,-50\,-25 \quad 0 \; 25 \; 50 \; 75 \; 100
\end{array}$$

4. (a) 8   (b) 8, -1, $-\frac{10}{2}$ (c) 8, -1, $\frac{4}{3}$, -3.25, $-\frac{10}{2}$

$$\begin{array}{c}
-\frac{10}{2}\; -3.25 \; -1 \; \frac{4}{3} \qquad 8 \\
\hline
-6 \;\; -4 \;\; -2 \;\; 0 \;\; 2 \;\; 4 \;\; 6 \;\; 8
\end{array}$$

6. $-5 < -3$ **8.** $-2 < 3$ **10.** $-\frac{7}{2} < \frac{5}{2}$

12. $50.5 < 53.5$

14. $6 > -2$ **16.** $2 > \frac{3}{2}$

$$\begin{array}{c}
-2 \qquad\qquad 6 \\
\hline
-2 \;\; 0 \;\; 2 \;\; 4 \;\; 6
\end{array}\qquad
\begin{array}{c}
\frac{3}{2} \; 2 \\
\hline
-1 \;\; 0 \;\; 1 \;\; 2 \;\; 3
\end{array}$$

18. $-\frac{7}{3} > -\frac{7}{2}$ **20.** $28.60 > -3.75$

$$\begin{array}{c}
-\frac{7}{2} \;\; -\frac{7}{3} \\
\hline
-4 \;\; -3 \;\; -2 \;\; -1 \;\; 0
\end{array}\qquad
\begin{array}{c}
-3.75 \qquad\qquad 28.60 \\
\hline
-5 \; 0 \; 5 \; 10 \; 15 \; 20 \; 25 \; 30
\end{array}$$

22. $-\frac{3}{8} > -\frac{5}{8}$ **24.** $2 < \pi$

$$\begin{array}{c}
-\frac{5}{8} \; -\frac{3}{8} \\
\hline
-2 \qquad -1 \qquad 0
\end{array}\qquad
\begin{array}{c}
2 \quad \pi \\
\hline
0 \;\; 1 \;\; 2 \;\; 3 \;\; 4
\end{array}$$

26. 5   **28.** 10

30. -2 **32.** 7.5

$$\begin{array}{c}
-2 \qquad\qquad 2 \\
\hline
-3 \;-2\; -1 \; 0 \; 1 \; 2 \; 3
\end{array}\qquad
\begin{array}{c}
-7.5 \qquad\qquad 7.5 \\
\hline
-8\,-6\,-4\,-2\; 0 \; 2 \; 4 \; 6 \; 8
\end{array}$$

Distance: 2   Distance: 7.5

34. $-\frac{3}{4}$ **36.** 3, 3   **38.** 2.4, 2.4

$$\begin{array}{c}
-\frac{3}{4} \qquad\qquad \frac{3}{4} \\
\hline
-1 \;\; -\frac{1}{2} \;\; 0 \;\; \frac{1}{2} \;\; 1
\end{array}$$

Distance: $\frac{3}{4}$

40. 6   **42.** 16.2   **44.** $\frac{9}{16}$ **46.** -43.8 **48.** -91.3

50. 0   **52.** $|525| = |-525|$ **54.** $|16| < |-25|$

56. $|1026| > |800|$ **58.** $\left|-\frac{7}{8}\right| < \left|\frac{4}{3}\right|$

60. $-|-64| < |-50|$ **62.** $|-4.9| < |-10.2|$

64.
$$\begin{array}{c}
-\frac{1}{2} \quad |-1.9| \;\; 3.7 \;\; \frac{16}{3} \\
\hline
-1 \; 0 \; 1 \; 2 \; 3 \; 4 \; 5 \; 6
\end{array}$$

66.
$$\begin{array}{c}
-|3.2| \; -2.3 \qquad |-2.3| \;\; 3.2 \\
\hline
-4 \,-3\, -2 \,-1 \; 0 \; 1 \; 2 \; 3 \; 4
\end{array}$$

68. 15.3, 27.3   **70.** 35.5, 49.5   **72.** $\frac{8}{4} = 2$, $\frac{7}{4} = 1.75$

74. -25; $|-25| > |10|$

76. The smaller number is located to the left of the larger number on the real number line.

78. False. $|0| = 0$ **80.** True   **82.** True

Section 1.2   *(page 24)*

2. 7   **4.** -11

$$\begin{array}{c}
\longleftarrow \longrightarrow \\
\hline
0 \; 1 \; 2 \; 3 \; 4 \; 5 \; 6 \; 7 \; 8 \; 9 \; 10
\end{array}\qquad
\begin{array}{c}
\longleftarrow \\
\hline
-10 \;\; -8 \;\; -6 \;\; -4 \;\; -2 \;\; 0
\end{array}$$

6. -3 **8.** 0   **10.** -1 **12.** 0   **14.** -50

16. 25   **18.** 32   **20.** 45   **22.** -10 **24.** -135

26. -976 **28.** 706   **30.** 40,431   **32.** -661

34. 5   **36.** 15   **38.** 26   **40.** -30 **42.** -190

44. 3100   **46.** -80 **48.** -5 **50.** 75

52. -290 **54.** 125   **56.** -100 **58.** 20

60. -36 **62.** $5 + 5 + 5 + 5 = 20$

64. $(-2) + (-2) + (-2) + (-2) + (-2) + (-2) = -12$

66. 0   **68.** -50 **70.** 160   **72.** 3000   **74.** 21

76. -80 **78.** 480   **80.** 72   **82.** -336

84. 260   **86.** 8190   **88.** 7   **90.** -7 **92.** 0

94. 5   **96.** -12 **98.** Division by zero is undefined.

100. 1   **102.** 82   **104.** -82 **106.** 310

108. 641   **110.** 713   **112.** 4110   **114.** 14,400

116. Prime   **118.** Composite   **120.** Composite

122. Composite   **124.** Composite   **126.** $2 \cdot 2 \cdot 13$

128. $3 \cdot 11 \cdot 17$ **130.** $5 \cdot 7 \cdot 7$

132. $2 \cdot 2 \cdot 2 \cdot 3 \cdot 11$ **134.** $3 \cdot 3 \cdot 13 \cdot 13$

136. \$2356.42   **138.** 7000 feet

140. (a) \$105.8 billion   (b) 16   **142.** 44 points

144. \$208   **146.** 900 square feet

148. (a) 82   **150.** 180 cubic meters

(b)

(c) $73 - 82 = -9$
$77 - 82 = -5$
$87 - 82 = 5$
$91 - 82 = 9$
The sum is 0.

152. (a) $2 + (-4) = -2$

(b) Adding two integers with unlike signs

(c) On the last two plays, the team gained 2 yards and lost 4 yards for a net loss of 2 yards.

154. There are 7 other twin primes. They are: 5, 7; 11, 13; 17, 19; 29, 31; 41, 43; 59, 61; 71, 73

156. (a) 1̸ 2 3 4̸ 5 6̸ 7 8̸ 9̸ 1̸0̸

11 1̸2̸ 13 1̸4̸ 1̸5̸ 1̸6̸ 17 1̸8̸ 19 2̸0̸

2̸1̸ 2̸2̸ 23 2̸4̸ 2̸5̸ 2̸6̸ 2̸7̸ 2̸8̸ 29 3̸0̸

3̸1̸ 3̸2̸ 3̸3̸ 3̸4̸ 3̸5̸ 3̸6̸ 37 3̸8̸ 3̸9̸ 4̸0̸

41 4̸2̸ 43 4̸4̸ 4̸5̸ 4̸6̸ 47 4̸8̸ 4̸9̸ 5̸0̸

5̸1̸ 5̸2̸ 53 5̸4̸ 5̸5̸ 5̸6̸ 5̸7̸ 5̸8̸ 59 6̸0̸

61 6̸2̸ 6̸3̸ 6̸4̸ 6̸5̸ 6̸6̸ 67 6̸8̸ 6̸9̸ 7̸0̸

71 7̸2̸ 73 7̸4̸ 7̸5̸ 7̸6̸ 7̸7̸ 7̸8̸ 79 8̸0̸

8̸1̸ 8̸2̸ 83 8̸4̸ 8̸5̸ 8̸6̸ 8̸7̸ 8̸8̸ 89 9̸0̸

9̸1̸ 9̸2̸ 93 9̸4̸ 9̸5̸ 9̸6̸ 97 9̸8̸ 9̸9̸ 1̸0̸0̸

(b) Prime

158. Subtract the smaller absolute value from the larger absolute value and attach the sign of the integer with the larger absolute value.

160. Positive

162. The product (or quotient) of two nonzero real numbers of like signs is positive. The product (or quotient) of two nonzero real numbers of unlike signs is negative.

164. Multiply the divisor and quotient to obtain the dividend.

166. $\frac{1}{0}, \frac{0}{0}$

Section 1.3   *(page 40)*

2. 45   **4.** 16   **6.** 2   **8.** 39   **10.** 2   **12.** $\frac{3}{4}$

14. $\frac{2}{7}$ **16.** $\frac{1}{5}$ **18.** $\frac{4}{7}$ **20.** $\frac{2}{3}$ **22.** $\frac{1}{2}$ **24.** $\frac{18}{35}$

26. 3   **28.** $\frac{1}{4}$ **30.** 2   **32.** $-\frac{1}{4}$ **34.** $\frac{21}{8}$

36. $\frac{12}{15}$ **38.** $\frac{12}{28}$ **40.** $\frac{11}{10}$ **42.** $\frac{1}{2}$ **44.** $\frac{10}{9}$ **46.** $\frac{7}{8}$

48. $\frac{67}{25}$ **50.** $-\frac{19}{36}$ **52.** $\frac{7}{20}$ **54.** $\frac{19}{28}$ **56.** $\frac{64}{9}$

58. $\frac{3}{16}$ **60.** $\frac{23}{3}$ **62.** $-\frac{7}{4}$ **64.** $\frac{21}{8}$ **66.** $\frac{301}{100}$

68. $\frac{277}{20}$ **70.** $\frac{27}{8}$ **72.** $\frac{19}{8}$ **74.** $-\frac{119}{20}$ **76.** $\frac{13}{60}$

78. $-\frac{10}{21}$ **80.** $\frac{1}{3}$ **82.** -1 **84.** $\frac{1}{36}$ **86.** $\frac{5}{24}$

88. $-\frac{28}{3}$ **90.** 35   **92.** $-\frac{51}{2}$ **94.** $-\frac{289}{10}$ **96.** $\frac{1}{14}$

98. $-\frac{9}{5}$ **100.** $\frac{1}{10}$ **102.** $\frac{12}{7}$ **104.** $\frac{3}{7}$ **106.** 0

108. Division by zero is undefined.   **110.** $\frac{5}{24}$ **112.** $\frac{11}{24}$

114. $\frac{11}{14}$ **116.** 0.625   **118.** 0.35   **120.** $0.8\overline{3}$

122. $0.5\overline{3}$ **124.** $0.\overline{238095}$ **126.** -7.47

128. 106.65   **130.** 4.30   **132.** -54.76 **134.** -0.51

136. ≈ 2 **138.** $5\frac{11}{12}$ yards   **140.** $\frac{7}{2}$ cups   **142.** $\frac{17}{48}$

144. $6.26   **146.** $1.302   **148.** $1.98

150. ≈ 14 minutes

152. The product is greater than 20, because the factors are greater than factors that yield a product of 20.

154. No. $-\frac{3}{4} + \left(-\frac{1}{8}\right) = -\frac{7}{8}$

156. If the fractions have the same sign, the product is positive. If the fractions have opposite signs, the product is negative.

158. No. $\frac{2}{3} = 0.\overline{6}$ (nonterminating)

160. There are 4 one-sixths in $\frac{2}{3}$.

162. True   **164.** False. $\frac{1}{2} \cdot \frac{1}{4} = \frac{1}{8}$ **166.** False

168. N. Since P and R are between 0 and 1, their product PR is less than the smaller of P and R but positive.

Section 1.4   *(page 51)*

2. $(-5)^4$ **4.** $(1.6)^5$ **6.** $\left(\frac{3}{8}\right)\left(\frac{3}{8}\right)\left(\frac{3}{8}\right)\left(\frac{3}{8}\right)\left(\frac{3}{8}\right)$

8. $(0.01)(0.01)(0.01)(0.01)(0.01)(0.01)(0.01)$

10. $\left(\frac{3}{11}\right)\left(\frac{3}{11}\right)\left(\frac{3}{11}\right)\left(\frac{3}{11}\right)$ **12.** Positive   **14.** Positive

16. 64   **18.** 125   **20.** -9 **22.** $\frac{64}{125}$ **24.** 5.0625

26. 12   **28.** 113   **30.** 17   **32.** 36   **34.** 34

36. 64   **38.** -24 **40.** 2   **42.** 21   **44.** $\frac{7}{80}$

46. $-\frac{1}{8}$ **48.** $\frac{12}{125}$ **50.** 5   **52.** 0   **54.** 2

56. 48,500   **58.** 328,000   **60.** 0.0623   **62.** 0.8235

64. Division by zero is undefined.   **66.** 366.12

68. 10.69   **70.** $4 - (6 - 2) = 4 - 6 + 2$

72. $\dfrac{8 - 6}{2} = \dfrac{8}{2} - \dfrac{6}{2} = 1$

74. Commutative Property of Addition

76. Commutative Property of Multiplication

78. Multiplicative Identity Property

80. Associative Property of Multiplication

82. Additive Inverse Property

84. Associative Property of Addition

86. Additive Inverse Property

88. Distributive Property

90. Distributive Property

92. Associative Property of Multiplication   **94.** $5 + y$

96. $-3(10)$ **98.** $5u + 5v$ **100.** $4x - xy$

102. $(12 \cdot 3)4$ **104.** $(10 + x) + 2y$

106. (a) -12 (b) $\frac{1}{12}$ **108.** (a) $\frac{1}{2}$ (b) -2

110. (a) $-5y$ (b) $\dfrac{1}{5y}$ **112.** (a) $-uv$ (b) $\dfrac{1}{uv}$

114. 20   **116.** 1

118. $7(x - 2) = 7x - 14$ **120.** $5\left(\frac{1}{5}\right) = 1$

122. $3 + 10(x + 1)$

$= 3 + 10x + 10$　　Distributive Property

$= 3 + 10 + 10x$　　Commutative Property of Addition

$= (3 + 10) + 10x$　　Associative Property of Addition

$= 13 + 10x$　　Addition of Real Numbers

124. $2(x + 3) + x$

$= 2x + 2 \cdot 3 + x$　　Distributive Property of Addition

$= 2x + x + 6$　　Commutative Property of Addition

$= (2 + 1)x + 6$　　Distributive Property

$= 3x + 6$　　Addition of Real Numbers

$= 3(x + 2)$　　Distributive Property

126. 128 square units　　**128.** 3,430,000

130. \$5,368,709.12

132. $30(30 - 8) = 30(30) - 30(8) = 660$ square units

134. $a(b - c) = ab - ac$　　**136.** Yes

138. No. $-6^2 = -36, (-6)^2 = 36$

140. (a) Perform operations inside symbols of grouping, starting with the innermost symbols.

(b) Evaluate all exponential expressions.

(c) Perform all multiplications and divisions from left to right.

(d) Perform all additions and subtractions from left to right.

142. $-9 + \dfrac{9 + 20}{3(5)} - (-3) = -9 + \dfrac{29}{15} + 3$

$= -6 + \dfrac{29}{15}$

$= \dfrac{-90 + 29}{15}$

$= -\dfrac{61}{15}$

144. Associative Property of Addition:
$a + (b + c) = (a + b) + c$,
$3 + (4 + x) = (3 + 4) + x$

Associative Property of Multiplication:
$a(bc) = (ab)c, 3(4x) = (3 \cdot 4)x$

146. (a) $2 \cdot 2 + 2 \cdot 3 = 4 + 6 = 10$

(b) $2 \cdot 5 = 10$

(c) $2 \cdot 2 + 2 \cdot 3 = 2(2 + 3) = 2 \cdot 5 = 10$

Review Exercises　*(page 56)*

2. $\dfrac{25}{3} > \dfrac{5}{3}$

4. $10.6 > -3.5$

6. 10.4, 10.4　　**8.** $-\frac{2}{3}, \frac{2}{3}$　　**10.** 3.4　　**12.** 9.6

14. $|-10| > |4|$　　**16.** $|2.3| > -|2.3|$　　**18.** 68

20. -95　　**22.** 0　　**24.** -670　　**26.** 120

28. -88　　**30.** 2560　　**32.** -460　　**34.** 13

36. -8　　**38.** 273　　**40.** -126　　**42.** 4516

44. 1,499,685　　**46.** 12,489　　**48.** Composite

50. Prime　　**52.** $2 \cdot 3 \cdot 11 \cdot 13$　　**54.** 1787

56. 22　　**58.** 11　　**60.** $\frac{3}{7} = \frac{12}{28}$　　**62.** $\frac{9}{12} = \frac{12}{16}$

64. $\frac{1}{4}$　　**66.** $-\frac{1}{3}$　　**68.** $\frac{29}{75}$　　**70.** $-\frac{43}{24}$　　**72.** $-\frac{3}{5}$

74. $-\frac{53}{20}$　　**76.** 1　　**78.** $\frac{1}{15}$　　**80.** $-\frac{21}{8}$　　**82.** $-\frac{3}{32}$

84. 0　　**86.** 87.36　　**88.** 5.04　　**90.** 1000.80

92. 25　　**94.** -16　　**96.** $(-3)^2 > (-3)^3$

98. $\left(\frac{2}{3}\right)^3 < \left(\frac{2}{3}\right)^2$　　**100.** $\frac{1}{108}$　　**102.** $-15,600$

104. 45　　**106.** 72　　**108.** -60　　**110.** 8

112. 14　　**114.** Division by zero is undefined.

116. Multiplicative Inverse Property

118. Associative Property of Multiplication

120. Commutative Property of Addition

122. Associative Property of Addition

124. Divisible by 9; 9, 18, 27, . . .

126. True　　**128.** \$300

130. (a) 86,000,000

(b) 25,000,000

(c) 77,000,000, 80,000,000, 86,000,000, 92,000,000, 91,000,000, 104,000,000, 95,000,000. Increased until 1988.

(d) The bar representing the winning candidate must be taller than the stacked bars of the other candidates. No.

132. $\frac{13}{24}$　　**134.** $\frac{27}{32}$ inches per hour

136. 108 cubic feet, 6739.2 pounds

Chapter 2

Section 2.1　*(page 68)*

2. $1.25n$　　**4.** $50x$　　**6.** Variable: y
　　　　Constant: 1

8. Variable: z　　**10.** $6x, -1$　　**12.** $5, -3t^2$
Constant: 3^2

14. $6x, -\frac{2}{3}$　　**16.** $x^2, 18xy, y^2$　　**18.** $16, -(x + 1)$

20. $10, -\dfrac{t}{6}$ **22.** $x^2, \dfrac{3x+1}{x-1}, 4$

24. 25   **26.** $\frac{1}{8}$ **28.** $\frac{3}{4}$ **30.** π

32. -5.32 **34.** $x \cdot x \cdot x \cdot x \cdot x \cdot x$

36. $5 \cdot 5 \cdot 5 \cdot x \cdot x$ **38.** $3 \cdot u \cdot v \cdot v \cdot v \cdot v$

40. $z^3 \cdot z^3 \cdot z^3 = z \cdot z \cdot z \cdot z \cdot z \cdot z \cdot z \cdot z \cdot z$

42. $a \cdot a \cdot y \cdot y \cdot y \cdot y \cdot y$

44. $2 \cdot x \cdot x \cdot x \cdot x \cdot z \cdot z \cdot z \cdot z$

46. $(s-t)(s-t)(s-t)(s-t)(s-t)$

48. $\left(\dfrac{2}{x+1}\right)\left(\dfrac{2}{x+1}\right)\left(\dfrac{2}{x+1}\right)$

50. $2 \cdot 2(a-b)(a-b)(a-b)(a-b)(a-b)(a-b)$

52. $\frac{1}{3}x^5$ **54.** $\left(\frac{1}{3}x\right)^5$

56. $y^2 z^4$ **58.** $8^3(u-v)^3$ **60.** $\left(\dfrac{r-s}{5}\right)^4$

62. (a) 2   **64.** (a) 0   **66.** (a) 0

   (b) -5 (b) -80 (b) 1

68. (a) 6   **70.** (a) -8 **72.** (a) $-\frac{1}{5}$

   (b) 10   (b) -12 (b) $\frac{3}{10}$

74. (a) 0   **76.** (a) 72   **78.** (a) 240

   (b) $-\frac{1}{10}$ (b) 1000   (b) 175

80. (a)

x	-1	0	1	2	3	4
$3-2x$	5	3	1	-1	-3	-5

   (b) -2 (c) $-\frac{3}{2}$

82. $(x+y)^2$, 169 square units

84. $x(x+3)$, 108 square units

86. Either n or $n-3$ is even. Therefore every product $n(n-3)$ is divisible by 2.

88. (a) 3.5, 4.625, 5.469, 6.102, 6.576, 6.932, 7.199
   Approaches 8.

   (b) 11, 10.25, 9.688, 9.266, 8.949, 8.712, 8.534
   Approaches 8.

90. Addition separates terms. Multiplication separates factors.

92. $10x$ is the base and 3 is the exponent.

Section 2.2   *(page 80)*

   2. z^4 **4.** $4y^4$ **6.** $-6x^6$ **8.** $8x^3$ **10.** $18u^3v^3$

12. $24x^3y^4$ **14.** v^6 **16.** $3p^4q^4$ **18.** $9z^2$

20. $s^{13}t^9$ **22.** $72y^7z^8$ **24.** $(t+1)^{10}$ **26.** $(x-3)^7$

28. $(-2x)^4 = (-2)^4x^4 = 16x^4 \neq -2x^4$

30. $(xy)^2 = x^2y^2 \neq xy^2$

32. Associative Property of Multiplication

34. Additive Identity Property

36. Associative Property of Addition

38. Distributive Property

40. Multiplicative Inverse Property

42. Distributive Property

44. Additive Inverse Property, Additive Identity Property

46. $(-5r)s = -5(rs)$
   Associative Property of Multiplication

48. $(4x-3y) + 0 = 4x - 3y$
   Additive Identity Property

50. $(2z-3) + [-(2z-3)] = 0$
   Additive Inverse Property

52. $(s-5) \cdot 1 = s - 5$
   Multiplicative Identity Property

54. $(2x-y)(-3) = -3(2x-y)$
   Commutative Property of Multiplication

56. $32 + 16z$ **58.** $-24 + 6t$ **60.** $6r - 6t + 6s$

62. $8y^2 - 4y$ **64.** $-5z + 2z^2$ **66.** $-x - y$

68. $2r^3 - rt$ **70.** $3x; 3y; 3(x+y) = 3x + 3y$

72. $a(b-c); ac; a(b-c) + ac = ab$

74. $-4xy, 2xz, -yz; -4, 2, -1$

76. $a^2, a^2; 5ab^2, -ab^2; -3b^2; 7a^2b$

78. $-\frac{1}{4}x^2, \frac{3}{4}x^2; -3x, x$

80. Variable factors are not alike. $x^2y^3 \neq x^2y$

82. $9x$ **84.** $4s + 3$ **86.** $5x - 4$ **88.** $10t + 5$

90. $r^2 + 2rs - 6$ **92.** $6x + 2$ **94.** $6x^2 + 3x$

96. $2rt - 5r^2t + 2rt^2$ **98.** $5\left(\dfrac{1}{x}\right) - 4x$

100. $10\left(\dfrac{a}{b}\right) + 1$ **102.** False. $-3(x-4) = -3x + 12$

104. False. $12y^2 + 3y^2 = 15y^2$ **106.** 174   **108.** 143.4

110. $35a$ **112.** $-5t$ **114.** $12y$ **116.** $-40t^3$

118. $2x$ **120.** $2x^2$ **122.** $21r^3s^4$ **124.** $-3x - 5$

126. $5x - 2$ **128.** $-13l + 30$ **130.** $-12r + 19s$

132. $-\frac{3}{8}y + 9$ **134.** 15   **136.** $-5x^2 + 6x$

138. $2z^2 + 2z + 5$ **140.** x^2 **142.** $-y^2 + 19y$

144. $\dfrac{y}{2}$ **146.** t **148.** $\dfrac{29x}{21}$ **150.** $-\dfrac{z}{12}$

152. $28,717.46   **154.** (a) $4ma^2L$ (b) $\frac{1}{2}k\pi a^4 L$

156. (a) Answers will vary.   (b) $\frac{57}{2}$

158. 46.8 square inches   **160.** Addition and multiplication

$$4x = x + x + x + x$$
$$x^4 = x \cdot x \cdot x \cdot x$$

162. Two terms are like terms if they are both constant or if they have the same variable factor(s). Like terms: $3x^2, -5x^2$; unlike terms: $3x^2, 5x$

164. $3(x + 9) = 3x + 3 \cdot 9$

166. (a) Perform operations inside symbols of grouping, starting with the innermost symbols.

(b) Evaluate all exponential expressions.

(c) Perform all multiplications and divisions from left to right.

(d) Perform all additions and subtractions from left to right.

168. $\dfrac{x}{3} + \dfrac{4x}{3} = \dfrac{5x}{3}$

Section 2.3   *(page 95)*

2. (a)   **4.** (f)   **6.** (c)   **8.** $25 + x$ **10.** $x - 7$

12. $10 + x$ **14.** $30x$ **16.** $\dfrac{x}{100}$ **18.** $\dfrac{1}{4}x$

20. $0.25x$ **22.** $3(x + 5)$ **24.** $\dfrac{x}{5} - 15$ **26.** $7 + 5x$

28. $|2x - 4|$ **30.** $2x^2 + 4$

32. A number increased by 9

34. Four decreased by 7 times a number

36. Nine decreased by $\frac{1}{4}$ of a number

38. Minus 10 times the difference of a number and 6

40. One-half decreased by a number divided by 5

42. The cube of a number, decreased by 1

44. $(6 + n)(5) = 30 + 5n$

46. $(4 + x) + [x + (-8)] = 2x - 4$

48. $x^2 + x(x + 1) = 2x^2 + x$ **50.** $4(x - 15) = 4x - 60$

52. $0.10d + 0.25q$ **54.** $0.022I$ **56.** $3r$

58. $12.50 + 0.75q$ **60.** $t = 14.2$ years

62. $t = 9.0$ years

64.

n	0	1	2	3	4	5
$7n + 5$	5	12	19	26	33	40
Differences		7	7	7	7	7

66. a **68.** $a = 4, b = 1$ **70.** $(-4x)(-4x) = 16x^2$

72. $\frac{1}{2}(2x^2)[(9x + 4) + (8 - x)] = 8x^3 + 12x^2$

74.

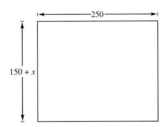

Area of the original lawn: 37,500 square feet
Area of the expanded lawn: $250(150 + x)$ square feet

76. $8w$ **78.** $4s$

80. (c) Center aisle: $3x$ feet; Side aisle: $2x$ feet

(d) $\frac{7}{6}$ feet; $7x + 14$ feet

(e) Rear aisle: $2x$ feet; Front region: $7 + 3x$ feet

(f) 1 foot; $19x + 22$ feet

(g) Center aisle: 6 feet
Width: 28 feet; Depth: 60 feet; 30×60 feet (canopy 4); Total cost: $1096

(h) Use plastic/aluminum chairs and/or decrease the width of the aisles.

82. Division

84. (a) No. Addition is commutative.

(b) Yes. Subtraction is not commutative.

(c) No. Multiplication is commutative.

(d) Yes. Division is not commutative.

Section 2.4   *(page 105)*

2. (a) Not a solution   **4.** (a) Solution

(b) Solution   (b) Not a solution

6. (a) Not a solution   **8.** (a) Solution

(b) Solution   (b) Not a solution

10. (a) Not a solution   **12.** (a) Solution

(b) Solution   (b) Solution

14. (a) Not a solution   **16.** (a) Solution

(b) Solution   (b) Solution

18. (a) Not a solution   **20.** (a) Not a solution

    (b) Solution   (b) Not a solution

22. (a) Solution   **24.** (a) Not a solution

    (b) Solution   (b) Solution

26. (a) Solution

    (b) Solution

28.

$14 - 3x = 5$	Given equation
$14 - 3x - 14 = 5 - 14$	Subtract 14 from both sides.
$14 - 14 - 3x = -9$	Commutative Property
$-3x = -9$	Additive Inverse Property
$\dfrac{-3x}{-3} = \dfrac{-9}{-3}$	Divide both sides by -3.
$x = 3$	Solution

30.

$\dfrac{4}{5}x = -28$	Given equation
$\dfrac{5}{4}\left(\dfrac{4}{5}x\right) = \dfrac{5}{4}(-28)$	Multiply both sides by $\frac{5}{4}$.
$x = -35$	Solution

32.

$x + 6 = -6(4 - x)$	Given equation
$x + 6 = -24 + 6x$	Distributive Property
$-x + x + 6 = -x - 24 + 6x$	Subtract x from both sides.
$6 = 5x - 24$	Combine like terms.
$6 + 24 = 5x - 24 + 24$	Add 24 to both sides.
$30 = 5x$	Combine like terms.
$\dfrac{30}{5} = \dfrac{5x}{5}$	Divide both sides by 5.
$6 = x$	Solution

34.

$\dfrac{x}{3} = x + 1$	Given equation
$3\left(\dfrac{x}{3}\right) = 3(x + 1)$	Multiply both sides by 3.
$x = 3x + 3$	Multiplicative Inverse and Distributive Properties
$-3x + x = -3x + 3x + 3$	Subtract $3x$ from both sides.
$-2x = 0 + 3$	Additive Inverse Property
$-2x = 3$	Additive Identity Property
$\dfrac{-2x}{-2} = \dfrac{3}{-2}$	Divide both sides by -2.
$x = -\dfrac{3}{2}$	Solution

36. 15   **38.** 48   **40.** A number decreased by 9 is 52.

42. Two times the difference of a number and 5 is 12.

44. The difference of a number and 2 divided by 10 is 6.

46. $4.5 = x + 1.2$ **48.** $225.98 = x - 64$

50. $3x + 4 = 16$ **52.** $120 - 6x = 96$

54. $\dfrac{x + 8}{4} = 32$ **56.** $0.25n + 7 = 8.75$

58. $24h = 72$ **60.** $4r + 24 = 200$

62. $x - 58 = 8695$ **64.** $\dfrac{d}{1100} = 3$

66. $48(158) - 6000 = I$ **68.** $10{,}120 + 1432 = x$

70. 375 miles   **72.** 9 dollars   **74.** 240 centimeters

76. Substitute the real number into the equation. If the equation is true, the real number is a solution. Given the equation $2x - 3 = 5$, $x = 4$ is a solution and $x = -2$ is not a solution.

78. Equivalent equations have the same solution set.

80. The total cost of a shipment of bulbs is \$840. Find the number of cases of bulbs if each case costs \$35.

Review Exercises   (page 110)

2. $5x^2, 5; -3x, -3; 10$ **4.** $\dfrac{x + 2y}{3}, \dfrac{1}{3}; -\dfrac{4x}{y}, -4$

6. $\left(\dfrac{3}{8}y\right)^4$ **8.** $3^3(y - x)^2$ **10.** (a) 0 (b) 56

12. (a) 0 (b) -7 **14.** y^6 **16.** t^{12} **18.** $3u^4$

20. $-6u^2v^3$ **22.** $45x^4$

24. Associative Property of Multiplication

26. Additive Identity Property   **28.** Distributive Property

30. $24s - 36t$ **32.** $6x + 24y$ **34.** $-3u^2 + 10uv$

36. $-42 + 12j$ **38.** $4c$ **40.** $-15x + 2y$

42. $\dfrac{19}{15}a + \dfrac{1}{6}b$ **44.** $-uv^2 + 12$ **46.** $3y^3 - y^2 + 1$

48. $-4\left(\dfrac{1}{u}\right) + 4\left(\dfrac{1}{u^2}\right)$ **50.** $10 - 3v$ **52.** $20x - 100$

54. $45 - 9y$ **56.** $13s + 10$ **58.** $24x - 21$

60. $2t^2 + 7t$ **62.** $100 - 5x$ **64.** $\dfrac{x}{10}$ **66.** $10 - \dfrac{x}{2}$

68. $15x - 2$ **70.** $|x + (-10)|$

72. Three times a number decreased by 2

74. Four times the sum of a number and 5

76. (a) Solution   **78.** (a) Not a solution

    (b) Not a solution   (b) Solution

80. (a) Solution   **82.** (a) Not a solution

    (b) Not a solution   (b) Not a solution

84. (a) Solution   **86.** $\frac{3}{4}b^2$ **88.** $0.05n + 0.25q$

(b) Solution

90. $6x - 2$

92. $(2n - 1) + (2n + 1) + (2n + 3) = 6n + 3$

94. 72,080   **96.** $a = 5, b = 4$ **98.** $135 = 45t$

100. $2L + 2(0.35L) = 2.7L = 72$

Chapter 3

Section 3.1   *(page 124)*

2. 11   **4.** 6   **6.** -9 **8.** 3

10. Original equation
Add 14 to both sides.
Combine like terms.
Divide both sides by 7.
Simplify.

12. Original equation
Add $3x$ to both sides.
Combine like terms.
Subtract 10 from both sides.
Combine like terms.
Divide both sides by 3.
Simplify.

14. -3 **16.** $\frac{3}{2}$ **18.** 3   **20.** 2   **22.** -2

24. $-\frac{5}{4}$ **26.** 4   **28.** $-\frac{1}{2}$ **30.** 3

32. No solution   **34.** -3 **36.** 0   **38.** $\frac{5}{2}$

40. Identity   **42.** $\frac{1}{5}$ **44.** 3   **46.** -1 **48.** -6

50. 2   **52.** $-\frac{7}{10}$ **54.** Identity   **56.** No solution

58. 80 inches × 40 inches   **60.** 75 centimeters

62. 6 hours   **64.** 500   **66.** 12 hours 30 minutes

68. 4   **70.** 62, 64, 66

72. Answers will vary. Examples are given.
Linear: $2x - 3 = 9, 2(x + 3) = x - 4$
Nonlinear: $x^2 - 3x = 0, xy = 4$

74. (a) Simplify each side by removing symbols of grouping, combining like terms, and reducing fractions on one or both sides.

(b) Add (or subtract) the same quantity to (from) both sides of the equation.

(c) Multiply (or divide) both sides of the equation by the same nonzero real number.

(d) Interchange the two sides of the equation.

76. Divide each side of the equation by 3. Multiplication Property of Equality

78. False

Section 3.2   *(page 134)*

2. 7   **4.** -7 **6.** 5   **8.** $\frac{22}{5}$ **10.** 7   **12.** 7

14. 2   **16.** Identity   **18.** 6   **20.** No solution

22. 2   **24.** 41   **26.** No solution   **28.** -26

30. $\frac{23}{6}$ **32.** $\frac{3}{2}$ **34.** -5 **36.** $\frac{16}{3}$ **38.** $-\frac{3}{4}$

40. $\frac{21}{2}$ **42.** $\frac{12}{7}$ **44.** No solution   **46.** $\frac{1}{2}$ **48.** -16

50. 6   **52.** 0   **54.** 12   **56.** $\frac{13}{4}$ **58.** 0   **60.** $\frac{5}{4}$

62. $-\frac{1}{4}$ **64.** 10.00   **66.** 13.24   **68.** -6.04

70. 0.19   **72.** 0.24   **74.** 6 hours

76. (a) 93.5

(b) No. A 100 on the final will yield only 89% for the course.

78. 4 gallons   **80.** 50 pounds   **82.** 2090 pounds

84. 2036   **86.** $-2(x - 5) = -2x + 10$

88. The least common multiple of the denominators is the simplest expression that is a multiple of all the denominators. The least common multiple of the denominators contains each prime factor of the denominators repeated the maximum number of times it occurs in any one of the factorizations of the denominators.

90. Because the expression is not an equation, there are not two sides to multiply by the least common multiple of the denominators.

Section 3.3   *(page 145)*

	Parts out		
Percent	of 100	Decimal	Fraction
2. 15%	15	0.15	$\frac{3}{20}$
4. 75%	75	0.75	$\frac{3}{4}$
6. 10.5%	10.5	0.105	$\frac{21}{200}$
8. 80%	80	0.80	$\frac{4}{5}$
10. 15%	15	0.15	$\frac{3}{20}$
12. 125%	125	1.25	$\frac{5}{4}$

14. 57%   **16.** 38%   **18.** 0.5%   **20.** 175%

22. 0.95   **24.** 0.085   **26.** 0.003   **28.** $0.\overline{3}$

30. 25%   **32.** 120%   **34.** $66\frac{2}{3}\%$ **36.** 150%

38. $66\frac{2}{3}\%$ **40.** $33\frac{1}{3}\%$ **42.** 744   **44.** 172

46. 200   **48.** 1462.5   **50.** 500   **52.** 84

54. 1221   **56.** 64,000   **58.** 39%   **60.** $\frac{2}{3}\%$

62. 100%   **64.** 15.5%

	Cost	Selling Price	Markup	Markup Rate
66.	$149.79	$224.87	$75.08	50.1%
68.	$680.00	$906.67	$226.67	$33\frac{1}{3}\%$
70.	$71.97	$119.95	$47.98	$66\frac{2}{3}\%$
72.	$269.23	$350.00	$80.77	30%
74.	$45.01	$69.99	$24.98	55.5%

	List Price	Sale Price	Discount	Discount Rate
76.	$18.95	$10.95	$8.00	42.2%
78.	$394.97	$259.97	$135.00	34.2%
80.	$50.99	$45.99	$5.00	9.8%
82.	$84.95	$29.73	$55.22	65%
84.	$315.00	$189.00	$126.00	40%

86. $11,550   **88.** 980   **90.** (a) 19.6%   (b) 1 out of 5

92. 4%   **94.** 6252

96. Buy now. The rise in price is more than the penalty for early withdrawal of the certificate of deposit.

98. 80   **100.** 35.3%   **102.** (a) 5.3%   (b) 6.9%

104. 1950s   19.7%   **106.** Percent means part of 100
1960s   23.4%
1970s   30.7%
1980s   25.0%
172.0 million

108. Percent to fraction: Divide by 100.
$37\% = \frac{37}{100}$

110. Divide and multiply the result by 100.
$\frac{3}{8} = 0.375 = 37.5\%$

112. No. $\frac{1}{2}\% = 0.5\% = 0.005$

Section 3.4   (page 156)

2. $\frac{3}{4}$ **4.** $\frac{10}{3}$ **6.** $\frac{4}{3}$ **8.** $\frac{2}{5}$ **10.** $\frac{5}{4}$ **12.** $\frac{4}{5}$

14. $\frac{1}{8}$ **16.** $\frac{1}{2}$ **18.** $\frac{1}{5}$ **20.** $\frac{8}{3}$ **22.** $\frac{1}{20}$ **24.** $\frac{11}{8}$

26. $\frac{3}{1}$ **28.** $0.1772   **30.** $0.1806   **32.** 3-pound tub

34. 18-ounce jar   **36.** 2.5-gallon container   **38.** $\frac{5}{2}$

40. 30   **42.** $\frac{25}{2}$ **44.** $\frac{7}{2}$ **46.** $\frac{2}{9}$ **48.** $\frac{9}{2}$ **50.** 10

52. 24   **54.** $\frac{11}{500}$ **56.** $\frac{23}{1}$ **58.** $\frac{3}{1}$

60. $\frac{13}{7}, \frac{13}{6}, \frac{13}{5}, \frac{52}{17}, \frac{26}{7}$; 1st gear   **62.** 0.82

64. $21\frac{1}{3}$ gallons   **66.** 75 pounds   **68.** $1523

70. 400   **72.** 5 cups   **74.** 64 pounds

76. $106\frac{2}{3}$ miles   **78.** 10   **80.** 81 feet   **82.** 20%

84. $283   **86.** $62

88. A ratio is a comparison of one number with another by division.

90. The units must be the same.   **92.** Answers will vary.

Section 3.5   (page 169)

2. $\dfrac{P - 2W}{2}$ **4.** $\dfrac{C}{2\pi}$ **6.** $\dfrac{V}{\pi r^2}$ **8.** $\dfrac{S}{1 - R}$

10. $\dfrac{A}{\left(1 + \dfrac{r}{n}\right)^{nt}}$ **12.** $\dfrac{Fr^2}{\alpha m_1}$ **14.** $\dfrac{3V}{4\pi a^2}$

16. $\dfrac{2S - n^2 d + nd}{2n}$ **18.** $\dfrac{150}{11}$ watts per volt

20. 320 feet   **22.** 8 seconds   **24.** 48 miles per hour

26. 3 feet   **28.** 144 square feet   **30.** 2.39 meters

32. 12π meters^3 **34.** 22 inches   **36.** 136 square inches

38. $262.50   **40.** $660.29   **42.** 8.6%   **44.** 3 years

46. $10,000   **48.** 0.139 hour or $\approx$ 8.3 minutes

50. 1665 miles   **52.** 360 meters per minute

54. 55 miles per hour for 3 hours
48 miles per hour for 1.25 hours

56. 40 minutes after the second jogger leaves, $3\frac{1}{3}$ miles

58. Solution 1: 4 liters   **60.** Solution 1: 18.75 gallons
Solution 2: 1 liter   Solution 2: 6.25 gallons

62. 20-cent stamps: 4   **64.** 32 dimes
33-cent stamps: 16   18 quarters

66. 16 dozen roses, 8 dozen carnations

68. 100 children
300 adults

70.

Metal A x	Metal B $5 - x$	Price per ounce of the alloy
0	5	$16.00
1	4	$23.20
2	3	$30.40
3	2	$37.60
4	1	$44.80
5	0	$52.00

(a) Decreases

(b) Increases

(c) Average of the two prices

72. $3\frac{3}{7}$ hours   **74.** 8   **76.** 64

78. Candidate A: 500 votes
   Candidate B: 300 votes
   Candidate C: 200 votes

80. Yes. $A = \frac{1}{2}bh$. If h is doubled, you have $A = \frac{1}{2}b(2h) = 2\left(\frac{1}{2}bh\right)$.

82. Divide by 2 to obtain 90 miles per hour and divide by 2 again to obtain 45 miles per hour.

$$r = \frac{d}{t} = \frac{180}{4} = 45 \text{ miles per hour}$$

84. Answers will vary.

Section 3.6   *(page 183)*

2. z is greater than 8.

4. x is greater than -3 *and* less than 4.

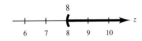

6. t is greater than -3.8 *and* less than or equal to -3.

8. (a) Yes   **10.** (a) No   **12.** (a) No   **14.** (a) No
   (b) No   (b) Yes   (b) Yes   (b) No
   (c) Yes   (c) Yes   (c) Yes   (c) Yes
   (d) Yes   (d) No   (d) No   (d) Yes

16. f   **18.** a   **20.** e

22. $t < 5$ **24.** $z > 2$

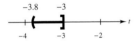

26. $x > \frac{3}{2}$ **28.** $x < -3$

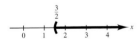

30. $x \le -16$ **32.** $x \le 4$

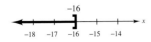

34. $x < 3$ **36.** $x \le 1$

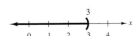 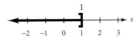

38. $x > -7$ **40.** $t < 3$

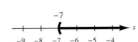

42. $z \le \frac{3}{11}$ **44.** $y < \frac{21}{2}$

46. $x \ge \frac{12}{7}$ **48.** $-2 < x \le 5$

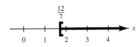

50. $-\frac{3}{4} \le x < \frac{1}{2}$ **52.** $-2 \le x < 8$

54. $\frac{5}{3} < x < \frac{9}{4}$ **56.** $2 \le x < 3$

58. $x \le -\frac{5}{2}$ or $x > 3$ **60.** $A = \{x \mid x \le 1\}$
                                            $B = \{x \mid x \ge 2\}$
 $A \cup B$

62. $A = \{x \mid x > 4\}$ **64.** $A = \{x \mid x < 12\}$
   $B = \{x \mid x < 10\}$ $B = \{x \mid x > 6\}$
   $A \cap B$ $A \cap B$

66. $A = \{x \mid x \ge -4\}$ **68.** $P \le 2$ **70.** $z \ge 3$
   $B = \{x \mid x \le -10\}$
   $A \cup B$

72. $t < 8$ **74.** $-2 \le x < 5$ **76.** $-4 < x \le 3$

78. Department A's budget is less than Department C's budget. Transitive Property

80. $1600   **82.** $x \ge 36$ **84.** $0 \le x \le 34$ bushels

86. $1 \le d \le 5$ miles

88. $a < b$ means that a is to the left of b on the real number line. $a \le b$ means that a is to the left of b or coincides with b on the real number line. $a > b$ means that a is to the right of b on the real number line. $a \ge b$ means that a is to the right of b or coincides with b on the real number line. $a = b$ means that a and b occupy the same position on the real number line.

90. Yes. Multiplication and Division Properties of Inequalities.

CHAPTER 3

92. The inequality symbol is reversed. If $x - 3 > 2$, then $-5(x - 3) < -10$.

94. $\geq$ **96.** True. Subtract 6 from both sides of the inequality.

98. False. $z \geq 0$

Section 3.7 *(page 190)*

2. No   **4.** Yes   **6.** $m + 4 = 3$ **8.** $3k - 5 = 7$
$m + 4 = -3$ $3k - 5 = -7$

10. ± 6 **12.** ± 3 **14.** No solution   **16.** ± 8

18. $-15, 35$ **20.** $-8, -4$ **22.** $1, 5$ **24.** 4

26. $-\frac{22}{3}, 4$ **28.** $-4, \frac{20}{3}$ **30.** $-\frac{7}{2}, 2$ **32.** $-24, 12$

34. $\frac{4}{5}, \frac{52}{15}$ **36.** $|3t - 5| = 7$ **38.** $|t - 10| = 4$

40. (a) No   **42.** (a) Yes   **44.** (a) No   **46.** (a) No
(b) Yes   (b) No   (b) No   (b) No
(c) No   (c) No   (c) Yes   (c) Yes
(d) Yes   (d) Yes   (d) Yes   (d) No

48. $-3 \leq x - 7 \leq 3$ **50.** $8 - x > 10$
$8 - x < -10$

52.    **54.**

56. $-5 < x < 5$ **58.** $x \leq -5$ or $x \geq 5$

60. $y < -7$ or $y > 7$ **62.** $-1 \leq u \leq 7$

64. $-8 < z < 2$ **66.** $-4 \leq z \leq 4$

68. $v < 0$ or $v > 8$ **70.** $s \leq -8$ or $s \geq 2$

72. d   **74.** b   **76.** $|x - 1| \leq 3$

78. $|x - 6| > 3$ **80.** $|x| > 2$ **82.** $|x| \geq 5$

84. $|x - 6| \leq 2$ **86.**
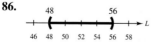

88. Greatest amount: 66 ounces   **90.** $|x - 2| = 0$
Least amount: 62 ounces

92. The solution is the set of all real numbers whose distance from 0 on the real number line is more than 3.

Review Exercises *(page 194)*

2. 7   **4.** 5   **6.** Original equation
Multiply both sides by 12.
Combine like terms.
Divide both sides by 7.
Simplify.

8. 11   **10.** 5   **12.** -7 **14.** 4   **16.** 8   **18.** $\frac{10}{3}$

20. -7 **22.** $-\frac{9}{2}$ **24.** $\frac{22}{5}$ **26.** 14   **28.** -52

30. $\frac{15}{8}$ **32.** 3.32   **34.** 3.58

36.

Percent	Parts out of 100	Decimal	Fraction
80%	80	0.80	$\frac{4}{5}$

38. 26   **40.** 340   **42.** 4%   **44.** $\frac{1}{16}$ **46.** $\frac{8}{3}$

48. 15   **50.** $\frac{25}{4}$ **52.** 2   **54.** $\frac{S + d - a}{d}$

56. 14.1 meters   **58.** 171 minutes

60. 40 kilometers per hour   **62.** $-3 < x < 0$

64. $x \geq 20$

66. $x \leq 3$ **68.** $x > 3$

70. $x \leq -3$ **72.** $n < -6$

74. $k > -24$ **76.** $y \leq \frac{76}{5}$

78. $-\frac{1}{2} < x \leq 2$ **80.** $9 < x \leq 18$

82. $A = \{x | x \leq -2\}$ **84.** $A = \{x | x > -3\}$
$B = \{x | x \geq -1\}$ $B = \{x | x < 4\}$
$A \cup B$ $A \cap B$

86. $A = \{x \mid x < 5\}$
$B = \{x \mid x > -1\}$
$A \cap B$

88. $A = \{x \mid x \geq 6\}$
$B = \{x \mid x \leq -1\}$
$A \cup B$

90. $x \geq 0$ **92.** $A \leq 100$ **94.** $P \geq 24$

96. $50, 250$ **98.** $-48, 48$ **100.** $-\frac{5}{2}, 4$

102. $u \leq -4$ or $u \geq 4$ **104.** $-10 < k < 2$

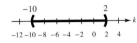

106. $n \leq -\frac{4}{3}$ or $n \geq 2$

108. 12 units   **110.** 2 feet, 8 feet   **112.** $19,290

114. Living with spouse: 10,540,530
Living with other relatives: 547,560
Living alone or with nonrelatives: 2,600,910

116. $4\frac{1}{2}$ cups   **118.** $\frac{4}{3}$ **120.** 1108.3 miles

122. 51.7 miles per hour

124. Candidate A: 400   **126.** 25 centimeters
Candidate B: 400
Candidate C: 500

128. 8%   **130.** $178.06   **132.** $\frac{24}{11} \approx 2.2$ hours

Chapter 4

Section 4.1   *(page 209)*

2.

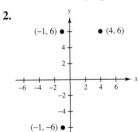

4.

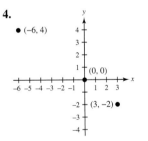

6.

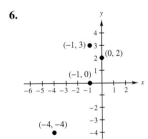

8.

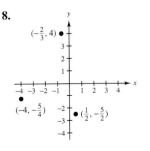

10.

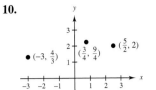

12. A: $(-3, 1)$
B: $(2, 4)$
C: $(-3, -3)$
D: $(5, -5)$

14. A: $(0, 3)$ **16.** Quadrant IV   **18.** Quadrant I
B: $(4, 0)$
C: $(-2, -2)$
D: $(3, -1)$

20. Quadrant II   **22.** Quadrant I or IV

24. Quadrant I or II   **26.** Quadrant I or III

28. $(-2, 0)$ **30.** $(12, -4)$

32.

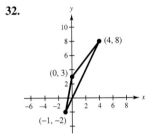

34.

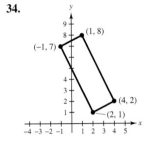

36.

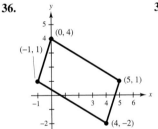

38.

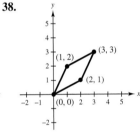

40.

x	-2	0	2	4	6
$y = \frac{1}{4}x + 1$	$\frac{1}{2}$	1	$\frac{3}{2}$	2	$\frac{5}{2}$

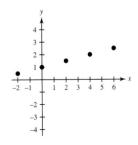

CHAPTER 4

42.

x	-4	-2	0	2	4
$y = -\frac{1}{2}x + 3$	5	4	3	2	1

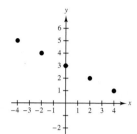

44.

x	-2	0	$\frac{1}{2}$	2	4
$y = -\frac{7}{2}x + 3$	10	3	$\frac{5}{4}$	-4	-11

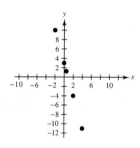

46. $y = -2x + 1$ **48.** $y = \frac{1}{2}x + 3$ **50.** $y = \frac{3}{4}x + \frac{7}{4}$

52. (a) Not a solution   **54.** (a) Solution

(b) Solution   (b) Solution

(c) Solution   (c) Not a solution

(d) Not a solution   (d) Not a solution

56. (a) Not a solution   **58.** (a) Not a solution

(b) Not a solution   (b) Solution

(c) Solution   (c) Solution

(d) Solution   (d) Solution

60.

x	0	2	4	6	8
$y = -800x + 9500$	9500	7900	6300	4700	3100

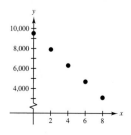

62.

x	2	5	8	10	20
$y = 0.50x + 10$	11	12.50	14	15	20

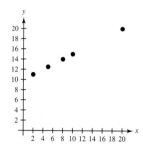

64. (a)

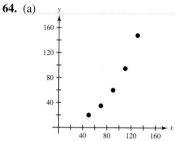

(b) Increasing at an increasing rate

66. (a)

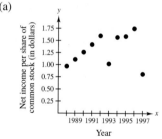

(b) Greatest increase: 1994
Greatest decrease: 1997

68. 1,000,000   **70.** 100,000; 7%   **72.** $23,400

74. 61%   **76.** 14%

78. (a) and (b)

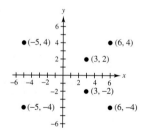

(c) Reflection in the x-axis

80. The *x*-coordinate measures the distance from the *y*-axis to the point. The *y*-coordinate measures the distance from the *x*-axis to the point.

82. First quadrant: $(+, +)$
Second quadrant: $(-, +)$

84. No. The scale will be determined by the magnitudes of the quantities being measured by *x* and *y*. If *y* is measuring revenue for a product and *x* is measuring time in years, the scale on the *y*-axis may be in units of $100,000 and the scale on the *x*-axis in units of 1.

Section 4.2   *(page 219)*

2. b   **4.** e   **6.** c   **8.** f

10.

x	−2	−1	0	1	2
y	−3	−2	−1	0	1

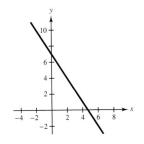

12.

x	−2	0	2	4	6
y	10	7	4	1	−2

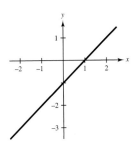

14.

x	−2	0	2	4	6
y	−6	−3	0	3	6

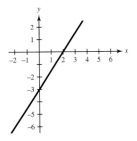

16.

x	−1	0	1	2	3
y	4	1	0	1	4

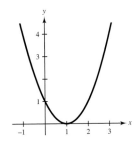

18. $(-5, 0), (0, 2)$ **20.** $(3, 0), (0, 4)$
22. $(-4, 0), (4, 0), (0, 4)$ **24.** $(-2, 0), (2, 0), (0, -4)$
26. $\left(\frac{5}{3}, 0\right), (0, 5)$ **28.** $(6, 0), (0, 3)$ **30.** $(10, 0), (0, 10)$
32. $\left(\frac{1}{3}, 0\right), \left(0, -\frac{1}{2}\right)$ **34.** $(-25, 0), (0, 10)$
36. $(2, 0), \left(0, \frac{3}{2}\right)$

38.

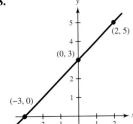

40.

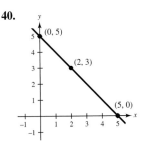

42.

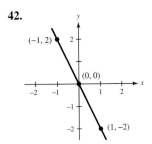

44.

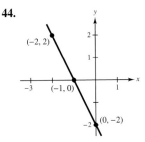

CHAPTER 4

46.
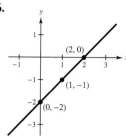

48.
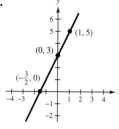

66.
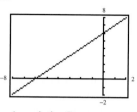
Associative Property
of Addition

68.
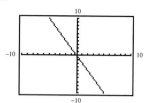

50.
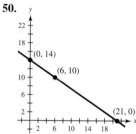

52.
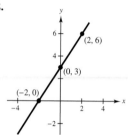

70.
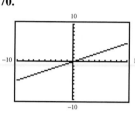

72.
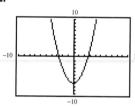

54.
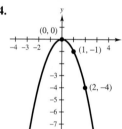

56.
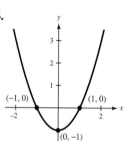

74.
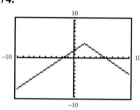

76.
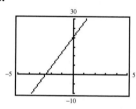

58.
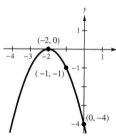

60.
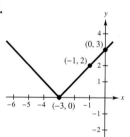

78.
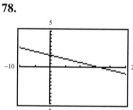

80.
Xmin = -15
Xmax = 15
Xscl = 1
Ymin = -10
Ymax = 10
Yscl = 1

62.
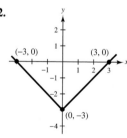

64.
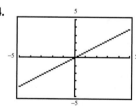
Associative Property of
Multiplication

82.
Xmin = -10
Xmax = 10
Xscl = 5
Ymin = -9
Ymax = 21
Yscl = 5

84. $C = 500 + 5x$
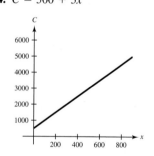

86. (a) and (b)

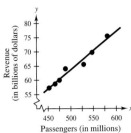

(c) $76.9 billion

90. (a)

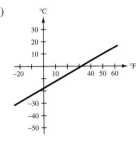

(b) *x*-intercept: Fahrenheit temperature when $C = 0$.
 y-intercept: Celsius temperature when $F = 0$.

92. The equation has an infinite number of solutions. The number of points you need to graph an equation depends on the complexity of the graph. For a line, you need only two points.

94. Substitute the coordinates for the respective variables in the equation and determine if the equation is true.

96.

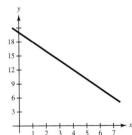

Section 4.3 *(page 229)*

2. Domain: $\{-5, -1, 4, 8\}$
 Range: $\{-2, 3, 5, 6\}$

4. Domain: $\left\{-6, 0, \frac{2}{3}\right\}$
 Range: $\left\{-4, 0, \frac{1}{4}\right\}$

6. Domain: $\{-2, -1, 1, 2, 3\}$
 Range: $\{1, 4, 9\}$

8. Function

10. Function   **12.** Function   **14.** Not a function

16. Function   **18.** Not a function   **20.** Not a function

22. Function   **24.** Function   **26.** Function

28. Not a function   **30.** Function   **32.** Not a function

88. $1000

34. Function   **36.** Function

38. (a) -4 **40.** (a) 3   **42.** (a) 0   **44.** (a) -36
  (b) 0   (b) -1 (b) 25   (b) 14
  (c) $\frac{12}{5}$ (c) 11   (c) 5   (c) 16
  (d) 1   (d) 0   (d) $\frac{7}{2}$ (d) $\frac{11}{3}$

46. (a) 0   **48.** (a) -1 **50.** (a) 6   **52.** (a) 0
  (b) -8 (b) -1 (b) 12   (b) 0
  (c) -18 (c) 139   (c) 4   (c) 15
  (d) -32 (d) $\frac{29}{4}$ (d) $\frac{7}{2}$ (d) -65

54. $R = \{-1, 0, 1, 2, 3\}$ **56.** $R = \{0, 1, 4\}$

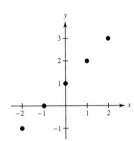
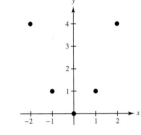

58. $R = \{-8, -1, 0, 1, 8\}$ **60.** $R = \{-2, 0, 2\}$

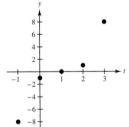
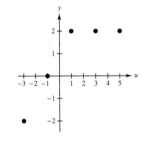

62. (a)

d	2	4	6	8
$L(d)$	400	1600	3600	6400

(b) Maximum safe load increases.

64. (a) 1116 feet per second
 (b) 1075.6 feet per second
 (c) 994.8 feet per second

66. College enrollment is a function of the year.

68. 13,800,000   **70.** $V = t^3$
           V is a function of t.

72. (a) $(24,000, 980), (7000, 640), (0, 500), (36,000, 1220)$

(b) Yes. Independent variable x represents "Weekly Sales."
 Dependent variable y represents "Weekly Earnings."

(c) Domain: $x \geq 0$; Range: $y \geq 500$

CHAPTER 4

74. No.   **76.** $y = x^2 + 4$, $\{(3, 9), (-2, 4), (2, 4)\}$

78. You can name the function $(f, g, \ldots)$, which is convenient when there is more than one function used in solving a problem. The values of the independent and dependent variables are easily seen in function notation.

80. (a) No   (b) Yes

Section 4.4   *(page 242)*

2. -2 **4.** 2 **6.** $\frac{1}{2}$ **8.** $-\frac{1}{2}$ **10.** $-\frac{2}{3}$

12. (a) L_2 (b) L_4 (c) L_3 (d) L_1

14. $m = -2$ **16.** $m = 3$
The line falls.   The line rises.

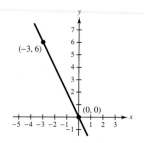   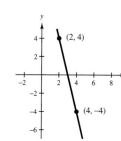

18. $m = \frac{3}{4}$ **20.** $m = -4$
The line rises.   The line falls.

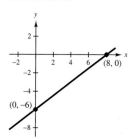

22. m is undefined.   **24.** $m = \frac{4}{3}$
The line is vertical.   The line rises.

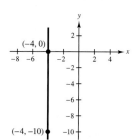

26. $m = \frac{8}{17}$ **28.** m is undefined.
The line rises.   The line is vertical.

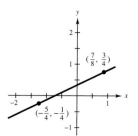   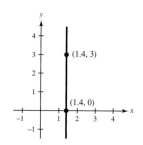

30. $m = 0$ **32.** m is undefined.
The line is horizontal.   The line is vertical.

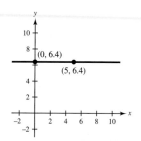   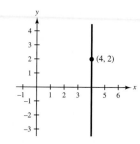

34.

x	-2	0	2	4
y	-2	4	10	16
Solution points	$(-2, -2)$	$(0, 4)$	$(2, 10)$	$(4, 16)$

$m = 3$

36. $y = -20$ **38.** $y = 8$

40.   **42.**

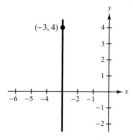   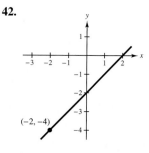

$(-3, 5), (-3, 8)$ $(-1, -3), (0, -2)$

44.   **46.**

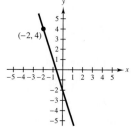

$(-1, 1), (1, -5)$ $(3, -2), (7, -3)$

48.

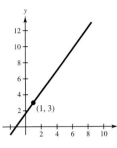

$(4, 7), (7, 11)$

50.

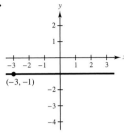

$(-2, -1), (3, -1)$

52.

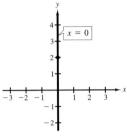

54.

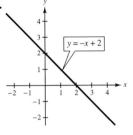

56.

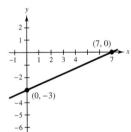

58.

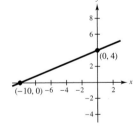

60.

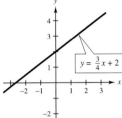

62.

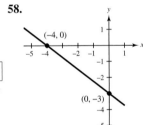

64. $y = x$

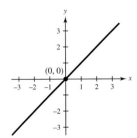

66. $y = 3x$

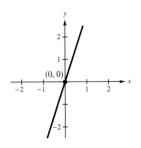

68. $y = x + 2$

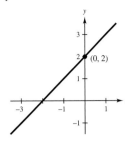

70. $y = \frac{3}{2}x - 1$

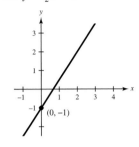

72. $y = -\frac{5}{3}x + \frac{1}{2}$

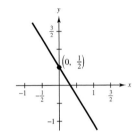

74. $y = -\frac{2}{3}x$

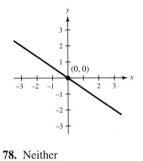

76. $y = 3$

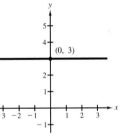

78. Neither

80. Perpendicular

82. Parallel

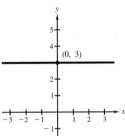

84. Perpendicular

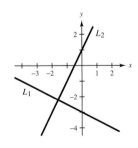

86. $\frac{40}{9}$ **88.** $\frac{1}{5}$

CHAPTER 4

90. (a) Estimated yearly increase in profits

(b) P_2

(c) $P_1(10) = 4.4$ million, $P_2(10) = 5.4$ million

(d)
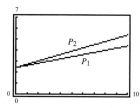

92. (a) Sales increase by 76 units.

(b) Sales do not change.

(c) Sales decrease by 14 units.

94. The slope is positive if the line rises to the right and negative if it falls to the right.

96. -5. The steeper line is the one whose slope has the greater absolute value.

98. For each 2-unit increase in x, y will increase by 3 units. Because there are four 2-unit increases in x, y will increase by 12 units.

100. No. y is not a function of x. (It may be possible using the draw feature or a mode other than the function mode.)

102. Yes. You are free to label either one of the points as (x_1, y_1) and the other as (x_2, y_2). However, once this is done, you must form the numerator and denominator using the same order of subtraction.

Section 4.5   *(page 253)*

2. $3x - y = 2$

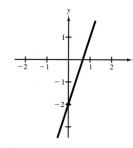

4. $x + 4y = 40$

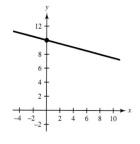

6. $x + y = -2$

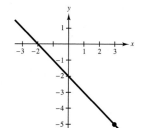

8. $2x + 3y = 36$

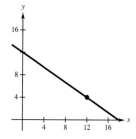

10. $y = 6$

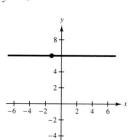

12. $3x - 4y = 10$

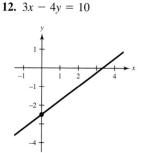

14. $67x - 100y = 702$

16. $y = -x + 7$

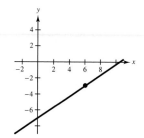

18. $y = 4x + 8$ **20.** $y = \frac{4}{3}x - 2$ **22.** $y = -5$

24. $y = \frac{1}{3}x + 3$ **26.** $y = -\frac{1}{2}x + \frac{7}{2}$ **28.** -3

30. -2 **32.** $\frac{5}{8}$ **34.** 0 **36.** Undefined   **38.** $-\frac{5}{4}$

40. $y = -2x + 4$ **42.** $y = \frac{2}{3}x + 1$

44. $y - 1 = \frac{3}{2}(x - 3)$

46. $y - 2 = -\frac{2}{5}(x + 3)$ or $y - 0 = -\frac{2}{5}(x - 2)$

48. $2x + y = 0$ **50.** $4x + 3y - 21 = 0$

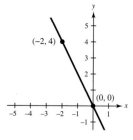

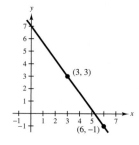

52. $3x + 2y = 0$ **54.** $3x + 5y - 8 = 0$

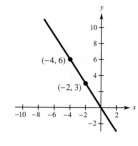

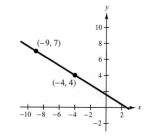

56. $y - 3 = 0$ **58.** $3x - 15y + 13 = 0$

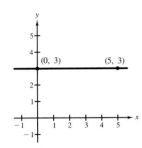

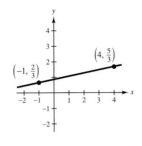

60. $x - 2y + 2 = 0$ **62.** $x + 4y - 16 = 0$

64. $2x + y + 3 = 0$ **66.** $x + 2y - 13 = 0$

68. $2x + y - 9 = 0$ **70.** $20x - 12y + 7 = 0$

72. $3x + 10y + 18 = 0$

74. (a) $x + y + 1 = 0$ **76.** (a) $5x + 3y - 69 = 0$

   (b) $x - y + 5 = 0$ (b) $3x - 5y - 55 = 0$

78. (a) $x + 5y + 5 = 0$ **80.** (a) $x - 2 = 0$

   (b) $5x - y - 27 = 0$ (b) $y - 5 = 0$

82. (a) $4x - 5y + 49 = 0$ **84.** $y = 3$

   (b) $5x + 4y + 10 = 0$

86. $x = \frac{1}{4}$ **88.** $y = 5$ **90.** $x = 3$

92.   **94.**

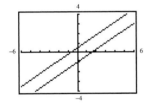

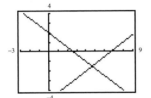

Parallel   Neither

96. $W = 2000 + 0.02S$ **98.** $C = 250 + 0.43x$

100. $d = 50t$

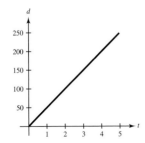

102. (a) $V = 5400 - 1100t$

   (b) \$2100

104. (a) $(50, 480), (47, 525)$

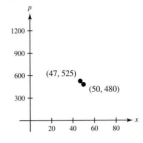

   (b) $15x + p - 1230 = 0$ (c) 45   (d) 49

   As the rent increases,
   the demand decreases.

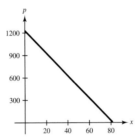

106. $-\dfrac{5}{7}, -\dfrac{a}{b}$

108. (d) The function is linear if the slopes are the same between the points (x, y), where x is the weekly sales and y is weekly earnings.

   (e) $m = 0.02$; 2%; Commission rate

   (f) $y = 500 + 0.02x$

   (g)

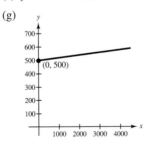

   The y-intercept is the weekly earnings when no ads are sold. The x-intercept does not have meaning.

110. No. The slope is undefined.

112. The coordinates of a   **114.** The lines are parallel.
   point on the line

Section 4.6   *(page 262)*

2. (a) Solution   **4.** (a) Not a solution

   (b) Not a solution   (b) Solution

   (c) Solution   (c) Solution

   (d) Not a solution   (d) Solution

CHAPTER 4

6. (a) Not a solution
   (b) Not a solution
   (c) Solution
   (d) Not a solution

8. (a) Not a solution
   (b) Not a solution
   (c) Solution
   (d) Not a solution

10. Solid   **12.** Dashed

14. c   **16.** a   **18.** a   **20.** d

22. $x \leq 0$

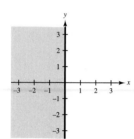

24. $y < -2$

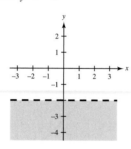

26. $y > -\frac{2}{3}x$

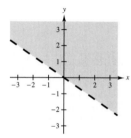

28. $y > -x$

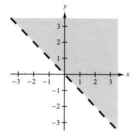

30. $y \geq -x + 3$

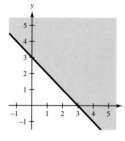

32. $y \geq 0.6x + 1$

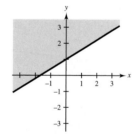

34. $y < -x + 3$

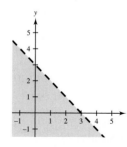

36. $y < 3x + 1$

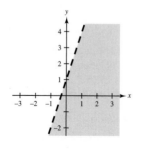

38. $y \leq -\frac{3}{4}x + 2$

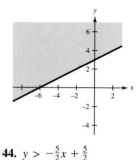

40. $y \geq \frac{1}{2}x + 3$

42. $y \geq -\frac{1}{4}x$

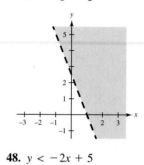

44. $y > -\frac{5}{2}x + \frac{5}{2}$

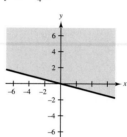

46. $y > -\frac{1}{2}x + 5$

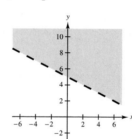

48. $y < -2x + 5$

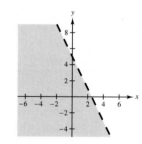

50. $y > x + 2$

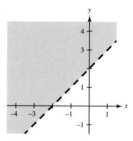

52. $y \leq 4 - 0.5x$

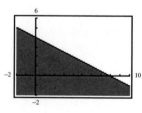

54. $y \geq x - 3$

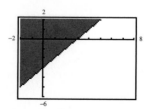

56. $y \leq -\frac{2}{3}x + 6$

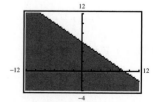

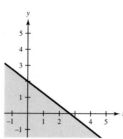

58. $y \leq \frac{3}{2}x + 2$

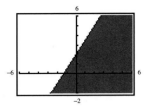

60. $x < -1$ **62.** $2x - 5y \leq 10$

64. $x + 3y < 3$

66. $0.10d + 0.25q \geq 25$
d: number of dimes
q: number of quarters
(d, q): $(250, 0)$, $(0, 100)$, $(300, 50)$

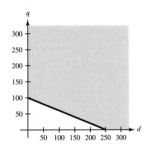

68. $2x + 3y \leq 30$
x: number of \$2000 computers
y: number of \$3000 computers
(x, y): $(0, 10)$, $(15, 0)$, $(10, 3)$

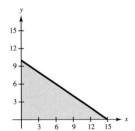

70. At least \$17,000

72. The inequality is true when x_1 and y_1 are substituted for x and y, respectively.

74. Test a point in one of the half-planes.

76. $y > 0$

78. $x + y < 0$

Review Exercises   *(page 266)*

2.

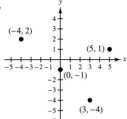

4.

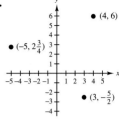

6. Quadrant IV   **8.** y-axis   **10.** Quadrant III

12. Quadrant III or IV   **14.** $y = -\frac{2}{3}x + 2$

16. $y = -\frac{1}{3}x - 3$

18.

x	-1	0	1	2
$y = -2x - 1$	1	-1	-3	-5

20. (a) Not a solution
(b) Solution
(c) Solution
(d) Not a solution

22. (a) Solution
(b) Solution
(c) Solution
(d) Solution

24.

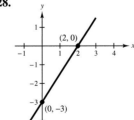

26.

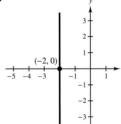

28.

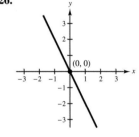

30.

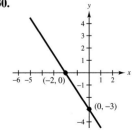

CHAPTER 4

32.

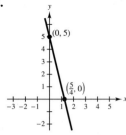

34.

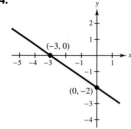

36.

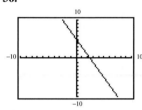

38.

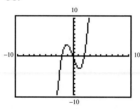

40.

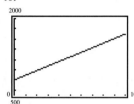

42.

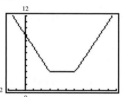

44. Domain: $\{-7, -1, 0, 4\}$
    Range: $\{1, 3, 5, 6\}$

46. Domain: $\{-3, -2, 1, 6\}$
    Range: $\{-9, 4, 5, 7\}$

48. Function   **50.** Not a function   **52.** Function

54. Not a function   **56.** Not a function

58. (a) 64   **60.** (a) 25   **62.** (a) -3

    (b) 63   (b) 25   (b) -3

    (c) 48   (c) 25   (c) 0

    (d) 0   (d) 25   (d) -2

64.

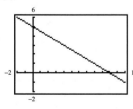

    $(10, 0), (0, 5)$

66.

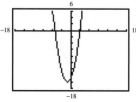

    $(0, -15), (-5, 0), (3, 0)$

68.

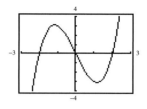

70.

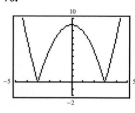

$(0, 0), (-2, 0), (2, 0)$ $(0, 9), (3, 0), (-3, 0)$

72. -2 **74.** a   **76.** d   **78.** $-\frac{12}{5}$

80. $-\frac{4}{3}$ **82.** 0   **84.** $\frac{1}{4}$ **86.** $\frac{3}{11}$ **88.** $\frac{4}{15}$

90. $y = 2x + 1$ **92.** $y = -\frac{1}{3}x - \frac{2}{3}$

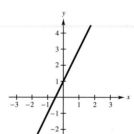 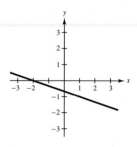

94. Perpendicular   **96.** Parallel

98. $(-1, 8), (0, 11)$ **100.** $(0, -1), (3, -3)$

102. $(6, 2), (6, -1)$ **104.** $3x - y + 17 = 0$

106. $x + y - 4 = 0$ **108.** $x + 6y + 12 = 0$

110. $8x - 5y - 42 = 0$ **112.** $y - 6 = 0$

114. $m = 0$ **116.** m is undefined.

118. $x - y + 2 = 0$ **120.** $x - 2 = 0$

122. $4x + 9y - 12 = 0$ **124.** $10x - 5y + 14 = 0$

126. (a) $25x + 5y - 1 = 0$ **128.** (a) $x + 2 = 0$

    (b) $5x - 25y - 21 = 0$ (b) $y - 1 = 0$

130.

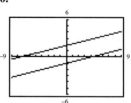

Parallel

132.

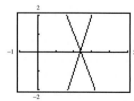

Neither

134. (a) Not a solution

    (b) Not a solution

    (c) Not a solution

    (d) Solution

136. $y < -3$

138. $y < \frac{3}{4}x - \frac{1}{2}$

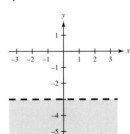

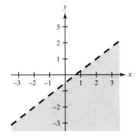

156. $2x + 3y \le 120$

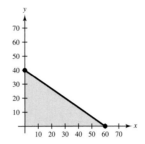

(x, y): $(10, 15)$, $(20, 20)$, $(30, 20)$

140. $y \ge -\frac{1}{2}x + \frac{3}{2}$

142. $x \ge -1$ **144.** $y > -\frac{1}{3}x$

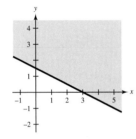

Chapter 5

Section 5.1   *(page 280)*

2. Polynomial

4. Not a polynomial because the exponent in the second term is not an integer.

6. Not a polynomial because the exponent in the second term is negative.

8. Polynomial

10. Polynomial: $2x - 3$
Standard form: $2x - 3$
Degree: 1
Leading coefficient: 2

12. Polynomial: $9 - 2y^4$
Standard form: $-2y^4 + 9$
Degree: 4
Leading coefficient: -2

146. (a) $\approx \$975,000$ (b) 1992 (c) $\approx 23\%$ increase

148.

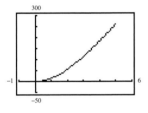

150. $y = 150 + 0.30x$

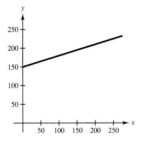

152. $\frac{2}{3}$

154. (a)

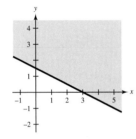

(b) The velocity decreases at a constant rate of 32 feet per second per second.

(c) 48 feet per second, 16 feet per second

(d) 1.5 seconds

14. Polynomial: $5x^3 - 3x^2 + 10$
Standard form: $5x^3 - 3x^2 + 10$
Degree: 3
Leading coefficient: 5

16. Polynomial: -32
Standard form: -32
Degree: 0
Leading coefficient: -32

18. Polynomial: $64 - \frac{1}{2}at^2$
Standard form: $-\frac{1}{2}at^2 + 64$
Degree: 2
Leading coefficient: $-\frac{1}{2}a$

20. Monomial   **22.** Trinomial   **24.** Binomial

26. $2z^4 + 7z - 2$ **28.** $6 - 2v^5$ **30.** 7

32. $-x - 2$ **34.** $6x^4 + 12x - 6$

36. $x^3 + 4x^2 - x - 8$ **38.** $4x^3 + 12x^2 + 4x + 6$

40. $5uv - 2$ **42.** $\frac{7}{8}x^3 + \frac{5}{2}$ **44.** $0.7x^2 + 7.2x - 1.4$

46. $16x - 3$ **48.** $7x^2 + 2$ **50.** $2z^3 + z^2 + z - 2$

52. $x^5 + 2x^4 - x^3 + x + 6$ **54.** $x^3 + 6x + 2$

56. $a^2 + 2a$ **58.** $3y^2 + 6y + 5$ **60.** $-7z^2 + 7z - 3$

62. $3.7x^4 + 8x^3 - 6.2x^2 - 16x + 17.6$ **64.** $-6x + 6$

66. 0 **68.** $2t^4 - 5t^2 + 5$ **70.** $z^3 + 1$

72. $4t^3 - 3t^2 + 4t - 3$ **74.** $6x - 2$ **76.** -4

78. $14x^3 + 7x^2 + 3x - 15$ **80.** $5z^3 - z - 4$

82. $-3s^2 - 10s - 3$ **84.** $3y^2 - 3y + 2$

86. $-y^5 + 4y^4 + y^2$ **88.** $3x^2 - 2x + 2$

90. $-2x^2 - 4$ **92.** $4z^4 - 2z^2 + 12$

94. $28x^4 - 13x - 34$ **96.** $y^3 - y^2 - 3y + 7$

98. $-5u - 36$ **100.** $-20x + 5$ **102.** $8y + 10$

104. $3x^2 - \frac{5}{3}x$ **106.** $11x^2 - 3x$ **108.** $\frac{3\pi}{4}r^2$

110. (a) $-x^2 + 60x - 100$

(b)

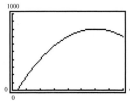

(c) \$800; If x is some value other than 30, the profit is less than \$800.

112. The degree of a term ax^k is k. The term of highest degree in a polynomial has the same degree as the polynomial.

114. Two terms are like terms if they are both constant or if they have the same variable factor(s). Numerical coefficients

116. Yes.   **118.** No. $(x^2 - 2) + (5 - x^2) = 3$

Section 5.2   *(page 292)*

2. $-3y^2$ **4.** $3u^5$ **6.** $\frac{3}{4}x^2$ **8.** $-12m^3$

10. $z^2 - 3z$ **12.** $-10t + 3t^2$ **14.** $-5u^3 - 20u$

16. $25v - 20v^2 + 25v^3$ **18.** $4y^3 + 2y^2 - 3y$

20. $-3x^2 + 9x$ **22.** $-2t^5 - 12t^4$

24. $2y^4 + y^3 - 5y^2$ **26.** $10u^7 - 15u^5 + 15u^4$

28. $-8x^4 + 8x^2$ **30.** $30y^5$ **32.** $x^2 + 5x - 50$

34. $28x^2 - 29x + 6$ **36.** $x^2 + 3xy + 2y^2$

38. $8x^2 + 2x - 3$ **40.** $-32x^2 + 64x - 30$

42. $7x^2 + 12xy + 5y^2$ **44.** $5x^4 - 5x^3 - 2x + 2$

46. $14x^4 - 34x^2 + 12$ **48.** $4t^2 + 16t - 10$

50. $14x^4 - 27x^2 + 12$ **52.** $x^2 + 2x - 3$

54. $6x^2 - 13x + 6$ **56.** $x^3 - 6x^2 + 13x - 12$

58. $x^3 + 1$ **60.** $x^3 + 8x^2 - 13x - 36$

62. $x^4 - 2x^3 + 6x^2 - 6x + 9$

64. $4x^5 + 8x^4 + 20x^3 - 2x^2 - 4x - 10$

66. $10x^2 - 3x - 1$

68. $8x^5 + 12x^4 - 12x^3 - 18x^2 + 18x + 27$

70. $2x^4 + 3x^3 + 7x^2 - 7x - 5$

72. $x^4 - x^2 - 2x - 1$ **74.** $x^3 + 9x^2 + 27x + 27$

76. $x^4 + 16x^3 + 96x^2 + 256x + 256$

78. $x^3 - 9x^2 + 24x - 16$

80. $10x^3 - x^2 - 53x + 30$ **82.** $x^2 - 25$

84. $y^2 - 81$ **86.** $9z^2 - 16$ **88.** $9u^2 - 49$

90. $25u^2 - 144v^2$ **92.** $64a^2 - 25b^2$ **94.** $16t^4 - 36$

96. $a^2 - 4a + 4$ **98.** $x^2 + 20x + 100$

100. $4x^2 - 32x + 64$ **102.** $1 - 10t + 25t^2$

104. $16s^2 + 24st + 9t^2$ **106.** $9u^2 - 48uv + 64v^2$

108. $x^2 + y^2 - 2xy - 6x + 6y + 9$

110. $4u^2 + v^2 + 4uv + 4u + 2v + 1$ **112.** $2u^2 + 50$

114. Yes   **116.** $x^3 + 3x^2 + 3x + 1$ **118.** $x^2 + 10x$

120. $x^2 + 5x + 4 = (x + 1)(x + 4)$

122. $4x^2 + 6x + 2 = (2x + 1)(2x + 2)$

124. $(x + 2)^2 = x^2 + 4x + 4$

$(a + b)^2 = a^2 + 2ab + b^2$

126. $(x + 4)(x + 5) = x^2 + 9x + 20$

128. $4x = (x + 4)(x + 3) - x^2 - 3x - 12$

130. 16 feet $\times$ 16 feet

132. (a)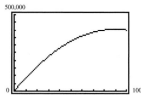

(b) $900x - 0.5x^2$

(c) \$325,000; Increase

134. $1200r^2 + 2400r + 1200$

136. Multiplying a polynomial by a monomial is a direct application of the Distributive Property. Multiplying two polynomials requires repeated application of the Distributive Property.

138. $(3x)^2 = 3^2 \cdot x^2 = 9x^2 \neq 3x^2$

140. The product of the terms of highest degree in each polynomial will be of the form $(ax^m)(bx^n) = abx^{m+n}$. This will be the term of highest degree in the product, and therefore the degree of the product is $m + n$.

142. False. $(x - 2)(x + 3) = x^2 + x - 6$

Section 5.3   *(page 302)*

2. $\dfrac{1}{4^2}$ **4.** $\dfrac{1}{z^2}$ **6.** $\dfrac{6}{x^2 y^3}$ **8.** $\dfrac{9}{u^5 v^2}$ **10.** $7x^2 y^3$

12. $\dfrac{5u^2 v^4}{6}$ **14.** 3^{-2} **16.** $7y^{-3}$ **18.** $3z^{-n}$

20. $9y^{-n}$ **22.** $5x^3 y^{-6}$ **24.** $\dfrac{1}{5^3} = \dfrac{1}{125}$

26. $\dfrac{1}{(-6)^2} = \dfrac{1}{36}$ **28.** 16 **30.** $4(3^2) = 36$

32. $\dfrac{1}{2(4^3)} = \dfrac{1}{128}$ **34.** $\left(\dfrac{4}{3}\right)^3 = \dfrac{64}{27}$ **36.** $\left(\dfrac{4}{5}\right)^3 = \dfrac{64}{125}$

38. 0.0042 **40.** 107.2741 **42.** $\dfrac{1}{5}$ **44.** $\dfrac{1}{a^3}$

46. 1 **48.** v **50.** z^6 **52.** $\dfrac{1}{x^5}$ **54.** $\dfrac{1}{t^4}$

56. $\dfrac{1}{z^6}$ **58.** $\dfrac{1}{a^9}$ **60.** 1 **62.** c^2 **64.** $\dfrac{x^9}{64 y^6}$

66. $-\dfrac{st^2}{2}$ **68.** $12y^2$ **70.** $\dfrac{z^2}{16}$ **72.** $\dfrac{125 x^9}{y^{12}}$ **74.** 1

76. $-\dfrac{3}{125}$ **78.** $\dfrac{10}{x^2}$ **80.** 1 **82.** 1 **84.** 9×10^8

86. 6.78×10^1 **88.** 8.367×10^{-3} **90.** 4.5×10^{-7}

92. 8.2×10^{-4} **94.** $234{,}500{,}000$ **96.** $94{,}675$

98. 0.00007021 **100.** 4.73 **102.** $69{,}000.4$

104. 1.5443×10^{14} **106.** 2.967×10^1

108. 1.7798×10^{47} **110.** 9.1125×10^{-14}

112. 1.2885×10^{10} **114.** 2.21×10^{-3}

116. 4.4647×10^{14} miles

118. (a)

t	0	2	4
$24{,}000(1.2)^{-t}$	\$24,000	\$16,667	\$11,574

t	6	8
$24{,}000(1.2)^{-t}$	\$8038	\$5582

(b)

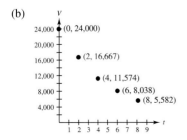

(c) When the car is 18 years old

120. 0.006 gallon   **122.** False. Let $x = 2$ and $y = 2$.

124. False. Let $x = 1$ and $y = 1$.   **126.** True

128. $a^m a^n = a^{m+n}$ **130.** $\dfrac{10^3}{4}$

$\dfrac{a^m}{a^n} = a^{m-n}$

$(ab)^m = a^m b^m$

$\left(\dfrac{a}{b}\right)^m = \dfrac{a^m}{b^m}$

$(a^m)^n = a^{mn}$

$a^{-n} = \dfrac{1}{a^n}$

$a^0 = 1$

Section 5.4   *(page 312)*

2. y^4 **4.** $\dfrac{1}{y^4}$ **6.** y^5 **8.** $\dfrac{z^2}{5}$ **10.** $9x^3$ **12.** 1

14. $\dfrac{v^3}{8}$ **16.** $4a^4$ **18.** $-\dfrac{16}{v^2}$ **20.** $2y^2$ **22.** $-\dfrac{7}{8c^3}$

24. $-\dfrac{9}{4x^2}$ **26.** $-\dfrac{7v^2}{4u^2}$ **28.** $\dfrac{a}{16}$ **30.** $-\dfrac{5v^3}{9u^7}$

32. $\dfrac{5}{9}$ **34.** $x + 1$ **36.** $u - 3$ **38.** $\dfrac{3}{5} - 2x$

40. $3 + 2x^2$ **42.** $16a + 5$ **44.** $-2c^3 + 6$

46. $x^2 + \dfrac{5}{3}x - \dfrac{4}{3}$ **48.** $l - 4 + \dfrac{8}{l}$ **50.** $-2y - 3$

52. $-3x^3 + 4x - 1 + \dfrac{5}{3x}$ **54.** $x - 3$ **56.** $x + 3$

58. $t - 2$ **60.** $10t - 4$

62. $2x^2 - 4x + 7 + \dfrac{2}{x + 1}$

64. $4 - \dfrac{9}{2x + 1}$ **66.** $x^2 - 3x + 9$

68. $y - 3 + \dfrac{12}{y + 3}$ **70.** $5y + 2$

72. $x^3 + x^2 + x + 1 + \dfrac{1}{x - 1}$

74. $7x - 10 + \dfrac{23}{x + 2}$

76. $x^2 - 4x - 12$ **78.** $2x^2 - x + 1$ **80.** $4x$

82. $2xy$ **84.** $5x - 5$

86. Error; You can only cancel common factors of the numerator and denominator.

88. Error; You cannot cancel digits of numbers.

90. (a) Yes

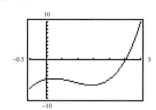

(b) $(2x - 5)(x^2 + 1) = 2x(x^2) + 2x(1) - 5(x^2) - 5(1)$
$$= 2x^3 + 2x - 5x^2 - 5$$

(c) $(2x^3 - 5x^2 + 2x - 5) \div (2x - 5) = x^2 + 1$

92. $x + 6$ **94.** $2x - 1$

96. Algebraically: Multiply.
Graphically: Use a graphing utility to graph the rational expression and the result of the division process. The graphs should coincide.

98. Divide each term of the polynomial by the monomial.

100. $2; m - n$

Review Exercises   *(page 316)*

2. Polynomial: $2x^2 + 9$
Standard form: $2x^2 + 9$
Degree: 2
Leading coefficient: 2

4. Polynomial: $6 - 3x + 6x^2 - x^3$
Standard form: $-x^3 + 6x^2 - 3x + 6$
Degree: 3
Leading coefficient: -1

6. Polynomial: $12x^2 + 2x - 8x^5 + 1$
Standard form: $-8x^5 + 12x^2 + 2x + 1$
Degree: 5
Leading coefficient: -8

8. Polynomial: $\frac{1}{4}t^2$ **10.** $7t^2$ **12.** $4x^5 - 2x^3 + x$
Standard form: $\frac{1}{4}t^2$
Degree: 2
Leading coefficient: $\frac{1}{4}$

14. $\frac{9}{2}x + 1$ **16.** 12   **18.** $2x^2 - 3x - 6$

20. $-x^2 + 5x - 24$ **22.** $-3x^2 + 2x - 3$

24. $-2z^2$ **26.** $7u^2 + 8u + 5$ **28.** $4a^3 + a + 4$

30. $5z^3 + z^2 - 6z - 7$ **32.** $-6y^4 - 6$

34. $3y^2 + 3y$ **36.** $u^2 + 3u - 10$ **38.** $4y^2 + 5y - 6$

40. $-14x^2 + 22x + 60$ **42.** $s^4 - 3s^3 + 4s^2 - 15s + 9$

44. $4x^3 + 26x^2 - 8x - 10$ **46.** 0

48. $x^2 - 10x + 25$ **50.** $81 - 36x + 4x^2$

52. $16 + 24b + 9b^2$ **54.** $r^2 - 9$ **56.** $9a^2 - 64$

58. $9a^2 + 6ab + b^2$ **60.** $16u^2 - 25v^2$ **62.** $\frac{1}{81}$

64. $\frac{1}{36}$ **66.** 125   **68.** 189   **70.** $\frac{1}{144}$ **72.** $\frac{16}{3}$

74. 200,000   **76.** 15,625   **78.** $\frac{1}{x^5}$ **80.** $-\frac{4}{u^3}$

82. $\frac{y^4}{2}$ **84.** $\frac{5}{u^2v^4}$ **86.** $\frac{1}{x^3}$ **88.** $-2u^5$ **90.** $27u^3$

92. 5   **94.** a^2 **96.** x^6 **98.** $\frac{x^4}{7}$ **100.** 1

102. $\frac{3}{2x^2} - \frac{1}{4x} + \frac{3}{4}$ **104.** $4u^2 + 2u$ **106.** $x - 4$

108. $7x + 6 + \frac{19}{3x - 2}$ **110.** $2x^3 - 9x$

112. $3x^2 + 3 + \frac{3}{x^2 - 1}$ **114.** $11x^2 - x$

116. $4r^2 - \pi r^2$

118. (a) $-\frac{1}{2}x^2 + 14x - 15$

(b) 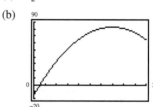   (c) \$83; Profit will decrease.

120. $3x - 4 + \frac{9}{x + 3}$

122. (a)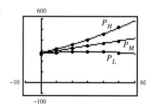

(b) $\frac{P_L + P_H}{2} = 0.003t^2 + 2.365t + 274.445$

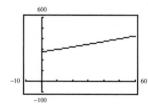

The graph is most similar to P_M.

(c) $P_H - P_L = 0.05t^2 + 2.07t + 7.47$

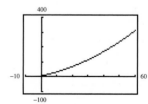

The vertical distance between P_L and P_H is increasing.

Chapter 6

Section 6.1   *(page 327)*

2. 5   **4.** 10   **6.** t^4 **8.** $18x^3$ **10.** rs

12. $15xy^3$ **14.** $5y$ **16.** $4xy$ **18.** $5(y + 1)$

20. $3(x - 1)$ **22.** $3(u + 4)$ **24.** $-7(2y + 1)$

26. $7(z^3 + 3)$ **28.** $-s(s^2 + 1)$ **30.** $12t^2(3t^2 + 2)$

32. $9z^4(z^2 + 3)$ **34.** No common factor

36. $3u(4 + 3u)$ **38.** $-24a(6a - 1)$

40. $6x^2y(x^2 + 2)$ **42.** $7xz(3x - 5)$

44. $3(3 - y - 5y^2)$ **46.** $7(6t^3 - 3t^2 + 1)$

48. $2a(16a^4 - a^2 + 3)$ **50.** $11y^2(y - 1)$

52. $(x + 6)(x + 3)$ **54.** $(q - 5)(y - 10)$

56. $(y + 4)(x^3 + y)$ **58.** $x(x - 2)(x^2 + 1)$

60. $y(x - y)$ **62.** $-(x - 3)$ **64.** $-(2x^2 - 9)$

66. $-6(x^2 + 2x - 3)$ **68.** $-x(x^3 + 2x - 1)$

70. $(x - 5)(x + 1)$ **72.** $(x + 25)(x + 1)$

74. $(ay + 3)(y + 3)$ **76.** $(s + 2)(3s^2 + 2)$

78. $(x - 5)(x^2 + 1)$ **80.** $(2u - 1)(2u^2 - 3)$

82. $(x - 3)(x^2 + 7)$ **84.** $(2x + 1)(5x^2 + 4)$

86. $5x - 1$ **88.** $12z + 3$ **90.** $10u - 15v$

92. $y_1 = y_2$ **94.** $y_1 = y_2$

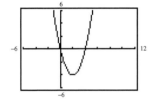

96. $x + 10$ **98.** $2x(x + 5)$ **100.** $20\pi x^2$

102. $P(1 + rt)$ **104.** $R = x(900 - 0.1x)$

$$p = 900 - 0.1x$$

106. $3x^3 + 3x^2 + 3x = 3x(x^2 + x + 1)$

108. Multiply the factors.

110. $2x + 4 = 2(x + 2)$

$$x(x^2 + 1) - 3(x^2 + 1) = (x - 3)(x^2 + 1)$$

Section 6.2   *(page 335)*

2. $x + 2$ **4.** $c - 1$ **6.** $y - 7$ **8.** $z - 1$

10. $(x + 1)(x + 10)$

$(x - 1)(x - 10)$

$(x + 2)(x + 5)$

$(x - 2)(x - 5)$

12. $(x + 18)(x + 1)$ **14.** $(x + 1)(x + 12)$

$(x - 18)(x - 1)$

$(x + 9)(x + 2)$

$(x - 9)(x - 2)$

$(x + 6)(x + 3)$

$(x - 6)(x - 3)$

16. $(x - 2)(x - 7)$ **18.** $(x + 4)(x + 6)$ **20.** Prime

22. $(x - 2)(x + 3)$ **24.** $(b - 5)(b + 3)$ **26.** Prime

28. Prime   **30.** $(x - 7)(x + 10)$ **32.** $(x + 9)(x + 12)$

34. $(r - 18)(r - 12)$ **36.** $(x - 2y)(x - 3y)$

38. $(u - 5v)(u + v)$ **40.** $(x + 5y)(x + 10y)$

42. $(y + 10z)(y - 6z)$ **44.** $4(x - 3)(x - 5)$

46. $5(x + 1)(x - 5)$ **48.** Prime   **50.** $6(x^2 - 4x - 1)$

52. $x(x + 2)(x - 1)$ **54.** $x^2(x - 2)(x + 5)$

56. $-5z(x - 5)(x + 2)$ **58.** $y(x^2 - 6xy + y^2)$

60. $x^2y^2(x + 2y)(x + y)$ **62.** $\pm 7, \pm 11$

64. $\pm 3, \pm 7, \pm 17$ **66.** $\pm 2, \pm 8, \pm 13, \pm 22, \pm 47$

68. $4, -14$ **70.** $14, -16$ **72.** $11, -13$

74. $y_1 = y_2$ **76.** $y_1 = y_2$

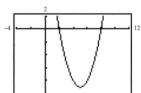   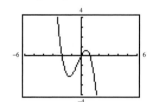

78. $(x + 4)(x + 1)$

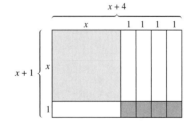

80. $(x + 1)(x + 5)$

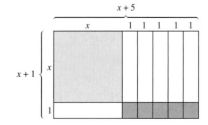

82. 200 square units **84. a:** Not completely factored
d: Completely factored

86. When attempting to factor $x^2 + bx + c$, find factors of c whose sum is b.

88. No. The factorization into prime factors is unique.

Section 6.3 (page 343)

2. $5x + 4$ **4.** $5c - 4$ **6.** $3y - 10$ **8.** $6z - 5$

10. $(5x + 21)(x + 1)$ $(5x - 21)(x - 1)$
$(5x + 1)(x + 21)$ $(5x - 1)(x - 21)$
$(5x + 7)(x + 3)$ $(5x - 7)(x - 3)$
$(5x + 3)(x + 7)$ $(5x - 3)(x - 7)$

12. $(5x + 36)(x + 1)$ $(5x - 36)(x - 1)$
$(5x + 1)(x + 36)$ $(5x - 1)(x - 36)$
$(5x + 18)(x + 2)$ $(5x - 18)(x - 2)$
$(5x + 2)(x + 18)$ $(5x - 2)(x - 18)$
$(5x + 12)(x + 3)$ $(5x - 12)(x - 3)$
$(5x + 3)(x + 12)$ $(5x - 3)(x - 12)$
$(5x + 9)(x + 4)$ $(5x - 9)(x - 4)$
$(5x + 4)(x + 9)$ $(5x - 4)(x - 9)$
$(5x + 6)(x + 6)$ $(5x - 6)(x - 6)$

14. $(3x + 1)(x + 2)$ **16.** $(3x - 1)(x + 2)$
18. $(3a - 2)(a - 1)$ **20.** $(3z + 2)(z - 1)$
22. Prime **24.** Prime **26.** $(3v + 2)(2v - 1)$
28. $(2y - 5)(3y + 4)$ **30.** $(2a - 3)(2a - 5)$
32. $(8s - 1)(3s + 5)$ **34.** $(2x - 3)(6x + 5)$
36. $(5t - 1)(2t + 9)$ **38.** $(7b + 3)(3b - 7)$
40. $(3x - 8)(4x - 3)$ **42.** $-(5x + 4)(x - 1)$
44. $-(4x + 3)(x - 5)$ **46.** $-(3x - 2)(2x + 1)$
48. $-(3x - 2)(4x + 1)$ **50.** $-(2x - 5)(5x + 4)$
52. $3a^3(a - 3)$ **54.** $8y(3y^2 - 2)$ **56.** $(x - 8)(x - 2)$
58. $4(z + 2)(z - 5)$ **60.** $5(y + 1)(y + 7)$
62. $2(3x - 2)(x + 2)$ **64.** $6(x - 3)(x + 2)$
66. $-y^2(2y - 3)(y + 5)$ **68.** $x(5x^2 - 3x - 4)$
70. $-7x(x - 5)(x + 1)$ **72.** $4x^3(3x^2 - 4x + 2)$
74. $\pm 7, \pm 8, \pm 13$ **76.** $\pm 1, \pm 7, \pm 13, \pm 29$
78. $0, \pm 7, \pm 10, \pm 18, \pm 32, \pm 45, \pm 70, \pm 143$
80. $2, -3$ **82.** $-5, -26$ **84.** $-9, 2$
86. $(x + 2)(2x + 1)$ **88.** $(5x + 1)(x - 3)$
90. $(4y + 1)(3y + 2)$ **92.** $(x - 1)(12x - 1)$
94. $(3z + 5)(z - 3)$ **96.** $(c + 1)(20c - 1)$

98. $(2y - 5)(5y + 6)$ **100.** $(2x + 3)(6x + 5)$
102. $(3x + 1)(x + 1)$

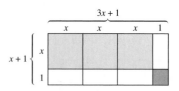

104. $w = 3d - 4$ **106.** $6x + 3$

108. (a) $-\dfrac{x^2}{120}(12 + x)$

(b)

110. First, Outer, Inner, Last
112. $9x^2 - 9x - 54 = 9(x^2 - x - 6)$
$= 9(x - 3)(x + 2)$
114. $x^2 + x + 1$ **116.** Yes, $9x^2 + 12x + 4 = (3x + 2)^2$

Section 6.4 (page 353)

2. $(y + 7)(y - 7)$ **4.** $(x + 2)(x - 2)$
6. $(9 + x)(9 - x)$ **8.** $\left(v + \frac{2}{3}\right)\left(v - \frac{2}{3}\right)$
10. $\left(u + \frac{5}{9}\right)\left(u - \frac{5}{9}\right)$ **12.** $(3z + 5)(3z - 5)$
14. $(4 + 9x)(4 - 9x)$ **16.** $(t + 5)(t - 1)$
18. $(a + 2)(a - 6)$ **20.** $3(x + 3)(x - 3)$
22. $a(a + 4)(a - 4)$ **24.** $(z^2 + 4)(z + 2)(z - 2)$
26. $(16 + u^2)(4 + u)(4 - u)$ **28.** $2(3 + x^2)(3 - x^2)$
30. $(3x + 1)(3x - 1)(9x^2 + 1)$ **32.** $(x + 5)^2$
34. $(a - 6)^2$ **36.** $(3x - 2)^2$ **38.** $(4z + 3)^2$
40. $\left(x + \frac{1}{5}\right)^2$ **42.** $\left(2t - \frac{1}{3}\right)^2$ **44.** $(4x - y)^2$
46. $(u + 4v)^2$ **48.** $(7m - 2n)^2$ **50.** ± 20 **52.** $\pm \frac{2}{3}$
54. ± 12 **56.** 25 **58.** 49
60. $(x - 3)(x^2 + 3x + 9)$ **62.** $(z + 5)(z^2 - 5z + 25)$
64. $(3s + 1)(9s^2 - 3s + 1)$
66. $(4v - 5)(16v^2 + 20v + 25)$ **68.** $8(t + 6)$
70. $x^2(x - 4)$ **72.** $12a(a - 2)$ **74.** $6(x + 3)(x - 3)$
76. $y^2(y + 7)(y - 7)$ **78.** $(3x - 1)^2$
80. $(2 + x)(8 - x)$ **82.** $x(4x^2 + 3x + 1)$
84. $y(2y + 3)(y - 5)$ **86.** $16(t + 3)(t - 3)$

88. $(t - 7)(t - 1)$ **90.** $(x + 7)(x - 13)$

92. $u(u + 3)(u - 1)$ **94.** Prime

96. $3(2x - 1)(4x^2 + 2x + 1)$ **98.** $2(3 - x)(9 + 3x + x^2)$

100. $2(x^2 + 4)(x + 2)(x - 2)$

102. $(3 - y)(3 + y)(9 + y^2)$

104. $(y + 2)(y - 2)(y + 3)$

106. $2x(2 + x)(3 + x)(3 - x)$

108. $(1 + y)(1 - y)(1 + y^2)(1 + y^4)$

110. $y_1 = y_2$ **112.** $y_1 = y_2$

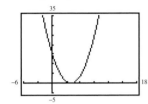   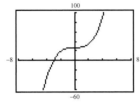

114. 2401 **116.** 896

118. $(x + 3)^2 - 1^2 = (x + 4)(x + 2)$

120. $x^2 + 2x + 1 = (x + 1)^2$

122. (a) $5 \times 5 = 25$ $8 \times 8 = 64$ $11 \times 11 = 121$

  $6 \times 4 = 24$ $9 \times 7 = 63$ $12 \times 10 = 120$

  (b) $13 \times 11 = 143$

  (c) $n^2 - 1 = (n + 1)(n - 1)$

124. (a) $x^3 - 8y^3$

  (b) $(x - 2y)(x^2 + 2xy + 4y^2)$

  (c) $y < \frac{1}{2}x$

126. $a^2 + 2ab + b^2 = (a + b)^2$

128. No. $(x + 2)^2 = x^2 + 4x + 4$

130. • Factor out any common factors.

  • Factor according to one of the special polynomial forms: difference of squares, sum or difference of cubes, or perfect square trinomials.

  • Factor by grouping—for polynomials with four terms.

  • Check to see whether the factors themselves can be factored.

  • Check the results by multiplying the factors.

Section 6.5   *(page 363)*

2. $0, 3$ **4.** $4, 10$ **6.** $-8, 3$ **8.** $\frac{2}{3}, \frac{5}{2}$ **10.** $-\frac{5}{4}, \frac{8}{3}$

12. $-8, 24$ **14.** $-25, 0, 3$ **16.** $-\frac{3}{5}, 0, 8$

18. $-12, 12$ **20.** $-2, 2$ **22.** $-2, 2$ **24.** $-2, 0$

26. $-12, 2$ **28.** $-\frac{1}{2}, 0$ **30.** $0, \frac{1}{3}$ **32.** $-2, 3$

34. $-2, 3$ **36.** -3 **38.** 5 **40.** $-\frac{7}{4}$ **42.** $-1, 9$

44. $-3, \frac{11}{2}$ **46.** $-\frac{1}{3}, -\frac{1}{4}$ **48.** $-2, 3$ **50.** -2

52. $-\frac{1}{5}, 3$ **54.** $-2, 3$ **56.** $-3, 10$ **58.** $-2, 0, 5$

60. $-\frac{1}{3}, 0, 2$ **62.** $-3, -1, 1$ **64.** $-2, 2$

66. $-3, 0, 3, 4$

68. $(-1, 0), (2, 0)$; The number of solutions equals the number of x-intercepts.

70. $\left(-\frac{3}{2}, 0\right), (1, 0)$; The number of solutions equals the number of x-intercepts.

72. $\left(-\frac{5}{2}, 0\right), (0, 0), (1, 0)$; The number of solutions equals the number of x-intercepts.

74. $(-4, 0), (0, 0), (2, 0)$; The number of solutions equals the number of x-intercepts.

76.   **78.**

   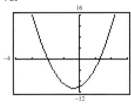

  $(0, 0), (4, 0)$ $(-2, 0), \left(\frac{5}{4}, 0\right)$

80.   **82.**

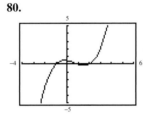   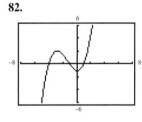

  $(-1, 0), (1, 0), (2, 0)$ $(-4, 0), (-1, 0), (1, 0)$

84. $15, 16$ **86.** $17, 19$ **88.** 16 feet $\times$ 20 feet

90. 20 inches $\times$ 30 inches   **92.** 6 inches $\times$ 6 inches

94. 5 seconds

96. (a)   (b) 40   (c) 40

98. (a) $15, 36, 55$ (b) Verification   (c) 20

100. $x(ax + b) = 0$

  $x = 0, -\dfrac{b}{a}$

102. (c) 7 feet $\times$ 9 feet $\times$ 12 feet

  (d) No. When the area of the base is 100 square feet, $x = 4$ and the volume of the bin is 1600 cubic feet.

  (e) $x = 2$, 4 feet $\times$ 8 feet $\times$ 8 feet

  (f) $V(x) = 4x(x + 6)(4x - 3)$

  No. $V(2) = 320$ cubic feet, which is larger than the bin.

CHAPTER 6

104. The Zero-Factor Property allows you to solve a quadratic equation by factoring and converting it into two linear equations.

106. Yes. $x^2 + 2x + 1 = (x + 1)^2 = 0$. There is one solution, $x = -1$.

108. False. $3(x - 2)(x + 5) = 0$ also has solutions $x = 2$ and $x = -5$.

Review Exercises   *(page 368)*

2. $3x^2$ **4.** 1 **6.** $7(1 + 3x)$ **8.** $u(u - 6)$

10. $7y(1 - 3y^3)$ **12.** $3u(2 - 3u + 5u^2)$

14. $(u - 2)(2u + 5)$ **16.** $(z - 5)(z^2 + 1)$

18. $(x - 5)(x^2 + 5)$ **20.** $(x + 3)(2x - 5)$

22. $(x - 8)(x + 5)$ **24.** $(y + 7)(y + 8)$

26. Prime   **28.** $(v + 2u)(v + 16u)$

30. $x(x + 3)(x + 6)$ **32.** $\pm 10, \pm 26$

34. $\pm 9, \pm 15$ **36.** $(2x - 3)(4x - 3)$

38. $(7 - 2x)(1 + x)$ **40.** $(16x - 3)(x + 1)$

42. $2x(4x^2 - 4x + 15)$ **44.** $(3x + 2)(x + 2)$

46. $\pm 4, \pm 14, \pm 31$ **48.** ± 4 **50.** $1, -8$

52. $(u + v)(u - v)$ **54.** $(6 + b)(6 - b)$

56. $(4b + 1)(4b - 1)$ **58.** $(y + 1)(y - 5)$

60. $(y + 12)^2$ **62.** $(v - 5)^2$ **64.** $(u - v)^2$

66. $yz(y + 2z)^2$ **68.** $(z + 2)(z^2 - 2z + 4)$

70. $(z - 5)(z^2 + 5z + 25)$ **72.** $5t(1 + 5t)(1 - 5t)$

74. $-11, 11$ **76.** $-\frac{1}{2}, 2$ **78.** $-2, 0, 3$

80. $-\frac{1}{5}, 0$ **82.** $-5, 3$ **84.** $-8, 3$

86. $-1, 1, 3$ **88.** $x(3x + 4)$

90. (a)

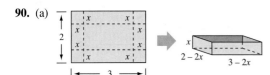

(b) $2x(x - 1)(2x - 3) = x(2 - 2x)(3 - 2x)$

(c)

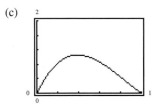

$x \approx 0.4$

92. 3 seconds   **94.** 10 inches $\times$ 10 inches $\times$ 5 inches

96. Multiply two binomials and give the product to your friend.

$(x + 2)(x - 3) = x^2 - x - 6$

$(2x + 1)(3x + 5) = 6x^2 + 13x + 5$

$(7 - 2x)(3 + x) = 21 + x - 2x^2$

Chapter 7

Section 7.1   *(page 380)*

2. (a) Not a solution   (b) Solution

4. (a) Solution   (b) Not a solution

6. (a) Not a solution   (b) Solution   **8.** $(-1, 1)$

10. $(3, 4)$ **12.** $(3, 0)$ **14.** No solution   **16.** $(2, 3)$

18. $(4, 4)$ **20.** $(2, 2)$ **22.** $(2, 2)$ **24.** $(4, 3)$

26. No solution   **28.** $(0, -3)$

30. Infinitely many solutions   **32.** $\left(4, \frac{3}{2}\right)$

34. $(-10, 2)$ **36.** $\left(1, \frac{3}{2}\right)$ **38.** No solution

40. Infinitely many solutions   **42.** No solution

44. $(2, 6)$ **46.** $(4, 5)$ **48.** $(-2, -1)$

50. $y = \frac{5}{8}x + 1$, $y = \frac{7}{4}x - \frac{7}{2}$, One solution

52. $y = -\frac{3}{8}x + \frac{7}{2}$, $y = \frac{4}{9}x + \frac{1}{9}$, One solution

54. $y = -\frac{2}{5}x + 3$, $y = \frac{2}{5}x - 1$, One solution

56. $y = \frac{3}{4}x + \frac{9}{8}$, $y = \frac{3}{4}x + \frac{9}{8}$, Infinitely many solutions

58. 9 feet $\times$ 12 feet   **60.** $x + y = 35$

$\qquad\qquad\qquad\qquad\qquad x - y = 11$

$\qquad\qquad\qquad\qquad\qquad (23, 12)$

62.

$p = \$44$

64. Because the slopes of the two lines are not equal, the lines intersect and the system has one solution: $(48, 50)$.

66. • Two lines that intersect in one point. The system has a unique solution.

   • Two lines that coincide. The system has an infinite number of solutions.

   • Two parallel lines. The system has no solution.

68. A system that has no solution

70. $x + 2y = 5$ **72.** $x + y = 3$

   $-x + 3y = 0$ $2x + 2y = 6$

Section 7.2   *(page 388)*

2. $(1, 0)$ **4.** $(-2, 3)$ **6.** $(-1, 4)$ **8.** No solution

10. $(2, 5)$ **12.** $(-17, 3)$ **14.** $\left(\frac{2}{3}, 2\right)$

16. No solution   **18.** $(5, 5)$ **20.** $(0, 0)$ **22.** $\left(4, \frac{1}{2}\right)$

24. $\left(\frac{4}{3}, \frac{4}{3}\right)$ **26.** $\left(-\frac{5}{3}, -1\right)$ **28.** $(-4, -18)$

30. $\left(\frac{26}{7}, \frac{76}{7}\right)$ **32.** Infinitely many solutions

34. No solution   **36.** No solution   **38.** $(-10, -10)$

40. $\left(-\frac{2}{3}, \frac{32}{3}\right)$ **42.** $\left(-9, -\frac{19}{2}\right)$

44. $(4, 8)$ **46.** $(3, 5)$

 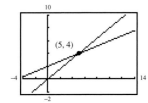

48. $(5, 4)$

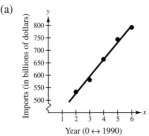

50. $2x + y = 5$ **52.** $4x + 5y = 3$ **54.** $15, 35$
      $-x + y = -7$ $2x + 3y = 2$

56. 5%: $10,000   **58.** 2   **60.** 50,000 miles
      8%: $5000

62. (a)

(b) $y_I = 68.0x + 390.4$

(c) $y_E - y_I = -20.7x - 52.4$

  Imports are increasing faster than exports.

64. $3x + y - 2 = 0$

66. (a) Solve one of the equations for one variable in terms of the other.

  (b) Substitute the expression found in Step (a) into the other equation to obtain an equation in one variable.

(c) Solve the equation obtained in Step (b).

(d) Back-substitute the solution from Step (c) into the expression obtained in Step (a) to find the value of the other variable.

(e) Check the solution in the original system.

68. Solve one of the equations for one variable in terms of the other variable. Substitute that expression into the other equation. If an identity statement results, the system has infinitely many solutions.

70. A consistent system of linear equations is a system that has at least one solution.

72. $b = 2$ **74.** $b = -\frac{1}{3}$

Section 7.3   *(page 398)*

2. $(-1, 1)$ **4.** $(3, 4)$ **6.** $(5, 2)$ **8.** $(12, 1)$

10. $(-1, -2)$ **12.** $(1, 1)$ **14.** No solution

16. $(2, 1)$ **18.** $(5, -4)$ **20.** Infinitely many solutions

22. $(-2, 3)$ **24.** $(3, 1)$ **26.** Infinitely many solutions

28. $\left(\frac{18}{11}, \frac{25}{11}\right)$ **30.** No solution   **32.** $(6, 3)$

34. $\left(\frac{3}{2}, 5\right)$ **36.** $(4, 3)$

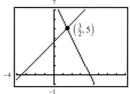 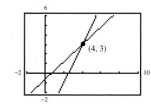

38. $(3, 4)$

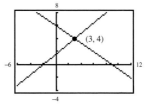

40. $(0.2, 0.5)$

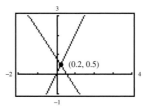

42. $(21, 7)$ **44.** $(-2, 8)$ **46.** $(4, 4)$ **48.** $(2, -1)$

CHAPTER 7

50. (4, 2)   **52.** (9, 10)   **54.** $\left(\frac{5}{4}, \frac{141}{8}\right)$

56. $x - 2y = 11$ **58.** $x + y = -5$

$2x + y = -8$ $x - y = 25$

60. Student ticket: \$2   **62.** \$3000   **64.** 58, 96
General admission: \$3

66. $x + 3y = 1$ is the equation of the upper ray because the slope of the line is negative. The focal length is 1.

68. $2x + y - 7 = 0$

70. (a) Obtain coefficients for x or y that differ only in sign by multiplying all terms of one or both equations by suitably chosen constants.

(b) Add the equations to eliminate one variable and solve the resulting equation.

(c) Back-substitute the value obtained in Step (b) into either of the original equations and solve for the other variable.

(d) Check your solution in both of the original equations.

72. When you add the equations to eliminate one variable, both are eliminated, yielding an identity. For example, adding the equations in the system $x - y = 3$ and $-x + y = -3$ yields $0 = 0$.

74. $x - 4y = 3$

$7x + 9y = 11$

76. Infinite. Since two solutions are given, the system is dependent.

Section 7.4   *(page 408)*

2. (a) (Amount at 10.5%) + (amount at 12%) = 12,000

(Interest from 10.5% fund) + (interest from 12% fund)

= (total interest)

(b) x = amount at 10.5%; y = amount at 12%

(c) $x + y = 12,000$

$0.105x + 0.12y = 1,380$

(d) \$4000 in 10.5% fund; \$8000 in 12% fund

4. 45, 30   **6.** 30, 16   **8.** 15, 45

10. 17 dimes, 4 quarters   **12.** 5 nickels, 30 quarters

14. 8 nickels, 20 dimes   **16.** 50 inches × 60 inches

18. 8 meters × 16 meters   **20.** 7.5 feet × 10 feet

22. \$85.65   **24.** \$343.75   **26.** \$895

28. Adult ticket: \$5.00   **30.** Large truck: \$52,000
Child's ticket: \$2.50   Small truck: \$35,000

32. Regular: \$1.09 per gallon   **34.** \$1.19
Premium: \$1.59 per gallon

36. 10 miles per hour

38. Plane in still air: 550 miles per hour
Speed of the wind: 50 miles per hour

40. 6 hours   **42.** 150 miles; 300 miles

44. 20% solution: $6\frac{2}{3}$ gallons   **46.** \$3.25 nuts: 9 pounds
50% solution: $3\frac{1}{3}$ gallons   \$5.85 nuts: 6 pounds

48. \$1.68 bird feed: 60 pounds   **50.** \$2000
\$0.83 bird feed: 40 pounds

52.

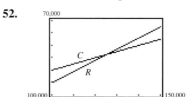

125,000 units
$R(125,000) = \$56,250$

54. $m = 2, b = 1$ **56.** $m = -\frac{5}{2}, b = 2$

58. (a) $y = -\frac{9}{14}x + \frac{13}{7}$

(b)

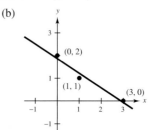

60. (a)

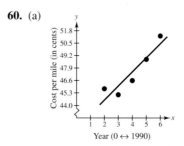

(b) $y = 1.51x + 41.54$

(c) The average change in cost per mile

62. Translation of the verbal description of a problem into the form of an equation using words.

64. Graphing, substitution, elimination

Review Exercises   *(page 413)*

2. (a) Not a solution   (b) Solution

4. (a) Not a solution   (b) Not a solution

6. b   **8.** c   **10.** (6, −4)   **12.** No solution

14. (2, −3)   **16.** No solution   **18.** (1, −3)

20. $(3, 5)$ **22.** $\left(-\frac{1}{5}, \frac{2}{5}\right)$ **24.** $(5, -2)$ **26.** $(3, 0)$

28. $(-9, -4)$ **30.** $(0.6, 0.5)$ **32.** $(4, 3)$

34. $(0, 4)$ **36.** $(8, -3)$ **38.** $\left(-3, -\frac{4}{3}\right)$ **40.** $(8, 12)$

42. $\left(\frac{4}{7}, -\frac{4}{7}\right)$ **44.** No solution   **46.** $(-1, 3)$

48. $(0, 0)$ **50.** $(-0.5, 0.8)$

52. $\begin{aligned} x + y &= 5 \\ -3x - y &= 1 \end{aligned}$ **54.** $\begin{aligned} -3x + y &= 7 \\ 9x + 2y &= 4 \end{aligned}$

56. $\begin{aligned} 2x - 3y &= 3 \\ -2x + 3y &= 6 \end{aligned}$ **58.** $\begin{aligned} x - 3y &= -3 \\ -2x + 6y &= 6 \end{aligned}$

60. 6 dimes, 9 quarters   **62.** 2

64.

828 units
$R(828) = \$3933$

66. 2 hours

Chapter 8

Section 8.1   *(page 423)*

2. Not rational since the denominator is not a polynomial

4. Rational   **6.** All real values of x such that $x \neq 6$

8. All real values of z such that $z \neq -8$

10. All real values of y **12.** All real values of x

14. All real values of z such that $z \neq -2$ and $z \neq 2$

16. All real values of x such that $x \neq -2$ and $x \neq -4$

18. All real values of x such that $x \neq -5$ and $x \neq 2$

20. All real values of y such that $y \neq -1$ and $y \neq \frac{3}{4}$

22. (a) 0 (b) -3 (c) $\frac{15}{2}$

(d) Division by zero is undefined.

24. (a) 1 (b) Division by zero is undefined.

(c) $\frac{8}{5}$ (d) Division by zero is undefined.

26. $\dfrac{-4}{y}, \dfrac{4}{-y}$ **28.** $-\dfrac{6 - x}{x + 1}, \dfrac{6 - x}{-1 - x}$ **30.** $(2x^2)$

32. $[2(x - 4)^2]$ **34.** $(5x)$ **36.** $[-(x + 2)]$

38. $(y - 1)$ **40.** $(z + 1)$ **42.** $\dfrac{y}{2}$ **44.** $5z^2, z \neq 0$

46. $\dfrac{3}{10y^3}$ **48.** $\dfrac{5}{b - 3}, b \neq 0$ **50.** $\dfrac{1}{b}, b \neq 2$

52. $-\frac{1}{2}, x \neq 5$ **54.** $x, xy \neq -1$ **56.** $-\frac{1}{3}, y \neq 3$

58. $x + 5, x \neq 5$ **60.** $x + 5z, x \neq 5z$

62. $-\dfrac{u + 1}{u + 4}, u \neq 4$ **64.** $u - 3, u \neq 3$

66. $\dfrac{z + 6}{5}, z \neq -6$ **68.** $\dfrac{x}{x - 1}, x \neq 7$

70. $\dfrac{y - 4}{y + 6}, y \neq 3$ **72.** $\dfrac{z + 3}{z + 8}, z \neq 6$

74. $\dfrac{t + 1}{t + 6}, t \neq 0, t \neq 1$ **76.** $\dfrac{1}{x + 1}, x \neq \pm 3$

78. $\dfrac{1}{z^2 + 1}, z \neq 3$ **80.** $1 - y$

82. $\dfrac{5x - 6}{2}, x \neq 0$

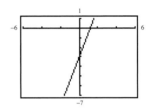

84. $2(x - 4), x \neq 4$

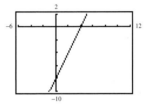

86. $\dfrac{x(x - 4)}{x^2 + 2}, x \neq 0$

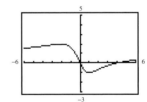

88.

x	0	0.5	1	1.5	2
$\dfrac{x - 1}{x^2 + 2x - 3}$	$\dfrac{1}{3}$	$\dfrac{2}{7}$	Undef.	$\dfrac{2}{9}$	$\dfrac{1}{5}$
$\dfrac{1}{x + 3}$	$\dfrac{1}{3}$	$\dfrac{2}{7}$	$\dfrac{1}{4}$	$\dfrac{2}{9}$	$\dfrac{1}{5}$

90. $\dfrac{240}{x + 5}$

92. (a) $\overline{C} = \dfrac{5000 + 12.50x}{x}$ (b) $\{1, 2, 3, 4, \dots \}$

     (c) $\$37.50$

94. (a) 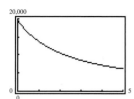   (b) $\$9615$

96. (a) Friend: $D = 60t$;   Yourself: $d = 50(t + 2)$

     (b) $\dfrac{6t}{5(t + 2)}$ (c) $t = 5 : \frac{6}{7}; t = 10 : 1$

98. $\dfrac{11}{x + 7}$ **100.** $\dfrac{5}{6}$

102. The domain of a rational expression consists of all values of the variable for which the denominator is not zero.

104. True   **106.** They are equivalent for $x \neq 0$.

108. $\dfrac{x}{x^2 + x}$

Section 8.2   *(page 433)*

2. (a) 0 (b) 8 (c) -8

     (d) Division by zero is undefined.

4. (8) **6.** (x^2) **8.** $(x + 3)$ **10.** $2x$

12. $(-x)$ **14.** $\frac{6}{35}$ **16.** $\frac{25}{64}$ **18.** 45 **20.** $\frac{6}{5}, x \neq 0$

22. $5x, x \neq 0$ **24.** $\dfrac{4x^2}{3y}, x \neq 0$

26. $-\dfrac{7v^2}{12}, u \neq 0, v \neq 0$ **28.** $1, x \neq -1$

30. $\dfrac{2}{3x}, x \neq 3$ **32.** $-1, t \neq 6$ **34.** $\dfrac{-2z(z - 4)}{z - 1}$

36. $\dfrac{3y}{4}, y \neq -4$ **38.** $y - 2, y \neq \pm 2$

40. $\dfrac{1}{2(r - 2)}, r \neq -3$ **42.** $-1, z \neq \pm 1$

44. $\dfrac{x - 3}{(x + 2)^2}, x \neq -5$ **46.** $\dfrac{8}{5}, y \neq 4x, y \neq -3x$

48. $\dfrac{2(y + 4)}{y^2(y - 2)}, y \neq 4$ **50.** $u^2 - 4, u \neq 2$

52. $\dfrac{1}{3x(x - 7)}, x \neq -7, x \neq 5$ **54.** $\dfrac{x - 1}{x(x + 1)^2}, x \neq -2$

56. $\dfrac{x + 1}{7}, x \neq 0, x \neq 7$

58. $z(z + 1), z \neq 0, z \neq -\frac{3}{2}, z \neq 2$

---

60. $\dfrac{(x + 4)(x + 5)}{x}, x \neq \pm 5$ **62.** $\dfrac{9}{16}$ **64.** $\dfrac{1}{18}$

66. $1, x \neq 0$ **68.** $\dfrac{5}{2x}$ **70.** $\dfrac{z + 3}{3z}$ **72.** $20, x \neq 3$

74. $\dfrac{2x(x + 1)}{3}, x \neq -1, x \neq 0$ **76.** $\dfrac{10}{x(x + 5)}, x \neq 5$

78. $\dfrac{x + y}{x - y}, x \neq 0, y \neq 0$ **80.** $-\dfrac{x + 1}{x + 2}, x \neq 2$

82. $\dfrac{x^2 + 1}{3(x + 3)}$ **84.** $-\dfrac{147}{64}$ **86.** $\dfrac{4y^3}{3}, y \neq 0$

88. $\dfrac{6r^2}{5t^2}, r \neq 0$ **90.** $-1, x \neq 4, x \neq 0$

92. $\dfrac{1}{3}, a \neq -4, a \neq \dfrac{5}{2}$ **94.** $\dfrac{x + 2}{5(x - 1)}, x \neq 4$

96. $\dfrac{3x + 1}{x^2}, x \neq -\dfrac{1}{5}, x \neq \dfrac{5}{2}$ **98.** $\dfrac{40}{9u}$

100. $\dfrac{16(x + 1)}{x - 1}, x \neq -1$

102. (a) $\dfrac{1}{24}$ minute   (b) $\dfrac{x}{24}$ minutes   (c) 5 minutes

104. (a) $\dfrac{200(149t + 2842)}{7(t + 24)(200 - 9t)}$

     (b)

Year, t	0	2	4	6
Monthly rate	$\$16.92$	$\$18.96$	$\$21.39$	$\$24.37$

106. To divide two rational expressions, invert the divisor and multiply.

108. 1. Multiplicative Inverse Property

110. Invert the divisor, not the dividend.

Section 8.3   *(page 443)*

2. $-x$ **4.** $\dfrac{17}{z^2}$ **6.** $\dfrac{1}{z}$ **8.** 1 **10.** -2

12. $\dfrac{x}{x + 3}$ **14.** $\dfrac{5s + 5}{s + 5}$ **16.** $24t^2$ **18.** $4x^3$

20. $54y^2(y - 3)$ **22.** $x^2(x + 7)(x - 7)$

24. $x^2(x - 5)(x - 25)$ **26.** $(t^2 + 3t + 9)(t^2 - 9)$

28. $x(x + 1)(x - 1)$ **30.** $\dfrac{32x}{4(x + 2)}, \dfrac{3}{4(x + 2)}$

32. $\dfrac{5t^2}{t(t - 3)^2}, \dfrac{4(t - 3)}{t(t - 3)^2}$

34. $\dfrac{3y^2}{y(y - 3)(y + 2)}, \dfrac{(y + 2)^2}{y(y - 3)(y + 2)}$

36. $\dfrac{29}{24z}$ **38.** $\dfrac{4x+3}{6x}$ **40.** $\dfrac{5z+6}{z^2}$ **42.** $\dfrac{2(6-u)}{9u^2}$

44. $\dfrac{9}{6-t}$ **46.** $\dfrac{3(3x+2)}{(x-1)(x+4)}$ **48.** $\dfrac{2}{2-x}$

50. $\dfrac{-5x+8}{x-1}$ **52.** $\dfrac{4x-7}{2x-5}$ **54.** $\dfrac{x+11}{(x-4)(x+1)}$

56. $\dfrac{2x-1}{2x(x-1)}$ **58.** $\dfrac{5z-9}{(z+2)(z-2)}$ **60.** $\dfrac{t+2}{t(t+1)}$

62. $\dfrac{x^2-4x+7}{(x+1)(x^2-2x+3)}$ **64.** $\dfrac{x^2-3x+1}{(x-1)(x^2-4)}$

66. $\dfrac{7x^2+38x-4}{(x+5)(x-5)}$ **68.** $\dfrac{10x-9}{x(x-3)}$ **70.** $\dfrac{4x^2-1}{2x(x+1)^2}$

72. $-\dfrac{2(2x^2-14x-33)}{3x(2x+5)}$ **74.** $\dfrac{2v}{3u},\ v\neq 0$

76. $\dfrac{x^2}{5+2x},\ x\neq 0$ **78.** $\dfrac{2(x-2)}{x^2}$

80. $\dfrac{4(x+2)}{1-16x},\ x\neq 0$ **82.** $\dfrac{5x}{x+5},\ x\neq 0$ **84.** $\dfrac{u-6}{1+6u}$

86. $\dfrac{8}{9},\ x\neq -5$ **88.** $\dfrac{4y+5}{5y},\ y\neq -\dfrac{1}{2}$ **90.** $\dfrac{5t}{18}$

92. $\dfrac{19x}{30}$ **94.** $\dfrac{23x}{36},\dfrac{17x}{18}$

96. (a) $\dfrac{1508t^2-731{,}651t-49{,}159{,}000}{100(13t-1000)}$ (b) $665{,}399$

98. $\dfrac{x+35}{x^2-25}=-\dfrac{3}{x+5}+\dfrac{4}{x-5}$

100. Add or subtract the numerators and place the result over the common denominator.

102. Determine the prime factorization of each polynomial. The least common multiple contains each prime factor, repeated the maximum number of times it occurs in any one of the factorizations.

104. When the numerators are subtracted, the result should be $x-(3x-4)=x-3x+4$.

Section 8.4   *(page 453)*

2. (a) Not a solution   (b) Solution   (c) Solution
   (d) Not a solution

4. (a) Solution   (b) Not a solution   (c) Not a solution
   (d) Not a solution

6. 13 **8.** -3 **10.** -40 **12.** 12 **14.** 10

16. $\dfrac{200}{3}$ **18.** 12 **20.** 4 **22.** -1 **24.** $\dfrac{1}{4}$

26. 2 **28.** 5 **30.** -5 **32.** $\dfrac{4}{7}$ **34.** $\dfrac{1}{2}$

36. $-\dfrac{2}{5}$ **38.** $-\dfrac{25}{2}$ **40.** $\dfrac{9}{7}$ **42.** 6 **44.** 10

46. 2 **48.** 6 **50.** 5 **52.** $-5,6$ **54.** $-\dfrac{1}{3},2$

56. $-12,2$ **58.** $-5,-2$ **60.** $-\dfrac{3}{2},1$

62. (a) 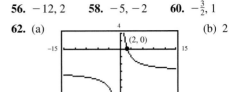   (b) 2

64. (a) 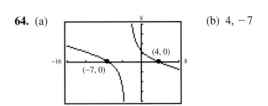   (b) $4,-7$

66. (a) 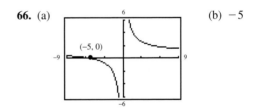   (b) -5

68. (a) 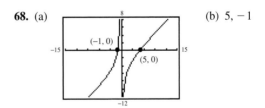   (b) $5,-1$

70. $\dfrac{3}{5},5$ **72.** $10,12$

74. First car: 50 miles per hour; Second car: 60 miles per hour

76. Car: 75 miles per hour; Bus: 60 miles per hour

78. 30 miles per hour

80.

Person #1	Person #2	Together
30 minutes	30 minutes	15 minutes
$6\frac{1}{2}$ hours	4 hours	$2\frac{10}{21}$ hours
a days	b days	$\dfrac{ab}{a+b}$ days

82. $33\frac{1}{3}$ minutes   **84.** 10 hours, 15 hours   **86.** 6 hits

88. 2000 units   **90.** 75%

92. The first is a rational equation and the second is a rational expression.

94. An extraneous solution is an extra solution found by multiplying both sides of the original equation by an expression containing the variable. It is identified by checking all solutions in the original equation.

96. Step (iii)

Review Exercises   *(page 458)*

2. All real numbers y such that $y \neq -3$

4. All real numbers x such that $x \neq 0$, $x \neq -2$, and $x \neq 2$

6. (a) $-\frac{3}{10}$ (b) $-\frac{1}{4}$ (c) Division by zero is undefined.
(d) $-\frac{1}{5}$

8. (a) $\frac{1}{3}$ (b) $\frac{2}{3}$ (c) 0   (d) Division by zero is undefined.

10. $3x$ **12.** $\frac{8z}{3}$, $z \neq 0$ **14.** $\frac{y}{3z^2}$, $y \neq 0$

16. $\frac{1}{5}$, $a \neq -\frac{5}{2}$ **18.** $-\frac{1}{3}$, $x \neq y$ **20.** $\frac{x+2}{x+3}$, $x \neq 2$

22. $\frac{x-2}{x^2-2x+4}$, $x \neq -2$ **24.** $\frac{x^2+2xy+y^2}{x^2-xy-y^2}$

26. $\frac{x-5}{x}$

28.

x	1	1.5	2	2.5	3
$\dfrac{x-2}{x^2-x-2}$	$\frac{1}{2}$	$\frac{2}{5}$	Undef.	$\frac{2}{7}$	$\frac{1}{4}$
$\dfrac{1}{x+1}$	$\frac{1}{2}$	$\frac{2}{5}$	$\frac{1}{3}$	$\frac{2}{7}$	$\frac{1}{4}$

30. $(x-3)$ **32.** $(x+2)$ **34.** $\frac{3}{20}$ **36.** $\frac{1}{8}$

38. $-\frac{y}{2}$, $y \neq 0$ **40.** $\frac{1}{3x}$ **42.** $\frac{1}{2x}$, $y \neq 0$ **44.** $\frac{5}{3z^4}$

46. $-\frac{1}{3}$, $u \neq 0$, $u \neq 1$ **48.** $-2(x+7)$, $x \neq 7$, $x \neq \frac{5}{4}$

50. 1, $v \neq 0$, $v \neq -5$ **52.** $\frac{2x(1-x)}{x-4}$

54. $\frac{5}{x+5}$, $x \neq 0$, $x \neq 1$, $x \neq -1$ **56.** $5y$, $x \neq 0$, $y \neq 0$

58. $\frac{x(x-3)}{4(x+4)}$, $x \neq -1$, $x \neq 3$

60. $\frac{8xy^2(y-1)}{y+4}$, $x \neq 0$, $y \neq 0$, $y \neq 1$

62. $36y^2z$ **64.** $10(x^3-1)$ **66.** $\frac{5t}{3}$

68. 1, $y \neq -\frac{1}{2}$ **70.** $\frac{23x}{24}$ **72.** $\frac{5x+13}{(x-3)(x+4)}$

74. $\frac{4x}{(x-1)(x+1)^2}$ **76.** $\frac{3x-1}{(x+6)(x-6)}$

78. $\frac{3x^2-7x-2}{x(x-1)(x+1)}$ **80.** $\frac{2x^2-3x+2}{(x+2)(x-2)^2}$

82. $\frac{x+2}{2-x}$, $x \neq 0$ **84.** $\frac{1}{xy(x+y)}$

86. $\frac{1}{5(x+1)}$, $x \neq 4$ **88.** $\frac{3}{2}$ **90.** $\frac{1}{2}$ **92.** 3

94. $-\frac{2}{3}$ **96.** $-4, 4$ **98.** 0, 5

100. (a) and (b)

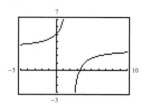

$\left(\frac{10}{3}, 0\right)$

102. (a) and (b)

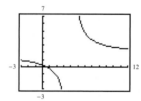

$\left(\frac{4}{7}, 0\right)$

104. (a) and (b)

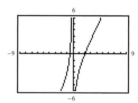

$(2, 0), \left(-\frac{1}{2}, 0\right)$

106. $\frac{2(a+1)}{2a+3}$ **108.** $4, \frac{1}{2}$

110. 45 miles per hour, 50 miles per hour

112. 21.6 hours, 27 hours

114. 3 hits

116. (a) $\dfrac{100}{x}, \dfrac{100}{y}, \dfrac{100}{x} + \dfrac{100}{y}$ (b) $\dfrac{2xy}{x+y}$

(c) $\dfrac{xy}{x+y} = 25$

(d) $y = \dfrac{25x}{x-25}, \; x > 25$

x	40	45	47	49	50
y	66.67	56.25	53.41	51.04	50

(e) The average of x and y is not 50 miles per hour except when $x = y = 50$.

Chapter 9

Section 9.1   (page 470)

2. 7   **4.** -13 **6.** $12, -12$ **8.** $5, -5$

10. $\frac{2}{5}, -\frac{2}{5}$ **12.** $\frac{5}{4}, -\frac{5}{4}$ **14.** Not possible

16. $0.5, -0.5$ **18.** Not possible   **20.** 1   **22.** 5

24. -3 **26.** $\frac{1}{3}$ **28.** Not possible   **30.** 8

32. -8 **34.** Not possible   **36.** -6 **38.** 15

40. Not possible   **42.** $\frac{2}{3}$ **44.** $-\frac{1}{5}$ **46.** $\frac{9}{20}$

48. $\frac{1}{2}$ **50.** 0.8   **52.** -0.3 **54.** 4   **56.** -3

58. -2 **60.** -3 **62.** -1 **64.** Rational

66. Irrational   **68.** Irrational   **70.** Irrational

72. Rational   **74.** Rational   **76.** Irrational

78. 6.164   **80.** Not possible   **82.** 12.247

84. 18.055   **86.** -35.355 **88.** 18.061   **90.** 0.845

92. -2.933 **94.** 32.683   **96.** -2.348 **98.** 18.121

100. Not possible   **102.** 9.487   **104.** 5.477

106. 11.180   **108.** 22.361   **110.** 0

112. $\sqrt{201} \approx 14.18$ **114.** $\dfrac{10\sqrt{3}}{2} \approx 8.66$ **116.** 3.6

118. 23 feet $\times$ 23 feet   **120.** 0.0260 inch

122. (a)

x	0	1	2	4	6	8
$\sqrt{x}$	0	1	1.41	2	2.45	2.83

x	10	12	14	16	18	20
$\sqrt{x}$	3.16	3.46	3.74	4	4.24	4.47

(b)
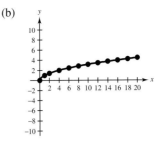

(c) y is a function of x.

124. a **126.** b is the square root of a if $b^2 = a$.

128. a is the radicand of $\sqrt{a}$.

130. $x < 0$. $\sqrt{(-4)^2} = \sqrt{16} = 4$

Section 9.2   (page 480)

2. $\sqrt{95}$ **4.** $\sqrt{105}$ **6.** $\sqrt{70}$ **8.** $\sqrt{3y}$

10. $\sqrt{15ab}$ **12.** $4\sqrt{3}$ **14.** $10\sqrt{3}$ **16.** $2\sqrt{3}$

18. $5\sqrt{2}$ **20.** $2\sqrt{5}$ **22.** $8\sqrt{2}$ **24.** $12\sqrt{3}$

26. $20\sqrt{2}$ **28.** $2\sqrt[3]{2}$ **30.** $2\sqrt[3]{5}$ **32.** $2\sqrt[4]{2}$

34. $4\sqrt[4]{2}$ **36.** $3x^2$ **38.** $7z^2\sqrt{z}$ **40.** y^4

42. $v^2\sqrt{v}$ **44.** $3b^4\sqrt{5}$ **46.** $a^2b^2\sqrt{a}$ **48.** $|xy^3|$

50. $8u^2v^3\sqrt{2v}$ **52.** $2x\sqrt[3]{x^2}$ **54.** $r\sqrt[3]{6r^2}$

56. $x\sqrt[4]{x}$ **58.** $2t\sqrt[4]{5t^3}$ **60.** $\sqrt{3}$ **62.** $\sqrt{6}$

64. $\sqrt{7}$ **66.** $2\sqrt{5}$ **68.** $4\sqrt{2}$ **70.** $\sqrt{5}, u \neq 0$

72. $4|y|, y \neq 0$ **74.** $3x^2|x|, x \neq 0$ **76.** $\dfrac{\sqrt{11}}{5}$

78. $2\sqrt{2}$ **80.** $\dfrac{\sqrt{6}}{3}$ **82.** $\dfrac{\sqrt{5}}{2|u|}$ **84.** $\dfrac{x^2}{2}$

86. $5x^2\sqrt{x}$ **88.** $\dfrac{u^2}{6v^2}$ **90.** $\dfrac{\sqrt{2}}{3x^2}$ **92.** $\dfrac{\sqrt{5}}{5}$

94. $\dfrac{\sqrt{10}}{10}$ **96.** $\dfrac{\sqrt{14}}{2}$ **98.** $\dfrac{\sqrt{6}}{4}$ **100.** $\dfrac{\sqrt{14}}{6}$

102. $\dfrac{\sqrt{5}}{4}$ **104.** $\dfrac{13\sqrt{2}}{2}$ **106.** $\dfrac{\sqrt{z}}{z}$ **108.** $\dfrac{\sqrt{3a}}{a}$

110. $\dfrac{\sqrt{6u}}{5u^2}$ **112.** $\dfrac{\sqrt{xy}}{5y}$ **114.** $\dfrac{2x}{y}$ **116.** $\dfrac{9\sqrt[3]{2}}{2}$

118. $\dfrac{5\sqrt[3]{4}}{2}$ **120.** $\dfrac{\sqrt[3]{3x^2}}{x}$ **122.** $\dfrac{\sqrt[3]{a^2}}{3a}$

124.
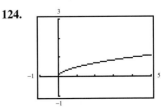

The equations are equivalent.

126.

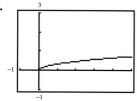

The equations are equivalent.

128. $\sqrt{300} > 12$

130. $4 < \sqrt{5} + \sqrt{10}$ **132.** 98   **134.** $\dfrac{9\sqrt{2}}{4} \approx 3.18$

136. $\dfrac{1.5\pi\sqrt{2}}{4} \approx 1.67$ seconds

138. If a and b are nonnegative real numbers and $b \neq 0$, then
$$\sqrt{\dfrac{a}{b}} = \dfrac{\sqrt{a}}{\sqrt{b}}.$$

140. $\sqrt{28} = \sqrt{4 \cdot 7} = \sqrt{4} \cdot \sqrt{7} = 2\sqrt{7}$

142. False. $\sqrt{3x^2} = |x|\sqrt{3}$

144. False. $(x + 4)^2 = x^2 + 8x + 16$

Section 9.3   (page 490)

2. $-5\sqrt{6}$ **4.** $8\sqrt{15}$ **6.** $2\sqrt{6}$

8. $-2\sqrt{17} + 8\sqrt{2}$ **10.** $\sqrt{6} - 2\sqrt{3}$ **12.** $10\sqrt[5]{4}$

14. $\sqrt[3]{3}$ **16.** $10\sqrt[4]{6}$ **18.** $7\sqrt[5]{2}$ **20.** $8\sqrt{y}$

22. $7\sqrt{v} - 3$ **24.** $10\sqrt[4]{a} + 8$ **26.** $5\sqrt[3]{x^2} + 5$

28. $7\sqrt[3]{b^2} - 8$ **30.** $24\sqrt{2}$ **32.** $7\sqrt{3}$

34. $7\sqrt{2} - 2\sqrt{3}$ **36.** $4\sqrt{t}$ **38.** $-4\sqrt{x}$

40. $9\sqrt{2u}$ **42.** $8\sqrt{v} + 2\sqrt{7v}$

44. $u^2\left(9\sqrt{5u} + 20\sqrt{3u}\right)$ **46.** $(3t^2 - s^2)\sqrt{st}$

48. $-\dfrac{1}{6}\sqrt{v}$ **50.** 6   **52.** $5\sqrt{3}$ **54.** $7\sqrt{3}$

56. 3   **58.** 3   **60.** $\sqrt{15} - 3\sqrt{3}$

62. $2\sqrt{7} + 3\sqrt{2}$ **64.** $2 - 3\sqrt[3]{4}$ **66.** $9\sqrt[4]{4} - 2$

68. $5 - \sqrt{15} + \sqrt{10} - \sqrt{6}$ **70.** $21 + 8\sqrt{6}$

72. -2 **74.** -1 **76.** $7\sqrt[4]{6} - 3\sqrt[4]{2} + \sqrt[4]{12} - 21$

78. $\sqrt[4]{36} + 6\sqrt[4]{6} + 9 = \sqrt{6} + 6\sqrt[4]{6} + 9$

80. $6\sqrt{7} + 16$ **82.** $28 - 16\sqrt{3}$ **84.** $3\sqrt{x} - x$

86. $u - 7\sqrt{u} + 12$ **88.** $25 - 10\sqrt{v} + v$

90. $16 - 9t$ **92.** $\sqrt{7} + 3, -2$ **94.** $\sqrt{10} - \sqrt{2}, 8$

96. $\sqrt{t} - 5, t - 25$ **98.** $\sqrt{a} - \sqrt{3}, a - 3$

100. $-\dfrac{\sqrt{10} + 5}{3}$ **102.** $-3\left(\sqrt{5} - \sqrt{6}\right)$

104. $-\dfrac{1}{2}\left(3 + \sqrt{21}\right)$ **106.** $\dfrac{\sqrt{7} - 3}{2}$ **108.** $\dfrac{6\left(\sqrt{x} + 1\right)}{x - 1}$

110. $\dfrac{6\left(2x + \sqrt{5x}\right)}{4x - 5}$ **112.** $\dfrac{t + 2\sqrt{t} + 1}{t - 1}$

114. $\dfrac{\sqrt{5} - 25}{5}$ **116.** $\dfrac{13\sqrt{3}}{3}$

118.

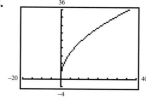

The equations are equivalent.

120.

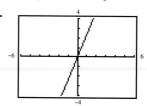

The equations are equivalent.

122. $\sqrt{5} - \sqrt{3} < \sqrt{5 - 3}$ **124.** $5 = \sqrt{3^2 + 4^2}$

126. Perimeter: $6\sqrt{17} + 18$; Area: $18\sqrt{17} + 34$

128. Perimeter: 20; Area: $4\sqrt{5} + 16$

130.

$v\backslash T$	0°	5°	10°
10 mi/hr	$-20.9°$	$-14.8°$	$-8.6°$
20 mi/hr	$-38.5°$	$-31.4°$	$-24.3°$
30 mi/hr	$-47.7°$	$-40.1°$	$-32.5°$
40 mi/hr	$-52.5°$	$-44.7°$	$-36.8°$

$v\backslash T$	15°	20°	25°
10 mi/hr	$-2.5°$	3.7°	9.8°
20 mi/hr	$-17.2°$	$-10.1°$	$-3.0°$
30 mi/hr	$-24.9°$	$-17.3°$	$-9.7°$
40 mi/hr	$-28.9°$	$-21.0°$	$-13.2°$

132. They have the same radicand.

134. $9\sqrt{7} - 3\sqrt{7} = (9 - 3)\sqrt{7} = 6\sqrt{7}$

136. Conjugates

138. No. Squaring yields $\frac{9}{2}$, whereas rationalizing the denominator yields $3\sqrt{2}/2$.

Section 9.4   (page 499)

2. (a) Solution (b) Not a solution (c) Not a solution
(d) Not a solution

4. (a) Not a solution (b) Not a solution (c) Solution
(d) Not a solution

6. 25   **8.** 9   **10.** 144   **12.** No solution

14. No solution   **16.** 8   **18.** 2   **20.** No solution

22. 13   **24.** $\frac{38}{5}$ **26.** -32 **28.** 15   **30.** -23

32. $\frac{13}{4}$ **34.** -1 **36.** 9   **38.** $\frac{3}{2}$ **40.** No solution

42. $\frac{1}{4}$ **44.** 5   **46.** $\frac{3}{2}$ **48.** 4   **50.** 1, 16

52. 2   **54.** 7   **56.** 2

58.

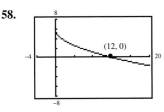

12

60.

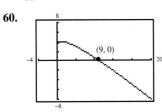

9

62. $5\sqrt{13} \approx 18.03$ **64.** 12   **66.** 7

68. $\sqrt{41} \approx 6.40$ **70.** $5\sqrt{5} \approx 11.18$

72. $\sqrt{122} \approx 11.05$ **74.** $4\sqrt{5} \approx 8.94$ **76.** 400 feet

78. 156.25 feet   **80.** 0.52 foot   **82.** 36 feet

84. 50 feet   **86.** $90\sqrt{2}$ feet   **88.** $16\sqrt{2}$ inches

90. 26.25 thousand passengers   **92.** Answers will vary.

94. A radical equation is an equation that contains one or more radicals with variable radicands.

96. No. The principal square root of a number is positive.

98. If a and b are the lengths of the legs of a right triangle and c is the length of the hypotenuse, then $a^2 + b^2 = c^2$.

Review Exercises   *(page 504)*

2. Not possible   **4.** 7   **6.** 0.3   **8.** $-\frac{8}{3}$ **10.** 2

12. $\frac{1}{3}$ **14.** 73.04   **16.** -2.37 **18.** -13.49

20. 0.34   **22.** $6\sqrt{2}$ **24.** $3\sqrt{5}$ **26.** $\frac{\sqrt{26}}{4}$

28. $\frac{3\sqrt{3}}{4}$ **30.** $2\sqrt[4]{3}$ **32.** $3\sqrt[3]{2}$ **34.** $9z$

36. $10u^2\sqrt{u}$ **38.** $5u^2v\sqrt{3}$ **40.** $1.2xy\sqrt{y}$

42. $2y\sqrt[4]{y}$ **44.** $a^2b^2\sqrt[4]{b^2}$ **46.** $\frac{\sqrt{70}}{10}$ **48.** $3\sqrt{5}$

50. $\frac{\sqrt{26}}{8}$ **52.** $\frac{5}{2}\sqrt[3]{2}$ **54.** $\frac{2}{3}\sqrt[3]{3}$ **56.** $\frac{7\sqrt{t}}{t}$

58. $\frac{2\sqrt{yz}}{z}$ **60.** $\frac{\sqrt{5}a}{2b}$ **62.** $\frac{\sqrt[3]{7y}}{y^2}$ **64.** $8\sqrt{15}$

66. $6\sqrt{2} - 3\sqrt{11}$ **68.** $189\sqrt{2}$ **70.** $58\sqrt{2}$

72. $5\sqrt[3]{7}$ **74.** $9\sqrt[4]{x^2} - 3\sqrt[4]{y^3}$ **76.** $12\sqrt{x}$

78. $6y^2\sqrt{7y}$ **80.** $10\sqrt{7} - 7$ **82.** $\sqrt[3]{20} + 2\sqrt[3]{5}$

84. 3   **86.** $2\sqrt{3} + 4$

88. $2\sqrt{6} - 6\sqrt{3} + 10\sqrt{2} - 30$ **90.** $\sqrt[4]{9} - 2\sqrt[4]{3} + 1$

92. $15\sqrt{z} - z$ **94.** $-(\sqrt{7} + 4)$ **96.** $5(\sqrt{6} - 2)$

98. $\frac{3s - \sqrt{s} - 2}{s - 1}$ **100.** 625   **102.** 100   **104.** 116

106. 3   **108.** 1   **110.** -3

112.

114. $3\sqrt{5} \approx 6.71$

116. $5\sqrt{2} \approx 7.07$ **118.** $\sqrt{202} \approx 14.21$

120. $\sqrt{274} \approx 16.55$ **122.** 3.0

124. 80 feet per second   **126.** 36 feet   **128.** 3

130. $3^2 + 6^2 = (3\sqrt{5})^2$ **132.** $10\sqrt{337} \approx 183.6$ feet

134. $\frac{1}{2}$; no   **136.** $\sqrt{10x} = \sqrt{10}\sqrt{x}$

Chapter 10

Section 10.1   *(page 515)*

2. $-5, 0$ **4.** 0, 4   **6.** $-4, 4$ **8.** $-\frac{9}{4}, \frac{9}{4}$

10. $-3, \frac{5}{2}$ **12.** $\frac{1}{4}, 3$ **14.** 3, 4   **16.** 5   **18.** $\frac{2}{3}$

20. $-\frac{4}{3}, 6$ **22.** $\frac{1}{2}, 2$ **24.** $-4, -1$ **26.** $-5, 5$

28. $-11, 11$ **30.** $-7, 7$ **32.** $-\sqrt{7}, \sqrt{7}$

34. $-\sqrt{11}, \sqrt{11}$ **36.** $-\frac{11}{4}, \frac{11}{4}$ **38.** $-\frac{1}{3}, \frac{1}{3}$

40. $-5, 5$ **42.** $-\frac{5}{4}, \frac{5}{4}$ **44.** No real solution

46. $-\frac{5}{9}, \frac{5}{9}$ **48.** $-\sqrt{5}, \sqrt{5}$ **50.** $-4\sqrt{2}, 4\sqrt{2}$

52. No real solution   **54.** $2 - \sqrt{11}, 2 + \sqrt{11}$

56. $-1 - \sqrt{10}, -1 + \sqrt{10}$ **58.** $-4, 18$

60. $10 - 2\sqrt{5}, 10 + 2\sqrt{5}$ **62.** $5 - 2\sqrt{2}, 5 + 2\sqrt{2}$

64. $-6 - 2\sqrt{6}, -6 + 2\sqrt{6}$ **66.** $\frac{1 - \sqrt{3}}{2}, \frac{1 + \sqrt{3}}{2}$

68. $\frac{-5 - \sqrt{10}}{4}, \frac{-5 + \sqrt{10}}{4}$ **70.** $\frac{7 - 4\sqrt{2}}{3}, \frac{7 + 4\sqrt{2}}{3}$

72. $\frac{2 - 2\sqrt{5}}{5}, \frac{2 + 2\sqrt{5}}{5}$ **74.** No real solution

76. $-\frac{1}{3}, \frac{7}{3}$ **78.** $-\frac{24}{5}, -\frac{6}{5}$ **80.** $-\frac{11}{4}, -\frac{1}{4}$

82. $\dfrac{14 - \sqrt{5}}{6}, \dfrac{14 + \sqrt{5}}{6}$ **84.** $-5, -1$ **86.** $-\frac{1}{2}, \frac{7}{2}$

88.

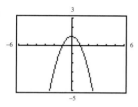

$1, -1$

90.

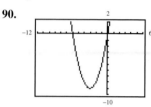

$0, -6$

92.

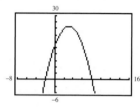

$8, -2$

94. 12   **96.** 2   **98.** 29.99 inches

100. $0.065 = 6.5\%$ **102.** $0.07 = 7\%$ **104.** 60 units

106. 2.5 seconds   **108.** 1.36 seconds

110. If $a = 0$, the equation would not be quadratic.

112. False. The solutions are $x = \pm 4$, because $4^2 = 16$ and $(-4)^2 = 16$.

114. (a) Extracting square roots   (b) Factoring

Section 10.2   *(page 524)*

2. $t^2 + 6t + 9$ **4.** $u^2 - 12u + 36$ **6.** 49   **8.** 16

10. 81   **12.** $\frac{81}{4}$ **14.** $\frac{121}{4}$ **16.** $\frac{25}{4}$ **18.** $\frac{1}{36}$

20. $\frac{4}{25}$ **22.** $-12, 0$ **24.** $0, 16$ **26.** $3 \pm \sqrt{2}$

28. $5 \pm \sqrt{10}$ **30.** No real solution   **32.** $-3 \pm 2\sqrt{3}$

34. $-1 \pm 3\sqrt{3}$ **36.** $-3, 9$ **38.** $\dfrac{-3 \pm \sqrt{5}}{2}$

40. $\dfrac{9 \pm \sqrt{101}}{2}$ **42.** $-3, -2$ **44.** $\dfrac{7 \pm \sqrt{29}}{2}$

46. No real solution   **48.** No real solution

50. $\dfrac{6 \pm \sqrt{15}}{3}$ **52.** No real solution   **54.** $\dfrac{3 \pm \sqrt{41}}{8}$

56. No real solution   **58.** $-5, 2$ **60.** $\dfrac{6 \pm \sqrt{30}}{2}$

62. $0, 2$ **64.** $-5, 3$ **66.** $-1, 8$ **68.** $-\frac{1}{2}, \frac{3}{2}$

70. $\dfrac{3 + \sqrt{5}}{2} \approx 2.62; \ \dfrac{3 - \sqrt{5}}{2} \approx 0.38$

72. $-2 + \sqrt{5} \approx 0.24; \ -2 - \sqrt{5} \approx -4.24$

74. $\dfrac{-3 + \sqrt{7}}{2} \approx -0.18; \ \dfrac{-3 - \sqrt{7}}{2} \approx -2.82$

76. $\dfrac{-1 + \sqrt{15}}{2} \approx 1.44; \ \dfrac{-1 - \sqrt{15}}{2} \approx -2.44$

78. $6 \pm \sqrt{30}$ **80.** $4 \pm 2\sqrt{2}$ **82.** $8 + \sqrt{33}$

84. 15   **86.** 10

88.

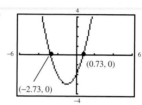

$-1 + \sqrt{3} \approx 0.73$

$-1 - \sqrt{3} \approx -2.73$

90.

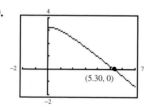

$\dfrac{7 + \sqrt{13}}{2} \approx 5.30$

92. $-1 + 4\sqrt{2}$ **94.** 20   **96.** 4, 5   **98.** 58 units

100. (a)

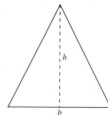

(b) $120 - h$

(c) $A = \frac{1}{2}(120 - h)h$
Height: 56 centimeters
Base: 64 centimeters

or

Height: 64 centimeters
Base: 56 centimeters

102. A perfect square trinomial is one that can be written in the form $(x + k)^2$. Example: $x^2 - 4x + 4$

104. Divide both sides of the equation by the leading coefficient and then follow the steps listed in the answer to Exercise 103.

106. Completing the square, because it is not easily factored.

108. False. Any quadratic equation with real solutions can be solved by completing the square.

Section 10.3   *(page 532)*

2. $2x^2 + 3x - 5 = 0$ **4.** $8x^2 + 3x - 2 = 0$ **6.** 1

8. 0   **10.** 2   **12.** 2   **14.** $-7, 2$

16. $\dfrac{-1 \pm \sqrt{13}}{2}$ **18.** No real solution   **20.** $5 \pm \sqrt{3}$

22. $\dfrac{-5 \pm \sqrt{17}}{2}$ **24.** 2, 10   **26.** $-2, -\dfrac{5}{3}$

28. $\dfrac{1}{4}, 3$ **30.** No real solution   **32.** $-1, \dfrac{9}{2}$

34. $\dfrac{-2 \pm \sqrt{7}}{3}$ **36.** No real solution   **38.** $\dfrac{-7 \pm \sqrt{97}}{6}$

40. $5 \pm \sqrt{35}$ **42.** $\dfrac{-5 \pm \sqrt{265}}{12}$ **44.** $\pm 3\sqrt{3}$

46. 0, 7   **48.** $-2, 5$ **50.** $8 \pm 2\sqrt{5}$ **52.** -7

54. $\dfrac{-10 \pm \sqrt{70}}{6}$ **56.** $\dfrac{3}{2}$

58. $\dfrac{-1 + 3\sqrt{109}}{14} \approx 2.166; \dfrac{-1 - 3\sqrt{109}}{14} \approx -2.309$

60. $\dfrac{21 + 2\sqrt{21}}{17} \approx 1.774; \dfrac{21 - 2\sqrt{21}}{17} \approx 0.696$

62. $\dfrac{3 \pm \sqrt{17}}{2}$ **64.** 6   **66.** 3.6 miles per hour

68. (a) 0 seconds; $\dfrac{9}{8}$ seconds   (b) 1.81 seconds

70. 22, 24   **72.** 6.2 inches $\times$ 4.3 inches

74. Compute $-b$ plus or minus the square root of the quantity b squared minus $4ac$. This quantity divided by the quantity $2a$ is the Quadratic Formula.

76. After the binomial factors are multiplied, the Quadratic Formula could be used. This would not be the most efficient method, because the quadratic is already factored.

78. $x^2 - 2 = 0$

Section 10.4   *(page 542)*

2. c   **4.** b   **6.** e   **8.** Down   **10.** Down

12. Up   **14.** Up   **16.** $(-6, 0), (6, 0), (0, -36)$

18. $(0, 0), (4, 0)$ **20.** $(0, 4)$ **22.** $(1, 0), (0, 1)$

24. $\left(\dfrac{1}{2}, 0\right), (3, 0), (0, 3)$ **26.** $(0, 7)$

28. $\left(-3 - 2\sqrt{3}, 0\right), \left(-3 + 2\sqrt{3}, 0\right), (0, -1)$

30. $(0, -3)$ **32.** $(-1, 2)$ **34.** $(6, -27)$

36. $\left(-\dfrac{3}{2}, \dfrac{7}{4}\right)$ **38.** $(3, 23)$ **40.** $\left(-\dfrac{2}{3}, -\dfrac{7}{3}\right)$

42.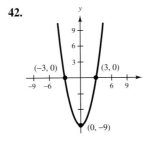

44.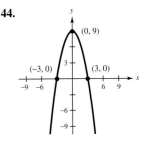

46.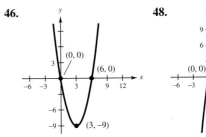

48.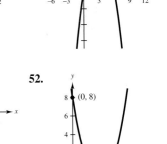

50.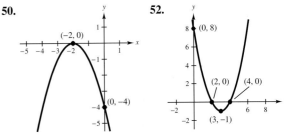

52.

54.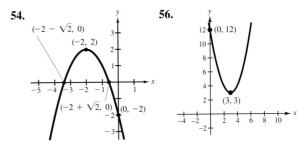

56.

58.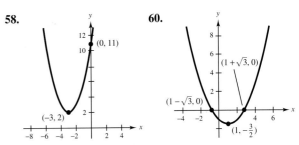

60.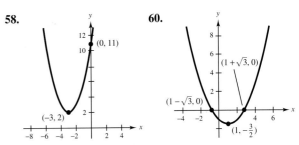

62.

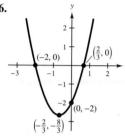

64.

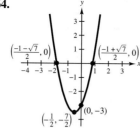

66.

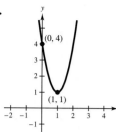

68.

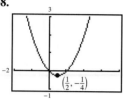

70.

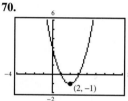

72.

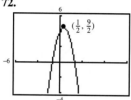

74.

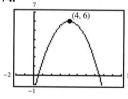

76.

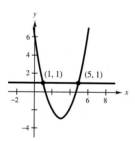

78.

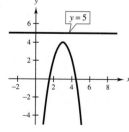

80.

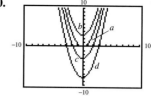

(a) The vertex is at the origin.

(b) The graph is shifted 3 units up from (a).

(c) The graph is shifted 3 units down from (a).

(d) The graph is shifted 8 units down from (a).

82.

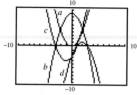

(a) The parabola opens upward with vertex at the origin.

(b) The graph opens downward and is shifted 9 units up.

(c) The graph is shifted 1 unit to the left and 4 units down.

(d) The parabola opens downward and is shifted 2 units to the right and 1 unit up.

84. $y = x^2 - 16$ **86.** $y = x^2 - 7x + 10$

     $y = 16 - x^2$ $y = -x^2 + 7x - 10$

88.

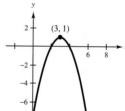

If the equation is in the form $y = (x - b)^2 + c$, the vertex is (b, c). Therefore, the vertex is $(3, 1)$.

90. $y = (x + 4)^2 - 2; (-4, -2)$

92. (a) 4 feet   (b) 24 feet   (c) $20 + 4\sqrt{30} \approx 41.9$ feet

94. Maximum height: 15 yards; Yard line: 38

96. Square   **98.** (g) 100 feet

100. The intercepts are the points where the graph intersects the x- and y-axes. Find the x-intercepts by setting $y = 0$ and solving the resulting equation. Find the y-intercepts by setting $x = 0$ and solving the resulting equation.

102. Discriminant is positive: Two x-intercepts
Discriminant is 0: One x-intercept
Discriminant is negative: No x-intercept

104. No. The relationship $f(x) = ax^2 + bx + c$ is a function and therefore any vertical line will intersect the graph at most once.

Section 10.5   *(page 550)*

2. 20, 21   **4.** 11, 13   **6.** 12, 14   **8.** 14, 15

10. 5 seconds   **12.** 10.39 seconds   **14.** 9.19 seconds

16. Width: 15 m; Length: 22.5 m; Area: 337.5 m²

18. Width: 34.64 cm; Length: 41.57 cm; Perimeter: 152.42 cm

20. Width: 4 in.; Length: 6 in.; Perimeter: 20 in.

22. Width: 2 ft; Length: 7 ft; Area: 14 ft²

24. Width: 10 ft; Length: 16 ft; Perimeter: 52 ft

26. $x(x - 7) = 144$; Width: 9 in.; Length: 16 in.

28. $x(x + 4) = 9600$; Length: 100 feet; Width: 96 feet

30. 112.8 feet   **32.** Base: 24 inches; Height: 72 inches

34. 6.24 feet   **36.** 8 miles or 6 miles

38. 18 inches × 24 inches   **40.** 75 feet

42. 6.14 hours; 8.14 hours

44. Printer A: 4.4 minutes; Printer B: 9.4 minutes

46. 24 people   **48.** 50 people

50. 50 miles per hour; 40 miles per hour

52. 7%   **54.** 9.5%

56. (a)

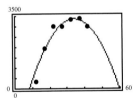

(b) 34

(c) $y = -3.82x^2 + 259.42x - 1871.08$

58. Equivalent equations have the same solution(s). The equations $x + 3 = 10$ and $2x + 6 = 20$ are equivalent.

60. Addition

62. (i) Write a verbal model that will describe what you need to know.

(ii) Assign labels to each part of the verbal model—numbers to the known quantities and letters to the variable quantities.

(iii) Use the labels to write an algebraic model based on the verbal model.

(iv) Solve the resulting algebraic equation and check your solution.

Review Exercises   *(page 555)*

2. 0, 12   **4.** $-3, \frac{2}{3}$ **6.** $-2, 2$ **8.** ± 9

10. $\pm 6\sqrt{2}$ **12.** $\pm 2\sqrt{2}$ **14.** $-2 \pm \sqrt{5}$

16. No real solution   **18.** $1 \pm 2\sqrt{3}$ **20.** $-\frac{9}{2}, -\frac{3}{2}$

22. No real solution   **24.** $-5 \pm \sqrt{13}$ **26.** $\dfrac{-3 \pm \sqrt{5}}{2}$

28. No real solution   **30.** No real solution   **32.** $-4, 5$

34. 1, 5   **36.** No real solution   **38.** $\dfrac{1 \pm \sqrt{161}}{4}$

40. $-\dfrac{1}{2}$ **42.** 0, 45   **44.** $\dfrac{31 \pm 3\sqrt{329}}{20}$

46. $\dfrac{-3 \pm \sqrt{73}}{4}$ **48.** $\dfrac{-1 \pm \sqrt{193}}{8}$ **50.** 5

52. Down   **54.** Up   **56.** Up

58.

60.

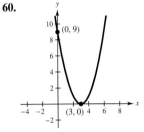

62.

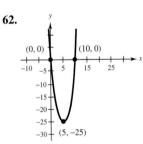

64.

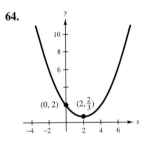

66.

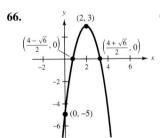

68.

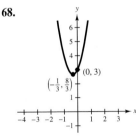

70.

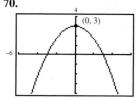

72.

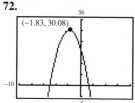

74. 13, 14   **76.** 5%

78. 5 seconds. The object was thrown upward from a height of 160 feet with a velocity of 48 feet per second. The object reaches its maximum height of 196 feet after $1\frac{1}{2}$ seconds.

80. 10 feet   **82.** 20 feet

84. Base: 4 inches; Height: 12 inches   **86.** 24 people

88. 55 miles per hour; 65 miles per hour

90. 29.03 hours; 31.03 hours

92. 26 centimeters × 35 centimeters

94. (a) 3 feet   (b) 4 feet   (c) 6 feet

96. (a) $x^3 - 8x + 15 = 0$ (b) $2x^2 - 7x + 3 = 0$
     (c) $x^2 + 5x + 4 = 0$ (d) $x^2 + 12x + 20 = 0$

Technology

Section 1.1   *(page 4)*

Between 3 and 4

Section 1.2   *(page 17)*

No, no, $1 = 0 \cdot 0$, $2 = 0 \cdot 0$. Division by zero is undefined; an error message

Section 1.3   *(page 36)*

-0.882. Rounding digit: 2; decision digit: 4

Section 1.4   *(page 44)*

$(-5)^4 = 625$, $-5^4 = -625$; $(-5)^3 = -125$, $-5^3 = -125$. If the negative sign is part of the base and the base is raised to an odd power, the result is negative. If the negative sign is part of the base and the base is raised to an even power, the result is positive. If the negative sign is not part of the base, the result is negative regardless of the power.

Section 3.5   *(page 163)*

$P = \$9580$

Section 4.2   *(page 215)*

The graph appears in the viewing window, but you cannot see where the x- and y-intercepts of the graph are located.

Xmin = -4
Xmax = 12
Xscl = 2
Ymin = -2
Ymax = 14
Yscl = 2

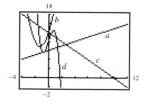

Section 5.3   *(page 298)*

≈ 170.6913258, ≈ 170.6913258. The expressions are equal.

Section 6.4   *(page 347)*

$16^2 - 9^2 = 175$ and $(16 + 9)(16 - 9) = 175$. The equation is true for all real numbers.

Section 6.5   *(page 359)*

Example 3:   Standard form: $x^2 - 8x + 16 = 0$
               x-intercept: $(4, 0)$

Example 4:   Standard form: $x^2 + 9x + 14 = 0$
               x-intercepts: $(-2, 0), (-7, 0)$

The number of solutions is the same as the number of x-intercepts.

Section 7.1   *(page 376)*

(a) $y = -\frac{3}{4}x + 3$
    $y = \frac{2}{3}x + 3$

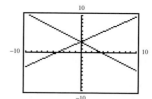

(b) $y = \frac{1}{2}x + 4$
    $y = \frac{1}{2}x - \frac{5}{4}$

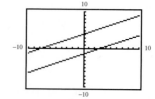

(c) $y = -x + 6$

$y = -x + 6$

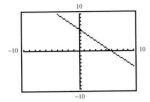

If the slopes are not equal, there is one point of intersection. If the slopes are equal, there may be no points of intersection or infinitely many points of intersection.

Section 7.1   *(page 378)*

The solution point is $\left(\frac{3}{2}, 1\right)$.

Section 7.2   *(page 387)*

The solution is (7000, 5000).

Section 8.1   *(page 418)*

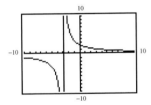

The y-value to the right of $x = -3$ is a large positive number, whereas the y-value to the left of $x = -3$ is a large negative number. When the table feature is used, at $x = -3$ the corresponding y-value displays an error. When an x-value is not in the domain of a rational expression, the graphing calculator displays a line connecting the two extremes on each side of the x-value.

Section 8.1   *(page 421)*

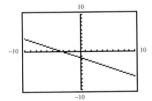

Section 8.4   *(page 449)*

The x-intercepts and the points of intersection of the graph(s) are the solutions in Example 6. The x-intercepts of a rational equation are the solutions of the equation.

Section 9.1   *(page 464)*

When a positive number is raised to an even or odd power, the answer is positive.

(a) 16   (b) -64 (c) 16   (d) -32

When a negative number is raised to an even power, the answer is positive. When a negative number is raised to an odd power, the answer is negative.

Section 9.1   *(page 467)*

(a) 8   (b) -8

(c) Error. The square root of a negative number is not a real number.

Section 9.4   *(page 496)*

There are no solutions to $\sqrt{2x} + 4 = 0$.

Section 10.2   *(page 522)*

The x-intercepts do occur at the two given x-values.

Section 10.2   *(page 523)*

The graph does not cross the x-axis. The vertex of the graph lies on the x-axis. The graph intersects the x-axis at two locations.

Section 10.3   *(page 531)*

The solution is the same as in Example 6.

Section 10.4   *(page 535)*

If the coefficient of the x^2-term is positive, the graph opens up. If the coefficient of the x^2-term is negative, the graph opens down. The graph opens down.

Section 10.5   *(page 547)*

The x-intercepts are the same as the solutions in Example 2.

Discussing the Concept

Section 1.1   *(page 8)*

Yes, $5 \geq 5$ is true.

Section 1.2   *(page 23)*

$3 \cdot (-1) = -3$	$-3 \cdot (-1) = 3$
$3 \cdot (-2) = -6$	$-3 \cdot (-2) = 6$
$3 \cdot (-3) = -9$	$-3 \cdot (-3) = 9$

Rules demonstrated: the product of integers with like signs is positive and the product of integers with different signs is negative.

Section 1.3   *(page 39)*

First method: 43.6; Second method: 42.1

Section 1.4   *(page 50)*

(a) No.   (b) $(4 + 8) \cdot 6 = 72$

(c) $93 - (25 - 4) = 72$ (d) 72

(e) $[(60 + 20) \div 2] + 32 = 72$ (f) 72

Section 2.1   *(page 67)*

The student substituted 4 instead of -4 into the term $(x - y)$. The correct work is:

$$y - 2(x - y) = -4 - 2[2 - (-4)]$$
$$= -4 - 2(6)$$
$$= -4 - 12$$
$$= -16$$

Section 2.2   *(page 79)*

Largest number using 2, 3, and 4 is:

$$2^{3^4} = 2^{81} \approx 2.418 \times 10^{24}$$

Section 2.3   *(page 94)*

The additional information of how much the person normally makes per hour is necessary. (You would also need to be sure that the person normally works 40 hours per week and that overtime is paid on time worked beyond 40 hours.)

Section 2.4   *(page 104)*

Red herring: that it took 45 minutes for the last 36 miles of the trip (this amount of time is beyond the first 3 hours of the trip).

Section 3.1   *(page 123)*

(a) Volume is measured in cubic feet, not square feet.

(b) 0.42¢ is less than 1 cent.

(c) Weight is measured in pounds (mass is measured in kilograms), not liters.

(d) Height is measured in meters, not square meters.

Section 3.2   *(page 133)*

In the last step of the problem, the student should not have divided both sides of the equation by the variable factor. The correct work is:

$$4(x + 2) - 8 = 3x$$
$$4x + 8 - 8 = 3x$$
$$4x = 3x$$
$$4x - 3x = 0$$
$$x = 0$$

Section 3.3   *(page 144)*

(a)

Year	Salary for Option 1	Raise for Option 1	Salary for Option 2	Raise for Option 2
2000	$28,000.00	$1500.00	$28,000.00	$1400.00
2001	$29,500.00	$1500.00	$29,400.00	$1470.00
2002	$31,000.00	$1500.00	$30,870.00	$1543.50
2003	$32,500.00	$1500.00	$32,413.50	$1620.68
2004	$34,000.00	$1500.00	$34,034.18	$1701.71
2005	$35,500.00	$1500.00	$35,735.89	$1786.79
2006	$37,000.00	$1500.00	$37,522.68	$1876.13
2007	$38,500.00	$1500.00	$39,398.81	$1969.94

For an 8-year contract, option 2 pays out a higher total over the 8 years than option 1, as well as eventually giving higher salaries.

(b) For both a 3-year contract and a 4-year contract, option 1 would be better because if you look at the table from part (a), you can see that you would make more money with option 1.

(c) The year 2002

Section 3.4   *(page 155)*

Answers will vary depending on the accuracy of the measurements. The ratio should be approximately 3.14 and does not depend on the size of the circumference.

Section 3.5   *(page 168)*

1-inch square cutouts:

volume $= 7 \times 10 \times 1 = 70$ cubic inches

2-inch square cutouts:

volume $= 5 \times 8 \times 2 = 80$ cubic inches

3-inch square cutouts:

volume $= 3 \times 6 \times 3 = 54$ cubic inches

Let $x =$ length of side of square cutout, then

$$V = (9 - x - x)(12 - x - x)x = (9 - 2x)(12 - 2x)x.$$

Section 3.6   *(page 182)*

No, because $3 < x - 2 < -3$ says that $3 < -3$, which is not true. Correct solution:

$$x - 2 > 3 \quad \text{and} \quad x - 2 < -3$$
$$x > 5 \quad \text{and} \quad x < -1$$

But the solution set should contain all real numbers that satisfy *both* inequalities, and because this is not possible, there is *no* solution.

Section 3.7 *(page 189)*

(a) $x = -4$ or $x = -\frac{2}{3}$ (b) No solution   (c) $x = -8$

(d) $-3 \le x \le 5$ (e) All real numbers   (f) No solution

Section 4.1 *(page 208)*

The graph on the left is misleading. The scale on the vertical axis makes it appear that the change in profits is dramatic, but the total change is only $3000, which is small in comparison with $3,000,000.

Section 4.2 *(page 218)*

Descriptions will vary. It appears that the van made stops for deliveries between minutes 5 and 8, minutes 10 and 12, and minutes 14 and 19 before coming to a stop (end of trip) at minute 22. Top speed during this trip was only 40 miles per hour.

Section 4.3 *(page 228)*

1. b   2. d (represents y as a function of x)

3. c   4. a (represents y as a function of x)

Section 4.4 *(page 241)*

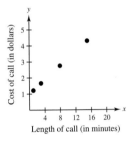

Yes. $m = 0.22$; y-intercept: $(0, 1)$

Section 4.5 *(page 252)*

Slope-intercept form

$$y = mx + b$$
$$y = -2x + b$$

Point-slope form

$$y - y_1 = m(x - x_1)$$
$$y - 2 = -2(x + 3)$$

Substitute $(-3, 2)$:

$$2 = (-2)(-3) + b$$
$$b = -4$$

So, $y = -2x - 4$.

Section 4.6 *(page 261)*

$y \ge 2x$, $y \le x + 2$

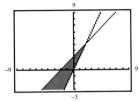

Section 5.1 *(page 279)*

Answers will vary. The key point is that you can combine only like terms.

Section 5.2 *(page 291)*

$(x + 1)^7 = x^7 + 7x^6 + 21x^5 + 35x^4 + 35x^3 + 21x^2 + 7x + 1$

Section 5.3 *(page 301)*

Equivalent pairs: $\dfrac{2}{x^{-3}}$ and $2x^3$, $\dfrac{1}{2x^3}$ and $\dfrac{x^{-3}}{2}$, $\dfrac{1}{(2x)^{-3}}$ and $8x^3$, and $\dfrac{1}{8x^3}$ and $(2x)^{-3}$

Section 5.4 *(page 311)*

Answers will vary.

Section 6.1 *(page 326)*

Answers will vary.

Section 6.2 *(page 334)*

$x^3 + 5x^2 - 3x - 15 = (x^2 - 3)(x + 5)$

$x^3 - 7x^2 + 2x - 14 = (x^2 + 2)(x - 7)$

Section 6.3 *(page 342)*

Factoring by grouping:

$$6x^2 - 13x + 6 = 6x^2 - (4x + 9x) + 6$$
$$= (6x^2 - 4x) - (9x - 6)$$
$$= 2x(3x - 2) - 3(3x - 2)$$
$$= (3x - 2)(2x - 3)$$

$$2x^2 + 5x - 12 = 2x^2 + (8x - 3x) - 12$$
$$= (2x^2 + 8x) - (3x + 12)$$
$$= 2x(x + 4) - 3(x + 4)$$
$$= (x + 4)(2x - 3)$$

$$3x^2 + 11x - 4 = 3x^2 + (12x - x) - 4$$
$$= (3x^2 + 12x) - (x + 4)$$
$$= 3x(x + 4) - (x + 4)$$
$$= (x + 4)(3x - 1)$$

DISCUSSING THE CONCEPT

Section 6.4   *(page 352)*

Box 1: $(a - b)a^2$ Box 2: $(a - b)ab$ Box 3: $(a - b)b^2$

The sum of the volumes of boxes 1, 2, and 3 equals the volume of the large cube minus the volume of the small cube, which is the difference of two cubes.

Section 6.5   *(page 362)*

The student should have written the equation in standard form before factoring, and then set each factor equal to 0, not 10. Correct solution:

$$x^2 + 3x = 10$$
$$x^2 + 3x - 10 = 0$$
$$(x + 5)(x - 2) = 0$$
$$x + 5 = 0 \Rightarrow x = -5$$
$$x - 2 = 0 \Rightarrow x = 2$$

Section 7.1   *(page 379)*

Examples will vary.

Section 7.2   *(page 387)*

$$y = 2x - 3$$
$$y = 5x - 9$$

Solution point: (2, 1)
The "system" $x^2 - 1 = 2x - 1$ has two solution points.

Section 7.3   *(page 397)*

Yes, the claim is valid for the one-solution case, but it is not possible to distinguish further between the no-solution and many-solution cases.

Section 7.4   *(page 407)*

Examples will vary.

Section 8.1   *(page 422)*

Both students used incorrect cancellation techniques—only *factors* in the numerator and denominator may be canceled. Neither of these expressions may be simplified any further than their original forms.

Section 8.2   *(page 432)*

No; $\dfrac{3x^2 + 4x - 4}{2x^2 + 5x + 2} = \dfrac{(3x - 2)(x + 2)}{(2x + 1)(x + 2)} = \dfrac{3x - 2}{2x + 1}$;

$x = -\frac{1}{2}$ and $x = -2$ are excluded from the first expression, and $x = -\frac{1}{2}$ is excluded from each of the other expressions.

Section 8.3   *(page 442)*

$$\frac{1}{2x - 12}, x \neq -6$$

Section 8.4   *(page 452)*

Because you are given $x = 1$ and $x - 1 = 0$, you have division by zero in Step 4, which is undefined.

Section 9.1   *(page 469)*

First triangle: 1 and $\sqrt{3}$ are the lengths of the sides and 2 is the length of the hypotenuse. Second triangle: 1 and 2 are the lengths of the sides and $\sqrt{5}$ is the length of the hypotenuse.

Section 9.2   *(page 479)*

1. False; 2. True; 3. False; 4. True
Examples will vary.

Section 9.3   *(page 489)*

Examples will vary; one possibility is $\sqrt{3} \cdot \sqrt{3} = 3$. Another example of a subset closed with respect to multiplication is the integers.

Section 9.4   *(page 498)*

The solution $x = -2$ is extraneous. The no-solution case would appear graphically as having no x-intercepts.

Section 10.1   *(page 514)*

Explanations will vary. Suggested revision: restrict values of c to $c \leq 0$ so that solutions will be real.

Section 10.2   *(page 523)*

Area required to complete the square: 1
Figures for $x^2 + 5x$:

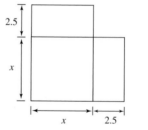
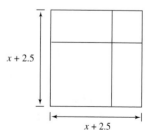

The value $(2.5)^2$ was added to complete the square.

Section 10.3   *(page 531)*

Two solutions: for $a > 0$, the vertex is below the x-axis;
            for $a < 0$, the vertex is above the x-axis.

One solution: vertex lies on the x-axis.

No solutions: for $a > 0$, the vertex is above the x-axis;
            for $a < 0$, the vertex is below the x-axis.

Examples will vary.

Section 10.4   *(page 541)*

$$-(x - 2)(x - 6) = -x^2 + 8x - 12$$
$$-2(x - 2)(x - 6) = -2x^2 + 16x - 24$$
$$2(x - 2)(x - 6) = 2x^2 - 16x + 24$$

Section 10.5   *(page 549)*

Answers will vary.

Appendix A   *(page A6)*

2.
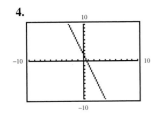

4.
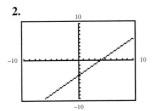

6.
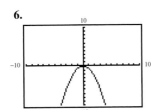

8.
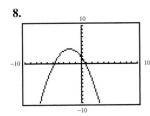

10.
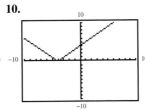

12.
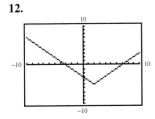

14.
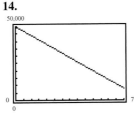

16.
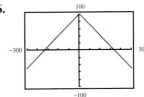

18.
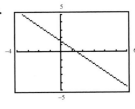
Xmin = 8
Xmax = 16
Xscl = 1
Ymin = 14
Ymax = 22
Yscl = 1

20.
Xmin = -18
Xmax = -6
Xscl = 1
Ymin = -16
Ymax = 10
Yscl = 1

22.
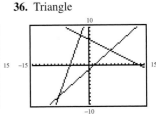

Distributive Property

24.
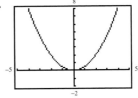

Commutative Property of Multiplication

26. $(-1, 0), \left(\frac{5}{3}, 0\right), (0, -5)$

28. $(0.268, 0), (3.732, 0), (0, 1)$

30. $(-4, 0), (4, 0), (0, 4)$ **32.** $(-2, 0), (0, 0), (2, 0)$

34. Triangle   **36.** Triangle
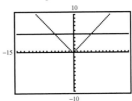

38. (a) Increasing

(b) Increasing. Revenues from periodicals are not increasing as rapidly as revenues from first-class mail.

Appendix B

Section B.1   *(page A14)*

2. Answers will vary.   **4.** a and c
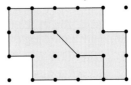

6.

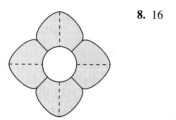

8. 16   **10.** 3   **12.** True

14. False   **16.** c   **18.** a   **20.** a, b, and c

22. Interior   **24.** b   **26.** e   **28.** a

30. $\angle M \cong \angle N$, $\angle L \cong \angle O$, $\angle P \cong \angle Q$

32. $\triangle ONQ$ must be isosceles because the triangles have congruent sides.

34. $\angle X$ **36.** NO **38.** 2; No   **40.** 2; No

42. 3 inches by 4.5 inches   **44.** $(1, -1)$

46. Four. Remove the toothpicks marked with an "X."

Section B.2   *(page A21)*

2.

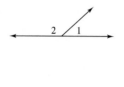

4.

6.

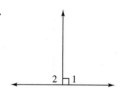

8. Adjacent compl. $\angle$

10. Vertical $\angle$ **12.** Adjacent suppl. $\angle$ **14.** True

16. True   **18.** True   **20.** 150°   **22.** 43.5°   **24.** 10°

26. $\angle 1$ and $\angle 5$, $\angle 2$ and $\angle 6$, $\angle 4$ and $\angle 8$, $\angle 3$ and $\angle 7$

28. $\angle 2$ and $\angle 8$ *or* $\angle 1$ and $\angle 7$

30. $m\angle 1 = 120°$ by the Corresponding Angles Postulate; $m\angle 2 = 120°$ because $\angle 2$ and $\angle 1$ are vertical angles.

32. $m\angle 1 = 80°$ by the Alternate Exterior Angles Theorem; $m\angle 2 = 100°$ because it forms a linear pair with $\angle 1$.

34. $a = 80°$, $b = 110°$ **36.** $a = 150°$, $b = 30°$

38. $\angle 1$, $\angle 3$, $\angle 4$, $\angle 6$, $\angle 8$ **40.** 105°   **42.** 40°   **44.** False

46. True   **48.** $m\angle 1 = 75°$, $m\angle 2 = 55°$, $m\angle 3 = 55°$, $m\angle 4 = 40°$, $m\angle 5 = 140°$, $m\angle 6 = 40°$, $m\angle 7 = 75°$, $m\angle 8 = 65°$, $m\angle 9 = 115°$

50.

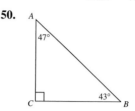

$m\angle B = 43°$

52.

54. 35°, 60°, 85°   **56.** 40°, 50°, 90°

Appendix C   *(page A33)*

2.

Stems	Leaves
0	62 65 66 67 80 89 93 98
1	01 09 24 46 90 96
2	40 55 61 92
3	35 68
4	12 38 80 96
5	18 50 66 70 81
6	00 01 34 44
7	00 61 66
8	11 41 57 90
9	
10	
11	33 59 60
12	92
13	17 19 37
27	22
31	32
46	80
65	14

4.

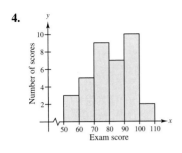

6. Organize the data by using a stem-and-leaf plot.

Stems	Leaves
1	3.0 3.0 5.7 8.7 8.9 9.1
2	1.1 1.3 1.5 1.6 1.8 1.8 3.3 3.8 5.8 6.2 9.0 9.2
3	0.7 1.0 2.1 2.3 3.6 4.4 8.0 9.8
4	2.1 4.6 7.5 9.0

8.

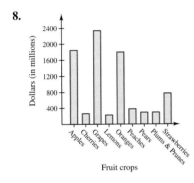

10. 30 million tons   **12.** 1960 to 1986

14. Answers will vary. Because there are fewer and fewer places to put it. More is being recycled.

16.

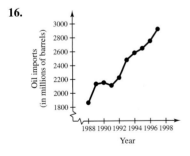

18.

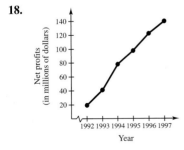

20.

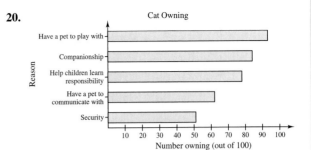

22. There is some duplication.

24. Yes, one hit can produce up to four runs.

26. Positive correlation   **28.** No correlation

30. They have a negative correlation.   **32.** 28,000 feet

34. Because y tends to increase as x increases, the points are positively correlated.

36. No, the model is not accurate for large values of x.

38. Because v tends to decrease as h increases, the points are negatively correlated.

40. Because the model yields $v = 830.3$ feet per second when $h = 70$, we see that the model is inaccurate for large values of h.

42. $y = 2.2286x + 43.0857$ **44.** $y = -6.0512x + 148.0349$

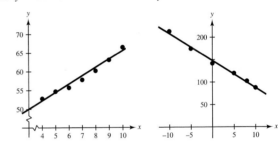

46. (a) $S = 384.1 + 21.2x$; $479.50

(b)   (c) $r \approx 0.996$

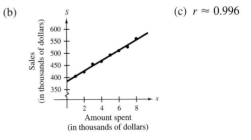

48. Mean: 33.86; median: 33; mode: 32

50. Mean: 32.43; median: 33; mode: 32

52. Mean: 320; median: 320; mode: 320

54. (a) Average number of hits $= 1$

(b) Batting average $= 0.250$

56. One possibility: $\{4, 4, 6, 7.5, 8.5\}$

58. The median and mode give the best descriptions.

APPENDIX

Index of Applications

Index